ROBERT F. BARNES

									H 1 / 1 / 1−, 1+	He 2 / 2 / 0
				B 5 / 2,3 / 3+	C 6 / 2,4 / 2±, 4±	N 7 / 2,5 / 4+, 3+, 3−, 5±	O 8 / 2,6 / 1−, 2−	F 9 / 2,7 / 1−	Ne 10 / 2,8 / 0
				Al 13 / 2,8,3 / 3+	Si 14 / 2,8,4 / 2±, 4±	P 15 / 2,8,5 / 3−, 3+, 5+	S 16 / 2,8,6 / 4+, 2−, 6+	Cl 17 / 2,8,7 / 1+, 7+, 5+, 1−	A 18 / 2,8,8 / 0
Co 27 / 15,2 / 3+, 2+	Ni 28 / 16,2 / 2+	Cu 29 / 18,1 / 1+, 2+	Zn 30 / 18,2 / 2+	Ga 31 / 18,3 / 3+	Ge 32 / 18,4 / 4±	As 33 / 18,5 / 3−, 3+, 5+	Se 34 / 18,6 / 2−, 4+, 6+	Br 35 / 18,7 / 1+, 5+, 1−	Kr 36 / 18,8 / 0
Rh 45 / 16,1 / 3+	Pd 46 / 18 / 4+, 2+	Ag 47 / 18,1 / 1+	Cd 48 / 18,2 / 2+	In 49 / 18,3 / 3+	Sn 50 / 18,4 / 2+, 4+	Sb 51 / 18,5 / 3−, 5+, 3+	Te 52 / 18,6 / 6+, 4+	I 53 / 18,7 / 7+, 1+, 5+, 1−	Xe 54 / 18,8 / 0
Ir 77 / 32,17 / 4+, 3+	Pt 78 / 32,17,1 / 2+, 4+	Au 79 / 32,18,1 / 1+, 3+	Hg 80 / 32,18,2 / 1+, 2+	Tl 81 / 32,18,3 / 3+, 1+	Pb 82 / 32,18,4 / 4+, 2+	Bi 83 / 32,18,5 / 3+	Po 84 / 32,18,6 / 2+	At 85 / 32,18,7	Rn 86 / 32,18,8 / 0
9b	10b	1b	2b	3a	4a	5a	6a	7a	0

Eu 63 / 25,8,2 / 2+, 3+	Gd 64 / 25,9,2 / 3+	Tb 65 / 27,8,2 / 3+	Dy 66 / 28,8,2 / 3+	Ho 67 / 29,8,2 / 3+	Er 68 / 30,8,2 / 3+	Tm 69 / 31,8,2 / 3+	Yb 70 / 32,8,2 / 2+, 3+	Lu 71 / 32,9,2 / 3+
Am 95 / 25,8,2 / 6+, 5+, 4+, 2+, 3+	Cm 96 / 25,9,2 / 3+	Bk 97 / 27,8,2 / 4+, 3+	Cf 98 / 28,8,2 / 3+	99	100			

GENERAL CHEMISTRY

THE MACMILLAN COMPANY
NEW YORK · CHICAGO
DALLAS · ATLANTA · SAN FRANCISCO

THE MACMILLAN COMPANY
OF CANADA, LIMITED
TORONTO

Electron photomicrograph of tobacco virus protein crystals. Note the close packing of the approximately spherical macromolecules. From R. W. G. Wyckoff, *Electron Microscopy, Technique and Applications*. Copyright 1949. Interscience Publishers, New York–London.

GENERAL CHEMISTRY

L. E. STEINER *and* **J. A. CAMPBELL**

PROFESSORS OF CHEMISTRY, OBERLIN COLLEGE

ILLUSTRATED BY **PAUL B. ARNOLD**

ASSISTANT PROFESSOR OF FINE ARTS, OBERLIN COLLEGE

The Macmillan Company, New York

COPYRIGHT, 1955, BY THE MACMILLAN COMPANY

PUBLISHED SIMULTANEOUSLY IN CANADA

All rights reserved—no part of this book may be reproduced in any form without permission in writing from the publisher, except by a reviewer who wishes to quote brief passages in connection with a review written for inclusion in magazine or newspaper.

PRINTED IN THE UNITED STATES OF AMERICA

FIRST PRINTING

PREFACE

THE PLACE of science in a college education is now accepted, but the numbers and kinds of first courses in chemistry to fill that place are still questions for debate and choice. At one extreme are institutions which offer separate beginning chemistry courses for every large group of students with special interests. At the other extreme are institutions which offer only one beginning course to be taken both by preprofessional students and by terminal students.

Our college is in the latter group. For years we have tried to give a course which has meaning in a liberal arts setting, is rigorous enough to give the student some feeling for the nature of fact and proof in chemistry as a science and comprehensive enough in scope to test a student's desire for more work in chemistry. A single beginning course is possible if one accepts the idea that future chemists can benefit from a first college course in which emphasis is on broad, fundamental concepts rather than on details of inorganic chemistry. For the first semester only, we form a separate section for those without high school chemistry, another section for upper classmen, and others for freshmen with high school chemistry; but by the beginning of the second semester the sections are interchangeable.

Some devices for achieving a wide scope are: beginning with concepts and experiences which are not covered in typical high school courses, yet which are within the grasp of beginners; discussing the theoretical bases of chemistry with a breadth of illustration beyond the confines of descriptive inorganic chemistry; grading the text and problems through differential emphasis, so that the most fundamental ideas are approached and used repeatedly with different accents while advanced and narrowly applicable material is handled more succinctly. The whole is tied together by continual emphasis on the interpretation of properties and reactions in terms of structural relationships.

Education has been said to be the continual rediscovery of the obvious by the uninformed. But ideas become obvious only when they fit into an over-all pattern. Establishment of such a pattern by fiat is a most tempting way to shorten an introductory subject and to come to grips with the present state of knowledge. Yet patterns change even in a science and one test of a student's education is his ability to adapt himself to new patterns. When he understands the experimental reasons behind our contemporary ideas he will find it much easier to see both the strengths and weaknesses of the ideas, to evaluate new suggestions critically, and to maintain a reasonable comprehension not only through his final examination in beginning chemistry, but through the much more important interval beyond. Nor is it too much to hope that he will transfer this feeling for well-grounded tentativity to other studies. And, not least, the future research chemist will be encouraged to exercise his imagination from the beginning.

All the included material we believe can be read with profit, but the average student will not be able to comprehend in detail everything he reads. No set of lectures of reasonable scope can discuss all the material in this book, nor should this be necessary. The important ideas reappear often and are used continually, and they are given fullness by details not to be memorized. Thus, the best student should find enough to keep him interested, but the poorer student should not be overwhelmed and lost. The exposition is designed to encourage correlation and reasoning by the student rather than episodic feats of memory. The material is selected to illustrate methods of experiment and thought in chemistry and the patterns to which they lead. It will be clear to all that the patterns are incomplete, and changing.

Each teacher will recognize the concepts requiring skilled teaching and will fill out in more detail those parts he wishes to stress. Each teacher may also wish to advise his students, as they learn, to differentiate between the material they should understand but not memorize and the facts indispensable to the understanding of chemical concepts and behavior. We would encourage the student to use the index to find data when needed. We would also expect him to become familiar with other sources of data.

The textbook is designed for use in conjunction with experimental work in the laboratory, where the student learns to differentiate fact from verbalization. The laboratory work is a vital part of the course. Here are discovered the bases for the whole pattern of chemical thinking and comprehension. Our own schedule assigns each student his laboratory work for the whole semester at the first meeting and lets him proceed at his own pace. Within the assignment each student does what he can do in the allotted time. The better students are expected to do more work than the poorer ones. Under this program the better students are always ahead of the classroom work and thus really make their own experimental discoveries which are later discussed in the class. The less gifted students automatically fall somewhat behind, and their work tends to coincide with, or come slightly later than, the class discussions. The schedule is self-regulatory. The farther ahead the best student gets, the harder he must work to learn and the greater independence he acquires; the farther behind the poorer student gets the greater the help available to him from the class work. The experimental nature of chemistry is also emphasized in the classroom by both demonstrations and displays. Few meetings indeed can achieve their maximum profit without recourse to experimental illustrations, the backbone of any study of science.

We thank our students of the last five years, who studied, with little complaint, from mimeographed material, and who, by their questions, helped to improve the course. We thank our colleagues at Oberlin for their criticism. In particular, Professor G. T. Scott for his suggestions on biochemistry and Professor W. B. Renfrow for his on organic chemistry.

The faults, dear reader, are but our own. Toward their correction let John Dryden be the guide.

>But find you faithful friends that will reprove,
>That on your work may look with careful eyes,
>And of your faults be zealous enemies.
>
>(translation of Boileau's *Art of Poetry*)

L. E. STEINER
J. A. CAMPBELL

CONTENTS

1	INTRODUCTION	1
2	KINDS OF SUBSTANCES	5
3	THE FUNDAMENTAL PARTICLES OF NATURE	18
4	ELEMENTS AND ATOMS	32
5	COMPOUNDS AND FORMULAS	49
6	THE ATMOSPHERE	64
7	CARBON AND ELEMENTARY CRYSTAL CHEMISTRY	76
8	SOME COMPOUNDS OF CARBON	85
9	THE BEHAVIOR OF GASES	98
10	THE KINETIC THEORY OF GASES	120
11	LIQUIDS AND SOLIDS	131
12	PERIODIC CLASSIFICATION OF THE ELEMENTS	149
13	NUCLEAR STRUCTURE IN ATOMS	160
14	ELECTRONIC STRUCTURE OF ATOMS	174
15	CHEMICAL BONDING	197
16	CHEMICAL REACTIONS	225
17	SOLUTIONS	250
18	CHEMICAL EQUILIBRIUM	271
19	THE SULFUR FAMILY	290
20	THE HALOGENS	310
21	NUCLEAR CHEMISTRY	334
22	THE NITROGEN FAMILY	351
23	PRINCIPLES OF QUALITATIVE ANALYSIS	373
24	SOLUBILITY OF SALTS AND CRYSTAL STRUCTURES	391
25	OXIDES AND THEIR REACTIONS WITH WATER	407
26	ELECTROCHEMISTRY AND ELECTRICAL CELLS	429
27	METALS FROM ORES: METALLURGY	450
28	THE HIGHLY ELECTRO-POSITIVE ELEMENTS	468
29	THE RARE EARTH ELEMENTS, AND SCANDIUM AND YTTRIUM	487

30	ELEMENTS IN THE CENTRAL REGION OF THE PERIODIC TABLE—I	496
31	ELEMENTS IN THE CENTRAL REGION OF THE PERIODIC TABLE—II	516
32	METALS AND ALLOYS	534
33	SILICATES	543
34	COLLOIDS	555
35	THE HYDROCARBONS	566
36	ORGANIC COMPOUNDS CONTAINING OXYGEN	591
37	OTHER HYDROCARBON DERIVATIVES	605
38	POLYMERS	616
39	BIOCHEMISTRY	633
	APPENDIX A: REVIEW PROBLEMS	653
	APPENDIX B: SOME CONVERSION FACTORS	659
	INDEX	661

GENERAL CHEMISTRY

INTRODUCTION

THE SCIENCE of chemistry deals with the substance of the physical universe and with its alterations. It consists of descriptive material, expressed in terms of certain concepts, and of theories to explain why substances behave as they do. Full comprehension of the scope and purpose of chemistry can come only after long experience, but a brief orienting statement may help those of you who are just beginning to study chemistry.

WHY STUDY CHEMISTRY?

Some students take up chemistry intending to enter the profession of chemistry or of another science. Some have a desire to broaden their education, to inquire into the nature of things, to seek answers to particular, even trivial, questions—what makes atomic bombs explode, what makes water wet, what makes the sun shine, what makes soap a cleanser, in short, what makes the universe run! Others study chemistry, or "just take the course," because it is a requirement, because Dad is a chemist, or because Mother "enjoyed it so much when she took it."

Whatever the reasons behind your own choice, your decision was aided in its formulation and execution by chemical processes; for you are, among other things, a very complicated chemical factory. You eat food and inhale air, and you transform these substances into different substances in such a way as to maintain a dynamic, living chemical system. The chemical reactions are energy producing, and, at the age of most students, they produce a net growth.

When you think, as you did in deciding to study chemistry, chemicals, substances produced by chemical reaction, supply the energy necessary for thought. Chemicals also supply the paths necessary to communicate this thought to the appropriate muscles (also chemical systems) for action, which again requires chemical processes. Thus, some of the blame for any inability of yours to understand chemistry may conceivably be placed on a lack of proper chemical facilities in your own body. In such a case, certain drugs (chemicals again) may be prescribed by your physician to help remedy the deficiency. But you can't blame all your lacks on chemistry for you respond, as a living person, to stimuli—light, sound, and other energy—not chemical

2 GENERAL CHEMISTRY

in nature. For instance, speech, which certainly has effects on the hearer of the words, is not matter. It is not a substance.

The science of chemistry lays claim, then, to all material, known or to be known, as its field of study. It concerns itself with analyzing this material into its simpler components, if any. It concerns itself with synthesizing known as well as new substances from the available material. It concerns itself with studying quantitatively the properties and the interactions of materials and with developing generalizations (or laws) to correlate them. In short, chemists want to know the structure and properties of all the substances in the universe; they want to discover how to duplicate every substance, and to produce even more desirable new substances; they want to know, in terms of correlations between properties and structures, why substances behave as they do.

BRANCHES OF CHEMISTRY

While it may be true, as Alexander Pope has said, that the "proper study of mankind is man," the human body, as a chemical system, is far too complicated in structure to serve as a suitable study for a beginning chemist. A detailed study of the chemistry of life processes would not even be attempted in an introductory course because a student must understand many simple reactions of substances before he can understand what happens when many reactions occur simultaneously.

The possible interactions of substances are so many that no one person can even hope to know all of that which has been discovered. Beginning students, therefore, should strive for a broad basic training which will serve as background for general comprehension of what chemists are doing. Then communication with understanding is possible. In addition each chemist must decide for himself where his main interests lie so that he may be thoroughly prepared to comprehend that smaller field and to make contributions to its further growth. Consequently, there have arisen in chemistry, as in other fields of knowledge, specialized branches. These in turn have led to the courses to be found listed in college catalogs.

One way of listing the branches of chemistry is given in Table 1.1. The listing—introductory or general, qualitative analysis, quantitative analysis, inorganic, organic, physical, and biochemistry—is not the only possible one. On the other hand, all the branches, no matter how listed, overlap. The analytical, the inorganic, the physical, and the biochemist are all interested in the tendency of water to evaporate from a salt solution, for instance.

CHEMISTRY AND THE OTHER SCIENCES

Chemistry is subdivided into branches but is itself only a branch of the broad field of natural science. Here again the branches overlap more and more each year, differing primarily in general approach to a subject rather than in goals. All aim to increase our knowledge of the physical universe. Many of the research results published in the *Journal of Chemical Physics* come from men who call themselves chemists, and articles in the *Journal of Physical Chemistry* may come from persons identified as physicists. There is even less point here than in most classification systems in attempting a rigid distinction between the various fields for all have fundamental methods and aims in common. It has been shown over and over again that the most rapid progress in solving a new problem is made when persons with training in each of the fields work on it simultaneously. The need for men trained thoroughly in several branches of science is greater than ever before and there are no fields of science which hold greater promise for enterprising researchers than those lying in the regions where the sciences overlap most.

Table 1.1
Branches of Chemistry

Introductory or General Chemistry—study of the basic concepts for comprehension of the relations between the structures and properties of matter.
Qualitative Analysis—study of the methods of determining the composition of substances in terms of kinds of simpler substances.
Quantitative Analysis—study of the methods of determining the composition of substances in terms of the amounts of simpler substances.
Inorganic Chemistry—study of all the elements and their compounds with the exception of most carbon compounds.
Organic Chemistry—study of the compounds of carbon.
Physical Chemistry—study of the quantitative relationships between properties and structure.
Biochemistry—study of the chemistry of life processes.

PROGRESS IN CHEMISTRY

The scope of science today is far different than in the fourth century B.C. when one man, Aristotle, was able to cover authoritatively in his writings the field of known science, and to have his writings remain the practically unchallenged authority among scientific treatises for almost a thousand years. Today there are hundreds of thousands of chemists alone. The monthly content of the chemical journals is far too great for any one person to read, let alone comprehend, even were he to possess a photographic memory and the highest degree of intellectual genius. In 1953 articles appeared in the chemical literature at the rate of two hundred per day making it impossible for a single chemist even to find those articles pertaining only to his own specialty without help and the rate increases each year. Since 1906, therefore, the American Chemical Society has published Chemical Abstracts. This is now a semimonthly periodical containing brief summaries of, and full references to, each of the articles having any bearing on chemistry which appears in any of some five thousand journals. The part time services of more than nine hundred chemists are needed to find the articles, read them, and prepare the summaries and references. The abstracts are then classified into one of thirty-one general fields of interest, and those within any given field again grouped as to

4 GENERAL CHEMISTRY

similarity of content. Publication of annual indexes and decennial indexes renders even easier the use of the Abstracts.

Chemistry, you can see, is a rapidly growing subject. An introductory course will not only fail to cover the whole field, but it will change both in content and emphasis from year to year as new facts and new interpretations arise. As with any well-organized construction, so with chemistry, most of the changes, both replacements and additions, will occur in the superstructure. Occasionally a small change in the foundation is necessary and very occasionally a major alteration of the basic concepts of science is required. The introductory course will concern itself with an outline of the basic fundamentals of science in general and chemistry in particular. The incorporation of future changes will have to be made by each student. If he understands thoroughly the organization of the present structure, and the interrelationships of the various parts, he will be able to understand the necessity for change and the over-all effect of a given change. Only a well-grounded understanding in the fundamental concepts and the methods used to reach them will give lasting value to the study of introductory chemistry.

Problem 1.1. How would you proceed to find reports of the latest research on some problem in chemistry? Apply your method to one of the following subjects: synthetic ruby or sapphire, penicillin, plutonium, ink, liquid helium, nylon, polyethylene, Vitamin K, or any other substance in which you are interested.

Problem 1.2. Visit the library and glance through some of the chemical journals and books.

Problem 1.3. How do you account for the rapid rate of increase in the quantity of scientific research literature as contrasted with the slower rate in the arts and in literature itself?

---

2 KINDS OF SUBSTANCES

ONE OF the most obvious observations about the universe is that it is heterogeneous, that it shows differences. The view has been expressed that no two things in the universe are alike. No two trees, or even two single leaves are the same. No two grains of sand are perfect twins, snow flakes differ from one another, and each mass-produced milk bottle differs from the rest of the lot. If differences were all-important there would be no science. Fortunately, likenesses also occur. Trees have certain features in common, as do their leaves. Grains of sand are similar in some respects; all snow flakes (or milk bottles) have certain shared properties. Thus we use differences to distinguish objects and materials and likenesses to group them together.

Behind every scheme of arranging things according to likenesses there is an idea, a point of view, which dictates the particular kinds of likenesses that are emphasized in the arrangement. Trees are classified by botanists according to certain differences and likenesses, and sand is classified by geologists. Chemists, who deal with all substance wherever it is found, also classify the substance of trees and of sand, but according to their own ideas. What distinguishes one science from another and from the nonscientific studies is the central point of view as much as the material with which it deals. We can rather quickly get an introduction to the science of chemistry by seeing what ideas the chemist uses to classify the different substances of the universe, that is, to distinguish among the "kinds of substances."

Chemists do more than search for the kinds of substances in the universe. They also try to analyze each of these into simpler substances and to interpret the properties of the more complex substance in terms of those of the simpler substances composing it. The hope is always present that one may discover a small number of "fundamental" substances in terms of which the composition and behavior of all substances may be interpreted. In this chapter we shall consider some of the methods chemists use to search for simpler substances and shall describe some of the results.

THE SENSES

Since man is primarily limited to the five senses, sight, smell, touch, hearing, and taste, we may marvel that he can have as many different experiences as he does. Yet, whether other senses exist or not, we interpret most of each day's sensations with the aid of these five. Since these senses are our basic tools we shall consider them for a moment.

Each of the senses is able to make two kinds of distinctions, one as to the quality of the sensation and the other as to the intensity of the sensation. By quality we mean the ability of sight to distinguish red from blue, of smell to discriminate between perfume and cheese, of touch to detect temperature or roughness, of hearing to recognize high or low musical tones, and of taste to detect sweet or bitter. Intensity, on the other hand, is exemplified in the distinction between brightness of sunlight by sight, dosages of perfume by smell, degrees of roughness by touch, loudness of sounds by hearing, and degrees of sweetness by taste. The physiological basis of none of the senses is completely understood but the average man can detect and classify several hundred thousand different hues and colors with his eyes, an undetermined number of different odors with his nose (though it has been claimed that there are only four basic odors), several hundred different tones with his ears, four different tastes with his tongue (salt, sour, sweet, and bitter), and an undetermined number of different responses with his other nerves.

Although all scientists use instruments in their work they still rely heavily on their senses. The scientist, as well as the nonscientist, distinguishes between oak and pine wood, granite and sandstone, aluminum utensils and enamelware, copper wire and iron wire with his unaided senses. Because there is no substitute for first-hand experience based on the senses all the sciences use the laboratory as an integral part of their instruction. Only through sensory experience do the concepts and theories give us the knowledge we call science.

INSTRUMENTS

Modern civilization could not have arisen if man depended solely on the unaided senses. We are familiar with the growth of civilizations in coordination with instruments used as apparatus and tools, a common growth summarized in terms such as the Stone Age and the Iron Age. But instruments may be used for more than tools to make things. They may also be used to extend observations of the senses. The experimental sciences grew when man began to use instruments in this way. Instruments extend the range of observation of the senses and greatly sharpen the distinctions which can be made both in quality and in quantity. Indeed, they enable the observer to assign numerical values to qualities, values that can be agreed to by men working independently. The numbers can then serve as a basis for quantitative statements. The telescope and the microscope extend the range of vision, and mechanical color comparators discriminate quantitatively between hues and depths of color no unaided eye can distinguish. The thermometer and the balance extend the range within which one can observe differences in temperature and mass, and they increase enormously the discrimination with which one can note the differences. They permit the numerical values necessary for precise concepts as well as for accurate description.

One should not leap to the conclusion that sciences, even the physical sciences, depend completely on modern instrumentation. Ideas, concepts, points of view, are as fundamental to the sciences as observations, as any one studying the great scientific "discoveries" will learn. Some of the basic concepts of chemistry, once revolutionary, rested on a minimum of data obtained with relatively crude apparatus. Even today some important discoveries result from keen interpretation of rather simple experiments (penicillin) while others (heavy hydrogen) rest on observation of differences indicated with highly sensitive instruments.

PROPERTIES OF MATTER

The chemist, being interested in the substance of the universe, identifies and describes this matter by its properties—by its qualities as detected by the senses or by instruments, and by its behavior under different treatments. If differences alone existed in the world there would usually be no point in recording properties for the description would fit only one specimen. Because of the likenesses found among substances chemists divide matter into classes with common qualities and behavior and then record the properties of representative samples of each class.

All students in a chemical laboratory, whatever the state or nation of their origin, agree in identifying the liquid that flows from the pipe at the lecture desk as water. They, as well as the trained chemist, recognize it as a particular kind of substance. Sugar and salt are other substances having characteristic properties which may be used to describe and identify them. Properties, in modern thinking, are inherent in substances and not accidental or casually associated qualities. This point of view did not always prevail.

From ancient times to the chemical revolution in the latter part of the eighteenth century it was common to explain the properties of substances in terms of the presence or absence of certain *principles* or *essences* which were regarded as qualities without mass. Some of the work of the alchemists was spent in trying to remove essences from substances in an effort to change their properties. Because the principles and essences were thought to be qualities without mass and because there was no experimental method for measuring them, it is not surprising that much of the alchemical work was mystical rather than scientific. Today we accept the idea that a vitamin or new drug will not be a mysterious, unweighable essence but, instead, a definite weighable substance with definite properties and, consequently, definite physiological actions.

Properties may be separated into two categories: those which depend on the amount of material, the *extensive properties*, and those independent of the amount, the *intensive properties*. The latter are usually the ones used to differentiate between or to identify substances. When men say in common speech that lead is "heavier" than iron they are really comparing an intensive property, density, rather than the extensive property, mass. They mean that the lead in a lump of a given size as measured by the eye has a greater "heft" when lifted by the hand than a lump of iron of corresponding size. This concept is expressed quantitatively in science by *density*, defined as the mass per unit volume. In each system of weights and measures definite values of the densities of lead and iron can be determined and their ratio can then be calculated when wanted.

Many of the terms in chemistry used to designate properties were introduced for this reason. The concepts they represent are not new but they are accurately defined and unambiguous whereas words in common use have different meanings and shades of meaning. Definite numerical values obtained with standard instruments or by standard procedures can then be measured and reported as properties in books and journals for ready reference.

Although chemists need such "scientifically" determined properties to describe and help identify the hundreds of thousands of different known substances they rely solely on their senses for much practical work. They learn to identify many substances by direct observation. The place where a substance is found is often a useful clue, not as extraneous as may appear at first glance. Substances may be found in certain places or environments *because* of their properties. Water flows from the pipe in the laboratory because water has properties which induced someone to lay the pipes to bring it there.

HOMOGENEOUS SYSTEMS AND PHASES

We have already commented on the fact that the universe is heterogeneous. The air about us, the waters of the earth, whether they are fresh or salt, and the solid earth, are different in kind and behavior. Even the air is heterogeneous, for we see that it contains clouds and dust. However, if we take a sample of air free from clouds and filter out the dust, we have a homogeneous substance alike in all its parts as judged by properties of different samples of it. Similarly, by separating the seaweed and visible suspended matter from sea water we obtain a clear homogeneous liquid.

The solid earth has much more heterogeneity than the air or waters. To separate homogeneous samples of solids from the rest of the earth is more difficult than to separate homogeneous gas or liquid but solids can be separated by hand sorting or by the various processes known to chemists. It is convenient to designate as a *system* any body or material we wish to consider and to call any homogeneous system of material a *phase*.

A *homogeneous phase* is, then, a region which is the "same" in all its parts, whereas a *heterogeneous substance* differs from region to region. But what experimental criteria does one use to detect these differences? A large rock which appears homogeneous from a distance may show markedly different phases on closer examination. Consider the granite mountain which on microscopic examination proves to be made up of five phases as in Figure 2.1. A powder homogeneous to the naked eye may be seen to contain many different kinds of crystals when viewed under the optical microscope or the electron microscope. And all known substances are heterogeneous when examined with a beam of x-rays, for the beam is always diffracted differently in different regions of the sample. Thus it appears that if we are to use the

Figure 2.1.
Granite rock (Half Dome, Yosemite National Park). Distant and microscopic views. The phases are (1) plagioclase, (2) quartz, (3) orthoclase, (4) biotite, and (5) hornblende.

term "homogeneous" we must make a rather arbitrary statement as to how closely one should examine a substance before arriving at a decision. As your knowledge of the structure of matter grows some of this arbitrariness will be resolved. For the moment you may consider a substance homogeneous if the tools at hand during the examination reveal no different regions in the material. Even the most advanced studies usually draw the line at the limit of observation with optical microscopes.

SEPARATION OF PHASES

All gas phases have important properties in common, properties familiar to anyone who has observed the behavior of air. All liquid phases also have common properties, familiar to anyone who has observed the most common liquid—water. Solid phases have other common properties. The differences in properties between gas phase, liquid phase, and solid phase are ordinarily so great that even the tyro can separate a gas phase from a liquid or solid phase, or a liquid phase from gas or solid phases. Two liquid phases can be separated since the phases, being different, probably have different densities. Then the lighter liquid will float on the heavier liquid and the two can be separated by mechanical devices. A solid phase can be readily separated from gas or liquid phases but less readily from other solid phases. A piece of granite is an example of a system with different solid phases, there being at least three. In Figure 2.1 there were five. A system of ice water has at least two different phases, the liquid phase and the ice phase. Observe that we do not speak of more than one ice phase even though there are many lumps of ice floating in the water. Similarly, all the grains of sugar in a sugar bowl belong to the same phase, sugar phase, since all the grains of sugar are homogeneous and have the same intensive properties. One does not create new phases simply by subdividing old ones.

PHASES AND PURE SUBSTANCES

When liquids boil they change to gases, and when liquids freeze they change to solids. A sample of substance may happen to be in a solid, a liquid, or a gaseous phase depending on the temperature and energy of the sample. High temperatures (and energies) favor the existence of gas phases and low temperatures favor the existence of solid phases. If the prevailing temperatures on earth were 100° colder, some substances we know as gases would be liquids and many we know as liquids would be solids. If the prevailing temperatures were 100° warmer some substances we know as solid would be liquids and many we know as liquids would be gaseous. Since substances may be in any one of the phases, solid, liquid, or gas, it appears that the phases themselves can not tell us what the constituent substances of the universe are.

Then too, not all homogeneous samples of natural waters are alike. A homogeneous sample of sea water, for example, tastes salty whereas a homogeneous sample of rain water does not. There are other definite, though small, differences; among them, differences in boiling and freezing temperatures. The water distilled from sea water has properties like that of rain water, but a salty solid is left behind when the water is evaporated completely. On the other hand, in water, whatever its source, we recognize a kind of substance with a unique set of properties which are the same regardless of whether the water was obtained as rain from the sky or as a distillate collected from sea water.

A thermometer placed above boiling rain water registers a definite and constant temperature (near 100°C.) as the liquid water boils away. If the water vapor is collected and condensed to liquid again, a thermometer in the condensing vapor will register the *same* temperature as that of the boiling liquid. The condensate has exactly the same properties as the liquid from which it came. From the fact that the thermometer registers a constant temperature we may deduce that the last of the water to boil away is exactly like the first. If either the original rain water or the condensate is frozen to ice, a thermometer in the ice-water mixture registers 0°C. temperature during the process. If some of the ice is removed and melted, a thermometer in this ice-water mixture registers the same temperature, 0°C., and the water obtained has the same properties as the original water. A substance meeting these tests of constant temperature during the changes of phase is called a *pure substance*. The last part of each pure substance to freeze or evaporate is identical with the first part to change phase. Phase changes may be used to separate one kind of pure substance from another, for example water from salt; they are the most common method used to obtain pure substances from other homogeneous phases, solutions.

SOLUTIONS

Not all homogeneous systems, containing substance in a single phase, are pure substances. A phase that is not pure is called a *solution*. Sea water is an example. Its density is greater than that of pure water and it has a salty taste. It begins to boil at a temperature higher than that of pure water and the temperature rises gradually as the water boils away. At the same time the density, and saltiness, of the sea water increases gradually. Curves showing how the boiling temperatures of pure water and of sea water change with time are shown in Figure 2.2. When some of the vapors of the boiling solutions are collected and condensed, they meet the tests of pure water—density about one gram per milliliter, condensation temperature constant at about 100°C., freezing temperature constant at 0°C., etc. By the distillation process pure water is separated from the sea water solution, leaving behind a solution of changed properties and composition (greater density and saltiness). If distillation is continued, crystalline salts begin to appear in the boiling solution, and finally, when all the water has evaporated, a mass of solid salts remains behind. Because the sea water can, through distillation accompanied by a regular rise in temperature, be separated into the component parts, water and the salts, we regard it as a solution. If the water which was boiled away and condensed again is now added to the solid salts the resulting solution will be like the original.

Solutions behave in a similar way on freezing. Salt water will not begin to freeze until its temperature is below the freezing temperatures both of pure water and of salt. When the temperature is lowered enough, either crystalline water (ice) or crystalline salt separates from the solution as a separate phase, depending on the relative amounts of water and salt in the solution. As the solid phase grows, the proportions of the components of the solution (water

12 GENERAL CHEMISTRY

and salt) change and the freezing temperature becomes progressively lower. At the same time the other properties of the solution—density, boiling temperature, etc.—also change.

We have already noted that the constant boiling and freezing temperatures of pure liquids depend on the fact that the liquid remaining behind is exactly like the part that has boiled away or frozen. Therefore, when energy is added evenly, all parts of the sample change at the same rate. But when solutions boil or freeze the different components change phase at different rates. Then the new phases that are formed have different compositions from the original solution and their properties are also different.

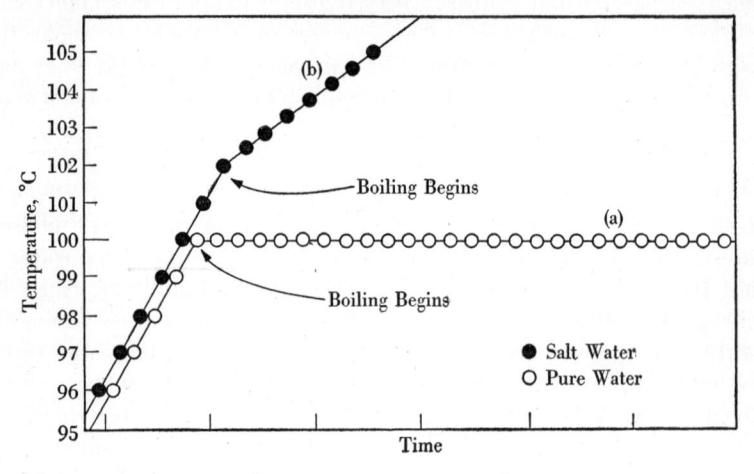

Figure 2.2.
Variation of boiling temperature with time for pure water (a) and for salt water (b).

In certain special cases solutions have a constant boiling temperature because both components evaporate at the same rate to produce a vapor with the same proportions of the components as the mother liquor. In other special cases both components of a solution crystallize out of the solution in the same proportion as they have in the mother liquor. Fortunately, constant-boiling solutions do not remain so when the pressure is changed, and, in general, a constant-freezing solution does not have a constant-boiling temperature so that we shall not need to be concerned with this problem unless we deal with different pure substances that are very similar in all their properties. So important and useful are the boiling and freezing temperatures of pure substances as means for distinguishing and identifying them that they are among the first properties of a pure substance to be mentioned.

Phase changes, then, not only allow us to distinguish between solutions and pure substances, but they also allow us to separate solutions into their component pure substances. The distillation of the solution, crude oil, into natural gas, gasoline, kerosene, lubricating oils, etc., is a step in this direction. In this particular process it is not commercially feasible or desirable to accomplish a complete separation, so that natural gas, gasoline, kerosene, and lubricating oil are all solutions in turn, though each contains fewer components than did the parent crude oil. A further step in the purification of many lubricating oils is a chilling process in which many of the waxes and other easily solidified components separate from the liquid solution as solids.

We have seen that our heterogeneous universe may be separated into its homogeneous parts, solutions and pure substances. As may be guessed, solutions are more commonly found than pure substances. Air is a gaseous solution. Most waters are solutions, containing, in addition to the principal component, water, variable amounts of other substances. The solutions may be separated into pure substances by suitable changes in phase.

CLASSES OF PURE SUBSTANCES—COMPOUNDS AND ELEMENTS

From the infinite variety of heterogeneities, through the billions of possible heterogeneous substances, chemists have found a few million pure substances, but the number known increases each day. It was one of the goals of the early chemists to see whether further simplification was possible, to see whether all known pure substances could be made from a smaller number of simpler substances. Such an idea had been considered by the early Greeks who postulated a set of four "elements"—earth, air, fire, and water. These correspond roughly to the four modern terms: solid, gas, energy, and liquid. In 1661, Robert Boyle proposed an idea of chemical elements modern in character: All pure substances are either elements or compounds, the elements being the simple, primitive "bodies," not made of other "bodies" or one another, which are the ingredients of compounds and into which compounds may be resolved.

Boyle's proposal was weak since it did not include practical criteria for deciding whether a particular substance was a simple one—whether it was an element or a compound. A hundred years passed before Lavoisier, a French chemist, developed a logical and experimental method of distinguishing compounds from elements. Prior to Lavoisier's work (in the 1770's) chemists had learned that substances could be made from other substances but they did not pay enough attention to the quantities of material involved. The element oxygen, one of the most common elements, was not recognized before 1774. When Lavoisier began to measure and to weigh the materials consumed and the materials produced in reactions, he proposed an important generalization now known as the *law of conservation of mass*. As applied to chemical reactions it may be stated: The sum of the masses of the reacting substances (*reagents*) always equals the sum of the masses of substances produced (*products*) when new substances are made from old ones (*chemical change*). This principle gives

14 GENERAL CHEMISTRY

a criterion of simple substances (elements): The mass of each of the simpler substances must be less than that of the compound substance but the sum of their masses must equal the mass of the compound substance.

Water is a pure substance and hydrogen is a pure substance but are either of them "simple" substances? In Lavoisier's time it was known that hydrogen burned to form water. Water can be decomposed to form hydrogen. Is one "simpler" than the other? When heated to very high temperatures some water is decomposed to form a gaseous solution of hydrogen and oxygen each of which may be separated out as a pure substance. Hydrogen and oxygen are also produced from water when it is decomposed with electrical energy rather than with thermal energy. Measurements show that the sum of the masses of the hydrogen and oxygen produced is equal to that of the water which has decomposed. Similarly, when a given amount of hydrogen burns, a definite amount of oxygen is required and the mass of the water produced is equal to the masses of hydrogen and oxygen that are consumed. Thus, water can be made of two fragments, hydrogen and oxygen, or it can be decomposed into those fragments. Water must be a compound substance. The experiment does not tell us whether oxygen and hydrogen are compounds or elements. If they can not be fragmented further they are "simple" and are elements.

Although water can be fragmented into hydrogen and oxygen this does not prove that water "contains" hydrogen and oxygen, for it is possible to form substances from materials which do not contain them as such. Sugar, for example, on heating decomposes into carbon and water, but sugar contains no carbon or water as such and was erroneously labeled a carbohydrate, meaning a compound of carbon and water, by the early chemists. The name is still used, however, for it is convenient even though its connotations are false. The fact that, upon the addition of energy, two substances, carbon and water, are obtained from sugar and that, in turn, two substances, hydrogen and oxygen, are obtained from water does prove that sugar and water are not "simple" substances. Both can be separated into different fragments which are pure substances. Thus, sugar and water are compounds.

One should note, even in these apparently clear-cut examples, that a large assumption is made. The assumption is that one need not be concerned with the energy necessary to decompose the sugar into carbon and water or to decompose water into hydrogen and oxygen. To put it another way, we do not consider energy a substance even though it is essential to the process. Energy is not appreciable in weight and not matter, though it is present in all matter. The terms substance and matter are limited to objects having mass.

And what is *mass*? Everyone knows that some bodies are harder to move (or stop moving) than others. The tendency to remain at rest if at rest, or to remain in motion if in motion, is called inertia. The masses of bodies are directly proportional to their inertias, so that by shoving or pulling them we can make a rough estimate of their masses and with proper instruments we can determine their masses accurately. A second way of measuring mass, and the one commonly used, is weighing. The method depends on the attraction of the earth for the substance under specified conditions. The force of this attraction is called gravity. In chemistry mass is usually measured by means of a *balance* on which the mass of one object is balanced by weights of known masses. Then the attraction of the earth is the same for the masses on the two pans of the balance.

CHEMICAL ELEMENTS

The methods of Boyle and Lavoisier for finding what pure substances are chemical elements may seem crude for they rest on the skill of the experimenter in decomposing compounds. The first lists of chemical elements contained some substances we now know to be compounds. For example, lime, a compound of calcium and oxygen, was included among the elements because the early chemists were not able to decompose it. After calcium was prepared in 1808 it was shown to combine with oxygen to form lime, hence lime must be a compound. Indirect methods of this kind, the forming of a given mass of pure substance from two or more different substances according to the principle of conservation of mass, showed that most known pure substances were compounds. The pure substances that remained, those which could not be decomposed into simple substances or synthesized from simpler substances, formed the list of chemical elements. Over the years the number of known chemical elements increased slowly as compounds of the less abundant elements were discovered and the elements were isolated from them.

It is now well known that each of the chemical elements may, in turn, be decomposed into still simpler (less massive) fragments. These fragments differ from the elements in that they can not be stored in large quantities by any known method but must be observed shortly after the element has been fragmented to form them. Nevertheless, the idea of the chemical element is still a useful one. The chemical elements are the simplest pure substances which can be isolated, bottled, and put on the shelf for storage. Their properties, boiling and freezing temperatures, densities, etc., can be determined. Under controlled conditions they may react in known ways with one another to form compounds, which in turn are pure substances that can be bottled and stored.

Carbon, hydrogen, oxygen, nitrogen, sulfur, sodium, iron, copper, and gold are examples of chemical elements. In 1945 there were some 90 chemical elements known and in 1954 100 were known. The evidence is very strong that no others will be found in nature on earth, although it may be possible for chemists and physicists to synthesize a few more, perhaps as many as ten, in the laboratory. The hundred chemical elements must, according to our argument, be able to combine to give us the million or so known chemical compounds which in turn must form all known solutions and heterogeneous systems. From the great apparent diversity of the universe we have arrived at the concept of about one hundred simple chemical substances through whose combinations all matter is constructed.

16 GENERAL CHEMISTRY

ULTIMATE PARTICLES

Up to now we have considered only the kinds of substances that can be isolated and stored. No claim has been made that the chemical elements are the simplest fragments or building blocks in nature. The theory that elements consist of characteristic atoms was proposed at the beginning of the nineteenth century. One hundred years passed before experiments were devised showing the effects of individual atoms. Since that time we have learned how to detect small particles lighter in mass than those of individual atoms. Up to 1932 it was generally accepted that there were two such particles, electrons and protons. Since electrons could be obtained from any of the elements they were thought of as being one of the kinds of ultimate particles from which all chemical elements were made and they were therefore designated as "fundamental particles." Protons were also regarded as the fundamental particles responsible for most of the mass of the elements. In the last twenty years a number of other "sub-atomic" particles have been detected. The continued search for the fundamental particles of nature is one of the most exciting of current scientific researches and the answers do not appear to be close at hand. We now know that particles such as electrons, protons, neutrons, positrons, and mesons, are related to one another and, under certain conditions, can interact to form one another. The term, fundamental particles, is still applied to them but "fundamental" has taken on a new and restricted meaning. In the next chapter we shall consider some of the present knowledge of these particles.

UNDERSTANDING CHEMISTRY

You will have noted that formal definitions were not given in the preceding material and that no sentences are emphasized by special type. There will be little of "you must know this," or "remember this" in following chapters to jog your mind and encourage you to memorize particular statements of fundamental ideas. Formal definitions and too forceful emphasis on certain statements tend to encourage feats of memory which interfere with critical thinking about the ideas themselves. You should not need arbitrary emphases for you will find that the most important words, facts, and ideas are used again and again.

None can deny that memory is important in learning chemistry. By the end of the year, if you are successful in your studying, you will have accumulated a large store of chemical information in your "memory." But, again assuming you have applied yourself, most of this material will not be at your command because you sat down and deliberately memorized it. It will have come from your direct experiences with materials, particularly in the laboratory, and with your quantitative and qualitative measurement of their properties. Through repeated use you will remember certain numerical values. You will remember the properties and behaviors you use to identify and classify

KINDS OF SUBSTANCES

the substances you work with and you will learn to extrapolate your experience to new substances. In this way you will do most of your memorizing subconsciously.

Memory, a recall of information, is useful only if the material recalled is usable. To be most usable, it must be understood. A good memory is helpful but it can never be effective without thought, that is, without understanding of relationships. Real comprehension will be yours only when you have learned to use information. Good ways of testing your understanding and your mastery of information are to apply them to new situations (problems) and to explain your solutions to a fellow student. Then you will quickly find the gaps in your understanding.

Problem 2.1. Matter is sometimes said to include anything which has mass and occupies space. Is the first part of the definition alone sufficient, that is, is there anything which has mass but is not matter? Do we know anything about space entirely apart from matter?

Problem 2.2. Which of the following substances are homogeneous and which heterogeneous: wood, sugar, water, iron rust, brass, granite, coin silver, molasses, wine, brick, glass, air, salt, mercury, coal? State your reasons.

Problem 2.3. Which of the homogeneous substances listed in Problem 2.2 are pure substances and which are solutions? Of the pure substances which are compounds and which are elements?

Problem 2.4. Name some properties that serve to differentiate metals and nonmetals.

Problem 2.5. Compose an outline showing the relationship between the kinds of substances discussed in this chapter, starting with heterogeneous substances and progressing to the elements. Indicate the experimental test to be applied to each type of substance and the method of decomposing each of the more complex substances into the next simpler form.

Problem 2.6. How would you proceed to test the statement that air is a solution? You should be able to describe at least three conclusive, but mutually independent, methods.

Problem 2.7. Minerals of aluminum are relatively abundant. Why is aluminum more expensive than iron?

Problem 2.8. Airplanes are known as "heavier-than-air" machines, and dirigibles as "lighter-than-air." How do you interpret these two terms?

Problem 2.9. Which of the following substances can burn in air: iron, salt, sugar, concrete, gold, magnesium, kerosene, water, oxygen, carbon dioxide, glass?

Problem 2.10. All of us identify water subconsciously when we see it. What experience and what properties of water do we use in making the identification?

Problem 2.11. List some of the criteria used to determine whether or not a substance is pure.

3 THE FUNDAMENTAL PARTICLES OF NATURE

WE HAVE seen that heterogeneous systems found in nature can be segregated into component homogeneous parts, that these can be identified as solutions or pure substances, and that the solutions can be separated by phase changes into the pure substances of which they are composed. All the pure substances are made up of the chemical elements (of which 100 are now known) either as themselves or combined with one another in the form of new pure substances, called compounds. The whole world, therefore, consists of the chemical elements combined in various ways. These chemical elements may be further decomposed under special conditions involving very high energies, but the fragments so obtained are of short life and cannot be stored in any large amount. We shall now examine the nature of these fragments which may be obtained by the decomposition of the chemical elements.

NATURAL TRANSMUTATIONS OF THE CHEMICAL ELEMENTS

The chemical elements may indeed be stored but not with equal ease or permanence. We are not referring here to any possible interaction with the container but to the inherent possibility that the element itself will undergo a change. If one were to obtain one hundred separate containers each holding a sample of one of the hundred elements known in 1954, twenty-eight of the hundred would be found to be continually changing. In each of these twenty-eight bottles the element originally placed in the bottle would be found to be undergoing a transformation into one or more of the other known chemical elements. Can we still use our ability to bottle and store as a test for chemical elements when more than one-fourth of the elements so stored undergo spontaneous change? The answer is yes, for in each case that portion of the original element remaining has unchanged properties and the element formed from the portion that has changed has the properties characteristic of the daughter element. Here we find occurring naturally the transmutation of the elements which early chemists, then known as alchemists, sought so vigorously.

RADIOACTIVITY

Careful examination of every elementary sample undergoing a transmutational change reveals that radiation is being emitted by the sample. Such elements are said to be radioactive. Certain substances—for example naphthalene, zinc sulfide, the powder inside a fluorescent lamp—emit visible light when struck by the invisible radiations from a radioactive material. They fluoresce. The rate of emission of radiation in some radioactive transformations may be so low that very careful experimentation is required to detect it with fluorescent materials, but each of the elements in Table 3.1 may be shown to be undergoing a transmutation. Table 3.1 lists only the parent element and a

Table 3.1
Typical Transmutations Occurring Among the Chemical Elements

PARENT ELEMENT	DAUGHTER ELEMENT	PARENT ELEMENT	DAUGHTER ELEMENT
Potassium	→ calcium	Radon	→ polonium
Rubidium	→ strontium	Francium	→ radium
Technetium	→ ruthenium	Radium	→ radon
Indium	→ tin	Actinium	→ thorium
Prometheum	→ samarium	Thorium	→ radium
Samarium	→ neodymium	Protoactinium	→ uranium
Lutetium	→ hafnium	Uranium	→ thorium
Rhenium	→ osmium	Neptunium	→ plutonium
Thallium	→ lead	Plutonium	→ uranium
Lead	→ bismuth	Americium	→ neptunium
Bismuth	→ polonium	Curium	→ plutonium
Polonium	→ lead	Berkelium	→ americium
Astatine	→ bismuth	Californium	→ curium

daughter element and does not show the radiations emitted during the transmutations. Some of the parent elements undergo several different types of transmutation simultaneously as evidenced by the fact that several daughter elements are formed and that several different types of radiation are being emitted.

Not only may the radiations cause fluorescence, as has already been stated. They may also affect a photographic plate as does visible light. Indeed, the first evidence of their existence was the discovery by Henri Becquerel in 1896 that certain radiations were able to pass through the black paper protecting his photographic plates from visible light. The radiations were found to penetrate considerable thicknesses of matter impervious to visible light, indicating that the radiations possess high energy. They cause gases, which are ordinarily electrical insulators, to become electrical conductors. These facts led to an investigation of the electrical properties of the rays themselves. Thin beams of the radiations from the various radioactive substances, when passed between plates of opposite electrical charge, behave in one of three ways (see Figure 3.1). Some beams pass through the electrical field undeflected, hence they have no electrical charge associated with them. Some beams are deflected toward the positive electrical plate, hence a negative charge is associated with them. Finally, some beams are deflected toward the negative electrical plate, hence there is a positive charge on the beams. These observations are interpreted by the primary rule of electrostatics—that like electrical charges repel and unlike electrical charges attract each other. For convenience, since the full nature of the beams was an enigma, the positively charged beams were called alpha rays, the negatively charged beams were called beta rays, and the electrically

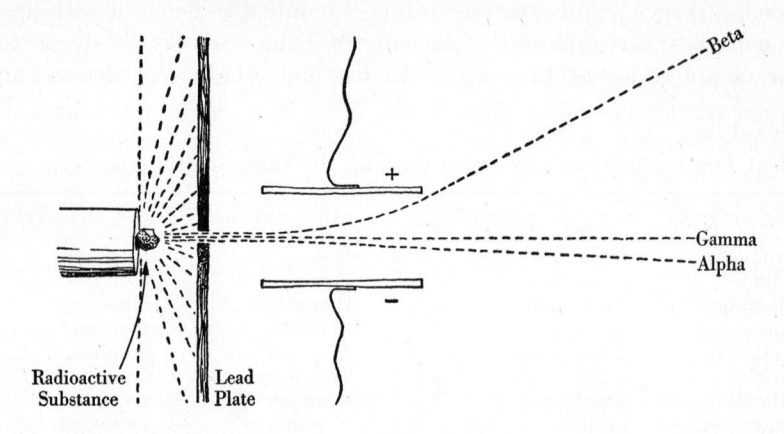

Figure 3.1.
Deflection of alpha, beta, and gamma rays in an electric field.

neutral rays were called gamma rays after the first three letters of the Greek alphabet. These names are still used.

PARTICLES OR STREAMS OF RADIATION?

Thus far we have tacitly assumed that materials can be fragmented, that is, broken up into particles, but this assumption is not necessarily true. We must ask ourselves, for instance: Are the alpha, beta, and gamma rays composed of individual particles or are they merely continuous streams of some type ejected by the elements much as a continuous stream of water seems to be ejected by a hose? The fluorescent screen gives the most direct answer. At first glance the screen appears to emit a steady, even glow as one would expect to result if it were being struck by a continuous stream, but closer examination with a microscope shows that the apparent steady glow is in reality composed of thousands of individual flashes or scintillations and that the fluorescence consists of intermittent bursts or flashes of light originating in very small regions. The most direct interpretation is that the individual scintillations are caused by individual particles. However, a possible interpretation is that the screen receives a continuous stream of energy but that this energy must be stored in small localities until enough has accumulated to cause the screen to emit a flash of light.

RADIATION COUNTERS

The question of individual particles versus continuous stream may be resolved by studying two other properties of rays, the property of making gases electrically conducting, and the property of containing considerable energy. For the moment let us consider only the beams having no electrical charge, the gamma rays. Rays from all samples emitting gamma radiation have the ability to make gases conductive and the degree of conductivity is found to vary with the total energy of the radiation. Let us construct an apparatus for determining the electrical conductivity of a gas and study this variation. Such an apparatus might consist schematically of two metallic plates, one charged negatively and the other positively, with a gas between them. There must also be some sort of a recording device to register the number of times the gas becomes conductive and the amount of electricity it conducts each time it is in the conductive condition. When such an apparatus, called a radiation counter, is placed so that the radiations must pass through the gas, discrete periods of conductivity are recorded just as discrete flashes of light were obtained on the fluorescent screen. This fact could mean either that the gamma radiation consists of discrete particles or merely that the gas has to absorb a certain amount of energy from the beam before it can become conductive (with time required for the absorption of enough energy.) A clear test of these two alternatives is possible for one can test the relation between amount of energy and number of flashes.

Let two sources of radiation, known to be of different energies be used. The difference in energy may be measured by interposing metal sheets between a screen and the two sources of radiation, and observing how the fluorescence is inhibited. The metal sheets will absorb a much higher fraction of the less energetic beam. If the radiation is continuous and the intermittent action of the counter is a result of the storage of energy until the critical amount necessary to start current flow has been accumulated, each period of conductivity should represent the passage of the same amount of electrical current having this stored up energy. Each "pulse" should then be identical. Variations in the energy content of different radiation beams will appear as varying numbers of periods of conductivity. High energy beams will give many pulses per second, while low energy beams will give fewer pulses per second since it will take the system longer to accumulate the energy required to cause current to flow in the counter tube. On the other hand a radiation beam composed of discrete particles will render the tube conducting each time a particle passes through it, and the amount of current which flows in each pulse will depend on the energy associated with the particle. High-energy particles will allow more current to flow per pulse than will low-energy particles, since their higher energy will generate more electrical current. With proper apparatus experimental observation shows that pulses from high-energy rays and low-energy rays may come with equal frequency but that the former pulses do indeed represent a higher current through the counter tube. These facts are consistent with the particle theory but not with the continuous stream theory of gamma radiation.

Similar results are obtained for all three types of beam: alpha, beta, and gamma. Alpha rays, being electrically positive, are beams of positively charged particles, beta rays, being negatively charged, consist of negatively charged particles, and gamma rays consist of particles with no electrical charge.

Study of electricity shows that flow of electricity can occur only through

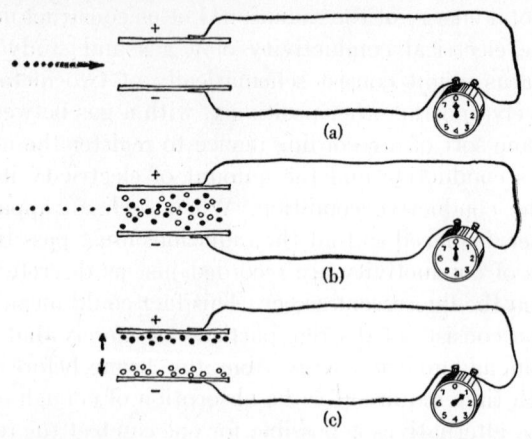

Figure 3.2.
Operation of a counter tube (schematic): (a) radiation approaches tube, (b) radiation produces charged particles, (c) charged particles reach plates—current flows.

the motion of charged particles. Thus the function of radiation in rendering a gas conductive must be to form charged particles in the gas. Figure 3.2 gives a diagrammatic representation of the action of a radiation counter. (Radiation counters are of many types, for example, Geiger counters, ionization chambers. The type we have described is known as a proportional counter.)

WILSON CLOUD CHAMBER

A more direct indication of particle nature in radioactivity is possible since the paths of individual alpha, beta, and gamma rays may be made observable to the naked eye. We have already seen that the radiations make a gas electrically conducting as they pass through it. Other experiments show that water vapor condenses preferentially in the conductive regions to form droplets of liquid water. Consequently, when water vapor under proper conditions is present, the vapor condenses to form small visible droplets along the paths of the rays. These "cloud tracks" outline the actual paths of the rays. The apparatus usually used for observing the cloud track is called a Wilson cloud chamber. Figure 3.3 shows a typical observation. Occasionally the ray path shows a sharp deflection from linearity; apparently the radiation particle struck something in the gas and changed direction.

The tracks formed by the radiation resulting from any given transmutation have about the same length. This fact is interpreted as meaning that the original radiations had the same energies. It requires energy to render the gas conductive so that finally the radiated particle loses its energy and the track ceases. Since particles having the same initial energy lose it at the same rate in passing through the gas, the length of track in a given medium is a measure of the energy of the radiated particle.

Additional evidence could be cited for the particle nature of alpha, beta, and gamma rays but the fluorescence effect and the behavior in radiation counters and in cloud chambers can be most simply interpreted in terms of individual particles. If alpha, beta, and gamma radiation consist of particles and some of them are charged two further questions suggest themselves: (1) How large are the electrical charges on the particles and (2) how massive are the particles?

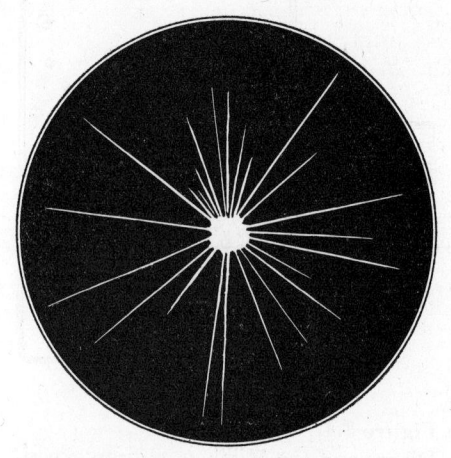

Figure 3.3.
Diagram of Wilson cloud chamber fog tracks. The tracks are of equal length but go in all directions, thus some are foreshortened.

THE NATURE OF ELECTRICAL CHARGES

The determination of a thing's magnitude is customarily a much more difficult task than the determination of a thing's existence, and electrical charge is no exception. The concept of positive and negative charge has been known for two hundred years, but the determination of the magnitude of the unit of charge is of relatively recent origin. Here again, as for the radiation from radioactive elements, the problem of particle versus stream presents itself. Can electricity be subdivided into indefinitely smaller units of charge or is there some small unit of charge which must be taken in multiples to make up all larger charges so that all quantities of electricity are multiples of this unit charge? This problem was originally solved unambiguously by Stoney in 1874. He showed that there was a single unit of negative electricity, determined its approximate magnitude, and named it the *electron* charge. But the first accurate measurements of magnitude were made by Millikan during the years 1906–16.

24 GENERAL CHEMISTRY

Millikan utilized the fact, to which we have already referred, that opposite charges attract and like charges repel. He reasoned that if a small object were electrically neutral, its rate of fall in the earth's gravitational field would be unaffected by the presence of a positively charged electrical plate above it and a negatively charged plate below. If such an object should be charged positively, however, its rate of fall would be increased by such an arrangement, whereas a negatively charged particle would fall at a slower rate under these conditions or might even rise. If the two plates were present but not charged, any charge on the object would have no effect on its rate of fall. Millikan's experiment involved the rate of fall of oil drops which had been given an electrical charge by exposure to a source of natural radioactivity and the change in that rate of fall when various electrical charges were imposed on the plates above and below the drop. His apparatus is represented schematically in Figure 3.4. This and other experiments have been done thousands of times and all the results lead to the conclusion that all electrical charges, both positive and negative, are multiples of a single unit of charge. This unit is often expressed in "electrostatic units" or "electromagnetic units" but for our purposes it is most convenient to call this smallest possible electrical charge a charge of one, or unit electrical charge. All other charges then are simple multiples of unity.

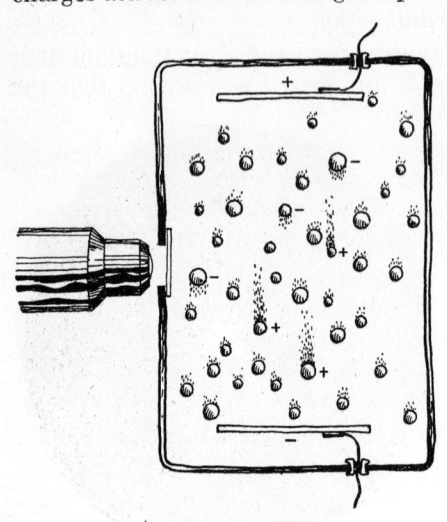

Figure 3.4.
Diagram of the Millikan oil drop experiment (schematic). The rate of fall of a given drop is observed in the microscope and measured with the plates charged and with them uncharged. From the two rates and the known properties of the oil and the gas through which the droplets move the magnitude of the charge on each drop can be calculated. All charges prove to be multiples of the same unit charge.

ELECTRICAL CHARGES OF ALPHA AND BETA PARTICLES

We know that gamma particles are uncharged but what is the magnitude of the charges on alpha and beta particles? Since all electrical charges are multiples of a unit charge, the alpha particles, being positively charged, must each bear a charge of 1+, 2+, or some other integral positive value and each beta particle, being negatively charged, must bear a charge of 1−, 2−, or some other integral value. The assignment of magnitude of charge to alpha particles and beta particles is an extremely difficult experimental problem which we shall not attempt to describe here. It is relatively easy to determine the ratio of the charge of a particle to its mass but if we do not know the mass we are unable to calculate the value for the charge. We can report that a tremendous amount of evidence leads to the conclusion that the charge on an alpha particle is 2+ and the charge on a beta particle is 1−.

MASS AND CHARGE OF RADIOACTIVE RADIATIONS

We are now left with the problem of the mass of these particles. We have already intimated that mass may be calculated directly from experiments if the charge on the respective particles is known. In this determination one again utilizes the fact that like electrical charges repel and unlike attract. Our proof that alpha and beta rays have an electrical charge was obtained by passing them between oppositely charged plates and noting the direction of their deflection (see Figure 3.1). It is possible to measure not only the direction of this deflection but also its magnitude, and a brief consideration of the factors affecting this magnitude will show where mass enters in. The deflection itself is due to the difference in charge of plates and particle and will be larger the greater the charge on the plates, and the greater the charge on the particle. But the amount of deflection also depends on the length of time the particle spends between the plates, that is, on its speed—deflection is less the higher the speed. In addition the mass of the particle will have an effect, for a more massive particle will be harder to deflect from its path than a lighter one and therefore will deviate less from a straight-line path. Knowing the velocity of the particle, the strength of the electric field through which it passes, the charge on the particle, and radius of curvature of its path we can calculate the mass of the particle. Values for the masses of alpha, beta, and gamma particles are listed in Table 3.2.

Table 3.2
Mass and Charge of Particles Found in Natural Radioactivity

PARTICLE	MASS (IN GRAMS)	CHARGE (ELECTRON = 1−)	OTHER IDENTIFICATION
Alpha	6.6×10^{-24}	2+	helium ions
Beta	9.1×10^{-28}	1−	electrons
Gamma	0	0	energy (photons, quanta)

The beta particles with their charge of 1− have the same mass and charge as other particles obtained from known stable materials. From their behavior, beta particles are known to be electrons travelling at high speeds and with high energy.

When alpha particles with their charge of 2+ lose their energy and high velocity they pick up electrons from the surroundings and their charge becomes neutralized. They then behave like helium gas. The first experimental test

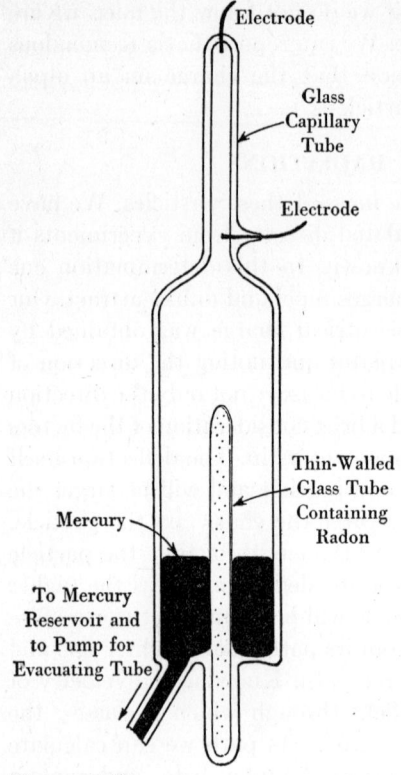

Figure 3.5.
Diagram of apparatus for collecting helium gas formed by alpha particles from radon. Radon is sealed in the small, thin-walled center tube. Alpha particles from the radon go through the thin glass wall but are trapped in the surrounding enclosed space. From time to time this trapped gas is compressed into the small capillary by allowing the mercury level to rise, and voltage is applied to the two electrodes. The trapped gas then emits light identical to that obtained from gaseous helium under similar conditions. The intensity of the light increases with each compression, indicating that the amount of helium in the tube increases as more and more alpha particles are trapped.

for this is outlined in Figure 3.5. Similarly, if ordinary helium gas is made conductive and accelerated to high velocities, rays with the characteristics of alpha particles result. These facts indicate that alpha particles are particles of helium gas each carrying a charge of 2+. They also show the particle, or atomic, nature of the element helium. Its charged atoms, for example, He^{2+}, are called *ions*.

A summary of the information we have collected on alpha, beta, and gamma particles is presented in Table 3.2. Only these three particles are obtained during radioactive processes observed in naturally occurring materials. These processes are called natural radioactivity.

The observant student will notice that the method of mass determination described above cannot be used on gamma particles. Why? Their masses are, therefore, obtained in other ways and prove to be zero as listed in Table 3.2. But particles with zero mass are not matter and cannot be called substances, as was indicated in Chapter 2. Gamma rays, therefore, since they lack mass, are "pure energy." We are thus led to the conclusion that not only can mass come in packets, alpha and beta rays for instance, but energy also may. These energy particles, or packets, are sometimes called photons, and sometimes quanta. (We should comment here that experimental difficulties in obtaining and using electric fields in general prevent their use in quantitative deflection experiments unless combined with magnetic fields. Charged particles are deflected not only by electric fields, but also by magnetic fields. This experimental fact does not affect the arguments presented, however.)

INDUCED RADIOACTIVITY

But what of the other seventy-two elements which are not naturally radioactive? Are they stable because they are grossly different from the twenty-eight radioactive ones? Or is it perhaps that they do not have enough energy of themselves to emit the highly energetic radioactive rays? Suggested possibility—supply them with a great deal of energy. The simplest way is to bombard them with radiations from some of the naturally radioactive materials, but to produce bombarding beams of very high energy and intensity requires complicated machines (cyclotrons, synchrotrons, betatrons, linear accelerators, etc.). The effects of the high-energy cosmic rays may also be studied. Such bombardments lead to the expected results, but give some new phenomena in addition. During bombardment with high energy particles many of the normally nonradioactive elements begin to emit alpha, beta, or gamma radiations themselves. But just as commonly they emit radiations which are not alpha, beta, or gamma rays. These new radiations, which are characteristic only of bombardment experiments and induced radioactive processes (as opposed to natural radioactivity), may be measured in ways similar to those used for the alpha, beta, and gamma rays. (The properties of some of them

Table 3.3
Mass and Charge of Some Particles Found in Bombardment Experiments

PARTICLE	APPROXIMATE MASS (in grams)	CHARGE (compared to electron = 1−)	APPROXIMATE MASS (compared to neutron)
Neutron	1.7×10^{-24}	0	1
Proton	1.7×10^{-24}	1+	1
Deuteron	3.4×10^{-24}	1+	2
Triton	5.1×10^{-24}	1+	3
Positron	9.1×10^{-28}	1+	$\frac{1}{2000}$
Neutrino	Very small	0	Very small, not zero
Meson	Any one of about a dozen particles whose mass lies between that of the electron and the proton, and whose charge is apparently 0, or 1+, or 1−. The mean lifetime of a meson is usually less than 10^{-6} seconds. They are formed only in very high energy reactions. Thus they are of no current importance in chemistry though of great interest because of what they may reveal about fundamental particles.		

are cataloged in Table 3.3.) Furthermore, some of them may be used as bombarding particles to induce still further changes.

The charges on all particles in Table 3.3 are integral multiples of the electron (beta particle) charge, but the masses bear no such simple relation to one another. Some semblance of order may be obtained, however, if we neglect the very light particles (less than 10^{-24} g.) for a moment and compare the masses of the proton and neutron. They are approximately the same, and the masses of the deuteron, triton, and alpha particles are approximately integral multiples of this proton or neutron mass. We shall, therefore, call the approximate mass of the proton or neutron *unit mass* (analogous to calling the electron charge unity) and tabulate the masses of other particles in terms of it, as in the last column of Table 3.3. It is an important fact that although the charges are exactly integral multiples of the electronic charge, the actual masses deviate slightly (less than one per cent) from integral numbers.

We have seen that the naturally radioactive elements are transformed to other elements (as in Table 3.1) while they are emitting the radiations shown in Table 3.2. In the same way the ordinarily stable elements when bombarded so that radioactivity is induced in them are transmuted to daughter elements while their own radiations are being emitted. The daughter elements formed depend on the kind of beams used as well as on the nature of the parent elements. Radioactive forms of all the elements are now known. The changes will be discussed more fully in Chapter 22 on Nuclear Chemistry.

THE FUNDAMENTAL PARTICLES

The data in Tables 3.2 and 3.3 show certain regularities. All charges are multiples of the unit electron charge and the masses of all heavier particles are approximate multiples of the proton or neutron mass. Is each of the listed particles a fundamental particle or are some of them combinations of simpler particles? This question has not yet been answered definitely but we may assume that some are combinations. The deuteron may be considered to be a combination of a proton and a neutron which would give it its charge of 1+ and its mass of 2. Likewise, the triton may be considered to be composed of a proton and two neutrons and the alpha particle to be composed of two protons and two neutrons. Thus, all the heavier particles may be considered to be formed by combination of protons and neutrons. The electrons and other light particles do not fit into this scheme.

If a particle were truly "fundamental" one would expect that it could not be subdivided further and that when it reacted with other materials it would contribute its own characteristics, charge and mass, for example, to the product. However, processes are known in which protons are converted to neutrons either by gaining electrons or losing positrons. And it is possible for a neutron to change into a proton by uniting with a positron or by emitting an electron. Yet there is no evidence that there are individual neutrons or positrons within a proton, or that neutrons "contain" protons or electrons as such. Each merely contains the ingredients, such as charge and mass, essential for the creation of other particles. (Remember that water can be obtained from sugar even though there is no water in sugar.) The problem of the ultimate constitution of these particles is an unsolved mystery.

We have already commented on the fact that electrons and protons were

THE FUNDAMENTAL PARTICLES OF NATURE

thought to be fundamental particles when they were discovered. In the same way some of the other small particles in turn were thought to be fundamental particles. Even though we now know that they may be converted into one another we still call all the simpler ones "fundamental," because to designate any of them as truly fundamental would involve a choice not warranted by the present experimental evidence. We shall hereafter drop the quotation marks from "fundamental" because the limited meaning of the term should now be understood. For most of the purposes of beginning chemistry we shall be concerned primarily with the fundamental particles, protons, neutrons, and electrons. We pass over, for the present, positrons, neutrinos, and mesons, primarily because their short mean life times (less than 10^{-6} seconds) makes them rare, but partly because they are found only in high-energy reactions.

INTERCONVERSION OF MASS AND ENERGY

It will be noted in Table 3.2 that the gamma particles are unique in that they do not exhibit mass. These massless particles also have no charge and thus can be described as "pure energy." It is not, however, correct to say that an element loses no mass when it emits gamma radiation, for mass and energy are two different aspects of the same thing. Any system which loses energy also loses mass. The relationship between the two is given by the famous Einstein equation: $\Delta E = c^2 \times \Delta m$, where ΔE is the energy change, Δm is the change in mass, and c is the speed of light, which enters as the square in the equation and is a very large number.

The amount of energy in a closed system undergoing change may thus vary widely, whereas the amount of mass varies only slightly. This follows from the very large conversion factor c^2 between mass and energy changes and shows why the law of conservation of mass, mentioned previously, holds so well within experimental accuracy even though it is really violated in every change involving energy shifts. In other words, the changes in mass are seldom detectable by present experimental methods. The statement should really be that mass-energy is neither created nor destroyed in any change, and that transformations of mass to energy and vice versa follow the Einstein equation. This statement is known as the law of conservation of mass-energy.

An interesting consequence of the law of conservation of mass-energy is met when a massive particle acquires energy and begins to move at a higher speed. Einstein predicted that the increase in speed would be accompanied by an increase in mass according to the equation

$$m = m_0 \frac{1}{\sqrt{1 - \left(\frac{v}{c}\right)^2}} \tag{3.1}$$

where m_0 is the mass of the particle when it is at rest (speed is zero), c is the speed of light and m is the mass of the particle when its speed is v. The

30   GENERAL CHEMISTRY

equation has been tested extensively experimentally and Einstein's prediction justified.

LOW ENERGY RADIATIONS FROM CHEMICAL ELEMENTS

As is now common knowledge, the energy associated with radioactivity is very great. That necessary to induce radioactivity is of the order of a million electron-volts per disintegration. (The electron-volt is a unit of energy. It is the energy gained by a single electron which is accelerated across a potential gap of one volt. An electron-volt is equal to 1.6×10^{-12} ergs or 3.8×10^{-20} calories.) Physicists and chemists were able to detect radioactivity because they had developed experience with such common radiations as ordinary light, or flame, or a low-energy electric discharge. The energy associated with such common radiations is only about one-millionth that found in radioactive processes.

Beams of high intensity may be developed in electrical discharge tubes, called *Crookes tubes*, containing two electrodes and a gas at low pressure. Connection of a high voltage source of about a thousand volts to the electrodes produces electrical discharge through the gas. Three types of beams are found. One type causes a fluorescent screen to scintillate, showing that the beam consists of particles. The beam is attracted toward the positive plate in an electric field, showing that the particles are negatively charged. A determination of the mass and electrical charge of the beam particles shows that these particles are electrons, yet they have been obtained with the use of low energies and are not themselves emitted with the very high energies characteristic of beta-ray electrons, though identical with them in every other way. These lower-energy electrons may be obtained from any of the hundred elements by suitable excitation, though beta rays can not be obtained from some. Evidently there are two sources of electrons in the elements which differ at least in the energy necessary to give up the electrons and perhaps in other ways as well. Because the low-energy electrons are obtainable from all elements they are considered by chemists to be one of the fundamental particles forming the elements.

In some discharge tubes a second radiation called x-radiation was formed. The x-rays were found to be without charge and mass, just as we have found the gamma rays to be. Consequently, x-rays are energy, like light. They have, in general, less energy than gamma rays.

A third type of rays in discharge tubes was found to be attracted toward the negative plate of the electric field. The rays are therefore positively charged. They consist of particles much more massive than electrons. Their nature depends on the nature of the gas in the discharge tube. Hydrogen gas gives positive rays with the same charge and mass as protons, and helium gas gives positive rays like alpha particles. Furthermore, the masses of the particles in the rays correspond to the masses proposed by chemists for the atoms of the elements. It appears, therefore, that the low-energy positive rays obtained from the elements are charged atoms or molecules, called ions. Here again we find evidence for the particle nature of matter among the chemical elements as well as among the fundamental particles. Later we shall see in more detail how the atoms of the elements may be composed from the fundamental particles.

In this chapter we have shown how our highly heterogeneous world gives evidence of being composed of some ten or so fundamental particles. The relations between these particles are not clear at present. As students of chemistry we are primarily interested in their gross effect, if any, on the properties of bulk material we can handle and store and we shall try to explain as many of the properties of pure substances as possible in terms of the behavior of fundamental particles. It will be convenient to make some of the correlations indirectly, that is, to explain the properties of atoms of the elements in terms of protons, neutrons, electrons, etc., and then to use the atoms to explain the properties of the chemical elements and compounds and all the homogeneous and heterogeneous materials that can be made from them. However, we shall have continuing reasons on occasion to refer to the properties of the fundamental particles themselves. For instance, we shall interpret negative charges in terms of electrons, positive charges (and accompanying mass) in terms of protons, and mass unaccompanied by charge in terms of neutrons.

Problem 3.1. Using the Crookes' tube data and Table 3.3, suggest a possible composition of hydrogen atoms and of helium atoms in terms of the fundamental particles.

Problem 3.2. Under what conditions would the conversion of a neutron into a proton and an electron be consistent with the law of the conservation of mass-energy? That is, what relations may exist between the mass of the neutron and that of the proton?

Problem 3.3. Does the fact that the elements emit discrete particles in radioactive processes prove that the elements themselves are composed of particles, i.e., are atomic in character?

Problem 3.4. Tabulate the relative masses and charges of electrons, protons, and neutrons.

Problem 3.5. A substance emits an alpha particle. What else must be lost by the substance if it is to retain its electrical neutrality?

Problem 3.6. Occasionally the tracks in a Wilson cloud chamber are observed to split into two separate tracks, forming a Y-shaped track as a whole. Suggest two possible interpretations of this effect.

Problem 3.7. In Millikan's oil drop experiment some of the oil drops fell more rapidly when the plates were charged, some fell less rapidly, and some at the same rate as when no charge was on the plates. How do you account for these observations?

Problem 3.8. What would you expect to observe if you looked through a microscope at the luminous figures on a watch dial, the room being dark? Give reasons for your answer.

4 ELEMENTS AND ATOMS

WE HAVE already seen that the material of the heterogeneous universe can be separated into pure substances having definite properties which can be used to identify and describe them. Some of the pure substances, the compounds, can be decomposed into other pure substances, the chemical elements. The millions of known compounds can be decomposed into, or synthesized from, the hundred known elements. We have also seen that the chemical elements themselves, or their compounds can yield certain simpler particles of fugitive existence. The larger of these particles, though carrying an electric charge when travelling at a high speed, become electrically neutral when they have lost their excess energy and then have a more stable existence as atoms of elements which can be bottled and stored.

CHEMICAL ELEMENTS AND ATOMS

Two points of view about the nature of matter are now evident. The first concerns itself with the things we can detect directly with our senses, the things we can handle, see, taste, and smell. The chemical elements are the simplest of these. When the chemical elements react to form compounds they do so in definite relative amounts and according to the principle of conservation of mass. We find today, as Lavoisier did in his time, that a fixed weight of carbon when burned combines with $2\frac{2}{3}$ times its weight of oxygen and that the weight of carbon dioxide produced is the sum of the weights of the carbon and oxygen. When we buy coal, or fuel oil, or gas to heat our houses, we expect for each kind of fuel that the heat produced is directly proportional to the weight of fuel burned. From a ton of sulfur we can make a definite amount of sulfuric acid, and twice as much from two tons of sulfur. Even the diluted vitamins we buy in capsules are present in weighable amounts, expressed in milligrams, for example.

On the other hand our ideas about the way things react become clearer when we think in terms of tiny particles of elements, the atoms. We have already seen experimental evidence for the particle nature of matter but, a hundred years before we had such direct evidence, chemists had invented the idea of the atoms and molecules as the simplest logical way of explaining the results of chemical reactions. Furthermore, the properties of the substances themselves are most simply explained in terms of the ways in which the atoms of the different elements are arranged and in terms of the forces with which the atoms hold neighboring atoms.

However, chemists do not work with single atoms. A very small speck of substance weighing no more than a milligram has an extremely large number, about 10^{19}, atoms in it and a tiny sample, one-thousandth as large, one microgram or one millionth of a gram, has 10^{16} atoms. Chemists think in terms of atoms but usually in terms of enough atoms so that the sample behaves like bulk matter, that is, in terms of weighable amounts of substance. In this chapter, therefore, we shall consider both the weight relations among reacting elements and the interpretation in terms of atomic behavior. The dual point of view gives us a fuller picture of the way things behave than either would alone.

DEFINITE COMPOSITION OF PURE SUBSTANCES

Even after they accepted the principle of conservation of mass, the early chemists were not agreed on the composition of compounds. Not all experimenters were equally skillful and the samples analyzed were not always pure. There were no chemical supply houses so that each researcher had to prepare his own chemicals and build his own equipment. Accurate melting and boiling temperatures were difficult to determine and other criteria of purity had not been developed and accepted widely. Although Lavoisier assumed definite composition in his experiments, another French chemist, Berthollet, in 1799, maintained that the properties and composition of compounds depend on the proportion of the ingredients used to make them. Proust, a professor of chemistry at the University of Madrid, disagreed. He carried on a great many experiments over a period of eight years to test the statement, analyzing minerals from all parts of the world. His conclusions were:

We are forced to recognize that the composition of true compounds is as invariable as their properties: between pole and pole they are identical in these two respects. The cinnabar of Japan has the same properties and composition as that of Spain: silver chloride is identically the same, whether obtained from Peru or Siberia: in all the world there is but one chloride of sodium, one saltpeter, one sulphate of lime, or one baryta. The native oxides have the same composition as the artificial. These are facts which analysis confirms at every step.

Even so the controversy did not entirely die down. As late as 1860, Marignac, who worked with rare earths, revived the idea that pure substances might have slight variations in composition. Undoubtedly he was led to this opinion because the rare earth elements and their compounds are very difficult to isolate in pure form so that the specimens he analyzed did actually vary in composition. Stas, a Belgian chemist, undertook to retest the idea of a definite composition. As the result of a series of very careful experiments he confirmed the ideas of Proust.

34 GENERAL CHEMISTRY

We have considered these controversies primarily to illustrate how the principles of a science develop. There frequently are differences of opinion about interpreting the results of single experiments, in part because of the possibilities of error in the experiments. Each interpretation, however, leads to certain conclusions. On the basis of these conclusions one can predict what will happen if certain other experiments are carried out. The new experiments then serve as tests for the different explanations. Chemists avoid ideas and theories that can not be tested by experiment. Only those theories that meet the test of experiments are acceptable in the framework of chemistry.

CONSTANT MASS AND ERROR

The principle of definite composition of pure substances could not be established until there were reliable methods for measuring the amounts. After the chemical balance was developed in the eighteenth century, amounts could be measured accurately by weighing, that is, by measuring the masses of substances. Gases are harder to weigh than liquids or solids because they must be confined in vessels, which weigh more than the gases themselves and which are buoyed up by air in the balance. Volumes of gases are easily measured but equal volumes of different kinds of gases have different weights. Furthermore, the mass of gas in any particular volume varies with the pressure and temperature of the gas. Therefore, for each kind of gas, the relation between mass and volume (at definite temperatures and pressures) had to be determined. Density is such a measure. Then chemical reactions involving gases as well as liquids or solids could be tested to see whether the principles of conservation of mass and of definite composition were valid. The measurements of Lavoisier were not very accurate—the work of pioneers rarely is—but they were good enough for him to see the underlying relationships.

In the years following Lavoisier's proposal many experiments, among them very accurate ones, have been carried out to test the principle of conservation of mass. Although the experiments always show some disagreement they do not contradict the idea nor do they limit its usefulness. In order to understand how principles may be accepted in spite of disagreement, and to recognize the nature of the so-called "natural laws," one must know something about the nature of experimental proof. One of the reasons a chemistry student works in the laboratory is that after he has carried out experiments he has a better understanding of the interpretation of the data obtained by other experimenters.

Every experiment has inherent in it sources of error. Errors may be the result of the method, of the instruments and manipulations used to carry out the experiment, or of the limitations of the experimenter himself. If the experimenter is a student, errors may appear in the recording of the data and in the numerical computations. Even the most careful scientist taking every known precaution finds that there are limits to the reproducibility of his results when he makes his measurements accurately enough. For example, during a weighing an undetected piece of dust may settle on one piece of apparatus or an unnoticed air current may blow very gently on the balance. Heat radiated from some warm body outside the balance case may cause one balance arm to expand more than the other. All these and many more are possible. A critical evaluation of possible errors often allows the experimenter to estimate their probable size, or even their maximum effect on the results, and then to designate the probable error or the maximum error.

Table 4.1 contains some of the experimental weights of hydrogen and oxygen in their reaction to form water obtained by Morley, an expert chemist. They

Table 4.1

Weights (in Grams) of Hydrogen Gas and Oxygen Gas Reacting to Give a Measured Weight of Water
(Experiments of Morley)

WEIGHT OF HYDROGEN	WEIGHT OF OXYGEN	WEIGHT OF HYDROGEN PLUS WEIGHT OF OXYGEN	WEIGHT OF WATER
3.2559	25.8531	29.1090	29.1052
3.8382	30.4700	34.3082	34.3151
3.8523	30.5818	34.4341	34.4327
3.8211	30.3429	34.1640	34.1559

are the results of an expert working with difficult experiments requiring the accurate weighing of gases. Note that the weight of water produced does not exactly equal the sum of the weights of the hydrogen and oxygen used. The maximum difference is about 8 units in 34,000, or 0.02 per cent. In other reactions easier to measure the conservation of mass has been confirmed to about 0.001 per cent. Since few chemical experiments are attempted to an accuracy of more than 0.1 or 0.01 per cent, they lie within the range within which the idea of the conservation of mass is completely valid.

DEFINITE COMPOSITION AND THE COMPOSITION OF WATER

The experimenter making quantitative measurements in the laboratory first records numerical values he observes. Thus, the weights recorded in column (1) of Table 4.2 represent the actual weights of materials in different experiments. What can such weights tell us about the composition of water? Even a casual inspection of the data shows that larger amounts of hydrogen will always react with larger amounts of oxygen to produce larger amounts of water. But one not trained in the interpretation of numbers may fail to see that the weights of hydrogen, oxygen, and water are directly proportional. We see this clearly if we calculate for each experiment the amount of oxygen combined with 1 g. of hydrogen. The results of the calculation, listed in column (2) of Table 4.2, show that in each experiment 7.94 g. of oxygen (in rounded-off numbers) combine with the gram of hydrogen. We may prefer to follow the

36 GENERAL CHEMISTRY

Table 4.2

Relative Weights of Hydrogen and Oxygen Combining to Form Water

(1) EXPERIMENTAL		(2) FOR 1 GRAM OF HYDROGEN		(3) FOR 100 GRAMS OF OXYGEN		(4) FOR 8 GRAMS OF OXYGEN	
Hydrogen	Oxygen	Hydrogen	Oxygen	Hydrogen	Oxygen	Hydrogen	Oxygen
3.2559	25.8531	1	7.9404	12.594	100	1.0075	8
3.8382	30.4700	1	7.9386	12.597	100	1.0077	8
3.8523	30.5818	1	7.9386	12.597	100	1.0077	8
3.8211	30.3429	1	7.9409	12.593	100	1.0074	8
Average		1	7.9396	12.595	100	1.0076	8

example of some of the early chemists and calculate the weight of hydrogen combining with 100 g. of oxygen. The value is approximately 12.60 g., as shown in column (3). Or, we may, following the example of other early chemists, calculate the weight of hydrogen combining with 8 g. of oxygen. The value is 1.008 g. as shown in column (4). The calculations indicate that within Morley's experimental error all the water he formed had the same composition, that is, the same elements combined in the same ratios.

Problem 4.1. Show that the following pairs of numbers represent the same ratio: 3.2559, 25.8531; 1, 7.9404; 12.594, 100; 1.0075, 8.

When hydrogen and oxygen react they release energy. The amount of energy is directly proportional to the amounts of the combining elements and of the water formed. Water, in turn, can be decomposed in an electrolytic cell into hydrogen and oxygen on addition of electrical energy. In accordance with the principle of the conservation of mass the weights of the products, hydrogen and oxygen, equal the weight of the water decomposed. Furthermore the relative amounts of hydrogen and oxygen correspond to those which react to produce water. Within the experimental error all experimenters, whether they form water from elements or decompose it to the elements, find that the water has a definite composition, always the same.

The various relationships among the amounts of hydrogen, oxygen, and water may be expressed neatly in the form of equations, the reacting substances being shown on the left side of the equation and the product of the reaction on the right side.

```
    1     g.   hydrogen +   7.94 g.  oxygen =   8.94 g.  water
   12.6   "       "      + 100   "     "    = 112.6   "    "
    1.008 "       "      +   8   "     "    =   9.008 "    "
    2.016 "       "      +  16   "     "    =  18.016 "    "
    3.024 "       "      +  24   "     "    =  27.024 "    "
    1.008 tons    "      +   8   tons  "    =   9.008 tons "
   11.2   "       "      +  88.8  "    "    = 100     "    "
```

Observe that the numbers in all the equations are relative numbers. An equation remains an equality when both sides of it are multiplied by the same number. Therefore, on multiplication by suitable definite numbers (constants) any equation in the list may be transformed to any other equation. Any weight unit may be used. Observe also that all the equations rest on the conservation principle.

We have already indicated that the amounts of gases may be measured conveniently by measuring volumes of the gases. The reacting volumes of hydrogen gas and oxygen gas (under the same pressure and temperature) combining to form water have a simple relationship—almost exactly two volumes of hydrogen gas combine with one volume of oxygen gas. This statement does not contradict any of the previous statements since a given volume of oxygen weighs nearly sixteen times as much as an equal volume of hydrogen. However, the volume of water formed is very small compared to the volume of the reacting gases since water is a liquid at room temperature and pressure and much more dense than gases. Under the circumstances we found it simpler to represent the amounts of reacting substances by their masses rather than by their volumes. However, the simple ratio in the volumes of reacting gases is too important to be neglected. We shall return to it when we consider the problems of the relative weights of molecules of gases and the relative weights of the atoms of hydrogen and oxygen.

THE ATOMIC THEORY

In the period 1803–1805, twenty-five years after Lavoisier laid the quantitative foundation of chemistry, the British chemist, Dalton, proposed an atomic theory of matter. Each element, according to Dalton, consists of individual indivisible atoms alike in size and weight. He proposed that when the atoms of different elements combine with each other they do so in a one-to-one ratio. However, Dalton knew that some elements, nitrogen and oxygen, for example, can combine with each other in different proportions to form different compounds. He, therefore, suggested that in some compounds the atoms combine two of one element to one of the other or three of one element to two of the other, etc.

Here we have a theory simple and logical in nature, yet it did not have much impact on the chemists of his time. One of the reasons was that Dalton had some faulty ideas about the nature of gases. Another is a reason already noted, namely, that not all contemporary chemists accepted the principle of the definite composition of compounds. A third reason was that many chemists were skeptical about speculations on the nature of matter and were more interested in the experimental relations just being discovered. Their modern counterparts are those who insist that they have more interest in "facts" than in "theory."

When proper allowance was made for experimental error, Dalton's ideas were consistent with various experimental facts. They were consistent with

38　GENERAL CHEMISTRY

the principle of the conservation of mass—in chemical reactions atoms combine with one another in different ways but they do not change in mass. They were consistent with the definite composition of pure substances—each element consists of only one kind of atom of definite mass, and compounds are formed from specific kinds of atoms of definite masses combined in simple relative numbers. We shall also see that they were consistent with the principle of constant combining weights.

EQUIVALENT WEIGHTS OR COMBINING WEIGHTS

The work of Proust, and later of men like Morley, established and confirmed the principle of constant composition of pure substances. Each compound, according to this principle has a definite *analysis*, which specifies the kinds and relative amounts of the elements which may be used to make the compounds or into which the compound may be decomposed.

The first step in an analysis is to measure the actual weights for a particular sample, weights such as those in column (1) of Table 4.2. For example, a piece of aluminum foil weighing 1.53 g. is caused to react with oxygen. It will not react at room temperature because of the very thin but adherent coating of aluminum oxide on the surface, which stops further action. However, if the foil is placed in a bomb with excess oxygen gas under high pressure, 40 atmospheres for example, and then ignited it burns completely until the aluminum is consumed and only the solid, aluminum oxide, and gaseous oxygen remain. The solid aluminum oxide is weighed—its weight is found to be 2.89 g. The conclusion is: 2.89 − 1.53, or 1.36 g., of oxygen combined with the 1.53 g. of aluminum to form 2.89 g. of aluminum oxide. The analysis may be expressed in decimal fractions. Thus, the fraction $\frac{1.36}{2.89}$ or 0.471 of the weight of the aluminum oxide is attributable to oxygen and $\frac{1.53}{2.89}$ or 0.529 to aluminum. In terms of percentages these values become 47.1 per cent oxygen and 52.9 per cent aluminum. These values appear in columns (b) and (c) of Table 4.3. A second way of expressing the analysis is to indicate the weight of aluminum combining with 1 unit weight or with 100 unit weights of oxygen. For 1 unit weight the value for aluminum is $\frac{1}{1.36}$ of 1.53, or 1.12, and for 100 unit weights of oxygen the value for aluminum is 112 unit weights. These values appear in columns (d) and (e) of Table 4.3. A third way of expressing the analysis is in terms of the weight of aluminum combining with 8 grams of oxygen. This value is, obviously, 8 times the amount combining with 1 gram of oxygen, that is, 8 times 1.12, or 8.96 grams. This value appears in column (g) of Table 4.3.

Beginners often believe that percentages are the simplest way of expressing ratios, forgetting that not all things come in units of one hundred. In Table 4.3

ELEMENTS AND ATOMS 39

are listed the analyses of several oxygen compounds as calculated from the experimental data in the three different ways. The values in columns (b) and (c) are expressed in terms of the per cents of the two constituent elements. Observe the percentage values for the two oxides of hydrogen, water and hydrogen peroxide. The relation between them is not at all obvious. Percentages represent correctly the number of weight units of the elements per 100 weight units of the compound but they disguise certain regularities. We find it is not good chemistry to compare equal weights (100 units) of different compounds.

Table 4.3

Analysis of Some Oxides Expressed in Different Ways, but Always Showing the Relative Weights of Different Elements That Combine to Form the Oxides

SUBSTANCES	ANALYSIS					
	Per Cent by Weight of		Combining Weights (Oxygen = 100)		Combining Weights (Oxygen = 8)	
(a)	Oxygen (b)	Other Element (c)	Oxygen (d)	Other Element (e)	Oxygen (f)	Other Element (g)
Aluminum oxide	47.1	52.9	100	112	8	8.96
Carbon dioxide	72.7	27.3	100	37.5	8	3.00
Carbon monoxide	57.2	42.8	100	75.0	8	6.00
Copper oxide (black)	20.1	79.9	100	398	8	31.8
Copper oxide (red)	11.2	88.8	100	795	8	63.6
Hydrogen peroxide	94.1	5.9	100	6.3	8	0.500
Water	88.8	11.2	100	12.5	8	1.00
Magnesium oxide	39.7	60.3	100	152	8	12.2

Let us express the analyses of all the compounds in Table 4.3 in terms of the weights of the other elements that combine with a fixed weight of oxygen. The values shown in column (e) are obtained when the fixed weight of oxygen is one hundred units (column [d]). Observe what has happened to the numbers representing the weights of carbon, copper, and hydrogen in their oxides. Two oxides are listed for each of these elements. The one oxide of carbon, for example, contains twice as much carbon per 100 weight units of oxygen as does the other oxide. The weights of the different elements that combine with a fixed weight of oxygen are called _combining weights_ or _equivalent weights_. In modern usage the fixed weight selected for oxygen is 8 units (rather than 100) and the term equivalent weight is applied only to the relative weights of the elements calculated on this basis. Column (g) contains the values of the equivalent weights. They may, of course, be calculated (how?) from the values in the other columns because they represent the analyses of the same compounds. Observe that some of the equivalent weights are whole numbers. For this, and other reasons (see page 45), chemists have come to agree on this system of equivalent weights based on 8 units of oxygen as a standard.

40 GENERAL CHEMISTRY

If we enlarge our list of compounds to include compounds other than oxides we find an important relation among the equivalent weights. Consider the equivalent weights of chlorine, magnesium, sodium, and hydrogen, obtained from the analysis of the oxides of these elements, as shown in the first four lines of Table 4.4. The same equivalent weights express the analysis of the other compounds formed by reaction between the various elements as shown in the last four lines of Table 4.4. Figure 4.1 illustrates relations among

Table 4.4
Some Equivalent Weights

SUBSTANCE	ANALYSIS: RELATIVE WEIGHTS OF				
	Chlorine	Hydrogen	Magnesium	Oxygen	Sodium
Chlorine monoxide	35.5			8.00	
Magnesium oxide			12.2	8.00	
Sodium oxide				8.00	23.0
Water		1.0		8.00	
Magnesium chloride	35.5		12.2		
Sodium chloride	35.5				23.0
Hydrogen chloride	35.5	1.0			
Sodium hydride		1.0			23.0

sodium, oxygen, hydrogen, and chlorine in six of the compounds they form. It appears that the weights of the various elements equivalent to a fixed weight of oxygen are equivalent to each other. This interrelationship is known as the Law of Combining Weights.

At this point the alert student will wonder how one may speak of a law of combining weights when some elements have more than one equivalent weight. Table 4.3 shows that each of the elements carbon, copper, and hydrogen has at least two equivalent weights since each forms more than one compound with oxygen, the compounds having different analyses. When elements combine to form more than one compound they combine in more than one ratio but each of the compounds has a unique, definite composition and a unique set of properties characteristic of the compound. Furthermore, when an element has more than one equivalent weight, the equivalent weights stand in a simple ratio to each other. This statement is usually called the Law of Multiple Proportions. The ratios are not always 2 to 1 as in Table 4.3 but may have such values as 3 to 2, 5 to 2, or 3 to 1. The Law of Combining Weights is consistent with Dalton's atomic theory for if one atom of A combines with one atom of B or one atom of C then one atom of B may be expected to combine with one atom of C. In fact, Dalton's theory enabled him to predict the Law of Multiple Proportions which was later confirmed by experiment. One of the tests of good theory is always its usefulness in making predictions about unknown situations.

ELEMENTS AND ATOMS 41

On the other hand there was no "theory" connected with our deriving of equivalent weights. We did nothing more than take the analytical values as measured in the laboratory and find relatively simple ways of expressing them, ways that brought to light significant regularities and relationships. Scientists always try to express experimental values in forms that show fundamental and simple relations among themselves and with other data. Such calculations require less imagination than new theory does but they are often the first step toward the development of new ideas. In the laboratory, each student will be expected to scrutinize his own data for relationships. Isolated, unrelated facts, though they may be perfectly valid, are not useful to anyone who wishes to predict what will happen in new situations.

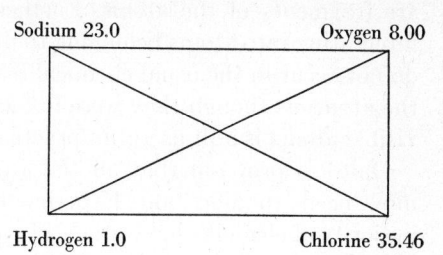

Figure 4.1.
Reciprocal combining quantities of several elements. The quantity of each element indicated at a corner of the diagram will combine with the listed quantity of each of the three elements at the other corners.

Sodium 23.0 — Oxygen 8.00 — Hydrogen 1.0 — Chlorine 35.46

MODERN ATOMIC THEORY

Dalton's atomic theory was consistent with the experimental facts of his time, but consistency is not proof, as the early chemists well knew. Usually more than one explanation will fit a given set of facts. Though all are consistent with the facts, all can not be true. To prove a theory one must show not only that it is consistent with the facts but also that it is the only theory which will fit them. In science few theories meet the latter test. In the absence of definitive tests, one of the rules used to choose between rival theories is that of simplicity—one does not use a complicated theory when a simple one does just as well. A second rule is that of generality—one uses a theory explaining a variety of phenomena over one explaining but a few. Because of human limitations we do not test all possible theories. Consequently, the most we can say about our best theories is that they are highly probable rather than true.

Great advances in science often arise from intuitive judgments such as those of Dalton. Dalton and his contemporaries did not have good values for the combining weights of elements. Like many great originators Dalton was able to see beyond erratic fragmentary data containing error to a unifying idea behind the data. This deserves full credit. New theories are often not "proved" by their originators but by others who help to fill in the logical gaps.

The concept of atoms has stood the test of time and of many experiments of various kinds. The details of the theory have needed to be modified but the details have confirmed the idea that atoms can and do exist. Modern experiments on the particle theory of matter show that atoms of the elements are not indivisible. The fundamental particles discussed in the previous chapter are fragments of the atoms. Furthermore, some atoms are radioactive, disintegrating into atoms belonging to different elements. Since these phenomena do not occur in the usual chemical reactions, we may, for most purposes, treat the atoms as though they were in fact indivisible. Hence, the concept of indivisible atoms is still useful in practice.

Dalton's proposal that all the atoms of an element are alike in size and mass needs modification. Experiments with individual atoms show that the majority of elements have atoms of more than one mass. For example naturally occurring chlorine has atoms with masses 35 and 37, mixed in such a ratio that the average mass is 35.46. Since the reactions of the two kinds of chlorine atoms (called isotopes) are very nearly the same, most reactions do not change the ratio of the isotopes present. Hence, for practical purposes we may usually treat chlorine as though it consisted of atoms with an average mass of 35.46.

The idea that atoms usually combine in a one-to-one ratio had to be modified almost from the beginning. Dalton had recognized the other possible simple ratios but none of them involved many atoms. Relatively few of the now known substances have the simple ratios proposed by Dalton. In most compounds, structures based on many atoms are found. Even a relatively simple organic substance such as ordinary sugar has twelve carbon atoms, twenty-two hydrogen atoms, and eleven oxygen atoms in the simplest sugar particle, the molecule.

CHEMICAL SYMBOLS

If there are atoms, each with a definite mass, it becomes natural to represent the atoms of different elements by symbols. Dalton used the symbol ○ for hydrogen, ⊙ for oxygen, ⊕ for nitrogen, and ● for carbon. The atomic weights he assigned to these are a 1.0 for hydrogen, 5.66 for oxygen, 4.0 for nitrogen, and 4.5 for carbon. We now recognize these as combining weights rather than atomic weights and rather poor values at that. The formula he wrote for water was ○⊙. Our modern chemical symbols were proposed by Berzelius, a Swedish chemist, who became interested in Dalton's atomic theory and who prepared the best early lists of "atomic weights." The alchemists had used symbols, many of which were borrowed from astronomy, but there was a certain amount of mysticism connected with their use and they did not represent specific amounts. Some alchemical symbols are shown in Figure 4.2.

Instead of such arbitrary symbols, Berzelius proposed that the first letter or the first letter and one other in the Latin name of the element stand for a definite quantity of the element. Because Latin was an international language known to educated men, Berzelius' set of symbols could be accepted internationally. The names of the elements known to the ancients varied widely from nation to nation (compare the English, French, and German names, iron, fer, and Eisen, for the same common element), so that symbols based on any

ELEMENTS AND ATOMS 43

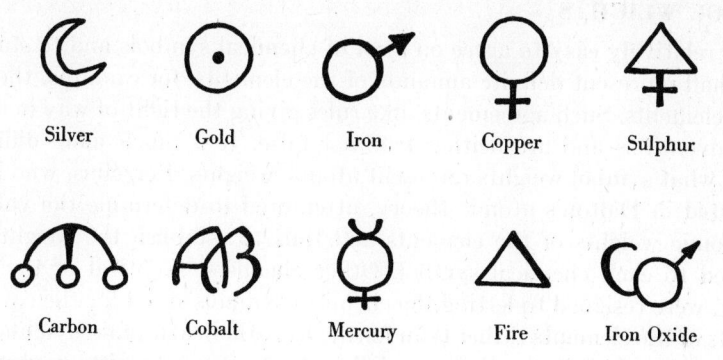

Figure 4.2.
Some alchemical symbols.

one modern language would not have been accepted generally. A great majority of the elements discovered in modern times bear names accepted by chemists of all nationalities. The symbols for these elements present no problem—they can be derived from the common name. Chemical symbols have been established by international agreement. American students will

Table 4.5
Related Names and Symbols of Elements Whose International Symbols Are Not Derivable from Their American Names

AMERICAN NAME	SYMBOL	SYMBOL SOURCE	AMERICAN NAME	SYMBOL	SYMBOL SOURCE
Antimony	Sb	Stibnum	Potassium	K	Kalium
Copper	Cu	Cuprum	Silver	Ag	Argentum
Gold	Au	Aurum	Sodium	Na	Natrium
Iron	Fe	Ferrum	Tin	Sn	Stannum
Lead	Pb	Plumbum	Tungsten	W	Wolfram
Mercury	Hg	Hydrargyrum			

find that only eleven of the standard international symbols are unrelated to the American name for the element. The symbols of the seven elements known to the ancients are derived from their Latin names. The eleven elements are listed in Table 4.5.

The symbols for the remaining elements may be obtained from the first letter of the current American name, or the first plus one other letter when it is necessary to differentiate elements having the same initial (cerium, cesium). The symbols composed of Latin letters are used even in countries with non-Latin alphabets. The advantages of an international set of chemical symbols is so great that American students can not reasonably object to the few symbols not derivable from the American names of the elements.

SYMBOL WEIGHTS

It is relatively easy to agree on a set of chemical symbols and to state that they shall represent definite amounts of the elements, for example, the atoms of the elements. Such agreements, like rules giving the right of way in driving, are conventions and are neither true nor false. It is much more difficult to decide what symbol weights represent atomic weights. Berzelius, who became interested in Dalton's atomic theory, attempted to determine the values for the atomic weights of the elements and thus to establish the weights to be assigned to each chemical symbol. Other chemists, skeptical of the atomic theory, were resigned to letting the chemical symbols stand for the equivalent weights of the elements rather than for the hypothetical atomic weights. Needless to say confusion arose because different schools of chemists used different weights for the chemical symbols. Not until after 1860 did chemists finally agree on the criteria for recognizing and establishing atomic weights and the weights to be assigned to chemical symbols.

How can one determine the relative mass of atoms without measuring the masses of individual atoms? We have already seen that chemists work not with individual atoms but with enormous numbers of atoms. The mass spectrograph enables one to determine the masses of individual atoms but interpretation of experimental results is not easy unless the atomic weights of the elements are known approximately. Since most elements, like carbon, have more than one equivalent weight, it follows that the equivalent weights as a rule do not represent atomic weights. Berzelius understood that the atomic weight of an element may be a multiple of its equivalent weight, the question always being: What multiple? He published his first table of atomic weights in 1813 and a more extensive one in 1826. It is remarkable that many of these values, when translated to our modern basis, $O = 16$, are very near to our best modern values. Others in his list were simple multiples or fractions of our modern values.

Since we do not work with individual atoms, all the chemical methods for determining atomic weights depend on comparing the weights of different elements having the same number of atoms. It does not matter how many atoms are present as long as the number always remains the same. The only assumption made here is that all the atoms of an element have the same mass. If they do not, then the so-called atomic weights can represent only the average mass of the atoms. It is inherent in the chemical methods of determining the atomic weights that they yield only such average masses. Let us take, for example, 1.00 g. of hydrogen and the number of atoms of hydrogen present in it. By methods to be considered in later chapters we find that a sample of oxygen containing the same number of atoms of oxygen weighs 15.88 g. Therefore, the average oxygen atom weighs 15.88 times as much as the average hydrogen atom. A system of atomic weights can be built on this basis.

For a number of reasons it is preferable to select a definite number of atoms for the standard sample of an element, by convention the number present in 16 g. of oxygen. The same number of atoms of hydrogen weighs 1.008 g. Changing the number of atoms considered does not affect the ratio between weights of the oxygen and hydrogen atoms—oxygen atoms weigh 15.88 times as much as hydrogen atoms. Some of the reasons for selecting oxygen as the standard element and 16 as its symbol weight are: oxygen combines directly with most of the other elements so that combining weights may be determined directly, most oxides are easy to handle in chemical experiments, oxygen is common and itself easy to handle, all symbol weights are greater than unity when 16 is chosen as the standard weight for oxygen, the smallest symbol weight (that of hydrogen) is approximately one, and many of the other symbol weights are approximately integral.

It is important to note that by using equal numbers of atoms we can find the relative average mass of atoms without knowing what the number of atoms actually is. For example, one may know that the number of bolts and nuts in boxes are equal without knowing what the number is, and by weighing bolts and nuts separately get the relative weights of the two.

In chemical practice the relative numbers, 16 for oxygen and 1.008 for hydrogen, are associated respectively with the chemical symbols O and H. Chemists usually use the gram as a unit of mass and let the symbol O represent 16 grams of oxygen and H represent 1.008 g. of hydrogen. These weights are often called *gram-atomic weights*. Over the years a number of different experiments have been carried out to measure the number of atoms in one gram-atomic weight of an element. All agree on the order of magnitude, a very large number. The best modern value is 6.0238×10^{23}. Consequently, since 16 g. of oxygen contain this number of atoms, the average mass of an oxygen atom is $\frac{16}{6.0238 \times 10^{23}}$ g., or 2.6561×10^{-23} g. A new unit of weight, called the *avogram*, has been defined to represent $\frac{1}{16}$ of this value, or 1.6601×10^{-24} g. In terms of this unit the average oxygen atom has a mass of 16 avograms and the average hydrogen atom a mass of 1.008 avograms. We shall rarely use this unit since for most purposes we are not concerned with the actual weight of individual atoms. The number of atoms in 16 grams of oxygen or in the gram-atomic weight of any other element, 6.0238×10^{23}, is called the *Avogadro number*, in honor of the man who first suggested methods for obtaining equal numbers of atoms of the elements.

Sometimes chemists use the chemical symbols to represent single atoms rather than the Avogadro number of atoms. Then the average weights associated with the symbols O and H are 16 and 1.008 avograms rather than 16 and 1.008 g. The names of the elements, their international symbols, and the weights associated with the symbols (atomic weights) are shown in Table 4.6.

Table 4.6
International Atomic Weights—1953 *

	SYMBOL	ATOMIC NUMBER	ATOMIC WEIGHT *		SYMBOL	ATOMIC NUMBER	ATOMIC WEIGHT *
Actinium	Ac	89	227	Neodymium	Nd	60	144.27
Aluminum	Al	13	26.98	Neptunium	Np	93	[237]
Americium	Am	95	[243]	Neon	Ne	10	20.183
Antimony	Sb	51	121.76	Nickel	Ni	28	58.69
Argon	A	18	39.944	Niobium			
Arsenic	As	33	74.91	(Columbium)	Nb	41	92.91
Astatine	At	85	[210]	Nitrogen	N	7	14.008
Barium	Ba	56	137.36	Osmium	Os	76	190.2
Berkelium	Bk	97	[245]	Oxygen	O	8	**16.0000**
Beryllium	Be	4	9.013	Palladium	Pd	46	106.7
Bismuth	Bi	83	209.00	Phosphorus	P	15	30.975
Boron	B	5	10.82	Platinum	Pt	78	195.23
Bromine	Br	35	79.916	Plutonium	Pu	94	[242]
Cadmium	Cd	48	112.41	Polonium	Po	84	210
Calcium	Ca	20	40.08	Potassium	K	19	39.100
Californium	Cf	98	[248]	Praseodymium	Pr	59	140.92
Carbon	C	6	12.011	Promethium	Pm	61	[145]
Cerium	Ce	58	140.13	Protactinium	Pa	91	231
Cesium	Cs	55	132.91	Radium	Ra	88	226.05
Chlorine	Cl	17	35.457	Radon	Rn	86	222
Chromium	Cr	24	52.01	Rhenium	Re	75	186.31
Cobalt	Co	27	58.94	Rhodium	Rh	45	102.91
Copper	Cu	29	63.54	Rubidium	Rb	37	85.48
Curium	Cm	96	[245]	Ruthenium	Ru	44	101.1
Dysprosium	Dy	66	162.46	Samarium	Sm	62	150.43
Erbium	Er	68	167.2	Scandium	Sc	21	44.96
Europium	Eu	63	152.0	Selenium	Se	34	78.96
Fluorine	F	9	19.00	Silicon	Si	14	28.09
Francium	Fr	87	[223]	Silver	Ag	47	107.880
Gadolinium	Gd	64	156.9	Sodium	Na	11	22.991
Gallium	Ga	31	69.72	Strontium	Sr	38	87.63
Germanium	Ge	32	72.60	Sulfur	S	16	32.066
Gold	Au	79	197.0	Tantalum	Ta	73	180.95
Hafnium	Hf	72	178.6	Technetium	Tc	43	[99]
Helium	He	2	4.003	Tellurium	Te	52	127.61
Holmium	Ho	67	164.94	Terbium	Tb	65	158.93
Hydrogen	H	1	1.0080	Thallium	Tl	81	204.39
Indium	In	49	114.76	Thorium	Th	90	232.05
Iodine	I	53	126.91	Thulium	Tm	69	168.94
Iridium	Ir	77	192.2	Tin	Sn	50	118.70
Iron	Fe	26	55.85	Titanium	Ti	22	47.90
Krypton	Kr	36	83.80	Tungsten	W	74	183.92
Lanthanum	La	57	138.92	Uranium	U	92	238.07
Lead	Pb	82	207.21	Vanadium	V	23	50.95
Lithium	Li	3	6.940	Xenon	Xe	54	131.3
Lutetium	Lu	71	174.99	Ytterbium	Yb	70	173.04
Magnesium	Mg	12	24.32	Yttrium	Y	39	88.92
Manganese	Mn	25	54.94	Zinc	Zn	30	65.38
Mercury	Hg	80	200.61	Zirconium	Zr	40	91.22
Molybdenum	Mo	42	95.95				

[ ] Value given in brackets denotes the mass number of the most stable known isotope.
* Journal of the American Chemical Society, [**76,** 2033 (1954)].

USE OF SIGNIFICANT FIGURES

We have already seen that numbers derived from experimental data are limited in precision by the experimental error. Morley's experiments on the equivalent weight of hydrogen, though carried out with great skill, showed disagreement when pressed far enough, the average value being 1.0076. This number contains five *significant figures*, the value of the last being uncertain. Multiplications and divisions using these data can never give a result containing more than five significant figures. In reporting experimental data it is good practice to report one, but not more than one, uncertain figure. The best modern value for the equivalent (and atomic) weight of hydrogen is 1.0080, a number in good agreement with that of Morley. The last figure, a zero in this number, is also a significant figure. It indicates that the "true value" is more likely to be 1.0080 than 1.0079 or 1.0081. Terminal zeros are always retained in a number when they are significant figures.

The position of the decimal point does not influence the number of significant figures. The numbers 1470, 1.47, 0.147, and 0.00147 are identical except for the size of units in which they are expressed, just as $1.23 and 123 cents represent the same value. Each is known to three significant figures, hence to the same accuracy. A decimal point merely indicates the size of unit and not the accuracy of a number.

In column (1) of Table 4.2 the experimental weights of hydrogen are given to five significant figures and those of oxygen to six significant figures. Therefore, numbers derived from these can be good only to five figures, as is illustrated by the figures in the remaining columns. In column (2) the weight of hydrogen is taken as a standard without error with a value 1.00000—, ad infinitum, so that all the errors are concentrated in the values for oxygen. In columns (3) and (4) the values of oxygen are taken as the exact numbers 100.0000—, and 8.00000—, respectively, all errors appearing in the values for hydrogen. In Table 4.3 the number of significant figures given in the data limits the values derived from them to three significant figures. In all multiplications and divisions the number of significant figures in the result is determined by and equal to the number in that datum having the least number of significant figures.

For convenience we often *round off* numbers thereby decreasing the numbers of significant figures shown. The atomic weight of chlorine, 35.457, is known to five significant figures. When only four significant figures are desired this number is rounded off to 35.46. It may be further rounded off to 35.5 and to 35. Which of these numbers we use depends on our purposes in using the numbers. Observe that a bargain at $3.98 when properly rounded off becomes $4.0, not $3.9, or $4 not $3. If data are to be used in multiplication and division it is good practice to round each number off until it contains the same number of significant figures as that datum which originally had the least number of significant figures.

Problem 4.2. Indicate the significant figures in each of the following numbers: 10.1 tons, 0.6849 grams, 0.026 liters, 1.000 kilograms, 0.0140 inches.

Problem 4.3. Round off each of the following atomic weights by one significant figure at a time, until you have one significant figure remaining: (Na) 22.991, (Ag) 107.880, (Cu) 63.54, (Al) 26.98, (Rb) 85.48.

Problem 4.4. The combining weight of chlorine has been calculated very exactly by the following method. Very pure silver oxide is analyzed and found to contain 6.9037 per cent oxygen, the rest being silver. Calculate the value for the combining weight of silver. Very pure silver chloride has the analysis, 24.737 per cent chlorine, the rest being silver. From the previous value for the combining weight of silver calculate the combining weight of chlorine. (In these calculations use five-place logarithms.)

Problem 4.5. The analysis of hydrogen fluoride is 5.0380 per cent hydrogen, the rest being fluorine. What is the combining weight of fluorine?

Problem 4.6. From the values for the combining weights of hydrogen and oxygen estimate how many grams of each are required to form 10 grams of water. How many tons of each are required to form 10 tons of water?

Problem 4.7. One hundred tons of pure barium chloride are formed from 34.05 tons of chlorine and 65.95 tons of barium. What is the percentage analysis by weight of the barium chloride? What weights of the elements are required to form 100 grams of barium chloride? If the combining weight of chlorine is 35.46 what is the combining weight of barium?

Problem 4.8. Use the combining weight of barium found in Problem 4.7 to calculate the percentages of barium and oxygen in barium oxide.

Problem 4.9. From the values of the combining weights of the elements given in the textbook, predict the number of grams of magnesium, sodium, aluminum, copper, and carbon that combine with 35.46 g. of chlorine.

Problem 4.10. Calculate the relative numbers of symbol weights (atomic weights) of the elements corresponding to the weights listed in Table 4.4. In chlorine monoxide, for instance, there is one symbol weight of chlorine combined with one half of a symbol weight of oxygen, or $Cl_1O_{\frac{1}{2}}$. This is generally written Cl_2O to avoid non-integral subscripts.

Problem 4.11. An element X forms both a fluoride and an oxide. When 0.560 g. of the fluoride are treated with water 0.340 g. of the oxide are produced. Calculate the value for the equivalent weight of X. (The equivalent weight of fluorine is 19.)

Problem 4.12. In an experiment 2.00 g. of oxygen react with 7.6637 g. of a metal. What is the equivalent weight of the metal? What is the per cent of oxygen in the compound?

Problem 4.13. What are the possible meanings of each of the following symbols: H, Cl, Mg, Ce, K, S, Na, Mn, Hg, Fe?

5 COMPOUNDS AND FORMULAS

IN THE preceding chapter we considered the relative weights of elements combining to form compounds and found that they can be expressed in the form of equivalent weights. The fact that compounds have definite compositions and that the combining weights equivalent to a third element are equivalent to each other was most simply explained in terms of an atomic theory. The individual atoms so postulated were found many years later among the heavier particles associated with the fundamental particles of the matter. We shall next consider the compounds formed when atoms of elements combine with one another.

ATOMS AND MOLECULES

In his consideration of the "ultimate particles" of elements and compounds Dalton called them atoms, whether they were particles of an element or of a compound, though he sometimes called the particles of compounds "compound atoms." On the other hand Avogadro called ultimate particles molecules, distinguishing between the "molécule intégrante" (usually applied to compounds), "molécule constituante" (applied to molecules of elements), and "molécule elementaire" (applied to atoms of elements). In modern usage the term *atom* is restricted to the simplest particle of an element. On the other hand the term *molecule* is applied to the particle of a gas, whether element or compound, and to corresponding particles in liquids and solids.

A molecule of a gas represents the characteristic particle of a gas, the particle which gives the gas its characteristic physical behavior. The molecules of some elementary gases, argon and helium, for example, consist of single atoms. The molecules of other gases, oxygen, hydrogen, and nitrogen, for example, consist of two atoms. Other numbers of atoms in molecules of elements are three as in ozone, four as in white phosphorus, or eight as in sulfur. In the molecules of compounds the numbers of atoms may range from two to large numbers, and the atoms are not all alike but are those characteristic of the elements which go to form the compounds.

In gases one can easily determine the masses of the molecules. For example, neutral molecules, like atoms, can be changed to ions and caused to flow as molecular beams through electrical and magnetic fields. Their masses can then be determined as discussed on page 25. But what happens when gases containing molecules are condensed to form liquids or solids? In many liquids experimental evidence shows that molecules exist and that they contain the same numbers and kinds of atoms found in the molecules of gas. Typically, solids formed by freezing liquids or condensing gases also contain electrically neutral molecules. They are called molecular solids to distinguish them from other types of solids which do not have small neutral molecules. The latter solids, either macromolecular solids or ionic solids, are difficult to melt or to evaporate, precisely because their atoms are not associated in simple molecules which can behave independently and evaporate to form gases. The forces that bind atoms together to form molecules or to form larger units than molecules will be considered in many of the following chapters but in particular in Chapter 15 on Chemical Bonding. We shall consider here some of the experimental evidence for deciding that molecules exist and for finding their relative masses.

COMBINING VOLUMES OF GASES

In the previous chapter we found that relative weights of hydrogen and oxygen gases combining to form water are 1 of hydrogen to 8 of oxygen (more exactly 1.008 to 8). In 1805, Gay-Lussac, a French chemist and physicist, and von Humboldt observed that the volumes of the two gases combining are two volumes of hydrogen to one of oxygen. Even though an excessive amount of one gas or the other was used, the relative volumes that combined were always the same. From more experiments of his own and from results of other experimenters Gay-Lussac concluded, in 1808, that the volumes (measured at the same pressure and the same temperature) of the different gases that are

Table 5.1
Some Reacting Volumes of Gases Found by Gay-Lussac *
(In each experiment the volumes were measured at the same pressure and the same temperature.)

---

2 volumes hydrogen and 1 volume oxygen produce 2 volumes water (gas)
2 volumes "carbonic oxide" (carbon monoxide) and 1 volume oxygen produce 2 volumes "carbonic gas" (carbon dioxide)

2 volumes ammonia produce 3 volumes hydrogen and 1 volume nitrogen
2 volumes "nitrous oxide" (dinitrogen oxide) produce 2 volumes nitrogen and 1 volume oxygen
2 volumes "nitrous gas" (nitrogen oxide) produce 1 volume nitrogen and 1 volume oxygen

1 volume ammonia and 1 volume muriatic acid (hydrogen chloride) produce a neutral salt
1 volume ammonia and 1 volume "carbonic gas" (carbon dioxide) produce (with water) a salt
2 volumes ammonia and 1 volume "carbonic gas" produce (with water) another salt

---

* Read before the Philomanthic Society, Dec. 31, 1808.

formed or consumed in chemical reactions are in the ratios of small whole numbers. This relation is known as *Gay-Lussac's Law of Combining Volumes of Gases*. Some volumes of reacting gases are shown in Table 5.1.

In interpreting the results of other experimenters Gay-Lussac took the analysis of the compounds expressed in relative weights and calculated from the known densities of the gases what the combining volumes were. Because of experimental error both in the analysis and in the densities, the numbers were not exactly simple ratios. For example, using the analytical values of Davy for some oxides of nitrogen he obtained the following ratios:

	VOLUMES OF NITROGEN	OXYGEN
"Nitrous oxide"	100	49.5
"Nitrous gas"	100	108.9
"Nitric acid"	100	204.7

He saw that the volumes of oxygen combining with the 100 volumes of nitrogen were 50, 100, and 200 after allowance was made for experimental error. Here again we see the ability of a good theorist to find underlying principles behind inaccurate data.

Gay-Lussac thought that the simple ratios he found confirmed the atomic theory of Dalton though Dalton disagreed. Three years later, in 1811 the Italian physicist, Avogadro, proposed an explanation for the simple ratios of Gay-Lussac's volumes: *Equal volumes of gases contain equal numbers of particles (molecules)* the temperature, and the pressure, being the same. In accordance with this theory he concluded that, since in his experiments oxygen gas is fifteen times as dense as hydrogen gas, the oxygen molecule must weigh fifteen times as much as the hydrogen molecule (we now know that the correct ratio is 15.88 to 1). Furthermore, according to the theory, the explanation of the observed ratio of combining volumes is that two molecules of hydrogen and one molecule of oxygen produce two molecules of gaseous water. Therefore, each molecule of oxygen must be divisible by two, that is, it must contain two atoms or four atoms or some other even number since the molecules of water formed always have the same number of oxygen atoms in them. The combining volumes of Gay-Lussac for other compounds showed that the molecules of hydrogen and nitrogen must also be divisible into two parts and thus contain an even number of atoms. Avogadro, in accordance with the practice of scientists, used the simplest explanation possible, namely, that oxygen, hydrogen, and nitrogen molecules each contain two atoms since no larger number such as four, or six, or eight was needed to explain the facts. For these gases no larger number than two has ever been needed.

Here we see a method of determining the relative weights of molecules and of finding the numbers of atoms within the molecules. Then, by simple arithmetic, one could determine the relative weights of the atoms. Berzelius used the reacting volumes of gases in determining the relative atomic masses of the elements which form gaseous compounds but Dalton, the father of the atomic theory, never accepted them, particularly because his own less accurate experiments did not yield the same simple ratios among the combining volumes.

Problem 5.1. Apply the arguments of Avogadro to the compounds in Table 5.1 to show the number of part-molecules (atoms) in each molecule of nitrogen and hydrogen.

FORMULA FOR WATER

The chemical symbols H and O with the accurate weights, 1.008 and 16, assigned to them, may be used to express the composition of water neatly and precisely. The experimental analyses, earlier considered, show that 1.008 g. of hydrogen combine with 8.000 g. of oxygen to form 9.008 g. of water. In terms of the chemical symbols this amount of water may be represented by the formula $HO_{\frac{1}{2}}$ where H represents as before one symbol-weight of hydrogen and $O_{\frac{1}{2}}$ one half symbol-weight of oxygen. But 2.016 g. of hydrogen react with 16 g. of oxygen to form 18.016 g. of water. This amount of water is represented by the formula H_2O, where H_2 represents two symbol-weights of hydrogen. The formulas, $H_3O_{\frac{3}{2}}$ and H_4O_2 also represent the correct composition of water. By agreement chemists do not write formulas with fractional subscripts for to do so would involve fractions of atoms whenever the symbols stand for the atoms themselves. We must still select between the formulas H_2O, H_4O_2, H_6O_3, etc.

Since all of the formulas represent the correct weight relations and relative numbers of atoms, it follows that weight relations or relative numbers of atoms alone do not permit us to distinguish between them. One can never read more information from a formula than is needed to write the formula in the first place. Part of this information is expressed in the chemical symbols themselves and part in the subscripts indicating the number of symbol units in the formula. The information is:

1. The constituent elements of the substance.
2. The relative number of atoms of each kind in the substance.
3. The relative weights of the constituent elements in the substance.

Let us now use Avogadro's theory to determine the relative weight of the water molecules. Since water can be changed to a gas we will compare the weights of equal volumes of water vapor and of oxygen (at the same pressure and temperature), which is known to be diatomic and to have the formula O_2. The volume that holds 32 g. of oxygen, corresponding to the formula O_2, holds 18 g. of water. Therefore the water molecule has the relative weight of 18. The formula corresponding to this weight is H_2O. It is a molecular formula. If we can assume that liquid water has the same size molecules as gaseous water, the formula H_2O also is the molecular formula for liquid water.

The volume relations, the weight relations, and the equations in terms of the chemical symbols for the formation of gaseous water from hydrogen and oxygen gases are shown in Figure 5.1. The combining volumes shown in the figure are valid only when the substances are gases, but the weight relations and the chemical equations are valid whether the reacting substances are gaseous, liquid, or solid: When a given amount of a substance changes from one phase to another it does not change its weight or the number of atoms in it. This fact needs emphasis because we can write formulas for solids and

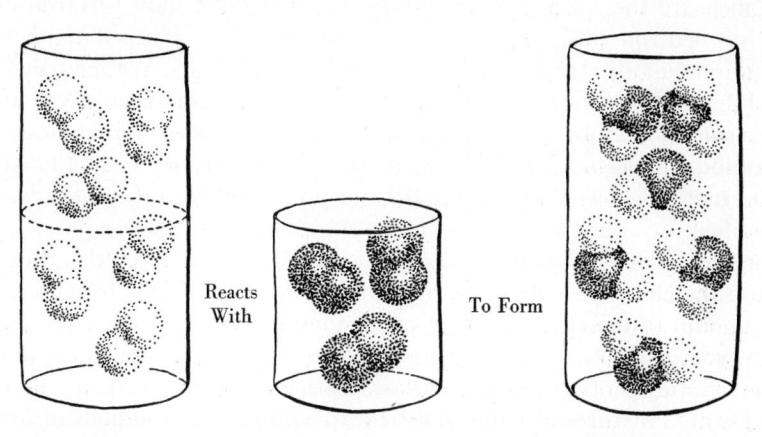

Figure 5.1.
Combining volumes of gases—Gay-Lussac's relation. 2 volumes of gaseous hydrogen plus 1 volume of gaseous oxygen yields 2 volumes of gaseous water. 4 grams of hydrogen plus 32 grams of oxygen yields 36 grams of water. $2H_{2(g)} + O_{2(g)} = 2H_2O_{(g)}$

liquids even though they do not contain molecules. If they do not contain molecules the formulas obviously cannot stand for molecules.

FORMULAS FOR THE ELEMENTS

If formulas based on chemical symbols are to represent the molecules of elements they can not be written unless the size of molecule has been determined by some experimental means. Free isolated atoms are rare on the earth, because the atoms of most elements tend to combine with one another to form larger structural units. But, a group of inert elements exists of which helium and argon are examples. Their atoms do not combine with any others. Hence a molecule of helium gas contains only one atom per molecule and the molecule may be represented by the symbol He. For argon, the symbol would be A.

Most atoms are combined at room temperature, if not with atoms of other elements then with atoms of their own kind. In many of the common elementary gases the atoms are combined in pairs. The molecules of oxygen, nitrogen, and hydrogen gases consist of such atom pairs and are represented by the formulas O_2, N_2, and H_2, respectively. When sulfur is evaporated at not too high temperatures the gas is found to consist of molecules containing eight atoms; its formula then is S_8.

What formulas shall we use to represent elements in liquids or solid phases? Under some circumstances we may measure molecular weights in liquids. They are frequently, but not always, the same as the molecular weights of the substances as gases. In solids the only way to determine the size of molecules is to measure the spacing of the atoms by x-ray diffraction, electron diffraction, or neutron diffraction. Certain atoms may be grouped more closely around one another than they are to neighboring atoms. We may then infer that the group of closely associated atoms represents a molecule. Or, we may melt a solid or dissolve it in a liquid and then use one of the liquid methods for determining molecular weight. If we do this we assume, of course, that the size of the molecule has not changed in the process. This assumption is often unjustified.

For those elements whose molecular weights have not been determined we can use the chemical symbol representing one atomic weight to represent the unit amount of the element. Most of the metallic elements are represented in this way. Even sulfur, which we now know to have eight atoms per molecule in the crystal, is often represented as S rather than S_8. Chemists, like other persons, are creatures of habit and tend to continue old methods of formulation even though newer information is available. Except for H_2, N_2, O_2, F_2, Cl_2, Br_2, and I_2, therefore, the formulas for elements are usually represented as "monatomic."

FORMULAS OF COMPOUNDS

Many formulas used to represent compounds express actual molecular weights. Thus, H_2O_2 rather than HO is used for hydrogen peroxide because it corresponds to the observed molecular weight of the substance. Whenever a formula is written in which the numbers of atoms of the different elements are not expressed in the simplest possible ratio the student may safely deduce that it represents a molecular weight determined experimentally. Grape sugar is represented by the formula $C_6H_{12}O_6$ rather than by the formula CH_2O. It is a solid but it can be dissolved and its molecular weight can be determined in the liquid solution.

Many solids do not contain small molecules. Among them is quartz, a crystalline form of silicon dioxide in which the silicon and oxygen atoms are bound together to make a large structural unit. The formula for such a substance is usually expressed in its simplest form, for example, SiO_2 and called an empirical formula. The formula Fe_3O_4 for the black, magnetic iron oxide is of this type. Common salt, sodium chloride, does not have molecules, the sodium atoms and chlorine atoms being arranged in such a way that each sodium atom is equidistant from six chlorine atoms and each chlorine atom is equidistant from six sodium atoms in the form of a three-dimensional lattice. Therefore, the formula, NaCl, does not represent any molecule. It expresses the information, summarized in the section on Formula for Water, namely, the constituent elements, sodium and chlorine, the relative number of atoms of each, 1 to 1, and the relative weights, 23 to 35.46. The composition of salt by weight may also be expressed as $\frac{23}{58.46}$ sodium and $\frac{35.46}{58.46}$ chlorine, in terms of corresponding percentages, or in any other way that does not change the fundamental ratio. The formulas of most inorganic compounds, thus, are empirical formulas which merely represent the composition in terms of the simplest possible whole number of symbols, and do not pretend to represent molecules.

MOLE

The unit of a substance represented by the formula weight in grams is so useful to chemists that it is given a name, the *mole*. A mole of oxygen is the amount represented by the formula, O_2, when $O = 16$ g. It weighs 32 g. The number of molecules in a mole is called the Avogadro number, in honor of the man who first suggested a method for getting samples of different substances containing the same number of molecules. We have seen that the best present value of the Avogadro number is 6.0238×10^{23}. A mole of water, represented by the formula H_2O, weighs 18.016 g. and contains the same number of molecules, the Avogadro number, whether the water be water vapor, liquid water, or ice. The concept of the mole is so useful that it is extended in practice even to such crystalline substances as salt and quartz which do not have molecules. The formula weight of salt in grams, 58.46 g., corresponding to the formula NaCl will also be called a molar weight or formal weight. The formula SiO_2 with a weight of 60.06 g. likewise represents a mole of quartz. The mole of an element such as copper is represented by the symbol weight in grams. This weight of an element is often called the gram-atomic weight.

The mole is a convenient unit of substance to use for expressing values of extensive properties—properties which depend on the amount of material. One of the extensive properties is volume. The volume of one mole is, obviously, a molar volume. The molar volumes of gases are relatively large. At room temperature and pressure the molar volume of gases is approximately one cubic foot. The water molecule is relatively small so that liquid water has a small molar volume, 18 milliliters. A tea cup of water holds about ten moles (180 ml.). Twenty copper pennies (U. S.) contain about one mole of copper. A mole of salt occupies about 27 ml., 1.5 times the molar volume of liquid water. The mole of ordinary sugar, represented by the formula $C_{12}H_{22}O_{11}$, is relatively large. Its weight is 342 g. and its volume is 220 ml., only slightly less than one measuring cup. These molar volumes are indicated in Figure 5.2. Observe that a molecule of this sugar contains more atoms than are present in 11 molecules of water so that it is not surprising to find the molar volume of sugar to be greater than that of 11 moles of water. Molar volumes are always large for substances with many atoms per molecule, although some atoms are larger than other atoms. We shall, in later chapters, pay some attention to the relative sizes of atoms.

Many properties associated with chemicals are usually tabulated per mole of substance. Thus, the reported heat of combustion, 68,300 calories, for the

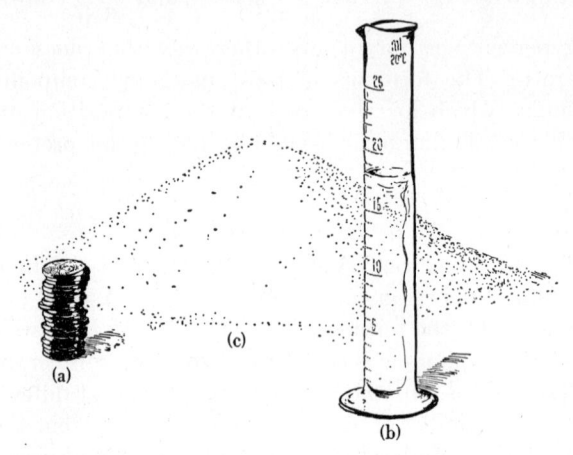

Figure 5.2.
Molar volumes of some common substances (to scale).
(a) copper, 20 pennies (b) water, 18 ml. (c) common sugar (sucrose), ¾ of a pound.

combustion of hydrogen and oxygen is the amount of energy released when one mole of liquid water is formed.

THE STRUCTURE OF MOLECULES

Molecules exist, molecules that can be represented by definite formulas. Why do they form? Why is their composition so specific? Do they have structures that explain the properties of the finite samples of substances? How do they react to form other substances? These are fundamental chemical problems.

The structures of many simple molecules are now well established. For example, electron diffraction experiments show that the molecules of oxygen gas, O_2, consist of pairs of atoms, the two atoms of each pair being closer to each other than they are to atoms of neighboring molecules. The molecule is not symmetrical like a sphere but, rather, is dumbbell shaped with the two atom centers a very short distance apart; the equilibrium distance between the atom centers is 1.20×10^{-8} cm, or 1.20 Å. All diatomic molecules, that is, molecules containing two atoms, are of this type. The carbon monoxide molecule, with the formula CO (C—O distance is 1.13 Å.), has a dumbbell shape but the two ends of the dumbbell are not alike. The carbon dioxide molecule (C—O distance is 1.15 Å.), with the formula CO_2, contains three atoms. The atom centers are arranged in a line with the carbon atom in the center. Its structure may then be represented as OCO. The water molecule (H—O distance 0.97 Å.), also with three atoms, has a different shape. The two hydrogen atoms are attached separately to the oxygen atom but the molecule has a bent form represented by the structure

H—O
    \
     H   the angle of bending being 105°.

Consequently, the water molecule is more unsymmetrical than the carbon dioxide molecule. After we have considered the atomic structure in more detail we will understand why water and carbon dioxide molecules differ in spatial arrangement. An adequate atomic theory will explain differences in behavior of this kind. The geometry of each of the above four molecules is shown in Figure 5.3.

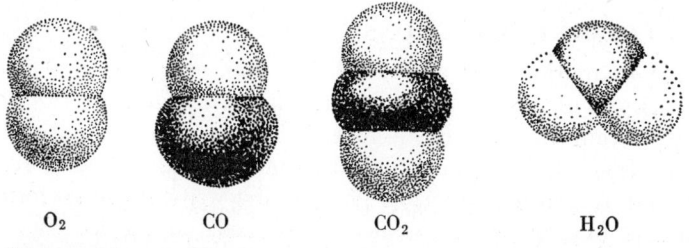

O₂   CO   CO₂   H₂O

Figure 5.3.
Sketches (to scale) for oxygen, carbon monoxide, carbon dioxide, and water molecules.

If the two hydrogen atoms of a water molecule are attached separately to the oxygen atom we may think of the oxygen atom as consisting of two halves, each of which is able to form a chemical bond with a single hydrogen atom. This concept explains the observed combining weights; only half an oxygen atom, with a mass of 8, is required to hold a hydrogen atom with a mass of 1. A hydrogen atom represents one equivalent for it forms only one bond per atom but an oxygen atom contains two equivalents. Therefore, the equivalent weight of oxygen is one-half of the atomic weight. Using this concept we are able to derive a value for the equivalent weight of carbon since each carbon atom can combine with two oxygen atoms each of which contains two equivalents by definition. A carbon atom must contain four equivalents. The equivalent weight of carbon in carbon dioxide is, therefore, one-fourth of 12, or 3. Similarly, in carbon monoxide the equivalent weight of carbon is six. These are the equivalent weights of carbon shown in Table 4.2.

The equivalent weights of elements may be derived from the formulas of compounds in a formal way without reference to the way the atoms are bonded. From the formula for quartz, SiO_2, we may deduce that there are four equivalents of silicon to combine with the four equivalents of oxygen, the equivalent weight of silicon being one fourth of 28, or 7. We get this information without knowing the structure of quartz. As a matter of fact, in quartz each silicon atom is attached to four different oxygen atoms and each oxygen to two different silicon atoms, with the result that there is no simple molecule but rather a three-dimensional structure extending to the boundaries of the crystal.

The differences in structure of solid silicon dioxide and carbon dioxide explain why quartz remains a solid up to very high temperatures whereas carbon dioxide with its simple molecular structure evaporates readily at temperatures well below room temperature. In order to understand the properties of substances we need to go beyond the formula, which sometimes represents the molecule and sometimes does not, to the arrangements of the atoms in substances. The resulting structures are determined by the ways in which atoms are bonded to one another in space.

WRITING CHEMICAL EQUATIONS

A chemical equation, like any other equation, expresses an *equality* (but not necessarily an identity). Given the formulas of the substances in a reaction, how can we obtain the equation? A general logical method, applicable to complicated reactions, will be illustrated and applied to the familiar reaction of hydrogen and oxygen to form water. Let us first write down the formulas for hydrogen and oxygen, the substances consumed, on the left side and the formula for water, the substance produced, on the right side, and connect them by an inequality sign, for the statement is not yet an equation. Thus,

$$H_2 + O_2 \neq H_2O$$

The statement can be made into an equation if numbers showing the relative numbers of moles of reacting substances are inserted. These numbers may be represented by x, y, and z as in the equation

$$xH_2 + y\,O_2 = z\,H_2O \tag{5.1}$$

The values of x, y, and z are relative, but when the value of any one is fixed the others have unique values consistent with it. These values may be found by logic. For example, let $z = 1$. Then we are concerned with the formation of one mole of water. But one mole of water, with its two symbol weights of hydrogen requires the number of moles of hydrogen that furnishes this quantity. Therefore x *must be* 1. The mole of water requires one symbol weight of oxygen which is supplied by one-half mole of oxygen. Therefore y must be $\frac{1}{2}$. Equation 5.1 then becomes

$$1H_2 + \tfrac{1}{2}O_2 = 1H_2O \tag{5.2}$$

Observe that the method does not use any "trial and error" or guessing. The equation yields the information that 1 mole of hydrogen (weighing 2.016 g.) reacts with $\frac{1}{2}$ mole of oxygen (weighing 16.000 g.) to form 1 mole of water (weighing 18.016 g.). A corresponding statement in terms of molecules cannot be as precise. It would indicate correctly the relative numbers of molecules (and atoms) but not the relative weights of the individual atoms, for not all the hydrogen atoms (or oxygen atoms) have the same mass. The equation will become precise for individual molecules if the masses of the individual atoms are indicated. We shall show how such equations are written when we consider the reactions of individual atoms and molecules.

If we are interested in the formation of two moles of water we assign a value of 2 to z. Then x must be 2 and y must be 1, as in the equation

$$2H_2 + 1O_2 = 2H_2O \tag{5.3}$$

Equations are usually written in as simple a form as convenient. Whichever of the equations 5.2 or 5.3 (or others) is considered more convenient depends on whether one is interested in one mole of water or two, or even on whether one dislikes fractions. Experienced chemists omit 1 as a coefficient, this number being understood when no other coefficient is used. Beginners should use such symbols as x, y, and z and should retain coefficients of unity until the logic of writing equations is perfectly clear.

Problem 5.2. Using a logical method derive the chemical equations for the following reactions:
  a. Carbon burns with oxygen to form carbon dioxide.
  b. Carbon monoxide burns with oxygen to form carbon dioxide.
  c. Iron burns with oxygen to form magnetic iron oxide, with the formula Fe_3O_4.

ENERGY IN CHEMICAL REACTIONS

Each substance has energy characteristic of it and of the state it is in. This energy, called the *internal energy*, is an extensive property. Another extensive property of a substance is its *heat capacity*, the quantity of heat required to raise its temperature 1°. At higher temperatures a substance always has more internal energy than at lower temperatures. When a substance is not permitted to do work while its temperature is raised all the heat absorbed by it becomes part of its internal energy. (The unit of energy most commonly used in chemistry is the *calorie*. One calorie equals 4.184 joules. The earlier definition of the calorie as the amount of heat required to change the temperature of one gram of water by one degree centigrade is sufficiently accurate for our purposes.)

That each substance has a characteristic internal energy is also shown by the fact that when substances react to form new substances definite amounts of energy are released (or absorbed), even though the reacting substances and the products are at the same temperature. Thus, when a mixture of hydrogen and oxygen gases at room temperature is ignited, water is formed and a great deal of energy is released. If the water is brought to room temperature and the total energy released is measured, the energy is always found to have a characteristic value directly proportional to the amount of water formed. In

60   GENERAL CHEMISTRY

other words, a mole of water has less energy by a characteristic amount than the mole of hydrogen and half-mole of oxygen from which it was formed. The energy released in the reaction may appear as heat which can be measured in a calorimeter or as work which can be measured in terms of its ability to move matter from one place to another. Since the work effects of most chemical reactions are small compared with the heat effects we may measure the energy differences of the reacting substances roughly in terms of the heat released. The heat released on formation of one mole of liquid water from the elements at room temperature (25°C.) is 68,300 calories. That is, a mole of water may be said to have a *heat content* less by 68,300 calories than the elements. This fact can be expressed in the form of an equation:

$$\text{heat content of 1 mole hydrogen gas} + \text{heat content of } \tfrac{1}{2} \text{ mole oxygen gas} = \text{heat content of 1 mole liquid water} + 68{,}300 \text{ calories} \qquad (5.4)$$

A thermal equation of this kind is often added to a chemical equation to give a combined, thermochemical, equation which may be written as follows

$$H_{2(g)} + \tfrac{1}{2}O_{2(g)} = H_2O_{(liq)} + 68{,}300 \text{ cal.} \qquad (5.5)$$

Thermochemical equations are dual equations. They show an equality of atoms and of their weights in terms of a unit of mass such as the gram. They also show an equality in heat content in terms of an energy unit, such as the calorie. When no work, such as work of expansion against the atmosphere, is done during the reaction they also show an equality in energies. Because of the interconvertibility of mass and energy one could express both mass and energy in terms of a single unit, but this is not feasible practically; the values of the energies expressed in mass units would be extremely small numbers. We shall continue the dual set of units, especially since they are not ambiguous or confusing.

A reaction in which heat is released to the environment, the products having less heat content than the reacting substances, is called an *exothermic* reaction. Equation 5.5 when read from left to right represents an exothermic reaction. It also indicates that if we wish to decompose a mole of water into its elements we must supply this amount of energy. Such a reaction, represented by equation 5.5 read from right to left, is called an *endothermic* reaction. The heat of formation of water from the elements is expressed as a negative number, $-68{,}300$ calories, emphasizing the fact that water has less energy than the elements from which it is made. Thus, for exothermic reactions the heats of reaction are listed as negative numbers. In reaction 5.5 the change in heat content would be given as $-68{,}300$ calories.

In thermochemical equations the states of the reacting substances as well as their formulas must be shown because the energies and heats of reactions depend on those of the reacting materials and these in turn depend on their states (phase, temperature, pressure, and concentration). Unless otherwise specified each reaction is assumed to be occurring at room temperature, under a total pressure of one atmosphere, and with each substance present in its phase most stable under these conditions.

A mole of gaseous water at room temperature and atmospheric pressure has more energy than a mole of liquid water under these conditions. Indeed, it is unstable and tends to condense to form liquid water. The thermochemical equation for the formation of gaseous water at 25°C. is

$$H_{2(g)} + \tfrac{1}{2}O_{2(g)} = H_2O_{(g)} + 57{,}800 \text{ cal.} \tag{5.6}$$

The condensation of gaseous water to liquid water with evolution of heat may be represented by the equation

$$H_2O_{(g)} = H_2O_{(liq)} + 10{,}500 \text{ cal.} \tag{5.7}$$

Thermochemical equations, like any equations, may be added or subtracted. We may add equations 5.6 and 5.7 as follows

$$H_{2(g)} + \tfrac{1}{2}O_{2(g)} = H_2O_{(g)} + 57{,}800 \text{ cal.} \tag{5.6}$$
$$H_2O_{(g)} = H_2O_{(liq)} + 10{,}500 \text{ cal.} \tag{5.7}$$
$$\overline{H_{2(g)} + \tfrac{1}{2}O_{2(g)} = H_2O_{(liq)} + 68{,}300 \text{ cal.}} \tag{5.5}$$

The result is equation 5.5.

We have already seen that heats of reaction are proportional to the amounts of reacting materials. For the formation of two moles of water, as in equation 5.3, the heat of reaction is double that in equation 5.5.

$$2H_{2(g)} + O_{2(g)} = 2H_2O_{(liq)} + 136{,}600 \text{ cal.} \tag{5.8}$$

Even when we do not write thermochemical equations we will often find it instructive to designate the phases of reacting substances. The formulas for substances as gases are variously represented by $H_{2(g)}$, $H_2 \uparrow$, or $\bar{H}_2$, those for substances in a liquid phase by $H_2O_{(liq)}$ or $H_2O_{(l)}$, or the formula without any special notation, and those for substances in a pure solid phase by $NaCl_{(c)}$, $NaCl_{(s)}$, $NaCl \downarrow$, or $\underline{NaCl}$. All these notations may be found in chemical writings.

Heats of reaction are important to chemists for two reasons. In the first place, they enable us to find the internal energies of chemical substances, energies which are one of the important factors in the stabilities of the substances. In the second place, many chemical reactions are carried out because they are heat producing. We use the tendency of substances to produce other substances with less energy to furnish us with heat. Fuels are energy-rich substances. They combine with oxygen to form energy-poor products, such as carbon dioxide and water, with much less internal energy. Whether they be used for cooking, for the running of automobiles or factories, or for propulsion of rockets, all fuels have these characteristics. The substances now used for fuels were synthesized earlier by endothermic reactions from other natural substances with the aid of solar energy. Accurate knowledge of heats of re-

Table 5.2
Some Heats of Combustion of Some Substances with Oxygen

(Values in kilocalories per formula weight (mole). A negative sign means that heat is evolved in the reaction.)

SUBSTANCE	FORMULA WEIGHT	COMBUSTION PRODUCTS	HEAT OF COMBUSTION AT 25°C. (IN KILOCALORIES)
Hydrogen	$H_2 = 2.016$	$H_2O_{(liq)}$	−68.32
"	"	$H_2O_{(g)}$	−57.80
Sulfur	$S = 32.06$	SO_2	−70.92
Carbon (graphite)	$C = 12.010$	CO_2	−94.05
Carbon monoxide	$CO = 28.010$	CO_2	−67.64
Methane	$CH_4 = 16.042$	CO_2 and $H_2O_{(liq)}$	−212.80

action is necessary if we are to compare the merits of different fuels or to test the efficiency with which they are utilized.

A few heats of combustion, that is, heats of reaction with oxygen, are given in Table 5.2.

Problem 5.3. List all the experimental facts we must have before we can write the formula H_2O for water.

Problem 5.4. The formula for hydrogen peroxide is H_2O_2. Why is the formula not expressed as HO? Can the percentage analysis of hydrogen peroxide tell us which formula is correct?

Problem 5.5. Complete the following:

$$Fe_{(s)} + Cl_{2(g)} = Fe_2Cl_{6(s)}$$
$$Mn_{(s)} + O_{2(g)} = Mn_3O_{4(s)}$$
$$Na_{(s)} + P_{4(s)} + O_{2(g)} = Na_3PO_{4(s)}$$
$$Na_{(s)} + H_{2(g)} + S_{8(s)} + O_{2(g)} = NaHSO_{4(s)}$$
$$C_{(s)} + H_{2(g)} + O_{2(g)} + N_{2(g)} = HNC\,(C_2H_5)OC_2H_{5(s)}$$
$$C_{12}H_{22}O_{11(s)} + O_{2(g)} = CO_{2(g)} + H_2O$$
$$KClO_{3(s)} = KCl_{(s)} + O_{2(g)}$$

Problem 5.6. The analysis of a compound is: carbon, 38.70 per cent; hydrogen, 9.74 per cent; and oxygen, 51.56 per cent. By an independent method to be studied later the molecular weight of the compound is found to be approximately 64. What is the formula of the compound? What is its exact molecular weight?

Problem 5.7. Derive a formula for a compound having the analysis 47.09 per cent oxygen and 52.91 per cent aluminum.

Problem 5.8. Ten g. of aluminum are burned in 10 g. of oxygen until one of the reagents is consumed. Is either aluminum or oxygen present in excess? What weight of aluminum oxide is formed? See Problem 5.7 for data.

Problem 5.9. When enough aluminum is burned in air to form a molar weight of aluminum oxide in grams, 400,000 cal. of energy are released as heat. How much energy is released when 1 g. of aluminum burns?

Problem 5.10. How much phosphoric acid, formula, H_3PO_4, is formed when 142 g. of "phosphorus pentoxide," formula, P_4O_{10}, are treated with enough water? How many moles of water are required?

Problem 5.11. Write the missing words for the numbered spaces in the following: The ___(1)___ Al$_2$O$_3$, indicates that aluminum and oxygen are united in the proportion of two ___(2)___ of aluminum to three of oxygen; that aluminum and oxygen are ___(3)___ while Al$_2$O$_3$ is a ___(4)___ . The letters Al are the ___(5)___ for aluminum; 27.0 g. of it is called one ___(6)___ .

Problem 5.12. What weight of sulfuric acid, formula, H$_2$SO$_4$, may be made from 12 tons of sulfur by the process based on the following reactions:

$$S + O_{2(g)} = SO_{2(g)}$$
$$SO_{2(g)} + \tfrac{1}{2} O_{2(g)} = SO_{3(g)}$$
$$SO_{3(g)} + H_2O = H_2SO_4$$

Problem 5.13. When a mixture of potassium chlorate, formula, KClO$_3$, and potassium chloride, formula, KCl, weighing 3.00 g. is heated thoroughly, 0.400 g. of oxygen is liberated. Calculate the per cent by weight of potassium chlorate in the sample.

Problem 5.14. (a) Air is passed over 1.000 g. of hot copper until the copper is completely converted to the black copper oxide. What weight of copper oxide is formed? What weight of oxygen reacts with the copper?

(b) A stream of hydrogen is passed over the copper oxide prepared in (a) while it is kept hot. What weight of copper is formed? What weight of water is formed? What is the weight of the oxygen in the water? The weight of hydrogen?

Problem 5.15. Repeat the calculations in Problem 5.14, but this time for a sample of copper whose weight equals the gram-atomic weight of copper. Of what practical value is the chemist's concept of the gram-atomic weight?

6 THE ATMOSPHERE

THE CHEMICALS with which most chemists work are not ordinarily found pure in nature. They must be obtained from the naturally occurring raw materials by manufacturing and purifying processes. Until about 1875 each chemist had to prepare most of his own chemicals from natural materials, but now he can obtain any of thousands of pure chemicals from numerous manufacturers and supply houses. It is, however, still interesting to know natural sources and the treatments necessary to produce pure substances from them.

There are three general sources of raw materials: the atmosphere; the oceans, lakes, and rivers, called the hydrosphere; and the land, called the lithosphere. The atmosphere contains primarily gaseous substances; the hydrosphere contains water and certain water-soluble substances; and the lithosphere contains all other raw materials, primarily solids, which include by far the major fraction of substances in variety and amount. Land must be thoroughly prospected for its minerals, ores, and other raw materials because they are found in localized areas, whereas the oceans and the atmosphere have their constituents rather uniformly distributed. The atmosphere has an important advantage as a source of raw materials in that it is available at any spot on the earth's surface. This means that there is no transportation problem or cost; the atmosphere in these respects constitutes an ideal raw material source. The materials themselves are also of fundamental interest to the chemist. We shall, therefore, first consider the composition of the atmosphere.

AIR AS A SOLUTION

There is evidence that a Chinese scholar named Mao-Khoa recognized that air is not an element as early as the eighth century, but the first unambiguous reference to this fact by a European was made by Leonardo da Vinci near the beginning of the sixteenth century when he noticed that air was consumed, but not completely consumed, in respiration and combustion processes.

Clear-cut proof that air is a solution rather than a pure substance is obtained by liquefying it at temperatures of approximately $-200°C.$ and distilling the liquid. As moist air is chilled to 0°C. liquid water condenses from it. Below 0°C. most of the remaining water vapor condenses to ice but a little vapor always remains. When the dried air is cooled below −78.5°C. solid carbon dioxide crystallizes and separates. On further cooling the elements, nitrogen, oxygen, argon, neon, krypton, and xenon liquefy, but at different rates. For example, at about −190°C. oxygen liquefies more readily than nitrogen so that oxygen becomes more concentrated in the liquid phase and nitrogen in the gas phase. The separation may be made more complete if the liquid phases are further boiled and liquefied. In this way all the above gases may be separated and obtained pure on a commercial scale.

Traces of elementary hydrogen and helium, and of ozone, carbon monoxide, methane, and nitrous oxide in the atmosphere may be detected with a spec-

Table 6.1
Composition of a Certain Sample of Dry Air and the Boiling Points of the Constituents

SUBSTANCE	VOLUME PER CENT	WEIGHT PER CENT	B. P. (°C.)
Nitrogen	78.09	75.51	−195.8
Oxygen	20.95	23.15	−183.0
Argon	0.93	1.28	−185.8
Neon	0.0018	0.0013	−245.9
Krypton	0.0001	0.0003	−152
Xenon	0.000008	0.00004	−108.0
Helium	0.00052	0.00007	−268.9
Hydrogen	0.00005	0.000003	−252.6
Carbon Dioxide	0.03	0.05	—

Traces (less than 0.0002% by volume) of formaldehyde, oxides of nitrogen, hydrogen peroxide, ozone, carbon monoxide, methane, ammonia, iodine, and radon are also known to be present in the atmosphere as gases.

troscope. Industrial areas may have a rather high atmospheric content of many other chemicals. Sulfur dioxide and hydrocarbons (compounds of hydrogen and carbon) are common examples. These are known as contaminants for they would not be present except for man-made industries. The presence of such contaminants seems to be critical for inducing atmospheric conditions such as "industrial haze," also known as "smog" or "smaze." Occasionally these contaminants accumulate in lethal concentrations as when 4000 people died in London in a 1953 "fog."

The water content of air is so variable that air is often dried before being analyzed. The analysis of a sample of dry, uncontaminated air, expressed in percentages, is shown in Table 6.1. However, not all samples of air have the same analysis. The relative amounts of oxygen in a large number of samples of dry, uncontaminated air from various localities are summarized in Table 6.2. The variation in per cent by volume, from 20.72 to 21.18, is appreciable. Thus air, if free from suspended particles, is a gaseous solution of variable composition, but with variations confined to a rather narrow range.

Table 6.2

Oxygen in Different Samples of Dry Air

SOURCE OF SAMPLES	NUMBER OF SAMPLES	\multicolumn{4}{c}{VOLUME PER CENT OF OXYGEN}
		Minimum	Maximum	Difference	Average
Cape Horn	20	20.72	20.97	0.25	20.86
Manchester	32	20.78	21.02	0.24	20.94
Mountains of Scotland	34	20.80	21.18	0.38	20.97
Heidelberg	28	20.840	20.970	0.130	20.924
Dresden	46	20.877	20.971	0.094	20.930
Cleveland, Ohio	45	20.90	20.95	0.05	20.93
Bonn	45	20.901	20.989	0.038	20.922
Paris	100	20.913	20.999	0.086	20.960

COMPOSITION EXPRESSED IN PER CENTS

Gases can be weighed by weighing an evacuated container, then introducing the gas into the container, sealing it, and weighing it again. The difference in the two weights gives the weight of the gas. The fraction, by weight, of a component in the gas may be found by determining the loss in weight of a known weight of gas when that component is removed. The fraction by weight of oxygen in air, for instance, may be determined by passing weighed samples of air over hot copper which combines with the oxygen to produce a solid oxide. Capturing and weighing the remaining gas then permits one to find the weight of oxygen originally present in terms of the loss in weight of the sample. Or the gain in weight of the copper may be measured. This weight will also represent the weight of oxygen originally present in the sample but now combined in the copper oxide. From these data the composition of the gas in terms of the per cent by weight of its components may be derived. The equation for the reaction of copper with oxygen is

$$\underset{\text{red}}{Cu_{(s)}} + \tfrac{1}{2}O_{2(g)} = \underset{\text{black}}{CuO_{(s)}} \tag{6.1}$$

It is far more common to present the composition of gases in terms of per cent by volume rather than per cent by weight, partly because volumes of gases may be more easily measured than weights and partly because volume relationships in gases prove to correlate simply with molecular behavior. Composition by volume may be determined by measuring the volume of the gas when it is confined over mercury at a given pressure and temperature, letting it react with appropriate reagents to remove a certain component, reconfining it over the mercury, and noting the new volume when the pressure and temperature are the same as in the original measurement. Mercury is used as a confining agent since it is a liquid of very low volatility and so does not contribute any appreciable amount of gas to the volume being measured, and because it does not dissolve or react with most gases.

A composition expressed in percentages when applied to gases means per cent by volume unless otherwise qualified. The percentages used in expressing the composition of liquids or solids, unless qualified, mean per cent by weight.

NITROGEN

The main constituent of the atmosphere is nitrogen which makes up almost 80 per cent by volume of the gas. Nitrogen is rather inert chemically. In fact, elementary nitrogen is so stable with respect to its compounds that many nitrogen compounds decompose readily to form the element. Most chemical explosives are nitrogen compounds for this reason.

Bacteria on the roots of leguminous plants are able to extract the nitrogen from the air and synthesize nitrogen compounds from it. The electrical energy of a lightning bolt is able to bring about combination of nitrogen and oxygen in the atmosphere on an appreciable scale. Industrial methods have likewise been found for synthesizing nitrogen compounds from the nitrogen of the air and most industrialized countries can now make all the nitrogen compounds they need, using atmospheric nitrogen as a raw material. Such methods are known as nitrogen-fixation processes. Several million tons of nitrogen are "mined" from the atmosphere in this way each year.

Neither man, animals, or plants, with the exception of the legumes and their bacteria previously mentioned, have physiologies which enable them to utilize directly the nitrogen in the air, yet all living organisms require nitrogenous materials to survive. Death brings on decay which returns an appreciable fraction of the nitrogenous material to elementary nitrogen so that those processes which recombine the nitrogen are an important part of one of the many cycles in nature. The rate of passage around any cycle is determined by the rate of the slowest step, and, for many parts of the world, the slowest step in the nitrogen cycle was known, by the end of the nineteenth century, to be the recombination of atmospheric nitrogen into a form usefully available to plants. That is, many soils were depleted in available nitrogen. The discovery, early in this century, of industrial methods for producing fertilizers from atmospheric nitrogen has now removed the possibility that this particular lack will act as the limiting control on agriculture, and has led to the doubling and trebling of yields of crops per acre of land. It must be remembered, of course, that any balanced fertilizer also contains components other than available nitrogen.

OXYGEN

Oxygen composes about one fifth of the air by volume. It is rather inert in dry air at temperatures usually found in the atmosphere but is by far the most reactive constituent. It would be foolish to say that oxygen is the most important constituent, however, for at least three other components of the atmosphere—nitrogen, carbon dioxide, and water—are essential to life as we know it, and are therefore equally important.

Much more oxygen than nitrogen is removed from the air and many millions of tons of oxygen appear in saleable chemical products. About half a million tons of relatively pure oxygen are obtained from the air by liquefaction annually of which nine-tenths is used to weld and cut metals. But the greatest industrial use of oxygen by far is to burn fuels, and the oxygen, obtained directly from the air, is then vented back to the atmosphere in combustion products such as carbon dioxide and water vapor. Living organisms participate in a similar oxygen cycle.

One of the more important roles of elementary oxygen is in the physiology of animals where it enters into energy-producing reactions having the general nature of combustions and then is eliminated in carbon dioxide and water. The animals use the energy so obtained to maintain their life processes. Plants, on the other hand, obtain their energy primarily from the sun. They need to absorb little oxygen, but do require large amounts of carbon for growth. This they extract from carbon dioxide, freeing oxygen in the process. In both plants and animals some of the oxygen is incorporated into the organic structure but not most of that which enters the system. In contrast, the nitrogen compounds of living organisms are generally incorporated in the structure of the organisms for relatively long periods of time. Thus the oxygen cycle moves much more rapidly than the nitrogen cycle and the demand for oxygen from the atmosphere at any given time is much the greater of the two. The oxygen supply of the atmosphere is renewed on the average of once every three thousand years, whereas the nitrogen supply is renewed about every hundred million years.

Oxygen may also be contrasted with nitrogen in the stability of its compounds for most oxygen compounds are very stable with respect to evolution of elementary oxygen. Large amounts of energy must ordinarily be expended to free oxygen from its chemical combinations. To liberate one pound of oxygen from water requires over two kilowatt-hours of energy, or almost two million calories. Further evidence for the tendency of oxygen to form compounds may be drawn from the fact that ninety-two of the chemical elements are known to form binary compounds of oxygen. That there is any free oxygen in the atmosphere is due to the slowness with which oxygen reacts with most combustible material at ordinary temperatures, for there is more than enough combustible material near the earth's surface to combine with all the oxygen. During the early stages of the earth's formation when the temperatures were considerably higher than at present there was no elementary oxygen in the atmosphere. Some process or processes which liberated free oxygen had to occur before most of the present forms of life were possible.

COMBUSTION

We now all recognize the fundamental part the atmosphere, and particularly oxygen, plays in combustion processes. In fact we treat this knowledge as though it were obvious. But there is little in the appearance of a fire to indicate the role of the atmosphere in maintaining it. More obviously flames are leaving the fire. On the basis of this observation the early chemists believed that combustion was a process in which a volatile substance, phlogiston, escaped in the form of fire into the atmosphere, leaving behind a calx, or ash, which could be considered dephlogisticated material. Smothering prevented the escape of phlogiston, water cooled the material and reduced the volatility of phlogiston, heating increased the volatility of phlogiston and led to flame formation. The ease and vigor with which things burned depended on the tightness with which they held their phlogiston and the amount of phlogiston each contained. Thus, the theory explained many of the observed facts. It is interesting to note that the two men who are credited with the discovery of oxygen, Scheele and Priestley, both believed firmly in the phlogiston theory of combustion until their deaths in 1786 and 1804 respectively. In fact, Priestley called oxygen "dephlogisticated air" since substances burned so much more brightly in it that he presumed their phlogiston could escape more readily into this new substance. The gases obtained when flames were confined in closed volumes until they smothered themselves were thought to be saturated with phlogiston. Addition of dephlogisticated air, oxygen, to them, rejuvenated their ability to support combustion by reducing the phlogiston concentration.

It was Lavoisier, in 1775, who first arrived at the present interpretation of combustion as the combination of a substance with the "purest and most salubrious part of air" (oxygen). He showed that heating mercury at low temperatures in contact with air in a closed system diminished the volume of air by about one-fifth while a red powder formed on the mercury surface, and that the residual gas would not support combustion. He then raised the temperature of the system, causing the red powder to disappear and the gas to recover the normal properties of air. He also showed that the red powder weighed more than the mercury it contained. These facts seemed to indicate that matter was leaving the gas and combining with the mercury, rather than leaving the mercury and entering the gas. Nevertheless many chemists did not agree with Lavoisier's deduction and thirty years elapsed before the phlogiston theory was discarded. During this period phlogiston was given such odd attributes as a negative weight to account, for instance, for the gain in weight when mercury was converted to the red powder. Thus, one notes that science has its share of men who refuse to change their concepts in the face of new and even overwhelming evidence.

THE INERT GASES

Until near the end of the nineteenth century chemists considered the atmosphere as made up of nitrogen and oxygen plus variable amounts of carbon dioxide and water. True, Cavendish, in England in 1785, had sparked a mixture of air and excess oxygen until all the nitrogen should have combined with the oxygen to give nitrogen oxides soluble in basic solution. (Remember the reaction between oxygen and nitrogen when lightning occurs.) Cavendish

70   GENERAL CHEMISTRY

placed the resulting gas in contact with base and then removed the excess oxygen only to find that a small bubble, less than 1 per cent of the volume of the original sample, remained. He made no comment on its composition and the general assumption was that the sparking had not been continued long enough.

Over a hundred years later, in 1894, Lord Rayleigh, also in England, prepared nitrogen (1) by removing the oxygen from air, (2) by burning ammonia in air, and (3) by heating ammonium nitrite. The equations for the latter processes are:

$$2NH_{3(g)} + \tfrac{3}{2}O_{2(g)} = N_{2(g)} + 3H_2O_{(g)} \qquad (6.2)$$
$$NH_4NO_2 = N_{2(g)} + 2H_2O \qquad (6.3)$$

Presumably, when the water (and unreacted ammonia) was removed from the gas produced by reactions 6.2 and 6.3 pure nitrogen remained, but the samples of "nitrogen" prepared by the three different methods had different densities. The sample from air alone (1) had a density of 1.2572 g. per l. at 25°C. and 1 atmosphere pressure, that from ammonium nitrite (3) 1.2505 g. per l., and that from ammonia and air (2) an intermediate value depending on the relative amounts of the two used. Some observers might have overlooked the discrepancy as an experimental error but Rayleigh felt the differences were significant. The experiment of Cavendish was then repeated by Rayleigh and Ramsay who showed that the residual gas was not nitrogen or oxygen but a hitherto undiscovered element, which they named argon. Further search by the same men led to the subsequent discovery of neon, krypton, and xenon in the atmosphere. Simultaneously, Ramsay showed that helium, previously discovered in the sun by Lockyer in 1868 through spectroscopic evidence, was present in ores containing uranium. Later, traces of helium were shown to exist in the atmosphere.

The five elements, helium, neon, argon, krypton, and xenon, form no strong chemical bonds. Radon, discovered in radium ores in 1900, is a sixth element with similarly inert chemistry. These six are known as the inert gases. The forces of attraction of their atoms for other atoms are very small. That the attractions for atoms of their own kind is also small is shown by the low boiling points of the elements listed in Table 6.1. The attractive forces between atoms of helium are the smallest inter-atomic forces known. Evidently, the inert gases have highly stable atomic structures which cannot gain in stability by combining with any other substances.

As a result of their inertness, helium and argon are much used when a nonreactive atmosphere is desired; for example, helium around a torch for welding aluminum, or argon around the white hot filament of an electric light bulb. Helium, which has the greatest lifting power of any gas except hydrogen, is used for filling balloons, blimps, and dirigibles since it lacks hydrogen's inflammability in air. (Lifting power may be defined as the weight which can be lifted by a unit weight of any substance when it is buoyed up by a second substance. Or it may be defined as the difference in density of the first and second substance.) Neon is familiar as the gaseous substance which is excited to emit the orange-red light of "neon signs," and krypton has been widely used recently as the filler in photographers' "repeating flash lamps." The claim made in 1949 that xenon is an anesthetic is most interesting in the light of xenon's general chemical inertness.

The amount of helium in the atmosphere is far too small to be of economic significance. Some natural gas wells in Texas and Kansas contain as much as 16 per cent of helium and are the commercial sources of the gas. There is evidence that the atmosphere at one time contained much more helium, neon, and hydrogen than at present but that these substances have diffused into outer space during the geological history of the earth.

Ordinarily we think of gas, liquid, and solid as terms covering all the possible types of phases of matter. Helium when cooled to very low temperatures ($-271°C$.) has properties which place it outside this scheme. Above this temperature helium is a normal liquid or gas, but below it it acts like a liquid by filling the bottom of its container. It then has less viscosity than any gas, and better heat conductivity than most solids. The interpretation of this behavior is still not adequate so that "liquid helium II" is one of the most fascinating of chemical substances.

CARBON DIOXIDE

The relative amount of carbon dioxide in air varies considerably, averaging about 0.03 per cent in country areas. In cities, the percentage is higher, and poorly ventilated rooms may contain as much as 1 per cent. The amount of carbon dioxide in the air is very important to life. Too much carbon dioxide in the air, above about 6 per cent, makes it impossible for the lungs to accomplish their function of eliminating carbon dioxide from the blood and suffocation will result from prolonged breathing of such a high percentage of the gas. On the other hand a small amount is necessary to maintain the supply of carbon dioxide in the blood, for it stimulates the brain centers controlling respiration.

The role of carbon dioxide in plant metabolism is equally important for it is from this raw material and water that plants synthesize sugars and starches photosynthetically. In the process elementary oxygen is produced by the plants. Thus the complementary arrangement of plants utilizing carbon dioxide and releasing oxygen whereas animals inhale oxygen and exhale carbon dioxide works to the mutual benefit of both. The carbon cycle, as indicated in Figure 6.1, is far faster than either the oxygen (three thousand years) or nitrogen (one hundred million years). Land plants, for instance, assimilate carbon at a rate equivalent to using up all the carbon dioxide in the atmosphere in ten years. But the oceans, the principal reservoirs of water, are also the principal reservoirs of carbon dioxide, partly present as dissolved carbon dioxide

72 GENERAL CHEMISTRY

and partly combined into other chemical substances. If we consider the carbon reserves of the ocean and the ocean plant demands, the carbon cycle lengthens, but is still only one hundred years. We shall discuss the chemistry of carbon dioxide further in following chapters.

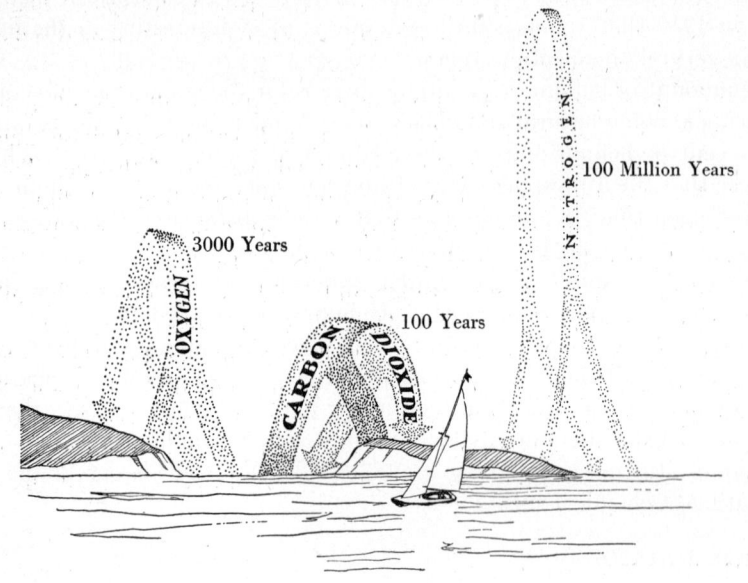

Figure 6.1.
Time cycles for renewal of nitrogen, oxygen, and carbon dioxide in the atmosphere.

WATER VAPOR

The variation in the amount of water vapor in air is particularly great. As dry air moves over ice or water, net vaporization of water into the air will occur, and the concentration of gaseous water in the air will increase to a maximum value (if contact time is sufficient) which is determined by the temperature. When this maximum is reached at any temperature, the wet air is said to be in vapor equilibrium with the ice or water, or to be saturated with water vapor. Ice at −30°C. will be in vapor equilibrium with air (at standard pressure) containing 0.04 per cent by volume of water vapor whereas water at 30°C. will be in vapor equilibrium with air containing about 4 per cent by volume of gaseous water. As air moves from colder to warmer regions, its water content can thus increase if a source of water is available. Conversely, movement of warm air with a high water vapor content to colder regions will result in the precipitation of the water as clouds, dew, rain or snow when the vapor content of the atmosphere exceeds the equilibrium value at the resulting atmospheric temperature.

Cloud formation is of particular interest. Air containing water vapor is less dense than dry air and thus tends to rise. As it rises in the earth's atmosphere, the pressure decreases and the gas expands. This expansion requires expenditure of energy. The only source of energy available is the thermal energy of the gas so that some of this thermal energy is used up and the gas cools. The cold gas is no longer able to maintain a high water content and droplets of liquid water form. These droplets may be so small that they have little tendency to settle but stay suspended in the atmosphere and form a cloud. If the temperature becomes low enough the droplets may consist of undercooled water (liquid water below its normal freezing temperature) or may freeze into tiny ice particles. Ice clouds are quite common at high altitudes. Any mechanism which would allow the small particles to coalesce would enhance the possibilities of large rain droplets forming or large ice crystals (snowflakes) forming in the clouds. This would lead to precipitation. The present day methods of inducing rainfall or snowfall attempt to supply such a mechanism by providing nuclei on which undercooled water may crystallize (the silver iodide method), by strongly cooling the cloud locally to induce crystallization (the dry ice method), by neutralizing the electric charge present on the cloud droplets and thus enhancing their chance of collision (the electrostatic method), or by actually introducing droplets of water into the cloud (the water spray method).

HUMIDITY AND LIFE PROCESSES

One of the prime means of regulating the temperature of the human body is through the evaporation of perspiration from the skin. This process requires energy, the heat of evaporation, which comes from the thermal energy of the body with resulting cooling. Evaporation can occur with a net loss of heat only if the vapor particles are carried away so that they do not recondense on the skin. Thus any breeze aids the cooling process. If the breeze consists only of air which is already saturated with water vapor, however, there is no net evaporation into it and no cooling effect. The usual unit for measuring water content of air is relative humidity, the relative humidity being that percentage of the total possible equilibrium water content which is actually present in the sample of air. Thus 100 per cent relative humidity means that the air already contains that concentration of water vapor which would be in equilibrium with liquid water at the same temperature, whereas air of 50 per cent relative humidity contains only half as much water vapor. It thus becomes clear why the relative humidity is of much importance in determining whether one is comfortable or not, and why the statement "it isn't the temperature, it is the humidity that determines comfort" has some validity.

On the other hand, if the humidity becomes too low, desiccation occurs. This is equally deleterious to human welfare and to life in general. It is interesting to study the varieties of plants and animals which grow in regions of greatly different temperatures and humidities and the structural features which allow them to live in a given environment. The smooth, almost poreless, rounded shapes of the cactus minimize surfaces from which evaporation may occur, while the succulent, broad-leaved jungle plants provide maximum area for the processes of photosynthesis to utilize the abundant light, water, and carbon dioxide available to them.

The fact that water is involved in photosynthesis necessitates its inclusion in the cyclical scheme which already involves nitrogen, oxygen, and carbon dioxide. It can be shown that, on the average, all the water in the hydrosphere and the atmosphere is decomposed once every two million years.

WINDS AND WEATHER

About the only time we are really conscious of the atmosphere is when it is in motion or we are in motion, that is, when it is flowing past us. The flow of the atmosphere past stationary objects will always be from regions of high pressure to regions of low pressure so that a glance at a weather map which gives local pressures will allow one to judge the probable direction of the winds. This problem is complicated by the fact that the earth is a sphere rotating on its polar axis giving rise to the "prevailing westerlies" and the clockwise rotation of wind vortices in the northern hemisphere. As the gas flows from high to low pressure areas it expands and cools as we have already shown. This cooling encourages cloud formation and precipitation so that rain and snow are most apt to fall in low pressure areas. Thus the concept that a rising barometer (higher pressure) means fair weather, and a falling barometer (low pressure) means bad weather. A very rapid fall in pressure results in the onset of high winds, great cooling, and very bad storms, such as tornadoes and hurricanes.

These storms are apt to follow a period of hot weather for the hot air is less dense than colder air and tends to rise into the atmosphere lowering the pressure and allowing the surrounding cool air to rush in from all sides.

MOLECULAR SOLIDS

In air, a gaseous solution, molecules of the component substances, water, carbon dioxide, nitrogen, oxygen, and the inert gases, are present. When these components are cooled and separated as liquids the same molecules are present in the liquids. Similarly, when the liquids are frozen to solids, the solids are crystalline, having characteristic crystal faces and angles between the faces. Furthermore, the crystals are shown by x-ray analysis to be made up of molecules arranged in orderly ways. Thus, study of solid carbon dioxide shows that it is crystalline and that molecules with the formula, CO_2, exist as units in the crystals. Solid nitrogen and oxygen are also crystalline, being built up of molecules represented by the formulas, N_2 and O_2, respectively. The molecules of the gaseous inert elements consist of single atoms. When the inert gases are frozen, the solids are crystalline and the molecules (single atoms) are arranged in such a way as to produce symmetrical crystals. Such crystals, built up of small, individual molecules, are called *molecular crystals*.

We have already commented on the low temperatures at which the components of air liquefy and freeze. Low liquefying and freezing temperatures indicate that the attractive forces between the molecules are feeble. One characteristic of molecular crystals is that they melt and evaporate to gases rather easily. Consequently, when we have a solid which melts and evaporates at or below room temperature we may safely deduce that it is built of rather simple molecules with little attraction for one another. Conversely, hard or high melting solids evidently are not made up of small molecules with weak attractions for one another. The latter are not molecular crystals.

Problem 6.1. Can you suggest any reason for the relative constancy of the oxygen content of the atmosphere in Cleveland as contrasted with the other localities listed in Table 6.2?

Problem 6.2. Suggest a reason for the fact that dew forms more often on leaves of grass than on bare ground or tree trunks.

Problem 6.3. If you were going to attempt to prepare a compound containing one of the inert gases, which one of them would you select for the trial?

Problem 6.4. Lavoisier, in his work on oxygen, heated mercury in contact with an enclosed volume of air for twelve days. Why do you suppose he did not use a shorter time? A longer time?

Problem 6.5. Why should the density of the nitrogenous gas Rayleigh obtained from burning ammonia in air vary, depending on the relative amounts of ammonia and air which were mixed in the burner?

Problem 6.6. Breathing into and out of a paper bag is sometimes effective in stopping hiccoughs. Suggest a possible interpretation and a more effective treatment.

7 CARBON AND ELEMENTARY CRYSTAL CHEMISTRY

MANY ESTIMATES of the abundance of elements forming the earth have been made, but at best they rest on guesses made about the relative abundance of different minerals. All experts agree that oxygen, silicon, and aluminum are the most abundant elements but differ in their estimates for the remaining elements. Table 7.1 lists one order for the relative abundance of atoms in igneous rocks of the earth, in meteorites, in the sun's atmosphere, in a star, and in a nebula. There is little doubt but that the nebular order represents, more closely than any of the others, the relative order in the universe as a whole. The order of abundance in the earth's crust, including the oceans, differs in detail from that in the igneous rocks. Hydrogen, of course, is the most abundant element in oceans, there being two hydrogen atoms for every oxygen atom in water.

The geologic abundance of elements, however, is not a measure of the frequency with which they are met in every-day life nor of their importance to us. Carbon is near the tenth or twelfth position on most lists but it is a vital element in living organisms and it is the most abundant element in coal, the mineral used in by far the greatest quantities in the world. We shall now consider carbon not only because it appears in so many familiar materials but also because it illustrates, both in its elementary forms and in its compounds, an important type of chemical bonding.

FORMS OF CARBON

There are two forms of pure carbon at room temperatures: graphite and diamond. All other forms of carbonaceous matter, such as carbon blacks, charcoals, and cokes, may be considered as different-sized particles of graphite or as impure carbon or carbon compounds.

Pure carbon is a rarity in nature. Natural graphite is found in many countries but this supply must be amplified through the production of syn-

CARBON AND ELEMENTARY CRYSTAL CHEMISTRY 77

thetic graphite. When anthracite coal is heated at electric furnace temperatures of about 3500°C. in the absence of air the carbon compounds in the coal decompose into the elements and the remaining carbon atoms rearrange to give solid graphite.

Table 7.1
Order of Abundance of the Atoms of the Most Abundant Elements *

ABUNDANCE	IGNEOUS ROCKS (UPPER LITHOSPHERE)	METEORITES	SUN'S ATMOSPHERE	τ SCORPII	NEBULA NGC 7027
Highest...	O	O	H	H	H
	Si	Si	He	He	He
	Al	Fe	O	Ne	C
	Na	Mg	N	O	O
	Ca	S	C	N	Si
	Fe	Al	Si	C	N
	Mg	Ca	Mg	Si	B
	K	Ni	Na	Mg	Ne
	Ti	Na	Fe	(Fe)	S
	C	Cr	K	Al	P
	P	K	Ca		V
	Mn	Mn	Al		Li
	S	P	Ni		Be
	F	Cl	F		Al
	Cl	Ti	Mn		Mg
	Li	Co	Cr		Cl
	Cr	C	S		Fe
	Rb	Cu	Co		Na
	V	Zn	Ti		A
	Zr	F	V		Ca
	Ba	Ge	Cu		Cr
	Sr	Zr	B		Mn
	Ni	V	Zn		Ti
	Zn	Li	P		K
			Sc		Sc
Lowest...			Sr		F
			Ba		

* Kalervo Rankama and Th. G. Sahama, *Geochemistry*, The University of Chicago Press, Chicago. Copyright 1950 by the University of Chicago, p. 42.

Diamonds are also rare. They are generally found in volcanic rocks. The larger, naturally occurring diamonds are cut into gem stones which, by virtue of their brilliance and "flash," have achieved a value far above production costs. This brilliance is a result of the transparency of the diamond coupled with a very high refractive index. Most of the light entering a cut diamond undergoes internal reflections and leaves the stone through one of the top facets causing the observed flash. Smaller diamonds are much used in industry in cutting and grinding operations, for diamond is by far the hardest substance known. Over 95 per cent by weight of the diamonds sold in this country are used as abrasives. Less than 5 per cent are marketed as jewels.

Although diamond is very hard, graphite is very soft. The hardness of diamond would indicate the presence of strong forces holding the solid together. The softness of graphite would indicate only weak forces in that solid. Yet both diamond and graphite have melting points probably higher than any

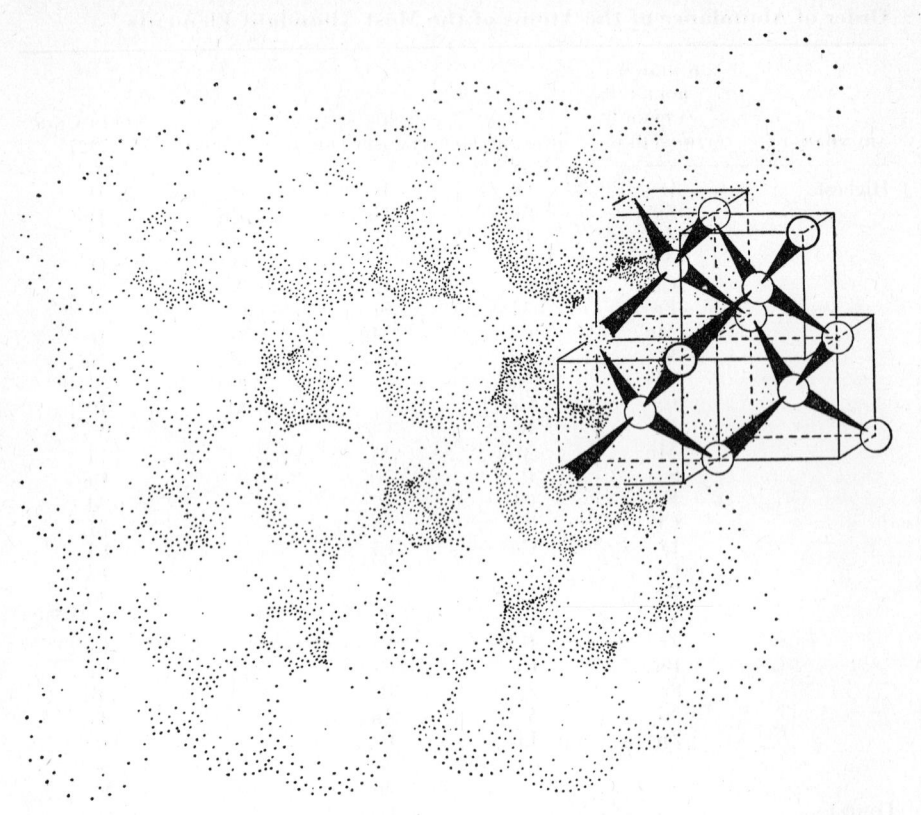

Figure 7.1.
Crystal structure of diamond. Note tetrahedral arrangement.

other substance. This behavior would indicate strong bonding in both solids. X-ray diffraction studies of diamond and graphite show that in the former each carbon atom is surrounded tetrahedrally by four equivalent carbon atoms at a distance of 1.54 Å. between atom centers. Each of these, in turn, is surrounded tetrahedrally by three more carbons and so on throughout the whole three-dimensional substance as shown in Figure 7.1. Each atom is indistinguishable from its neighbors as far as surroundings go and the attractive forces are strong in three dimensions. In graphite each atom is surrounded by only three others at the corners of an equilateral triangle and all four lie in the same plane. Each of the three holds on to two more atoms in turn and continues the planar arrangement indefinitely as shown in Figure 7.2. The distance between the centers of atoms in adjacent planes (3.40 Å.) is about two and one-half times the distance (1.42 Å.) between atom centers in the same plane and the attractive forces are accordingly smaller between the planes. The planes slide over one another readily giving graphite the softness and lubricating qualities noted in pencil lead for instance. It should be pointed out that the neighboring atoms in a layer of atoms in graphite are even closer together than are neighboring atoms in diamond (1.42 Å. versus 1.54 Å.).

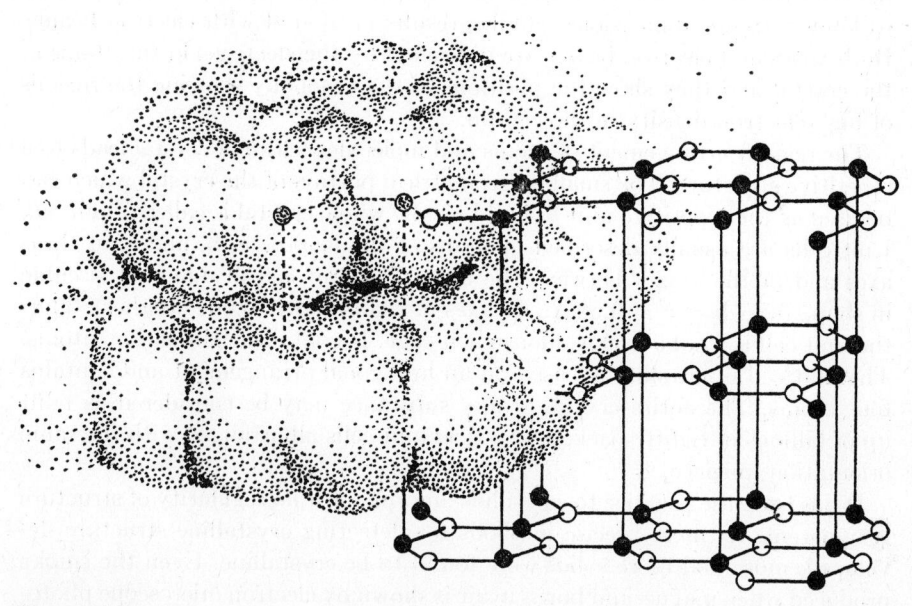

Figure 7.2.
Crystal structure of graphite. Note hexagonal arrangement.

Consequently the bonds in graphite are actually stronger in two dimensions than the bonds in diamond. It is only the fact that diamond bonds extend in three dimensions whereas strong graphite bonds are limited to two that makes graphite so soft. A melting process, as contrasted to a deformation, must break the solids down into small units. Quite clearly, neither diamond nor graphite is a molecular solid (see page 74). Thus, we can see why both diamond and graphite have such high melting points.

CRYSTALS AND AMORPHOUS MATERIALS

Historically, the term *crystal* was applied to transparent substances such as quartz whose particles or grains have plane faces meeting at characteristic angles with each other. When these large crystals with faces and angles visible to the naked eye are crushed they fracture to form smaller particles with new surfaces but with the same characteristic faces and angles. Under the microscope even fine powders may be seen to be crystalline. The simplest explanation is that the geometrical pattern of crystals results from a regular arrangement of the atoms, molecules, or ions in the solid.

This idea could not be put to the test until after 1913 when Max von Laue and W. H. and W. L. Bragg showed that crystals produce regular diffraction patterns when a beam of x-rays is reflected from or passed through them. From photographs of the patterns the Braggs could calculate the distances between the diffraction centers in the crystals; these distances corresponded to known atomic dimensions. Similar results are found with electron beams. Both x-ray and electron beams are diffracted by the electrons in the atoms of the crystal and they show the positions of the atoms by showing the regions of high electron density in the crystal.

The regular arrangement of atoms and molecules within a crystal leads to a repetitive structure. The smallest geometrical portion of the crystal which can be used as the repetitive unit to build up the whole crystal is called a *unit cell*. Unit cells are usually described in terms of the lengths a, b, and c, of three axes and of the angles between the axes. The unit cell in diamond is cubic in shape (a = b = c = 3.56 Å., all axes at right angles to one another). Thus the unit cell is a cube 3.56 Å. along each edge. It contains eight carbon atoms. The unit cell in graphite is based on an hexagonal arrangement and contains four atoms. The entire crystal of any substance may be considered as built up of billions of tightly packed, identical unit cells all arranged with the same orientation in space.

It has been the practice to call solids amorphous if no regularity of structure is apparent. As more precise methods for detecting crystalline structure developed, more and more solids were found to be crystalline. Even the smoke produced when magnesium burns in air is shown by electron microscope photographs to be crystalline, consisting of regular cubes as small as 400 Å. on an edge.

Tiny crystals produced by grinding contain only enough molecules, atoms, or ions to form a few unit cells. Then the interatomic distances are less regular because a high fraction of the atoms are in crystal edges and surfaces. When the geometric arrangements are distorted in this way the solids do not show sharp diffraction patterns and are classed as amorphous. Some carbon blacks and charcoals are amorphous according to their x-ray diffraction patterns but many are crystalline, showing the characteristic pattern of graphite. Other amorphous substances, lacking completely repetitive packing of atoms, are known. In glasses, for example, the atoms, ions, or molecules have random arrangements. Gases and most liquids are also amorphous. Figures 7.3 and 7.4 illustrate the difference between a crystal with its repeating unit cell pattern and an amorphous arrangement with no repetitive pattern.

We have already pointed out that in diamond each carbon atom is tightly bonded to four and only four other atoms. Each atom has four nearest neighbors. In graphite each carbon has three nearest neighbors, the atoms in another plane being more distant. In solid argon the atoms are packed in such a way that each atom has twelve nearest neighbors but is weakly bonded to these. Thus diamond and graphite form very large molecules (a *macromolecular crystal*) in which each atom is tightly bonded to its neighbors whereas crystalline argon consists of relatively independent single atoms attracted to neighbors only by weak intermolecular forces (a molecular crystal). We shall find that other types of binding in crystals also exist.

RELATIVE STABILITY OF GRAPHITE AND DIAMOND

Carbon is not peculiar in having different crystalline forms. Iron, phosphorus, tin, and sulfur are well-known examples of elements with more than one; sulfur has four forms. Some compounds have an ever greater number. Different crystal forms of a given substance may be due to different possible packings of a single type of molecule and/or to the existence of more than one type of molecule of the element. Oxygen, for instance, has two different molecular forms. One, the prevalent form has the molecular formula, O_2. A gas at room temperature, oxygen becomes liquid on cooling to low temperatures, and solid at lower temperatures. There are three different crystalline forms of the solid, O_2, known as alpha, beta, and gamma oxygen resulting from different spatial arrangements of the molecules. The other molec-

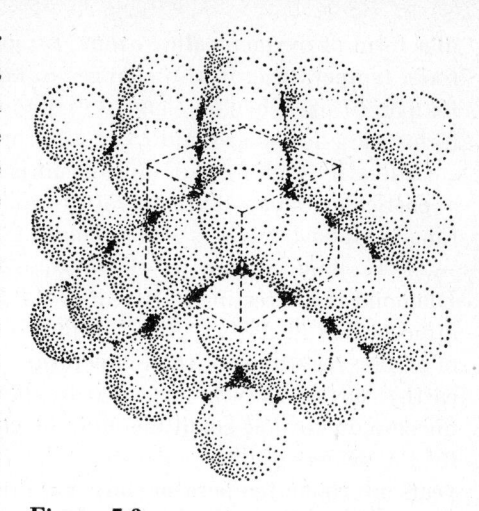

Figure 7.3.
Structure of a crystalline solid. The dotted cube outlines the unit cell for this crystal. An atomic nucleus is situated at each corner of the cubic cell (one eighth of each corner atom lies within the cell), and an atomic nucleus is situated in the center of each face (one half of each face atom lies within the cell).

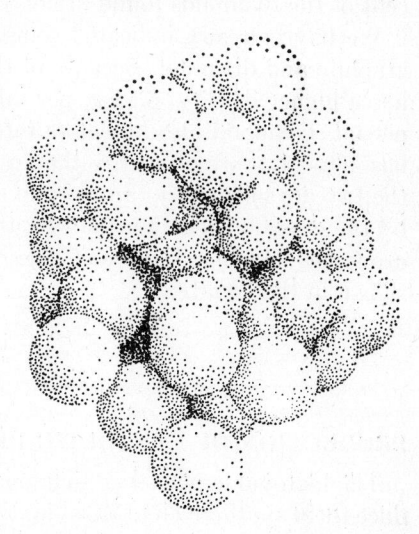

Figure 7.4.
Example of an amorphous solid. Note lack of any repeating structure.

ular form of oxygen, called ozone, is represented by the formula O_3. A gas at room temperature, it also changes to liquid and to a crystalline solid at low temperatures. When an element exists in several molecular and/or crystalline forms these forms are said to be allotropes.

Ordinarily each form of an element is stable with respect to the others over a particular range of temperature and pressure but unstable outside this range. Alpha oxygen is stable below $-250°C.$, beta oxygen from $-250°$ to $-230°C.$, and gamma oxygen from $-230°$ to the melting point, $-218°C.$ Diamond is interesting in that it is stable only at very high pressures (16,000 atmospheres at 25°C.). At all ordinary pressures graphite is the stable form of carbon regardless of the temperature. This means that all diamonds on the earth's surface may be expected to change to graphite eventually. It is not uncommon to find small amounts of graphite in diamonds but, fortunately for the owners of diamonds, the rate of transition is so small that millions of years at room temperature are required for significant change. At higher temperatures the rate of this reaction, like that of all reactions, increases.

While it is true that pure carbon is found only as diamond or graphite, each of these in turn exists in two slightly different crystal modifications known as Type I and Type II diamond, and alpha and beta graphite. Alpha and beta graphite, for instance, are identical in the structural arrangement within the planes of carbon atoms and differ only in the arrangement of the planes one above the other. The two forms have very nearly the same general properties. The second-named modification of each crystal is quite rare. Only about 1 per cent of the diamonds found are of Type II.

We have already indicated some of the differences in properties between graphite and diamond. Because of the closer packing of atoms in diamond, it has a higher density, 3.51 g. per ml., than graphite whose density is 2.26 g. per ml. Diamond also has more internal energy—a mole of diamond (12 g.) has 450 cal. more of energy than a mole of graphite. This means that when the two are burned to form carbon dioxide, 450 more cal. of heat are released by the diamond reaction than by the graphite reaction. Similarly, a mole of ozone has 34,000 cal. more of energy than $\frac{3}{2}$ moles of O_2. These relations are shown in the equations

$$C_{(diamond)} = C_{(graphite)} + 450 \text{ cal.} \quad (7.1)$$
$$O_{3(g)} = \tfrac{3}{2}O_{2(g)} + 34,000 \text{ cal.} \quad (7.2)$$

PRODUCTION OF SYNTHETIC DIAMONDS

The high value placed on diamonds has encouraged many attempts to produce them synthetically. Moissan, the famous French chemist and Nobel prize winner (1906), claimed to have produced very small diamonds in 1894 by sudden quenching of molten iron or silver containing dissolved carbon. The original theory behind the choice of this method was that high pressures would be engendered within the quenched metal as the outer surface solidified rapidly while the interior was still hot. As the carbon precipitated from the melt due to its decreasing solubility with falling temperatures, the high pressure ought to enhance the chances of forming diamond crystals since they are so much more dense than graphite. The high temperatures were thought necessary to give appreciable rates of reaction. The crystals which were obtained were small and were chiefly identified by their hardness, high refractive index, density, and single refraction. Moissan did burn some black crystals from his silver melts, and some transparent ones from the iron, and after correcting for the unburned ash, found that the carbon dioxide produced agreed almost quantitatively with the weight of carbon that should have been in the crystals. Apparently no one other than Moissan tested the crystals. At least half a dozen independent attempts have been made to repeat Moissan's work. Crystals have been produced, but in no case has it been possible to show unequivocally that diamonds were formed. Repeated search has, unfortunately, failed to locate any of Moissan's original diamonds. In 1928, C. H. Desch in England published a careful review of Moissan's work and other then-known attempts to synthesize diamonds. He, as had many others, reached the conclusion that "there was no satisfactory proof that diamonds had ever been obtained by any artificial process."

J. B. Hannay, a self-trained English consulting chemist, who had done work in synthesizing diamond well before Moissan, deposited in the British Museum twelve of the crystals he produced in 1879–80. These crystals were "rediscovered" in 1943 and examined by x-ray diffraction. The result has reopened the whole question of diamond synthesis, for eleven of the twelve show type II diamond structure and one is a fine but small sample of this rare type of diamond. In his earliest work Hannay heated hydrocarbons (compounds of carbon with hydrogen) and metallic lithium (to react with the hydrogen) in sealed glass tubes and occasionally obtained crystals which he identified as diamonds. Later he used iron tubes welded shut by a blacksmith's weld to withstand high pressures. These were two thirds filled with 90 per cent "paraffin spirits" (liquid hydrocarbons), 10 per cent "bone oil" (mainly pyridine) and some lithium, and heated to redness. The whole operation including the closing of the tubes containing highly volatile and combustible material was hazardous and nerve-racking. Most of the tubes exploded, yet from the black residue in the intact tubes he apparently isolated the transparent crystals in the British Museum, and others. Combustion of 14 milligrams of them showed that they were 97.85 per cent carbon.

Moissan tried to repeat Hannay's work but did not succeed in welding the tubes shut. About 1894 Hannay submitted for publication a further report on his diamond synthesis but was refused publication, perhaps because at least two of his papers on other subjects were strongly criticized as not having been written in good faith. Yet, as Desch points out in his latest review (1943) the fact that Hannay's diamonds still exist and are of the rare type II clearly increases the possibility that they are synthetic.

More recent attempts, as late as 1953, to transform graphite into diamond have failed. Hannay's work has still to be confirmed by others. The method, preparation of diamond from carbon compounds rather than from elementary carbon, would not require the high pressures needed to convert graphite to diamond. Many examples are known in which an inherently unstable crystalline form of a substance is produced by cooling a gas or liquid phase to temperatures at which the crystalline form is more stable than the gas or liquid. Of course, the stable crystal form must be absent. Otherwise, the substance would crystallize on it rather than on less stable forms.

Problem 7.1. Account for the high melting temperatures of both diamond and graphite in spite of their wide difference in hardness.

Problem 7.2. How large is the carbon molecule in a diamond? In a crystal of graphite?

Problem 7.3. Diagram the structure of a single layer of atoms in graphite.

Problem 7.4. How could you account for the occurrence of diamond rather than graphite in volcanic rocks? Why do not all volcanic rocks contain diamond?

Problem 7.5. Diamonds are sometimes found in Ohio, yet no volcanic rocks are near at hand. Could you explain these facts in terms consistent with the geological history of the state?

Problem 7.6. The unit cell in diamond is 3.56 Å. along an edge. Calculate from this and other knowledge about diamond crystals the number of atoms in 12.0 grams of diamond. Why does this number differ from the accepted value of the Avogadro number? Calculate a value for the volume of a unit cell of graphite and compare with the volume of a unit cell of diamond.

Problem 7.7. From what you know about the strength of metallic silver and metallic iron what chance is there that Moissan could have developed pressures of the order of 10,000 atmospheres within his quenched metal samples?

8 SOME COMPOUNDS OF CARBON

OVER ONE million compounds of carbon have been identified and the number of possible compounds of this element is almost limitless. In several later chapters we shall discuss some of these and the reasons for the variety of compounds and their complexities of structure. For the time being we shall consider only some of the simpler and more common carbon compounds.

NATURAL GAS

Natural gas is now piped in ever-increasing amounts from the wells which bring it from the interior of the earth to the great industrial areas. It consists primarily of compounds of carbon and hydrogen, called hydrocarbons. In certain areas natural gases rich in helium (up to 16 per cent), carbon dioxide (up to 92 per cent), or nitrogen (up to 80 per cent) are also found. The oxygen content in natural gases is usually low. Hydrogen is rarely present. The most abundant hydrocarbon is methane, with the formula CH_4. Other hydrocarbon gases present may be ethane (formula C_2H_6), propane (formula C_3H_8), and butane (formula C_4H_{10}).

Methane illustrates an important characteristic of carbon in its compounds. Each carbon atom is bonded to four hydrogen atoms, the hydrogen atoms being at positions represented by the four corners of a regular tetrahedron and the carbon atom being at the center. The angles between the bonds connecting carbon atom to hydrogen atom in methane are identical with the angles between the bonds connecting carbon to carbon in the diamond. In diamond, containing only carbon atoms, the bonding continues to the limits of the crystal but in methane each carbon atom is bonded to hydrogen atoms which in turn are bonded only to it (see Figure 8.1). The result is a unit, a molecule consisting of five particular atoms, which persists even when the methane becomes liquid or solid. The difference in structure between diamond and methane has important consequences. The diamond with its atoms tightly bonded in three dimensions to the limit of the crystal is the hardest known substance but methane is normally a gas consisting of individual molecules represented by the molecular formula CH₄. That a methane molecule has little attraction for other molecules is shown by the fact that it forms a liquid with difficulty. It must be cooled to −161.5°C. before it condenses to a liquid at atmospheric pressure, and cooled to −182.5°C. before it forms a solid. The solid, when formed, is crystalline. The unit cells, repeated in regular geometric arrangements throughout the crystal, contain a definite number of the same molecules as exist in the gas. To be sure, there must be attractive forces between separate molecules to enable methane to exist as a liquid or solid. Such forces between symmetrical molecules are known as *van der Waals forces*. The difficulty with which methane is liquefied indicates that its van der Waals forces are small.

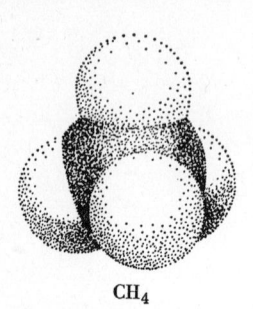

Figure 8.1. Structure of a methane molecule.

The second most abundant hydrocarbon in natural gases, ethane, with the molecular formula C₂H₆, illustrates another important characteristic of carbon in its compounds. From the ratio between the number of carbon and hydrogen atoms it might appear that each carbon atom is now bonded to only three hydrogen atoms. This is true, but the two carbon atoms are also bonded to one another so that each carbon atom is bonded to four other atoms. The angles between the bonds remain very near to the regular tetrahedral angles as in diamond. The structure of the ethane molecule is illustrated in Figure 8.2. In the plane of the paper the structures of methane and ethane are flattened out as

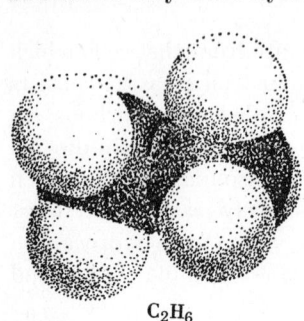

$$\begin{array}{c} H \\ | \\ H-C-H \\ | \\ H \end{array} \quad \text{and} \quad \begin{array}{c} H \; H \\ | \; | \\ H-C-C-H \\ | \; | \\ H \; H \end{array}$$

Figure 8.2. Structure of an ethane molecule.

In ethane the distance between the centers of the carbon atoms is 1.54Å. as in diamond but the distance from carbon center to hydrogen center is only 1.09Å., since a hydrogen atom is smaller than a carbon atom.

The molecule of ethane, containing eight atoms, is larger than the methane molecule with its five atoms. It has a larger volume and a larger surface to make contact with neighboring molecules. Consequently its van der Waals forces per molecule are greater and it is more easily condensed to a liquid. The boiling point (and condensation temperature at atmospheric pressure) of ethane is −88.6°C. but its freezing point is −183.2°C., slightly lower than that of methane. Apparently it is somewhat more difficult to arrange the elongated ethane molecules into a regular crystal system than it is the symmetrical methane molecules.

LIQUID HYDROCARBONS

Many carbon compounds appear when coal is heated. At high temperatures they are driven off as gases but some become liquid when cooled to room temperature. Various hydrocarbons are the principal products. Today, however, most hydrocarbons are obtained from petroleum. Petroleum is a solution containing a wide variety of carbon compounds, most of them hydrocarbons. Those with lighter, smaller molecules distill off at lower temperatures. Compounds with larger molecules distill at higher temperatures and those with the largest molecules do not distill at all because the temperatures required to change them to vapors are high enough to produce disruption of the molecules.

Relatively large molecules containing only the two elements, carbon and hydrogen, can exist because of the ability of carbon atoms to combine with other carbon atoms, seemingly without limit (compare diamond, and graphite). Gasoline, used as a fuel for automobile engines, consists of a mixture of hydrocarbons of intermediate molecular size. One component, called isooctane, with the formula C_8H_{18}, is a liquid at room temperature. Its boiling point of 99.2°C. is almost identical with that of water. Its freezing point, on the contrary, is much lower than that of water, being -107.4°C. The isooctane molecule is much larger than the water molecule, the molar volume being 165 milliliters. The molar volume of water is 18 ml. These facts would indicate that the attractive forces per unit of surface area are much less between molecules of hydrocarbons than between the molecules of water.

COMBUSTION OF CARBON AND ACTIVATION ENERGY

When carbon reacts with oxygen it forms a very stable compound—carbon dioxide. However, pure carbon in the form of diamond or graphite does not react with gaseous oxygen at a measurable rate at room temperature. At higher temperatures combustion begins, and it proceeds with the evolution of large amounts of energy till one or the other of the reacting materials is consumed. The reaction, an exothermic one, is represented by the equation:

$$C_{(s)} + O_{2(g)} = CO_{2(g)} + 94{,}000 \text{ cal.} \tag{8.1}$$

Equation (8.1) indicates that a mole of carbon dioxide has 94,000 calories less energy than its elements at room temperature. When the reaction is carried on at high temperatures the reacting carbon and oxygen have more energy and the carbon dioxide produced has more energy but the difference remains very nearly at the same value, 94,000 cal. Values of heats of reaction do in general vary with temperature. The values given are for 25°C. unless otherwise qualified.

We can best understand the influence of temperature on rate of burning if

88 GENERAL CHEMISTRY

we consider how the reaction must proceed. Since carbon is a solid at combustion temperatures, the gas, oxygen, must meet it at its surface. There the bonds holding the carbon atom in the crystal must be broken as new bonds form with the oxygen atoms. The bonds between the oxygen atoms in the molecules must also break as they become attached to the carbon atom to produce the molecule of carbon dioxide which has been shown to have the structure, OCO.

In this reaction, as in most reactions, more energy is required to break the old bonds in the early stages of reaction then is readily available. This "extra"

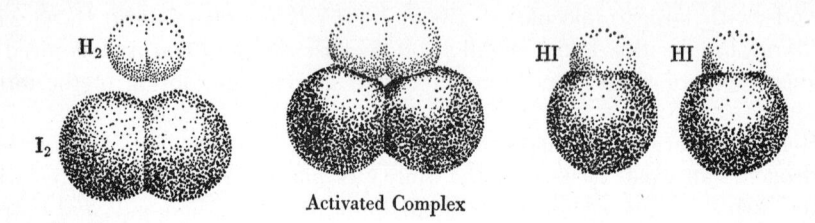

Figure 8.3.
Bond changes and the activated complex for the reaction between hydrogen and iodine.

energy must be supplied from some other energy source than old bonds themselves if the reaction is to proceed. At some critical point in the process the rate of energy production from formation of new bonds exceeds that required to break old bonds and the system begins to evolve energy. The energy necessary to take the reagents from their initial condition to this intermediate critical state is called the *activation energy*. It is always energy *absorbed* and thus the initial steps in such reactions are always endothermic. Similarly, the later steps are exothermic. Whether the over-all reaction is endothermic or exothermic depends on whether the activation energy is larger or smaller than the energy release in the final steps of the reaction. If an exothermic reaction (over-all) is to continue, some of the evolved heat must be absorbed by neighboring reagents to supply them with the necessary activation energy. Figure 8.3 illustrates the two steps schematically for the hydrogen-iodine reaction.

The need for activation energy explains the observed facts of combustion. A small isolated piece of graphite will not continue to burn. The heat evolved in the reaction on its surface is dissipated to the surroundings so rapidly that the particle of graphite cools. But the more the graphite cools the lower the rate at which it can burn for the less the chance that its atoms have the necessary activation energy. Thus the reaction rate decreases till it becomes negligible. Although a single piece of graphite will not continue to burn, the situation is different if it is broken into small pieces and arranged in a pile so that there is space between the particles. Then the heat of reaction from the surface of one particle is not lost directly to the surroundings but is radiated to another particle where it can furnish the necessary activation energy to keep the reaction going.

We have considered these questions in detail because they apply with equal force to the burning of other solids. An isolated log may not burn, but if it is split into two sections burning will continue between them, and still more effectively if the log is split into three or more pieces. Such reactions which can utilize reaction products to continue the reaction are known as *chain reactions*.

Coke and charcoal, prepared by heating coal or other organic materials, consist primarily of elementary carbon, often with graphitic structure, but contain some ash from the noncombustible, nonvolatile substances present in the original material. Coke and charcoal are much less dense than graphite, for pores extend through the apparently solid mass. The pores, many of which have very small diameters, represent spaces from which volatile substances were driven in the coking process. In consequence many carbon atoms are on surfaces and many of them are in particularly exposed positions on edges and corners. Some charcoals are therefore able to react to a limited degree even at room temperature. The rate remains slow and the reaction stops when the most exposed atoms have reacted. Because of their structures cokes and charcoals can be kindled at lower temperatures than can graphite, the *kindling temperature* representing the temperature at which a particular substance oxidizes fast enough to maintain reaction temperatures.

FORMATION OF CARBON MONOXIDE

Fortunately for us carbon dioxide is the usual product when carbon burns. At high temperatures carbon monoxide is also formed. This compound is poisonous for when breathed it forms a stable compound with hemoglobin of the blood, interfering with the normal transport of oxygen in the blood and thus leading to asphyxiation. Carbon dioxide in the presence of excess carbon can react to form carbon monoxide through an endothermic reaction represented by the equation:

$$41{,}000 \text{ cal.} + C_{(s)} + CO_{2(g)} = 2CO_{(g)} \tag{8.2}$$

Because the reaction is endothermic it can continue only if the proper amount of heat is supplied continuously to it. At room temperatures carbon dioxide is much more stable than carbon monoxide but at high enough temperatures (in the neighborhood of 700°C.) carbon monoxide becomes as stable as carbon dioxide in the absence of free oxygen. At a certain temperature, therefore, equal amounts of carbon dioxide and carbon monoxide are present, at higher temperatures carbon monoxide is in excess, and at lower temperatures carbon dioxide is in excess. At all reaction temperatures a definite ratio, called the equilibrium ratio, of the two will be present, provided, of course, that the carbon dioxide gas has ample opportunity to react with the solid carbon, as

90 GENERAL CHEMISTRY

in a deep bed of coke. The equilibrium amount of carbon monoxide becomes negligible at low temperatures (200° or 300°C.).

We have seen that carbon monoxide can exist in equilibrium with carbon dioxide and carbon. When oxygen (rather than carbon) is present, carbon monoxide becomes oxidized to carbon dioxide according to the reaction:

$$CO_{(g)} + \tfrac{1}{2}O_{2(g)} = CO_{2(g)} + 68,000 \text{ cal.} \tag{8.3}$$

The reaction of oxygen with carbon to form carbon dioxide proceeds without flame for it takes place on the solid. The reaction between carbon monoxide and oxygen to form carbon dioxide is a reaction between gases. It proceeds with a flame, light blue and almost invisible. This reaction, like the others, requires activation energy so that it does not proceed at a measurable rate at room temperature. When the gases are hot enough the reaction becomes self-sustaining. If sufficient oxygen is present the reaction proceeds almost to completion at temperatures even as high as 1,200°C. At that temperature the equilibrium concentration of carbon monoxide is only one hundred-thousandth that of the carbon dioxide.

For the sake of completeness we shall consider a reaction that may take place at very high temperatures. Then carbon may burn in oxygen to give carbon monoxide directly as represented by the equation:

$$C_{(s)} + \tfrac{1}{2}O_{2(g)} = CO_{(g)} + 26,000 \text{ cal.} \tag{8.4}$$

As already stated, the carbon monoxide produced will react with any excess oxygen to form carbon dioxide as shown in equation 8.3.

As was stated earlier, the listed heats of reaction are the values for room temperatures, (25°C.). These values, rather than values for the reactions at high temperatures, are given because if one starts with the reacting substances at room temperature and cools the products of the reaction to room temperature the values represent the net heat of reaction even though the actual reactions took place at high temperatures.

COMBUSTION OF CARBON COMPOUNDS

When compounds containing carbon and hydrogen burn with oxygen, the hydrogen atoms in the compounds appear in the product, water, and the carbon atoms appear in the product, carbon dioxide. The reactions are exothermic. For methane the reaction is represented by the equation:

$$CH_{4(g)} + 2O_{2(g)} = CO_{2(g)} + 2H_2O_{(liq)} + 213,000 \text{ cal.} \tag{8.5}$$

The amount of energy released is less than that found when one mole of carbon dioxide and two moles of liquid water are formed directly from the elements. Methane, like carbon dioxide and water, has less energy than its elements. When iso-octane burns the reaction is also exothermic; the equation for the reaction is

$$C_8H_{18(liq)} + 12\tfrac{1}{2}O_{2(g)} = 8CO_{2(g)} + 9H_2O_{(liq)} + 1{,}306{,}000 \text{ cal.} \qquad (8.6)$$

Problem 8.1. From the thermal data given in this chapter and in Table 5.2 calculate the amount of heat released when one mole of methane is formed from graphite and gaseous hydrogen.

Problem 8.2. Calculate the amount of heat released when one pound of each of the following is burned: Hydrogen, carbon (graphite), methane, iso-octane. On the basis of the heat released per pound of fuel which of the preceding substances would be preferable as a fuel?

Problem 8.3. Calculate the approximate number of cubic feet of air needed to burn one mole of iso-octane (see page 55). How many cubic feet of air must enter the carburetor of a car to burn one gallon of gasoline. Assume one gallon is equivalent to 25 moles of iso-octane.

Methane, being a gas, burns in a flame. In a gas burner the methane is mixed with air but the mixture does not burn until it is heated to the kindling temperature. Thereafter the heat of reaction supplies the necessary activation energy to maintain the reaction. Iso-octane also burns in a gas phase, as in the cylinder of an automobile. Liquid gasoline is classed as a dangerous inflammable material because the concentration of vapor above it is great enough when mixed with air to form an explosive mixture and to ignite readily. The heat released in the combustion then serves to evaporate more of the fuel.

Like carbon itself, most carbon compounds do not oxidize at an appreciable rate at room temperature. They begin to burn only when they are heated to their kindling temperatures. A spark contains enough energy to furnish the necessary activation energy and thus to initiate a reaction that can build up to very high rates in a short period of time if the reacting substances are already mixed as they can be in gases. Explosions are nothing more than very fast chemical reactions. Their rates are limited either by the speed with which the activation energy can be transmitted through the material or by the speed with which the reacting materials can meet. Certain carbon compounds, however, can react with atmospheric oxygen at appreciable rates even at room temperature. Coal and certain oils are examples. A pile of coal or a heap of oily rags may become warm through very slow oxidation if the heat of combustion is not dissipated to the surroundings. Then the material becomes hotter and hotter until it reaches the kindling temperature at which the rate of reaction is limited only by the rate at which the reacting substances meet. *Spontaneous combustion* of this kind does not occur, as may seem obvious, if the materials are kept from contact with air. It also does not occur if the materials are kept cool through proper ventilation.

Methane will burn even though insufficient oxygen is present to give the proportion called for in equation 8.5. Under such conditions the flame becomes yellow because of the presence of small particles of hot carbon (soot). When the

92 GENERAL CHEMISTRY

amount of oxygen is only half of that required for complete combustion, the reaction is represented by the equation:

$$CH_{4(g)} + O_{2(g)} = C_{(s)} + 2H_2O_{(g)} \tag{8.7}$$

Soot from combustion of methane is called *gas black*. Liquid petroleum when burned with a limited amount of oxygen furnishes *lamp black* in a similar way. The various blacks are used for printers inks or for compounding with rubber where a very finely divided carbon is desired. Their very high surface areas, with many atoms exposed, enables them to form tight bonding with rubber molecules to form a long-wearing product desirable in automobile tires.

We have already seen that both carbon dioxide and water are stable with respect to their elements. Why is water formed rather than carbon dioxide when there is not enough oxygen to form both? At low temperatures the pair of products, water and carbon, is more stable than the pair, carbon dioxide and hydrogen. However, the relative stabilities change with temperatures so that at about 700°C. the two pairs become equally stable. At higher temperatures gaseous hydrogen and carbon dioxide would be more stable products than carbon and water. For this reason the flames used to make the "blacks" are cooled. Conversely, the commercial preparation of hydrogen from methane by partial combustion with oxygen is carried on at high temperatures.

In the reactions leading to formation of carbon dioxide, carbon monoxide, and water we have seen that the substances produced in reactions with several possible products depend on the temperature of the reaction. One reason is that the stabilities of molecules decrease with increasing temperature. They do so at different rates so that relative stabilities change. Chemists, therefore, pay attention to the temperatures of reactions and control them where necessary. Because high temperatures increase the rate of all reactions, chemists may use higher temperatures than would otherwise be desirable in order to have the reactions proceed at satisfactory rates, even though the high temperatures also favor other reactions, producing substances they do not want.

COALS

The current rate of consumption of coal in the world is about two billion tons per year. Most of it is used for fuel but enormous amounts are used for making other substances. It is the most important industrial source of carbon —from 50 to 75 per cent of its atoms are carbon atoms.

Anyone examining an appreciable quantity of coal will note fossilized remains of plant stems, leaves, and fibers in the coal. The layered structure of coal indicates a sedimentary origin. Two origins are known: sapropel (the organic debris at the bottom of the ocean), and peat (the organic debris at the bottom of fresh waters). Lignin, a component of woody tissues (together with cellulose), is now thought to be the chief substance from which coal is formed. All coals contain moisture, and also materials which remain behind in the ash when the coal is burned. Some typical coals, and coal precursors, are listed in Table 8.1 together with their chemical analysis on a moisture-free, ash-free basis. Note particularly the per cent of atoms of each element in the different coals. Hundreds of coals are known and there are no clear distinctions, only gradations in properties from one to another. It is customary to treat anthracite as having undergone the most complete "coalification," and peat the least, and to grade coals on this basis.

Table 8.1
Chemical Compositions of Some Coals and Coal Precursors

MATERIAL	(PER CENT OF WEIGHT)				(PER CENT OF ATOMS)			
	Carbon	Hydrogen	Oxygen	Nitrogen	Carbon	Hydrogen	Oxygen	Nitrogen
Wood fiber	50	6	43	1	32	46	22	0.5
Peat	59	6	33	2	37	46	16	1
Brown Coal (lignite)	69	5.5	25	0.8	45	43	12	0.5
Bituminous coal	82	5	13	0.8	54	39	6.5	0.5
Anthracite	95	2.5	2.5	trace	75	24	1	trace

Some of the data from Kalervo Rankama and Th. G. Sahama, *Geochemistry*, The University of Chicago Press, Chicago. Copyright 1950 by the University of Chicago, p. 349.

Coalification consists mainly in the removal of oxygen, as can be seen from Table 8.1, with some loss in hydrogen and nitrogen. The oxygen is liberated primarily as carbon dioxide and water, the nitrogen as elementary nitrogen. Some of the hydrogen forms methane, the "fire damp," highly explosive when mixed with air, found in coal mines.

COKE AND CHARCOAL

When coal is heated in the absence of air, it decomposes into a number of different substances. Carbon dioxide, carbon monoxide, and water are evolved almost from the beginning. Methane is evolved below 100°C., and more complicated compounds of carbon and hydrogen as well as ammonia appear as the temperature rises. These gases are evolved only slowly until a temperature between 400°C. and 450°C. is reached at which the coal becomes quite soft due to production of liquid products. Many coals actually fuse at this temperature into a single body of fluid within which further, rather rapid, gaseous evolution leads to bubble formation. Further heating continues to drive out the volatile material, rigidity returns, and a tough substance with a cellular structure remains as the temperature passes 500°C. Continued heating, even to 1000°C., results in little further change in composition, though some volatiles are still evolved, but it does cause an increase in density, hardness, and strength of the solid. The solids obtained by heating coal in this manner to above 500°C. are known as cokes. They are about 95 per cent carbon by weight, the remaining 5 per cent or so being ash.

Heating wood in the absence of air gives a solid residue known as charcoal, or to be exact, wood charcoal. This material except for ash content is also almost entirely carbon but it is not as hard nor as dense as coke, partly because it has not been heated to as high temperatures. A good many oxygenated compounds of carbon are produced when wood is heated in this fashion as might be guessed from the composition data in Table 8.1. Blood charcoal and bone charcoal are obtained by similar heat treatments on the appropriate animal starting materials. Sugar charcoal may be prepared by heating sugar, whose formula is $C_{12}H_{22}O_{11}$.

$$C_{12}H_{22}O_{11} = 12C + 11H_2O \tag{8.8}$$

The sugar begins to decompose at its melting temperature and gaseous water, formed by disruption of the sugar molecules, leaves the fluid mass in bubbles. Temperatures are not high enough to permit the remaining carbon atoms to crystallize completely into large graphite crystals so the solid is filled with tiny voids. (Compare the behavior of coal on heating.)

Cokes and charcoals show the beginnings of graphitic structure under x-ray analysis and are at least partially composed of micro-crystalline graphite but they are usually classed as amorphous carbon. Coke and charcoal are much less dense than graphite, being filled with tiny pores. High-temperature coking reduces the number and volume of the pores.

When the distillate, consisting of the substances expelled in the heating of coal, is cooled to room temperature some of it is gaseous (coal gas), some liquid, and the remainder a black tarry mass, called *coal tar*. Carbon dioxide, carbon monoxide, and methane, are the principal constituents of *coal gas*, used as a fuel. Ammonia is also a gas but some of it dissolves in the liquid water appearing in the distillate. In commercial practice the ammonia is absorbed by sulfuric acid and serves as an important commercial source of nitrogen compounds. Other liquids, benzene, toluene, phenol, aniline, and other important organic compounds, are obtained commercially from the distillate, either directly, or from the coal tar when it is reheated.

COMMERCIAL GASES FROM COAL

Coke, when treated with steam, reacts according to the equation

$$31{,}000 \text{ cal.} + C_{(s)} + H_2O_{(g)} = CO_{(g)} + H_{2(g)} \tag{8.9}$$

The reaction is endothermic, requiring the addition of energy, for the mixture of one mole each of carbon monoxide and hydrogen has 31,000 more calories than the carbon and water from which they are made. The gaseous product containing approximately equal volumes of carbon monoxide and hydrogen is called *water gas*. It is widely used as a fuel or mixed with other gases where natural gas is unavailable. If coal rather than coke is used, many of the components of coal gas will also be present.

Water gas is produced at relatively high temperatures because high temperatures make it more stable compared with the starting materials (see page 89). High temperatures are also necessary to make the reaction proceed at an appreciable rate. The energy required to make the reaction proceed at all is supplied commercially in one of two ways. Sometimes steam and air are passed over the carbon alternately, so that part of the carbon is burned to carbon dioxide to furnish the heat necessary for the subsequent endothermic reaction. Or, air and steam are passed together over the fuel bed, their ratio being so adjusted that the necessary heat balance is maintained. Gas of this kind will contain nitrogen (from the air) and some carbon dioxide in addition to the combustibles found in water gas.

Since air is the source of oxygen, four moles of nitrogen will be present for every mole of oxygen used. This nitrogen appearing in the gas lowers its heating quality. A gaseous mixture of this kind is called *producer gas*. Because of its poor heating quality it is usually used directly from the gas producer while it still remains at high temperature. Table 8.2 lists some approximate compositions and heating values for various commercial gaseous fuels.

Table 8.2

Approximate Compositions and Heating Values (Heats of Combustions) of Various Fuel Gases

FUEL GAS	COMPOSITIONS IN VOLUME PER CENT						HEATING VALUE IN CALORIES PER 22.4 L. (S.T.P.)
	C_2H_6	CH_4	H_2	CO	CO_2	N_2	
Natural	16	83			0.2		230,000
Coal		30	53	6	2	7	110,000
Water		2	45	46	4	2	70,000
Producer			16	24	8	51	25,000

Problem 8.4. Commercial producer gas from coke contains about one third as much carbon dioxide as carbon monoxide by volume. Is this ratio consistent with an air-to-steam ratio adjusted to give a slightly exothermic reaction?

Problem 8.5. Calculate the heat released when a water gas mixture containing one-half mole of carbon monoxide and one-half mole of hydrogen is burned.

OTHER BINARY COMPOUNDS OF CARBON

Carbon can combine with many of the other elements to form binary compounds. *Binary compounds* are those with only two constituent elements. Examples of compounds formed by carbon with nonmetallic elements are carbon tetrachloride (formula, CCl_4) and carbon disulfide (formula CS_2). Both are liquids, the former boiling at 76.7°C. and the latter at 46.2°C. Both are used widely as commercial solvents. Carbon tetrachloride has the structure of methane but its molar volume is somewhat larger since chlorine atoms are larger than hydrogen atoms. That its van der Waals forces are somewhat larger may be deduced from the fact that it is a liquid rather than a gas at

96   GENERAL CHEMISTRY

room temperature. Carbon disulfide has molecules with a linear structure SCS corresponding to that of carbon dioxide, but somewhat larger because the sulfur atom is larger than the oxygen atom.

Unlike methane, carbon tetrachloride will not burn. Indeed, it is the fluid used in one type of portable fire extinguishers. Although useful for small fires it should not be used for hot fires because it forms the poisonous gas, phosgene, formula $COCl_2$, under these conditions. In general, substances with larger molecules tend to be decomposed at high temperature and substances with smaller molecules become relatively more stable.

Carbon tetrachloride is stable with respect to its elements up to high temperatures. Carbon disulfide, although it forms from the elements (charcoal and sulfur) at high temperatures, is unstable at room temperature. It does not violate our rule about temperature and relative stability for both carbon and sulfur at room temperature, exist, in "molecules" larger than those of carbon disulfide. Carbon disulfide is a highly flammable liquid, the vapors above it being combustible and in relatively high concentration. Both elements formed in its decomposition burn; the products of the combustion are carbon dioxide and sulfur dioxide as shown in the equation

$$CS_{2(liq)} + 3O_{2(g)} = CO_{2(g)} + 2SO_{2(g)} \tag{8.10}$$

Carbon forms binary compounds with many of the metallic elements; calcium carbide (formula, CaC_2) and iron carbide (formula, Fe_3C) are examples. Both of these are solids with very high melting points (above 1800°C.). Solids of this type cannot be represented by simple molecules held together by the relatively weak van der Waals forces. They contain macromolecules in which large numbers of atoms are strongly bonded in the crystals. The formulas, therefore, do not represent molecules but only the composition in terms of the simplest atomic or symbol ratio.

NOMENCLATURE IN BINARY COMPOUNDS

Some compounds, such as water and methane, have names which do not indicate their composition. Such names, called trivial names, are often those in common use before the composition was known. However, most chemical compounds bear names related in a more or less systematic way to their composition. The system of nomenclature used in chemistry will become clearer as more compounds are met, especially if several simple rules are understood. For binary compounds the names of both constituent elements appear in the name of the compound. The suffix -ide, used in binary compounds, is attached to the abbreviated form of one of the names. Thus, the systematic name for common salt, with the formula NaCl, is sodium chloride. Where necessary, the Greek numerical prefixes, mono-, di-, tri-, tetra-, penta-, hexa-, and hepta- in a name indicate the number of symbols of that element in the formula. The prefixes are often omitted, especially when a pair of elements form only one compound. The prefix mono- is usually omitted except when the pair of elements combine in several ratios to form different binary compounds. Table 8.3 illustrates usage.

Table 8.3

Nomenclature for Binary Compounds

FORMULA	COMMON NAME	COMPLETELY SYSTEMATIC NAME
H_2O	water	dihydrogen monoxide
CO	carbon monoxide	monocarbon monoxide
CO_2	carbon dioxide	monocarbon dioxide
SO_2	sulfur dioxide	monosulfur dioxide
NO	nitric oxide	mononitrogen monoxide
N_2O_3	nitrogen trioxide	dinitrogen trioxide
N_2O_5	nitrogen pentoxide	dinitrogen pentoxide
CCl_4	carbon tetrachloride	monocarbon tetrachloride
SF_6	sulfur hexafluoride	monosulfur hexafluoride
CaC_2	calcium carbide	monocalcium dicarbide
Fe_3C	iron carbide	triiron monocarbide

CARBONATES

Although carbon is a primary constituent of organic compounds, is found in the atmosphere as carbon dioxide, and occurs in certain carbides, most of the carbon in the earth is present in carbonates. The carbonates are not often used as sources of carbon since coal, gas, and petroleum are more "energy rich." Calcium carbonate, the principal component of limestone, marble, shells, pearls, and numerous other minerals, is the most common carbonate rock. On a tonnage basis, limestone is the third most important mineral in commerce, ranking behind coal, and sand and gravel. Wide-spread distribution with resulting low transportation costs favor its use as a raw material. Dolomite, another important carbonate mineral, has the formula, $CaCO_3 \cdot MgCO_3$. It is a compound, not a mixture of calcium carbonate and magnesium carbonate. Sodium carbonate (formula, Na_2CO_3) is also found in nature in certain dried-out rivers and lakes but only about 5 per cent of the industrial demand can be supplied directly from natural sources. Because carbonates are used primarily for other reasons than their carbon content we shall discuss them further under the chemistry of their respective metallic constituents: calcium, magnesium, sodium, etc.

The carbonates illustrate nomenclature for many *ternary* (three-element) *compounds*. The suffix, -ate, replaces -ide when the third element in the compound is oxygen. The term carbonate applies specifically to the group, CO_3, found in compounds, always with a third element, calcium, magnesium, etc.

Problem 8.6. How do you account for the fact that coal burns with a flame but coke does not to any comparable extent?

Problem 8.7. Why is coal dust considered an explosive although bulk coal is not explosive?

9 THE BEHAVIOR OF GASES

QUALITATIVE RELATIONSHIPS among pressure, volume, temperature, and amount of gas have been known for a long time. Bellows are very old instruments for moving air. Their operation depends on relationships among volume, pressure, and amount of gas moved. The relationship between gaseous volume and temperature was used as early as 300 B.C. by the Greeks when they drove simple machines by a stream of water ejected from an apparatus by the expansion of heated air. Even before then, Hesiod of Greece had attributed the winds to the effect of the sun's heat on the air. On the other hand, the first quantitative measurements on gases, needed to provide a sound basis for a theory of gaseous behavior, were not recorded until the seventeenth century. Thereafter, some two hundred years elapsed before all the quantitative relationships among pressure, volume, temperature, and amount (or weight) of gases were formulated.

MEASUREMENT OF PRESSURE

Early designers of pumps had discovered that water could not be raised more than about 34 feet with a lift pump and settled, for an explanation, on the phrase "Nature abhors a vacuum." Such a statement is hardly satisfactory in a science. In 1643 Torricelli came to the conclusion that this limit was set by the presence of a "sea of air" which could support a column of water exerting a pressure exactly equal to its own pressure, but no higher column. The science of hydrodynamics was already well advanced and the concepts of fluid pressure and the balancing of the pressure of one fluid by that of another was established. Torricelli's contribution was to treat the atmosphere as a fluid, albeit a very attenuated one. He reasoned that mercury being 13.6 times as dense as water would rise only $\frac{1}{13.6}$ times as high in a tube as would water. He therefore filled with mercury a long glass tube sealed at one end, placed his finger over the open end, inverted the tube, immersed the open end in a dish of mercury, and removed his finger. The mercury height fell until the column was about 30 in. or 76 cm. tall as required by his theory. He had invented the *mercury barometer*. Gas pressures were measurable in terms of the height of a column of liquid which the gas would support. Two common forms of a mercury barometer are shown in Figure 9.1.

Galileo, Torricelli's teacher, had already shown that air had weight by weighing a copper sphere before and after air was pumped into it. Torricelli's work allowed the calculation of the weight of the atmosphere over a unit of area of the earth's surface by measuring the weight of mercury (or some other fluid) per unit area which the atmosphere would support. The theory was further tested by noting the difference in height of the mercury column at the

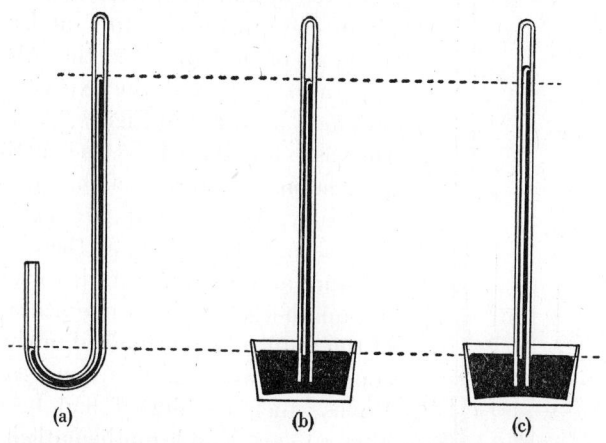

Figure 9.1.
Common forms of mercury barometers. Barometer (c) measures the same pressure as barometers (a) and (b) but is at a higher temperature. Its column of mercury is less dense and, therefore, longer.

bottom and top of a mountain. The lesser length of mercury column on the mountain top was consistent with the theory that the atmospheric weight was supporting the mercury since an ascent lessened the weight of air still above the barometer and led to a shortened column. Torricelli's ideas were early attacked on the basis that, if the mercury column were supported by the weight of the atmosphere, placing the barometer in a sealed box should give a very small mercury height since the weight of air in the box was so small. He quickly pointed out that these criticisms confused weight and pressure and that the pressure in the sealed box was exactly the same as it had been before the box was sealed so that the mercury height would remain unchanged. The barometer would always measure gaseous pressure. When open to the atmosphere it also served as a measure of the weight of the atmosphere.

Problem 9.1. Calculate the approximate weight of the atmosphere in grams per square centimeter at the earth's surface. In pounds per square inch.

100 GENERAL CHEMISTRY

The experiments of Robert Boyle confirmed these conclusions. In 1659 he perfected the air pump, earlier invented by Otto von Guericke, and used it to evacuate a container in which a barometer had been placed. As the gas was removed the height of the mercury column fell, conclusive proof of Torricelli's theory that it was indeed the gas which upheld the manometer fluid. This experiment firmly established the usefulness of a mercury column for measuring the pressure of gases.

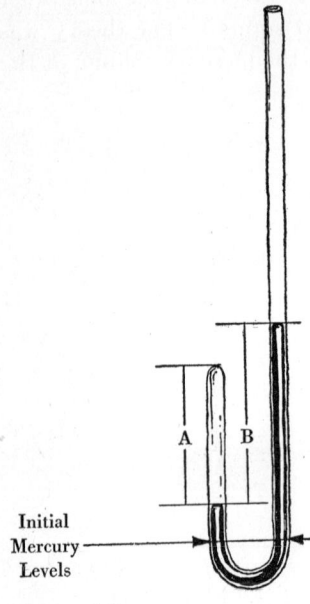

In one of many experiments, Boyle confined air in one arm of a U-tube and added varied amounts of mercury into the other arm. The apparatus used and the experimental results obtained are listed in Figure 9.2 and Table 9.1. He was evidently led to this experiment by the suggestions of three of his contemporaries (Townley, Hooke, and Brouncker) who had each separately arrived at the conclusion that pressure and volume were inversely related to one another when the temperature and amount of the confined gas remained unchanged. Their conclusions were based on some earlier work of Boyle which he himself had been unable to reduce to any simple mathematical relation and it is with evident satisfaction that his account, published in 1662, describes the simple mathematical result that, within experimental error, doubling the pressure reduced the volume of the confined gas to one-half, trebling the pressure reduced it to one third, etc. Later he continued the experiments, working with air at less than atmospheric pressure and noted that the relationship still held. Not enough was known about gases in Boyle's day to repeat the experiment on different gases but later experimenters did show that the principle of an inverse relationship between volume and pressure was applicable to all gases. Thus, any gas sample occupying 100 ml. at 1 atmosphere pressure would occupy $\frac{1}{2} \times 100$ or 50 ml. at 2 atmospheres, $\frac{1}{2.5} \times 100$ or 40 ml. at 2.5 atmospheres, etc., temperature and amount of gas remaining constant. By the end of the eighteenth century Boyle's results had been extended into the more general statement known as *Boyle's Law:* At a constant temperature and for a fixed amount of gas the pressure and volume vary inversely, that is, the product of pressure and volume remains constant.

Figure 9.2.
Diagram of Boyle's original apparatus. The shorter leg was graduated into 48 equal divisions. Mercury was added through the open end compressing air trapped in the shorter leg. The volume of trapped air is proportional to A. The pressure on this air is proportional to the height of the mercury barometer plus the height B of mercury.

Table 9.1

Compression of Air
(Adapted from Boyle's original data)

A	B	C	D	E	
48	00	$29\frac{2}{16}$	$29\frac{2}{16}$	$29\frac{2}{16}$	A. The number of equal spaces in the shorter leg, that contained the same parcel of air diversely extended.
46	$01\frac{7}{16}$	"	$30\frac{9}{16}$	$30\frac{6}{16}$	
44	$02\frac{13}{16}$	"	$31\frac{15}{16}$	$31\frac{12}{16}$	
42	$04\frac{6}{16}$	"	$33\frac{8}{16}$	$33\frac{7}{16}$	
40	$06\frac{3}{16}$	"	$35\frac{5}{16}$	35	
38	$07\frac{14}{16}$	"	37	$36\frac{4}{16}$	B. The height in inches of the mercurial cylinder in the longer leg, that compressed the air into those dimensions.
36	$10\frac{2}{16}$	"	$39\frac{4}{16}$	$38\frac{4}{16}$	
34	$12\frac{8}{16}$	"	$41\frac{10}{16}$	$41\frac{2}{16}$	
32	$15\frac{1}{16}$	"	$44\frac{3}{16}$	$43\frac{11}{16}$	
30	$17\frac{15}{16}$	"	$47\frac{1}{16}$	$46\frac{12}{16}$	
28	$21\frac{3}{16}$	"	$50\frac{5}{16}$	50	C. The height in inches of the mercurial cylinder that counter-balanced the pressure of the atmosphere.
26	$25\frac{3}{16}$	"	$54\frac{5}{16}$	$53\frac{11}{16}$	
24	$29\frac{11}{16}$	"	$58\frac{13}{16}$	$58\frac{4}{16}$	
23	$32\frac{3}{16}$	"	$61\frac{5}{16}$	$60\frac{12}{16}$	
22	$34\frac{15}{16}$	"	$64\frac{1}{16}$	$63\frac{9}{16}$	
21	$37\frac{15}{16}$	"	$67\frac{1}{16}$	$66\frac{8}{16}$	D. The aggregate of the two last columns B and C, exhibiting the pressure sustained by the included air.
20	$41\frac{9}{16}$	"	$70\frac{11}{16}$	70	
19	45	"	$74\frac{2}{16}$	$73\frac{9}{16}$	
18	$48\frac{12}{16}$	"	$77\frac{14}{16}$	$77\frac{10}{16}$	
17	$53\frac{11}{16}$	"	$82\frac{3}{16}$	$82\frac{4}{16}$	
16	$58\frac{2}{16}$	"	$87\frac{4}{16}$	$87\frac{6}{16}$	E. What that pressure in column D should be according to the hypothesis, that supposes the pressures and expansions to be in reciprocal proportion, using the initial readings as a basis of calculation.
15	$63\frac{15}{16}$	"	$93\frac{1}{16}$	$93\frac{3}{16}$	
14	$71\frac{5}{16}$	"	$100\frac{7}{16}$	$99\frac{12}{16}$	
13	$78\frac{11}{16}$	"	$107\frac{13}{16}$	$107\frac{8}{16}$	
12	$88\frac{7}{16}$	"	$117\frac{9}{16}$	$116\frac{8}{16}$	

Problem 9.2. Assume that Boyle's values at the highest pressure are correct (rather than those at the lowest pressure as did Boyle) and recalculate column E on this basis. Can you draw any conclusions from this recalculation? Tabulate the differences between columns D and E for each of the two sets of data. Are there any data in column D (and hence in column B) that would appear to be inconsistent with the others beyond the error of Boyle's measurements?

Boyle was familiar with the fact that his results were limited to a system containing a constant weight of gas at a constant temperature and he demonstrated, by warming the tube with a candle and by cooling it with water, that the temperature fluctuations in his own laboratory were not influencing his results appreciably. He did not extend his investigations to study the quantitative effect of temperature, possibly because there were no satisfactory temperature scales available at the time.

Note that the discovery of the relationship between pressure and volume in gases by Boyle depended on the prior invention of a device for measuring gas pressures, the barometer, and a device for varying gaseous pressures, the air

102 GENERAL CHEMISTRY

pump, and that his discovery was made within twenty years of the time the first of the tools was provided and within three years of the perfection of the second one. The frequent occurrence in science of the simultaneous discovery of some new fact by two people working quite independently may often be laid directly to the immediately prior discovery of some apparatus, chemical, or theory, which applied to their common problem. The obvious conclusion is that one must keep abreast of modern discoveries in order to make the greatest contribution to progress.

ABSOLUTE PRESSURES AND GAGE PRESSURES

The simple inverse relation between pressure and volume requires that the volume approach infinity when the pressure approaches zero, and that the volume approach zero when the pressure approaches infinity. There can be no negative volumes or pressures in such a system. This is consistent with our usual ideas of volume and pressure. Zero volume means the absence of volume and zero pressure means the absence of pressure.

On the other hand a tire gage used on a punctured tire gives a reading of zero, yet there certainly is some air in the tire—it can be expelled by stepping on the tire. Such pressure readings are called *gage pressures* and are defined as the difference between atmospheric pressure and the pressure in the system being measured. Negative gage pressures are possible. To get the total pressure in the system one must add the pressure of the atmosphere to the gage reading. Note that Boyle did this with the results in Table 9.1. The total pressure, as opposed to the gage pressure, is an absolute pressure—absolute in the sense that the zero is not arbitrarily defined but is, rather, chosen so that no negative values exist. Boyle's generalization will hold only when absolute pressures and volumes are used.

MEASUREMENT OF TEMPERATURE

Just as the discovery of pressure-volume relationships depended on prior invention of the barometer, so quantitative relationships involving temperatures remained undiscovered until thermometers were invented. We are now so accustomed to thermometers of mercury in glass that it may come as a surprise to know that the first thermometer used the effects of heating and cooling on a gas to measure temperature differences. Galileo is usually credited with the invention of the thermometer in about 1597, though it may have been discovered slightly earlier by another Italian, Giambattista della Porta. In any case, the early thermometers consisted of an air-filled bulb surmounted by a thin tube open to the atmosphere. A small drop of liquid (water or wine) in the tube served as an index, rising if the gas in the bulb was warmed, and falling if it was cooled. (Note that the position also varied with the atmospheric pressure.) Soon other methods of measuring changes in temperature were developed. In 1631, Jean Rey, a French physician, used a water filled thermometer to estimate the temperature of his patients and the mercury filled thermometer was introduced in 1680. These were much less sensitive to atmospheric changes.

One early thermometer made in the form of a turtle worked on a different principle. The turtle was filled with alcohol in which were placed glass balls of different density. The number of balls which floated when the turtle was placed on a patient's chest indicated the degree of fever.

In 1702 the physicist Amontons designed a thermometer having a confined sample of air in a bulb at constant volume and used the pressure of the gas in the bulb as a measure of temperature. His thermometer was so constructed that changes in atmospheric pressure did not influence the readings. He suggested that temperature be defined by the equation $\dfrac{T_1}{T_2} = \dfrac{P_1}{P_2}$ where T and P stand for the numerical values of the temperature and pressure respectively. Up to this time little progress had been made in producing thermometers with suitable temperature scales. Differences in temperature were measured in terms of arbitrary distances on the tube. Such "fixed points" or "reproducible" temperatures as the melting point of butter, the temperature of a deep cellar, or the temperature attained when some salt was added to ice were used as reference points with which to compare other temperatures. It is somewhat surprising, therefore, that Amonton's suggestion was neglected for well over a hundred years, and even more surprising in view of the fact that the method he suggested 250 years ago is still one of the most accurate ways of measuring temperatures. In the meantime Fahrenheit (1724), Reaumur (1730), and Celsius (1742) invented the temperature scales still used under their respective names, though the Celsius scale is often referred to as the Centigrade scale today.

TEMPERATURE SCALES

It is interesting to note the background of these three temperature scales. Fahrenheit chose the lowest temperature obtainable by adding ammonium chloride to ice as his zero, and the temperature of the human body as 96°. The other two men both used the melting point of ice and the boiling point of water as standards, Reaumur calling them 0° and 80°, respectively, and Celsius, 100° and 0°. These latter two temperature designations were reversed a year later giving the present Celsius or Centigrade temperature scale. It should be noted that neither of Fahrenheit's fixed points stood the test of time. The ammonium chloride-ice temperature is now called about 4°F. and the temperature of the normal human body is well known as 98.6°F. This resulted because the fixed points on the Reaumur and Centigrade scales proved so excellent that the Fahrenheit scale was redefined with the melting point of ice as 32°F. and the boiling point of water as 212°F.

The *melting point* of a substance is the temperature at which a mixture of the solid and liquid substance exist at equilibrium under a total pressure of one standard atmosphere (see page 104). The *boiling point* of a substance is the temperature at which the liquid and the gaseous substance exist at equilibrium under a pressure, due solely to the gaseous substance itself, of one standard atmosphere. Or, the boiling point of a substance is the temperature at which the liquid substance has a vapor pressure of one standard atmosphere.

Thus, between the two fixed temperatures, the melting point of ice and the boiling point of water, there are 180 Fahrenheit degrees, 80 Reaumur degrees, or 100 Centigrade degrees.

Not all the problems of establishing temperatures scales are solved by using the freezing and boiling points of water as fixed points. Both of the points vary with changes in atmospheric pressure. The boiling point of water rises and the melting point of ice falls with increasing pressure. For this reason a particular pressure is defined as standard atmospheric pressure. The influence of pressure on melting temperature is not great. That of ice is lowered only 0.01°C. when the pressure is increased to 2 standard atmospheres. On the other hand, the boiling temperature of water increases substantially, being 121°C. at two standard atmospheres. The standard atmosphere must therefore be defined precisely for accurate work.

STANDARD OF PRESSURE

The standard or normal atmosphere is defined by international agreement as the pressure due to a column of mercury 760 mm. high, having a density of 13.5951 g. per cm^3., subject to a gravitational acceleration of 980.665 cm/sec^2. The pressure of such a column is 1,013,250 dynes per sq. cm. This pressure is also expressed as 1.01325 bars or 1,013.25 millibars. A pressure of a standard mercury column 1 mm. high, usually called simply 1 mm., is $\frac{1}{760}$ of a standard atmosphere.

The rather complicated set of specifications is necessary if a mercury barometer is to be used to measure pressures. Both the height and density of the mercury are necessary, for they determine the mass of mercury supported by the gas pressure. The density of mercury, like that of other liquids, decreases with temperature so that a definite density, that of mercury at the melting point of ice (0°C.) is specified. When the barometer is at room temperature the density of the mercury is less and a longer column is required to balance the pressure of a standard atmosphere (see Figure 9.1c). The value for the acceleration of gravity is necessary for it determines the force of attraction between this column of mercury and the earth, and hence the force needed to support the mercury column. Gravitational attraction varies with latitude, the earth not being a perfect sphere, with altitude, that is, with distance above mean sea level, and even with the surrounding geological conformation.

To get an accurate value for the atmospheric pressure from a mercurial barometer reading one must always note the temperature of the barometer. Published tables may then be used to tell us how high the mercury column would be if the mercury were at standard density. The latter value, not the original barometer reading, represents the atmospheric pressure. On a day when the atmospheric pressure is 750 mm. (standard barometer) a mercury barometer at 20°C. reads 752.6 mm. and at 30° reads 753.9 mm. Barometer "corrections" of 2.6 and 3.9 mm., respectively, are subtracted from the barometer readings to give the value for the atmospheric pressure.

Similar corrections for deviations from standard gravity may also be made from tables. Some gravitational values (and the corresponding correction to be subtracted from the barometer reading) are Cleveland, 980.241 (0.3 mm.); Washington, 980.107 (0.4 mm.); Denver, 979.594 (0.8 mm.); London, 981.184 (−0.4 mm.); Honolulu, 979.108 (1.2 mm.).

Observe that pressure units and standard atmospheric pressure are defined in terms of the properties of matter and not as the pressure at any place. The pressures at sea level vary from day to day just as they do everywhere. At Oberlin, Ohio (altitude, 817 feet), the atmosphere has been observed to vary from 729 to 759 mm., the average value being about 740. At this pressure water boils at 99.3°C.

ABSOLUTE TEMPERATURES

The establishment of the temperature scales made it possible to study the quantitative effect of temperature changes on the volumes of gas samples. In 1802 Gay-Lussac repeated some work done by Charles in 1787. Both reached the same conclusion: Samples of all gases expand by the same fraction of their initial volume if heated over the same temperature range (if the pressure and amount are kept constant, of course). Later measurements with purer gases and more accurate equipment showed that all gas samples expand about $\frac{1}{273}$ of their volume at 0°C. for each degree Centigrade rise in temperature. The converse, that the gases will contract $\frac{1}{273}$ of their volume at 0°C. for each degree Centigrade fall in temperature, leads to the interesting conclusion that gases would have no volume at all if cooled to −273°C., an absurdity if our picture of atoms is correct. The plot of volume versus temperature (°C. and °K.) in Figure 9.3 illustrates the simplicity of their relationship. Actually, all gases liquefy before a temperature of −273°C. is reached, but there is ample other evidence to show that this is a unique temperature which, among other things, can never be attained but only approached more and more closely. Since it is the lower limit of all the temperature scales, it may be called *absolute zero*. Accurate experiments place the absolute zero of temperature at −273.16°C. Use of absolute zero removes any necessity of negative temperatures and leads to the simple relation for gases that the volume of any sample of gas is directly proportional to its absolute temperature provided the pressure remains constant. A sample whose volume is 100 ml. at 273°K. will occupy $\frac{546}{273} \times 100$, or 200 ml., at 546°K.; $\frac{1092}{273} \times 100$, or 400 ml., at 1092°K.; $\frac{137}{273} \times 100$ or 50 ml., at 137°K., etc., pressure and amount of gas remaining constant. The use of an absolute temperature scale rather than one based on the ice point as zero gives a simple arithmetical relationship for calculating gas behavior just as the use of absolute pressures rather than gage pressures did

106 GENERAL CHEMISTRY

earlier. The direct proportionality between volume and absolute temperature (on any scale) for a fixed amount of any gas at constant pressure is called *Charles' law* or *Gay-Lussac's law*. Because of Boyle's law, if the volume of a fixed amount of gas is kept constant the pressure is also directly proportional to the absolute temperature.

There are two commonly used absolute temperature scales, the Kelvin scale and the Rankine scale. Zero on each scale is placed at the absolute zero

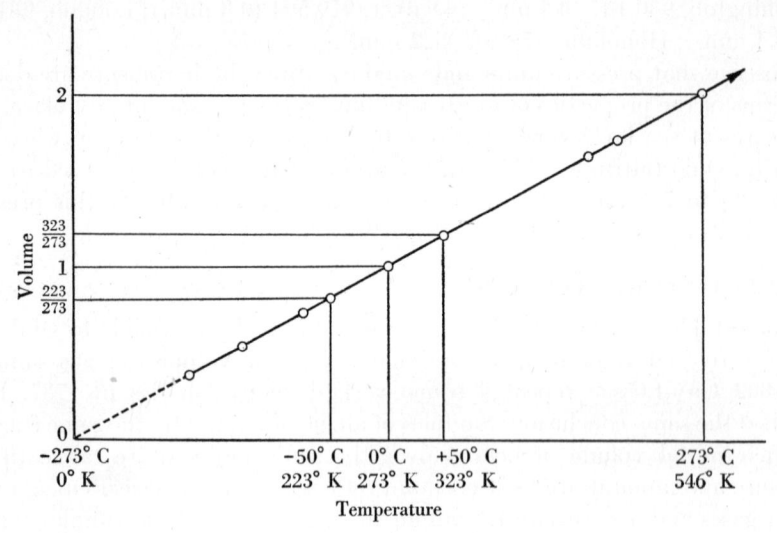

Figure 9.3.
Variation of volume of a gas with temperature. (Charles' law.)

of temperature. The Kelvin degree is defined as equal to the Centigrade degree and Rankine degree as equal to the Fahrenheit degree. The methods of defining the four common temperature scales and some comparison temperatures for them are summarized in Table 9.2. In order to convert a reading on one scale to another, it is only necessary to know the value each scale attributes to some one temperature, such as the melting point of ice, and the relative sizes of the two degrees.

Suppose we wish to find the Kelvin equivalent of 100°F. The melting point of ice is 32°F. or 273°K. 100°F. is 68 Fahrenheit degrees above the melting point of ice. One Fahrenheit degree is $\frac{5}{9}$ as large as a Kelvin degree; 68 Fahrenheit degrees therefore equal 68 × $\frac{5}{9}$ or 38 Kelvin degrees. Thus 100°F. is 38 Kelvin degrees above the melting point of ice and is identical with 273 + 38 or 311°K.

Laboratory temperatures are ordinarily read in °C. (or °F. in industrial plants), but the gas laws require absolute temperatures. The Centigrade-Kelvin conversion is particularly simple. Since the two degrees are the same size and 0°C. = 273°K., one can always convert °C. to °K. by adding 273 to

THE BEHAVIOR OF GASES

Table 9.2
Comparison of Standard Temperature Scales
(The temperatures of the Standard Fixed Points are on the International Temperature Scale. The Values Defining the Scales are in **Bold-Face** Type.)

NAME	CENTIGRADE	FAHRENHEIT	KELVIN	RANKINE
Symbol	°C.	°F.	°K.	°R.
Size of degree compared with centigrade degree	1	5/9	1	5/9
Standard Fixed Points (at 1 Standard Atmosphere)				
Silver-freezing	960.8	1761.44	1233.96	2221.13
Sulfur-condensing vapor	444.60	832.28	717.76	1291.97
Steam-condensing vapor	**100.**	212	373.16	671.69
Ice-melting	**0**	32	273.16	491.69
Oxygen-evaporating liquid	−182.97	−297.35	90.19	162.34
Absolute zero	−273.16	−459.69	**0**	**0**

the former. A comparison of some temperature readings on different temperature scales is given in Table 9.2

Problem 9.3. The gas pressure in a sealed bomb at 25°C. is 1 atmosphere. What will the pressure be at 300°C.?

Problem 9.4. A constant-pressure gas thermometer contains 0.628 liters of helium at 25°C. What would the volume be at the melting point of ice? At the boiling point of water?

Problem 9.5. A constant-volume gas thermometer showed a pressure of 732.9 mm. of mercury at the melting point of ice. When the thermometer was surrounded by dry ice (solid carbon dioxide) the pressure became 522.3 mm. What was the Centigrade temperature of the dry ice?

Problem 9.6. The pressure in a steel cylinder of hydrogen was 150 pounds per square inch on a day when the Fahrenheit temperature was 40°. Shortly thereafter the temperature was 30°F. What was the pressure in the cylinder then?

Problem 9.7. Air enters an automobile engine at 27°C. and 730 mm. pressure. The combustion products are exhausted at 200°C. and 800 mm. pressure. Compare the volume of nitrogen exhausted with the volume taken in.

Problem 9.8. An automobile tire is adjusted to a gage pressure of 32 one morning. A checkup a week later shows the gage pressure to be 34. How do you account for this result?

Problem 9.9. A commercial steel cylinder having an internal volume of 2 cubic feet is purchased, for laboratory use, filled with oxygen at a pressure of 2000 lb/sq in. What volume of oxygen at 750 mm. pressure will this cylinder supply to the laboratory? (One standard atmosphere expressed in pounds per square inch is 14.7.)

Problem 9.10. In some work at the Reichsanstalt in 1929 by Heuse and Otto, a constant volume helium gas thermometer exerted a pressure of 0.39024 meters of mercury at the ice point and 0.53310 meters of mercury at the steam point. Estimate the temperature of the ice point in °K. In another thermometer the two pressures were 0.7271

108   GENERAL CHEMISTRY

meters and 0.99450 meters respectively. Again estimate the ice point in °K. How do you account for the difference? Calculate the temperature of the first thermometer when its pressure reading was 0.24715 meters of mercury.

AMOUNT OF GAS

The amount of gas in a sample of the gas can always be expressed unambiguously in terms of its weight (and composition). If no gas is added or lost the volume depends on the pressure and temperature but the weight remains the same. Thus, the measured volume of 0.3 g. of oxygen obtained by heating potassium chlorate in the laboratory depends on the temperature and pressure of the oxygen. However, 0.6 g. of oxygen at that temperature and pressure occupies twice the volume of 0.3 g. Hence, at fixed pressure and temperature we can use the volume of the oxygen as a measure of the amount. Or, at fixed volume and temperature the pressure is directly proportional to the amount. Also, at fixed volume and pressure the absolute temperature is *inversely* proportional to the amount. Thus, a liter containing w grams of gas at pressure p and absolute temperature T becomes only $\frac{1}{2}$ liter at pressure p if the absolute temperature becomes $\frac{1}{2} T$. If we are to have one liter of gas at pressure p and at temperature, $\frac{1}{2} T$, we must have $2 w$ grams.

These relations are in common use. People buy "bottled gas" by weight, or city gas through the gas mains in cubic feet of volume (at average temperature and pressure). Either method relates cost to the amount of gas used. In the laboratory we buy oxygen in cylinders at high pressures in order to get much gas in a limited volume. As we use the gas, the pressure in the cylinder decreases proportionally. When air leaks from a bicycle tire the pressure drops. By adding more air the pressure is increased. In cold weather the pressure in an automobile tire decreases; more air restores the pressure.

As a typical problem involving changes in all the variables-volume, temperature, pressure, and amount—let us consider an automobile tire which contains 34.0 g. of air at a total pressure of 30.0 lb. per sq. in. and a temperature of 60°F. The volume of the air under these conditions is 10.0 l. This tire would be somewhat soft, the gage reading being only 15. When we inflate it to the proper operating conditions the volume changes to 10.2 l., the pressure to 40.0 pounds per square inch, and the temperature to 70°F. Let us calculate the weight of air now in the tire.

The gas laws have several arithmetical properties which make them easy to use. First, all the relationships are simple proportional ones; there are no squares or square roots for instance. Second, the laws are separable; the effect of changing one variable at a time may be studied. Third, the order in which one considers the various factors which are changing is immaterial; in algebraic terms the laws are commutative. This means that we may consider the effect on the amount of gas in the tire of changing the pressure either before or after considering volume and temperature effects, and also means that each may

THE BEHAVIOR OF GASES 109

be considered separately. It also means that only simple proportions between the quantities representing the initial and final conditions need be used. Thus, the final amount of air in the tire may be calculated by multiplying the initial amount by an expression which will contain three ratios: the ratio of the initial and final volumes, the ratio of the initial and final pressures, and the ratio of the initial and final temperatures. Which term, the initial or final condition, is in the numerator in each of the ratios can always be determined by noting whether the given change in that variable is in such a direction as to increase or to decrease the amount of gas.

In this problem the volume increases, tending to increase the amount; the larger volume will therefore be in the numerator of the volume ratio, $\frac{10.2}{10.0}$. The pressure increases, tending to increase the amount of gas in the tire; the larger pressure will therefore be in the numerator of the pressure ratio, $\frac{40.0}{30.0}$. The temperature increases from 60°F. + 460 = 520°R. to 70°F. + 460 = 530°R. It tends to decrease the amount of gas in the tire; the smaller temperature will therefore be in the numerator of the temperature ratio, $\frac{520}{530}$. The numbers in each ratio must have the same dimensions (pressures both in atmospheres, or both in millimeters of mercury, etc., volumes both in liters, or both in cubic feet, etc., temperatures both in Rankine or both in Kelvin degrees) and pressures and temperatures must be expressed on an absolute scale, *not* a gage scale for pressures, or Centigrade or Fahrenheit for temperatures. In order to make sure that the dimensions are those needed in the expression, one should record the dimension of each number. The complete solution for our problem then becomes:

$$\text{Final amount (in grams)} = 34.0 \text{ g.} \times \frac{10.2 \text{ l.}}{10.0 \text{ l.}} \times \frac{40.0 \text{ lb/in}^2}{30.0 \text{ lb/in}^2} \times \frac{520°\text{R.}}{530°\text{R.}} = 45.4 \text{ g.}$$

The relationships among changes in volume, pressure, temperature, and amount in gaseous systems are so simple that no symbolic formulas are necessary. A simple reasoning process applied to each new problem will lead to a much clearer understanding of the interrelationships than any formula would.

Problem 9.11. You have a bicycle tire containing air at an atmospheric pressure of 14 lb. per sq. in., and a tire pump with a cylinder one-tenth the volume of the tire. Assuming that at each stroke all the air in the cylinder is transferred to the tire, and that the volume of the tire and the temperature remain constant, calculate:
  a. The number of strokes required to raise the pressure to 28 lb.; 42 lb.
  b. The relative amount of air in the tire at 14 lb.; 28 lb.; 42 lb.
  c. The readings of a tire gage at the three pressures.
  d. The position of the piston in the pump cylinder when the air first enters the tire, the pressure of the tire being 28 lb.

CORRESPONDING AMOUNTS OF DIFFERENT GASES—THE MOLE OF GAS

We have already seen that all gases follow the same general relations between amount, volume, pressure, and temperature. What is the relation between the amounts of two different gases under the same conditions of volume, pressure, and temperature? Experimentally we find that the weight of oxygen is always 1.14 times as great as the weight of nitrogen under identical conditions. In Chapter 5 you learned of the hypothesis put forward in 1811 by Avogadro—equal volumes of all gases at equal pressures and temperatures contain equal numbers of molecules. The hypothesis is consistent with the known relations between amount, volume, pressure, and temperature and with Gay-Lussac's Law of Combining Volumes, and Avogadro was led to his conclusion only after the gas laws had been formulated. But his idea is not inherent in them; it is an additional step of extreme usefulness. It enables us, as Avogadro himself stated, to determine relative molecular weights directly. If a given number of oxygen molecules weighs 1.14 times as much as the same number of nitrogen molecules, each oxygen molecule weighs 1.14 times as much as each nitrogen molecule. It also enables us to employ a common unit of amount for all gases—the mole.

Since oxygen gas is diatomic, *one mole* of the gas weighs 32.0000 (*ad infinitum*) g. (2 × 16.0000 . . .) and the Avogadro number is the number of oxygen molecules in the mole. The volume of this amount of oxygen is, obviously, the *molar volume* of oxygen. Furthermore, the mole of any gas is defined as containing the Avogadro number of molecules of that gas. Then, according to the Avogadro hypothesis, all gases have the same molar volume at the same pressure and temperature and the molecular weights are proportional to the molar weights. Thus, since the molar volume of nitrogen weighs $\frac{1}{1.14}$ as much as the molar volume of oxygen, the molar weight of nitrogen is $\frac{1}{1.14} \times 32.0$ g. $= 28.1$ g. Before we extend the method to other gases we shall see how real gases deviate from the behavior predicted by the gas laws. But first we shall derive values of the molar volume from some data for oxygen. From published values the density of oxygen at 0°C. and one standard atmosphere is 1.42898 g. per l. Under these conditions the molar volume is $\frac{32.000000 \text{ g.}}{1.42898 \text{ g/l}}$, or 22.3939 l. (approximately 22.4 liters). At some higher temperature and lower pressure the density of oxygen may be 1 g. per l. Then the molar volume is 32 l. At the same temperature and pressure the molar volume of nitrogen has the same value.

THE IDEAL GAS AND REAL GASES

We stated earlier that no sample of gas follows exactly the simple rule of proportionality between volume and absolute temperature. Similarly no sample of gas follows the simple relationship between pressure and volume with exactness. It is not difficult to see why this is so: (1) Indefinitely great compression of the sample into small volumes must have a limit if the atoms occupy any space at all; (2) the fact that it is possible to liquefy and solidify all gases proves that all atoms have some attraction for neighboring atoms, thus tending to make compressive processes easier to accomplish. These two factors—the volume occupied by the molecules and the attractive forces between them—operate in such a way as to counteract one another partially. When they exactly balance, and no other forces are acting, the gas will behave as an "ideal gas" and will obey the simple gas laws exactly. Under other conditions the real gas will have either a little more volume (if the molecular volume effect predominates) or a little less volume (if the attractive forces predominate) than would be calculated from the ideal gas laws and the known pressure and temperature. The presence of other forces not so simply described may further complicate the picture. For most gases, at pressures and temperatures usually met, the deviations from the gas laws are not greater than 2 per cent of the calculated value, as illustrated by the experimentally measured molar volumes at 0°C. and 1 atmosphere pressure summarized in Table 9.3. If the ideal gas laws were followed these molar volumes would all equal

Table 9.3
Molar Volumes of Some Gases
(In liters at 0°C. and 1 standard atmospheric pressure. The molar volume of an ideal gas is 22.414 liters under these conditions.)

GAS	FORMULA	MOLAR VOLUME	GAS	FORMULA	MOLAR VOLUME
Hydrogen	H_2	22.428	Methane	CH_4	22.360
Helium	He	22.426	Carbon dioxide	CO_2	22.256
Neon	Ne	22.425	Hydrogen chloride	HCl	22.249
Nitrogen	N_2	22.404	Ethylene	C_2H_4	22.241
Carbon monoxide	CO	22.403	Acetylene	C_2H_2	22.19
Oxygen	O_2	22.394	Ammonia	NH_3	22.09
Argon	A	22.393	Chlorine	Cl_2	22.06
Nitric Oxide	NO	22.389			

22,414 ml. Ordinarily, therefore, the use of the ideal laws is justified in calculations of gaseous behavior.

Very involved equations have been suggested to describe the relations between amount of gas, pressure, volume, and temperature as exactly as they have been measured experimentally. No equation has succeeded in doing this and it is still essential to make experimental determinations of quantities which are to be used as the basis of important scientific work of great accuracy. In less demanding work the equations may be very useful.

112 GENERAL CHEMISTRY

Problem 9.12. From the known molar weights calculate the densities, in grams per liter, of oxygen, hydrogen, helium, argon, and methane at 20°C. and standard atmospheric pressure.

Problem 9.13. What is the molar volume of a gas at 0°C. at an altitude where the pressure is 600 mm.? If the gas is nitrogen what is its density in grams per liter?

Problem 9.14. Select some value for the room pressure and temperature you measured in the laboratory and calculate the value for the molar volume of an ideal gas under those conditions.

CALCULATION OF MOLAR WEIGHTS OF GASES

All methods of determining the molar weights (and molecular weights) of gases through the gas laws rest ultimately on the Avogadro hypothesis and the defined weight of oxygen. The method chosen depends on the ease of carrying out the experiment in each case.

a. The most direct method of determining a molar weight is to weigh a vessel containing a gas at any convenient pressure and temperature and then to weigh the vessel filled with oxygen at the same pressure and temperature. This method was applied on page 110 to nitrogen.

b. If the gas laws are utilized, the unknown gas and oxygen may be weighed at differing pressures, temperatures, and volumes but the values of these must then be known. From these values one can calculate the weight of oxygen that should occupy the volume of the unknown (at the temperature and pressure of the latter) and compare this weight with that of the unknown as before. Or, one can calculate the weight of the unknown needed to duplicate the volume of the oxygen at the experimental conditions for the oxygen. By either method equal volumes at the same conditions are obtained, and the ratio of the weight of unknown to that of oxygen is also the ratio of the molar weights of the two.

The values of the molar weights found in the above methods are most accurate when the experiments are carried out at conditions under which the gases obey the gas laws most closely. When the pressures are low and the temperatures are well above the boiling points of the substances, accurate molar weights may be obtained. Under these conditions the intermolecular forces are less important, and the effect of the molecular volume becomes negligible.

c. The experimenter who chooses to rely on the accuracy of the gas laws need not make any measurements on oxygen but can calculate the weight of the "unknown" per molar volume. With the gas laws we may calculate the molar volume of oxygen or any other gas at any temperature and pressure, say 20°C. and 740 mm. As the temperature rises the volume will increase in the ratio $\dfrac{293°K.}{273°K.}$, and as the pressure falls the volume will increase in the ratio $\dfrac{760 \text{ mm.}}{740 \text{ mm.}}$. Therefore the molar volume becomes:

THE BEHAVIOR OF GASES 113

$$\text{Molar volume} = 22.4 \text{ l.} \times \frac{293°K.}{273°K.} \times \frac{760 \text{ mm.}}{740 \text{ mm.}} = 24.8 \text{ l.}$$
(at 20°C. and 740 mm.).

If we have measured the density of the unknown gas under these conditions we can calculate the molar weight by multiplying the weight per liter by 24.8 l. (Since one cubic foot equals 28.3 l. it appears that the molar volume of a gas at the usual experimental condition is slightly less than one cubic foot.)

Using these principles one can also obtain the molar weight of a liquid such as water by changing it to a gas at a suitable temperature and measuring its weight, volume, pressure, and temperature. A simple gas law calculation then gives the weight of gaseous water in a molar volume.

Suppose we find that 835 ml. of a certain gas weighs 0.850 g. at 37°C. and a pressure of 562 ml. of mercury. What is the molar weight of the gas? We shall make the calculation in two equivalent ways.

1. First, the units must be consistent and absolute. We shall use liters, millimeters of mercury, degrees Kelvin, and grams. The weight of gas in 0.835 liters will increase in the ratio $\frac{760 \text{ mm.}}{562 \text{ mm.}}$ as the pressure increases from 562 mm. to 760 mm. The weight in this volume also increases in the ratio $\frac{310°K.}{273°K.}$ as the temperature decreases from 310°K. to 273°K. Therefore, the weight becomes

$$\text{Weight of gas} = 0.850 \text{ g.} \times \frac{760 \text{ mm.}}{562 \text{ mm.}} \times \frac{310°K.}{273°K.} = 1.305 \text{ g.} \quad (9.1)$$
(in 0.835 l.)

The weight of gas in a molar volume is greater in the ratio $\frac{22.4 \text{ l.}}{0.835 \text{ l.}}$

Therefore

$$\text{Molar weight} = 1.305 \text{ g.} \times \frac{22.4 \text{ l.}}{0.835 \text{ l.}} = 35.0 \text{ g.} \quad (9.2)$$

Equations 9.1 and 9.2 may be summarized in a single equation

$$\text{Molar weight} = 0.850 \text{ g.} \times \frac{760 \text{ mm.}}{562 \text{ mm.}} \times \frac{310°K.}{273°K.} \times \frac{22.4 \text{ l.}}{0.835 \text{ l.}} = 35.0 \text{ g.} \quad (9.3)$$

2. Let us first calculate the molar volume at the experimental conditions. Using the argument in (1) we find that:

$$\begin{matrix}\text{Molar volume at}\\ \text{experimental}\\ \text{conditions}\end{matrix} = 22.4 \text{ l.} \times \frac{760 \text{ mm.}}{562 \text{ mm.}} \times \frac{310°K.}{273°K.} = 34.4 \text{ l.} \quad (9.4)$$

The weight of gas in this molar volume is

$$\text{Molar weight} = 0.850 \text{ g.} \times \frac{34.4 \text{ l.}}{0.835 \text{ l.}} = 35.0 \text{ g.} \quad (9.5)$$

114 GENERAL CHEMISTRY

Equations 9.4 and 9.5 may be combined to give, directly

$$\text{Molar weight} = 0.850 \text{ g.} \times \frac{22.4 \text{ l.}}{0.835 \text{ l.}} \times \frac{760 \text{ mm.}}{562 \text{ mm.}} \times \frac{310°\text{K.}}{273°\text{K.}} = 35.0 \text{ g.} \quad (9.6)$$

Inspection shows that equation 9.6 is identical with equation 9.3. No matter what intermediate steps we use we always end with the same final equation. A student can always check his work by using two alternate methods and seeing whether they give the same equation and the same answer.

ATOMIC WEIGHTS FROM THE MOLAR WEIGHTS OF GASES

We have already seen that fifty years elapsed between the time Avogadro showed how to calculate the relative molecular weights from data on gases, and the time chemists used his methods on any wide scale. At a congress of chemists held at Karlsruhe in 1860 (the first international congress of scientists), Cannizarro circulated a publication he had prepared two years earlier on the application of Avogadro's hypothesis to determination of molecular weights and atomic weights. Cannizarro's argument may be expressed in the following terms. From the known densities of various gases we may obtain their molar weights relative to our standard, oxygen = 32.0000. From the analysis of these gases we know what fraction of the molar weight is due to each constituent element. If the atomic theory is correct, every molecule must contain one or two or three or some other integral number of atoms of each element. Therefore, the weights of any element in one mole of any of its compounds must be multiples of a certain weight which represents the atomic weight. We may illustrate the method by applying it to carbon compounds. Acetone has a molar weight of 58 grams. Analysis shows that the fraction 0.62 of this weight is carbon, that is, 0.62 × 58, or 36, out of the 58 grams are due to carbon. Carbon dioxide has a molar weight of 44, the fraction 0.27 being carbon. Therefore, 0.27 × 44, or 12 grams, of the 44 are due to carbon. The last column of Table 9.4 shows the weight of carbon in molar weights of various compounds.

The inspection of the column shows that the smallest weight is 12 and that every other weight is a multiple of 12. Every weight is also a multiple of 6 but no values are ever found in which 6, 18, or 30 grams of carbon are present in a molar weight. It appears, therefore, that 12 is the relative atomic weight of carbon.

In a similar way we find that the smallest weight of nitrogen ever found in a molar weight of nitrogen-containing substances is 14 grams or some multiple of this number. Therefore, the atomic weight of nitrogen is 14, or half the molar weight, and nitrogen gas must have the formula N_2, consistent with our tentative assumption made on the basis of the combining volumes of gases (page 51).

The method of Cannizarro was especially important for two reasons. It gave

Table 9.4

Molar Weights and Carbon Content of Some Carbon Compounds

COMPOUND	MOLAR WEIGHT OF COMPOUND	FRACTION OF CARBON IN COMPOUND	WEIGHT OF CARBON IN MOLAR WEIGHT OF COMPOUND
Acetone	58	0.62	36
Benzene	78	0.92	72
Butane	58	0.83	48
Carbon dioxide	44	0.27	12
Carbon monoxide	28	0.43	12
Ethane	30	0.80	24
Ethyl alcohol	46	0.52	24
Methane	16	0.75	12
Methyl chloride	50.5	0.24	12
Octane	114	0.84	96
Propane	42	0.86	36

a method for determining atomic weights of the nonmetallic elements all of which (except the inert gases) form gaseous compounds. (For the metallic elements [most of which do not form gaseous compounds] the principle of Dulong and Petit suggested in 1819 [see page 143] may be used to get atomic weights.) The Cannizarro method is important in the second place because it gave indirect evidence supporting the atomic theory, for its logic rests on the atomic theory. It did not prove the theory but it made the theory more plausible, for, experimentally, the weight of an element in a molar weight of its compounds is always a symbol weight or its multiple.

GASEOUS SOLUTIONS

The observations of Boyle, Charles, Gay-Lussac, and Avogadro on gaseous behavior apply not only to pure gases but also to gaseous solutions. Air, for example, obeys all the gas laws and may be used in a gas thermometer. In fact air thermometers have been used rather extensively. Dalton was the first to observe the comparable behavior of gaseous solutions and pure gases. He summarized his observations in the statement that each gas in a gaseous solution exerts the same pressure that it would if it were alone in the same container at the same temperature. This pressure is called the *partial pressure* of the gas. When one liter of oxygen at a pressure of one-third atmosphere and one liter of nitrogen at a pressure of two-thirds atmosphere are mixed (at the same temperature) to give one liter of gaseous solution the pressure will be $\frac{1}{3} + \frac{2}{3} = 1$ atmosphere. (Compare with what happens when both samples are the same gas.) If the gas laws are obeyed and the pressures are additive, volumes must also be additive. One-third liter of oxygen at one atmosphere plus two-thirds liter of nitrogen at one atmosphere when mixed (at the same temperature) give one liter of gaseous solution at one atmosphere. (Compare with what happens when both samples are the same gas.)

As a consequence of the Avogadro hypothesis another statement can be made. The gaseous solution prepared above will contain two times as many nitrogen molecules (or moles) as oxygen molecules (or moles). One third of the molecules are oxygen molecules and two thirds of the molecules are nitrogen molecules. The fractions, $\frac{1}{3} = 0.33$ and $\frac{2}{3} = 0.67$ representing the numbers of molecules (or moles) of one kind relative to the total number present, are called the *mole fractions* of the component gases. Dalton's statement may, therefore, be changed to the statement that the partial pressures of the gases in a gaseous solution are in the same ratio as the relative numbers of molecules of those gases. The mole fraction of a gas also represents the ratio of its partial pressure to the total pressure.

The principle of partial pressures is often applied in experiments in which a gaseous substance, A, is collected by displacing a liquid, B, from a container. All liquids have a tendency to evaporate to produce a gas or "vapor" having an equilibrium partial pressure, called the *vapor pressure*, at any given temperature. The gas collected by displacement of the liquid will, therefore, be a gaseous solution containing gaseous A together with some gaseous B. The total pressure in the container will be the sum of the various partial pressures. The partial pressure, or vapor pressure, of B will be determined by the temperature, and may be found in published tabulations for most common liquids. This partial pressure must be subtracted from the total pressure if the partial pressure of the gas A is desired. The partial pressure so calculated for the gas A will be the total pressure of gas at that volume and temperature if all the vapor of B is removed (by a dryer, for example). The equilibrium partial pressures of water vapor as a function of temperature are listed in Table 11.1, page 140.

A GENERAL PROBLEM INVOLVING GAS BEHAVIOR

Let us consider a problem which requires application of many of the principles discussed in this chapter for its solution. A sample of mercuric oxide ore weighing 1.362 g. is heated and the oxygen evolved is collected by the displacement of water from a calibrated tube. The resultant gas had a volume of 50.7 ml. Room temperature was 20°C. The barometric reading was 750 mm. What per cent of the ore was mercuric oxide? See Figure 9.4 for a diagram of the final conditions of the experiment.

If only the mercuric oxide in the ore liberated any gas, this problem becomes one of finding the weight of mercuric oxide that will give the measured volume of the gas (oxygen). Note that only three significant figures need be used since volume and pressure are determined only to this degree of accuracy. The equation for the reaction is known to be

$$HgO_{(s)} = Hg_{(liq)} + \tfrac{1}{2}O_{2(g)} \tag{9.6}$$

which indicates that one mole (217 g.) of mercuric oxide will yield one-half mole (16 g.) of oxygen. If we knew the weight of oxygen formed we could calculate the weight of mercuric oxide originally present. The weight of oxygen can be calculated with the aid of the gas laws if its temperature, volume, and pressure are known. The temperature was 20°C., the volume 50.7 ml., but the pressure of the oxygen was not directly observed, only the reading of the barometer in the room.

At 20°C. the barometer reading is 2.6 mm. higher than the atmospheric pressure (page 104). Thus the atmospheric pressure was 750 − 2.6 = 750 −

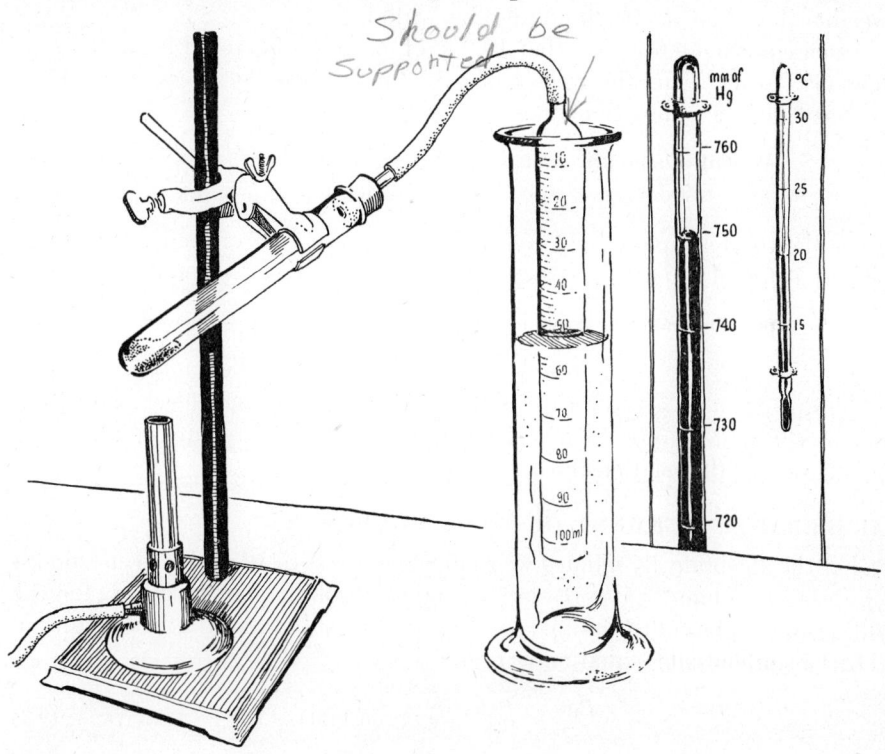

Figure 9.4.
Apparatus for correlating volume of a gas with its weight.

3 = 747 mm. (The gravity correction on the barometric height, 0.3 mm., may be neglected.) But the collected gas was not pure oxygen. It was collected by water displacement and so was saturated with water vapor. At 20°C. the vapor pressure of water is 17.51 mm. (see page 140). Since the water levels inside and outside the calibrated tube are identical the total pressures must also be the same and equal to 747 mm. Since the water vapor is exerting a pressure of 17.51, or 18, mm. inside the tube, the oxygen pressure there must be 747 − 18 = 729 mm.

Now we know that 32 g. of oxygen occupy 22.4 l. at 760 mm. pressure and 0°C. (273°K.). Therefore, we can calculate the weight of oxygen in 50.7 ml. (0.0507 liters) at 729 mm. and 20°C. (293°K.).

118   GENERAL CHEMISTRY

$$\text{Weight of oxygen collected} = 32.0 \text{ g.} \times \frac{729 \text{ mm.}}{760 \text{ mm.}} \times \frac{273°K.}{293°K.} \times \frac{0.0507 \text{ l.}}{22.4 \text{ l.}}$$
$$= 0.0647 \text{ g. of oxygen.}$$

Note that the ratios are consistent with the fact that the pressure in the experiment is less than standard (giving a smaller weight), the temperature is greater (giving a smaller weight), and the volume is less (giving a smaller weight) than that of the standard 32 g. sample.

From equation 9.6 we see that 16.0 g. of oxygen is liberated from 217 g. of mercuric oxide. Thus the weight of oxide in this sample is less than 217 g. just as 0.0647 g. is less than 16.0 g. of oxygen.

$$\text{Weight of mercuric oxide in sample} = 217 \text{ g.} \times \frac{0.0647 \text{g. oxygen}}{16.0 \text{ g. oxygen}}$$
$$= 0.877 \text{ g. of mercuric oxide.}$$

Since the total sample weight was 1.362 g., the per cent of mercuric oxide in the ore is found thus:

$$\text{per cent mercuric oxide in ore} = 100 \times \frac{0.877 \text{ g. mercuric oxide}}{1.362 \text{ g. ore}}$$
$$= 64.4\%.$$

This problem uses most of the mathematical relationships developed within Chapter 9. Other problems may be simpler but few will require greater comprehension of the relationships.

ALGEBRAIC STATEMENT OF THE GAS LAWS

For the algebraically minded we shall here express relations between amount of gas, n, its volume, v, its pressure, P, and its absolute temperature, T. Let the subscript $_1$ represent the initial condition and the subscript $_2$ the final condition. Then a summarizing equation is:

$$\frac{P_1 v_1}{n_1 T_1} = \frac{P_2 v_2}{n_2 T_2} = c \text{ (a constant)} \tag{9.7}$$

or

$$Pv = ncT \tag{9.8}$$

When the amount n is expressed in number of moles of gas, the constant c becomes the *universal gas constant* R. Then equation 9.8 may be written

$$Pv = nRT \tag{9.9}$$

Problem 9.15. A liter of pure oxygen at 30°C. and 730 mm. is bubbled through water at 30°C. The vapor pressure of water at this temperature is 32 mm.
(a) If the resulting gaseous solution is measured at 730 mm. and 30°C., what will be its volume?
(b) What will be the mole fractions of oxygen and water vapor in the gaseous solution in (a)?
(c) If the water vapor of the gaseous solution in (a) is removed, what will be the pressure of the oxygen remaining?

(d) If the water vapor of the gaseous solution in (a) is removed and the pressure made equal to 730 mm. what will be the volume of the oxygen?

Problem 9.16. Assuming that air contains 78 per cent nitrogen, 21 per cent oxygen, and 1 per cent argon, calculate:
(a) the mole fraction of each gas;
(b) the weight of air in a molar volume.
(Remember that the compositions of gaseous mixtures expressed in percentages are per cent by volume.)

Problem 9.17. Humid air is "lighter" than dry air. Explain.

Problem 9.18. When 240 ml. of a gas are collected at 730 mm. pressure and the pressure is changed to 760 mm. what is the final volume, the temperature remaining unchanged?

Problem 9.19. When 200 ml. of a gas are collected at 730 mm. pressure and the pressure changed to 700 mm. what will be the final volume, the temperature remaining unchanged?

Problem 9.20. A liter of gas at 1.00 atmosphere pressure and 0.0°C. is heated to 25.0°C. If the volume remains unchanged what will be the new pressure? If the pressure remains unchanged what will be the new volume?

Problem 9.21. A liter of gas measured at 750 mm. pressure and 0°C. is heated to 1°C. If the pressure remains constant what will be the new volume? What will be the new volume when a liter of gas at 20°C. and 750 mm. is heated at constant pressure to 21°C.?

Problem 9.22. When 120 ml. of dry gas at 740 mm. pressure and at 26°C. is bubbled through water at the same temperature what will be the final volume of the gas, the total pressure and temperature remaining unchanged?

Problem 9.23. At what temperature Centigrade will a flask contain 1.10 g. of carbon dioxide gas at 1.05 atmospheres if it contains 2.50 g. at 87°C. and 2.40 atmosphere?

Problem 9.24. If helium gas can be produced at $0.08 per cu. ft. measured at 1 atm. and 25°C., what is the helium worth in a tank having a capacity of 1.35 cu. ft. filled to 2000 lb. per sq. in. pressure at 20°C.?

Problem 9.25. What weight could be lifted by a balloon containing 200 kg. of helium?

Problem 9.26. Hydrogen sulfide, formula H_2S, is toxic at a concentration of 0.0100 mg/l. What is its partial pressure at this concentration?

Problem 9.27. 0.800 gram of a certain solid element, Z, combines with 1.200 gram of oxygen to produce 300 ml. of a gas measured at 37°C. and 1,611 mm. pressure. What is the molecular weight of the gas formed? If one molecule of this gas contains one atom of Z what is the atomic weight of Z?

Problem 9.28. If 200 g. of calcium carbonate on heating gave 10.0 l. of carbon dioxide measured at 15°C. and 1.20 atm., what per cent of the calcium carbonate was decomposed?

Problem 9.29. A gaseous compound of carbon and hydrogen is 80.0 per cent by weight carbon; 560.0 ml. of this compound at 0.100 atm. pressure and 0°C. weigh 0.0750 g. What is the molecular formula of the compound?

Problem 9.30. Analyses of a series of compounds containing element Z and oxygen give the following data. From these data what is the most probable atomic weight of Z?

Molar Weight of Compound	122.8	90.8	176.2	149.6
Per cent of Z	60.9	82.4	63.7	100

10 THE KINETIC THEORY OF GASES

YOU MAY have noted that the interrelationships among temperature, amount, pressure, and volume of gases discussed in Chapter 9 are based entirely on experimental observations made on ordinary samples of gases. They represent changes in the gross or bulk properties. The derived laws, except for Avogadro's hypothesis, do not depend for their validity on the existence of atoms or molecules. On the other hand, our concepts of atoms and molecules must be consistent with the experimental observations made on bulk materials. In this chapter we shall use a theoretical approach, interpreting gaseous behavior in terms of the atoms and molecules in the gas and of their motion or kinetic behavior. We shall find that the theory does explain the facts quantitatively and in addition gives us a point of view in terms of molecular behavior that can be extended profitably to other phenomena.

KINETIC ENERGY

It is convenient to classify energy into two types, kinetic energy, or energy of motion, and potential (latent) energy. The latter is due to position in a field of force and may be possessed by particles not in motion. We shall consider it in more detail in Chapter 11.

All particles in motion have kinetic energy. For translational motion, that is, motion of the particle in space from one place to another, the translational kinetic energy is represented by the equation

$$\text{K.E.} = \tfrac{1}{2}mu^2 \qquad (10.1)$$

in which m is the mass of a particle and u is its translational velocity. Similar equations apply to rotatory motion, in which the center of mass remains fixed and the parts of the body rotate about it, and to vibratory motion, in which the center of mass again remains fixed and the various portions of the particle vibrate with respect to the center of mass. Figure 10.1 illustrates these three types of motion. It is in terms of these motions that the kinetic theory interprets the behavior of gases.

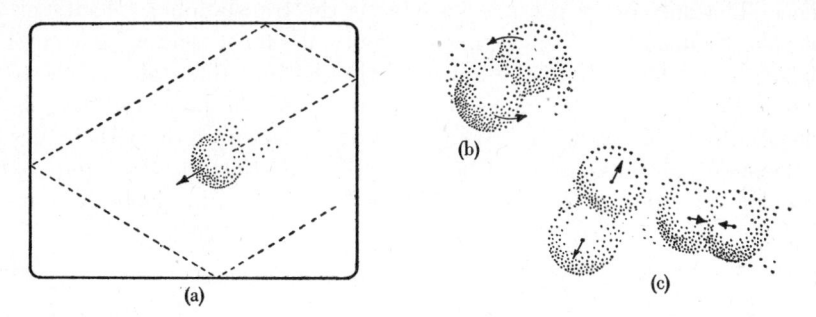

Figure 10.1.
Types of motion. In translational motion, a, the center of gravity of the particle moves. In rotational motion, b, the mass of the particle rotates about the center of gravity which remains stationary. In vibrational motion, c, the mass alternately moves toward and away from the center of gravity which remains stationary.

GASEOUS DIFFUSION AND MOLECULAR VELOCITIES

Thomas Graham's discovery in 1829 that different gases diffuse at different rates was a great step toward a complete understanding of gases in terms of the behavior of atoms and molecules. He sealed gases in a piston with a small escape hole, and measured the time it took for a given volume of the different gases to escape through the hole. The rates of escape (at the same pressure and temperature) were found to be inversely proportional to the square root of the density of the gases. That is, a gas with a density of 4 grams per liter would diffuse out the hole only half as fast as a gas with a density of 1 gram per liter.

$$\frac{(\text{rate})_1}{(\text{rate})_2} = \frac{\sqrt{1}}{\sqrt{4}} = \frac{1}{2} \tag{10.2}$$

Now density is a measure of weight per unit volume, and the weight of a given volume of gas will depend on the number of molecules present and the weight of each one. But, according to Avogadro, the number of gaseous molecules which diffuse out of the piston under Graham's conditions of equal volumes at equal pressures and temperatures will be identical for all gases. If the same number of molecules are allowed to escape, what is it that causes the variation in the time for this escape? The diameter of the hole is the same, the pressure is the same, the volume is the same, the temperature is the same, and the number of molecules escaping is the same; only the molecular weight is known to vary. If the hole were very tiny, it is conceivable that the more massive (hence, in general, larger) molecules might diffuse more slowly because of frictional effects as they rubbed along the sides. The effusion holes used in these experiments, however, were roughly 100,000 times larger than molecular diameters so it is hard to conceive that the walls of the hole had much influence. The only other possible variable is the translational velocity of the molecules themselves. The more massive molecules must be moving from place to place more slowly than the lighter molecules and thus take longer to go through the hole. Furthermore, the average translational velocity of the molecules must be inversely proportional to the square root of their masses. Or, the molecular mass, m, must be inversely proportional to the square of the molecular velocities, u. This statement may be written in algebraic terms as

$$\frac{\sqrt{m_1}}{\sqrt{m_2}} = \frac{u_2}{u_1}, \text{ or } \frac{m_1}{m_2} = \frac{u_2^2}{u_1^2}, \text{ or } m_1u_1^2 = m_2u_2^2 \tag{10.3}$$

The subscripts refer to the two separate gases. If one now knows that the translational kinetic energy of a particle is given by the equation 10.1:

$$\text{K.E.} = \tfrac{1}{2}mu^2$$

it is apparent that equations 10.3, rewritten in the form

$$\tfrac{1}{2}m_1u_1^2 = \tfrac{1}{2}m_2u_2^2, \tag{10.4}$$

indicate that the average translational kinetic energies of the gaseous molecules in the diffusion experiments are the same.

Further experiments show that the magnitude of this average kinetic energy for any gas depends only on the temperature. It is unaffected by changes in pressure, volume, or amount of gas. Study of diffusion rates as a function of temperature also shows that the translational kinetic energy is directly proportional to the absolute temperature of the gas. In algebraic terms:

$$cT = \tfrac{1}{2}mu^2 = \text{K.E.} \tag{10.5}$$

where c is a constant, the same for every gas, and T is the absolute temperature. Thus, doubling the absolute temperature doubles the translational kinetic energy of the gas molecules, and, conversely, decreasing the absolute temperature decreases the translational kinetic energy proportionally. Since the molecular weight of any particular gas is a constant this means that molecular velocity is uniquely determined by the temperature of the gas, and will, in fact, be proportional to the square root of the absolute temperature. At room temperature the average velocity of a hydrogen molecule is 200,000 centimeters (about one mile) per second, and that of an oxygen molecule 50,000 centimeters per second. With these values you should now calculate the value of "c" in equation 10.5. The numerical value of the constant obviously depends on whether the absolute temperature scale is the Kelvin or the Rankine scale, and on the units used for mass and velocity.

THE KINETIC THEORY OF GASES 123

Problem 10.1. One of the earliest objections to the kinetic theory was that the high molecular velocities predicted were not consistent with the slow rates with which gases diffuse. How would you answer this objection?

Problem 10.2. Calculate the value of c in equation 10.5 from the average velocities of hydrogen and oxygen molecules.

In equation 10.5 we have a very simple concept of temperature in terms of average molecular behavior in gas. Temperature is a measure of the translational kinetic energy of the gas, and, since molecular weights do not change with temperature, a rising temperature merely means that the molecules are moving with greater average velocities. A falling temperature indicates that molecular velocities are diminishing.

HEAT CAPACITY OF GASES

We have already observed that energy is needed to raise the temperature of a substance. The heat required to raise the temperature of a sample one degree is called its *heat capacity*. The heat capacity is an extensive property depending on the size of sample. It also depends somewhat on the temperature. The heat capacity of one gram of substance is defined as its *specific heat capacity*, sometimes called its specific heat. (The specific heat capacity of water varies slightly with the temperature but at all temperatures is approximately 1 calorie per gram per degree Centigrade.) Chemists usually compare moles of substances rather than grams and are therefore interested in the heat capacity per mole rather than per gram. We shall find that many generalizations can be made if the heat capacities per mole of substance, the *molar heat capacities*, are compared. The values we shall use will be in calories absorbed per degree (Centigrade or Kelvin) rise in temperature.

There are two standard measurements of the heat capacities of gases—heat capacity at constant volume, C_v, and heat capacity at constant pressure, C_p. The latter is always the larger since a gas expands when heated at constant pressure though not at constant volume. This expansion does work in pushing back the surrounding atmosphere, and the heat capacity at constant pressure will be greater than that at constant volume by the amount of the work done in expansion. Some typical heat capacities of gases at 25°C. are given in Table 10.1. Note that $C_p - C_v$ is a constant, consistent with the idea that the work against the atmosphere will be independent of the gas doing the work. (If this work term is measured more accurately, deviations from constancy will be noted since the gas may do work against its own intermolecular forces while expanding and these forces vary from gas to gas. It is this work done against their own intermolecular forces which causes all gases to cool upon expanding into a vacuum if the temperature before expansion is not too far removed from the boiling point of the substance. These same intermolecular forces cause liquefaction and solidification when any gas is sufficiently cooled.)

Table 10.1 also shows that some of the substances mercury, sodium, potas-

124 GENERAL CHEMISTRY

sium, helium, and argon—have the same heat capacity. Similarly, the heat capacities of hydrogen, nitrogen, oxygen, and hydrogen chloride are very close to being the same, but higher than those in the first group. Each of the first group of substances is monatomic in the gaseous state, and each of the second group is diatomic. The constant heat capacity of the monatomic substances can at once be seen to be completely consistent with the relation between translational kinetic energy and temperature discussed above. The translational kinetic energies of all gases are the same at the same temperature, therefore the difference in translational kinetic energy between the same

Table 10.1
Heat Capacities of Some Gases at 25°C.

GASEOUS SUBSTANCE	C_v (CAL/MOLE °C.) HEAT CAPACITY AT CONSTANT VOLUME	C_p (CAL/MOLE °C.) HEAT CAPACITY AT CONSTANT PRESSURE	$C_p - C_v$
Mercury	3.0	5.0	2.0
Sodium	3.0	5.0	2.0
Potassium	3.0	5.0	2.0
Helium	3.0	5.0	2.0
Argon	3.0	5.0	2.0
Oxygen	5.0	7.0	2.0
Nitrogen	5.0	7.0	2.0
Hydrogen	4.9	6.9	2.0
Hydrogen chloride	5.0	7.0	2.0
Water	6.0	8.0	2.0
Methane	6.5	8.5	2.0
Carbon dioxide	6.9	8.9	2.0

two temperatures must also be the same for every gas. Monatomic gases, whose particles can acquire neither rotational or vibrational kinetic energy, will change only in translational kinetic energy when heated and thus will all have the same heat capacity, 3.0 calories per mole per degree Centigrade. The heat capacity of diatomic molecules is higher than that of monatomic molecules since the diatomic molecules not only acquire translational energy, but also increase their rotational energy and their vibrational energy when heated. When the molecules contain more atoms there are more modes of vibration in the molecule. Therefore the amount of heat necessary to raise the temperature a fixed amount, the heat capacity, becomes larger as the number of atoms in the molecule increases.

At the time when the above theory was developed very few gases were known to be monatomic. Mercury was one, for measurement on its vapor shows that one mole of the gas had the same weight as the gram-atomic weight of the element. Its heat capacity, $C_v = 3$, was that predicted by the kinetic theory. Later the inert gases were discovered. Their molar weights were readily determined but there are no chemical methods for determining their atomic weights since they form no compounds. However, their heat capacities were $C_v = 3$, as predicted for monatomic gases and found experimentally for mercury. The conclusion was that the inert gases are monatomic, and that their atomic weights are identical with their molecular weights.

MEAN FREE PATH

A gas under approximately standard conditions occupies about 1000 times as much volume as the solid or liquid into which it may be made by cooling. Thus gaseous molecules are ordinarily much more widely separated than those in the liquid and solid phases. We have shown that they are traveling at high speeds of the order of 50,000 cm/sec. Separated though they are, the molecules are bound to collide, and to collide with great frequency because of their high velocities. The average path between collisions will be short under ordinary conditions and will depend on two quantities only, the number of molecules per cubic centimeter and the size of the molecules. Most gases at the usual room conditions have mean free paths of about 10^{-5} cm. That is, each molecule on the average undergoes a collision every one hundred thousandth of a centimeter of its travels. If it travels 50,000 cm/sec, it is easy to see that it will undergo about 5×10^9, or five billion, collisions per second. Some of these collisions will be with other gaseous molecules and some with the walls of the container.

A mean free path of 10^{-5} cm. may be expressed as 10^3 Å. (or 1000 Å.). The molecules themselves have diameters of the order of 4 Å. and their average spacing in the gas is of the order of 40 Å. It follows that on the average a molecule passes by many other molecules before it collides with one of them.

Problem 10.3. Calculate the total number of collisions in one second in one mole of hydrogen.

Problem 10.4. Liquid oxygen has a density of 1.14 g. per ml. at $-183°C$. Calculate the average distance between the centers of the oxygen molecules in the liquid. Calculate the average distance between the centers of molecules in gaseous oxygen at standard conditions. Compare the two distances.

PRESSURE AND THE KINETIC THEORY

In view of the above discussion we can now picture a gas as an assemblage of widely separated molecules in rapid, random motion, continually colliding with velocities which are determined only by the molecular mass and by the absolute temperature. Pressure within a container becomes comprehensible in terms of continual bombardment of the walls by these rapidly moving molecules. The total pressure will be determined by the number of such collisions per unit time and by the force of each collision.

The number of collisions per unit time will depend on the number of molecules (n), per unit of volume (V), that is, on $\frac{n}{V}$, and on the molecular velocity,

(u), and it is proportional to the product $\frac{n}{V} \times u$. The force per collision depends on the mass of the molecule, (m) and the molecular velocity and is proportional to their product, $m \times u$. The total effect on the walls is the product of these separate effects so that we see that pressure is proportional to $\frac{n}{V} \times u \times m \times u$, or to $\frac{nmu^2}{V}$. This relation may be written

$$P = \frac{c_1 nmu^2}{V} \tag{10.6}$$

where c_1 is a constant, the same for all gases. Equations 10.5 and 10.6 sum up all our previous discussion on the behavior of gases in terms of molecular properties. Equation 10.5 relates temperature to molecular mass and velocity, and equation 10.6 relates pressure, volume, and amount of gas to the same quantities and hence to temperature. It is now possible to interpret all these interrelationships in terms of what the molecules are "doing," that is, in terms of the kinetic theory which describes their motion.

For instance, equation 10.6 shows that increasing the amount of gas in a container (increasing n) must be accompanied by an increase in pressure (P), if the volume (V) and the temperature (proportional to mu^2) remain unchanged. Or an increase in temperature (volume and amount constant) is accompanied by an increase in molecular velocity (according to equation 10.5), and hence P increases since the number of molecular collisions and the force per collision both increase. Changes in volume, V, must be accompanied by appropriate changes in pressure, amount, or temperature.

We may summarize the kinetic theory by pointing out that according to it temperature completely determines the average translational kinetic energy ($\frac{1}{2} mu^2$) of gaseous particles and thus the average velocity with which the molecules of a given mass move. Pressure on the walls of the vessel is caused by molecular collisions and increases if more collisions occur per second (more molecules per unit volume or higher molecular velocities), and also increases if more force ($m \times u$) is exerted per collision (greater molecular velocity due to a rise in temperature). We have thus interpreted gaseous behavior in terms of three molecular properties: molecular mass, molecular velocity, and number of molecules per unit volume. Thus the atomic theory and the kinetic theory are consistent.

DISTRIBUTION OF MOLECULAR VELOCITIES

Throughout the above discussions we have used only the concept of an average molecular velocity. For most chemical discussions average velocities are adequate, but the kinetic theory is much more elegant in its entirety. On a purely theoretical basis Maxwell calculated that molecular velocities would actually be distributed over a very long range. In any gas some molecules would be stationary, more would be moving slowly, many would be moving with the average velocity, some would have still higher velocities, and a very few molecules would have velocities ten times the average or even greater. His predictions have been checked by many experiments. Any particular molecule has a definite velocity between collisions but in its billions of collisions per second it exchanges energy with other molecules. As a result of such exchanges it sometimes has smaller velocities and sometimes greater velocities than the average. Thus, the distribution of molecular velocities about the average represents that of any molecule over a period of time as well as that of all the molecules at any single instant.

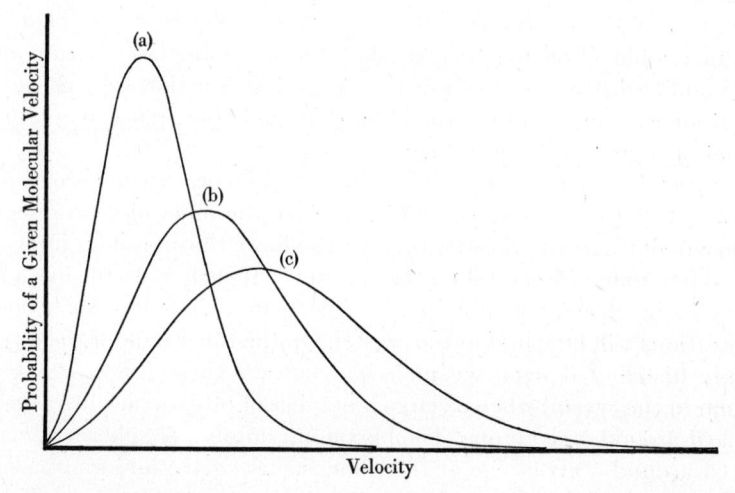

Figure 10.2.
Distribution of molecular velocities of oxygen at different temperatures, (a) 100°K = −173°C, (b) 273°K = 0°C, (c) 500°K = 227°C.

Figure 10.2 shows the distribution of molecular velocities of oxygen at several temperatures. Other gases behave similarly. At low temperatures the molecular velocities tend to bunch up close to the average. As the temperature rises a smaller fraction of the molecules approximate the average in velocity, and many of them attain velocities much higher than the average. Thus the number of molecules with high velocities, and, hence, high kinetic energies rises very rapidly with rise in temperature. Since it is these molecules with high kinetic energies of translation that possess the activation energy necessary to initiate chemical reactions, it is easy to see why raising the temperature only slightly can often greatly accelerate the rate of a chemical reaction.

CONDENSATION OF GASES

We have often referred in the preceding material to the fact that actual gases do not follow the simple gas laws exactly, for molecules do have volume of their own and do exert forces on one another. An ideal gas, on the other hand, would consist of infinitely small particles exerting no attractive forces whatever on one another under any conditions. An ideal gas could never be converted to a liquid or a solid since there would be no forces to hold the liquid or solid together. Real gases all condense to liquids or solids if cooled sufficiently.

The condensation of gases to liquids and solids may be interpreted in terms of the kinetic theory through the relationship between kinetic energy and temperature. As the temperature falls the kinetic energy of the gas molecules decreases. Collisions become less forceful and rebounds less vigorous. Eventually a state is reached in which the attractive forces between the molecules are able to prolong the collision to give a cluster of molecules. That is, the molecules remain close together so that the attractive forces can interact strongly and their translational kinetic energy is so low that they do not often escape from the cluster but rather bump around from place to place in it. A droplet of liquid has been formed.

Further cooling decreases the kinetic energy still more, the molecular motion becomes less and less vigorous, and eventually the molecules arrange themselves in a definite geometric structure which allows the molecular interactions to be at a maximum. A crystal has been formed. If each molecule has a strong tendency to bond another molecule in a particular direction, such bonds at fixed directions will be found in the crystal. On the other hand if the forces are uniformly distributed over the molecular surface these forces can be at a maximum in the crystal when as large a number of other molecules as possible are packed around a given one. The maximum number of spheres which may be placed around a given one of the same size is twelve and many elements crystallize in such a structure. Neon, argon, krypton, and xenon are known to crystallize in this way, consistent with the very small interatomic forces known in these substances.

THE CRITICAL STATE

Gases may often be liquefied when the pressure is increased (without change in temperature) for the higher pressure forces the molecules closer together. At these smaller distances the intermolecular forces are stronger and liquid formation is encouraged. For every gas there is, however, a temperature above which even the highest pressure is insufficient to lead to liquid formation. Above this temperature the kinetic energy of the molecules is so great that it can overcome the tendency of the intermolecular attractions to give droplet formation even at the closest distances of approach. This temperature is called the *critical temperature*. The pressure which will just give liquid formation at the *critical temperature* is called the *critical pressure*, and the molar volume at these conditions is the *critical volume*. High pressures at temperatures greater than the critical temperature may give a fluid more dense than the liquid substance, yet this fluid will not have the properties of a typical liquid because of the high kinetic energy.

There is considerable discussion in the literature these days as to the changes which occur near the critical temperature. No adequate theoretical interpretation of the phenomenon of condensation is known partly because the theory of liquids is not as well developed as the theory of gases.

Problem 10.5. (a) A liter of oxygen at 1 atmosphere pressure is forced into a liter vessel containing hydrogen at two atmospheres pressure. If the temperature remains unchanged at 20°C. and no reaction occurs what will be the pressure in the liter of mixed gas?

(b) The mixed gas in (a) is ignited in a strong liter vessel. After the vessel has cooled to 20°C. what will be the pressure of gas in the vessel?

Problem 10.6. When a mixture of hydrogen and oxygen gases is ignited as in Problem 10.5 an explosion occurs. After the reaction fewer molecules of gas exist than before and yet the sudden high pressure developed may break the vessel. Account for this sudden high pressure.

Problem 10.7. State the quantitative effect (a) on the number of molecular impacts per square centimeter per second, and (b) on the force of each impact when the air pressure in an automobile tire is slowly increased from 15 to 30 pounds per square inch gage pressure.

Problem 10.8. Two volumes of a certain gas react with one volume of oxygen at constant temperature and pressure to form two volumes of another gas. Give the reasoning and assumptions by which, from this result, you can conclude that the molecule of oxygen contains an even number of atoms.

Problem 10.9. If the gas phase reactions represented by the following equations are carried out in a closed vessel at constant temperature, what will be the quantitative effect on the pressure in each case?

a. $2NO = N_2 + O_2$
b. $2SO_2 + O_2 = 2SO_3$
c. $2NH_3 = N_2 + 3H_2$
d. $2O_3 = 3O_2$
e. $CO_2 + C_{(s)} = 2CO$

Problem 10.10. Some air was passed through an ozonizer in which an electric discharge changed part of its oxygen into ozone with the formula O_3. If the air diminished in volume by 2 per cent, what fraction of the oxygen was changed to ozone?

Problem 10.11. What is meant when one says that the atomic weight of nitrogen is 14.00?

Problem 10.12. A gaseous solution of two moles of hydrogen and one mole of oxygen at 400°C. is sparked until complete reaction has occurred, then allowed to return to 400°C., all in a constant volume. Compare quantitatively (a) the pressure, (b) the number of collisions per second with the walls, and (c) the force per collision before and after reaction.

Problem 10:13. Sound is energy transmitted through the atmosphere by molecular collisions. What factors will determine the velocity of sound in a gas? Is your theory consistent with the velocity of sound at the earth's surface: about 1100 ft-sec.? How do you account for the fact that the velocity of sound in the earth's atmosphere decreases with altitude?

Problem 10.14. Given initial and final conditions. Indicate relationship by $=$, $<$, $>$, or ?:

a. $m_1 = m_2$, $T_1 = T_2$, $n_1 > n_2$	P_1	P_2
b. $n_1 = n_2$, $P_1 = P_2$	s_1	s_2
c. $s_1 = s_2$, $u_1 = u_2$	m_1	m_2
d. $P_1 = P_2$, $m_1 = m_2$, $s_1 = s_2$	T_1	T_2
e. $u_1 < u_2$, $T_1 = T_2$	m_1	m_2

m = molecular wt.
T = temperature
n = no. of molecules/cc
s = no. of collisions/sec
u = velocity of molecules
P = pressure

Problem 10.15. Can you suggest a kinetic theory interpretation of the common adage that "wet cold weather is much more penetrating than dry cold"?

11 LIQUIDS AND SOLIDS

LIQUIDS AND solids differ strikingly from gases in the distances between molecules (or atoms). The molar volumes of liquids and solids are of the order of 100 milliliters, whereas those of gases are about one thousand times as great, being about 24,000 milliliters at the usual temperature and pressure. The widely spaced gas molecules are relatively independent of one another so that gases are able to expand indefinitely, and to "fill" all the space available to them. On the other hand, molecules of liquids and solids are close together, they cohere, and they form "surfaces" at the limits of the liquid and solid phases. The surfaces of liquids and solids, and the greater density, distinguish them from gases.

Rigidity is a property commonly used to distinguish between liquids and solids. Liquids can flow whereas solids retain definite shapes and are elastic when deformed under pressure unless excessive pressures are imposed. However, the test of rigidity is not always easy to apply. We have already found that most solids are crystalline, having the particles arranged in characteristic patterns. But some are noncrystalline, glasses being common examples. In noncrystalline solids the more random particle arrangement characteristic of most liquids is coupled with the rigidity of crystalline solids but the rigidity disappears as the temperature is raised. In this chapter we shall neglect noncrystalline solids and concern ourselves only with solids which are crystalline. Thus, solid will refer to a crystalline substance, liquid to an amorphous substance having a "surface," and gas to an amorphous substance having no "surface."

We have seen how the properties of gases may be interpreted in terms of a kinetic theory of rapid, random motion of individual molecules whose average kinetic energy is proportional only to the absolute temperature. But gases when cooled condense to liquids, which on further cooling freeze to solids. And many solids when heated melt to liquids and evaporate to form gases. We shall now see whether the idea of motion of atoms and molecules enables us to interpret such properties of liquids and solids as diffusion, thermal expansion, viscosity, surface tension, evaporation and vapor pressure, freezing, and heat capacity.

MOTION IN LIQUIDS AND SOLIDS

As long ago as 1817 an English botanist, Robert Brown, observed the violent random motion of tiny particles suspended in liquids. The motion of these particles, visible under a microscope, was as helter-skelter as that of the dust particles in air made visible by a sunbeam. Study of the "Brownian" motion showed that the extent of the motion and its variation with temperature was consistent quantitatively with the kinetic theory. Lighter particles move more rapidly than heavier ones and the velocities of both increase with rise in temperature. The simplest explanation of the Brownian movement is that the illuminated particles are being bombarded by the invisible molecules of the surrounding liquid (or gas) and acquire kinetic energy as a result of the bombardment.

In crystals the motions of atoms and molecules must be highly restricted because these particles occupy "fixed" positions in the crystal lattice. See, for instance, Figures 7.1, 7.2, and 7.3. However, there is good evidence that the atoms have some random motion about their "fixed" lattice positions. X-ray photographs, showing patterns dependent on the regular spacing of the diffraction centers (the atoms) in the crystal, become more and more "fuzzy" as the temperature of the crystal rises. Apparently the exact positions of the atoms become less and less certain. Furthermore, when a vibrating crystal is used as a standard of frequency, as in radio broadcasting, the accuracy of the desired frequency is limited by the random "thermal" motion of the atoms. This "thermal noise" is the limiting factor in the design of much electronic equipment, for the signal to be transmitted must, of course, be more energetic than the thermal motions themselves.

THERMAL EXPANSION

Most solids and liquids, like gases, expand when heated, a fact readily explained in terms of the kinetic theory. In all crystals, even at absolute zero, the atoms are in motion but the orderly structure of the crystal restricts the motions to vibrations about mean positions. Since the atoms in the crystal are moving (vibrating) at all temperatures, one cannot strictly speak of absolute distances between their centers, but only of a mean distance. These mean distances, however, are characteristic of each crystalline substance at each temperature. A higher temperature means more kinetic energy for the atoms, more energy of vibration, and, therefore, a greater amplitude in the vibration. Hence, the distance between atom centers becomes greater with rising temperature, the atoms become less closely packed, the volume increases, and the density falls. Thermal expansion has occurred. Direct evidence for this theory of increasing amplitude of vibration with rising temperature rather than merely of greater separation of the atoms comes from the x-ray photographs cited above.

The only liquids and solids that do not undergo thermal expansion are those of substances in which heating results in a radical change in structure. Water is such a substance in the neighborhood of 0°C. The liquid is more dense than the solid, and the liquid contracts still further when heated from 0°C. to 4°C., although from 4°C. upward it expands as do most substances. At 8°C. liquid water is as dense as it was at 0°C. There is evidence that, just above the melting point, liquid water retains some of the structure of ice, a structure in which the water molecules are oriented by fairly strong intermolecular bonds into a rather open framework. Increasing the temperature increases the kinetic energy of the molecules. Then directive bonds holding the molecules far apart in the solid (and in water at low temperatures) are broken, the molecules pack more closely, the volume decreases as in the range 0 to 4°C. Thereafter the closely packed liquid expands with rising temperature but the liquid water does not become as voluminous as ice is at 0°C. until the water temperature reaches 150°C. (under high pressure).

Problem 11.1. You will remember that some of the earliest thermometers were filled with water. Would such thermometers be useful in the range below 8°C.?

DIFFUSION

The rapid distribution of a gas uniformly throughout a container and the speed of intermixing, or diffusion, of different gases placed in a single container is readily interpreted in terms of the very high velocities of the gaseous molecules, and the relatively large distances separating the molecules (see page 125). Diffusion in liquids is much slower than that in gases and diffusion in solids is much slower still but each is appreciable. Alcohol and water layered into the same container become uniformly mixed even if no bulk currents, as by stirring, occur. The diffusion of a colored liquid into a colorless one may be readily observed though it may take months for any appreciable quantities to become uniform.

The much slower diffusion in solids is more difficult to measure. Perhaps the simplest method is to place a radioactive material in contact with a non-radioactive one and measure the rate at which the radioactive substance penetrates the other. Such experiments may be carried out in a reasonable length of time (of the order of months) because of the ease of detecting very small numbers of radioactive atoms, whereas all geological time (several billion years) has not sufficed for the interdiffusion of even very narrow mineral veins, say 1 mm. thick, with the surrounding rock. The presence of any diffusion at all indicates that atomic motion is definitely present. The slowness of the diffusion is due to the randomness of the motion, but even more importantly to the close packing of molecules in liquids and solids, plus the high degree of structural order to be overcome in solids. A man who can walk rapidly from one place to another in an open area is considerably slowed down by a crowd, particularly if it is arranged in a closely packed regular array with few open spaces.

Problem 11.2. Discuss the effects which an increase in temperature would have on diffusion rates in solids.

VISCOSITY

Not only does molecular flow, or diffusion, take place; bulk flow also occurs in which large clusters of molecules move. The *viscosity* of a substance is a measure of its resistance to such bulk flow. Crystals are usually very viscous, whereas gases have a very low viscosity. Liquids ordinarily have viscosities intermediate between those of gases and solids.

The principal effect contributing to high viscosities in liquids and solids is intermolecular bonding, the stronger the bonding the higher the viscosity. Crystals of a given substance exist at a lower temperature than the liquid and have less kinetic energy with which to break the intermolecular bonds. Hence the high viscosity of the crystalline state. When heated, the crystal eventually reaches a temperature at which the kinetic energy is great enough to overcome the strong directional bonding and the crystal melts. The liquid molecules are only slightly farther apart than those in the solid so that many intermolecular bonds still exist. They are not at maximum strength, however, for most are no longer oriented in the directions giving greatest attraction. Continued heating increases the kinetic energy of the liquid, the effectiveness of the intermolecular bonding diminishes still more, and the viscosity continues to decrease.

A few substances are known in which the viscosity remains practically constant over a considerable range of temperatures (certain silicone oils for instance), and there are a few (e.g., liquid sulfur) which actually increase in viscosity as the temperature increases through certain ranges. As in the case of thermal expansion, so here, these exceptions arise because of gross structural changes which occur as the liquid is heated. The silicone oils contain long-chain molecules which at low temperatures are coiled into roughly spherical shapes. Heating tends to uncoil the molecules and the resulting long chains intertangle, thus increasing the resistance to flow, the viscosity. This effect almost exactly counterbalances the kinetic energy effect on the intermolecular bonding and the viscosity remains approximately constant. Sulfur, at low temperatures is in the form of ring molecules, S_8. At higher temperatures the rings open up into chains which intertangle. In this instance the change occurs over a narrow range of temperature and the viscosity undergoes a very sharp increase in this range.

Viscosity may be simply estimated by stirring (for a liquid) or bending (for a solid). It gives a ready and simple estimate of the strength of the intermolecular bonds in the substances. One must of course, always allow for the possibility of other structural factors such as the presence of chain molecules, planar molecules, etc., which also affect the viscosity.

SURFACE TENSION

The existence of "self-imposed" boundary surfaces in liquids and solids indicates the presence in such substances of intermolecular bonding strong enough to hold the molecules together in a cluster. A molecule within the bulk material will form these intermolecular bonds in all directions, but a molecule in the surface will be unable to form bonds above the surface. Surface molecules thus form fewer bonds than bulk molecules. The most stable system, however, is the one with the most strong bonds so that as few molecules as possible will be present in the surface. It is for this reason that liquids assume spherical shapes when suspended freely in space. The sphere, of all shapes, has the least area for a given volume. Work must be done against the intermolecular forces if the surface area is to be increased. The force against which this work is done is called the *surface tension*.

Surface tensions can be quite large, particularly in liquids with strong intermolecular bonds. Water is such a liquid. Metal gauzes, needles, and water fowl, for instance, may be "floated" on water because of its high surface tension. The surface is resistant to stretching and breaking and thus buoys up the overlying material.

There are many substances known which show a marked ability to diminish surface tension, particularly of liquids. Soaps and detergents are such substances when dissolved in water. These materials tend to concentrate in the surface where they form weaker bonds than does water. Less work is, therefore, required to form new surfaces, the surface tension is lower, and the solution now "wets" other substances much more readily, that is, they penetrate its surface with less work. Water fowl will sink somewhat in such solutions for they now break through the surface which formerly supported them.

Surface tension decreases with rising temperature because the higher energies associated with the higher temperatures make it more probable that a molecule will have enough energy to break its intermolecular bonds with surrounding molecules. There is less and less difference between the bonding of a molecule in the surface and one in the bulk liquid. Continued heating of liquids eventually leads to a temperature at which the surface tension becomes zero. All the molecules are then alike in bonding and there no longer is any surface—the substance has become a gas. This temperature is the critical temperature of the substance (see also page 128).

ENERGIES OF DIFFERENT PHASES AT EQUILIBRIUM

If we place a mixture of ice and liquid water at 0°C. in an insulated container with space for water vapor we know that the three phases, gas, liquid, and solid, will all be present. According to the kinetic theory the water molecules, whether they be in the ice, in the liquid, or in the gas, have kinetic energies characteristic of the temperature. Since the temperature does not change, the kinetic energies of the water molecules in the three different phases do not change with the passage of time—they are equilibrium kinetic energies. The

136 GENERAL CHEMISTRY

temperature of each phase remains at 0° and no phase gains energy at the expense of the others. Yet we know that if we melt ice to form liquid water we must supply heat even though the liquid water is at the same final temperature as the ice from which it came. Similarly, if we evaporate liquid water to gaseous water at the same temperature we must supply heat. It is evident that there are energy differences between the three phases. If the water molecules in the three phases at equilibrium have equilibrium kinetic energies how can one explain the increase in energy required to go from solid to liquid and from liquid to gas phase?

POTENTIAL ENERGY

Energies of motion, called kinetic energies, are relatively easy to visualize, but every-day experience tells us that other kinds of energy are also important. Whenever we lift a weight from the ground we are aware that we must expend energy to lift it. A pound-weight three feet above the ground has more energy, even though not moving, than it has resting on the ground. If released, it falls back to the ground. Indeed, it can be made to do work for us in falling in the earth's gravitational field to its former position. The extra energy of the weight when raised is an example of *potential energy*. Another example of potential energy is a stretched rubber band, which may do work, as in driving a mechanical toy, in returning to its relaxed position. Potential energies appear whenever we move objects between which some force is acting—if we must do work in separating them, they in turn can do work for us when they return to their former position.

We currently talk of several types of fields of force—gravitational, electrical, magnetic, molecular, nuclear—and potential energy may be associated with any of them. One of the most challenging unsolved problems in theoretical science at present is that of treating all these apparently unrelated force fields in a single mathematical formulation. This is called the problem of the unified field theory and appears most complicated. Fortunately the simple methods available at present are quite adequate for our purposes in chemistry and we shall deal with these forces as though they were unrelated.

POTENTIAL ENERGY AND CHEMISTRY

In gases we were able, for the most part, to ignore the forces between molecules. They may annoy us by causing real gases to deviate somewhat from the ideal gas laws but they do not affect behavior greatly in gases not too near their liquefaction temperatures and not too highly compressed. The situation is different in liquids and solids where the attractive and repulsive forces play important roles.

Attractive and counterbalancing repulsive forces between atoms are necessary to explain the continued existence of any form of matter consisting of more than one atom. The two atoms of oxygen in a molecule are held together by strong attractive forces and must be held apart by forces just as strong since it is clear that they do not coalesce. Yet the resulting molecules formed from the two paired atoms do not attract or repel each other very much. The energies associated with the formation of molecules are sometimes called chemical energies, but they are an example of potential energies which result from the position of the atoms in one another's fields of force. Since some bonds are stronger than others it must be possible for the forces to concentrate in certain directions.

In liquids or solids consisting of molecules we may for convenience consider separately the potential energies associated with the forces between molecules and those associated with the forces between the atoms within the molecules. The latter forces are usually much stronger than the former. In many solids, however, the unit is not the molecule but individual atoms, as in graphite or diamond. The attractive forces here may be very great, corresponding to those which hold the pairs of oxygen atoms together in oxygen molecules. We have already indicated that one type of the relatively weak forces attracting molecules together is called van der Waals forces. The relatively strong forces holding atoms together will be discussed after we have considered the structure of atoms.

CHANGE FROM LIQUID TO GAS PHASE

One of the effects observed when a liquid evaporates to a gas is that heat is absorbed, the amount depending on the amount of liquid evaporating. If less than the necessary energy is supplied from other sources, the liquid cools as it evaporates. About 10,000 calories must be supplied when one mole of liquid water is evaporated to water vapor if the temperature of liquid and gas are to remain the same. Conversely, the same amount of heat is released when one mole of gaseous water is condensed to liquid water at the same temperature. The heat is called *heat of evaporation* or *heat of condensation* depending on which process occurs. Heat of evaporation is often called heat of vaporization.

The heat of evaporation is an example of the effects of potential (or latent) energy in a chemical system. Although molecules in the gas phase and those in the liquid phase have the same average kinetic energies, (fixed by the temperature) they differ in potential energy. A molecule in a liquid is held to neighboring molecules by the intermolecular forces. In the gas it is not. The molecules in the gas have been separated from one another against the attractive forces acting in the liquid. Energy is required for the separation just as energy is required to separate two objects tied together by a rubber band. For the evaporation of water we may write the thermochemical equation

$$10{,}000 \text{ cal.} + H_2O_{(liq)} = H_2O_{(g)} \qquad (11.1)$$

identical in form with the thermochemical equations written in previous chapters. The energy term represents the change in the potential energies of the substances as a result of their change of phase. However, the energy of separation of the liquid molecules, the energy of evaporation, is not quite identical with the heat of evaporation. The gas occupies more volume than the liquid from which it came so that some work must be expended to push back the atmosphere to make room for the gas. The heat of evaporation includes both the energy of evaporation and the energy of expansion.

A slightly different kinetic picture of the evaporation process may be represented as follows: A molecule of liquid is held to neighboring molecules by attractive forces. The average kinetic energy of the molecules in the liquid is fixed by the temperature but some molecules have more kinetic energy and some less than the average. Some molecules on the surface may momentarily have enough kinetic energy to enable them to break away from the attractive forces. They lose some of their kinetic energy as they pull away but they still have more than enough energy to escape. But, if kinetic energy is lost the average energy of the system is less and the temperature is less. Enough energy must be added from outside sources to provide the breaking-away energy if the temperature is to remain constant. The large cooling effect of ether or alcohol placed on the skin demonstrates this. The opposite effect takes place on condensation. Molecules of vapor on colliding with the surface of the liquid are attracted by the liquid molecules and move faster. Then the temperature of the system rises until the extra kinetic energy resulting from the potential energy is removed.

The molar heat of evaporation of water has a value characteristic of the class of liquids called polar liquids. Methyl alcohol and ethyl alcohol, other polar liquids, have molar heats of evaporation of 9,000 and 10,000 calories, respectively. So-called normal liquids in which van der Waals forces predominate have heats of evaporation in the neighborhood of 5,000 or 6,000 calories per mole. The differences between the values for polar liquids and normal liquids represents the differences in attractive forces between molecules in the two classes of liquids. It should be clear that the intermolecular forces are greater in the polar liquids.

Chemists usually compare heats of evaporation per mole of substance because they represent energies for equal numbers of molecules. The value of the molar heat of evaporation of water is like that of other polar liquids but its heat of evaporation per gram, 555 calories at room temperature, is high. The reason is simple. Water has a lower molar weight than almost any other substance and consequently more molecules in a gram. When the intermolecular forces do not differ greatly, the heat of evaporation accompanying the separation of liquid molecules to form gas is primarily a function of the number of molecules separated.

LIQUID-GAS EQUILIBRIUM AND VAPOR PRESSURE

The kinetic description of evaporation and condensation in the preceding section enables us to explain the fact that at any temperature each liquid has a definite concentration of vapor which may be in equilibrium with it. At any temperature a definite number of molecules pass through unit surface of the

LIQUIDS AND SOLIDS 139

liquid per unit time from the liquid to the gas phase. Consequently, more vapor is formed and its concentration tends to increase. At the same time the rate of condensation of the vapor depends on the number of molecules entering the liquid from the gas per unit time, and this number depends on the concentration of the vapor. When the two rates—that of evaporation and that of condensation—are equal, no further change is apparent and the system is at

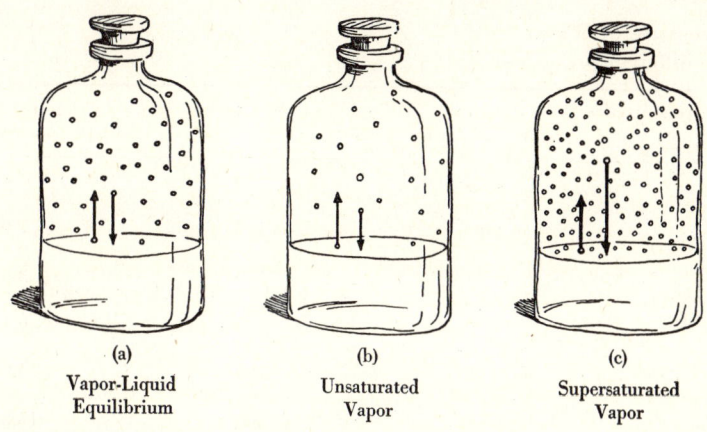

(a) Vapor-Liquid Equilibrium   (b) Unsaturated Vapor   (c) Supersaturated Vapor

Figure 11.1.
Migration of molecules between liquid and gas. (a) at equilibrium, (b) vapor unsaturated, (c) vapor supersaturated.

equilibrium (see Figure 11.1a). However, individual molecules are still evaporating and condensing. All chemical equilibria are of this dynamic type—a balancing of opposing and continuing processes.

The partial pressure of the vapor in equilibrium with a liquid is called the *vapor pressure* (or the saturated vapor pressure) of the liquid. It is a convenient measure of the concentration of vapor at equilibrium. If the vapor is "unsaturated" its concentration is less and more molecules pass from the liquid to the gas than return (see Figure 11.1b). In this way the concentration of the vapor builds up to the equilibrium value. If the vapor is "supersaturated" its concentration is greater than at equilibrium and more molecules pass from the gas to the liquid than return (see Figure 11.1c). Then the concentration of the vapor is reduced to the equilibrium value.

The number of molecules of the liquid having kinetic energies great enough to enable them to evaporate increases very rapidly as the temperature (and average kinetic energy) increases. Consequently, the rate of evaporation increases rapidly as the temperature rises. Then the partial pressure of the vapor necessary for equilibrium must also increase. Table 11.1 and Figure 11.2 show how the vapor pressure of water increases with temperature. The general trend of rapidly increasing vapor pressure with increase in temperature is characteristic of the vapor pressures of all liquids.

The change of liquid-vapor equilibrium with temperature is only one example covered by a very general *equilibrium principle* enunciated by *Le Chatelier*, a French chemist. According to the principle, any system at equilibrium and subjected to a change will adjust in such a way as to counteract the change. Thus, if a liquid-vapor system at equilibrium is heated, that is, if energy is added so that its temperature tends to rise, that process will occur

Table 11.1
Vapor Pressure of Water
(Note the different pressure units)

TEMPERATURE °C.	PRESSURE MM. OF MERCURY	TEMPERATURE °C.	PRESSURE IN ATMOSPHERES
0	4.59	100	1.00
10	9.20	120	1.96
20	17.51	140	3.57
21	18.63		
22	19.80	160	6.10
23	21.04		
24	22.35	180	9.90
25	23.73		
26	25.18	200	15.35
27	26.71		
28	28.32	220	22.90
29	30.01		
30	31.79	240	33.04
40	55.29	260	46.33
50	92.49	280	63.35
60	149.39	300	84.79
70	233.72	320	111.4
80	355.86	340	144.2
90	525.86	360	184.3
100	760.	374	218.0

which absorbs the added energy and minimizes the temperature rise. In this case, since evaporation of the liquid is endothermic, the liquid evaporates, absorbing energy, until a new equilibrium is reached. If the final temperature is higher, more of the substance will be in the gas phase and the vapor pressure will be higher. But the temperature will not have risen as much as if no net evaporation had occurred.

CRITICAL TEMPERATURE AND PRESSURE

Since the vapor pressures of liquids rise rapidly with temperature (see Table 11.1 or Figure 11.2) we may ask whether there is an upper limit to the

LIQUIDS AND SOLIDS 141

vapor pressure of a liquid. Experience shows that liquids do have maximum temperatures for their existence, the critical temperature, and a maximum vapor pressure, the critical pressure. A discussion of the critical temperature and critical pressure in terms of the kinetic theory is given on pages 128 and 135.

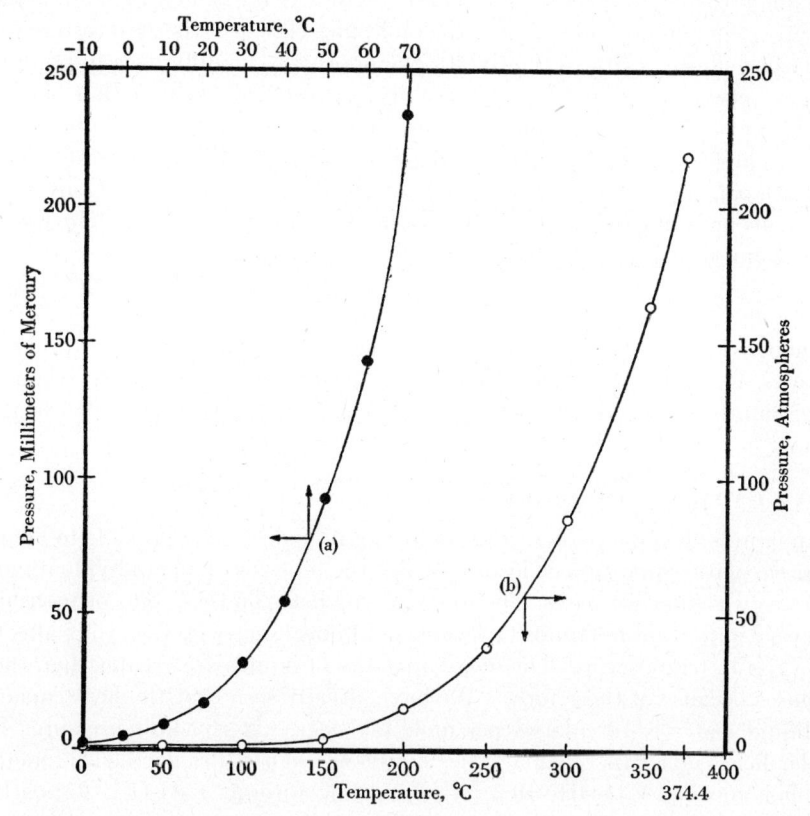

Figure 11.2.
Change of vapor pressure of water with temperature—vapor pressure curves. (a) Pressure in millimeters of mercury, (b) pressure in atmospheres.

Critical pressures are generally of the order of fifty atmospheres, but critical temperatures vary considerably depending on the strength of the intermolecular forces. The critical temperature of water is slightly above 374°C. and the critical pressure is slightly above 218 atmospheres. The common substances in air—oxygen, nitrogen, and argon—have molecules with little attraction for one another so that their critical temperatures lie far below room temperature, at −119°C., −147°C., and −122°C., respectively. Their critical pressures are 49, 33, and 48 atmospheres, respectively. Therefore, at room temperature no pressure, however great, will change these gases to liquids.

142 GENERAL CHEMISTRY

They must be cooled below their critical temperatures before applied pressure will cause liquefaction.

TRANSITION OF LIQUID TO SOLID PHASE

The arguments applied earlier to the evaporation of a liquid may be used to explain the crystallization of a liquid. Attractive forces in a crystalline solid are great enough not only to hold the molecules close together but also to hold them in definite positions relative to one another. The difference in potential energy between solid and liquid is usually not nearly as great as that between liquid and gas, since the difference in separation of molecules is much less. When a mole of liquid water freezes the heat released, called the *heat of freezing*, is 1,436 cal. per mole (compare with the heat of evaporation). Conversely, when one mole of ice melts the heat absorbed, called the *heat of melting*, has the same numerical value. Thus,

$$1{,}436 \text{ cal.} + H_2O_{(ice)} = H_2O_{(liq)} \qquad (11.2)$$

Although ice has a normal heat of melting per mole, its value per gram, 80 calories, is much higher than that of most solids, the reason again being the large number of molecules per gram. Heat of melting is often called heat of fusion.

HEAT CAPACITY OF LIQUIDS

In liquids the kinetic picture is complicated, making it impossible to predict heat capacities quantitatively in terms of the motions of the individual molecules as was done for gases. The forces acting between the atoms or molecules are very important in liquids but we do not know exactly how they are affected by a rise in temperature. The heat capacities of liquids are greater than those of gases because of these forces. We have already seen that the heat capacity of liquid water is 18 calories per mole per degree at constant pressure. The molar heat capacities of some other liquids in calories per degree are: methyl alcohol, formula CH_3OH, 19.5; ethyl alcohol, formula C_2H_5OH, 27; carbon tetrachloride, 20; carbon disulfide, 18. These values are much higher than those for the same substances as gases. (Compare with typical values for gases in Table 10.1.)

HEAT CAPACITY OF SOLIDS

There is considerably less freedom of movement in solids than there is in liquids. Fewer bonds can be stretched or broken without destroying the phase and leading to melting. Hence the heat capacity of a solid is normally lower than that of the corresponding liquid. And, as the temperature is lowered, the heat capacities of solids decrease more or less continuously, becoming zero at the absolute zero. Fairly comprehensive theories to account for this behavior have been developed but they are beyond the scope of beginning chemistry.

HEAT CAPACITY OF SOLID ELEMENTS

In the early nineteenth century two French physicists, Dulong and Petit, became interested in the atomic theory and its relation to bulk properties such as heat capacity. Using much of their own heat capacity data and Berzelius' values for atomic weights they reached the conclusion, in 1819, that the heat capacities of the amounts of elements represented by the then current "atomic weights" had very nearly the same value or were some multiple of this value. Feeling that it was more likely that all would have the same heat capacity rather than merely multiples of the same value they argued that some of the atomic weights were wrong, being based on incorrect multiples of the accurately known equivalent weights. Using simple fractions of the wrong atomic weights they found a constant "atomic" heat capacity for the great majority of their samples.

The statement—the heat capacity per gram-atomic weight (or per atom) is the same for all solid elements near room temperature—is known as the *Law of Dulong and Petit*. The principle holds for the metallic elements and for heavier nonmetallic elements such as sulfur, but fails for the lighter nonmetallic elements such as carbon. Because it failed for the lighter elements the principle was not accepted by many of their contemporary chemists, though it did give a simple method for determining the atomic weight of most of the elements. The only question was, which ones? For the great majority of solid elements the gram-atomic heat capacity is 6 calories per degree, within about fifteen per cent.

We now interpret the principle of Dulong and Petit, using our knowledge that the metals crystallize as atoms. In the crystal lattice the atoms vibrate individually. It can be shown from the kinetic theory that one mole of such atoms when vibrating fully should have a heat capacity of 6 calories per degree at ordinary temperatures, and that the heat capacity should decrease at low temperatures and become zero at the absolute zero. The observed behaviors follow these predictions very closely. The lighter elements do not conform because their atoms, being more tightly bonded together (remember the hardness of diamond) are not vibrating fully at room temperatures. At higher temperatures they too approach a heat capacity of 6 calories per mole per degree. Note that this value for solid elements is just twice the value of C_v for monatomic gases (on page 124). In monatomic gases the heat capacity represents a change in kinetic energy only. In monatomic solids there is the same change in kinetic energy plus an equal change in potential energy.

HEAT CAPACITIES AND ATOMIC WEIGHTS

We have shown on page 124 how the constant heat capacity of monatomic gases allows the calculation of their atomic weight. In the same way the approximately constant heat capacity of the solid elements, 6 calories per mole per degree, allows an estimation of their atomic weights.

The specific heat capacity of the elements is readily determined since it is

144 GENERAL CHEMISTRY

merely the amount of heat in calories required to change the temperature of one gram of the element by one degree Centigrade. These specific heat capacities vary widely from element to element since the number of atoms per gram varies greatly. Thus, the specific heat capacity of tin is 0.054 while that of magnesium is 0.25. There must be fewer atoms per gram of tin than per gram of magnesium since less heat is required for the tin. The atomic weight of tin

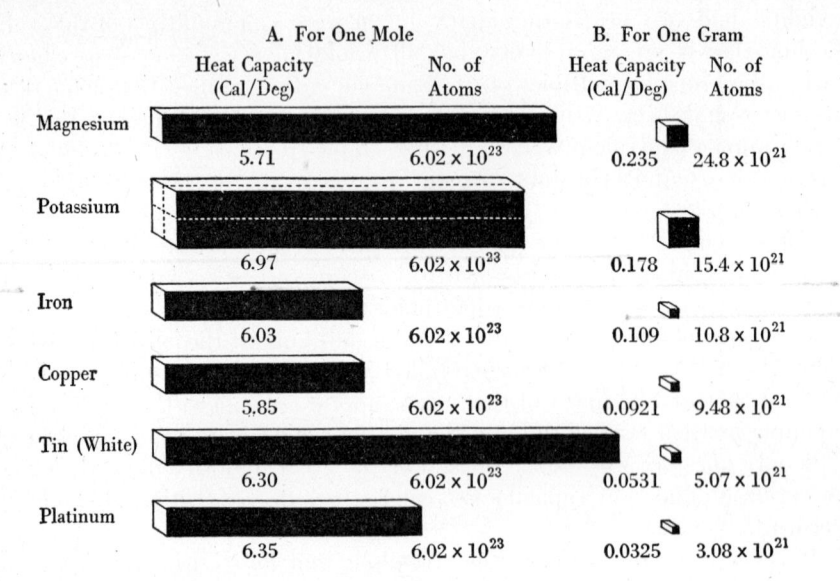

	A. For One Mole		B. For One Gram	
	Heat Capacity (Cal/Deg)	No. of Atoms	Heat Capacity (Cal/Deg)	No. of Atoms
Magnesium	5.71	6.02×10^{23}	0.235	24.8×10^{21}
Potassium	6.97	6.02×10^{23}	0.178	15.4×10^{21}
Iron	6.03	6.02×10^{23}	0.109	10.8×10^{21}
Copper	5.85	6.02×10^{23}	0.0921	9.48×10^{21}
Tin (White)	6.30	6.02×10^{23}	0.0531	5.07×10^{21}
Platinum	6.35	6.02×10^{23}	0.0325	3.08×10^{21}

Figure 11.3.
Dulong and Petit's Law. Gram-atomic volumes and the volumes occupied by one gram of various elements, with the heat capacities and numbers of atoms corresponding to each. Note the degree of validity of the law of Dulong and Petit.

must be greater than that of magnesium. The molar heat capacity of each element, however, is about 6 calories per degree. The atomic weight in grams is thus readily calculated by dividing the molar heat capacity, 6, by the heat required for a single gram, the specific heat capacity. Thus, the approximate atomic weight of tin is $\frac{6}{0.054} = 111$ and that of magnesium is $\frac{6}{0.25} = 24$. Analytical data give 59.35 and 29.68 as the equivalent weights of tin, and 12.16 as the equivalent weight of magnesium. The accurate atomic weights are therefore chosen as 118.70 for tin and 24.32 for magnesium in order to be consistent both with the equivalent weight data ($2 \times 59.35 = 4 \times 29.68 = 118.70$ and $2 \times 12.16 = 24.32$) and the heat capacity data (111 and 24) respectively.

The gram-atomic volumes and the volumes of one gram of several elements are indicated in Fig. 11.3, and the heat capacities per gram-atomic weight and per gram are listed. Note the relative constancy of the heat capacity per gram-atomic weight and the regular decrease in heat capacity per gram as the atomic weight increases as pointed out by Dulong and Petit.

PHASE DIAGRAMS

The particular phase—solid, liquid, or gas—in which a substance is found depends on its temperature and pressure. The temperature determines the kinetic energy and hence the tendency to overcome the intermolecular bonds.

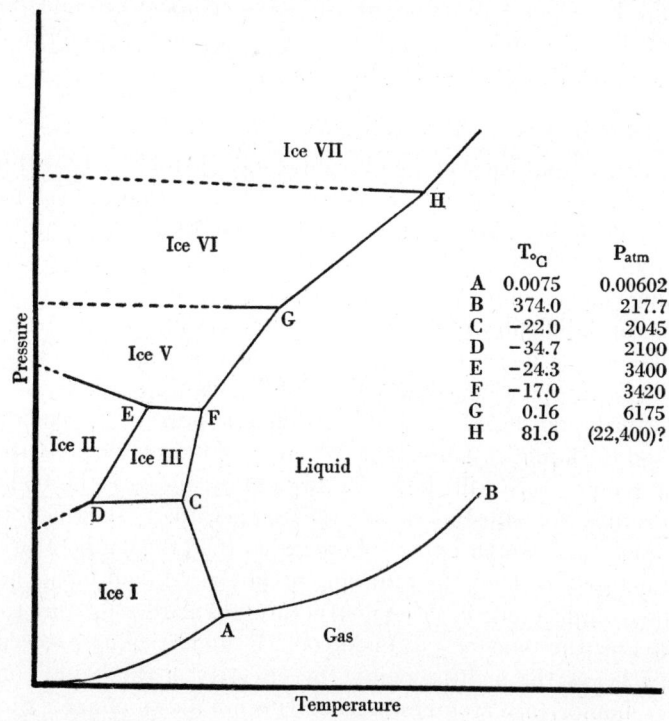

	$T_{°C}$	P_{atm}
A	0.0075	0.00602
B	374.0	217.7
C	−22.0	2045
D	−34.7	2100
E	−24.3	3400
F	−17.0	3420
G	0.16	6175
H	81.6	(22,400)?

Figure 11.4.
Solid-liquid-vapor equilibria—phase diagram for water (schematic). The numerical values of the actual coordinates of each point indicated by a letter are given in the tabulation at the right of the figure.

The pressure helps to determine the distance apart of the molecules and hence the effectiveness with which the intermolecular bonds can act. Low temperatures (low kinetic energies) and high pressures (small intermolecular distances) favor the existence of solids, whereas high temperatures and low pressures favor the existence of gases. There is for each substance a definite range of temperatures and pressures over which each of its phases is stable. These ranges may be represented on a two-dimensional diagram known as a *phase diagram*. The phase diagram for water is given in Figure 11.4. Each phase is stable within the pressure and temperature range bounded by the lines in the diagram. It is interesting to note that there are several forms of ice (five forms are now known) differing from one another in the arrangement of the molecules within the crystal, each stable over a particular range. The curves represent the pressures and temperatures at which the phases in each of the two neighboring regions can be in equilibrium with one another. The line B—A contains all points which represent pressures and temperatures at which liquid water and gaseous water can be in equilibrium. The intersections of the curves represent the pressures and temperatures at which three phases can be in equilibrium. Thus point A represents the only temperature and pressure at which ice I, liquid water, and gaseous water can be in equilibrium. Similar diagrams may be drawn for other substances.

UNDERCOOLING AND SUPERHEATING

While it is true that each phase of a substance is stable only within a given range of pressures and temperatures, one can often cool liquids well below their freezing points or heat them above their evaporation temperatures at any pressure and still have liquid remaining. These phenomena are known as undercooling (supercooling) and superheating respectively. They occur because of the structural difficulty of forming the initial crystal within the liquid as it cools to the melting point, or of forming the first gas bubble as it heats. In a liquid under atmospheric pressure the bubbles can grow only if the vapor pressure of the liquid slightly exceeds atmospheric pressure. Then new bubbles can form and the liquid is said to boil. When the atmospheric pressure changes, the boiling temperature will change accordingly. However, the boiling points usually recorded for substances are the temperatures at which the vapor pressure equals one standard atmosphere rather than the temperature at which the liquid actually boils at the atmospheric pressure found in the laboratory.

The more complicated the crystal structure, the harder to start the pattern and the greater the tendency to undercool. As undercooling proceeds further and further below the melting point, the viscosity of the liquid continues to rise further, hampering crystal formation. It is not uncommon for the viscosity to become so high that crystal formation is effectively inhibited and the undercooled liquid remains apparently stable, though far below its freezing point. Quartz glass and window glass are cases in point.

Superheating never continues indefinitely since the viscosity effect is in the reverse direction. At some temperature the local energy becomes high enough to form the first "hole" or bubble in the liquid. The superheated liquid rapidly vaporizes into the bubble which then grows to a large size. The growing bubble may violently eject the liquid lying above it from the container. Geysers are an example. Superheating may be minimized by placing porous material in heated liquids. These serve as sources of the original bubbles.

SUMMARY

We thus arrive at a picture of gases as composed of rather widely separated molecules, (some ten molecular diameters apart on the average) in rapid (500 meters per second), random motion, colliding and rebounding in a chaotic manner. The kinetic energy of an individual molecule will vary greatly from time to time, and any group of molecules will contain some with very high and some with very low energies, yet the average kinetic energy per molecule depends only on the absolute temperature, increasing at the same rate that the temperature increases.

Liquids and solids also contain atoms or molecules, which may be electrically neutral or electrically charged, undergoing similar random motions, but the close packing in these substances prevents a molecule from traveling far in any given direction before it strikes another molecule and rebounds. This is particularly true in solids where the regular crystalline structure makes it very difficult for a molecule to move from one lattice site to another. Thus the molecular motion in crystals is essentially a rapid vibration about a mean position.

Liquids are almost as closely packed as solids so that long continued molecular motion in any given direction is again impossible. The less orderly structure compared to solids and the slightly greater average spacing do make diffusion more easy than in solids so that molecular motion in liquids is essentially a rapid vibration accompanied by occasional diffusion. Thus the liquid may be considered somewhat like a solid which has lost its regular structure.

We have now used the concept of atoms and molecules in a kinetic theory describing their motion. We have learned how to determine relative weights of these atoms and molecules and we have shown how they give us a logical interpretation of the chemical composition in pure substances. In Chapter 13 we shall present other evidence for the existence of atoms and molecules. The evidence, supplementing that already discussed, increases the conviction of chemists that atoms are real even though invisible. There are many details about atoms and molecules not yet known. Nevertheless, one can be as sure of their reality as of the reality of a tree or mountain peak seen at a distance but not yet examined in complete detail.

Problem 11.3. The solubility of sodium chloride in water, that is, the number of grams of sodium chloride that will dissolve in a fixed amount of water, changes very little with a change in temperature. If you wished to make up a saturated solution of sodium chloride quickly would hot water or cold water be better? Give reasons for your choice.

Problem 11.4. Ten grams of ice are melted at 0°C. How much energy is required to melt the ice? If an equal quantity of energy is applied to the liquid water obtained from the ice at 0°C., to what temperature will the water be raised?

Problem 11.5. When 18 g. of steam at 100°C. are condensed to liquid water which is cooled to 0°C. and then frozen to ice how much heat is evolved?

Problem 11.6. In deserts, drinking water is sometimes stored in canvas bags hung where they are exposed to the hot winds. The water in the bag becomes cooler than the surrounding air. Explain.

Problem 11.7. In Severance Chemical Laboratory the usual boiling temperature of water is between 99 and 99.5°C. and never at 100°C. Does water have abnormal properties in Oberlin? Explain.

148 GENERAL CHEMISTRY

Problem 11.8. How many molecules are there in one liter of gas at standard conditions? If this gas is condensed to a liquid, how many molecules are there in the liquid?

Problem 11.9. Compare the number of molecules in 1 gram of ice and in 1 gram of carbon tetrachloride. How long would it take to count these at the rate of five per second?

Problem 11.10. Some ice is put into a bottle which is then stoppered and packed in an ice bath. Indicate all the different equilibria which might exist within the bottle.

Problem 11.11. What volume of liquid water, density 1 gram per milliliter, would be formed by condensing 1 liter of water vapor measured at 0°C. and 0.500 cm. of mercury?

Problem 11.12. An element is discovered which is metallic and has a specific heat capacity of 0.0276 cal/g; 1.161 g. of the metal gives 1.321 g. of a white oxide when heated in oxygen. What is the atomic weight of the element?

Problem 11.13. Summarize the methods of determining atomic weights so far discussed.

Problem 11.14. Suggest an interpretation of the fact that geyser action may be set off by throwing soap into the geyser hole.

12 PERIODIC CLASSIFICATION OF THE ELEMENTS

MANY ELEMENTS were discovered prior to the middle of the nineteenth century but no systematic relations among them were known nor was there any method of correlating their properties with the structures of the various atoms. The situation was similar to that found today among the fundamental particles.

Almost one hundred years elapsed between the time in the last quarter of the eighteenth century when Lavoisier and his associates derived a practical way for identifying the elements and the time, 1869, when a comprehensive scheme for classifying the elements in a systematic way became established. The lapse in time occurred for two reasons: (1) a systematic arrangement could not become apparent until enough elements were known to furnish an outline of it, and (2) the systematic relations depend on an order roughly related to the relative masses of atoms. The latter were not known or agreed on during the long period in which the atomic weights and the equivalent weights of elements were confused. The structural reasons for the order were developed much later, about 50 years after the order itself was established through the periodic table.

DISCOVERY OF THE ELEMENTS

The chemical elements known to the ancient world were those found uncombined in nature or those that could be readily prepared from available ores. They included the metallic elements: gold, silver, copper, iron, lead, tin, and mercury, and the nonmetallic elements: sulfur, and carbon. Distinctions between metals and nonmetals could be made by the ancients. Metals are ductile and malleable and retain their strength after deformation. They are lustrous and good conductors of heat. The nonmetals lack these qualities. From the medieval period up to the latter part of the seventeenth century several other elements were discovered. The name arsenic had been applied in the ancient world to a variety of poisonous substances but the metal itself was probably first prepared in the thirteenth century. Metallic antimony may have been known to the ancients but it was certainly known in the alchemical period. Bismuth, although found earlier, had not been differentiated from tin and lead until this period. Phosphorus, first prepared by an alchemist, Brandt in 1669, is the first element whose discoverer is definitely known. Among the elements isolated in the first seventy years of the eighteenth century were zinc, cobalt, nickel, manganese, and platinum. All these were recognized as distinct substances but not as chemical elements.

The discovery of nitrogen in 1772, of oxygen in 1774, and Lavoisier's recognition of these together with hydrogen, earlier discovered, as elements

Table 12.1
Discovery of the Elements. Time Chart *

Au				V							He		
Ag				Cr							Eu		
Cu				Be							Kr		
Fe				Nb	Na								
Pb	As		H	Ta	K					Ga Pr	Ne		Tc
Sn	Sb		N	Ce	Ba Li					Yb Nd	Xe		Fr
Hg	Bi		O	U	Pd Ca Cd	La		Cs	Sm Gd	Po		At Am
S	P	Co	Cl Mo Sr	Rh Mg Se Al Tb	Rb	Sc Dy Ra		Np Pm
C	Zn	Pt Ni	Mn W Ti	Os B Si Br Er	Tl	Ho Ge Ac	Hf	Pu Bk
			F Te Y	Ir I Zr Th Ru	In	Tm A Rn	Lu Pa Re	Cm Cf

Ancients	Alchemists	←—17 Hundred and—→	←———18 Hundred and——→	←—19 Hundred—
		35 45 55 65 75 85 95	05 15 25 35 45 55 65 75 85 95	05 15 25 35 45
		45 55 65 75 85 95	05 15 25 35 45 55 65 75 85 95	05 15 25 35 45 —

* S. C. Lind, "Chemistry at Mid-Century," *Chemical and Engineering News*, October 6, 1952, p. 4144. Copyright 1952 by the American Chemical Society.

enabled him to start on the modern list of elements. The first step was to decide which of the known pure substances were elements. The second was to recognize compounds of new elements and then to obtain the elements from their compounds. Fluorine may be taken as an extreme example of the span required. One of its compounds, hydrogen fluoride, was described as early as 1768 but fluorine itself was not isolated as an element for one hundred years although many able workers had worked with its compounds, suffering poisoning from them. Moissan prepared the first elementary fluorine in 1886. In the intervening years fluorine compounds were known, and recognized, and used in reactions. These reactions and the analysis of the other constituents in the compounds enabled chemists to determine the equivalent weight of fluorine, its atomic weight, and many of its properties (in compounds) and thus to prove its existence long before it was isolated. Berthelot's 1826 list of atomic weights included a rather good value for fluorine. Obviously the properties of the pure element, such as the boiling point, could not be determined in this way. It is, therefore, difficult to assign exact dates of discovery to many of the elements but Table 12.1 summarizes the data now widely accepted.

DOBEREINER'S TRIADS

By 1828 fifty-four elements had been recognized and some of their properties determined. The properties were those of the pure elements, including their tendencies to react with one another, and those of the compounds formed. In 1828 Döbereiner recognized a number of groups, each containing three elements, in which the central element had chemical properties intermediate between those of the other two, and he showed that the equivalent weight of the middle one was the average of the equivalent weights of the other two. Because the elements in a triad have similar properties and have the same number of equivalents per atomic weight Döbereiner's statement would have applied equally to atomic weights. His triads were: chlorine, bromine, and iodine; calcium, strontium, and barium; lithium, sodium, and potassium; sulfur, selenium, and tellurium; platinum, iridium, and osmium, and silver, lead and mercury. The last triad, on the basis of what we now know about properties, is a false one. The argument based on the other triads was limited, for numerous exceptions to the rules could be found.

NEWLANDS' OCTAVES

In the thirty-five years following Döbereiner's proposal only a few more elements were identified. Among them were thorium, ruthenium, rubidium, thallium, and indium. Although the discoveries were important in adding to the number of known elements, the most important single development in this time was Cannizarro's proposal on atomic weights made in 1860 (see page 114). Cannizarro's method enabled chemists to agree on the relative atomic weights of the different elements. In particular, the atomic weights of fluorine and silicon could be fixed. These were crucial elements since they completed the list of elements of low atomic weight (except for the inert gases which were not discovered until the eighteen nineties).

Newlands, an English chemist, arranged the elements in order of increasing atomic weights and numbered them, starting with hydrogen as number 1. He then noted that "the numbers of analogous elements, when not consecutive, differed by seven or a multiple of seven." Analogous elements were those with similar properties. Thus Döbereiner's triad—lithium, sodium, potassium—had numbers of 2, 9, and 16, respectively in Newlands' system. An analogous element was found in every eighth successive element, hence Newlands designated his system as a "law of octaves." Newlands saw that it was necessary to rearrange the order of the atoms in certain cases and ascribed this to errors in the values of the atomic weights. His system had the vital flaw that it merely correlated known information and did not allow any gaps for undiscovered elements. The only new knowledge it could predict was revised values for certain atomic weights. Newlands' system worked well only for the first two periods. Thereafter, elements not analogous in properties were placed as though they were because Newlands left no gaps for missing elements. When he read his paper before the Chemical Society of London it was received with ridicule. So little importance did chemists attach to atomic weights as a guide for correlations that a wit asked him whether he "had ever examined the elements according to the order of their initial letters." The Society rejected his paper as "not adapted for publication."

The German chemist and physicist, Lothar Meyer, simultaneously with Newlands in 1869, proposed a similar incomplete periodic table with this important difference—Meyer left blank spaces, putting the known elements only where they fitted and he predicted that other elements would be discovered to fill these spaces. By 1869 he had arranged 56 elements in a table consisting of groups and sub-groups based on similarities in such properties as chemical formulas and gram-atomic volumes.

THE MENDELEEFF PERIODIC TABLE

Mendeleeff, a brilliant Russian chemist, is generally given most credit for developing the present periodic table of the elements. In 1869 he presented his

Table 12.2

Comparison of Properties of Germanium (Discovered in 1886) with Those Predicted by Mendeleeff (in 1871) for Ekasilicon

PROPERTY	MENDELEEFF'S PREDICTION FOR EKASILICON (Es)	OBSERVED FOR GERMANIUM (Ge)
Atomic weight	72	72.60
Density (g/ml)	5.5	5.47
Gram-atomic volume (ml)	13	13.2
Specific heat capacity (cal/g °C.)	0.073	0.076
Formula of oxide	EsO_2	GeO_2
Density of oxide (g/ml)	4.7	4.703
Molar volume of oxide (ml)	22.	22.16
Formula of chloride	$EsCl_4$	$GeCl_4$
Boiling point of chloride (°C.)	under 100°	86°
Density of chloride (g/ml)	1.9	1.887
Molar volume of chloride (ml)	113.	113.35

paper on "The Relation of the Properties to the Atomic Weights of the Elements." His work, independent of that of Newlands in England and Meyer in Germany, was somewhat more complete. He noted that practically all of the known properties of the elements, as well as of their corresponding compounds, varied in a regularly repeating pattern (periodic pattern) when the elements were listed in order of increasing atomic weight if occasional blank spaces were left for undiscovered elements. Some of the properties he used are listed in Table 12.2. The properties of lithium and of its compounds were very similar to the corresponding properties of sodium, potassium, rubidium, and cesium and of their compounds. These elements made up a family called the alkali metals. Beryllium, magnesium, calcium, strontium, and barium (the alkaline earth elements) were similarly related and each of these latter immediately

Table 12.3. Periodic Table. (A long form)

Period																		
I								1 H 1.0080										2 He 4.003
II	3 Li 6.940	4 Be 9.013											5 B 10.82	6 C 12.01	7 N 14.01	8 O 16.0000	9 F 19.00	10 Ne 20.18
III	11 Na 22.99	12 Mg 24.32											13 Al 26.98	14 Si 28.09	15 P 30.98	16 S 32.07	17 Cl 35.46	18 A 39.94
IV	19 K 39.10	20 Ca 40.08	21 Sc 44.96	22 Ti 47.90	23 V 50.95	24 Cr 52.01	25 Mn 54.94	26 Fe 55.85	27 Co 58.94	28 Ni 58.69	29 Cu 63.54	30 Zn 65.38	31 Ga 69.72	32 Ge 72.60	33 As 74.91	34 Se 78.96	35 Br 79.92	36 Kr 83.80
V	37 Rb 85.48	38 Sr 87.63	39 Y 88.92	40 Zr 91.22	41 Nb 92.91	42 Mo 95.95	43 Tc [99]	44 Ru 101.1	45 Rh 102.9	46 Pd 106.7	47 Ag 107.9	48 Cd 112.4	49 In 114.8	50 Sn 118.7	51 Sb 121.8	52 Te 127.6	53 I 126.9	54 Xe 131.3
VI	55 Cs 132.9	56 Ba 137.4	57 * La 138.9	72 Hf 178.6	73 Ta 180.9	74 W 183.9	75 Re 186.3	76 Os 190.2	77 Ir 192.2	78 Pt 195.2	79 Au 197.0	80 Hg 200.6	81 Tl 204.4	82 Pb 207.2	83 Bi 209.0	84 Po 210	85 At [210]	86 Rn 222
VII	87 Fr [223]	88 Ra 226.0	89 + Ac 227	90 Th 232.1	91 Pa 231	92 U 238.1	93 Np [237]	94 Pu [242]	95 Am [243]	96 Cm [245]	97 Bk [245]	98 Cf [248]						
Group	1a	2a	3b	4b	5b	6b	7b	8b	9b	10b	1b	2b	3a	4a	5a	6a	7a	0

*Rare earth elements

58 Ce 140.1	59 Pr 140.9	60 Nd 144.3	61 Pm [145]	62 Sm 150.4	63 Eu 152.0	64 Gd 156.9	65 Tb 158.9	66 Dy 162.5	67 Ho 164.9	68 Er 167.2	69 Tm 168.9	70 Yb 173.0	71 Lu 175.0

+Actinium elements

90 Th 232.1	91 Pa 231	92 U 238.1	93 Np [237]	94 Pu [242]	95 Am [243]	96 Cm [245]	97 Bk [245]	98 Cf [248]	99	100			

153

followed an alkali element when the elements were arranged in order of increasing atomic weight. These families appear in the two left-hand columns of Table 12.3.

All the elements appearing in Periods II and III (except the inert gases in the extreme right-hand column) were known to Mendeleeff. However, the next known element after calcium in order of increasing atomic weight was titanium. Mendeleeff knew from its properties that it belonged in a family with silicon rather than with aluminum. He, therefore, left room for an element to be discovered. The elements after titanium followed in a regular order on the basis of their properties but after zinc another gap occurred. Zinc had certain relations to magnesium, and arsenic, the next known element, had properties similar to phosphorus. This meant that there should be elements similar to aluminum and silicon. Mendeleeff left space for these two elements also. In this way he developed the first long period in his periodic table. The next long period followed in order, there also being gaps in this period due to missing elements. Mendeleeff went further, predicting the properties of the missing elements. The missing element just preceding arsenic he called ekasilicon. The properties he listed for this element are shown in Table 12.2 together with the observed properties of the element germanium discovered 15 years later.

One property of which Mendeleeff made great use depended on crystal structure. He reasoned that if families of elements did exist the elements would not only have similar bulk properties but similar atomic properties. For instance elements in the same family should pack similarly in crystals either of the elements or of their compounds. Thus the crystal structures of, for instance, the oxides of the alkali elements should be the same; the compounds should be *isomorphous*. He thus used the concept of isomorphous crystals as an important guide in placing the elements into certain families rather than others.

Mendeleeff's first table was essentially the same as that shown in Table 12.3 except that he left no spaces for the then unknown inert gases or the elements following uranium and was unable to specify the total number of the rare earth elements. On the other hand these elements do fit into the general form of his table with no major revision.

Each element, including each missing element, may be given an order number in the table, called its atomic number. The modern atomic numbers are listed in Table 12.3. The modern atomic weights are also listed. Comparison shows that there are several elements whose atomic numbers are not consistent with the order of atomic weights. Tellurium and iodine, for instance, should be interchanged on the basis of atomic weight data alone. Mendeleeff noted this discrepancy, placed the elements in positions consistent with their other properties, and stated that one or the other or both of the atomic weights was incorrect. Exact work shows that these atomic weights are correct, though Mendeleeff correctly diagnosed some others as being wrong. Other pairs of elements with modern atomic weights not in the same order as the atomic numbers may be found in the table, but this fact is no longer of concern.

Arrangement of the elements in the periodic table is now based on atomic structure rather than on atomic weight. The elements with atomic numbers higher than uranium, for instance, were placed as shown not because of any weight relationships but because of their atomic structure.

THE INERT GASES

We have already discussed the recognition and isolation of argon as a new element by Rayleigh and Ramsay. It obviously did not fit into any of the then known periodic tables. Since it was inert and had no chemistry, Ramsay suggested that a new column be prepared for it and that other inert gases would be found to fill analogous spaces in each period. The logic of this argument encouraged Ramsay to succeed in finding the other stable, inert gases. Radon, a radioactive gas emitted by natural radioactive materials and called "emanation" by the early workers, fills the last vacant space. Thus, by the beginning of the twentieth century the periodic table with the present number of columns and periods was developed. The new radioactive elements then being discovered and those prepared in the nineteen forties could be fitted into this table.

FORMS OF PERIODIC TABLES

Many forms of periodic tables have been proposed. Mendeleeff and Meyer themselves used several types of arrangement. A "long form" such as that in Table 12.3 accents the periodic recurrence of similar appearance, chemical reactiveness, gram-atomic volume of the solid, boiling points, etc., among the elements. The latter two quantities are plotted versus atomic number in Figures 12.1 and 12.2. Sharp peaks in the gram-atomic volume curve at atomic numbers of 3, 11, 19, 37, 55, and 87 correspond in every case to an alkali metal. The intervals in atomic numbers between peaks are not constant, being 8, 8, 18, 18, and 32, respectively, but it is interesting to note that successive periods may have the same length. The long forms of the table accent this fact. Exactly the same periodicity is seen in the plot of boiling points versus atomic numbers in terms of the intervals between marked minima in the curve. These minima occur at atomic numbers of 2, 10, 18, 36, and 54, corresponding to the inert gases. The intervals between minima 8, 8, 18, 18, are the same as those indicated above, though the actual atomic numbers at the minima are different.

A slightly different long form is shown in Figure 12.3. Here the periodicity of atomic size or volume (labeled spheres) is shown in the rows. The relative sizes of some ions, atoms which have gained or lost electrons, is also shown by the unlabeled spheres below and slightly to the right of many of the labelled atomic size spheres.

Another of Mendeleeff's types, sometimes called the "short form" accents similar chemical formulas as shown in Table 12.4. The groups in this form must

156   GENERAL CHEMISTRY

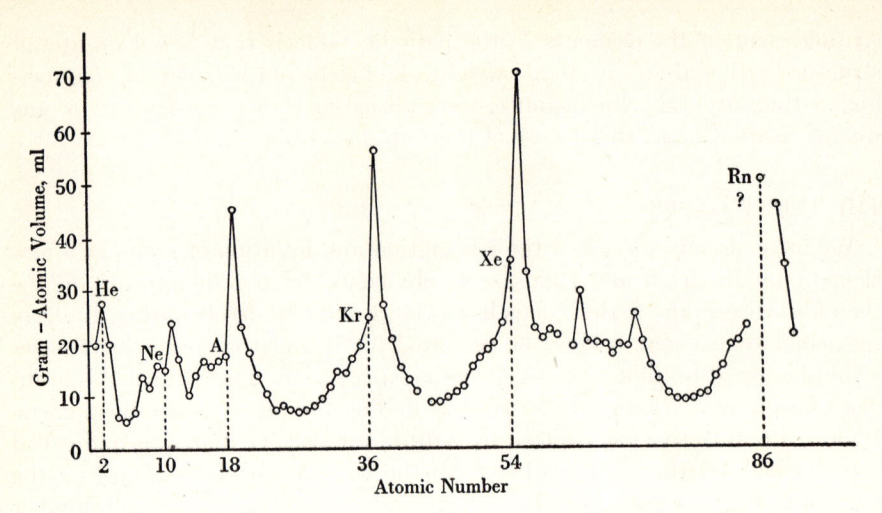

Figure 12.1.
Gram-atomic volume *vs* atomic number.

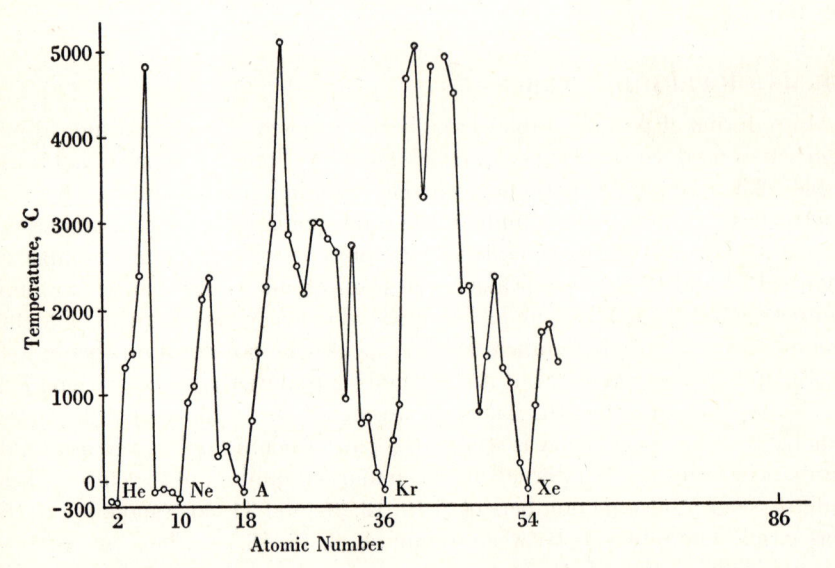

Figure 12.2.
Boiling points of the elements in °C. *vs* atomic number.

be divided into "a" and "b" sub-groups to bring together elements with similar chemical properties. Thus all the elements listed in Group 2 form oxides with the formula MO, where M stands for the symbol of the various elements. On the other hand the general properties of the elements in the "a" column are appreciably different from those in the "b" column so that it is convenient to divide them into these two sub-groups. For instance, in Group 1 the "a"

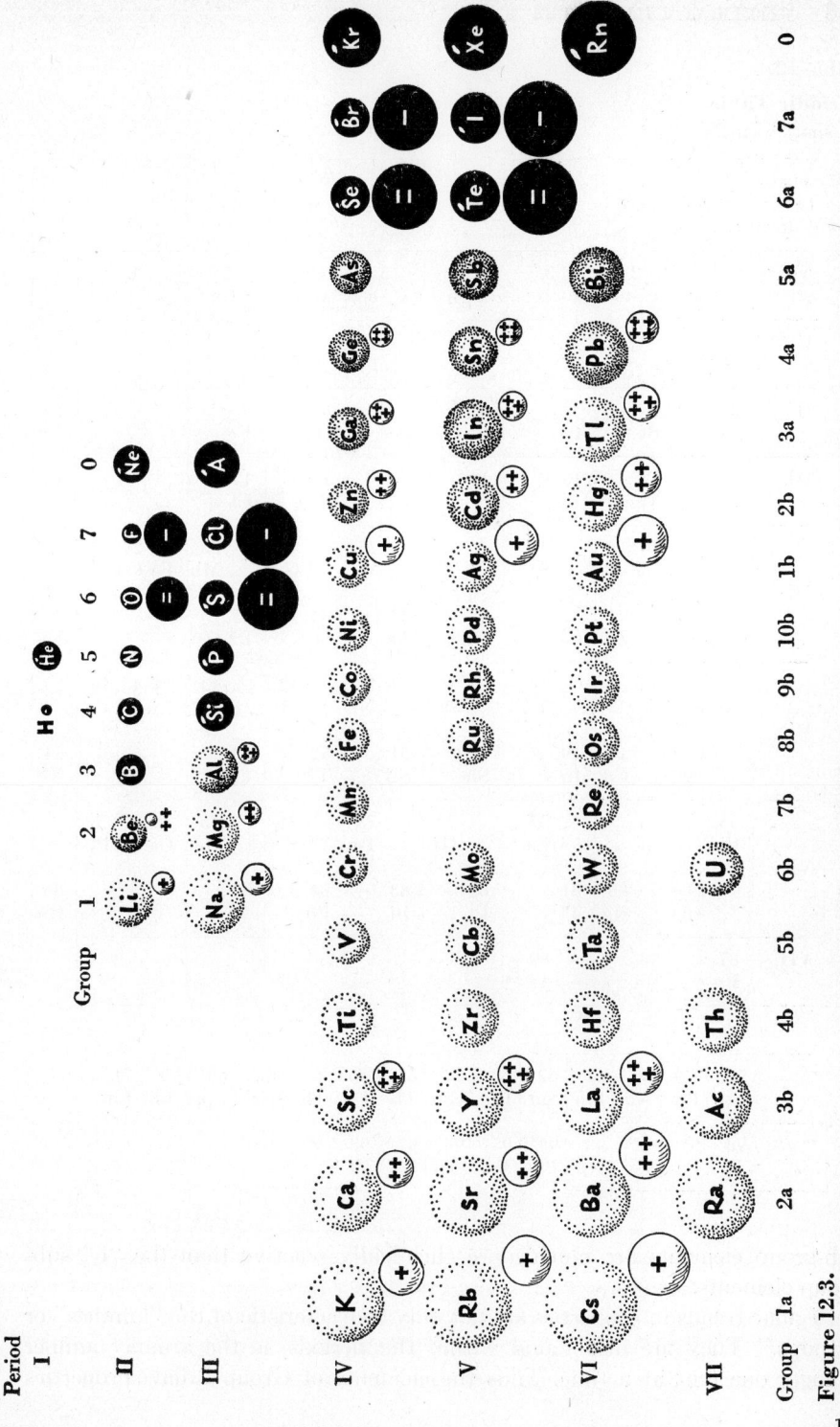

Figure 12.3.
Relative sizes of atoms and ions arranged according to the periodic table. The ions correspond to the elements above them.

157

158   GENERAL CHEMISTRY

Table 12.4
Periodic Table
(A short form)

FORMULA OF OXIDE	M₂O	MO	M₂O₃	MO₂	M₂O₅	MO₃	M₂O₇		
GROUP	1 A B	2 A B	3 A B	4 A B	5 A B	6 A B	7 A B	8	0
I	1 H								2 He
II	3 Li	4 Be	5 B	6 C	7 N	8 O	9 F		10 Ne
III	11 Na	12 Mg	13 Al	14 Si	15 P	16 S	17 Cl		18 A
IV	19 K 29 Cu	20 Ca 30 Zn	21 Sc 31 Ga	22 Ti 32 Ge	23 V 33 As	24 Cr 34 Se	25 Mn 35 Br	26 27 28 Fe Co Ni	36 Kr
V	37 Rb 47 Ag	38 Sr 48 Cd	39 Y 49 In	40 Zr 50 Sn	41 Nb 51 Sb	42 Mo 52 Te	43 Tc 53 I	44 45 46 Ru Rh Pd	54 Xe
VI	55 Cs 79 Au	56 Ba 80 Hg	57 La * 81 Tl	72 Hf 82 Pb	73 Ta 83 Bi	74 W 84 Po	75 Re 85 At	76 77 78 Os Ir Pt	86 Rn
VII	87 Fr	88 Ra	89 Ac **						

*	58 Ce	59 Pr	60 Nd	61 Pm	62 Sm	63 Eu	64 Gd	65 Tb	66 Dy	67 Ho	68 Er	69 Tm	70 Yb	71 Lu
**	90 Th	91 Pa	92 U	93 Np	94 Pu	95 Am	96 Cm	97 Bk	98 Cf	99	100			

sub-group elements are much more chemically reactive than the "b" sub-group elements.

Regular trends in properties are not only characteristic of the "families" or "groups." They are also found within the periods as the atomic number changes one unit at a time. Thus the elements of Group 2 have properties which are, in general, intermediate between those of Group 1 and Group 3, and so with the other Groups as well.

Dozens of other tabular forms have been suggested, each accenting different points. Familiarity with the general basis of the table and the types of correlation possible will enable a student to use many of the forms with equal ease.

In most modern periodic tables a particular vertical column of the table contains the elements of a given *group* or *family*. They are the analogous elements of Newlands and Döbereiner. The horizontal rows in the table contain all the elements in a particular *period*.

CORRELATION OF PROPERTIES

Periodic tables are still useful for predicting properties. When the new radioactive elements and their compounds were prepared the amounts were invisible. The periodic classification enabled experimenters to predict their properties on the basis of the properties of known elements. Predictions were made about the properties of plutonium, for example. These properties were then used to isolate and concentrate plutonium and its compounds. Work with a new element is facilitated enormously when one can make good guesses about its behavior, especially when only tiny amounts are available. The properties of curium, element 98, were predicted so well that it was possible to identify it in an original sample containing only about 3000 atoms of the element.

A student of chemistry finds the periodic table equally useful for correlating and predicting properties. The amount of information any individual, whether student or chemist, can carry in his head is limited. Knowledge of the periodic table and of the properties of key elements in it enables one to remember the properties of other elements or to predict properties that may not be known. Hereafter, students will find it advantageous to consider all the properties of an element in terms of its position in the periodic table.

Problem 12.1. Work out the relationship between Table 12.3 and Table 12.4, showing how one is converted into the other.

Problem 12.2. How does the ratio of the equivalent weight of an element to its atomic weight correlate with atomic number? See Table 12.4.

Problem 12.3. What compound would you expect between hydrogen and tellurium? Between sulfur and potassium? Between silicon and chlorine?

Problem 12.4. How do you account for the fact that positive, monatomic ions are smaller than the neutral atoms from which they come? See Figure 12.3.

Problem 12.5. Newlands insisted until his death that he should have received credit for discovering the periodic system. Evaluate his claim versus that of Mendeleeff.

13 NUCLEAR STRUCTURE IN ATOMS

MOST OF our attention thus far has been to the concept of individual atoms of the elements and to using these concepts to interpret the behavior of substances. Yet we have dealt mainly with the atoms in bulk quantities, not with the nature of the individual atoms. We shall now return to the questions raised in Chapter 3 concerning the composition and structure of the atoms in relation to the fundamental particles: protons, neutrons, and electrons.

A valid study of the composition and structures of atoms should include methods which deal with individual atoms rather than with large numbers in bulk. For instance, the methods of determining atomic weight discussed up to now have involved weighing equal numbers of atoms of various elements. After denoting the average weight of an oxygen atom as 16.0000 we calculated the average weights of other atoms in terms of this standard. But it should be clear that these weights are *averages*. As far as the measurements go, it would be quite possible for the weights of the individual atoms of each element to vary over a very large range, perhaps overlapping those of all the other elements, provided, of course, that different samples of an element had the same average. A similar statement could be made for any other properties, including tendency to undergo chemical reaction. In every instance the observed property would actually be the average for all the atoms. Since the number of atoms dealt with is always large, the average property could be the same regardless of the particular sample of the element used.

Fortunately there are a good many methods of detecting behavior due to isolated, individual atoms and some of these give us rather direct insights about the internal structure of atoms.

CHARGED ATOMS AND MOLECULES

Electrons may be obtained from all elements (see pages 30, 31) and may, therefore, be presumed to be present in all substances. (Though remember the discussion on pages 14 and 28.) Beams or "rays" of electrons were first found in glass tubes containing gas at very low pressure and having electrodes charged at different potentials. Such tubes are called Crookes tubes in honor of Sir William Crookes who prepared them in 1874. See also pages 30 and 31.

About ten years later, another type of beam or ray was detected in Crookes tubes. These beams traveled in the opposite direction from that of the electrons. The beams had momentum—therefore they consisted of particles having mass. The beams when passed through electrical fields at right angles were deflected toward the negative plate—therefore the particles were charged positively. The amount of deflection of the beams was much less than that of electron beams—therefore the particles in the beams had much greater mass than that of the electrons or they had much greater velocity. The apparent mass of the particles in the beam depended on the nature of the gas filling the tube, corresponding to the molecular weight of the gaseous substance—therefore, the particles were positively charged molecules of the gas. These observations were not made at once nor in the order indicated but series of experiments on these positive rays established all the indicated facts.

Further experiments showed that positively charged gaseous molecules or atoms, called ions, may be formed in other ways. Heat will produce them. Gaseous ions appear in the air surrounding the flame of a bunsen burner. A beam of gas passing over a heated wire will become ionized. Some negatively charged gaseous ions also exist. They are formed when neutral gas molecules capture free electrons temporarily. However, in very dilute gases the positively charged ions predominate over the negatively charged ions.

MASS SPECTROGRAPH

J. J. Thomson, the brilliant British physicist who first measured the mass of the electron, also studied the deflection of gaseous ions. He found that a beam of gaseous ions, passed through a slit to give the beam a definite cross-sectional shape, could be bent by a combination of electric and magnetic fields so that all particles with the same ratio of mass to charge, $\frac{m}{e}$, impinged on a single line in a photographic plate. The plate, when developed, showed this line. His observation was the foundation of the mass spectrograph, which enables us to determine the masses of gaseous ions with high precision. Thomson's work was extended by Aston who used the method to measure the relative masses of many atoms and molecules.

Figure 13.1 shows a schematic diagram of a mass spectrograph. A hot wire placed in a beam of molecular or atomic particles produces positively charged ion beams. The radius of curvature of these beams in an electric field will depend on the field itself, which can be kept constant, and on the charge, mass, and velocity of the particles passing through the field. The same factors apply to the radius of curvature of the beams in a magnetic field, but the relations between charge, mass, and velocity are somewhat different. When the two fields are properly balanced the charge and mass determine the path of the particles and all particles with the same ratio of $\frac{m}{e}$ can be focused on a single line on the photographic plate even though their velocities differ. Since the number of singly charged particles almost always predominates greatly over the number of doubly charged particles one can tell from the intensities of the lines which one corresponds to the charge, e = 1, and which corresponds to the

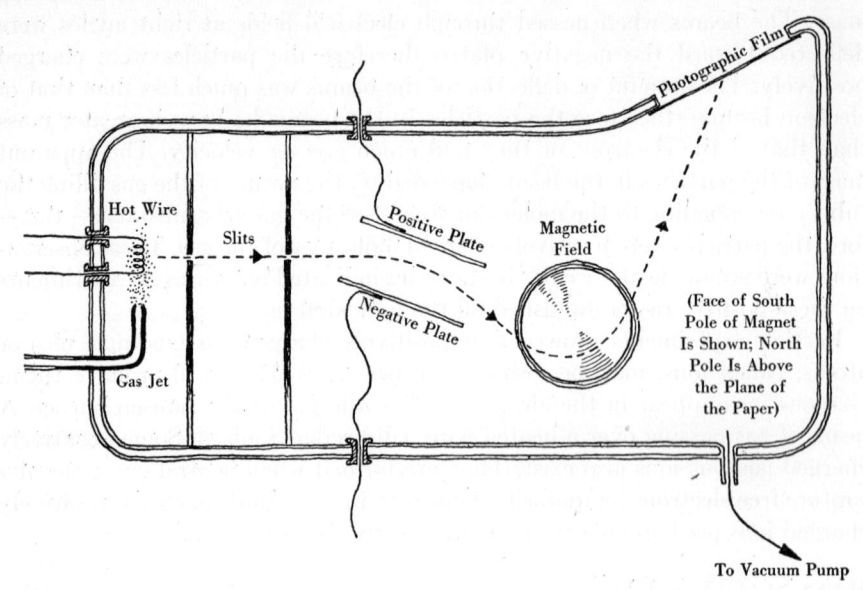

Figure 13.1.
Diagram of a mass spectrograph (schematic). Neutral molecules from the gas jet are ionized by the hot wire into electrons and positive ions. Some of the positive ions move through the slits, where they are accelerated by an electrical field which is not shown. The positive ions are then bent from their straight line path, first by the electric field and then by the magnetic field. The amount of bending will depend on the charge of the ion, the velocity of the ion, the strengths of the fields, and the mass of the ion. Each of these, except the mass, can be measured from the known properties of the apparatus. The mass is then calculated from the position at which the beam strikes the photographic film and the known properties of the apparatus.

charge, e = 2. When e = 2, $\frac{m}{e}$ has exactly one half the value of that for the singly charged particles for which e = 1.

RELATIVE WEIGHTS OF ATOMS AND MOLECULES; ISOTOPES

Analysis of positive rays in a mass spectrograph, as contrasted with other atomic weight determination we have discussed, gives us weights of the individual atoms or molecules, for it is these individuals which travel in the beam and are segregated according to their ratio of mass to charge.

In his early work on the separation of beams into parts containing particles with the same $\frac{m}{e}$ ratio, J. J. Thomson found an unexpected result. Some of the lines (called a mass spectrum by analogy with an optical spectrum), appearing on the photographic plate yielded values for the gaseous ions in agreement with their known molecular weights. Thus, a spectrum with air as a sample had relatively heavy lines corresponding to mass 28 for singly charged nitrogen molecules, 32 for singly charged oxygen molecules and 40 for singly charged argon molecules. There was also a line for neon molecules of mass 20. But, in addition, there was a faint line corresponding to $\frac{m}{e} = 22$. The latter was shown not to be due to a possible doubly charged carbon dioxide molecule $\left(\frac{m}{e} = \frac{44}{2}\right)$. By partial fractionation of some neon, Aston was able to show that the 22 line was, rather, due to neon. Now the atomic weight of neon obtained from its molar weight is 20.2. No such line appeared in the mass spectrum—only the principal line for mass 20 and the weak line at mass 22 appeared. Apparently neon has at least two kinds of atoms, thus accounting for the average mass, 20.2.

Chlorine had been subject to extensive investigation by the early chemists because its atomic weight is so far from being a whole number. The mass spectrum of chlorine shows that it has no atoms of mass 35.5 corresponding to its gram-atomic weight. The lines actually found are for masses 35 and 37 the former being about three times as intense as the latter. Ordinary chlorine is, therefore, a mixture containing about three atoms of mass 35 to every atom of mass 37. Copper, with the average atomic weight of 63.6, consists of atoms of mass 63 and mass 65, the line for the former being about two and a half times as intense as the latter.

A complete survey of the naturally occurring elements shows that about four out of every five of them are composed of atoms which differ in mass. These elements are said to be composed of several *isotopes*, each isotope consisting of all the atoms of an element having the same mass. Thus, there are two stable isotopes of chlorine and two of copper. Neon actually has three, about three atoms in a thousand having mass 21.

MASS NUMBERS AND SYMBOLS FOR ISOTOPES

After mass spectrographs were refined, more exact measurements of the $\frac{m}{e}$ values showed that for isotopes of all elements the masses of the individual atoms were *very nearly* whole numbers on the scale O = 16 but not exactly whole numbers (see Table 13.1). The integral numbers used heretofore for the approximate masses are called *mass numbers*. The actual mass, M, of an atom differs slightly from the mass number, A, for reasons which we shall discuss on page 169. Isotopes are distinguished by the chemical symbol of the element together with the mass number of the atoms of the particular isotope. The isotopes of chlorine and copper are designated, respectively, by the symbols Cl^{35} and Cl^{37}, and Cu^{63} and Cu^{65}. Somewhat less than half of the naturally occurring elements with odd atomic numbers have stable atoms of one mass number only. For example, all stable atoms of sodium have mass number 23 and all stable atoms of fluorine have mass number 19. However, we have now

Table 13.1

Mass and Mass Number of Some Neutral Atoms
(Physical Scale)

ATOMIC NUMBER	ELEMENT	ISOTOPIC SYMBOL	MASS NUMBER	MASS (PHYSICAL SCALE) $O^{16} = 16$
1	Hydrogen	H^1	1	1.008128
		H^2 or D	2	2.014718
		H^3 or T	3	3.017029
2	Helium	He^3	3	3.017016
		He^4	4	4.003880
6	Carbon	C^{12}	12	12.0385
7	Nitrogen	N^{14}	14	14.007539
8	Oxygen	O^{16}	16	16.0000
		O^{17}	17	17.0045
		O^{18}	18	18.0040
10	Neon	Ne^{20}	20	19.99872

learned how to prepare at least one radioactive isotope of every element. Consequently, in discussing isotopes, we find it necessary to designate the mass number of every atom, for example, Na^{23}.

STANDARD FOR ATOMIC MASS

Oxygen was chosen as the standard for atomic mass in the mass spectrograph for many of the same reasons that led to its choice as standard for atomic weights based on chemical methods (see page 45). Very precise observations have since shown that ordinary oxygen is a mixture of isotopes, atoms with mass numbers 17 and 18 having been discovered. They were not found in the mass spectrum until other experiments on oxygen had proved their existence, and a deliberate search was made for them in the beams of a mass spectrograph. About 99.76 per cent of oxygen atoms have mass number 16, 0.04 per cent have mass number 17, and 0.20 per cent have mass number 18. The chemical standard, O = 16.000, is based on an isotopic mixture of this kind. For mass spectrograph measurements, it is much easier to select the mass of the most abundant isotope of oxygen, O^{16}, as being equal to 16.0000. On this scale, called the physical scale, the average atomic weight of oxygen may be calculated to be 16.00445. The difference between the physical scale and the chemical scale is not great and may be neglected for most purposes. For certain measurements, however, the difference is important and the scale used must be clearly understood. Chemists continue to use the chemical scale because it represents the experimental weight effects observed for the naturally occurring isotopic mixtures of the elements and because there is usually no great shift in the relative isotopic abundance during chemical reactions. The chemical atomic mass unit is 1.000275 times as great as the physical unit. Recorded atomic weights may be changed from one basis to another by this conversion factor.

Problem 13.1. Using only the masses of the oxygen isotopes (Table 13.1) and their known abundance, calculate the gram-atomic weight of oxygen on the physical scale.

ABSOLUTE MASSES OF ATOMS AND THE AVOGADRO NUMBER

The relative masses of atoms may be determined with high precision in the mass spectrograph. Modern spectrographs can distinguish between lines such as those produced by oxygen, mass 17.0045, and OH^+, mass 17.008, or between the lines for doubly charged helium atoms and singly charged heavy hydrogen atoms, for both of which $\frac{m}{e}$ is very nearly equal to 2.

Absolute masses of atoms can be determined if the strengths of the electric and magnetic fields and the velocity of the atoms are known. Thus, the absolute mass of O^{16} atoms is determined to be about 2.66×10^{-23} grams. The absolute weights of atoms in grams are not often used, since atomic weights based on $O = 16$ are very nearly whole numbers and lend themselves more readily to rapid calculations.

ATOMS AND THE FUNDAMENTAL PARTICLES

In Chapter 3 we considered a number of fundamental particles. Among them were the proton and the alpha particle. Both of these are positively charged, as are the ions found in a mass spectrograph. Both have masses corresponding to atomic masses. Protons may be obtained from positive rays of hydrogen. They have the mass and charge of hydrogen atoms which have lost an electron. Alpha particles have the charge and mass of helium atoms which have lost two electrons. On the other hand, the collision diameters of protons and alpha particles show that they are very small, the diameters being of the order of $\frac{1}{100,000}$ those of ordinary atoms. Diameters of neutral atoms may be calculated from observed internuclear distances in crystals. Collision diameters may be measured by determining the scattering which occurs when two beams, of alpha particles for instance, cross one another at right angles. If one knows the concentration of particles in each beam (from radiation counters) he can calculate effective particle diameters from the frequency with which the particles are deflected from a straight-line path. How are these particles, and the positively-charged particles obtained from other elements, related to the neutral atoms and molecules of these elements? And how can the existence of isotopes be related to atomic structure?

THE RUTHERFORD THEORY OF ATOMIC STRUCTURE

A crucial set of experiments by Rutherford and his co-workers gave important evidence on the structure of atoms. They examined a beam of alpha rays which had passed through various metal foils, platinum for instance. The metal, although in a very thin sheet, had a thickness corresponding to many layers of atoms. It might be expected that the alpha particles could be scattered in at least two ways: (1) by any massive particles present in the heavy platinum atoms, atomic weight 195; (2) by any positively charged particles present in the platinum. (The positive particles were assumed present to offset the negative charge due to the presumed presence of electrons in each atom.) But the kind of scattering observed was unexpected. A large fraction of the beam passed through the foil without any significant scattering at all, as though the platinum atoms were not present. A few of the alpha particles were scattered, however, and usually widely deflected from their original path. Apparently the scattering particles were small and seldom struck, but were also highly effective scatterers when struck, that is, were massive and/or highly positive in electrical charge.

From the results of the scattering experiment it was possible to show that each platinum atom contained one small, massive, positively charged scattering center and to calculate that the positive charge of this center was 78 within experimental error (the actual calculation gave 77.4). Experiments with copper and silver foil gave similar results but the scattering was less, for the positive charges in these atoms are 29 and 47 respectively. (The experimental values were 29.3 and 46.3.) The most interesting discovery was that the number of positive charges on an atom center, called the atomic nucleus, corresponded to the ordinal number of the element in the periodic classification, and therefore represented the atomic number.

In 1911 Rutherford proposed an atomic structure which these experiments and all subsequent work support. The entire positive charge of an atom and practically all the mass of the atom is concentrated in a tiny *nucleus* at the atom center surrounded by enough electrons to balance the positive charge on the nucleus. The mass of the electron is negligible compared with the mass of the nucleus, but the electron field is responsible for the size of the atom. The atomic model based on this theory is called the "Rutherford atom."

Further evidence for the presence of a positive nucleus, relatively independent of the electrons, is obtained by ionizing the atoms. In all cases the maximum charge obtainable on the positive ion is identical with the atomic number of the element, e.g., He^{2+}, C^{6+}, F^{9+}, K^{19+}, etc. In the following chapter we shall consider the electron field around the nucleus. For the present we shall restrict ourselves to the structure of atomic nuclei.

STRUCTURE OF NUCLEI

Any theory of the structure of nuclei must explain such experimental facts as the following: The nucleus is positively charged, the charge being equal to the atomic number; all the mass of an atom (except a small electronic mass) is concentrated in the nucleus; the relative nuclear masses are very close to whole numbers; certain fundamental particles may be ejected from or added to atomic nuclei to form new nuclei with new charge or mass or both; the element to which a nucleus belongs is determined by the charge of the nucleus and not by its method of formation or its mass.

Structures composed of two fundamental particles, protons and neutrons, allow interpretation of all these facts: The magnitude of the positive nuclear charge is equal to the number of protons within the nucleus; the integral mass of the nucleus is made up of the protons (mass $\cong 1$), which give the appropriate charge, plus an integral number of neutrons (mass $\cong 1$); nuclear changes result from changes in numbers of neutrons and protons present; all isotopes of a given element have the same nuclear charge. Thus the nuclear charge, not the mass, determines the chemical properties of an atom.

According to this theory hydrogen atoms, atomic number 1, would have nuclei bearing a single positive charge. Such a nucleus would contain a single proton. In the same way helium, atomic number 2, has two protons in its nucleus to give it a charge of positive two, and oxygen, atomic number 8, has eight protons in its nucleus. For the atoms of any element, the number of protons in the nucleus is represented by the atomic number, Z, of the element.

Inspection of the masses of the different stable isotopes of all the elements shows that the mass number (except in the lightest isotope of hydrogen) is numerically greater than the atomic number. For some of the isotopes of the lighter elements and for all the isotopes of the heavier elements the mass number is more than twice as great as the atomic number. This extra mass, beyond the mass of the protons, may be attributed to the fundamental particles having mass but no charge, the neutrons. Since neutrons actually appear in many atomic disintegrations it is reasonable to represent the uncharged mass in nuclei in terms of the number of neutrons present. We have already indicated that helium, with atomic number 2 and mass number 4, has two protons in its nucleus. Two neutrons in addition to the two protons gives the helium nucleus the observed mass number of 4. Oxygen, with atomic number 8 and mass number 16, has eight protons. Eight neutrons in its nucleus in addition to the eight protons give it the observed mass number of 16. Sodium, with atomic number 11 and mass number 23, has 11 protons and 12 neutrons in its nucleus. In general, if mass number is indicated by A and atomic number by Z the number of neutrons in a nucleus is equal to $A - Z$. One may think of the neutrons as diluting the protons and diminishing the repulsion due to their positive charges.

Note that this neutron-proton theory does not have any electrons in the nucleus. There is much experimental evidence that there are no nuclear electrons—the simplest one being that the radius of an electron as measured in collision and other experiments is bigger than the radius of a nucleus.

We have already found that ordinary oxygen is a mixture of isotopes. Almost all the oxygen atoms have mass number 16 but a few have mass number 18 and still fewer have mass number 17. All the oxygen isotopes have the same number of protons but different numbers of neutrons, oxygen 18 having ten neutrons in the nucleus and oxygen 17, nine neutrons. Heavy hydrogen, sometimes called deuterium, has a mass number of two. Its nucleus consists of one proton and one neutron. A still rarer isotope of hydrogen, sometimes called tritium, has mass number 3. Its nucleus consists of one proton and two neutrons.

An isotopic description of an atom may be given by writing its atomic number on the lower left-hand corner of the symbol in addition to writing its mass number on the upper right-hand corner. Thus, the isotopes of hydrogen may be represented as $_1H^1$, $_1H^2$, and $_1H^3$. The atomic number and the symbol are not both necessary to distinguish an element but it is often convenient to have both indicated.

Sometimes the atoms of different elements have the same mass number. For example, an isotope of sulfur, $_{16}S^{36}$, has the same mass number as an isotope of argon, $_{18}A^{36}$. Thus we see again that it is the nuclear charge, rather than the mass, which determines the element. We shall find that differences in isotopic masses do cause small differences in chemical properties, for example, the rate at which the atoms undergo reaction, but these effects are usually outside the experimental error of ± 0.2 per cent ordinarily attained in routine work.

The description of the composition of nuclei in terms of number of protons and neutrons is consistent with the facts but is not necessarily a true one. This distinction is important for, as our knowledge of the nucleus changes, we may wish to modify the kinds of fundamental particles used to describe it. What we have done is to give the simplest explanation we can in terms of the fewest fundamental particles, the principle being that one does not postulate a more complicated structure than is necessary to explain the data he wishes to consider. The simple explanation is consistent with the experimental facts and any other explanation must also be consistent with the facts. But consistency, as we have mentioned earlier, is not proof. The charge and mass of a nucleus are known, for they may be measured, but the particles responsible for the charge and mass have not yet been proved by experiment.

EXACT ISOTOPIC MASSES

We have already found that the relative masses of all atoms on the scale $O = 16$ are very nearly whole numbers. We shall now consider the exact masses of atoms and the meaning of the qualification, "very nearly." Since we shall be dealing with the fundamental individual particles, we shall use the physical scale of atomic weights in this discussion, remembering that each of these masses may be converted to the chemical atomic weight scale by dividing by 1.000275. In Table 13.2 are listed the most recent, accepted values for the masses of some particles.

We have postulated that the nucleus of heavy hydrogen, the deuteron, is composed of a proton and a neutron. If we add the masses of these two particles as listed in Table 13.2 we find that the total mass is 2.016517 whereas the actual mass of the deuteron is less, being 2.014169. But what has "become" of the difference in mass, 0.002348?

It is clear that if a deuteron is to be made up of a stable combination of two particles—proton and neutron—the combination must have less energy than the two particles. The difference in energy, evolved when combination occurs, is called "binding energy." It may be measured in terms of the accompanying

Table 13.2
Exact Masses of Some Particles

NAME	SYMBOL	CHARGE	MASS (PHYSICAL BASIS) (O^{16} = 16)
Electron	e	1−	0.0005486
Neutron	n	0	1.008938
Proton	p	1+	1.007579
Deuteron	d	1+	2.014169
Triton	t	1+	3.016480
Helium 3 (nucleus)	He^3	2+	3.015919
Helium 4 (nucleus)	α or He^4	2+	4.002783
Copper 63 (nucleus)	Cu^{63}	29+	62.949

loss of mass according to the Einstein equation, $\Delta E = c^2 \Delta m$, where ΔE is the binding energy, c the speed of light, and Δm the change in mass. From the relationship we find that a nuclear transformation involving the loss of one mass unit corresponds to the release of 1.49×10^{-3} ergs so that the energy released for a mass loss of 0.002348 units is 3.50×10^{-6} ergs. Thus, this energy is released for each atom of deuterium which is formed. How much energy, in calories, is released per mole of deuterium formed?

The energy released when an appreciable amount of material is transformed is enormous. For example, if one gram-atomic weight of deuterium atoms were formed from protons and neutrons the loss in mass would be 0.002348 grams. This corresponds to the release of 2.11×10^{18} ergs, or 5.05×10^{10} calories. The energy released when substances react in chemical reactions is often of the order of magnitude of 100,000, or 10^5, calories per mole. The energy released in the formation of the nuclei of deuterium is 500,000 times greater. Thus, 5 tons of coal would have to be burned to release as much energy as would come from the formation of 2 grams of deuterium.

All nuclei have smaller masses than the sum of the masses of the protons and neutrons indicated as being present. The alpha particle is 0.030251 atomic mass units smaller than the sum of the masses of its protons and neutrons. For Cu^{63} nuclei the sum of the masses of 29 protons and 34 neutrons, is 63.524 whereas the observed value for the mass is 62.949, the difference being 0.575 units. Atomic Cu^{63} has a mass of 62.965. All these values are on the scale

170 GENERAL CHEMISTRY

$O^{16} = 16.0000$. We now see one of the advantages of retaining oxygen as a weight standard on the physical scale as well as on the chemical scale. With oxygen as a standard the weights of the different atoms are more nearly whole numbers than if the mass of hydrogen were taken as a standard, for we note that the mass of Cu^{63} is only slightly less than the whole number, 63. For some atoms the mass is slightly more than a whole number. We need not consider the deviations from whole numbers unless we are interested in the numerical values of the energies released in nuclear transformations.

Similarly, on the chemical atomic weight scale the atomic weight of elements having only one kind of atom may differ slightly from being a whole number. For example, sodium, which consists entirely of Na^{23} atoms, has an atomic weight, 22.991, and aluminum, which consists entirely of Al^{27} has an atomic weight of 26.98. For many purposes we may use the rounded-off numbers, 23 and 27.

NUCLEAR TRANSFORMATIONS IN NATURE

From what has been said in the previous sections, it appears that the nuclei of atoms might react with release of enormous energy to give new products, the products being new kinds of atoms. This kind of behavior is called radioactivity. For example, uranium 238 is known to emit alpha particles and to form an isotope of thorium (see Table 3.1). Further transformations occur until a stable isotope of lead is formed. Each of these particles is emitted with an energy of roughly 1,000,000 electron volts, an energy which corresponds to 23,000,000,000 calories per mole. These particles must, therefore, originate in the nucleus, since energies of this order of magnitude are never found in other reactions. This radioactive transformation may be expressed in terms of an equation similar in form to our ordinary chemical equations.

$$_{92}U^{238} = {_2}He^4 + {_{90}}Th^{234} + \text{energy} \tag{13.1}$$

Equation 13.1 shows that the nucleus of the uranium atom, mass number 238, atomic number 92, has split to give two new nuclei: one is that of helium, (mass number 4, atomic number 2), and the other is that of thorium, (mass number 234, atomic number 90). Observe that the total nuclear positive charge remains unchanged—the sum of the positive charges of the helium and thorium produced, 2 + 90, is identical with 92, the charge of the uranium atom. Similarly, the total mass number, does not change, for the sum of the mass numbers of the helium nucleus and the thorium nucleus, 4 + 234, equals the mass number of the original uranium atom, 238. However, the actual mass of U^{238} is not exactly 238 nor are the masses of He^4 and Th^{234} exactly equal to 4 and 234, respectively. There is a slight loss in mass during the reaction. This reappears as energy, in the form of radiant energy (gamma rays) or in the kinetic energies of the alpha particle and the thorium atom produced in the reaction. Note that emission of an alpha particle is interpreted as the loss of a particle containing 2 neutrons and 2 protons in terms of our nuclear theory.

Thus the daughter element has an atomic number 2 less and a mass number 4 less than the parent.

Transformations involving emission of beta rays may be treated similarly, Thorium 234 disintegrates with the emission of a beta ray. This beta ray has such high energy that it must also originate in the nucleus. But the nucleus that we have postulated does not contain electrons, it consists only of protons and neutrons. It must, therefore, be possible to form electrons from the fundamental particles in the nucleus. If an electron of unit negative charge is formed in the nucleus then an additional positively charged particle must be formed simultaneously. The process may be of the type

$$_0n^1 = {}_1p^1 + {}_{-1}e^0 \tag{13.2}$$

When the electron is emitted the positive charge of the remaining nucleus (and the atomic number of this nucleus) must increase by one unit. The mass of an electron is negligible compared to unity so that the mass number of the nucleus does not change even though a slight amount of additional mass is lost to give the electron its escape energy. The disintegration of the thorium 234 may be represented by equations 13.3a and b.

$$_{90}Th^{234} = {}_{-1}e^0 + {}_{91}Pa^{234} + \text{energy} \tag{13.3a}$$

or

$$_{90}Th^{234} = {}_{-1}\beta^0 + {}_{91}Pa^{234} + \text{energy} \tag{13.3b}$$

When the electron is emitted from the thorium nucleus a new kind of atom is formed, namely that of protoactinium with mass number 234 and atomic number 91. The energy appearing is that corresponding to the small differences in mass discussed previously. Part of the energy is carried by the fast moving electron, part by the protoactinium atom, but some is emitted as gamma rays.

Some transformations are known in which only a gamma ray is emitted. Then, there is no change in nuclear charge or mass number for a tiny amount of mass loss is sufficient to provide the energy represented by the gamma ray. The resulting isotope is so nearly like the one from which it was formed that it may, for most purposes, be represented by the same notation as that for the original atom. The only change which has occurred is that the protons and neutrons have rearranged themselves into a more stable nuclear structure, the energy loss appearing as a gamma ray.

Only alpha particles, electrons, and gamma rays are emitted by naturally occurring isotopes. Synthesized isotopes may emit several other kinds of particles, as we shall discover, but their emission is still interpreted in terms of nuclei containing only neutrons and protons.

HALF LIFE OF RADIOACTIVE ATOMS

There is no predicting when a particular unstable nucleus will disintegrate, for its disintegration is equally probable at any time. When a large number of atoms is considered, the ability to predict is increased since the laws of mathematical probability apply to the problem. For example, in a sample containing

172   GENERAL CHEMISTRY

a large number of atoms, we find that the number of atoms disintegrating in any time interval is directly proportional to the number of atoms present. If a certain number of U^{238} atoms in a one-gram sample disintegrate in one minute, twice as many atoms disintegrate in a two-gram sample and one half as many disintegrate in a 0.5-g. sample in the same time interval. This means that in a definite interval, characteristic of each radioactive isotope, half the atoms in any sample of that isotope will disintegrate. This time interval is called the *half-life period*, or simply the *half life*. At the end of a half-life period

TABLE 13.3
Some Half-Life Periods

PARENT ISOTOPE	EMITTED PARTICLE	ENERGY OF RADIATION (MILLION ELECTRON VOLTS)	HALF LIFE
U^{238}	α	4.18	4.5×10^9 years
Th^{234}	β^-	0.20	24 days
Sm^{152}	α	2.1	1.0×10^{12} years
Po^{212}	α	8.78	3×10^{-7} seconds
Pb^{210}	β^-	0.03	22 years
Ag^{106}	β^+	2.0	24.5 minutes
C^{10}	β^+	2	20 seconds
C^{14}	β^-	0.15	5000 years

one half of the original atoms still remain. At the end of a second half-life period one quarter of the original atoms remain, and at the end of a third half-life period one eighth of the original atoms remain, and so on until the number of atoms remaining is so few that the laws of probability do not apply. Table 13.3 shows the half-life period and one of the disintegration products for some typical radioactive isotopes. Note the very large range in half lives.

STABLE ISOTOPES AND THEIR ABUNDANCE

Although the different stable isotopes of the various elements and their relative abundance are now known for practically all the elements, we do not yet have an adequate theory for explaining the stability or instability of nuclei. We can predict successfully that certain isotopes, when prepared, will be radioactive, for we know that atoms having smaller or larger mass than those for the stable atoms are unstable and will disintegrate according to the probability principle, with definite half-life periods. We also know that only those reactions involving a loss in mass can proceed spontaneously. Present theory, however, is not yet adequate for explaining the observed results in terms of general concepts.

One striking fact is that a certain type of isotope is unusually stable in lighter elements. Among the most common elements found on the earth and in the rest of the universe are those whose atomic numbers are even and whose principal isotopes have mass numbers exactly double the atomic number.

Indeed, the nuclei of such atoms might be considered as made up of a number of alpha particles. The list includes $_2$He^4, $_6$C^{12}, $_8$O^{16}, $_{10}$Ne^{20}, $_{12}$Mg^{24}, $_{14}$Si^{28}, $_{16}$S^{32}, $_{20}$Ca^{40}. The atoms in this list have nuclei whose composition could be indicated as 1, 3, 4, 5, 6, 7, 8, and 10 alpha particles, respectively. Significantly absent are $_4$Be whose mass number is 9, not 8, and $_{18}$A whose most abundant isotope has mass number 40, not 36. More than half the atoms on the earth are $_8$O^{16} atoms. The cosmic importance of the above series will be appreciated on review of Table 7.1 which shows the relative abundance not only in the rocks of the earth and in meteorites but also in the sun's atmosphere, a star, and a nebula.

Some other general statements may be made about stable isotopes. As a group, the even-numbered atoms are much more abundant than odd-numbered atoms. In general, the mass numbers of odd-numbered elements are odd and those of even-numbered elements are even, although important exceptions occur. In other words, the great majority of nuclei contain an even number of neutrons. An exception is beryllium, an even-numbered element whose mass number is 9. About one half the odd-numbered elements consist of only one kind of atom. Examples are fluorine, sodium, aluminum, phosphorus, scandium, vanadium, manganese, and cobalt. Most of the other odd elements have only two isotopes and these have odd mass numbers which differ by two units. In general the even elements have two or more stable isotopes. Tin has ten, and others have eight or nine stable isotopes.

Significant also is the list of the elements within the periodic table which have no stable isotopes. They include: element 43, technicium; element 49, indium; element 61, promethium, and all elements of atomic number greater than 83. Some are so unstable that they have not been found in nature, though all have been synthesized.

Problem 13.2. Calculate a value for the energy released when one mole of Cu^{63} is formed from protons, neutrons, and electrons. Do you need to consider the mass of the electrons in this calculation? Explain. What will be the mass of a Cu^{63} atom on the physical scale? On the chemical scale?

Problem 13.3. For each of the isotopes listed in Table 13.3, one of the products formed in a radioactive transformation is listed. Write an equation for each of the transformations, indicating clearly the second product formed, together with its mass number and atomic number.

Problem 13.4. Which of the oxygen isotopes would you expect to be most stable on the basis of their masses? Explain.

Problem 13.5. From the data in Table 13.2 compare the masses of doubly charged helium atoms, and singly charged heavy hydrogen atoms H^2. Could the lines formed by these particles in a mass spectrograph be distinguished from one another? How could you tell whether H^3 or He^3 were giving a line at about m/e = 3 in a mass spectrograph?

Problem 13.6. One of the following reactions proceeds with a half life of about half an hour. Predict which it is. What bearing has your answer on the situation within a nucleus?

$$_0n^1 = {_1p^1} + {_{-1}e^0}$$
$$_1p^1 = {_0n^1} + {_1e^0}$$

14 ELECTRONIC STRUCTURE OF ATOMS

FROM THE scattering of alpha particles and other rapidly moving particles by atomic nuclei we find that the diameter of a nucleus is of the order of 10^{-13} cm., or 10^{-5} Ångstrom units. The distance between nuclei in a solid element is much greater, of the order of 10^{-8} cm., or 1 Å. This latter distance also corresponds to the diameter of atoms as calculated from collision experiments in gases or from the number of atoms in crystals. Thus, the diameter of the nucleus is only about $\frac{1}{100,000}$ of that of an atom as a whole so that the neutrons and protons occupy only a minute fraction of the volume of an atom. We shall now consider the structure of the rest of the atom in terms of the electrons which surround the nucleus.

VOLUME OF ATOMS

Although atoms occupy a very real volume they can not be regarded as though they were solid spheres. The volume of the electrons around a nucleus is not enough in itself to explain observed volumes, the collision diameter of an electron being only slightly larger than the nuclear diameter of about 10^{-13} cm.

The apparent volumes of atoms and of gaseous molecules may be calculated from collision volumes but volumes calculated in this way vary with the speed of the colliding particles. Apparently, atoms colliding at high speeds move closer together before the repulsive forces reverse the motion than do atoms moving at low speeds. The situation is analogous to the collision of tennis balls. If one were to measure the diameter of tennis balls by observing how close their centers approach before the balls rebound one would find that the apparent diameter of the balls varies with the speed. Nevertheless, the volumes measured in this way are definite in any experiment.

Another way of calculating volumes of atoms is to find how many of them are present in a crystal and to calculate the diameters and volumes from the space to be attributed to each atom. Since the number of uniform spheres or

ELECTRONIC STRUCTURE OF ATOMS   175

other geometric bodies that may be packed in a given volume depends on the mode of packing as well as on the diameter of the bodies, the calculated volume of an atom will vary with the assumed packing. But if the mode of packing is known, then the diameter of an atom can be calculated with greater certainty. Even this figure will vary with temperature as the crystal expands or contracts.

When solids or liquids are subjected to pressure they decrease in volume at a small but measurable rate. Some of the effects may be explained in terms of a closer packing of the atoms or molecules but some must be explained in terms of the compression of the atoms themselves. At pressures of the order of about 30,000 atmospheres, the maximum decrease in volume is about twenty-five per cent (except for helium whose volume is reduced one half at pressures of 3000 atmospheres [Dugdale and Simon, 1953]). The changes in volume of liquids or solids caused by the normal changes in atmospheric pressure are insignificant, although the changes are appreciable for gases in which the atoms and molecules are widely separated and not in contact with one another, as we have already shown.

When two atoms combine to form a molecule, the volume of the molecule, as measured by any of the available means, is slightly less than the sum of the independent atomic volumes. The effect may be interpreted as an overlapping of volumes so that the nuclei of atoms within a molecule have a shorter distance between them than the distance between the nuclei of atoms not in the same molecule. If electrons are responsible for the volume of atoms, the decrease in total volume when two atoms combine in a molecule may be attributed to the mutual sharing of some of the electrons.

All these lines of evidence show that the atomic volume occupied by the electrons is relatively easily deformed. Thus, electrons in atoms do not occupy a hard sphere nor create a rigid surface. By allowing for all the above effects, however, we can arrive at rather definite values for the effective volumes and diameters of atoms at rest or moving at low speeds. The values for the atomic diameters lie in a rather small range from 1 Å. to 5 Å. How, then, do the electrons "occupy" this space?

ELECTRONS IN ATOMS

Let us summarize briefly what we have said about electrons in atoms. We have seen that electrons may be rather easily removed from atoms by heating or by other means of providing the necessary energy of separation. However, if an atom is to be electrically neutral, the number of electrons around the nucleus must be equal to the number of positive charges on the nucleus, that is, to the atomic number. These electrons form an electronic field about the nucleus which excludes other atoms and gives each atom its volume. The atoms of different elements, having differing numbers of electrons attracted by nuclei of differing charge, occupy differing volumes. The volume does not increase uniformly with atomic number. It fluctuates in a periodic fashion

176 GENERAL CHEMISTRY

(see Figure 12.1). The volume corresponding to the electronic field is somewhat fuzzy and not bounded by a distinct "surface." It is easily distorted, but, nevertheless, requires very great forces to compress it appreciably. The atom with its electronic field to give it volume behaves more like a tennis ball than like a billiard ball.

We have already noted that most of a beam of alpha particles can pass through a thin sheet of metal without being deflected. Some of the alpha particles which miss the nuclei of the atoms will encounter electrons and drive them out of the atoms but the electrons do not serve as effective scattering centers because their masses are too small. For the same reason, electrons do not scatter protons and neutrons. The electron, with a mass of only $\frac{1}{1800}$ that of the proton, is about as effective in deflecting a proton as a bean would be in deflecting a fifty-caliber rifle bullet. Such scattering experiments, therefore, reveal little concerning electron structure in atoms. X-rays are scattered by electrons and it is from such scattering that direct evidence is obtained concerning electron distribution.

According to modern theory, the electrons in an atom are in rapid motion. If an atom were enlarged until the nucleus became one inch in diameter, each electron might be represented by a sphere a few inches in diameter moving rapidly about the nucleus, the farthest electron being at a distance of about one mile from the nucleus. Thus, the volumes of the electrons themselves would not interfere with the free motion of the electrons. The motion itself is not simple, as can be seen from the fact that the single electron in a hydrogen atom moves about so as to give a spherical symmetry to the atom. Although the electrons do not move in regular "planetary" orbits about the nucleus as postulated by Bohr, they are, for historical reasons, often called orbital electrons.

All the forces operating between the orbital electrons in an atom are not clearly understood, but it is evident that when there are several orbital electrons in an atom their motions cannot be entirely independent, for the repulsive forces between the negatively charged electrons extend far beyond their volumes as determined from collisions. A consequence is that the motions of different electrons in the same atom are oriented to one another. Thus, all the orbital electrons remain outside the nucleus and may orient themselves so that the energy of the atom is at a minimum value. Atoms in this state of minimum energy are said to be in their *ground state*.

ELECTRONIC ENERGY LEVELS

One of the best-known facts about atoms is that they may exist in different energy states, each with a definite energy. When they are "excited" out of the ground state by the introduction of energy they emit light of definite wave lengths (or frequencies) as they return to their ground states. The "light" may be ordinary visible light or it may be similar radiant energy in the infrared, ultraviolet, or x-ray range of frequencies. These facts we shall interpret in terms of the electrons in the atoms.

All radiant energy travels with the speed of light and may be interpreted in terms of a wave motion. Infrared waves have very long wave lengths and low energies; x-rays have short wave lengths and high energies. The *frequency* of a wave is defined as the number of wave fronts that pass a point in unit time. Long wave lengths mean that relatively few wave fronts pass per second and, therefore, correspond to low frequencies. Since the energies of waves are directly proportional to their frequencies but inversely proportional to wave length, we shall use frequency rather than wave length to characterize radiant energy. Visible light represents only a small part of the possible frequencies (or wave lengths), for the eye can detect only the energy absorbed by the

Table 14.1
Colors Imparted to Flames by Compounds of Certain Elements

ELEMENT	COLOR	ELEMENT	COLOR
Lithium	Scarlet	Calcium	Dull Red
Sodium	Yellow	Strontium	Bright Red
Potassium	Violet	Barium	Green
Rubidium	Red	Copper	Blue
Cesium	Blue	Boron	Green

molecules in the eye in enough quantity to produce certain chemical changes without disrupting the light-gathering molecules. Ultraviolet light has higher frequencies and higher energies than visible light. X-rays have still higher values and cosmic rays have the highest frequencies and energies of all.

The light emitted by atoms may be separated into its different components by passing it through a narrow slit into a spectrograph. This separates the light of different frequencies into different "lines" falling on a photograph plate. Each spectral line of different color corresponds to a different energy change in the atom.

A simple demonstration of the differences in energy changes in different atoms can be made with an ordinary Bunsen flame. That such flames probably contain free electrons may be readily demonstrated from their very high electrical conductivity as evidenced, for instance, by the great tendency of a charged object to discharge by sparking to a flame. Introduction of a compound of sodium into the flame gives the flame a bright yellow color. Sodium chloride contains positively charged sodium atoms, or ions, and these, when vaporized, gain electrons from the flame with the resulting evolution of energy in the form of light. This is the basis of the flame tests used to identify several of the chemical elements in their compounds as listed in Table 14.1. In these instances certain energy changes predominate, giving only a few spectral lines

178 GENERAL CHEMISTRY

and the resulting color. So many transitions are possible in iron, on the other hand, that the spectral lines combine to give white light.

The electronic interpretation of the different energy states is that the orbital electrons may exist in definite configurations of differing energy. When an atom is excited, electrons are moved from lower energy levels (which may be said to be nearer the nucleus) to higher energy levels (farther from the nucleus). After the excitation, the electrons may drop back to the lower energy levels, emitting their excess energy as light. If the difference in energy be-

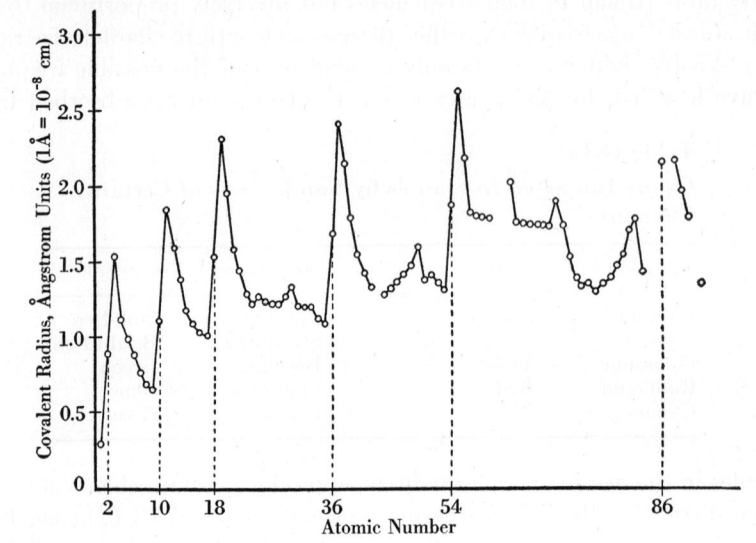

Figure 14.1.
Covalent atomic radius *vs* atomic number of the element.

tween the different levels is fixed, the light emitted will have a definite energy (and frequency). The observed lines and their frequencies fully confirm the idea that the electrons in atoms exist in well-defined energy levels, only certain energies being absorbed or evolved as electrons go to higher or lower levels.

A second method for gaining information about the energies of the different energy levels is to measure the energy required to remove electrons completely from atoms so that positive ions and free electrons are produced. This method readily gives information on the outer energy levels for it is the electrons least tightly bound by the nucleus which are the most easily removed. If a potential of one volt is required to remove an electron, the *ionization potential* is one volt and the energy required is one electron-volt. The corresponding energy to remove one electron each from an Avogadro number of such atoms is 6×10^{23} electron-volts, or 23,000 calories. In practice, the term "ionization potential" is applied to the energy (in electron-volts) required to remove electrons.

ELECTRONIC STRUCTURE OF ATOMS   179

The ionization potential of most of the elements are listed in Table 14.2, together with their atomic and ionic radii. See pages 80 and 470 for a discussion of the measurement of these radii. The ionization potentials are for the removal from the neutral atom of the least tightly bound electron. The data may be more meaningful if they are plotted in a diagram. The values of the atomic radii as ordinates against the atomic numbers as abscissas are plotted in Figure 14.1. Similarly, the values for the ionization potentials are plotted

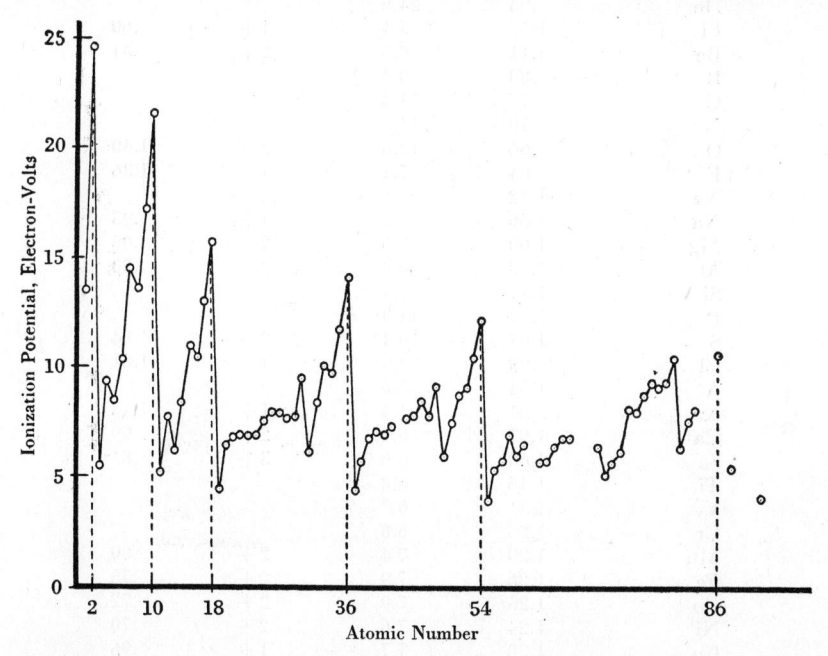

Figure 14.2.
Ionization energy of the first electron in electron-volts *vs* atomic number of the element.

against atomic numbers in Figure 14.2. These two figures should be compared with one another and with Figure 12.1, page 156.

The marked periodicity in the tendency of the elements to undergo comparable chemical reaction as the atomic number increases is further evidence for a periodicity in the electron structure, for it is the electrons that interact, not the nuclei. The nuclei remain quite remote from one another in the usual laboratory reactions.

Further information concerning electron arrangements is obtained from the energies required to remove a second or third electron. Some of these energies are listed in Table 14.3. They may be interpreted on the basis of the following considerations: if the laws of electrostatics hold, the attraction of a nucleus for an electron will depend on (1) the effective charge of the nucleus and (2)

Table 14.2
Atomic Ionization Potentials and Atomic and Ionic Radii

ELEMENT	COVALENT ATOMIC RADIUS (Å.)	IONIZATION POTENTIAL (ELECTRON VOLTS)	CHARGE	ION RADIUS (Å.)
H	.30	13.60	1−	2.08
He	.93	24.6		
Li	1.52	5.4	1+	.60
Be	1.11	9.3	2+	.31
B	.88	8.3		
C	.77	11.3		
N	.70	14.5		
O	.66	13.6	2−	1.40
F	.64	17.4	1−	1.36
Ne	1.12	21.6		
Na	1.86	5.1	1+	.95
Mg	1.60	7.6	2+	.65
Al	1.43	6.0	3+	.50
Si	1.17	8.1		
P	1.10	11.0		
S	1.04	10.4	2−	1.84
Cl	.99	13.0	1−	1.81
A	1.54	15.8		
K	2.31	4.4	1+	1.33
Ca	1.97	6.1	2+	.99
Sc	1.60	6.6	3+	.81
Ti	1.46	6.8		
V	1.31	6.7		
Cr	1.25	6.8		
Mn	1.29	7.4	2+	.80
Fe	1.26	7.9	2+	.75
Co	1.25	7.9	2+	.72
Ni	1.24	7.6	2+	.70
Cu	1.28	7.7	1+	.96
Zn	1.33	9.4	2+	.74
Ga	1.22	6.0	3+	.62
Ge	1.22	8.1	4+	.53
As	1.21	10.±		
Se	1.17	9.7	2−	1.98
Br	1.14	11.8	1−	1.95
Kr	1.69	14.0		
Rb	2.44	4.2	1+	1.48
Sr	2.15	5.7	2+	1.13
Y	1.80	6.6	3+	.93
Zr	1.57	7.0		
Nb	1.43	6.8		
Mo	1.36	7.2		
Tc	—			
Ru	1.33	7.5		
Rh	1.34	7.7		
Pd	1.38	8.3		
Ag	1.44	7.6	1+	1.26
Cd	1.49	9.0	2+	.97
In	1.62	5.8	3+	.81

Table 14.2—*Continued*

ELEMENT	COVALENT ATOMIC RADIUS (Å.)	IONIZATION POTENTIAL (ELECTRON VOLTS)	ION CHARGE	ION RADIUS (Å.)
Sn	1.4	7.3	4+	.71
Sb	1.41	8.6		
Te	1.37	9.0	2−	2.21
I	1.33	10.4	1−	2.16
Xe	1.90	12.1		
Cs	2.62	3.9	1+	1.69
Ba	2.17	5.2	2+	1.35
La	1.87	5.6	3+	1.15
Ce	1.82	(6.9)	3+	1.01
Pr	1.82	(5.8)	3+	1.00
Nd	1.82	(6.3)	3+	.99
Pm			3+	.98
Sm		5.6	3+	.98
Eu	2.04	5.7	3+	.97
Gd	1.79	6.2	3+	.96
Tb	1.77	(6.7)	3+	.95
Dy	1.77	(6.8)	3+	.94
Ho	1.76		3+	.93
Er	1.75		3+	.92
Tm	1.74		3+	.91
Yb	1.93	6.2	3+	.89
Lu	1.74	5.0	3+	.89
Hf	1.57	5.5±		
Ta	1.43	6±		
W	1.37	8.0		
Re	1.37	7.9		
Os	1.34	8.7		
Ir	1.35	9.2		
Pt	1.38	9.0		
Au	1.44	9.2	1+	1.37
Hg	1.55	10.4	2+	1.10
Tl	1.71	6.1	3+	.95
Pb	1.75	7.4	4+	.84
Bi	1.46	8±		
Po	1.65			
At	—			
Rn	2.2	10.7		
Fr	—			
Ra	2.20	5.3		
Ac	2.0			
Th	1.80			
Pa	—			
U	1.4	4±	3+	1.11
Np			3+	1.08
Pu			3+	1.06
Am			3+	1.04
Cm			3+	1.02
Bk			3+	1.01
Cf			3+	1.00

the distance of the electron from the nucleus. We refer to effective charge, rather than to the nuclear charge represented by the atomic number, since an electron distant from the nucleus will be shielded from the nucleus by any electrons between itself and the nucleus and will be less strongly attracted to it. The electrons nearest the nucleus will experience the attraction of the full nuclear charge. Those farther away will be less strongly attracted, not only because of the greater distance but also because the intervening electrons reduce the effectiveness of the nuclear charge on them.

Table 14.3

Electron-Volts Required to Remove First, Second, and Third Electrons

ELEMENT SYMBOL	ELECTRON REMOVED		
	First	Second	Third
H	13.60		
He	24.58	54.40	
Li	5.39	75.62	122.42
Be	9.32	18.21	153.85
B	8.30	25.15	37.92
C	11.26	24.38	47.87
N	14.54	29.60	47.43
O	13.61	35.15	54.93
F	17.42	34.98	62.65
Ne	21.56	41.07	64$\pm$

Data from National Bureau of Standards Circular No. 467, "Atomic Energy Levels," June 15, 1949.

That other forces are present becomes evident on inspection of Table 14.2, but the simple principles we have assumed give us much insight into the behavior of the orbital electrons. Thus, a potential of 13.60 volts is required to separate the electron from the hydrogen nucleus, charge 1+, but 24.58 volts are required to separate one of the two electrons from the helium nucleus, charge 2+. The potential for ionizing the second electron is much larger, being 54.40 volts. However, the potential required to separate a single electron from the lithium nucleus, charge 3+, represents a much lower energy than that for either the hydrogen or helium electrons, the potential being 5.39 volts. For this reason, and others, we believe that the electron separated from the lithium was in a different energy level, one farther from the nucleus than the level in hydrogen and helium. We shall interpret the other ionization potential values when we consider the detailed electronic structure of the different elements.

Note also that the first ionization potential of hydrogen (13.60 volts), the second ionization potential of helium (54.40 volts), and the third ionization potential of lithium (122.42 volts), are in the ratio of $1^2:2^2:3^2$, that is, they are proportional to the square of the nuclear charge of each atom. These values are consistent with Coulomb's law of electrostatics which states that the energy of attraction between electrical charges is proportional to the square of the charge acting.

THE HYDROGEN ATOM

The simplest atom is that of the most common isotope of hydrogen, consisting of a single proton and a single orbital electron. The energy necessary to remove this electron, to ionize the atom, may be measured; it is 13.60 electron-volts. This value may be readily checked by determining the energy of the light emitted when the electron returns to the atom. When the electron returns to its former level, the energy emitted is found to be 13.60 electron-volts. If less energy is added the electron may still absorb energy but then it does not leave the atom. The least amount of energy effective in removing an electron from the ground level of hydrogen is 10.1 electron-volts, the next effective amount is 11.9 electron-volts, and the next is 12.6 electron-volts. Always definite amounts of energy are required to raise an electron to a higher energy level.

Once the electron is in a higher level it may return spontaneously to a lower level, emitting the appropriate amount of energy as light. The lowest energy level is called the *1*, or *K*, level and the next higher the *2*, or *L*, level. If the electron is in the *2* level it may return to the *1* level emitting, as light, energy of the amount 10.1 electron-volts. If the electron was in the *3* or the *4* level, it emits energy of 11.9 or 12.6 electron-volts, respectively, on returning to the *1* level. These changes in energy are illustrated in Figure 14.3. In a sample containing many hydrogen atoms, some of each of these transitions occur and the light emitted may be separated into a spectrum of lines, called the Lyman series. The lines have wave lengths which place them in the ultraviolet part of the spectrum. A second set of spectral lines is found when visible light is emitted by hydrogen. This light corresponds to the energy required to raise electrons from the *2* level to higher levels. When the electrons then return to the *2* level they emit light having energy corresponding to the difference in energies between the *3* and *2* levels, the *4* and *2* levels, the *5* and *2* levels, etc. These lines appearing in the visible part of the spectrum are called the Balmer series. Other series are known. They represent the shift of electrons from higher levels to the *3* level and to the *4* level.

The energy level picture obtained in this way is consistent with all the experimental evidence. The numerical values for the differences in energy between the different levels can be derived from any of the spectral series, the values always being in agreement. When an electron moves from the *3* level to the *1* level the total energy emitted is the same whether it moves in one step or whether it first moves to the *2* level and then to the *1* level.

In a hydrogen atom there is only one electron. This electron can be in only one level at a time. When the atom is in the ground state, the electron is in the

184 GENERAL CHEMISTRY

1 level. When the atom is excited, the electron is in one of the higher levels. The same principles apply to more complex atoms. In each atom an electron may be in one of several different energy levels but its energy is determined by the level in which it is. If it moves to a higher level it absorbs a definite amount of energy and when it returns to the former level it emits that same amount of energy.

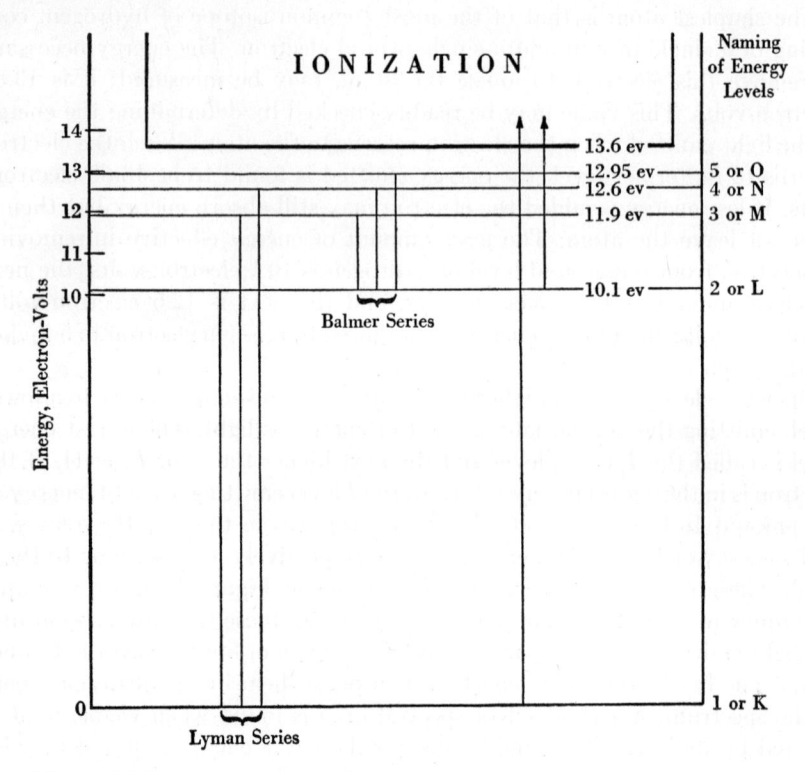

Figure 14.3.
Electronic energy levels for hydrogen atoms.

Problem 14.1. Compare the differences in energy (in electron-volts) between the first five electronic energy levels in hydrogen.

THE HELIUM ATOM

It is clear from the data plotted in Figure 14.2 that much more energy is required to remove an electron from an atom of helium than from an atom of hydrogen. Helium differs from hydrogen in having a nuclear charge of two and, consequently, two electrons in the available energy levels. A study of the spectrum of ionized helium, helium nuclei with only one electron, shows that it is identical with the hydrogen spectrum if correction is made for the doubly charged nucleus attracting the single electron more strongly. This means that the same arrangement of energy levels is present in each atom but each electron is held more tightly to the nucleus in helium by the higher attracting charge. Analysis of the spectrum of neutral helium shows that both its electrons are in the same lowest-lying energy level and that this corresponds to the lowest energy level in hydrogen. Thus this first level can hold at least two electrons simultaneously.

THE ELEMENTS LITHIUM THROUGH SODIUM

For lithium the ionization potential is much less than for either hydrogen or helium, in spite of the increase in the nuclear charge. An increase in radius (see Figure 14.1) is also apparent now that three electrons are present in the atom. That the general arrangement of the energy levels is the same here as in hydrogen or helium is shown by the fact that the spectrum of singly ionized lithium, lithium nuclei holding only two electrons, is identical with that of helium if a correction is made for the increased nuclear charge, and further that the spectrum of doubly ionized lithium, lithium nuclei with only one electron, is the same as that of hydrogen atoms again applying a correction for the trebling of the nuclear charge. The first two lithium electrons are, therefore, in the same energy level as were the hydrogen and helium electrons. If the third lithium electron were also in this level one might expect an increase in ionization potential in going from helium to lithium similar to that found in going from hydrogen to helium and attributable to the same cause, an increase in nuclear charge. As a matter of fact a decrease in the ionization energy is observed. A logical interpretation is that the third lithium electron enters a new energy level where it is less attracted to the nucleus. This is proved to be true by a detailed examination of the transitions observed in the spectrum. The increase in atomic size in going from helium to lithium indicates that this third electron is farther from the nucleus and thus more readily removed.

With beryllium an increase in potential is observed compared to that of lithium. Note also that beryllium atoms are smaller than lithium atoms. Interpreted as above, this fact would mean that fourth beryllium electron entered the same energy level as did the third electron. The spectral data confirm this interpretation. For boron a decrease in ionization potential is observed, interpreted again as the beginning of a new energy level—an interpretation proved correct by spectral data.

This third new energy level does not differ from the second one in the same way the second differs from the first, however, for certain properties of the electrons in the second and third levels are identical. It is true the electrons differ in energy but the mathematics used to describe them also shows that some of the description is common to both levels. These second and third levels are, then, said to be separate parts of a main level, or main shell, and will be called the first and second sub-levels of the second main level. This arrangement is analogous to a cabinet in which the carpenter has placed a series of shelves to which have been added secondary shelves for closer sorting of the contents. The main levels will be numbered *1, 2, 3, 4*, etc., out from the nucleus, and the sub-levels will be labelled *s, p, d*, and *f*. (The choice of *s, p, d*, and *f*, for identification of the sub-levels was based on certain properties of the corresponding spectral lines by which the lines were originally characterized as sharp, principal, diffuse, or fundamental.) The least tightly held (fifth) boron electron is then known as a *2p* electron, the two most tightly held being *1s* and the other two, *2s* electrons.

Element 6, carbon, again shows an increase in ionization potential indicating another *2p* electron, as does also element 7, nitrogen. These assignments are again borne out by detailed spectroscopic investigations. But note, the *1s* and the *2s* levels were filled by two electrons each whereas the *2p* level already has three electrons in it and may not yet be filled. Oxygen, the next element, with a total of eight electrons shows another drop in ionization potential, hitherto an indication of the start of a new shell. Spectroscopic investigation shows that this last electron is also a *2p* electron, however, and that no new level is started. Fluorine adds another *2p* electron and element 10, neon, still another *2p* electron. At this point a very large drop in ionization potential and a very large increase in atomic volume are found when we go to element 11, sodium. As first observed for lithium, the abrupt changes are again due to the beginning of a new main level, for sodium the *3s* level containing only a single electron. Apparently the *2p* level can hold no more than 6 electrons, just as an *s* level can hold only 2 electrons.

Thus lithium and sodium, members of the same column or family in the periodic table, both have a single electron in their outermost energy level, an *s* level. It is this similarity in outer electron structure that gives family relationships in the tables. Thus, one would expect potassium, the next member of this family, to have a single *4s* electron, rubidium a single *5s* electron, etc. This prediction is borne out by experiment.

You will note that the abrupt changes in ionization potential between helium and neon repeat themselves exactly as one proceeds from neon to element number 20, calcium, and each such change is interpretable in the way outlined above. It also becomes clear why the chemistries of those elements in the same column of a Mendeleeff table are so similar; they have the same electron configurations in their outer energy levels. It is these outer levels which determine chemistry since it is the outer levels which interact when atoms approach one another.

The electronic structure of calcium may, then, be written as *$1s^2$; $2s^2$, $2p^6$; $3s^2$, $3p^6$; $4s^2$*, where the superscripts give the number of electrons in each of the sub-levels indicated by main level number and sub-level symbol. The electronic structure may also be written 2, 8, 8, 2 in terms of main levels only. Again one could predict that the valence electrons of strontium would be *$5s^2$*, of barium *$6s^2$*, and of radium *$7s^2$*.

PAIRED AND UNPAIRED ELECTRONS

But what about the drop in ionization potential in going from nitrogen with three $2p$ electrons to oxygen with four $2p$ electrons? Or the similar drop between phosphorus and sulfur?

In our discussion of the properties of electrons we have mentioned that they had other properties besides those of charge, mass, and size. One of these additional properties, called *electron spin*, exhibits itself by endowing single electrons with magnetic properties. These magnetic properties disappear when two electrons pair up, the scientific terminology being that the spins are then opposed. Now it is fairly easy to determine the number of unpaired electrons in an atom by studying the effect of a magnetic field on the atom, since the field of the external magnet interacts with the magnetic field of the electron in a calculable manner. Substances containing unpaired electrons are pulled into a magnetic field, the force being greater the greater the number of unpaired electrons. These substances are said to be paramagnetic. Pairing of electrons destroys this interaction.

Table 14.4

Number of Unpaired Electrons in a Single Atom of Each of First Eleven Elements in the Periodic Table

ELEMENT	H	He	Li	Be	B	C	N	O	F	Ne	Na
TOTAL NO. OF ELECTRONS	1	2	3	4	5	6	7	8	9	10	11
NO. OF UNPAIRED ELECTRONS	1	0	1	0	1	2	3	2	1	0	1

The number of unpaired electrons per atom for the first eleven elements in the periodic table are listed in Table 14.4. This table illustrates the fact that electrons in a given atomic energy level often remain unpaired. It should be noted that every atom of odd atomic number (odd number of electrons) must, of course, have at least one unpaired electron, but there is no obvious reason that more than one unpaired electron should exist in any atom. Yet carbon, nitrogen, and oxygen all contain more than one unpaired electron even though the unpaired electrons are in the same energy level and supposedly could be paired. Evidently unpaired electrons are more stable than paired electrons in these atoms where the energy level is far from full of electrons. The fourth, fifth, and sixth p electron, on the other hand, go into electron pairs—it appears that there can be a maximum of only three unpaired electrons in a p level. We shall find it to be a general rule that the first electrons to enter an energy level remain unpaired but that the number of unpaired electrons in any energy level cannot exceed half the total number of electrons that level can hold. We shall also find much evidence that atoms containing electron structures in which a level is exactly half full are rather stable.

The tendency to unpair electrons in single atoms and the rather high stability of exactly half full energy levels account for the lower ionization potential of oxygen atoms compared to nitrogen atoms. The fourth p electron in oxygen is relatively easy to remove since the tendency to form pairs is not strong, and the structure of the resulting singly positive oxygen ion is quite stable since it contains a p level which is exactly half full. Thus the difference in energy between the atom and ion (that is, the ionization potential) is small.

ELEMENTS BEYOND SCANDIUM

From the above we would expect a drop in ionization potential between calcium and element 21, scandium, but a rise is actually observed. Unless we have been misguided, all the lower levels are full, each "s" level holding its two electrons and each "p" level its six, so that a new level must be started at this point—a new level has always resulted in a decrease in ionization potential. Investigation shows that a new level does indeed start but that the characteristics of these added electrons are such that they belong to main level 3 rather than 4. In other words, main levels 3 and 4 overlap so that 4 begins to fill before 3 is really full. Since this 21st electron goes into the third sub-level of main level 3 it is known as a $3d$ electron. Hence scandium is in Group 3b of the periodic table, for its outer electron structure ($4s^2$, $3d$), while similar to aluminum ($3s^2$, $3p$), is not the same so that the two elements have some rather large differences in chemical behavior. We shall, in fact, define "b" Group elements as those which contain d electrons but differ from the atoms of neighboring atomic number in the number of d electrons they contain.

Additional evidence of the occurrence of the new sub-level in main level 3 comes from the observation that there are eight atomic numbers, or elements, between helium and neon and eight between neon and argon (these three elements—helium, neon, and argon—belonging to the same column in the periodic table), but that the next element in this column, krypton, is eighteen atoms later, or eight plus ten. Further examination shows that this ten corresponds exactly to the maximum number of $3d$ electrons. The order in which they enter the atoms is shown in Table 14.5. This order correlates very well with the ionization potentials, the minima at chromium and copper in Figure 14.2 being interpreted as due to the existence of only one $4s$ electron in these two atoms compared to two $4s$ electrons in all the rest from calcium through zinc. The apparent anomalies in chromium and copper cease to be anomalies if we remember the tendency of atoms to assume completely full levels or exactly half-full levels as in the singly-positive oxygen ion. Here the tendency for the $3d$ level to become exactly half full or to become completely full overcomes a similar tendency in the $4s$ level, with the observed results. Furthermore, the single $4s$ electron can be removed rather easily, that is, it has a low ionization potential. It may be noted that the same abrupt changes in ionization potential that were observed when the $2p$ and $3p$ levels filled are again observed in Figure 14.2 as the $4p$ level fills.

The electronic structures of most of the elements have now been deduced experimentally. The rest have been deduced from the trends in the periodic table. The currently accepted structures for all the known elements are listed in Table 14.5, which also shows the final completion of the 4th main level to its maximum of 32 with the acquisition of the fourteen 4f electrons (elements 58 through 71).

Table 14.5

Electronic Structures of Single Atoms of the Elements

		K 1s	L 2s 2p	M 3s 3p 3d	N 4s 4p 4d 4f	O 5s 5p 5d	P 6s 6p 6d	Q 7s
H	1	1						
He	2	2						
Li	3	2	1					
Be	4	2	2					
B	5	2	2 1					
C	6	2	2 2					
N	7	2	2 3					
O	8	2	2 4					
F	9	2	2 5					
Ne	10	2	2 6					
Na	11	2	2 6	1				
Mg	12			2				
Al	13			2 1				
Si	14		10	2 2				
P	15		Neon Core	2 3				
S	16			2 4				
Cl	17			2 5				
A	18			2 6				
K	19	2	2 6	2 6	1			
Ca	20				2			
Sc	21			1	2			
Ti	22			2	2			
V	23			3	2			
Cr	24		18	5	1			
Mn	25		Argon core	5	2			
Fe	26			6	2			
Co	27			7	2			
Ni	28			8	2			
Cu	29	2	2 6	2 6 10	1			
Zn	30				2			
Ga	31				2 1			
Ge	32				2 2			
As	33		28		2 3			
Se	34		Copper core		2 4			
Br	35				2 5			
Kr	36				2 6			
Rb	37	2	2 6	2 6 10	2 6	1		
Sr	38					2		
Y	39				1	2		
Zr	40				2	2		
Cb	41				4	1		
Mo	42		36		5	1		
Tc	43		Krypton core		6	1		
Ru	44				7	1		
Rh	45				8	1		
Pd	46				10			

Table 14.5—Continued

		K 1s	L 2s 2p	M 3s 3p 3d	N 4s 4p 4d 4f	O 5s 5p 5d	P 6s 6p 6d	Q 7s
Ag	47	2	2 6	2 6 10	2 6 10	1		
Cd	48					2		
In	49					2 1		
Sn	50			46		2 2		
Sb	51			Silver core		2 3		
Te	52					2 4		
I	53					2 5		
Xe	54					2 6		
Cs	55	2	2 6	2 6 10	2 6 10	2 6	1	
Ba	56			54			2	
La	57			Xenon core		1	2	
Ce	58	2	2 6	2 6 10	2 6 10 2	2 6	2	
Pr	59				3		2	
Nd	60				4		2	
Pm	61				5		2	
Sm	62				6		2	
Eu	63				7		2	
Gd	64				7	1	2	
Tb	65			46	9	8	2	
Dy	66			1s to 4d	10	5s, 5p	2	
Ho	67				11		2	
Er	68				12		2	
Tm	69				13		2	
Yb	70				14		2	
Lu	71				14	1	2	
Hf	72	2	2 6	2 6 10	2 6 10 14	2 6 2	2	
Ta	73					3	2	
W	74			68		4	2	
Re	75			Hafnium core		5	2	
Os	76					6	2	
Ir	77					9		
Pt	78					9	1	
Au	79	2	2 6	2 6 10	2 6 10 14	2 6 10	1	
Hg	80						2	
Tl	81						2 1	
Pb	82			78			2 2	
Bi	83			Gold core			2 3	
Po	84						2 4	
At	85						2 5	
Rn	86						2 6	
Fr	87	2	2 6	2 6 10	2 6 10 14	2 6 10	2 6	1
Ra	88					5f		2
Ac	89						1	2
Th	90						2	2
Pa	91					2	1	2
U	92					3	1	2
Np	93			86		5		2
Pu	94			Radon core		6		2
Am	95					7		2
Cm	96					7	1	2
Bk	97					9		2
Cf	98					10		2

190

DESCRIPTION OF ELECTRON STRUCTURES

It is customary, in writing electron structures, to enumerate all the electrons in a given main level together rather than to list all the electrons according to the sub-level they occupy. Thus, the electron structure of tungsten is given as 2, 8, 18, 32, 12, 2, showing the number of electrons in each of the six main levels which are fully or partially occupied, rather than as $1s^2$; $2s^2$, $2p^6$; $3s^2$,

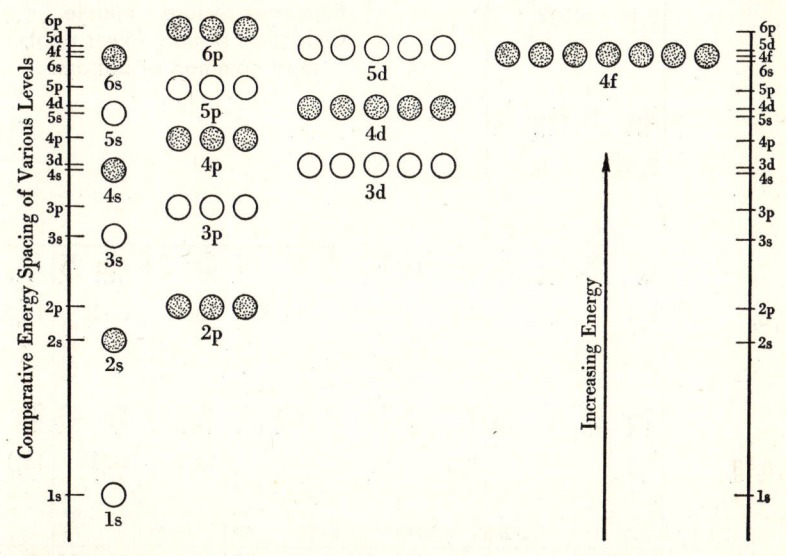

Figure 14.4.
Diagram of atomic energy levels of the gaseous atoms of the elements.

$3p^6$, $3d^{10}$; $4s^2$, $4p^6$, $4d^{10}$, $4f^{14}$; $5s^2$, $5p^6$, $5d^4$; $6s^2$ which lists all the electrons by sub-level. It should be clear that the simpler form gives, in much less space, almost as much information as the more complicated method, and that the sub-level division of the electrons may be determined from it by applying the generalizations already made. These may be summarized here as: (1) electrons will go into the lowest available energy level, (2) electrons tend to unpair to the maximum extent in individual atoms; (3) energy levels tend to become completely full, or exactly half full of electrons.

Each unpaired electron and each pair of electrons are said to occupy an *orbital*. Thus there is a single *s* orbital, three *p* orbitals, five *d* orbitals, and seven *f* orbitals in each appropriate level. A graphical method of presenting the order of filling of the orbitals and energy levels is given in Figure 14.4. Each circle (orbital) can contain a pair of electrons. Electrons enter the lowest available circle (orbital). When two or more circles have the same height (energy) the electrons spread out (unpair) as much as possible in those circles. When every

Table 14.6
Periodic Table of the Elements

KEY: Symbol – upper left
Atomic number – upper right
Electron structure – middle
Oxidation states – lower right, most common at bottom.

Period (Row)									
I	**H** 1 1 1− 1+								
II	**Li** 3 2,1 1+	**Be** 4 2,2 2+							
III	**Na** 11 2,8,1 1+	**Mg** 12 2,8,2 2+							
IV 2,8,	**K** 19 8,1 1+	**Ca** 20 8,2 2+	**Sc** 21 9,2 3+	**Ti** 22 10,2 2+ 3+ 4+	**V** 23 11,2 2+ 3+ 4+ 5+	**Cr** 24 13,1 2+ 3+ 6+	**Mn** 25 13,2 2+ 3+ 4+ 7+ 2+	**Fe** 26 14,2 2+ 3+	
V 2,8,18,	**Rb** 37 8,1 1+	**Sr** 38 8,2 2+	**Y** 39 9,2 3+	**Zr** 40 10,2 4+	**Cb** 41 12,1 3+ 5+	**Mo** 42 13,1 6+	**Te** 43 14,1 4+ 6+ 7+	**Ru** 44 15,1 4+ 3+	
VI 2,8,18,	**Cs** 55 18,8,1 1+	**Ba** 56 18,8,2 2+	57–71 Rare earths 18,9,2 to 32,9,2	**Hf** 72 32,10,2 4+	**Ta** 73 32,11,2 5+	**W** 74 32,12,2 6+	**Re** 75 32,13,2 6+ 4+ 7+	**Os** 76 32,14,2 4+ 3+	
VII 2,8,18,32,	**Fr** 87 18,8,1 1+	**Ra** 88 18,8,2 2+	89– 2nd Rare earths 18,9,2 to	4b	5b	6b	7b	8b	
Group (Column)	1a	2a	3b						

Rare earths (Lanthanides) 2,8,18,

| **La** 57
18,9,2
3+ | **Ce** 58
20,8,2
4+
3+ | **Pr** 59
21,8,2
3+ | **Nd** 60
22,8,2
3+ | **Pm** 61
23,8,2
3+ | **Sm** 62
24,8,2
2+
3+ |

2nd Rare earths (Actinides) 2,8,18,32,

| **Ac** 89
18,9,2
3+ | **Th** 90
18,10,2
4+ | **Pa** 91
20,9,2
5+ | **U** 92
21,9,2
3+
4+
6+ | **Np** 93
23,8,2
3+
6+
4+
5+ | **Pu** 94
24,8,2
5+
3+
6+
4+ |

Table 14.6—*Continued*

								H 1 1	He 2 2 1− 1+ 0
			B 5 2,3 3+	C 6 2,4 2± 4±	N 7 2,5 4+ 3+ 3− 5+	O 8 2,6 1− 2−	F 9 2,7 1−	Ne 10 2,8 0
			Al 13 2,8,3 3+	Si 14 2,8,4 2± 4±	P 15 2,8,5 3− 3+ 5+	S 16 2,8,6 4+ 2− 6+	Cl 17 2,8,7 1+ 7+ 5+ 1−	A 18 2,8,8 0
Co 27 15,2 3+ 2+	Ni 28 16,2 2+	Cu 29 18,1 1+ 2+	Zn 30 18,2 2+	Ga 31 18,3 3+	Ge 32 18,4 4±	As 33 18,5 3− 3+ 5+	Se 34 18,6 2− 4+ 6+	Br 35 18,7 1+ 5+ 1−	Kr 36 18,8 0
Rh 45 16,1 3+	Pd 46 18 4+ 2+	Ag 47 18,1 1+	Cd 48 18,2 2+	In 49 18,3 3+	Sn 50 18,4 2+ 4+	Sb 51 18,5 3− 5+ 3+	Te 52 18,6 6+ 4+	I 53 18,7 7+ 1+ 5+ 1−	Xe 54 18,8 0
Ir 77 32,17 4+ 3+	Pt 78 32,17,1 2+ 4+	Au 79 32,18,1 1+ 3+	Hg 80 32,18,2 1+ 2+	Tl 81 32,18,3 3+ 1+	Pb 82 32,18,4 4+ 2+	Bi 83 32,18,5 3+	Po 84 32,18,6 2+	At 85 32,18,7	Rn 86 32,18,8 0
9b	10b	1b	2b	3a	4a	5a	6a	7a	0

Eu 63 25,8,2 2+ 3+	Gd 64 25,9,2 3+	Tb 65 27,8,2 3+	Dy 66 28,8,2 3+	Ho 67 29,8,2 3+	Er 68 30,8,2 3+	Tm 69 31,8,2 3+	Yb 70 32,8,2 2+ 3+	Lu 71 32,9,2 3+
Am 95 25,8,2 6+ 5+ 4+ 2+ 3+	Cm 96 25,9,2 3+	Bk 97 27,8,2 4+ 3+	Cf 98 28,8,2 3+	99	100			

orbital in a given set (energy level) contains two electrons, the next electron will enter the next higher orbital.

(We should mention here that the relative order of the levels does not remain constant from atom to atom. Rather, as the nuclear charge becomes larger, the sub-levels within the same main level tend to segregate and the overlapping which occurs among the main shells when the electrons are first introduced disappears as more and more additional electrons are added. This behavior need not concern us, for chemistry involves changes in the outer electrons only [and these are the ones which were most recently added] rather than changes in levels which have become segregated as further levels were added. Spectroscopists who are concerned with the energy relationships among all the levels are not so fortunate.)

The electron structure of most of the elements may be predicted from Figure 14.4 by placing the requisite number of electrons in the lowest available orbitals (circles), 2 electrons per orbital as a maximum. The dozen or so exceptions to this simple generalization may be interpreted in terms of the other two rules summarized above. Correlating Figure 14.4 with Table 14.5 should give a clear picture of the order in which electron orbitals are filled as atomic number increases.

It may be interesting to note that all is not chaos in the description of these levels, numerically speaking. The maximum number of electrons in each of the main levels, 2, 8, 18, 32, etc., may be expressed by squaring the number of the level and multiplying by two. Thus, the fourth level can hold a maximum of $2 \times 4^2 = 32$ electrons. Furthermore, the numbers of electrons in each of the sub-levels, 2, 6, 10, 14, etc., are just twice the successive odd numbers, 1, 3, 5, 7, etc.

We thus arrive at a picture of the atom in which the small, massive, positively charged nucleus is surrounded by electrons each of which has a definite energy. We have learned that these energies differ in such a way that one may picture the electrons located in energy levels arranged outside the nucleus. The main energy levels, designated by a number sometimes called "the principal quantum number" (*1, 2, 3, 4, 5, 6, 7,* etc.), are in turn, composed of sub-levels (*s, p, d, f,* etc.) of such energies that the main levels may overlap one another in energy at times. Good generalizations may be formulated for describing the order in which the electrons occupy these levels and sub-levels. The recurrence of chemical properties periodically as the atomic number increases correlates with a recurrence of similar configurations of outer orbital electrons since it is these electrons which interact when atoms approach one another. The electron configurations are summarized in Table 14.6 in the form of a Bohr-Thomsen periodic table (see page 153). The similar outer electron arrangements within each column or family of elements is apparent. The oxidation number represents the apparent number of electrons lost by the element in forming its compounds. It is discussed at greater length on page 236.

ELECTRONIC STRUCTURE OF ATOMS

DEFINITION OF ELEMENT

Heretofore we have not been able to give a rigid definition of an element, though, in practice, we can always tell to what element a particular kind of atom belongs by its properties. All the atoms of oxygen undergo the same kind of reactions with the atoms of other elements to form compounds of definite structure. The atoms of other elements will undergo different reactions to form different compounds. We now have a further way of distinguishing the atoms of an element. In every element all the atoms of that element, regardless of the masses of the individual atoms, carry the same positive charge on the nucleus, a charge represented by the ordinal number of that element in the periodic classification, that is, the atomic number. Every atom, to be electrically neutral must, then, have enough of the negatively charged electrons around the nucleus to balance the positive nuclear charge. In consequence, an element may be defined in terms of the identity of the electronic fields of the neutral atoms of that element and/or the identical nuclear charge of the atoms.

This identity of nuclear charge and electronic fields for a given element, and a means of differentiating the elements from one another in terms of it was first established experimentally by Moseley in 1913. His method is the one still used to establish the existence of a new element beyond question. The essence of the method is to ionize the atoms by removing one of the electrons from the energy level closest to the nucleus, the 1 level, and then to observe the energy of the light emitted when an electron from outside the atom falls into this level. This emitted energy lies in the x-ray range for most of the elements, and since the energy arises from an electron entering the 1 level, or K level, the radiations are known as K x-rays. The electrons in this innermost shell are exposed to the full attractive force of the nucleus since no other electrons lie between them and the nucleus. Therefore, according to Coulomb's law of electrical attraction, the energy of attraction should be proportional to the square of the charge on the nucleus. After Rutherford suggested the nuclear picture of atomic structure, Moseley undertook a systematic study of the K x-rays of the elements and found the energies were indeed proportional to the square of the atomic number. He proved that cobalt should come before nickel in the periodic table in spite of the atomic weight order and he showed just how many of the elements remained to be discovered, a thing which Mendeleeff had been unable to do because of uncertainty with respect to the number of rare earth metals.

The new definition of element in terms of structure also had predictive power. The theory showed that element 72 belongs in the zirconium family. Hafnium was discovered, in 1922, in zirconium ores. Earlier workers had looked for this element, in vain, in ores containing the rare earth elements.

Problem 14.2. Make some general statements about atomic structure that apply to all atoms.

196 GENERAL CHEMISTRY

Problem 14.3. Complete the following table. If no answer is possible place an X.

ELEMENT	AT. NO.	AT. WT.	NO. OF NEUTRONS	NO. OF PROTONS	ELECT. STRUC.
Q			0	1	
R	15				
T		14			2, 4

Problem 14.4. Account for the fact that it is easier to remove a third electron from nitrogen than it is to remove a third electron from carbon. Why is this not true of the removal of the first and second electrons? See Table 14.3 for data.

Problem 14.5. Predict the number of unpaired electrons present in single atoms of each of the elements from argon to krypton in the periodic table.

Problem 14.6. Explain very briefly the origin of spectral lines.

Problem 14.7. Would you expect the K x-ray energy of cobalt to be greater or less than that of nickel? See page 153. How do you make your conclusion compatible with the atomic weight data?

Problem 14.8. Use Figure 14.3 to sketch the origin of a third family, or series, of lines in the hydrogen spectrum. In what portion of the spectrum—ultraviolet, visible, or infrared—would you expect to find these lines?

Problem 14.9. The electronic structure for technetium, element 43, is not definitely established. Can you think of any reason to question the description of that element given in Table 14.4?

Problem 14.10. Outline three or four ways one could determine the atomic number of an unknown element.

Problem 14.11. The x-ray wave length for copper and molybdenum are 1.54 Å. and 0.707 Å., respectively, for the process of an electron falling into the K shell. Show that these data are consistent with Moseley's interpretation. Calculate the wave length corresponding to this same transition in chromium and in tungsten.

Problem 14.12. Why are neon signs orange-red?

15 CHEMICAL BONDING

IN THE preceding chapters we discussed the evidence for the structure of atoms in terms of nuclei and of orbital electrons. But relatively few of the atoms in nature are isolated from one another. In the air the molecules of most of the gases each contain two or more atoms and in the hydrosphere and the lithosphere the atoms of the liquids and solids are relatively closely packed. The molecules of the gases are highly stable combinations of atoms. Liquids and solids are dense and viscous, and solids are hard. It is evident that the atoms in the various natural assemblies are held to other atoms by comparatively strong forces or bonds.

Yet it is also apparent that substances differ widely in cohesiveness. There must be great differences between the forces within the water molecule and those between water molecules in ice, water, or steam. Diamond and sugar, both containing carbon atoms, differ in hardness and ease of melting. Metals and salts differ markedly in rigidity and in other obvious ways. All the kinds of forces between atoms, holding them together, are known by the general term *chemical bonds*. We may expect as many types of chemical bonds as there are types of forces between atoms. To the nature of these bonds, as interpreted in terms of the nuclear and electronic structure of the atoms, we now turn our attention. We shall find that many of the properties of substances may be correlated rather simply in terms of the ways electrons can interact to form chemical bonds.

ATOMIC KERNELS AND VALENCE ELECTRONS

We have already seen (Chapter 12) that the arrangement of the elements in the periodic table, originally based only on the similarities in properties of the elements, is one which, a half century later, brings together into families the elements with the same outer electron structure (Chapter 14). The number of inner electron levels filled differs from element to element in a family but the number in the outer level generally does not. Apparently, only the electrons in the outer energy levels of atoms participate appreciably in chemical reactions and interactions.

The outer electrons, for historical reasons, are called *valence electrons*. The

198 GENERAL CHEMISTRY

rest of the atom, the nucleus and the electrons in the inner levels, is called the *kernel* of the atom or the *atomic kernel*. By definition, the valence electrons include those in the outermost, or highest, energy level only if the number of electrons is less than the maximum possible in that level. All completed levels are included in the kernel.

The description of atomic structure in terms of kernel and valence electrons will be illustrated for the oxygen atom, whose electronic structure is 2, 8, 6. Let the nucleus and the 2, 8 electrons, the kernel, be represented by the

Table 15.1
Valence Electrons, Kernel, and Structural Notation for Some Typical Elements

ELEMENT		HYDRO-GEN	OXY-GEN	NEON	CHLO-RINE	CHRO-MIUM	GER-MANIUM	ER-BIUM
ATOMIC STRUCTURE	Nuclear Charge	1+	8+	10+	17+	24+	32+	68+
	No. of Electrons	1	2, 6	2, 8	2, 8, 7	2, 8, 13, 1	2, 8, 18, 4	2, 8, 18 30, 8, 2
KERNEL STRUCTURE	Nuclear Charge	1+	8+	10+	17+	24+	32+	68+
	No. of Electrons		2	2, 8	2, 8	2, 8, 13	2, 8, 18	2, 8, 18 30, 8
NO. OF VALENCE ELECTRONS		1	6	None	7	1	4	2
NOTATION		H·	:Ö·	Ne	:Cl·	Cr·	·Ge·	Er·

chemical symbol O, and the six valence electrons by dots (or crosses). Of the valence electrons only two are unpaired. Hence the structure of the oxygen atom may be represented as :Ö·. Examples of kernel structure, number of valence electrons, and notation for some representative atoms are given in Table 15.1. We must immediately point out that we shall find some reactions, including very common ones, in which the kernel as defined above is altered and other reactions in which some of the valence electrons are not involved. The rules given are, however, very useful and we shall deal with the apparent exceptions when they occur.

The elements in Groups 1a, and 2a, for instance, ordinarily react in such a manner that only their outermost *s* electrons are involved. They customarily achieve oxidation states of 1+ and 2+ respectively in their compounds by forming the corresponding 1+ and 2+ ions. They, thus, have the same kernel in all their compounds. However, most elements have several possible oxidation states (see Table 14.6) and one should not be surprised to find various numbers of electrons involved in the bonding. This may or may not affect the nature of the kernel and the number of valence electrons. Thus chlorine (electron structure 2, 8, 7) shows oxidation numbers in its compounds varying from $1-$ to $7+$. Yet the first two electron levels (2, 8) are apparently never disturbed so that the kernel is always (2, 8) and there are always seven valence electrons. On the other hand, chromium (electron structure 2, 8, 13, 1) may lose two electrons to give Cr^{++} (2, 8, 12), or 3 electrons to give Cr^{+++} (2, 8, 11), or may form $CrO_4^=$ in which the unaffected kernel appears to be (2, 8, 8). Thus the number of valence electrons in these three cases would be 2, 3 and 6 respectively and each kernel is different from the others.

BOND ENERGIES

Atoms undoubtedly do attract one another. On the other hand, they do not interpenetrate to any great extent. There must be a field of force about each atom. When two atoms approach, their fields of force interact until there is a balance between the attractive and repulsive forces. The situation is analogous to that found when a meteor and the earth approach one another. The gravitational fields of the meteor and the earth interact strongly, and the bodies approach one another more and more closely until strong repulsive forces stop the relative motion and bring the meteor to rest on the earth's "surface." At the earth's surface, the attractive forces of the gravitational fields are exactly balanced by the repulsive forces which prevent interpenetration of the meteor and the earth, and the two bodies remain in a fixed position with respect to one another. We know that the attractive force is great because it takes a good deal of work to lift a large meteorite, and we know the repulsive force is equally great since it exactly balances the attraction.

The system meteor-earth is in a state of minimum potential energy. The force fields around atoms are more complicated to describe mathematically than gravitational fields. They are not purely electrical in nature as one might expect from a simplified view of the atomic structure, but they are analogous to electrical fields. They lead to a net attractive force at distances greater than a few Ångstrom units and net repulsion at distances of less than a few Ångstrom units. Just as a meteor stops when the gravitational force and the repulsive force become equal at the earth's surface, so also, for two interacting atoms, there exists a distance of separation at which the attractive forces and repulsive forces balance. Then the potential energy will be at a minimum. For most atoms the equilibrium distance between adjacent nuclei will be of the order of a few Ångstrom units. This distance is known as the *bond distance* for the interacting atoms, and the energy necessary to separate them from one another when they are initially at this distance is known as the *bond energy* for that pair of atoms.

Bond energies vary widely from substance to substance, and even from atom to atom in the same substance. For example, the element nitrogen consists of diatomic molecules regardless of whether it is in the gas, the liquid, or the solid phase. The bond between the two nitrogen atoms in the same molecule is one of the strongest bonds known between any two atoms. Relatively great energy (225 kilocalories per mole) is required to separate the two atoms so that they can move independently of each other. On the other hand the bonding forces between two nitrogen atoms in different molecules are very weak (binding energy of less than one kilocalorie per mole). As a result the atoms within each nitrogen molecule remain bonded together even though two molecules collide with one another.

Other molecules are known to exchange atoms when they collide. The molecules of liquid water, for instance, can exchange hydrogen atoms. One would deduce that the bonds in water molecules are weaker than those in nitrogen molecules. They happen to be, but activation energy and the geometry of the collision are more important in determining whether exchange of atoms occurs or not. These factors will be dealt with later.

THE INERT GAS ELEMENTS

Of all the elements in the periodic table only the Group 0 elements are not found in combination. Indeed, they exist as monatomic gases in which each molecule contains but a simple atom. They are, therefore called the *inert gas* or *noble gas* elements. Perhaps we can learn something about chemical bonding from the elements which do not form strong bonds between atoms, even those of their own kind.

The simplest of the noble gases is helium, atomic number 2. Each atom of helium has a nucleus carrying a 2+ charge and when neutral also has an electronic field containing 2 electrons. In the normal helium atom both of these electrons are in the *1s* energy level. The pair of electrons is the maximum number possible in this level. The next element in the noble gas family is neon, atomic number 10. Each of the atoms has a nuclear charge of 10+ and the neutral atoms have an electronic field containing ten electrons, two in the *1* level and eight in the *2* level. The two in the *1s* level are the maximum for this level. The other eight are distributed among the following orbitals: two in *2s* orbitals and six in *2p* orbitals. For neon, both the *1* and *2* energy levels contain the maximum number of electrons. The third noble gas element, argon, atomic number 18, has atoms with a nuclear charge of 18+. In the electronic field of eighteen (2, 8, 8) electrons, the two *1s* and the two *2s* and six *2p* orbitals are occupied. The remaining eight electrons are in the *3* energy level, there being two *3s* and six *3p* electrons. Thus, argon, like neon, has four pairs of electrons in its outer level, apparently a stable number, although not the maximum number possible in the *3* energy level. Krypton, atomic number 36 (2, 8, 18, 8), has its three lowest energy levels complete. It has two *1s* electrons, two *2s* and six *2p* electrons, two *3s*, six *3p*, and ten *3d* electrons. The *4* energy level is not completely filled, having two *4s* and six *4p* electrons or eight in all. Xenon (2, 8, 18, 18, 8), like the other elements in the family also has eight electrons in its outer level, its atoms having two $5s$ and six $5p$ electrons. The 4 energy level does not have the maximum possible in the level but has 18 electrons, the two $4s$, six $4p$, and ten $4d$ orbitals being occupied.

One may draw the following conclusions: When an atom has eight electrons, the maximum number of s and p electrons, in its outmost energy level it is so stable that it does not form bonds with other atoms. The outer energy level may have eight electrons if the lower levels have certain stable numbers of electrons. As we shall see, similar stable electronic structures are achieved by the atoms of other elements when they combine with one another.

Table 15.2
Electronic Structure of the Noble Gases

NOBLE GAS	ELECTRON STRUCTURE IN DETAIL	ELECTRONS ACCORDING TO MAIN LEVEL ONLY
He	$1s^2$	2
Ne	$1s^2; 2s^2, 2p^6$	2, 8
A	$1s^2; 2s^2, 2p^6; 3s^2, 3p^6$	2, 8, 8
Kr	$1s^2; 2s^2, 2p^6; 3s^2, 3p^6, 3d^{10}; 4s^2, 4p^6$	2, 8, 18, 8
Xe	$1s^2; 2s^2, 2p^6; 3s^2, 3p^6, 3d^{10}; 4s^2, 4p^6, 4d^{10}; 5s^2, 5p^6$	2, 8, 18, 18, 8
Rn	$1s^2; 2s^2, 2p^6; 3s^2, 3p^6, 3d^{10}; 4s^2, 4p^6, 4d^{10}, 4f^{14}; 5s^2, 5p^6, 5d^{10}; 6s^2, 6p^6$	2, 8, 18, 32, 18, 8

The electron structures of the noble gases are summarized in Table 15.2. (See also Table 14.1 and Figure 14.5.) Note that each has four pairs of electrons in its highest energy level.

COVALENT BONDS

The great majority of the atoms on the earth are bonded to other atoms. Many of them are bonded into relatively stable groups containing definite kinds and numbers of atoms. These groups are called molecules. They can exist because the bonding between atoms in the same molecule is stronger than that between an atom within the molecule to one outside the molecule and the distances (internuclear) between the strongly bonded atoms are shorter than that between weakly bonded atoms. Furthermore, the atoms in the molecules are not arranged at random but according to definite geometric patterns. These are facts to be explained in terms of the valence electrons.

Among the molecular substances are such elements (and molecular formulas) as hydrogen, H_2, chlorine, Cl_2, sulfur, S_8, and phosphorus (white), P_4. The single atoms of these elements have unpaired electrons in their valence orbitals but each of the molecules has only electron pairs. Indeed, with few exceptions, all stable molecules contain an even number of electrons. This fact, together with the known stability and inertness of the noble gas family of elements, suggests that the bonding within molecules results from an electron structure of low energy—one in which all electrons are paired, perhaps one in which each atom has acquired, by sharing of electrons, the electron structure of an inert gas atom. The shared pairs of electrons, being held jointly by two atoms, are common to both so that the volumes of the bonded atoms may be considered to be overlapping. A consequence is a shortening of the internuclear distance. The <u>bond formed by sharing of a pair of electrons is called a *covalent bond.*</u> When the two atoms share the electrons equally the bond is said to be *nonpolar*, since the electrons will, on the average, be half-way between the two atoms. <u>In general only like atoms form strictly nonpolar bonds.</u>

When a single hydrogen atom, with its single electron, pairs this electron with that of another hydrogen atom an electron pair is formed. The bond between the atoms will be nonpolar, since both nuclei have equal attraction for the electron pair. Furthermore, the stable helium electron structure, one pair of $1s$ electrons, has been formed. This structure we know to be stable. The hydrogen molecule is more stable and has less energy (104 kilocalories per mole less) than the separate atoms with their unpaired electrons have. In terms of the kernel and valence electrons the relation between bonded pair and isolated atoms is

$$H \cdot + H \cdot = H : H + 104{,}000 \text{ cal/mole}$$

The single chlorine atom also has a single unpaired electron as shown by the notation $:\overset{..}{\underset{..}{Cl}}\cdot$. It can pair this electron with that of another chlorine atom as in

$$:\overset{..}{\underset{..}{Cl}}\cdot + \cdot\overset{..}{\underset{..}{Cl}}: = :\overset{..}{\underset{..}{Cl}}:\overset{..}{\underset{..}{Cl}}: + 29{,}000 \text{ cal/mole}$$

There are only seven electron pairs of valence electrons but each atom is surrounded by four pairs. By the pairing process each chlorine atom has achieved the stable electron structure of argon. This structure has less energy than others and is more stable; that is, a rather large amount of energy (29 kilocalories per mole) is required to break the bond. Other examples of covalent bonding in elements are illustrated in Table 15.3.

Stable, covalent bonds are formed also by electron pairs shared between unlike atoms. For example, hydrogen and chlorine atoms are bonded in the hydrogen chloride molecule and hydrogen and oxygen atoms in the water molecule.

$$H_x + \cdot \overset{..}{\underset{..}{Cl}}: = H \overset{..}{\underset{..}{:}} \overset{..}{\underset{..}{Cl}}:$$

$$2H_x + \cdot \overset{..}{\underset{\cdot}{O}}: = H \overset{..}{\underset{\cdot x}{:}} \overset{..}{O}:$$
$$\phantom{2H_x + \cdot \overset{..}{\underset{\cdot}{O}}: = HHHH}H$$

CHEMICAL BONDING 203

In water, the hydrogen atom has, by electron pairing, achieved the helium electron structure and the oxygen atom has achieved the neon electron structure. In hydrogen chloride, the hydrogen atom has the helium electron structure and the chlorine atom the argon electron structure. Note that we count the shared pair as belonging to both atoms. Other examples of covalent bonding in molecules of compounds are shown in Table 15.4. (The different symbols, × and ·, for the electron have identical meaning. They are used only for convenience in counting electrons.)

Table 15.3
Covalent Bonding in the Molecules of Some Elements

ELEMENT	HYDROGEN	CHLORINE	OXYGEN	NITROGEN	SULFUR
ATOM	H ·	: Cl ·	: O ·	: N ·	: S ·
MOLECULE	H : H	: Cl : Cl :	: O : O : or : O ⋮ O :	: N : N :	(S₈ ring) NO

Covalent bonds, resulting from the sharing of electron pairs, may involve more than one electron pair. If two electron pairs are shared the bond is called a *double bond*. Similarly, if three electron pairs are shared the bond is called a *triple bond*. The bonds between carbon and oxygen in carbon dioxide (Table 15.4) are double bonds and that in nitrogen is a triple bond. Another example of a double bond is found in ethylene, for which the structure is

$$\begin{matrix} H & & & H \\ & \cdot_x & \cdot & \cdot_x \\ & \cdot C & \vdots & C \cdot \\ H & ^x & & ^x H \end{matrix}$$

Similarly acetylene, H ⋮ C : C ⋮ H, has a triple bond.

Since all electrons are alike we should not be surprised to find that both electrons in an electron pair need not have been contributed by different atoms. If both electrons in a pair are furnished by one of the atoms the bond is sometimes called a *coordinate bond* or a *dative bond*. Examples are found in sulfur dioxide and sulfur trioxide (Table 15.4), the sulfur being called the *donor* atom and the oxygen the *acceptor* atom.

One might deduce from the structure for sulfur dioxide and sulfur trioxide shown in Table 15.4 that the different oxygen atoms are bonded differently to the central sulfur atoms and should, therefore, have somewhat different

Table 15.4
Covalent Bonding in Some Molecules

SUBSTANCE	HYDROGEN CHLORIDE	WATER	AMMONIA	METHANE
Atoms	H ˟ , : Cl ·	H ˟ , · O :	H ˟ , · N :	H ˟ , · C ·
Molecules	H ⁝ Cl :	H ⁝ O : ˟ H	H ⁝ N : ˟ H	H ⁝ C ⁝ H ˟ H

SUBSTANCE	NITROGEN	CARBON DIOXIDE	SULFUR DIOXIDE	SULFUR TRIOXIDE
Atoms	˟N˟ · N :	˟C˟ , · O :	˟˟S˟ , · O :	˟˟S˟ , : O ·
Molecule	˟N⁝N:	:O⁝C⁝O:	S / \ O O :	:O: S / \ O O:

properties. Experiments, however, do not show such differences. The explanation is that the electrons are mobile and that the real electron structure is a hybrid structure.

Electron pair bonds are usually indicated by a dash rather than two dots or x's, for example, H—Cl : , H—H, O=C=O, : N≡N : . In many cases the electrons not engaged in bonding are not shown, for example, H—Cl, O=C=O, N≡N. Thus the formulas : N : : : N : , : N ⁝ N : , : N≡N : , and N≡N all indicate identical nitrogen molecules. You should be able to write and to recognize any of the forms.

COVALENT BOND DIRECTIONS

The sharing of electron pairs in an effort to reach electron stability explains both the shortening of the distance when atoms are bonded and the number of covalent bonds formed by an atom. But we also know that molecules have definite shapes. Those for water, carbon dioxide, methane, and others were described on pages 57 and 86. How do covalent bonds explain the observed shapes?

For many molecules the electron pairs about an atom tend, on the average, to be as far apart as possible. If there are four electron pairs about an atom the greatest separation of pairs will occur when they are in positions represented by the apexes of a regular tetrahedron. Bonds directed from a central atom toward the apexes will have angles of 109.5° between them. This angle, called the *tetrahedral angle*, represents the angles between the carbon-hydrogen bonds in methane. The actual shape of the methane molecule, being tetrahedral, requires three dimensions to describe it; it cannot be represented well in the plane of the paper. The diagram H—C—H represents only the numbers and kinds of atoms bonded but not the resulting shape of the molecule.

The tetrahedral angles are fairly well preserved in water and ammonia even though only two and three, respectively, of the electron pairs are bonding pairs. Thus the ammonia molecule has the shape of a pyramid rather than a plane and the water molecule has a bent rather than a linear shape. In water the H—O angle is 105° rather than the tetrahedral value, 109.5°.

The sulfur molecule, outlined in Table 15.3, consists of a ring of eight atoms, each sulfur atom forming two covalent bonds with two other sulfur atoms. But, because the bond angles are very nearly the tetrahedral angle, the ring is not flat. An end view shows a zigzag ring.

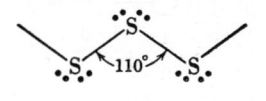

In white phosphorus, the molecule P_4 has a three-dimensional structure in which the bond angles cannot be tetrahedral. They are, rather, 60°. In the figure each line represents an electron pair. Observe that only one electron pair per atom does not participate in the bonding. See also Figure 22.1.

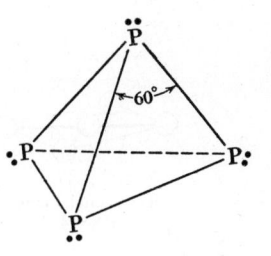

Many molecular shapes are possible and all the factors determining the final shape are not understood. Good correlations can be obtained, however, between the orbitals used in bonding and the resultant shape. Some of these correlations are summarized in Table 15.5. The more common ones are in bold face. Thus oxygen uses two p orbitals (p^2) to hold the hydrogen electrons so that water is angular; nitrogen uses three p orbitals (p^3) for the hydrogen electrons in ammonia to form a pyramidal molecule. Carbon uses one s and three p orbitals (sp^3) in tetrahedral methane, but auric ions (2, 8, 18, 32, 16) use one d, one s, and two p orbitals (dsp^2) forming the square, planar $AuCl_4^-$ ion. This table does not apply to molecules containing multiple bonds. The geometrical arrangements most commonly found are illustrated in Figure 15.1.

TABLE 15.5
Summary of Some Stable Bond Arrangements

COORDINATION NUMBER	BONDING ORBITALS	GEOMETRICAL ARRANGEMENT
2	sp	linear
	dp	linear
	p^2	angular
3	sp^2	trigonal plane
	p^3	trigonal pyramid
4	sp^3	tetrahedral
	dsp^2	tetragonal plane
	d^4	tetragonal pyramid
5	dsp^3	bipyramidal
	d^{2}sp^2	tetragonal pyramid
6	d^{2}sp^3	octahedral
	d^{4}sp	trigonal prism

VAN DER WAALS FORCES

Having considered the strong covalent forces which bind some atoms into discrete molecules we shall next consider the weak forces between molecules or between the atoms in different molecules. We know that such forces do

Linear
CN = 2

Angular
CN = 2

Trigonal Plane
CN = 3

Trigonal Pyramid
CN = 3

Tetragonal Plane
CN = 4

Tetrahedral
CN = 4

Octahedral
CN = 6

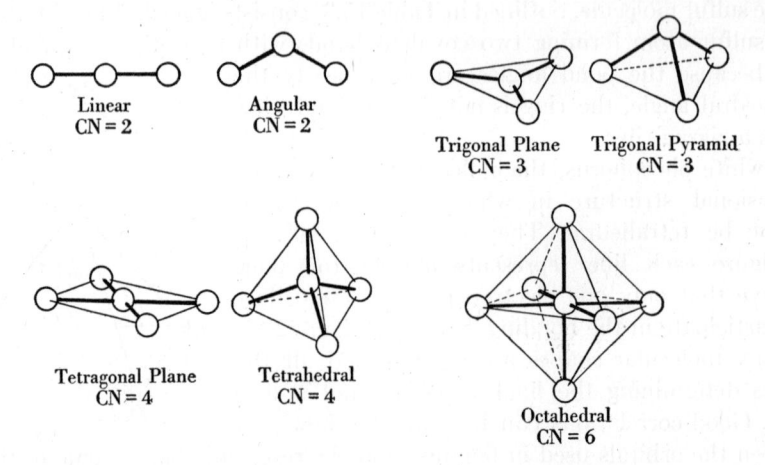

Figure 15.1.
Some atomic arrangements associated with different coordination numbers (CN).

exist because all molecular substances, including the inert gases with single atoms per molecule, may be liquefied and, at lower temperatures, frozen to crystalline solids.

Conversely most molecular substances may be melted and boiled (and so separated into their individual gaseous molecules) much more readily than they can be separated into individual atoms. These weak forces between the molecules are called *van der Waals forces*. In general, molecular crystals are softer and have lower melting points than other types of crystals, an indication of the weakness of the van der Waals forces.

In nitrogen gas the two nitrogen atoms strongly bonded in each molecule have a covalent bond (internuclear) distance of 1.10 Å. Below the critical temperature of 126°K. (−147°C.) nitrogen may be liquefied and at 63°K. it freezes to a soft crystal. In these condensed phases the closest distance between the nuclei of two atoms in *different* molecules is about 3.0Å. Such a distance is called the van der Waals distance. Since x-ray diffraction shows that in crystalline nitrogen some atoms are at distances of 1.10 Å. and others at distances of 3.0 Å. we conclude that the nitrogen molecule N_2 persists even in the solid phase. Both strong covalent and weak van der Waals bonds are present in the crystal. Kinetic energies corresponding to the critical temperature of 126°K. are sufficient to exceed the weak van der Waals attractions, but only very high energies corresponding to thousands of degrees Kelvin can cause appreciable dissociation of the covalent bond to give individual atoms.

The inert gases, Group 0 in the periodic table, constitute a set of substances in which van der Waals forces predominate. The monatomic nature of the gases at all temperatures, the low melting and boiling points, and the soft crystals all testify to the very small bond energies which are associated with van der Waals attractions.

Van der Waals forces arise in part because of the tendency of varying electric fields, such as those present in any atom, to cause a similar variation in the neighboring atoms and so lead to net attraction. Thus, an atom of an inert gas possesses a spherically symmetrical electric field if observed for any length of time, yet, instantaneously, certain portions of the atom will be positive and others negative. A positive section of an atom tends to cause a negative charge in the neighboring atom and a negative section tends to cause a positive section in its neighboring atom. These positive and negative sections in adjacent atoms attract one another to give the van der Waals forces. It should be clear that the intensity of this force will depend on the ease with which one atom can influence its neighbors' electron field, on the tightness with which the neighboring atom holds its electrons, and on the total areas of the molecules between which the forces can act.

We interpret the very small van der Waals attractions in helium in terms of the tightness with which helium holds its electrons (see the ionization potentials in Table 14.1) and the small size of the helium atom (see page 157) which exposes little surface over which attractions can be exerted. As the diameter of the inert gas atoms increases through neon and argon to radon, the peripheral electrons are held less tightly and each atom has greater surface area. Both factors increase the van der Waals forces and the boiling points show a corresponding rise (see Table 6.1). Similarly, in hydrocarbon molecules an increase in molecular size, actually surface area, increases the van der Waals force per molecule. It is this area factor rather than molecular weight which primarily affects melting and boiling points of molecular substances. The weight of the molecule as such has very little effect on these transition temperatures.

Although van der Waals forces are active in all substances, greater forces are also usually present. Often these other forces predominate so strongly that the van der Waals force is negligible by comparison and may be ignored in discussions of the properties of the substance.

MACROMOLECULAR COVALENT SUBSTANCES

There are many covalent substances which do not contain small molecular units. Diamond and graphite are examples. The "molecule" of these substances is limited only by the crystal faces, the boundaries of the carbon planes. Silicon carbide, silicon dioxide, and many other very hard, abrasive, high melting (greater than 1500°C.) substances have their constituent atoms joined by strong covalent bonds extending throughout the crystal in three dimensions. Asbestos is an example of a compound in which there is covalent bonding mainly in one direction to produce string molecules composed of long chains of atoms, and mica is, like graphite, an example in which very many atoms united by covalent bonds lie primarily in a plane. Cellulose, starch, and proteins are examples of organic substances having very many atoms covalently bonded in string-like molecules. Such very large molecules are called *macromolecules* and the substances are known as macromolecular substances (see Figures 7.1 and 7.2).

A common characteristic of the macromolecular substances having giant molecules extending in three dimensions is that they have high melting points. They have no small molecular aggregates which attract one another only through weak van der Waals forces. In contrast, almost all the low melting substances are covalently bonded materials with relatively few atoms per molecule.

SALTS

In contrast to the molecular and macromolecular substances, with covalent bonding between the atoms, and to another group of substances called metals (which we shall discuss later) there is a third important group of substances called salts. The classic example of a salt, giving its name to the class, is common salt, sodium chloride, with the formula NaCl. Salts are crystalline at room temperature and the melting points are rather high. The crystals are hard but relatively brittle. When they fracture the breaks are along well-defined crystal faces. In contrast to the metals, which reflect light, most salts transmit light, indicating that the electrons within the crystals are tightly held. However, the most important property distinguishing salts from other substances is their electrical behavior.

Crystalline salts are not electrically conducting; indeed they are electrical insulators. But, when the salts are melted or when they are dissolved in liquid solvents they become good conductors, whereas molecular substances are nonconductors of electricity in both the solid and liquid state. In contrast, metals, whether solid or liquid, are excellent electrical conductors. Since electrical conduction is the movement of electrical charges from one place to another and since electrical charges are associated with particles, electrical conduction may be described as the movement of charged particles. Only two kinds of charged particles (other than those originating only in atomic nuclei) exist: (a) electrons, which always have a unit negative charge, and (b) charged atoms or groups of atoms whose charges may be either positive or negative. The charged atoms or molecules are called *ions*. The differences in behavior of electrons and ions enable us to discover the structure of salts.

When a piece of metal such as a copper wire, for example, conducts electricity it may do so for an indefinite time without visible change in the metal. Since there is no evidence that atoms move in the metal we interpret electrical conduction as the movement of electrons from one atom to another. When copper or other metals melt, the mechanism and type of electrical conduction is not altered substantially. Since crystalline salts are not conducting it appears that they do not have free electrons as metals do. Why then do liquid salts conduct electricity? Perhaps the melting process frees electrons or perhaps ions in the crystal become free to move when the crystals melt.

If a molten salt conducted electricity by passing free electrons the salt itself should remain unchanged during the process, just as liquid or solid copper does when it conducts. But when a liquid salt, whether pure or in solution, conducts electricity, new substances are formed at the places where the electricity is introduced to or removed from the salt. These places are called *electrodes* and the processes occurring in their vicinity are called *electrode reactions*. Passage of an electric current through a substance or substances with the formation of new substances at the electrodes is called *electrolysis*. The fact of electrolysis in molten salts rules out conduction in the liquid by electrons only. Since ions are the only other means of electrical conduction, molten salts must contain positive and negative ions whose movements and changes account for the observed electrolysis.

ELECTROLYSIS

Consider an inert electric wire the two ends of which are immersed in a liquid salt. If the wire is attached to an electrical "pump," such as a generator or battery, electrons are moved from one end of the wire towards the other. The end having a deficiency of electrons becomes positively charged and the end having an excess of electrons becomes negatively charged. In the liquid salt positively charged ions (*cations*) will move toward the electron-rich electrode, called the *cathode*. At the cathode, ions or neutral molecules gain the electrons from the electrode and become new ions or molecules with different electron structure and different properties. At the same time negatively charged ions (*anions*) will move toward the electron-poor electrode, called the *anode*. At the anode, ions or neutral molecules lose electrons to the electrode and are also converted to different substances with different electron structure. Here we have an explanation of why new substances are always formed when a salt conducts electricity. There is no evidence that free electrons can travel through a salt. Instead the electricity moves through the liquid as ion charges. At the electrodes electrons are added to or taken from ions or molecules to produce new species, that is, new substances.

We may summarize as follows the events which occur during conduction by salts. All the events occur simultaneously.

1) Electrons are removed from the anode and supplied to the cathode by an electrical "pump."
2) Some ions or atoms must receive electrons from the cathode, becoming more negatively (or less positively) charged, and some ions or molecules must give up electrons to the anode, becoming more positively (or less negatively) charged.
3) Ions within the salt system must move towards the electrodes, negatively charged ion moving toward the anode and positively charged ion moving towards the cathode.

The mechansim of electronic conduction and of ionic conduction are shown schematically in Figure 15.2.

ELECTROLYSIS OF MOLTEN MAGNESIUM CHLORIDE

The electrolysis of fused magnesium chloride, formula $MgCl_2$, is a typical example of the behavior of a molten salt. This particular reaction is of great industrial importance since it is an integral step in the cheapest present industrial process of making metallic magnesium. In this process metallic magnesium is produced at the cathode and chlorine gas at the anode. The anode and cathode compartments are separated in such a way that the ions can move freely between them but that the elements formed do not come into direct contact with each other. Otherwise the elements would react immediately to re-form magnesium chloride. The fact that the electrically neutral magnesium forms at the cathode, the electrode at which the electrons are transferred to ions, indicates that the magnesium atoms in the molten salt have positive charge. Similarly, the chlorine gas, being electrically neutral, must have come from negatively charged atoms in the molten bath for it is formed by the removal of electrons from ions to the anode.

Molten magnesium chloride is, then, a liquid made up of positively charged magnesium ions and negatively charged chloride ions, the ratio of the numbers of the two kinds of ions being such that the liquid is electrically neutral as a whole. The liquid is an electrical conductor because the ions can move past one another towards the electrodes where they gain or lose electrons. If we stop the electrolysis at any point, we always find the bath electrically neutral. This means that in each interval of time the number of positive charges on magnesium ions and the number of negative charges on chloride ions that are removed must be the same. At the anode the ion which can lose electrons most readily, here the chloride ion, will do so and will become neutral chlorine atoms which then combine to form chlorine molecules. The molecules of chlorine assemble in gas bubbles which rise to the surface of the bath. At the cathode those ions which gain electrons most readily, here the magnesium ion, will do so. They become neutral magnesium atoms, which assemble to form metallic

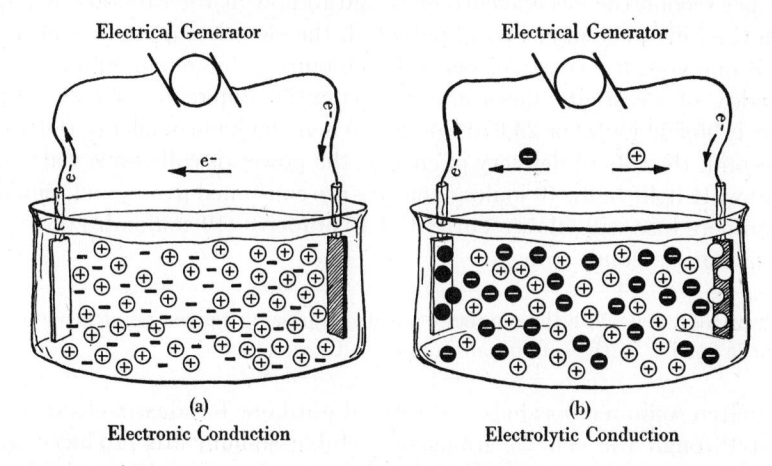

Figure 15.2.
Electronic and electrolytic conduction (schematic). (a) Electrons enter the liquid at right electrode (cathode) and leave at left (anode). The small electrons migrate quite freely from atom to atom in the liquid while the large and massive positive kernels remain practically stationary. (b) Electrons travel outside the electrolysis cell by metallic conduction but no free electrons are in the liquid within the cell. Positive ions gain electrons at cathode (right side) and become neutral. Negative ions lose electrons at left side (anode) and become neutral. Ions move within cell, positive ions toward right, negative ions toward left and thus cause current flow.

magnesium. If the electrolysis is to continue, magnesium ions (positively charged) must migrate towards the cathode to replace those removed and chloride ions (negatively charged) must migrate to the anode to replace the ions that have been removed there.

FARADAY'S LAWS OF THE ELECTROLYSIS

In 1834 Michael Faraday reported the fundamental observations on which our explanations of electrolysis are based:
    a. The amount of a substance produced at an electrode varies directly with the quantity of electricity passing through the cell.
    b. When a chemical equivalent of a substance is produced at one elec-

trode, a chemical equivalent of another substance is produced at the other electrode.

So important is the quantity of electricity producing 1 chemical equivalent of substance at each electrode, that it is designated as a *faraday*. One faraday represents 6.0238×10^{23} electrons, that is, the Avogadro number of electrons. The faraday also equals 96,500 coulombs.

The coulomb is a quantity of electricity. When one coulomb passes a given point per second the electric current is said to flow at the rate of one ampere. When the difference in electrical potential, the electrical pressure causing the flow, is one volt, the energy is one volt-coulomb or one joule. Similarly, when a faraday of electricity flows under a potential difference of one volt, the energy is 96,500 joules or 23,070 calories. When one joule of energy is delivered per second, the rate of delivery of energy, the power, is called one watt. Thus, in a 40-watt light bulb, 40 joules of energy are consumed per second. Similarly, a 10-ampere fuse will allow a current of 10 amperes (10 coulombs, or 6×10^{19} electrons, per second) to pass.

Problem 15.1. Calculate the number of electrons passing a given point per second if a current is flowing at the rate of one ampere in the conductor.

If molten sodium chloride is electrolyzed until one faraday of electricity has passed through the cell 23 grams of metallic sodium are produced at the cathode and 35.46 grams of chlorine gas are produced at the anode. Each of these amounts contains the Avogadro number of atoms. We conclude that 6×10^{23} sodium ions, Na^+, accept 6×10^{23} electrons to form 6×10^{23} atoms of neutral sodium and that 6×10^{23} chloride ions, Cl^-, lose 6×10^{23} electrons to form 6×10^{23} atoms or 3×10^{23} molecules of neutral chlorine.

When molten magnesium chloride is electrolyzed until one faraday of electricity has passed through the cell, 35.46 grams of chlorine gas are again produced at the anode. At the cathode the amount of magnesium produced is 12.16 grams, which is one equivalent weight or one-half mole of magnesium, containing only 3×10^{23} atoms. We conclude that 3×10^{23} doubly charged magnesium atoms, Mg^{++}, accept 2 electrons each so that 6×10^{23} electrons are accepted in all. When an aluminum compound is electrolyzed, one faraday of electricity yields 9 g. of aluminum at the cathode or 2×10^{23} atoms of aluminum. We conclude that aluminum ions are triply charged, Al^{+++}, each ion accepting 3 electrons. Three faradays are required to produce 1 mole of aluminum.

This method, based on Faraday's laws, was the first experimental method for determining the charge of ions. The chloride ion evidently carries a charge of 1−. Other negative ions carrying the same charge are the fluoride ion, the bromide ion, and the iodide ion. Oxide ions exist, though not in water solution, and they carry a charge of 2−. One faraday of electricity produces 8 grams or

3×10^{23} atoms of oxygen at the anode. The sulfide ion also carries a charge of 2−.

Problem 15.2. One mole of metallic calcium is produced for every mole of chlorine formed in electrolysis of molten calcium chloride. What is the simplest formula of calcium chloride and what must be the relative charges of the calcium ion and the chloride ion? Give your reasons in detail.

Problem 15.3. 1.08 g. of silver are deposited by the same amount of electricity that deposited 0.279 g. of iron. Calculate the value of the charge on the iron ions.

Problem 15.4. What weight of zinc could be electrolyzed to metal at a cathode immersed in zinc chloride if 10,000 coulombs passed through the cell? What weight of chlorine would be produced at the anode?

IONS IN SALT CRYSTALS

The evidence from electrolysis experiments shows beyond question that molten salts are composed of ions. Similar experiments in aqueous, and non-aqueous solutions of salts show that they also contain ions, but the lack of conduction in the solid salts does not tell us whether or not the solids contain ions. Either the ions are absent in the crystal and are formed in the melting process or they are so firmly fixed in position as to be unable to move through the crystal and so carry an electrical current. True there are a few salts, silver chloride for instance, which become ionic conductors when hot but still crystalline, but the great majority of salts do not. For definitive proof concerning the nature of crystalline salts we depend largely on x-ray diffraction measurements on the crystals themselves. Remember that it is always dangerous to base deductions about crystals on data obtained from the corresponding liquid or gas.

When x-rays impinge on atoms an interaction occurs. X-rays are a form of energy and the energy may be expressed in terms of electrical and magnetic fields. In other words, x-rays are a type of electromagnetic radiation. Visible light, radio waves, cosmic rays, and radiant heat are other electro-magnetic radiations. All have the property of being affected when passed through an electric field or a magnetic field under certain conditions. The stronger the field through which they pass the greater the effect. Atoms all contain electrons and have an electric field as a result. It is this atomic electric field which leads to all the interactions of light, radio waves, radiant heat, x-rays and other forms of radiant energy with matter. The extent of this interaction in the case of x-rays depends directly on the total number of electrons present in a given atom. This gives an experimental method of counting the number of electrons per atom in any substance and the method is particularly suitable for counting electrons per atom in a crystalline substance.

Table 15.6 summarizes some of the data on numbers of electrons per atom for certain salts. In these salts and in other salts, the atoms are found to be charged, to be ions (compare the number of electrons in an ion with the nuclear charge), so that crystalline salts are composed of ions just as are the corresponding liquids and gases. Each ion has its own set of electrons and there is almost no interchange of electrons between the ions. Note also that each ion has an even number of electrons as contrasted with the neutral atoms.

Table 15.6
Electrons Per Atom (Ion) in Some Salt Crystals from X-ray Diffraction Data

SALT	SODIUM CHLORIDE		MAGNESIUM CHLORIDE		MAGNESIUM OXIDE	
ION	SODIUM	CHLORIDE	MAGNESIUM	CHLORIDE	MAGNESIUM	OXIDE
No. of electrons on ion	10	18	10	18	10	10
Atomic number of element	11	17	12	17	12	8
Charge on ion	1+	1−	2+	1−	2+	2−

Many ions consist of single atoms which have gained or lost electrons to reach more stable electron configurations. (The inert gas configurations are common.) The metallic elements may form positive ions of this kind and the nonmetallic elements may form negative ions. However, not all ions consist of single atoms. Some groups of covalently bonded atoms can achieve stability only by becoming ions through gain or loss of electrons. An example is the

ammonium ion, $\begin{bmatrix} H \\ H : N : H \\ H \end{bmatrix}^+$ which has 8 valence electrons whereas the sum

of the valence electrons for the neutral atoms is 9. Hence the ion has a charge of 1+. In the nitrate ion, three oxygen atoms are bonded to a nitrogen atom, the number of valence electrons being $(3 \times 6) + 5$, or 23 electrons. By accepting one extra electron the group has 24 electrons and a charge of 1−, NO_3^-. Other common negative ions are carbonate, CO_3^{--}, sulfate, SO_4^{--}, phosphate, PO_4^{---}, hydrogen carbonate, HCO_3^-, monohydrogen phosphate, HPO_4^{--}, and dihydrogen phosphate, $H_2PO_4^-$. Such ions, containing more than one atom, are sometimes called radicals.

IONIC OR ELECTROVALENT BONDING

It can readily be shown experimentally that the attraction of two oppositely charged particles for one another at distances as small as those between the centers of ions in a crystal (a few Ångstrom units) is very much larger than any known van der Waals force and that the principal attractive force acting in salts is just this attraction between negative ions and positive ions in the vicinity. At the same time ions of like charge are repelling one another. Thus each ion tends to be surrounded with ions of charge opposite to its own. Such a tendency leads to an alternation of ions throughout the crystal with positive ions lying between negative ions and negative ions between positive ions. No small, electrically neutral molecules exist. Each positive ion is equally bonded or attracted to all its negatively charged neighbors and they, in turn, to their positively charged neighbors. Crystalline sodium chloride is typical of this

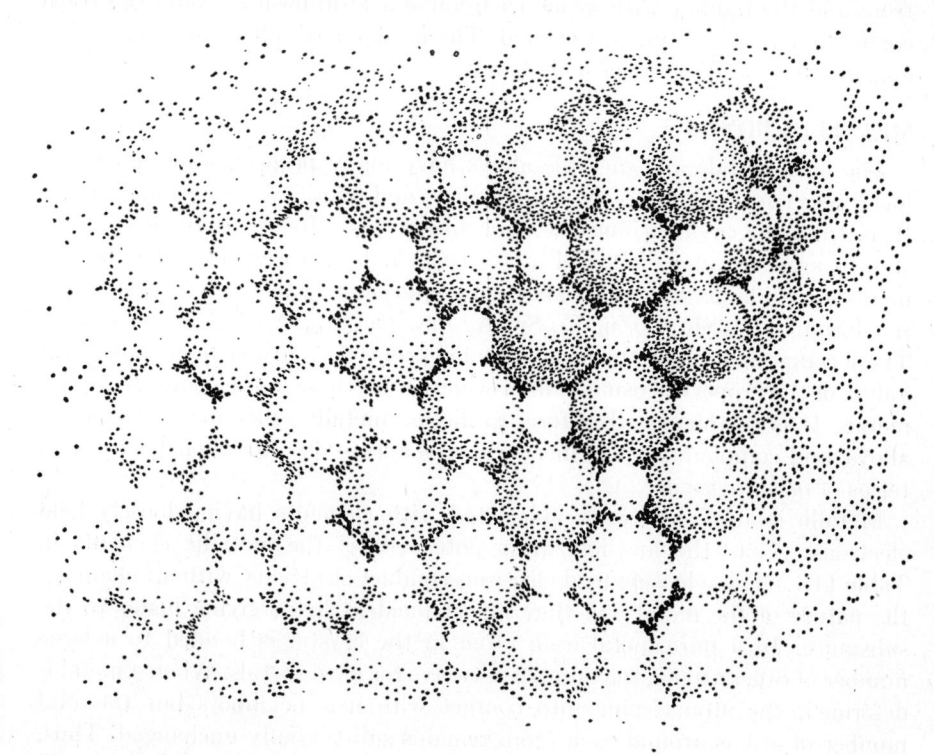

Figure 15.3.
Ionic crystal—sodium chloride. Note the alternating arrangement of sodium ions and chloride ions throughout the crystal. No individual molecules with formula NaCl are present.

alternating arrangement (see Figure 15.3). Each ion (except those on the surface of the crystal) has six neighbors of opposite charge. In cesium chloride each ion has eight neighbors of opposite charge.

Substances, such as the salts, which are held together primarily by attraction between oppositely charged ions are said to be held together by *ionic bonding* also called *electrovalent bonding*. Each ion, with its own set of electrons, has little electron interchange with its neighbors.

The brittleness of salt crystals is readily interpreted in terms of the packing arrangement of the ions. Deformation of the crystal, that is, sliding of one plane of atoms past another, for a distance of about one ion diameter, brings ions of like charge into contact. Their strong mutual repulsion breaks the crystal. The break occurs between the planes of atoms and leads to new crystal faces. The transparency of salt crystals is explained by the tightly held electrons of the individual ions. These electrons are not able to interact with light of low energy so that most salts transmit visible light. The tightly held electrons and the rigidity with which each ion is held in position make electrical conduction very difficult in the solid. The hardness of salt crystals is further evidence for the strength of ionic bonds.

METALLIC BONDS

The pure metals and metallic alloys have many properties in common—luster, electrical conductivity, malleability, and ductility. These differentiate them from the covalent and the ionic substances. Most of the metallic substances are hard and melt well above room temperatures. The metallic elements form a large number of solid compounds among themselves: those with the formulas Cs_3Sb, $CuZn$, Cu_5Sn, Ag_5Zn_8, $Cu_{31}Sn_8$, Au_5Al_3, are examples. These compounds show the usual metallic properties, although the numerical values of the properties usually differ widely from those of the component pure metals. It is customary, therefore, to discuss metallic substances—elements, alloys, and compounds—together as a class and to describe their behavior in terms of *metallic bonds*.

Metallic bonds are always associated with elements having loosely held electrons. (Note the low ionization potentials of the metallic elements in Table 14.1.) These loosely held electrons conduct electricity without changing the nature of the metal and they reflect incident light, giving luster to the substance. In a pure metal each atom in the crystal is bonded to a large number of other atoms; the number is twelve for most metals. When a metal is deformed, the atoms come into contact with new neighbors but the total number of atoms around each atom remains substantially unchanged. Thus, metals are malleable and ductile because new bonds are formed when the old ones are broken, and metals are strong because the atoms are strongly bonded to one another. High melting temperatures are a consequence of the strong bonding. A structure typical of many metals is shown in Figure 15.4. Each atom in this structure is bonded to twelve nearest neighbor atoms, but sliding can occur along the interatomic planes with little disturbance to the bonds.

In alloys the situation is more complicated because more than one kind of atom is present. For some types of alloys the properties can be readily interpreted in terms of atomic structure and atomic arrangement, but in other types, notably those in which intermetallic compounds exist, there is still no adequate theory to explain why certain of the compounds exist while others do not, although certain rules are known.

Metallic compounds differ from many chemical compounds in that they are stable only in the crystalline phase. On melting or evaporation they decompose into the individual atoms. Even in the crystalline phases they do not exist as molecules set apart from one another. In the compound with formula CuZn, for instance, each copper atom is at the center of a cube whose eight corners are occupied by zinc atoms, and each zinc atom is similarly surrounded by

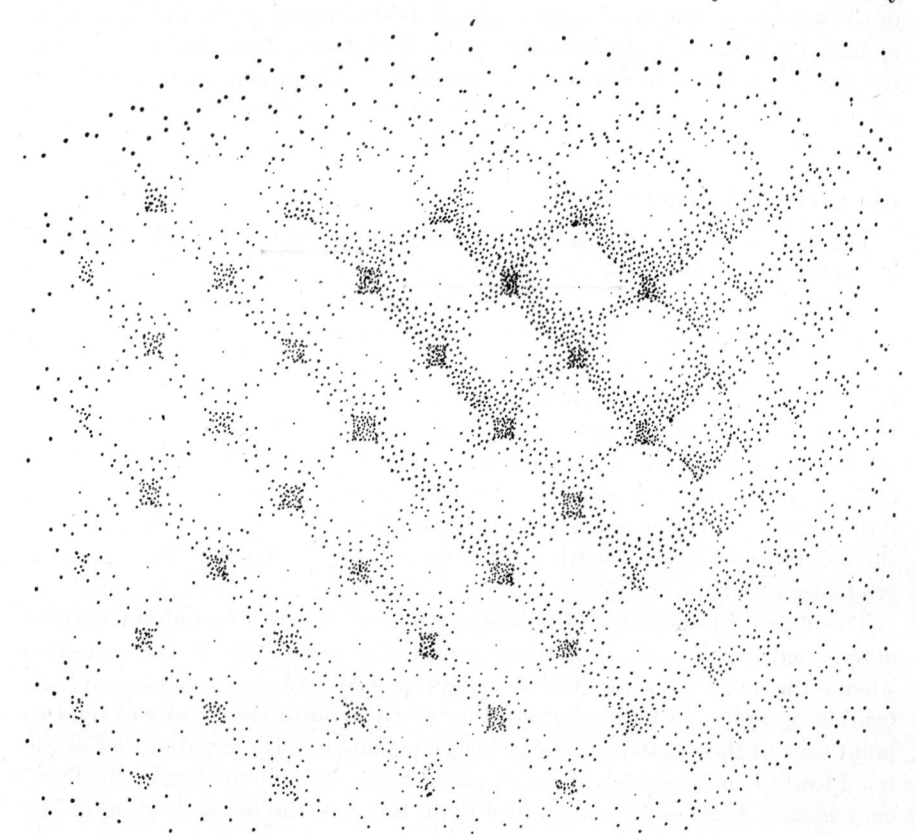

Figure 15.4.
Metallic crystal—aluminum, copper, silver, lead, and others. Each atom is surrounded by twelve other atoms (CN = 12) to give the most compact packing possible with spherical particles.

eight copper atoms. The geometry is like that of the salt, cesium chloride, but the bonds are different. There is no pair of atoms which is any different from any other pair. No discrete molecules exist. Each atom is bonded to eight other atoms and each of the eight bonds to any given atom is identical. The chemical formulas, here as with the salts, indicate only the composition of the compound and are not molecular formulas. They are empirical formulas only.

The simplest reasonable picture of metallic bonding is to consider the positively charged atomic kernels as surrounded by valence electrons which

218   GENERAL CHEMISTRY

continually exchange between neighboring atoms. The process of exchange leads to an attraction between the atoms. Since all the neighboring atoms have loosely held valence electrons, this exchange can occur between any set of neighbors and strong bonds are formed in all directions. Since the valence electrons may move from atom to atom they account for metallic conduction in the solid as well as in the liquid phase. If the crystal is deformed, another metallic atom moves in to replace each one forced away from a given spot and the bonds can thus remain strong at all times. This picture accounts for the hardness, ductility, high melting point, etc., as well as the electrical conductivity and luster.

RELATIVE ELECTRONEGATIVITY

The tendency of an atom to pair its electrons by gaining more electrons can be expressed in terms of *relative electronegativity*. A very electronegative atom is one with a great tendency to acquire electrons. An electropositive atom, which is another term for an atom of low electronegativity, has a great tendency to lose electrons. It becomes possible to predict the bonding situation between two atoms if their relative electronegativities can be determined. If the difference in electronegativity is high, ions will result. If the difference in electronegativity is zero a nonpolar bond will result (covalent between atoms of nonmetallic elements, metallic between atoms of the metallic elements), and if the difference in electronegativity is small a polar bond will form. The greater the difference in electronegativity, the more polar the bond will be, merging gradually into ionic status.

The approximate degree of polarity in a bond between two atoms may be determined experimentally if there is only one polar bond in the molecule. Then if the molecule containing the bond is placed between two metallic plates bearing opposite electrical charges, the positive end of the bond will tend to point toward the negatively charged electric plate and the negative end of the bond toward the positively charged plate. For a diatomic molecule this tendency is easy to measure and to express in terms of the *dipole moment* of the molecule. The dipole moment is the product of the electric charge on the ends of the molecule and the effective distance of separation of the ends. Thus the bigger the charge, the higher the dipole moment, and the longer the molecule the higher the dipole moment. Since it is possible to determine the internuclear distance in the molecule by other means such as x-ray or electron diffraction, we can use the dipole moment to determine the effective charge on the two atoms, or poles, of a diatomic molecule. Such calculations are carried out for a few simple molecules in Table 15.7.

It will be noted that the size of the charge varies. This variation may be considered as indicating that the shared electron pair is moving, as the polarity increases, from a point half-way between the two atoms as in chlorine, steadily toward the atom with the higher attraction for electrons.

The tendency of an atom to attract electrons proves to be a fairly constant quantity, independent of the other atoms in the vicinity. Hence the final nature of a bond, that is, its relative covalent and ionic character, will depend on the difference in the electronegativities of the two atoms involved.

A table of electronegativity values, on an arbitrary scale, for some of the chemical elements is given in Figure 15.5. The trends in electronegativity with position in the periodic table are clear and follow the predictions that would have been made on the basis of ionization potentials or dipole moments. This should not be surprising when one realizes that the electronegativity values

Table 15.7
Polarity of Molecules

MOLECULE	DIPOLE MOMENT (CM. × CHARGE IN E.S.U.)	INTERNUCLEAR DISTANCE IN MOLECULE (IN CENTIMETERS)	AVERAGE CHARGE ON POLES COMPARED TO CHARGE ON A SINGLE ELECTRON AS UNITY. (ELECTRON CHARGE = 4.8×10^{-10} E.S.U.)
Cl_2	0	2.01×10^{-8}	0.000
ICl	1.0×10^{-18}	2.30×10^{-8}	0.087
HI	0.38×10^{-18}	1.62×10^{-8}	0.049
HBr	0.78×10^{-18}	1.43×10^{-8}	0.114
HCl	1.04×10^{-18}	1.28×10^{-8}	0.170

are actually based, in part, on these two types of data. As a rough rule one may say that a compound of two elements differing in electronegativity by more than 1.5 units is essentially ionic, while one formed from elements differing in electronegativity by less than 1.5 units is primarily covalent in character.

It must be emphasized again that the change from covalent, nonpolar bonding to electrovalent, ionic bonding in a comparable series of compounds may be made by gradual steps and that there is really no sharp point of transition. Rather, all covalent bonds have a certain amount of ionic character, and all ionic bonds have some covalent character.

Fortunately most of the compounds with which we shall deal are either primarily ionic or primarily covalent in nature so that we shall not be too much bothered by the borderline cases. These transitions should be borne in mind, however, in interpreting the chemistry of the substances studied.

DIPOLE BONDS

The properties of the macromolecular substances—salts, metals, and substances like diamond—may be readily interpreted in terms of a single bond type for each of the three classes, that is, ionic, metallic, and covalent, respectively. The weak bonds between molecules containing nonpolar bonds are interpreted in terms of van der Waals forces. The presence of polar bonds in a substance leads to a form of attraction between the molecules which is somewhat different than the covalent, ionic, metallic, or van der Waals bonding we have already

220　GENERAL CHEMISTRY

discussed. Dipole moment measurements on hydrogen chloride, formula HCl, for instance, show that the chloride end of the molecule is somewhat negative and the hydrogen end somewhat positive in electrical charge (see Table 15.7). If two hydrogen chloride molecules approach one another, the positive end of one molecule will tend to attract the negative end and to repel the positive end of the other molecule. Thus the two molecules will tend to orient themselves so that the hydrogen of each molecule is near the chlorine of the other and vice versa. This type of bonding is similar to ionic bonding in that it stems from

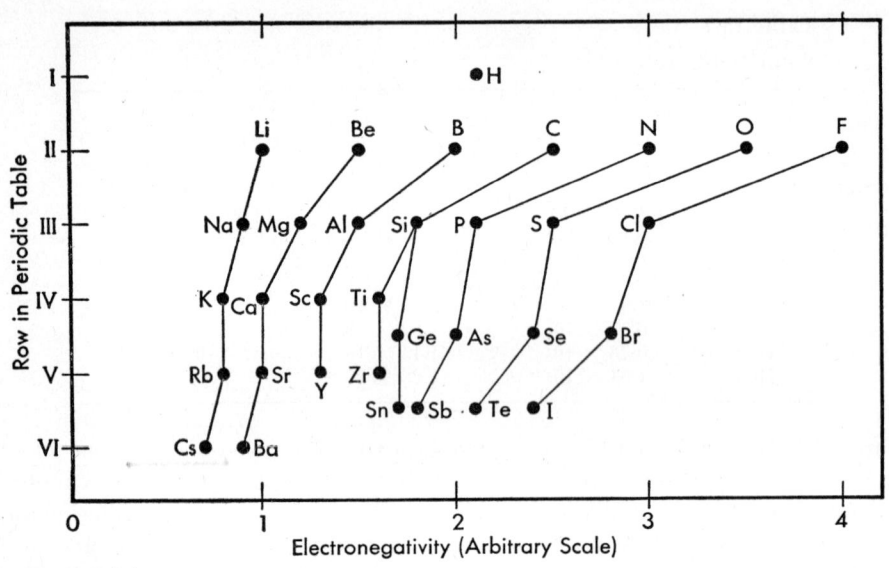

Figure 15.5.
Electronegativity scale of the elements. (Linus Pauling, *The Nature of the Chemical Bond*, Second Edition, p.65. The Cornell University Press, Ithaca N. Y. Copyright, 1945.)

forces of attraction and repulsion between electrical charges. Dipolar forces are much weaker than ionic forces, however, partly because the effective charges are smaller. On the other hand, dipolar forces and dipole bonds are stronger than van der Waals forces and bonds because of the greater effective electrical charges which are acting in dipole bonds.

All intramolecular polar bonds will tend to serve as a source of intermolecular dipole bonds, but in certain substances the net effect of the polar bonds on intermolecular attractions may be very small or zero because of the symmetry of the molecule. In water the bond angle is 105° so that the two polar bonds give a polar character to the water molecule as a whole. In carbon dioxide, on the other hand, the bond angle is 180°. Even though the bonds are polar in carbon dioxide, the molecule as a whole is not polar, since the two bonds are identical but oppositely directed in space. The two ends of the molecule are then identical and it is impossible to identify poles with the molecule. Yet it should be remembered that the oxygen atoms are slightly negative and the carbon atoms slightly positive. As a result carbon dioxide crystallizes in such a fashion that the oxygen atoms in a given molecule tend to approach the carbon atom of a neighboring molecule so that each carbon-oxygen bond "points" toward the carbon of a neighboring molecule. The weakness of the attraction is attested, however, by the low sublimation temperature, $-80°C.$, of carbon

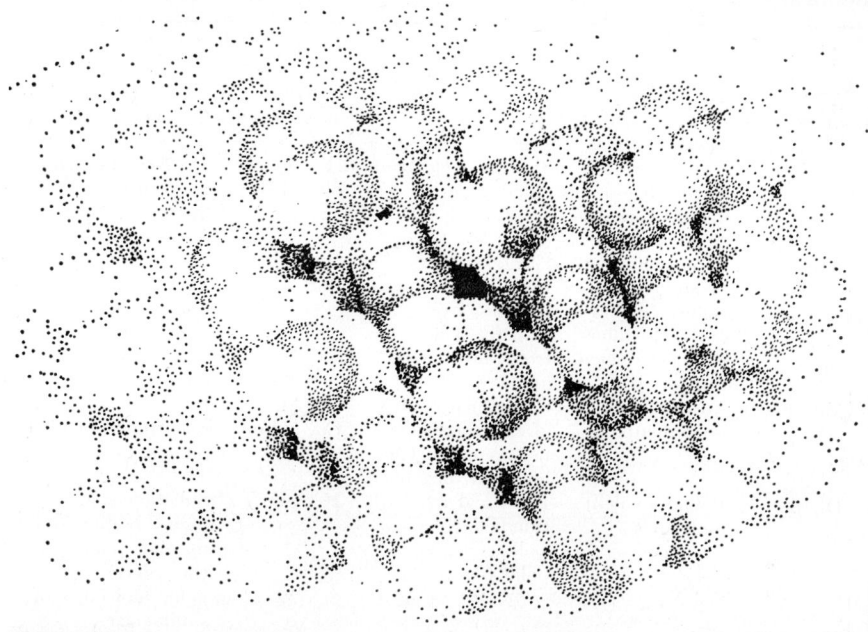

Figure 15.6.
Molecular crystal—carbon dioxide. Note individual O-C-O molecules.

dioxide. Water, on the other hand, boils at 100°C., consistent with its over-all polar character. Solid carbon dioxide is a typical molecular crystal, that is, it is composed of small discrete molecules. Its structure is shown in Figure 15.6.

In carbon tetrachloride each bond is again polar in character but the bond angles are all identical at 109.5°, the tetrahedral angle. The result is to produce a nonpolar molecule since each bond is identical and so directed in space that the outside of the molecule is almost uniformly negative, not polar. This uniform external surface of a carbon tetrachloride molecule prevents the formation of dipole bonds and leads to the interesting phenomenon of free rotation of the molecule even in the crystalline phase since the bonds (van der Waals) can be almost equally strong in any direction. At low temperatures this rotation ceases because the surface of the molecule is not quite uniform. Forces which are too weak to restrict the molecule at room temperatures can bind it when the kinetic energy becomes low at low temperatures.

HYDROGEN BONDS

Certain polar substances have intermolecular bonds which are much stronger than the dipole moment alone would indicate should exist. Their melting and boiling points are abnormally high. The viscosity of the liquid phase is abnormally high, and the molecules sometimes have a marked tendency to cluster

Table 15.8
Chemical Bond Types

BOND TYPE		GENERALLY FORMED BETWEEN	BOND FORMED BY	FORMULAS OF SUBSTANCES WITH BOND TYPE	PROPERTIES ASSOCIATED WITH BOND TYPE
INTERATOMIC	Covalent	Atoms of nonmetallic elements of similar electronegativity	Sharing of electron pairs	H_2, Cl_2 SiC, C_2H_6	Stable nonionizing molecules, not conductors of electricity in any phase
	Ionic	Atoms of metallic and nonmetallic elements of widely different electronegativities	Electrical attraction between ions resulting from transfer of electrons from one atom to another	NaCl, K_2O, BaS, LiH	Charged ions in gas, liquid, and solid. Solid is electrically nonconducting; gas and liquid are conductors
	Metallic	Atoms of metallic elements	Common exchange of valence electrons between atoms of low electronegativity	Na, Au, CuZn, Fe_3C	Electrical conductors (electronic) in all phases. Luster
INTERMOLECULAR	Dipole	Polar, covalent molecules	Electrical attraction between dipoles resulting from polar bonds	ICl, SO_2	Substances have higher boiling and melting points than those having nonpolar molecules of similar size
	Hydrogen	Molecules having hydrogen attached to atom of high electronegativity	Attraction of exposed proton to electronegative atom in neighboring molecule	H_2O, HF	Substances have much higher boiling and melting points than those having nonpolar molecules of similar size
	Van der Waals	Nonpolar molecules	Weak electrical fluctuations which destroy spherical symmetry of electronic fields about atoms	He, A Cl_2, CH_4	Substances have soft crystals and comparatively low melting and boiling points

into groups even in the gaseous phase. HF, H_2O, NH_3, HCl, and $CHCl_2$ are formulas for some typical substances. The "extra" bonding is most noticeable in hydrogen fluoride and decreases in the other substances listed in the order given. These substances, and all others in which the phenomenon has been observed, contain a hydrogen atom attached to a highly electronegative atom or group of atoms. This type of bond is, therefore, called a *hydrogen bond*.

The strength of the hydrogen bond, intermediate between dipole and ionic bonds, is attributed to the presence of only two electrons about a hydrogen nucleus. If these electrons are strongly attracted to an electronegative atom covalently bonded to the hydrogen, the hydrogen nucleus lies exposed at the end of the bond. This hydrogen nucleus will attract any negatively charged atoms strongly. The kernels of all atoms, other than hydrogen, contain electrons which shield the nucleus and make this type of bonding impossible for them. Thus, bonding of this kind is present only in compounds where hydrogen is connected to highly electronegative atoms and groups. It is associated with a high bond dipole rather than with the dipole moment of the whole molecule.

SUMMARY OF BOND TYPES

The different bond types and the accompanying properties of substances having them are so important to an understanding of chemistry that they are outlined in Table 15.8. The very strong attractions between individual atoms which lead to such effects as formation of molecules, high boiling points, or hard solids are interpreted in terms of covalent, ionic, or metallic bonding. The weaker attractions between molecules which already contain covalently bonded atoms are interpreted in terms of dipole, hydrogen, and van der Waals bonding. Soft substances, generally with low melting and boiling points, result when bonds of any of the last three types are present.

This system of bond classification should not be considered either complete or final. Chemical compounds are continually being discovered; many of the newer ones have properties which cannot be readily interpreted in terms of the bond types listed in Table 15.8. The number of such compounds is still relatively few, however, and we shall discuss only a very small number of them. Their existence does illustrate the necessity of maintaining an open mind in the face of the ever growing body of knowledge.

Problem 15.5. List the various types of chemical bonds in order of increasing average bond strength.

Problem 15.6. The density of gaseous hydrogen fluoride is 2.30 g/l at 28°C. and 1 atm. Calculate the apparent molecular weight. How do you interpret this value?

Problem 15.7. Identify all the types of bonds you would expect to find in each of the following crystals: (a) argon, (b) water, (c) methane, (d) carbon monoxide, (e) silicon, (f) aluminum, (g) calcium chloride, (h) potassium chlorate, (i) sodium cyanide, (j) hydrogen cyanide.

Problem 15.8. Outline the structure of the ordinary hydrogen atom; the ordinary hydrogen molecule; the deuterium atom; the deuterium molecule; the molecule consisting of one atom of hydrogen and one of deuterium.

Problem 15.9. The density of sodium chloride is 2.16 g/ml. The arrangement of the atoms is cubic with alternate sodium and chlorine atoms. Calculate the distance between the centers of adjacent sodium and chlorine atoms.

Problem 15.10. Which substance in the following list: sodium, diamond, chlorine, neon, iodine chloride, lithium fluoride, hydrogen, magnesium oxide, do you regard as the best example of (a) solid with electron pair bonding, (b) a molecule with electron pair bonding, (c) an ionic solid, (d) a monatomic molecule, (e) a polar, electron-pair bond, (f) an electrically conducting solid?

Problem 15.11. Explain the difference between the three types of crystal lattice—ionic, molecular, and macromolecular—in terms of bonds and their formation.

Problem 15.12. How do you account for the following properties in terms of the crystal structure of the solid:
  a. Hardness of diamond
  b. Lubricating qualities of graphite
  c. Plane surfaces formed when a sodium chloride crystal is broken
  d. Sublimation of "dry ice"
  e. Very high melting point of silicon carbide, formula SiC; very low melting point of carbon monoxide, formula CO?

Problem 15.13. How does deuterium differ from hydrogen in (a) atomic weight, (b) atomic number, (c) atoms per molecule, (d) weight of 10.0 l. under identical conditions?

Problem 15.14. State whether each of the following can conduct an electric current at low voltage, and, if so, what the mechanism is: (a) aluminum, (b) solid iodine, (c) solid sodium chloride, (d) fused sodium chloride, (e) gaseous iodine, (f) gaseous aluminum.

Problem 15.15. The majority of inorganic oxides and fluorides have salt structures. How do you account for this fact in terms of the electron structure and size (see Figure 12.3) of these atoms? Would you expect cesium compounds to be covalent or ionic?

Problem 15.16. List some simple experimental tests which would allow you to decide whether a given solid was primarily bonded with covalent, ionic, or van der Waals bonds.

Problem 15.17. According to Smeltzer and MacIntosh (1953) the electrical conductivity of carbon is decreased when the surface of each minute crystal is covered by a layer of adsorbed hydrocarbons, such as C_3H_8. Can you suggest a mechanism for this decrease?

Problem 15.18. Elements A, B, and C have atomic numbers of 5, 16, and 9, respectively. Tell which are nonmetallic and which metallic and give the formulas of any compounds they form among themselves.

Problem 15.19. Elements X, Y and Z have atomic numbers of 5, 15, and 1 and atomic weights of 12, 29, and 1 respectively. Give the atomic structure of each as far as possible. Write the formulas of any compounds these may form among themselves.

Problem 15.20. Calculate the shape of each of the following molecules: $HgCl_2$, H_2S, NH_4^+, $SiCl_4$, $AsCl_3$.

Problem 15.21. How do you reconcile, in terms of bond type, the softness of asbestos with its very high melting point? The brittleness of mica, contrasted to the malleability of graphite?

Problem 15.22. How could you account for the fact that sugar is much more soluble in water than cellulose is?

16 CHEMICAL REACTIONS

WE HAVE just considered the various types of bonding of atoms in the substances found in nature and in the substances prepared by man. These bond types help us to explain the stability of substances as they exist but they do not tell us when existing bonds will be broken so as to produce different substances with different arrangements of the atoms and different bonding. In this chapter we shall consider the problem of formation of new arrangements of atoms from existing ones—the problem of chemical reactions.

REACTIONS OF THE INERT GAS ELEMENTS

The atomic numbers, nuclear charge, and number of orbital electrons of the inert gas elements are: helium, 2; neon, 10; argon, 18; krypton, 36; xenon, 54, and radon, 86. The corresponding electron structures were shown in Table 15.2. Each inert gas atom has 4 pairs of electrons (s^2, p^6) in the outermost level and all other electrons are in exactly full sub-levels.

The only known "compounds" containing any of the neutral inert gas elements are crystals in which inert gas atoms fit into cavities which would otherwise be empty, cavities resulting from the shape and packing of the surrounding molecules. Thus, argon atoms can fit into the holes left by the water molecules in ice crystals. Obviously such "compounds" decompose when the crystal is melted or when it dissolves in a solvent. They owe their existence primarily to geometric factors rather than to strong specific forces of attraction between inert gas atoms and other atoms. These geometrical compounds are known as *clathrate compounds*.

When the noble gases are ionized so that the atoms have lost some of their electrons the number of electrons remaining is no longer the stable number. Thus, diatomic ions such as He_2^+ have been found in gaseous helium but they remain stable only so long as the molecule is charged. The diatomic molecules are not found in neutral helium.

FORMATION OF SALTS FROM THE ELEMENTS

One type of reaction, proceeding vigorously even at room temperature, is the reaction of the metallic elements on the left side of the periodic table (see

Figure 12.3) with the nonmetallic elements on the right side to form ionic compounds called salts. For example, each of the alkali metal elements, the family in the first column of the periodic table, has an atomic number greater by one than the inert gas element just preceding it and has an unpaired s electron in its electronic field (see Table 14.6). The bonding in the metal is relatively weak as evidenced by the softness, malleability, and low melting points of the metals, with the possible exception of lithium (at. no. 3). That the outer electron is weakly held to the atom is indicated by the low ionization potentials of the alkali metal elements. The halogen family of elements, on the other hand, immediately precedes the noble gas family in the periodic system. Each halogen atom has an electronic field containing one less electron than the stable number held by the succeeding noble gas atom. In consequence, each halogen atom has seven electrons in its outer energy level (see Table 14.6). In terms of our previous definition of valence electrons (see page 198), the halogen atoms have seven valence electrons and the alkali metal atoms have one valence electron.

The halogens, unlike the alkali metals, are molecular substances. At room temperature fluorine and chlorine are gases, bromine is a liquid, and iodine is a crystalline solid but each consists of diatomic molecules with the formulas F_2, Cl_2, Br_2, and I_2, respectively. It appears that in the pure element the halogen atoms join by a covalent bond with the result that each atom by sharing a pair of electrons with its neighbor has the four pairs of electrons in its outer level corresponding to the number in the stable noble gas structure as shown in Table 15.3. The resulting structure is

$$: \overset{..}{\underset{..}{Cl}} : \overset{xx}{\underset{xx}{Cl}} \overset{x}{\underset{x}{}}$$

So great is the tendency of the atoms to pair (see page 202) that dissociation of the diatomic chlorine molecules occurs to an appreciable extent only at high temperatures. At room temperature only about one molecule in one billion (1 in 10^9) will be monatomic.

REACTION BETWEEN SOLID AND GAS

When metallic sodium and gaseous chlorine are brought into contact, crystalline sodium chloride is formed. The reaction proceeds until either one of the reactants is consumed. There is no doubt about the tendency of sodium and chlorine to react, but the rate at which reaction proceeds may not be a measure of the tendency to react for the simple reason that the reacting substances cannot react faster than they can come into contact with each other. Thus, we must distinguish between "tendency to react" and "rate of reaction."

Since sodium is a solid and chlorine is a gas, chlorine, being the more mobile substance, is most likely to determine the rate of reaction. According to the kinetic theory the molecules of chlorine gas will bombard the surface of the metal and there meet the sodium atoms with which they react. There must, of course, be some motion of the sodium atoms if they are to leave the metal with its crystal structure and enter the different crystal structure of the salt that is formed. The salt, being also a solid, forms on the surface of the metal and there interferes with the meeting of sodium atoms and chlorine molecules to form more salt. Hence, this reaction, like most chemical reactions, proceeds at a relatively slow rate though the reaction will proceed with explosive violence if the reacting substances can come into contact with each other very rapidly, for instance, when both sodium and chlorine are gaseous.

ELECTRON TRANSFER IN SALT FORMATION

If the sodium-chlorine reaction were to be between atoms only, the equation could be represented as

$$\underset{\text{Atoms}}{Na_x} + \underset{\text{Atoms}}{\cdot \ddot{\underset{..}{Cl}}:} = \underset{\text{Ions in salt crystal}}{(Na)^+ (\ddot{\underset{..}{:Cl}}:)^-} \equiv NaCl \tag{16.1}$$

(The sign $\equiv$ means "is identical with.") In the reaction the neutral sodium atom, with its single valence electron, loses the electron to the chlorine atom which has seven valence electrons. As a result the sodium becomes an ion with a charge $1+$ and the chlorine atom becomes an ion with a charge $1-$. Each ion has the electron structure of noble gas atoms. Large numbers of these ions, necessarily present in equal numbers (why?), form the crystal of salt. (Note that while salts are composed of ions, as shown in $Na^+ Cl^-$, their formulas are usually written with the charges not indicated, as in NaCl. The student should remember their ionic nature, however.)

Equation 16.1 does not give an adequate picture of the reaction because we have already found that the overwhelming majority of the chlorine atoms are present, not as single atoms, but as atom pairs in diatomic molecules. It is much more probable that when a molecule of chlorine meets the metallic sodium one of each pair of chlorine atoms gains an electron from sodium to form a sodium ion, a chloride ion, and a neutral chlorine atom. The neutral chlorine atom could then meet another sodium atom to form more ions. Such a series of reactions may be represented by the equations

$$\underset{\substack{\text{atom in}\\\text{solid}}}{Na} + \underset{\substack{\text{diatomic}\\\text{molecule}}}{Cl_2} = \underset{\substack{\text{ions}\\\text{in salt}}}{Na^+Cl^-} + \underset{\text{atom}}{Cl} \qquad \text{(Step A)}$$

$$\underset{\substack{\text{atom in}\\\text{solid}}}{Na} + \underset{\text{atom}}{Cl} = \underset{\substack{\text{ions}\\\text{in salt}}}{Na^+Cl^-} \qquad \text{(Step B)}$$

The sum of Steps A and B is

$$\underset{\substack{\text{atoms in}\\\text{solid}}}{2Na} + \underset{\substack{\text{diatomic}\\\text{molecule}}}{Cl_2} = \underset{\substack{\text{ions}\\\text{in salt}}}{2Na^+Cl^-} \equiv \underset{\substack{\text{solid}\\\text{salt}}}{2NaCl} \tag{16.2}$$

In terms of molar quantities equation 16.2 may be written

228   GENERAL CHEMISTRY

$$\underset{\substack{\text{1 mole of}\\\text{metal}}}{Na_{(s)}} + \underset{\substack{\frac{1}{2}\text{ mole}\\\text{of gas}}}{\tfrac{1}{2}Cl_{2(g)}} = \underset{\substack{\text{1 mole}\\\text{of salt}}}{Na^+Cl^-_{(s)}} \equiv NaCl_{(s)} \qquad (16.3)$$

Another useful way of viewing the reaction as a sum of successive steps makes a separation at the point of transfer of the electrons from the one element to the other. For the loss of electrons by sodium metal, where one electron or one mole of electrons is represented by e^-,

$$Na_{(s)} = Na^+ + e^- \qquad \text{(Step A)}$$

and for the gain of electrons by neutral chlorine gas

$$e^- + \tfrac{1}{2}Cl_{2(g)} = Cl^- \qquad \text{(Step B)}$$

The sum of Step A and Step B gives us equation 16.3.

FORMATION OF IONS FROM METALLIC ELEMENTS

We have seen that metallic sodium may give up electrons to become sodium ions with charge 1+ if negative chloride ions are formed when chlorine accepts the electrons. Since salt is neutral even though it consists of ions, the ions must be present in such numbers as to preserve electrical neutrality. If this principle is clear, we may ignore the negative ions for the moment without acquiring faulty ideas about the nature of the reactions.

When a neutral sodium atom with its eleven electrons loses one electron to an atom of another element, ten electrons remain. There are two $1s$ electrons, two $2s$ and six $2p$ electrons, or ten in all. The sodium ion, Na^+, has the same electron structure as the neutral neon atom. The stability of this structure explains the stability of the sodium ion. In the same way the other alkali metals tend to lose one electron per atom to form ions with charge 1+. All the resulting alkali metal ions have inert gas structures: Li^+ (helium structure), K^+ (argon structure), Rb^+ (krypton structure), Cs^+ (xenon structure), and Fr^+ (radon structure). The details of the structures may be obtained from Table 14.5 or 15.2. The *partial equations*, that is, the equations for the part of the reaction of immediate interest are

$$\begin{aligned} Li &= Li^+ + e^- \\ Na &= Na^+ + e^- \\ K &= K^+ + e^- \\ Rb &= Rb^+ + e^- \\ Cs &= Cs^+ + e^- \\ Fr &= Fr^+ + e^- \end{aligned} \qquad (16.4)$$

The elements of the alkaline earth family (Group 2a) have atomic numbers greater by two than the corresponding inert gases and have two electrons per atom in their outmost energy levels. From the ionization potentials we know that these two valence electrons are held more tightly than the valence electron in the alkali metals. The atoms are smaller, the metals are harder, and the melting points are higher than in the alkali metals. Nevertheless, the atoms of the alkaline earth elements have a great tendency to lose both electrons to

Table 16.1
Some Monatomic Ions (and Atoms) Having Inert Gas Electron Structures

ELECTRON STRUCTURE: INERT GAS, 2 OR 8 ELECTRONS IN OUTER LEVEL	\multicolumn{7}{c}{PERIODIC GROUP OF ELEMENT}
	6	7	0	1	2	3	4
He 2		H$^-$	He	Li$^+$	Be^{++}		
Ne 2, 8	O^{--}	F$^-$	Ne	Na$^+$	Mg^{++}	Al^{+++}	
A 2, 8, 8	S^{--}	Cl$^-$	A	K$^+$	Ca^{++}	Sc^{+++}	Ti^{++++}
Kr 2, 8, 18, 8	Se^{--}	Br$^-$	Kr	Rb$^+$	Sr^{++}	Y^{+++}	Zr^{++++}
Xe 2, 8, 18, 18, 8	Te^{--}	I$^-$	Xe	Cs$^+$	Ba^{++}	La^{+++}	Ce^{++++}, Hf^{++++}
Rn 2, 8, 18, 32, 18, 8		At$^-$	Rn	Fr$^+$	Ra^{++}	Ac^{+++}	Th^{++++}

Table 16.2
Some Additional Stable Electron Structures for Monatomic Ions

ELECTRON STRUCTURE	\multicolumn{4}{c}{PERIODIC GROUP OF ELEMENT}
	1B	2B	3B	4B
A. 18 electrons in outer level				
2, 8, 18	Cu$^+$	Zn^{++}	Ga^{+++}	
Pd°—2, 8, 18, 18	Ag$^+$	Cd^{++}	In^{+++}	Sn^{++++}
2, 8, 18, 32, 18	Au$^+$	Hg^{++}	Tl^{+++}	Pb^{++++}
B. 2 electrons in outer level overlying a level of 18 electrons.				
Zn°—2, 8, 18, 2			Ga$^+$	Ge^{++}
Cd°—2, 8, 18, 18, 2			In$^+$	Sn^{++}
Hg°—2, 8, 18, 32, 18, 2			Tl$^+$	Pb^{++}

form ions with the charge 2+ (and noble gas electronic structures). They can do this if they meet atoms of other elements that will accept the electrons to form negative ions. The partial reactions are

$$\begin{aligned} Be &= Be^{++} + 2e^- \\ Mg &= Mg^{++} + 2e^- \\ Ca &= Ca^{++} + 2e^- \\ Sr &= Sr^{++} + 2e^- \\ Ba &= Ba^{++} + 2e^- \\ Ra &= Ra^{++} + 2e^- \end{aligned} \quad (16.5)$$

Similar considerations, applied to the metallic elements in Groups 3a and 4a of the periodic system, lead to partial equations such as

$$Al = Al^{+++} + 3e^- \quad (16.6)$$
$$Ti = Ti^{++++} + 4e^- \quad (16.7)$$

The electronic structures of these and some other positive ions are shown on the right side of Table 16.1.

All metallic elements, under the proper conditions, lose electrons to become positive ions in the manner shown in the preceding partial equations. However, the resulting ions have the electronic structures of the inert gases only if the elements lie in families near that of the inert gases. For some metallic elements in the long periods of the periodic system a relatively stable electronic structure is reached when eighteen rather than eight electrons remain in the outer level as shown in Part A of Table 16.2 or when two *s* electrons remain in the outer level underlain by a level with eighteen electrons, as shown in Part B of Table 16.2. Other electronic structures are possible for monatomic ions but these three are the most common.

FORMATION OF IONS FROM NONMETALLIC ELEMENTS

We have already seen that the atoms whose number of electrons is slightly less than that of the inert gases tend to achieve a stable arrangment—four pairs of electrons in the outermost level—by sharing electrons to form covalent bonds. For the halogens the result was diatomic molecules. Each atom needs to gain an electron to have the inert gas structure and this can only be done if they share a pair cooperatively. In the presence of metallic elements, which are electron donors, each halogen atom may acquire the electron structure of an inert gas by gaining one electron to form a monatomic ion with a charge of $1-$. Partial equations may be written for these reactions.

$$\begin{align} e^- + \tfrac{1}{2}F_2 &= F^- \\ e^- + \tfrac{1}{2}Cl_2 &= Cl^- \\ e^- + \tfrac{1}{2}Br_2 &= Br^- \\ e^- + \tfrac{1}{2}I_2 &= I^- \end{align} \quad (16.8)$$

The oxygen atom, with six valence electrons, needs two electrons to achieve an inert gas structure. The sulfur atom, like the oxygen atom, needs two electrons to achieve an inert gas structure. In crystalline sulfur the atoms form rings of eight atoms, S_8, rather than small molecules but we often represent solid sulfur by the simple symbol, S. The partial equations for the formation of oxygen and sulfur ions become

$$\begin{align} 2e^- + \tfrac{1}{2}O_2 &= O^{--} \\ 2e^- + S &= S^{--} \end{align} \quad (16.9)$$

The electron structures of some negatively charged ions are shown on the left side of Table 16.1.

FORMATION OF HYDROGEN IONS

The hydrogen atom is a unique atom. It has but a single electron which one might expect it to lose just as the atoms of the alkali metals lose their single valence electrons to form ions with charge $1+$. But the ions of the alkali metals have inert gas structures whereas the positively charged hydrogen would consist of the bare nucleus of the hydrogen atom. For ordinary hydrogen atoms the nucleus consists of the proton so that for them the hydrogen ion would be the proton. A proton, however, is a highly reactive particle. For example, pure nitric acid is a poor conductor. The proton remains attached to the nitrate by a covalent bond. However, when water is added to the acid the conductivity increases sharply. The solution then shows evidence of large numbers of hydrogen ions and nitrate ions. For these and other reasons we believe that the hydrogen ion is a larger ion formed when the proton becomes attached to a neutral molecule such as that of the solvent. The partial equations for the formation, from hydrogen gas, of a hydrogen ion in water solution or in a solution containing the solvent X becomes

$$\frac{1}{2}H_2 + H_2O = H_2O \cdot H^+ + e^-$$
$$\frac{1}{2}H_2 + X = X \cdot H^+ + e^- \tag{16.10}$$

Thus, the "hydrogen ion" is a charged group of atoms just as the ammonium ion NH_4^+ is a polyatomic ion. The principal difference between the $H_2O \cdot H^+$ (or H_3O^+) ion and the NH_4^+ ion is in the strength with which the proton is attached to the water or ammonia molecule. For simplicity we often omit the solvent from the equations 16.10 which then become

$$\frac{1}{2}H_2 = H^+ + e^- \tag{16.11}$$

We may use partial equation 16.11 so long as we remember that H^+ is a solvated proton rather than the proton itself. In the same way we shall write formulas for other ions without regard to their solvation though we know it occurs.

Hydrogen atoms are unique in another respect. Like the halogen atoms they lack one electron of the following inert gas structure. That is, if the hydrogen atom gains one electron the resulting negative ion has the electronic structure of helium; the ion is $(H:)^-$. This ion does not exist in water solution but does form when hydrogen reacts directly with some metallic elements. The partial equation is

$$e^- + \frac{1}{2}H_2 = H^- \tag{16.12}$$

With sodium the reaction is

$$Na = Na^+ + e^-$$
$$\underline{e^- + \frac{1}{2}H_2 = H^-}$$
$$Na + \frac{1}{2}H_2 = Na^+H^- \equiv NaH \tag{16.13}$$

The resulting compound, sodium hydride, formula Na^+H^-, is saltlike in properties since it is a solid made up of ions. Similar reactions could be written for the reaction of hydrogen with many other metallic elements. Note that equation 16.13 is the sum of two partial equations. The electrons must cancel when the partial reactions are added, for the electron loss by the sodium must exactly equal the electron gain by the hydrogen.

FORMATION OF SALTS FROM THE ELEMENTS

On the basis of the preceding principles we are now able to make general statements about the formation of ionic compounds from the elements. Electrical neutrality is preserved since some atom must gain an electron for every

232 GENERAL CHEMISTRY

atom that loses an electron. When potassium loses its valence electrons to bromine, one positive ion, charge 1+, is formed for every negative ion, charge 1−, and the salt has the formula K^+Br^-. The equation may be derived from the appropriate partial equations in 16.5 and 16.8 by addition (and canceling of electrons)

$$\begin{array}{r} K = K^+ + \cancel{e^-} \\ \cancel{e^-} + \tfrac{1}{2}Br_2 = Br^- \\ \hline K + \tfrac{1}{2}Br_2 = K^+Br^- \equiv KBr \end{array}$$
(16.14)

Since sulfur gains two electrons per atom and potassium loses only one per atom the equation for the formation of potassium sulfide becomes

$$\begin{array}{r} 2K = 2K^+ + 2\cancel{e^-} \\ 2\cancel{e^-} + S = S^{--} \\ \hline 2K + S = K^+_2 S^{--} \equiv K_2S \end{array}$$
(16.15)

Similarly, for the formation of calcium iodide

$$\begin{array}{r} Ca = Ca^{++} + 2\cancel{e^-} \\ 2\cancel{e^-} + I_2 = 2I^- \\ \hline Ca + I_2 = Ca^{++}I^-_2 \equiv CaI_2 \end{array}$$
(16.16)

Problem 16.1. With the aid of partial equations write the equations for the formation of the following: lithium fluoride, sodium oxide, cesium chloride, magnesium bromide, barium sulfide, strontium oxide, rubidium fluoride, francium chloride, titanium sulfide, scandium chloride.

FORMATION OF COVALENT COMPOUNDS

When hydrogen chloride is prepared from hydrogen and chlorine gases, new covalent bonds replace the old. The change becomes clear when the "atom kernels" and valence electrons are shown.

$$H \overset{\cdot}{\underset{\times}{\,}} H \ + \ \overset{..}{\underset{..}{:}} Cl \overset{..}{\underset{..}{:}} Cl \overset{..}{\underset{..}{:}} \ = \ 2H \overset{\cdot}{\underset{\times}{\,}} \overset{..}{\underset{..}{Cl}} :$$
(16.17)

molecules in gas   molecules in gas   molecules in gas

The arrangement of atoms in hydrogen chloride is more stable at room temperature than the arrangement in the elementary gases but the reaction does not proceed at a measurable rate unless the reaction mixture is heated to temperatures of several hundred degrees or unless light of sufficient energy is absorbed in the mixture. The reason is that the hydrogen-to-hydrogen and/or chlorine-to-chlorine bonds must be broken before the hydrogen-to-chlorine bonds can form. The energy needed to break the bonds, the activation energy (see page 88), may be derived from the high collision energies at high temperatures or from light energy of the frequency absorbed by the individual molecules. The activation energy is more than recovered when the new bonds form. The energy (heat) of reaction represents the net effect. For these reasons equation 16.17 shows the over-all change when large numbers of molecules (for example molar quantities) react but it cannot show the way in which individual molecules of the reacting gases actually interact to form the hydrogen chloride molecules.

The reaction of hydrogen atoms with oxygen atoms would seem to be straight-forward since each of two hydrogen atoms has a valence electron to share and each oxygen atom has six valence electrons, four already paired and two unpaired. Thus

$$2H_x + \cdot \overset{..}{O} : = H \overset{..}{:} \overset{..}{O} : \\ \overset{..x}{H}$$

The final product, water molecules, would have a stable electronic structure at the moment of formation but very high energy since each of the bonds forms with the release of a large amount of energy. The reaction cannot go in this way because the excess energy must be removed if the water molecules are not to dissociate immediately. We must, therefore, be careful not to confuse the equations we usually write with the actual mechanisms by which reaction proceeds. The mechanisms are ordinarily much more complicated than the equations show.

When molecules of hydrogen and oxygen are the reacting particles, activation energy is necessary to separate the atoms held by existing bonds. At room temperature a mixture of hydrogen and oxygen gases is inert just as a mixture of hydrogen and chlorine is. However, when the necessary activation energy is introduced by a spark or otherwise, the reaction proceeds by a series of steps at explosive rates. The usual equation, thus, does not show the course of the reaction but only the over-all result.

$$H_2 + \tfrac{1}{2}O_2 = H : \overset{..}{\underset{..}{O}} : \\ \phantom{H_2 + \tfrac{1}{2}O_2 = H : }H \qquad (16.18)$$

Similar considerations apply to the reaction of hydrogen and nitrogen to form ammonia. Although ammonia is more stable than the elements at room temperature, high temperatures are required to produce an appreciable rate of reaction. In practice a third substance, a catalyst, is present to form temporary intermediate products whose activation energies are lower than those needed to dissociate the diatomic molecules into their gaseous atoms. The over-all reaction may be represented by the equation

$$3H \overset{x}{:} H + :N : : :N : = 2H \overset{..}{\underset{x\cdot}{:} N :} H \qquad (16.19) \\ H$$

These principles are illustrated further by the behavior of hydrogen and carbon. The substance methane,

$$\begin{array}{c} H \\ \cdot\cdot \\ H:C:H \\ \cdot\cdot \\ H \end{array}$$

is stable at room temperatures with respect to the elements, hydrogen and graphite or diamond, but cannot be formed by direct reaction. The carbon atoms are so strongly bonded to one another in diamond or graphite that at the temperatures necessary to rupture the carbon-carbon bonds the proposed compound, methane, becomes unstable. Methane must be formed at temperatures which do not cause its decomposition and so cannot be formed directly from the elements at high temperatures. (Contrast with hydrogen chloride and water.)

We see that knowledge of stable electronic structures of compounds helps us to understand what groupings of atoms form stable compounds. Each of the atoms in the compounds so far discussed has attained an inert gas structure. This knowledge is extremely useful but not sufficient. If it were sufficient, chemistry would be primarily a bookkeeping science. The problems of chemistry are harder problems. What we usually require of chemistry is that it tells us how to make new substances we want from the relatively stable substances already existing in the world. What we need to know are the principles under which new bonds are exchanged for old.

COMPETITIVE REACTIONS

We have already considered the fact that covalent bonds in compounds are usually formed by the same electrons that form covalent bonds between the atoms of elements themselves. Whether the compounds or the elements are more stable depends in part on the energies released on formation of the bonds and on the symmetries of the resulting structures. Each structure competes with the others in attempting to share the electrons in covalent bonds in the most stable fashion.

The competition is decidedly one-sided when a strongly electropositive substance reacts with a strongly electronegative substance to produce ions. For instance, the tendency of atoms of metallic elements to lose electrons and the tendency of halogens to gain electrons to form positive and negative ions, respectively, cooperate to produce the ionic salt. However, competition can become important if there are two potential electron donors and only one electron receiver.

If we place a lump of potassium and a lump of sodium into a bottle of chlorine gas, potassium chloride will form on the first lump and sodium chloride on the second lump even though the ionization potentials of the metals indicate that potassium loses electrons more readily than sodium. Both reactions have a great tendency to go and both will go as rapidly as the chlorine gas can meet the metals. If, however, the two metals are intimately mixed so that the same molecules of gas can react with either metal the competitive factor enters and potassium chloride rather than sodium chloride forms so long as potassium atoms are available. Similarly, if metallic sodium is melted with potassium chloride no reaction takes place (sodium atoms hold electrons more tightly than potassium atoms), but if potassium is melted with sodium chloride, potassium atoms become ions by losing their electrons to sodium ions which then become neutral atoms. This reaction may be represented by the equations

$$\frac{\begin{array}{r}K = K^+ + e^-\\ e^- + Na^+ = Na\end{array}}{K + Na^+ = Na + K^+} \qquad (16.20)$$

or

$$\begin{array}{r}K + Na^+Cl^- = K^+Cl^- + Na\\ K + NaCl = KCl + Na\end{array} \qquad (16.21)$$

A similar competitive situation may exist in a system in which sodium has the opportunity to react with either chlorine or bromine. It can react with either independently, but when the amount of sodium is limited and there is freedom of exchange so that either the chlorine or bromine may receive the electrons, the negative ion which holds the electrons more tightly is formed. In this case chloride ions would form since chloride ions hold electrons more tightly than bromide ions. In consequence, if bromine is bubbled through molten sodium chloride no reaction occurs but if chlorine is bubbled through molten sodium bromide the reaction may be represented by the equations

$$\frac{\begin{array}{r}e^- + \tfrac{1}{2}Cl_2 = Cl^-\\ Br^- = \tfrac{1}{2}Br_2 + e^-\end{array}}{\tfrac{1}{2}Cl_2 + Br^- = \tfrac{1}{2}Br_2 + Cl^-} \qquad (16.22)$$

or

$$\begin{array}{r}\tfrac{1}{2}Cl_2 + Na^+Br^- = \tfrac{1}{2}Br_2 + Na^+Cl^-\\ \tfrac{1}{2}Cl_2 + NaBr = \tfrac{1}{2}Br_2 + NaCl\end{array} \qquad (16.23)$$

Competitive reactions are not restricted to ionic compounds. If a limited amount of hydrogen is mixed with equal quantities of chlorine and bromine, much, much more gaseous hydrogen chloride than hydrogen bromide is formed. Similarly, if chlorine is mixed with hydrogen bromide at reaction temperatures, hydrogen chloride and bromine will form as shown by the equation

$$\tfrac{1}{2}Cl_2 + HBr = \tfrac{1}{2}Br_2 + HCl \qquad (16.24)$$

(This picture of competitive reactions above is somewhat oversimplified for one must actually consider more factors than have been listed. For instance, it may be true that potassium always loses electrons more readily than sodium, but it does not automatically follow that potassium bromide will have a greater tendency to form than sodium bromide. This would only be true if one ended up with identically isolated bromide ions in each instance, as well as individually isolated positive ions. Actually one often ends up with a crystalline solid and it is quite possible that the structure of solid sodium bromide is an exceptionally stable one. This would increase its tendency to form as compared with potassium bromide. Such stability might arise, for instance, from the ease with which spheres having the relative sizes of sodium and bromide ions could pack together as compared to spheres with the relative sizes of potassium and bromide ions. Many examples of such shifts in relative stability are known. Silver iodide is much more stable toward decomposition into the elements than one would guess from a knowledge of the behavior of silver chloride, the three ions—silver, chloride, and iodide, and the corresponding elements. The enhanced stability is due to the nature of crystalline silver iodide compared to crystalline silver chloride. Thus one must consider the actual states of materials involved in the reaction being studied, rather than an idealized abstraction of them, if he hopes to generalize on the nature of competitive processes.)

OXIDATION STATE AND NUMBER

The atoms of an element in a salt are present as ions, positively or negatively charged. For them the positive or negative number designating the amount of and the sign of the charge is called the *oxidation number*. Thus, in calcium chloride with the formula $Ca^{++}Cl^-_2$ the oxidation number of calcium is $2+$ and that of chlorine is $1-$. For the neutral elements the oxidation numbers are 0. In metallic calcium the calcium is said to be in the 0 oxidation state and in the calcium salts it is said to be in the $2+$ oxidation state. For reactions involving complete transfer of electrons—as in the formation of ionic compounds—the concepts of oxidation number and state add nothing new since the oxidation number of an ion is identical with its charge. But oxidation numbers are also useful in describing situations in which bonding electrons, though not transferred completely, are not shared equally by the participating atoms. In other words they are used in the discussion of polar covalent bonds.

We saw in Chapter 15 that the bonding electrons in hydrogen and chlorine gases are shared equally by the atoms so that the bonds are nonpolar. But the bond in hydrogen chloride has an electrical polarity because the bonding electrons are attracted more by the chlorine than by the hydrogen atoms. We may recognize this situation by making an arbitrary separation as shown by the dotted line and designating *oxidation numbers* as follows:

Oxidation
numbers →   0 0   0 0   1+ 1−   1+ 1−
           H ∶ H + ∶ Cl ∶ Cl ∶ = H ∶ Cl ∶ + H ∶ Cl ∶

In hydrogen chloride the hydrogen is said to be in the $1+$ oxidation state and the chlorine in the $1-$ state, just as it is in the ionic compounds. This assignment follows from the electronegativity series of the elements in that an element which combines with a more electronegative element acquires a positive oxidation state. Conversely an element combining with a more electropositive element acquires a negative oxidation state. Since hydrogen is more electropositive than the other nonmetallic elements, its oxidation number is 1+ in compounds with nonmetals. On the other hand, hydrogen is more electronegative than the metallic elements (see Figure 15.5). Hydrogen, therefore, is in the 1− oxidation state in its compounds with the metals. Such compounds of hydrogen (1−) with metals are called *metallic hydrides* (see page 473). Because oxygen is the most electronegative element with the exception of fluorine (see Figure 15.5), tending to accept two electrons to complete its valence shell to eight electrons, its oxidation number is 2− in almost all of its compounds. Thus, in water, formula H_2O, the oxidation number of oxygen is 2−. Since the water molecule is electrically neutral the oxidation number of the hydrogen must be 1+. In hydrogen peroxide, formula H_2O_2, the hydrogen again has an oxidation number of 1+, but the oxygen must then be 1−.

Since compounds as well as elements are electrically neutral, the total of the oxidation numbers summed for all the atoms present must be zero. Per molecule of water we have $2(1+) + 1(2-) = 0$. This rule enables us to find the oxidation number of a third element when those of the other two are known. For example, in sulfuric acid, formula H_2SO_4, we have for the hydrogen, $2(1+) = 2+$ and for the oxygen, $4(2-) = 8-$. Since the molecule has zero oxidation number as a whole, the oxidation number of the sulfur must be 6+, for $2(1+) + 4(2-) + 1(6+) = 0$.

Consider the competitive reaction resulting from the fact that sodium has a greater tendency to acquire a positive oxidation state than hydrogen. In metallic sodium the oxidation state is 0 but, in hydrogen chloride, hydrogen is in the 1+ oxidation state. Therefore, when sodium is placed in contact with hydrogen chloride it becomes 1+ and hydrogen becomes 0 as shown by the reaction

$$\text{Oxidation numbers} \quad \overset{0}{\text{Na}} + \overset{1+\ 1-}{\text{HCl}} = \overset{1+\ 1-}{\text{Na}^+\text{Cl}^-} + \overset{0}{\tfrac{1}{2}\text{H}_2} \quad (16.26)$$

Compare this reaction with that shown in equation 16.21. Because potassium has a greater tendency to acquire a 1+ oxidation state than sodium it follows that potassium would show a greater tendency to react than sodium in a reaction of the type shown in equation 16.26.

The more common oxidation numbers of the elements are listed in Table 14.6. These oxidation numbers should be correlated with electron structures and positions in the periodic system. Knowledge of the relative stabilities of these oxidation states allows one to correlate a great deal of information about chemical reactions in a rather simple way.

OXIDATION-REDUCTION REACTIONS

When an element changes to a more positive (higher) oxidation state it is said to be oxidized. When an element changes to a more negative (lower)

238 GENERAL CHEMISTRY

oxidation state it is said to be reduced. But, since all elements and compounds are electrically neutral, the gains and losses in electrons, whether real or assigned by definition, must balance. Consequently, when something is oxidized something else must be reduced to a comparable degree. For every oxidation there is a comparable reduction, the processes being necessarily paired. A reaction in which there are changes in oxidation states is called an *oxidation-reduction reaction*. The majority of reactions we have already considered in this course are oxidation-reduction reactions.

OXIDATION-REDUCTION IN ELECTROLYTIC REACTIONS

In ordinary laboratory or industrial vessels, oxidation-reduction reactions occur wherever the atoms and molecules of the reacting substances meet throughout the reaction vessel but in electrolytic cells the oxidation and reduction reactions are separated in space. The oxidation takes place at one electrode, the anode, while reduction takes place at the other electrode, the cathode. Ions migrate through the cell to maintain electrical neutrality around the electrodes. In a cell reaction, as in all other oxidation-reduction reactions, there must be a reduction for every oxidation so that for each equivalent of substance oxidized at the anode an equivalent of substance is reduced at the cathode, in accordance with Faraday's laws of electrolysis (page 211).

When there is more than one oxidizable substance or more that one reducible substance in a cell the principles of competitive reactions, discussed on page 234, tells us that the most easily reduced atoms or ions or molecules will accept the electrons at the cathode and the most easily oxidized atom, ions, or molecules will give electrons to the anode. Thus, if the only cations present are Na^+ and K^+ ions, metallic sodium will form at the cathode so long as sodium ions remain. After the sodium ions are used up, potassium ions will be discharged. Similarly, if Cl^-, Br^-, and I^- ions are present, I^- will be oxidized at the anode before the other ions.

Competition always enters when water solutions of salts are electrolyzed. Water is more easily reduced at the cathode, with evolution of gaseous hydrogen, than are sodium or potassium ions to the respective metals. On the other hand, the ions Cu^{++} and Ag^+ are more readily reduced than water and may be deposited as metals from water solution as in commercial plating of these metals. Similarly, in a water solution of a fluoride, oxygen gas is released at the anode rather than fluorine. The partial equations are:

$$\text{At the cathode: } H_2O + e^- = \tfrac{1}{2}H_{2(g)} + OH^- \qquad (16.27)$$
$$\text{At the anode: } \tfrac{1}{2}H_2O + e^- = \tfrac{1}{4}O_{2(g)} + H^+ \qquad (16.28)$$

Problem 16.2. 0.1 moles of cupric bromide and 0.1 moles of potassium chloride are dissolved in a liter of water. The solution is electrolyzed until 0.1 faraday of electricity has passed through the cell. What and how much of each is formed at each electrode? Write the partial equations for the half-reactions, indicating the electrode at which each occurs, and write the equation for the over-all reaction.

REACTIONS OF BASIC OXIDES WITH WATER

When solid sodium oxide, formula Na_2O, is added to water it reacts vigorously with the evolution of much heat to form a new substance, sodium hydroxide. This substance with the formula $NaOH$ can be isolated from the water solution as a solid if the water is removed. It is very soluble in water. The reaction is represented by the equation

$$Na^+_2O^{--} + H_2O = 2Na^+OH^-$$
$$Na_2O + H_2O = 2NaOH \quad (16.29)$$

The same reaction takes place if the solid sodium oxide is exposed to gaseous water (water vapor). It is not an oxidation-reduction reaction; there is no change in oxidation numbers. In the compounds shown, sodium and hydrogen have oxidation numbers of $1+$ and oxygen the oxidation number of $2-$. The reaction is a general one for a class of oxides called basic oxides and may be represented by the equation

$$\underset{\text{oxide ion}}{O^{--}} + H_2O = \underset{\text{hydroxide ions}}{2OH^-} \quad (16.30)$$

It is the oxide ions which gives the basic properties, not the metallic ions. Observe that in the hydroxide ion oxygen retains the oxidation number of $2-$ and hydrogen that of $1+$, so that the ion as a whole has the oxidation number and charge of $1-$. In water the doubly charged oxide ion reacts to form two singly charged hydroxide ions, thus distributing the O—H bonds more evenly and minimizing the charge per ion.

The elements forming ionic oxides are the metallic elements on the left side of the periodic table, notably those of Groups 1, 2, and 3. Calcium forms an ionic oxide, commonly called lime, which reacts with water to form calcium hydroxide (slaked lime).

$$Ca^{++}O^{--} + H_2O = Ca^{++}(OH^-)_2$$
$$CaO_{(s)} + H_2O = Ca(OH)_{2(s)} \quad (16.31)$$

All substances containing hydroxide ions belong to a class of substances called bases. Most oxides of metals are basic oxides which react with water to produce hydroxide ions.

REACTIONS OF ACIDIC OXIDES WITH WATER

The nonmetallic elements on the right side of the periodic table form oxides which are covalent rather than ionic in character. The bonds between the central atom and oxygen, though polar, remain essentially covalent. The central atom in many of these oxides can form additional covalent bonds with the oxygen atoms from water. At the same time the hydrogen atoms rearrange so that no oxygen atom forms more than two covalent bonds. For example, when sulfur dioxide is dissolved in water it forms a new substance called sulfurous acid.

$$\mathrm{OSO} + \begin{array}{c}\mathrm{H}\\\mathrm{HO}\end{array} = \begin{array}{c}\mathrm{H}\\\mathrm{O}\\\mathrm{OSOH}\end{array} \equiv \begin{array}{c}(\mathrm{HO})_2\mathrm{SO}\\\text{or}\\\mathrm{H}_2\mathrm{SO}_3\end{array} \qquad (16.32)$$

As a result of the reaction, three oxygen atoms (rather than two) are bonded to each sulfur atom and the hydrogen atoms are attached to different oxygen atoms.

Although sulfurous acid contains two hydroxyl groups, these being covalently bonded do not yield hydroxide ions. Instead, some of the hydrogen atoms leave their valence electrons with the oxygen and are transferred as protons to neighboring water molecules (compare page 231). It is these hydrated (or solvated protons) that are called *hydrogen ions*.

$$\begin{array}{c}\mathrm{HOSO}\\\mathrm{O}\\\mathrm{H}\end{array} = \mathrm{H}^+ + \left[\begin{array}{c}\mathrm{OSO}\\\mathrm{O}\\\mathrm{H}\end{array}\right]^- \qquad (16.33)$$

sulfurous acid   hydrogen ions   hydrogen sulfite ions

A lesser number of protons leave the hydrogen sulfite ion.

$$\left[\begin{array}{c}\mathrm{OSO}\\\mathrm{O}\\\mathrm{H}\end{array}\right]^- = \mathrm{H}^+ + \left[\begin{array}{c}\mathrm{OSO}\\\mathrm{O}\end{array}\right]^{--} \qquad (16.34)$$

hydrogen sulfite ion   hydrogen ion   sulfite ion

Sulfur trioxide has three oxygen atoms attached to each sulfur atom but by reacting with water a fourth oxygen atom becomes attached as in sulfuric acid.

$$\begin{array}{c}\mathrm{O}\\\mathrm{OSO}\end{array} + \begin{array}{c}\mathrm{HO}\\\mathrm{H}\end{array} = \begin{array}{c}\mathrm{O}\\\mathrm{HOSO}\\\mathrm{O}\\\mathrm{H}\end{array} \equiv \begin{array}{c}(\mathrm{HO})_2\mathrm{SO}_2\\\text{or}\\\mathrm{H}_2\mathrm{SO}_4\end{array} \qquad (16.35)$$

This reaction occurs even when gaseous water is used. The structural formula shown for the acid represents, as well as one can in the plane of the paper, the arrangements of the atoms in the molecule. Actually, the oxygen atoms are arranged at the corners of a regular tetrahedron with the sulfur atom at its center. There are two hydroxyl groups (but not hydroxide ions) per molecule.

When an excess of water is present, sulfuric acid ionizes even more readily than does sulfurous acid.

$$\begin{array}{c}\mathrm{O}\\\mathrm{HOSO}\\\mathrm{O}\\\mathrm{H}\end{array} = \mathrm{H}^+ + \left[\begin{array}{c}\mathrm{O}\\\mathrm{OSO}\\\mathrm{O}\\\mathrm{H}\end{array}\right]^- \qquad (16.36)$$

sulfuric acid   hydrogen ion   hydrogen sulfate ion

$$\begin{bmatrix} \text{O} \\ \text{HOSO} \\ \text{O} \end{bmatrix}^{-} = \text{H}^+ + \begin{bmatrix} \text{O} \\ \text{OSO} \\ \text{O} \end{bmatrix}^{--} \quad (16.37)$$

hydrogen sulfate ion   hydrogen ion   sulfate ion

Some of the metallic elements in the central part of the periodic system form oxides in which they have a high positive oxidation number. These oxides are acidic, reacting with water to form acids. Thus chromium trioxide reacts much like sulfur trioxide.

$$\begin{matrix} \text{O} \\ \text{OCr} \\ \text{O} \end{matrix} + \begin{matrix} \text{HO} \\ \text{H} \end{matrix} = \begin{matrix} \text{O} \\ \text{HOCrO} \\ \text{O} \\ \text{H} \end{matrix} = \text{H}^+ + \begin{bmatrix} \text{O} \\ \text{HOCrO} \\ \text{O} \end{bmatrix}^{-} \quad (16.38)$$

solid chromium trioxide   chromic acid in water   hydrogen ion   hydrogen chromate ion

Substances which release hydrogen ions in water solution belong to a class of substances called acids.

Problem 16.3. Draw electronic structural formulas for sulfur dioxide, sulfurous acid, sulfur trioxide, sulfuric acid, and chromic acid so that each atom except hydrogen has an outer level holding 4 pairs of electrons. Hydrogen always holds a single pair of electrons. Note that the kernel notation for chromium is such that there are six valence electrons.

PRELIMINARY DEFINITION OF ACIDS AND BASES

Acids have a sour taste in water solution. Even a solid acid has a sour taste since it dissolves in the saliva to form a water solution. However, one should not apply this test freely since some acids are powerful poisons and others are highly corrosive. Acids also produce characteristic color changes in many dyes. Litmus, a naturally occurring substance, has a red color in acids. Grape juice from colored grapes contains a vegetable dye that has a somewhat different red color in acids. Acids also have the property of counteracting the special properties of bases, the acid properties being destroyed at the same time. Thus, acids and bases neutralize one another when mixed in proper ratios.

Bases in water solution are soapy to the touch. They produce characteristic colors in dyes such as litmus. In bases litmus has a blue color, as does the vegetable dye in grape juice. Other dyes (tea, beet juice, and many pure substances) have different acid and base colors. Phenolphthalein is colorless in acid and red in basic solution and in a strongly basic solution becomes colorless again. And, as stated above, bases react with acids to neutralize them. Both the sour taste and the soapy feeling disappear, for instance, as solutions of acids and bases are mixed.

Because certain dyes change color when bases are added in excess to acids or when acids are added in excess to bases the dyes are called acid-base indicators, or, simply, *indicators*. They may be used to show when equivalent amounts of acid and base have been mixed.

The above definitions for acids and bases are operational ones, based on their behaviors as classes of substances. We shall now consider the structures responsible for the special properties.

NEUTRALIZATION

When one mole of sodium hydroxide is treated with one mole of nitric acid the following reaction takes place:

$$NaOH + HNO_3 = HOH + NaNO_3 \text{ (sodium nitrate)} \qquad (16.39)$$

Neutral water and a neutral salt, neither of which are acid or base, are formed. The reaction is a *neutralization reaction*. When one mole of sodium hydroxide is treated with one mole of sulfuric acid, water and an acid salt, sodium hydrogen sulfate, are formed. The latter can be isolated by boiling off the water.

$$NaOH + H_2SO_4 = HOH + NaHSO_4 \text{ (sodium hydrogen sulfate)} \qquad (16.40)$$

If another mole of sodium hydroxide is added more water and a neutral salt, sodium sulfate, are formed.

$$NaOH + NaHSO_4 = HOH + Na_2SO_4 \text{ (sodium sulfate)} \qquad (16.41)$$

When one mole of calcium hydroxide is treated with one mole of sulfuric acid water and a neutral salt, calcium sulfate, are formed.

$$Ca(OH)_2 + H_2SO_4 = 2HOH + CaSO_4 \qquad (16.42)$$

In the above examples the neutralizing ability of the base is measured by the available hydroxide ions, one equivalent of the base having the Avogadro number of OH^- ions, and the neutralizing ability of the acid is measured by the number of available hydrogen ions, one equivalent of acid having the Avogadro number of ionizable hydrogens. In each case covalently bonded water is formed from the hydrogen and hydroxide ions. The other pair of ions may be crystallized as a salt.

In spite of the usefulness of this view, we shall not use it exclusively, for the unhydrated oxides themselves act as acids and bases. Sodium oxide reacts with sulfur trioxide according to the reaction

$$Na_2O + SO_3 = Na_2SO_4 \qquad (16.43)$$

Here the acidic oxide and basic oxide react directly to form the salt. In the same way lime and sulfur trioxide react to form calcium sulfate.

$$CaO + SO_3 = CaSO_4 \qquad (16.44)$$

The principal reaction is

$$O^{--} + SO_3 = SO_4^{--} \tag{16.45}$$

Nor is it necessary to limit oneself to oxygen-containing acids and bases. Thus, neutralization of acidic and basic properties is obtained in the following

$$NH_3 + HCl = NH_4Cl \tag{16.46}$$

GENERAL THEORIES OF ACIDS AND BASES

We have treated acids and bases so far in terms of their experimental properties. But we can also apply theoretical interpretations. The most limited theoretical acid-base system is that of Arrhenius who identified acidic properties with hydrogen ions and basic properties with hydroxide ions. This system is useful in water solutions. However, typical acidic and basic properties are observable in solvents other than water, and often no hydrogen and/or no hydroxide ions are present.

Brønsted generalized the theory of acids to include all substances furnishing hydrogen ions, regardless of the presence or absence of hydroxide ions, by defining an acid as a *proton donor* and a base as a *proton acceptor*. Ammonia qualifies directly as a base in the Brønsted sense but not in the Arrhenius sense. In the Brønsted system hydrogen iodide, hydrogen bromide, hydrogen chloride, and hydrogen fluoride are acids, whether in water solution or not, but are increasingly weak ones in the order named, for all can donate protons to other substances but each has less tendency to do so than the preceding one. Also, oxide ion, O^{--}, hydroxide ion, OH^-, carbonate ion, CO_3^{--}, the ammonia molecule, NH_3, and chloride ion, Cl^-, are bases. They are arranged in order of decreasing strength as bases, that is, as proton acceptors.

We have listed in Table 16.3 some electronic structures for the acids and bases discussed in the preceding section. Examination of the list will show certain similarities in structure. All the bases listed have inert gas structures in which at least one unshared pair of electrons exists, often coupled with a net negative charge on the base. They have more than enough electrons to form single bonds throughout the molecule.

All the acids, on the other hand, have less than enough electrons to form single bonds throughout the molecule, sometimes coupled with a positive charge. Each acid, as a matter of fact, has "room" to accept at least one more pair of electrons.

G. N. Lewis generalized these observations by characterizing an acid as a substance capable of forming a covalent bond by accepting a pair of electrons. A base is, then, a substance capable of donating a pair of electrons for covalent bond formation. The ammonia and hydrogen ion reaction is typical:

$$H^+ + \begin{array}{c} H \\ | \\ :N-H \\ | \\ H \end{array} = \begin{array}{c} H \\ | \\ H-N-H^+ \\ | \\ H \end{array} \tag{16.47}$$

Table 16.3
Electron Structures of Some Acids and Bases

ACIDS		BASES	
H⁺	H⁺	OH⁻	:Ö—H⁻
SO₂	:Ö:—S(=Ö:)	O⁻⁻	:Ö:⁻⁻
SO₃	:Ö—S(=Ö:)(Ö:)	NH₃	H—N(H)—H
CrO₃	[:Ö: Cr :Ö: (=O)]ₙ	Cl⁻	:Cl:⁻

Other systems have been suggested, including the very general one that electron-deficient molecules are acids and electron-rich molecules are bases. Each system has wide use, the more general systems being valuable in advanced chemistry. The hydrogen ion-hydroxide ion system will continue to cover most of our needs in this course for we shall deal almost entirely with aqueous solutions.

THE OXYGEN MOLECULE

Our discussion of chemical bonding and chemical reactions thus far has been based on the observation that most substances contain an even number of electrons and that these electrons exist in pairs. We have attributed the tendency to form bonds to the tendency of electrons to pair and often to form inert gas structures. The oxygen molecule is an interesting exception to this generalization.

The formula of the oxygen molecule is known to be O_2. Each oxygen atom contains a total of eight electrons—two $1s$, two $2s$, and four $2p$ electrons—with two of the $2p$ electrons unpaired. From a comparison with the other substances we have discussed, one would expect the oxygen molecule, which contains an even number of electrons, to form by pairing these unpaired $2p$ electrons to form a double bond.

$$:\ddot{O}\cdot + \cdot\ddot{O}: = :\ddot{O}::\ddot{O}: \quad \text{(not a valid structure at room temperature)} \quad (16.50)$$

However, <u>oxygen gas is paramagnetic</u>, indicating that the oxygen molecule itself contains unpaired electrons. Various theories have been suggested to account for this, all of them stating that our past picture of chemical bonding is probably too simple. The most acceptable of the present theories points out that the energy levels in molecules may be quite different from those in atoms since the nuclei are so close together. These *molecular energy levels* will, therefore, not follow the scheme outlined in Figure 14.4. A common way of writing the oxygen molecule in terms of electron structures such as we have discussed is

$:\overset{..}{\underset{..}{O}}:\overset{..}{\underset{..}{O}}:$ but this formulation is not adequate to interpret many of the properties of the molecule.

Many other substances are known for which adequate electronic structures cannot be written in terms of atomic electronic levels. However, the atomic energy levels may be used for the great majority, say 99 per cent, of all molecules. Hence we shall use the simpler picture based on atomic orbitals rather than to develop the more adequate but much more complicated ideas of molecular orbitals.

SUMMARY

The great majority of stable substances found on earth contain an even number of electrons per chemical formula, and contain these electrons in pairs. Only a few substances contain unpaired electrons.

In many substances the most stable electron structure of each atom is found to correspond to that of an inert gas atom, that is, four pairs of valence electrons. On the other hand isolated atoms of most of the elements contain unpaired electrons, and only the atoms of the inert gases have electron fields sufficiently stable that the single, neutral atoms are the stable form of the element at room temperature. For all other elements at room temperature or lower, stable electronic systems are achieved only through formation of bonds between atoms. Nonpolar bonds will exist in any pure element since all its atoms are alike. These bonds will vary from metallic (for the elements which are metallic) to covalent (for the nonmetallic elements).

Some of the nonmetallic elements (primarily those in the upper right corner of the periodic table) exist in the form of small molecules with strong internal covalent bonds, but the majority of elements at room temperature exist in macromolecular structures: metallic, three-dimensional covalent (diamond, silicon), two-dimensional covalent (graphite), or one-dimensional covalent (tellurium). At higher temperatures sufficient kinetic energy is available to break these metallic and covalent bonds to some extent and all the elements can be evaporated to give relatively simple molecules and, eventually, monatomic gases.

Binary compounds may form when two elements are mixed if the new bonds lead to more stable electronic fields than those present in the elements.

The elements may be rated on an electronegativity scale, a scale which represents the tendencies of their atoms to capture an electron. The nature of the binary compounds of the elements may be explained rather easily in terms of this scale.

When the highly electropositive elements combine with the highly electronegative elements, electrons are transferred from the atoms of the first type to the atoms of the second to produce positive and negative ions, respectively. The resulting compounds are ionic. They are crystalline solids with high melting points. They are hard but brittle since the bonding forces between the ions in the crystals are strong so long as the positive ions are surrounded by negative ions (and vice versa) but become weak when the ions are displaced so that similarly charged ions are brought near each other.

When the difference in electronegativity of reacting elements is small, the atoms of the elements complete their electron shells by sharing electrons to form covalent bonds. These bonds have different degrees of polarity depending on the difference in electronegativity of the reacting elements. If stable electronic fields are obtained when only a few atoms combine, simple molecules are formed. When these are small the substances are usually gases at room temperatures. When they are larger so that there may be more interaction with neighboring molecules they are liquids or solids. Nevertheless, the melting and boiling points are relatively low, much lower than those of ionic substances. Formation of very large molecules (for example, diamond) gives very high melting points since many strong bonds must be broken to form the liquid.

Since elements differ in electronegativity it is convenient to recognize this fact by assigning oxidation numbers to them when they combine to form compounds. These numbers offer a convenient way of keeping track of electron transfers. They may be used for covalent compounds as well as ionic compounds. We have already noted that reactions are competitive since there are different ways by which atoms can acquire stable electronic fields. The oxidation numbers help us to keep track of electrons when and if reaction takes place but do not assist us in deciding which compound is most stable. We shall need to consider various forces in competitive reactions, forces called oxidation-reduction potentials, more fully in a later chapter.

Although simple molecules of compounds may be more stable than the molecules of the elements, the electronic fields around the molecules may have a high concentration of electrons or a relative deficiency of electrons around the atoms. Such molecules may often combine with each other to form larger molecules or ions which are more stable. Reactions of acidic and basic oxides with one another are examples of this type of reaction. In such reactions there is no change in oxidation numbers. Or molecules may react, with no change in atomic oxidation numbers, by forming new and more stable ionic or covalent bonds at the expense of the original, less stable ones.

In the overwhelming number of stable substances the electrons are paired, hence, the number of electrons in the unit represented by the chemical formula is even. This fact enables us to formulate some general rules useful for writing and remembering chemical formulas. Since odd-numbered elements have atoms with odd numbers of electrons they must pair to form compounds with an even number of electrons. Hence, if the formula contains one symbol weight of an odd-numbered element it must contain another. Examples: H_2, Cl_2, HCl, H_2O, ICl, ICl_3. There is no such limit to the numbers of atoms of even-numbered atoms per molecule. Examples: SO_2, SO_3, HClO, $HClO_2$, $HClO_3$, $HClO_4$.

One of the problems facing the chemist is that of synthesizing desired substances from the rather stable (low energy content) substances already present on the earth. In some cases he can do this merely by mixing naturally occurring materials; new, more stable bonds form, energy is evolved and the reaction proceeds spontaneously. More commonly, however, the chemist must decrease the stability (increase the energy content) of the naturally occurring raw materials before he can produce the desired spontaneous reaction.

Much of your study of chemistry from now on will be concerned with the relative stability of different substances under varying conditions, with a search for substances of high energy content useful in chemical reactions, and with methods for making these high energy substances from the low energy forms found in nature.

Problem 16.4. How much hydrogen can be obtained when 49 g. of sulfuric acid are treated with an excess of zinc? When 49 g. of the acid are treated with an excess of aluminum? When 49. g of the acid are treated with an excess of iron?

Problem 16.5. How much aluminum is required to release 1.008 g. of hydrogen from sulfuric acid? Comqare this value with the combining weight for aluminum listed on page 39. What is the ratio between the combining weight of aluminum and its gram-atomic weight? How does this ratio correlate with position in the periodic table?

Problem 16.6. For each of the following reactions, considered as going forward as written, give the information asked for in the table below:

a. $Zn_{(s)} + 2H^+ = Zn^{++} + H_{2(g)}$
b. $2Fe^{++} + Br_2 = 2Fe^{+++} + 2Br^-$
           brown   yellow
c. $MnO_{2(s)} + 4H^+ + 2Cl^- = Mn^{++} + Cl_2 + 2H_2O$
       black   yellow

	Reaction (a.)	Reaction (b.)	Reaction (c.)
Oxidizing agent			
Reducing agent			
Element oxidized			
Atom which gives up electrons			

Problem 16.7. What weight of sodium is required to release 1.008 g. of hydrogen from hydrochloric acid? What weight of magnesium? How are these weights related to the combining weights of these elements? To the gram-atomic weights?

Problem 16.8. Assign oxidation numbers to each of the atoms in each of the following compounds with formulas: $KMnO_4$, Na_2O_2, $CaSO_4$, H_3PO_4, NaI, Mn_3O_4.

248   GENERAL CHEMISTRY

Problem 16.9. Which of the following reactions do not involve oxidation-reduction? Indicate by (x). List the oxidizing agent in each of the other reactions.

                                        No oxidation-reduction   Oxidizing agent

a. $2Zn_{(s)} + O_{2(g)} = 2ZnO_{(s)}$
b. $Cu^{++} + 4NH_3 = Cu(NH_3)_4^{++}$
   blue   deep blue
c. $AgCN_{(s)} + CN^- = Ag(CN)_2^-$
d. $4Ag_{(s)} + 8CN^- + 2H_2O + O_{2(g)} = 4Ag(CN)_2^- + 4OH^-$
e. $Zn_{(s)} + Cu^{++} = Zn^{++} + Cu_{(s)}$
             blue   red

Problem 16.10. Give the oxidation number of each of the atoms indicated in each of the following formulas:

$$H_2O, H_2O_2, HCl, BaCl_2, NaClO_4, Cr_2O_7^{--}.$$

Problem 16.11. Assign oxidation numbers to each atom in the following substances. Which of the substances are ionic, which polar, and which nonpolar? Formulas: KCl, H_2O_2, Cl_2, $BaSO_4$, CO.

Problem 16.12. When 0.300 g. of a metal is treated with hydrochloric acid 400.0 ml. of dry hydrogen measured at 27°C. and 351 mm. pressure are produced. The atomic number of the element is 20; what is its atomic weight?

Problem 16.13. Answer the listed questions concerning the elements following:

ELEMENT	A	B	C	D	E	F
AT. NO.	2	8	14	37	54	4

a. Which element has the highest atomic weight?
b. Which element has the greatest atomic radius?
c. Which element is the best reducing agent?
d. Which element is the best oxidizing agent?
e. Which element has the lowest boiling point?

Problem 16.14. Arrange the following elements in order of nobility, the most noble last: iron, platinum, copper, tin and zinc. Interpret in terms of atomic size and nuclear charge.

Problem 16.15. If the electrical energy required to decompose calcium chloride into calcium and chlorine is greater than that required to decompose zinc chloride into zinc and chlorine, (a) which atom, zinc or calcium, loses its valence electrons more easily? (b) Which would reduce the other from its chloride? Explain.

Problem 16.16. Which atom in each of the following pairs would lose an electron more easily: (a) silver or lead, (b) helium or argon, (c) fluorine or chlorine, (d) which of all the above atoms would add an additional electron most strongly? Explain.

Problem 16.17. The radius of the atom of chlorine is 0.99×10^{-8} cm., that of iodine is 1.3×10^{-8} cm. How would this difference affect the relative heats of formation of solid barium chloride and barium iodide from the reaction of metallic barium with gaseous chlorine and iodine respectively?

Problem 16.18. Predict some of the properties you would expect for the following compounds: silicon carbide, radium fluoride, boron nitride, magnesium sulfate, scandium oxide, hydrogen iodide.

CHEMICAL REACTIONS 249

Problem 16.19. Under what conditions would you expect calcium oxide to react with phosphorus pentoxide? What would be formed?

Problem 16.20. What method would you use to test for the presence of unpaired electrons in oxygen molecules?

Problem 16.21. A cubic foot of methane, formula CH_4, at room temperature and pressure weighs about 19 g. How much water is formed when this quantity of methane burns?

Problem 16.22. Draw electronic structures for each of the substances with the following formulas and classify the substances as acids or bases according to the Lewis theory: $AlCl_3$, NCl_3, BF_3, Cl^-, S^{--}, CO_2. Comment on the stability of each of the following in terms of the Lewis theory: $AlCl_4^-$, NCl_4^-.

Problem 16.23. According to van Arkel *et al.* (1953), the conductivity of molten oxides decreases in the order Li_2O, PbO, TeO_2, MoO_3, Bi_2O_3, V_2O_5, Sb_2O_3, and CrO_3. Furthermore, for elements giving more than one oxide stable in the molten state, the oxide corresponding to the highest oxidation number has the lowest conductivity. Interpret these two trends in terms of the nature of chemical bonding in these oxides.

Problem 16.24. The charge on the electron can be shown from the Millikan oil drop experiment to be 1.602×10^{-19} coulombs. Calculate a value for Avogadro's number using this datum. Compare it with the value found in Problem 7.6 and with the generally accepted value.

17 SOLUTIONS

WE HAVE thus far concerned ourselves primarily with studying pure substances, both elements and compounds. Yet many homogeneous systems are not single pure substances. They are solutions. In fact, it is possible to maintain the position that no really pure substances exist, but that all actual homogeneous systems are solutions because of the minute amounts of impurities which are always present in any substance. It is, therefore, important to study the behavior of solutions in order to see what types of effects these impurities may cause as well as to understand the behavior of the solutions themselves. The fact that the great majority of chemical reactions are carried out in solutions also adds importance to their study.

Pure substances may be characterized by melting points and boiling points which are independent of the fraction of the sample melted or boiled. Solutions do not exhibit this constancy, as we indicated in Chapter 2. Usually, one of the component substances melts or boils more readily than the others; then the compositions of the various phases change during melting and boiling. As the compositions of the phases change, so also do the melting and boiling points and the other properties of the solution.

SUSPENSIONS

Finely divided samples of different pure substances, when intermingled, sometimes form heterogeneous systems called *suspensions*. The different substances in a solution do not separate appreciably into layers of differing concentration because of the Brownian motion, but suspensions tend to separate in spite of this effect. Thus, suspensions of dust in air, or clay in water, will settle and cream in milk will rise because of the difference in densities of the different parts of these heterogeneous systems.

COLLOIDAL SYSTEMS

The degree of dispersion of substances may vary. When the particles of intermingled substances are small molecules, the resulting systems are homogeneous and solutions. When the particles are of visible size, whether viewed with the naked eye or under a microscope, the systems are heterogeneous and are suspensions. However, particles of intermediate size may exist; particles larger than the small molecules, yet smaller than visible size. Systems containing particles in this range of sizes behave in intermediate ways, having properties intermediate between those of solutions and of suspensions. They are called *colloidal* systems. They are important enough to deserve special consideration at a later time (see Chapter 34). For the present we shall consider only solutions, that is, dispersions containing particles of small molecular dimensions.

SOLUTION PHASES

Solutions may be either gaesous, liquid, or crystalline just as pure substances may exist in these three phases, and the general differences mentioned in connection with pure substances in the three phases also apply to solutions. Thus a solid or crystalline solution is composed of molecules which are free to vibrate

TABLE 17.1
Types of Solutions

PHASE OF SOLVENT AND OF SOLUTION	PHASE OF THE SOLUTE USED TO MAKE THE SOLUTION	EXAMPLE
Gas	gas	dry air
	liquid	air containing water vapor
	solid	air containing vapor from "moth crystals" (paradichlorobenzene)
Liquid	gas	natural water containing dissolved air
	liquid	gasoline
	solid	salt water
Solid	gas	palladium-hydrogen alloy
	liquid	rubber containing ether
	solid	coin silver

about a given spot determined by the regular geometrical arrangement in the crystal. Little diffusion is possible. Both liquid and gaseous solutions have little geometric order but liquids have surfaces and surface phenomena, such as surface tension and vapor pressure and gases do not.

Table 17.1 lists the different kinds of solution phases with examples.

SOLVENT AND SOLUTE

When crystals or gases dissolve in a pure liquid to give a liquid solution the pure liquid is generally called the *solvent*, and the gases and crystals dissolved in it are called *solutes*. Thus the substance which does not undergo a change in

252   GENERAL CHEMISTRY

phase during the solution process is known as the solvent, and the solutes are said to dissolve in it with a change in phase. When solutions are formed by mixing two gases, two liquids, or two solids it is foolish to say that one gas dissolves in the other, or the first liquid dissolves in the second, etc. Each gas dissolves in the other, as does each liquid and each solid. In such cases, that pure substance which is the *major component of the resulting solution is ordinarily called the solvent*, and the others, solutes. Numerous exceptions are made, the most prominent being for water. Water is so commonly used as a solvent that it is said to be the solvent in almost any liquid solution containing water. For instance, there is less than 5 per cent by weight of water in concentrated sulfuric acid yet it is commonly called an aqueous solution. It should be clear that the distinction between solvent and solute is quite arbitrary and the choice should be clearly stated for every solution if the terms are to be used.

CONCENTRATION UNITS

In discussing pure substances, one seldom needs to use concentration units. The fact that the substance is pure characterizes it sufficiently well. Gases are a notable exception and we learned to specify the number of molecules or moles per unit volume, for instance, as a measure of the concentration of the gas. Solutions, however, vary in properties depending on the relative amounts of the components present. As a result, most of the properties of solutions are correlated in terms of the concentrations of the components.

Concentration units of many kinds are found in the chemical literature, but we shall restrict ourselves, for the most part, to only three of them: *mole fraction*, *molal*, and *molar* or *formal*. Unfortunately the three have a similarity of spelling and pronunciation which makes differentiation difficult for many students.

The *mole fraction* of a substance in solution is the decimal fraction of all the molecules present which are of that kind. About one fifth of the molecules in the atmosphere are oxygen, hence the mole fraction of oxygen in the atmosphere is 0.2. Water can be decomposed into a gaseous solution containing twice as many hydrogen molecules as oxygen molecules. The mole fraction of oxygen in this solution would be about 0.33. When 18 g. of water and 138 g. of ethanol, formula C_2H_5OH, are mixed the mole fraction of water in the resulting solution is 0.25, for 18 g. of water is 1 mole of water and 138 g. of ethanol is $\frac{138}{46}$ or three moles of ethanol. The total number of moles in the solution is thus four of which one out of four, or 0.25 of the total, is water. One fourth of the molecules are water molecules.

The *molality* of a solute is the number of moles of solute dissolved per 1000 g. of solvent. Since 1000 g. of a given solvent always contains the same number of moles of solvent molecules, molality represents the number of moles of solute compared to this fixed number of moles of solvent. Dissolving 32 g. of methanol, formula CH_3OH (mol. wt., 32), in 1000 g. of ethanol gives a one molal solution of methanol in ethanol. Similarly, dissolving 60 g. of acetic acid, formula CH₃COOH (mol. wt., 60), in 1000 g. of ethanol gives a one molal solution of acetic acid in ethanol; 1000 g. of ethanol contains $\frac{1000}{46}$ or 21.7 moles of ethanol. On the other hand 1000 grams of water contains $\frac{1000}{18}$ or 55.5 moles of water. Thus a one molal solution of methanol in water would contain a lower fraction of methanol molecules than a one molal solution of methanol in ethanol.

The *molarity* or *formality* of a solution is the number of moles or gram-formula weights of solute dissolved in one liter of total solution. Such solutions may be made by putting the desired number of moles of solute in a vessel of known volume and then adding sufficient solvent to fill the vessel exactly to the known volume. Placing 117 g. of sodium chloride (mol. wt., 58.5) in a vessel calibrated to hold one liter of liquid, adding enough water to dissolve the salt, and then just enough more to fill the container exactly to the calibration mark will give a 2 molar (2 formal), written $2M$ ($2f$), solution of sodium chloride in water, since 117 g. of sodium chloride salt is $\frac{117}{58.5}$ or two moles (gram-formula weights) of the salt. We would not know, without making a separate measurement, how much water had been added to the container and cannot, therefore, calculate the relative number of molecules of different kinds which are present. Should it be desirable to determine this relative number of molecules we would have to weigh the solution or determine its density. From these latter data and the known weight of sodium chloride present, one can calculate the weight of water, and hence the number of moles of water.

Since molarity indicates the number of moles, or molecules, of solute present in a unit volume of solution it is widely used, for volumes may be measured more readily than weights. Weights, however, can be measured with greater accuracy than volumes so that very accurate work is done in terms of molality or mole fraction. Molarity is affected by any change in temperature of the solution causing it to expand or contract, while molality and mole fraction are not thus affected.

IDEAL SOLUTIONS AND REAL SOLUTIONS

A common saying is that "like dissolves like." If the components of a solution are so closely alike that each molecule in the solution finds itself subjected to the same forces as it did in the pure substance we say that the solution is ideal. Experimentally this means that there are no heat effects on solution (if there is no change in phase) and that the bulk properties of the solution are merely the average of the bulk properties of the pure substances (of similar phase) based on the mole fraction of each substance in the solution. The values for the density, heat capacity, vapor pressure, and viscosity of an ideal solution made up of 0.25 mole per cent of substance A and 0.75 mole per cent of substance B would be exactly one fourth of the way between the corresponding values of the same properties for pure B and those for pure A, for instance.

Just as there are no gases known which follow the ideal gas laws exactly, so there are no solutions known which are "ideal" according to the above criteria.

But, again as with the gases, there are many systems known which approximate ideal behavior rather closely and we shall find the ideal solution not only an interesting concept but also a useful approximation in dealing with real systems.

In the ideal gas case it was necessary to have no forces whatever acting between the molecules if the laws were to be obeyed. The restrictions for ideal solutions would appear to be much less severe since it is only necessary that the *same* forces be present in the solution as in the pure substances. It is found experimentally, however, that deviations from ideality are ordinarily greater in liquid or solid solutions than in gases because of the much closer approach of the molecules to one another in the solutions. This closeness of approach greatly enhances any interactions. Deviations of five and ten per cent from the ideal are usual and deviations of hundreds of per cent are common. Fortunately it is often possible to predict with some success how closely a given system will approximate an ideal solution by investigating the forces which will be acting. The greater the difference in forces in the pure substances and the solution, the greater the deviations from ideality.

UNSATURATION, SATURATION, AND SUPERSATURATION

In some instances there is no limit to the amount of one substance which may dissolve in another, as with a solution of the gases oxygen and nitrogen, or the liquids alcohol and water, or the crystals silver and gold. Such pairs of substances are said to be *infinitely soluble* in one another. In general, substances are not infinitely soluble but form solutions which can exist in equilibrium with excess of solute in another phase, such as the systems benzene and water, or sodium chloride and water. In these equilibrium solutions the solute continues to dissolve in the solution from the solute phase while the dissolved solute passes from the solution to the solute phase at the same rate. There is then no net change in the concentration of the solution or the amount of any phase. Such an equilibrium solution is said to be *saturated* with respect to the solute. One may demonstrate this dynamic equilibrium between phases by shaking a radioactive solid with a solution previously saturated with respect to a nonradioactive form of the same solute. What results would you expect?

A solution containing a lower concentration of the solute than a saturated solution is said to be *unsaturated*. When more of the solute phase is placed in contact with the unsaturated solution, additional solute will dissolve until the saturation (equilibrium) concentration is reached. The saturation equilibrium involving equal rates of solution and separation will then keep the solution exactly saturated.

A solution containing a higher concentration of the solute than the saturated solution is said to be supersaturated. When some of the solute phase is placed in contact with the supersaturated solution, solute will separate or precipitate from the solution faster than it will enter and its concentration will drop to that of the saturated solution.

ESCAPING TENDENCY AND ITS KINETIC INTERPRETATION

These three situations—unsaturation, saturation, and supersaturation—are readily interpreted in terms of the kinetic theory. We have shown that the molecules in any phase are in continual rapid motion, and that, when two phases are in contact, molecules may attain sufficient energy to leave one pure phase and enter the other, as in evaporation or melting processes. In the same way, molecules may leave a pure phase to enter a solution. The tendency of a molecule to leave a given phase, which we may call its *escaping tendency*, will depend on the probability that a molecule of sufficient energy to escape is present.

The magnitude of the escaping tendency from any phase is determined by three principal factors: the strength of the bonding, the temperature, and the concentration of molecules in the phase. All of these affect the probability of there being a molecule with sufficient kinetic energy to escape. Strong bonding forces in a phase will always lead to a low escaping tendency since it will be difficult for a molecule to break the bonds to escape. A high temperature, on the other hand, means a higher average kinetic energy per molecule and thus greater likelihood that there will be molecules with enough energy to break the bonds. Similarly, an increase in the concentration of the molecules in a given phase will increase the escaping tendency, since, with the larger number of molecules present, it is more likely that some of them will have sufficient energy to escape.

At a given temperature, therefore, a pure substance has a definite escaping tendency, and the rate of escape of molecules from the phase is fixed. When this pure substance is placed in contact with a new phase, molecules will escape into the new phase. They may, for instance, form a solution in the neighboring phase. Initially the transfer will be all one way, from the pure phase to the solution, but as the concentration of escaped molecules builds up in the solution the probability of their escape from the solution increases; that is, it becomes more probable that they will collide with and return to the original pure substance. Eventually the rate of escape of molecules from the solution to the pure phase will exactly equal the rate of escape of molecules from the pure phase into the solution. The escaping tendency of the solute molecules will be identical in the two phases. Equilibrium has been attained and will be maintained subsequently. The solution is saturated with respect to this solute.

The escaping tendency of the solute from an unsaturated solution is less than from a saturated solution since there are fewer molecules present. Contact with excess pure solute will result in a rise in concentration in the solution since the escaping tendency of the pure substance is greater than that of the dissolved solute. In a supersaturated solution the reverse is true. The escaping tendency of the dissolved molecules is greater than that of the pure substance, so that the concentration will fall to the equilibrium value upon contact with pure solute for the solute molecules will leave the solution faster than they will enter it.

STRUCTURE AND SUPERSATURATION

Since the process of separation of pure solute from a supersaturated solution results in growth of the pure phase, one might well ask why it is necessary to add any pure phase. Why doesn't the pure phase form spontaneously? The three most common types of supersaturation involve gas dissolved in liquid, solid dissolved in liquid, or solid dissolved in solid. The supersaturation of gases in liquids results from the difficulty of bubble formation in a liquid. A hole must be made in the liquid and this requires work. Recently opened bottles of carbonated beverages are well-known examples of liquids supersaturated with gas. One may destroy the supersaturation readily by shaking the beverage and thus creating bubbles or by adding some porous substance whose small holes can serve as starters for bubble formation in the liquid. Then a violent frothing will occur. When the pure solute phase is solid, supersaturation in liquid solutions depends on the fact that the solute has to form a rather precise and complicated crystal structure before it can precipitate as a solid phase. When a pattern is supplied by addition of some of the crystal, or even some of another solid with the same crystal structure, precipitation begins and the supersaturation is destroyed. Supersaturation in solid solutions is obtained by rapid quenching (cooling) of the solution. The very high viscosity of the solid at low temperatures prevents, almost indefinitely, the aggregation of the solute molecules into a pure phase. Many steels are supersaturated solid solutions of carbon or iron carbide in iron.

It is interesting to note the very close analogy between superheating of pure liquids (see page 146) and supersaturation of gases in liquids, between undercooling of pure liquids and supersaturation of solids in liquids, and between the formation of glasses and the supersaturation of solids in solids. The structural causes are the same in each pair.

EFFECT OF CHANGE IN TEMPERATURE ON CONCENTRATION IN SATURATED SOLUTIONS

The concentration of unsaturated solutions is readily calculated from the amount of solute which has been added to the solvent, for all the solute dissolves. The concentrations of saturated solutions are not so simply determined for excess of the solute phase will exist in equilibrium with the solution. We have already pointed out that this equilibrium condition is attained when the escaping tendency of the solute from the pure substances and from the solution are identical. Under these conditions the rates of solution and separation of the solute are also identical. Any factor which changes the escaping tendency of the molecules in either pure substance or solution may cause a shift in the equilibrium and a consequent change in the concentration of the saturated solution. The most apparent factor which might cause such a change is the temperature since a change in temperature will change the average kinetic energy of the molecules both in the pure phase and in the solution.

An increase in temperature will always increase the escaping tendency in every phase but the greatest increase will come in that phase with the strongest bonds. This is because the number of molecules with the high kinetic energy necessary to break these strong bonds always increases faster with rising temperature than the number of molecules with lower kinetic energies. (See, for example, Figure 10.2, page 127 and the discussion there.) This means that rising temperatures ordinarily decrease the solubilities of gases in liquids, the bonds in the liquid being stronger than those in the gas. Similarly the solubility of solids in liquids usually increases since bonds in solids are usually stronger than bonds in liquids. Solubilities of liquids in liquids may either increase or decrease with almost equal probability since bonds in liquids are similar in strength.

The effect of increasing temperature may be generalized in somewhat different terms by saying that the equilibrium will always shift in that direction which will tend to absorb heat, since the heat for the reaction becomes more readily available at the higher temperatures (Le Chatelier's principle—see page 140). This shifting of the equilibrium in the direction which tends to absorb heat is exactly that predicted above when we said that the phase with the strongest bonds would tend to increase in escaping tendency most rapidly. The heat which is absorbed goes into breaking these stronger bonds and the heat content of the products is, as a result, higher than the heat content of the initial materials.

EFFECT OF CHANGE IN PRESSURE ON CONCENTRATION IN A SATURATED SOLUTION

Another factor of major importance in determining the concentration of a saturated solution is the pressure on the system. An increase in pressure always increases the escaping tendency of every phase, since it forces the molecules closer together, increases their concentration, and hence their escaping tendencies. The pressure increase will, however, cause the greatest increase in the escaping tendency of the phase which undergoes the greatest reduction in volume since the concentration increase will be greatest in this phase. Only for gases is the concentration change with moderate increase in pressure sufficient to change the solubility relationships appreciably. Since the concentration in the gas phase, and hence the escaping tendency, is always increased by an increase in pressure the solubility of gases in liquids and solids is always increased under these conditions. (Another application of Le Chatelier's principle.)

Concentration in gases is directly proportional to the pressure on the gas, assuming constant temperature. Escaping tendency is proportional to concentration. In gases, therefore, escaping tendency must be directly proportional to the pressure of the gas. Doubling the pressure doubles the escaping tendency. Decreasing the pressure by one third decreases the escaping tendency the same amount—one third.

The escaping tendency of a solute in dilute solution is also directly proportional to the concentration. If one has a gas in equilibrium with a saturated solution and doubles the partial pressure of the gas, the mole fraction of that gas in the solution must also double. This follows at once from the fact that the pressure increase doubles the escaping tendency in the gas phase. At equilibrium the escaping tendency from the liquid phase must also double as it will if the mole fraction of the dissolved gas doubles.

The relation between pressure of a gas and its solubility in liquids is known as Henry's Law. It may be stated: The mole fraction of solute in the solution is directly proportional to the partial pressure of the gas above the solution. Since molality is proportional, but not equal, to mole fraction in dilute solutions the law may also be stated as: Molalities of solutes are directly proportional to the partial pressures of their gases in the gas phase.

The pressure effect may be generalized in somewhat different terms by saying that an increase in applied pressure on a system will always cause that reaction to occur which tends to decrease the volume of the system. Thus, an increase in gas pressure over a liquid solution causes more gas to dissolve since this tends to decrease the volume of the system.

VAPOR PRESSURE OF SOLVENT IN A SOLUTION

We have said that a liquid is characterized by surface effects and by a lack of geometric regularity. One of the surface effects most commonly mentioned is evaporation and consequent vapor pressure. Addition of a solute of such low vapor pressure as to be called nonvolatile ought not add to the vapor pressure of the solution and would furnish an opportunity to study the variation in the vapor pressure of the solvent itself. In Figure 17.1 we have plotted the vapor pressure of water as a function of the molality of various nonvolatile solutes dissolved in it at 100°C. Molality is used since it keeps the number of solvent molecules in the sample constant while expressing the variation in number of solute molecules present.

All the data lie near one or the other of three straight lines which meet at the same point, the vapor pressure of pure water. Inspection of these three lines will show that all those substances giving data lying on solid line *a* contain only nonmetallic elements and would be expected to be covalent, those lying on lines *b* and *c* contain both nonmetallic and metallic elements and would be expected to be ionic. Furthermore, those on line *b* contain two possible ions per formula and those on line *c* contain three possible ions per formula. If we now calculate actual molality of particles by doubling the values on curve b and trebling those on curve c and plot these total molalities against vapor pressure we obtain the dotted extension of curve a. Note that the ideal law is not followed in the more concentrated solutions; the vapor pressure is lowered less than would be expected.

Evidently we have here a method of counting the number of dissolved particles in a dilute solution, for the lowering of the vapor pressure of the water is directly proportional to the molality of the solute particles in dilute solu-

SOLUTIONS 259

tions. This means that the escaping tendency of the water is decreased the same amount by the addition of a given number of particles regardless of the nature of the particles. The explanation is comprehensible in terms of the nature of evaporation as a surface phenomena if one notes that the fraction of the total number of molecules in the surface which are water determines the escaping tendency. Introduction of solute particles reduces the fraction of the

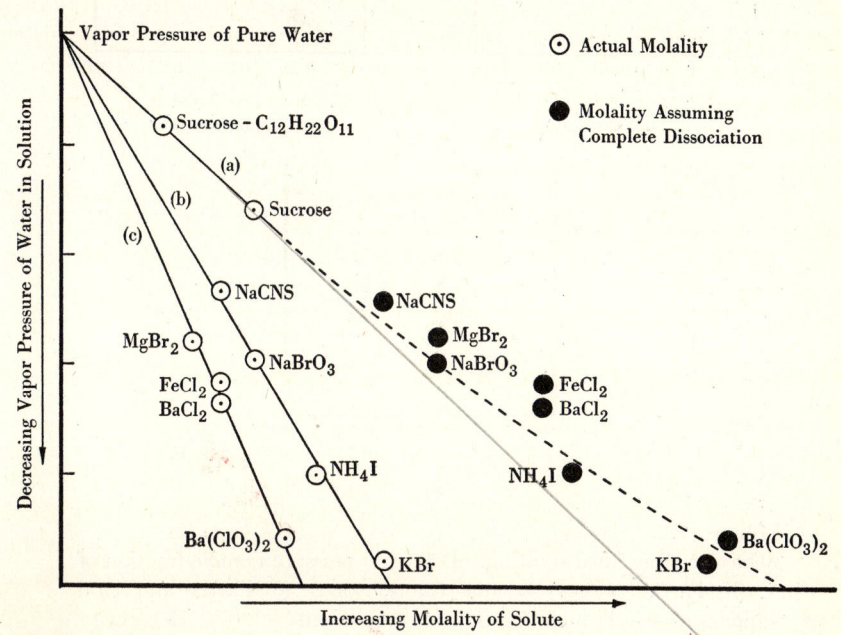

Figure 17.1.
Change in the vapor pressure of water produced by various solutes at random concentrations.

surface occupied by water molecules and hence lowers the vapor pressure accordingly, by decreasing the probability that a water molecule will evaporate. In other words, the process of evaporation is slowed up compared to the rate in pure water.

Figure 17.2 illustrates the variation in vapor pressure of each of the two components and of the solution as a whole when both components are volatile and an ideal solution is formed. The data in Figures 17.1 and 17.2 may be summarized in the statement that the vapor pressures of the volatile components in ideal solutions are directly proportional to their respective mole fractions. This statement is known as Raoult's law.

Example: The vapor pressure of pure A at 20°C. is 500 mm. and that of pure B is 300 mm. If the numbers of moles of A and B in a solution are equal, what will be the vapor pressure of A and B and the total pressure of the vapor? Assume ideal solutions.

260   GENERAL CHEMISTRY

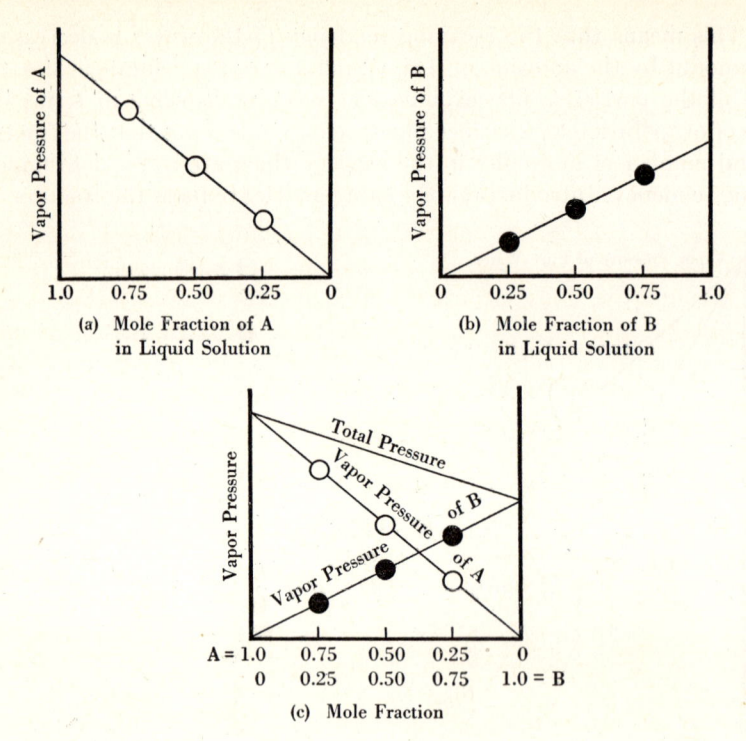

Figure 17.2.
Behavior of an ideal solution. (a) Partial pressure *vs* mole fraction of A. (b) Partial pressure *vs* mole fraction of B. (c) Partial and total vapor pressures *vs* mole fraction of components

The mole fractions of A and B are 0.5. The partial pressure of A will be 0.5×500 or 250 mm. The partial pressure of B will be 0.5×300 or 150 mm. The total pressure will be

$$250 + 150 = 400 \text{ mm.}$$

Note that there will be more moles of A than of B in the vapor phase, the ratio being 250 to 150. The more volatile component tends to concentrate in the vapor phase. This effect can be utilized to separate the components of a solution by distillation.

Salts and other ionic substances in water solutions do not follow Raoult's law, as shown by the several lines in Figure 17.1. Formula weights of salts lower the vapor pressure of a fixed amount of water several times as much as do formula weights of molecular solutes. In the first place, salts furnish several particles per formula weight and hence lower the mole fraction of water to a greater degree. In the second place, some of the water becomes associated with the ions, thereby lowering the mole fraction of free water still more. In the third place the ions are charged so that neighboring ions affect one another and the water so that the escaping tendency of the water molecules is changed by the ionic interactions as well as by the presence of the solute particles. The last two effects become increasingly important as the mole fraction of dissolved salt increases.

A KINETIC INTERPRETATION OF SOLVENT VAPOR PRESSURE

If one puts two containers, one containing pure water and one containing an aqueous solution, under a bell jar, the liquid level in the solution container will be found to rise slowly at exactly the same rate that the level in the pure water container falls (see Figure 17.3). In other words, the water is moving

Figure 17.3.
Transfer of vapor from pure solvent to solution in a closed system.

from the pure substance, through the gas phase, into the solution. We may interpret this in terms of escaping tendency. Evaporation can occur from the whole surface in the pure water for water covers the whole surface in that container. In the solution a certain fraction (determined by the mole fraction) of the liquid surface is not water but solute, thus the rate of evaporation of water from the solution will be lower than that from pure water. The rate of condensation of water in the two beakers will be identical, however, for water can condense on the whole liquid water surface and can also condense on the part of the surface occupied by solute molecules. Thus, more surface is available for condensation than for evaporation in the solution container, and the rate of condensation can exceed the rate of evaporation. The volume of the solution will increase. Or we may say that the vapor pressure of the pure water is greater than the vapor pressure of the water in the solution so that the total pressure of water vapor in the container will be greater than the equilibrium pressure for the solution.

The net movement of the water is analogous to the flow of gases which

262   GENERAL CHEMISTRY

always occurs from the region of greatest concentration (highest escaping tendency) to the region of lowest concentration (lowest escaping tendency). The effect of the flow is to make the concentrations, and hence the escaping tendencies, more equal until equilibrium is reached. Then the escaping tendency of each substance is the same in every portion of the equilibrium system and no net flow occurs, only equal flows in opposite directions.

BOILING POINTS OF AQUEOUS SOLUTIONS OF NONVOLATILE SOLUTES

Since the addition of solute to a liquid solvent lowers the vapor pressure of the solvent one must heat a solution containing a nonvolatile solute to a higher temperature than the boiling point of the pure solvent before the vapor

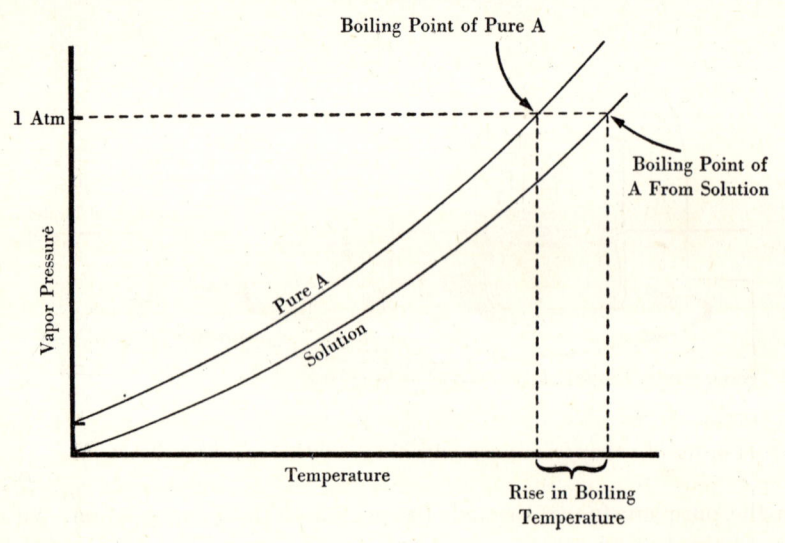

Figure 17.4.
Change of vapor pressure with temperature of a pure solvent and of its solution containing a nonvolatile solute.

pressure of the solvent in the solution can equal atmospheric pressure. Increasing the escaping tendency of the solvent by heating overcomes the decrease in escaping tendency due to the effect of the solute (see Figure 17.4). Data on the boiling points of some aqueous solutions are presented in Table 17.2.

Again the data fall into groups according to how many particles would be expected in the solution. All the data may be summarized in the generalization that the boiling point of water is increased 0.52°C. for each mole of particles present in 1000 g. of water. Thus, 0.1 mole of particles per 1000 g. of water raises the boiling point at standard pressure to 100.052°, an increase of 0.052°C. This increase is small and difficult to measure so that the change in boiling point is not a good measure of the concentration of very dilute solutions. The boiling points of concentrated solutions can be predicted only approximately because of increased solute-solute interactions as already noted. This approximation is well shown in Table 17.2.

Table 17.2
Boiling Point Rise in Aqueous Solutions (In °C.)

SOLUTE FORMULA	\multicolumn{4}{c}{MOLALITY OF SOLUTION}
	0.1	0.5	1.0	1.5
$C_{12}H_{22}O_{11}$	0.052	0.27	0.56	0.89
NaCl	0.103	0.48	0.99	1.53
NaBr	0.104	0.50	1.02	1.50
$KClO_3$	0.102	0.53	0.99	1.33
NH_4Br	0.102	—	0.95	1.40
$BaCl_2$	0.150	0.64	1.38	2.16
$Sr(NO_3)_2$	0.149	0.61	1.24	1.90
K_2CrO_4	0.148	0.57	1.15	1.70
$AlCl_3$	0.20	0.82	1.76	2.97
CdI_2	0.050	0.27	0.58	0.90

MELTING POINTS OF AQUEOUS SOLUTIONS

Not only do dissolved particles affect the vapor pressure and the boiling point of a liquid solution. They also alter the freezing point. Just as a solute makes evaporation and boiling more difficult, so it increases the difficulty of freezing the solvent from solution. Thus it lowers the freezing point compared to the freezing point of the pure solvent. In dilute solutions the freezing point of water is lowered at the rate of 1.86°C. for each mole of solute in 1000 g. of water. This limiting value of −1.86°C. is known as the *molal freezing point lowering of water*.

A practical application of the freezing point lowering of water by added solutes is the use of "antifreezes" in automobile radiators. Ethanol and ethylene glycol, formulas C_2H_5OH and $C_2H_4(OH)_2$, respectively, are common antifreezes. At the concentrations used their effects cannot be calculated from the limiting laws.

Changes in the freezing point of a substance are considerably easier to detect than changes in the boiling point. The main reason is that the boiling point is highly sensitive to pressure fluctuations whereas the freezing point is not. Even the freezing point method is not capable of detecting impurities of much less than 0.01 moles per 1000 g. of solvent. This may seem like a very small amount of impurity but we shall find that methods are available which

264 GENERAL CHEMISTRY

are capable of detecting as small an amount of impurity (solute in a solution) as 1 part in a million of solvent, and sometimes less.

Other liquids also have characteristic "molal freezing point lowerings." Some limiting values are: benzene, −5.1°C.; camphor, −40.0°C.; sulfuric acid, −6.8°C.; acetic acid, −3.9°C.

DETERMINATION OF MOLAR WEIGHTS OF SOLUTES FROM BOILING POINT, VAPOR PRESSURE, AND FREEZING POINT OF SOLVENT

An important use of boiling point rise, vapor pressure lowering, and freezing point lowering data is to determine the number of solute particles present in a dilute solution. If one knows the weight of solute dissolved in a fixed amount of solvent he can compare it with the number of particles (moles of particles) indicated by the experimentally observed changes in any of these three quantities and determine the average molecular weight. If the molar weight of solute is known he can find the extent to which the solute has apparently dissociated or ionized.

Each of these changes results from the lowering of the escaping tendency of the solvent molecules by the solute. When escaping tendency is lower the vapor pressure of the solvent will be lower, the boiling point of the solvent will be higher, and the freezing point of the solvent will be lower, for each of these shifts overcomes the decrease in escaping tendency of solvent caused by the solute.

It is essential to point out one limitation of this method which follows at once from the concept of the lowering of the escaping tendency of a solvent by a solute. This lowering is characteristic not only of liquid solutions but also of solid solutions. Thus, the escaping tendency of solid solvent from a solid solution is lowered by solute. This means that the vapor pressure of the solid solvent is lowered and also that the melting point of the solid solvent is raised. Note that the rise in melting point here is opposite to the lowering of the freezing point of liquid solutions. Thus, if the solute is soluble only in the liquid and not in the solid solvent the freezing point will be lower than that of the pure solvent. If the solute is soluble only in the solid solvent and not in the liquid solvent, the melting point, (or freezing point since they are the same) will be raised. If the solute is soluble in both the liquid and solid no safe prediction can be made. The system in which we are most interested, water as a solvent, exhibits one very nice feature in this respect for ice is an extremely poor solvent and forms almost no solid solutions of any appreciable concentration. Thus, the escaping tendency of the water from the ice is affected only by the temperature and not by any dissolved solute.

Two calculations will illustrate the application of these principles.

Example A. When 0.1 g. of the salt, sodium formate, formula $NaCHO_2$, is dissolved in 20 g. of water the freezing point of the solution is −0.270°C. How many particles (ions) are contributed per molecular formula of this salt? Per 1000 g. of water the amount of salt is

$$\frac{0.1 \text{ g. salt}}{20 \text{ g. water}} \times 1000 \text{ g. water} = 5 \text{ g. salt}$$

The weight of salt required to give one mole of particles is

$$5 \text{ g. salt} \times \frac{-1.86°C.}{-0.27°C.} = 35 \text{ g. salt}$$

The number of moles of particles per gram-formula weight (68 g.) is

$$\frac{68 \text{ g.}}{35 \text{ g.}} = 1.9^+$$

We conclude that sodium formate furnishes two ions per molecular formula weight.

Example B. A new organic compound has been prepared. It is soluble in benzene. Addition of 0.120 g. of the compound to 40 g. of benzene raises the boiling point of the benzene 0.422°C. (The molal boiling point elevation of benzene is 2.53°.) What is the molar weight of the compound? The molality of the solution is

$$\frac{0.422°C.}{2.53°C./m.} = 0.167 \text{ molal}$$

The weight of compound per 1000 g. of benzene is

$$\frac{0.120 \text{ g. compd.}}{40 \text{ g. benzene}} \times 1000 \text{ g. benzene} = 30 \text{ g. compd.}$$

Since 30 g. of the compound represent 0.167 mole, the molar weight is

$$\frac{30 \text{ g.}}{0.167 \text{ mole}} = 180 \text{ g/mole}$$

(Note that in these two examples the concentrations of solute were kept low so that the limiting laws would apply.)

SELECTIVE BARRIERS TO FLOW; OSMOSIS

It is possible to discover barriers which allow some substances to pass but hinder others. In the vapor pressure experiment of Figure 17.3, the gas phase served as a barrier to the passage of the dissolved salt since the salt was nonvolatile, but the gas was no great barrier to the volatile solvent. In other words, the water could traverse the region between the two phases but the salt could not do so with any facility.

In other systems, different types of barrier will inhibit the flow of certain substances while allowing the flow of others. Flow through such barriers is known as osmosis. If one clamps together two flasks, one containing ammonia gas and the other air, with a piece of wet filter paper between their mouths to form a gas-tight seal, and places a manometer on each flask to measure the pressure, he will note that the pressure in the ammonia flask initially falls and that in the air flask rises (see Figure 17.5). This in spite of the fact that the two pressures were originally identical. In other words, gas is flowing from a region of low total pressure to a region of higher total pressure. This result is readily explained if one considers the partial pressures of the gases (a measure of their escaping tendencies) and the wet filter paper barrier. Ammonia is very soluble in water whereas air is not. Thus the ammonia can dissolve in the water on one side of the filter paper, diffuse through the resulting solution, and evaporate into the air on the other side. At first the flow of ammonia will be entirely from the ammonia flask into the air, but as the concentration in the

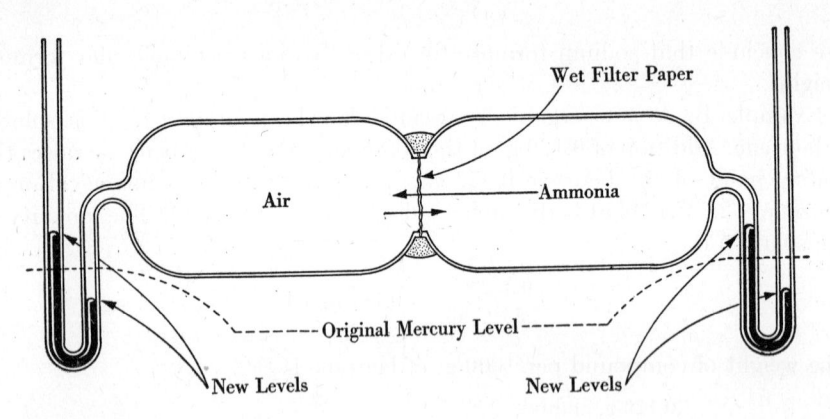

Figure 17.5.
Gas flow through a selective barrier.

air increases, more and more ammonia will flow back until, when the partial pressure of ammonia in the two flasks (the escaping tendency) is the same there will be no net flow of ammonia. Similarly, the air will tend to flow slowly from its flask through the wet paper into the ammonia flask. The very low solubility of air in water will keep the rate of this flow very low compared to the rate of ammonia flow so that the observed pressure difference builds up. If the system is allowed to stand for a sufficient length of time, the air too comes to equilibrium between the two flasks, since its solubility in water is not zero, and the total pressures in the two flasks again become identical.

SEMIPERMEABLE BARRIERS AND OSMOSIS

Systems can be set up in which one flow process is not merely slowed down by a barrier but is actually prohibited. To do this, one must find a barrier which is completely impermeable to some substance, while being permeable to another. Such a barrier is known as a *semipermeable membrane*. It may consist of a series of holes which are too small for one substance to enter. If the two substances are now separated by the barrier, one of them will be able to penetrate it while the other will not, and flow of only one of the substances will occur. The one substance will then flow back and forth through the barrier until its escaping tendency on each side is the same. The rates of flow in each direction will then be the same and the system is at equilibrium with respect to that one component, but, note carefully, not with respect to the other. Now we have already shown that escaping tendency is a function of concentration, temperature, and pressure. Assuming that this system is at constant temperature, the equilibrium concentration will be determined by the pressure. Pressure tends to force a substance through the barrier at a faster rate from the high pressure side to the low pressure side. The higher the pressure on the solution side, the lower the concentration of the diffusing substance must be for its escaping tendency from the solution to equal that from its pure phase. The pressure required to maintain the equilibrium flow through the membrane for any particular concentrations on the two sides of the barrier is known as the *osmotic pressure for that concentration difference.*

Such "equilibria" in which only some of the components are at equilibrium and in which pressure, or temperature, differences exist are called constrained equilibria, or, at times, *steady states*. The term steady state implies that no net changes are occurring but that complete thermal, pressure, and concentration equilibria may be lacking.

OSMOSIS AND LIFE PROCESSES

The phenomena of varying rates of flow through membranes are extremely important to life processes. The tendency of water, for instance, to flow from a region where it is concentrated (relatively pure) to a region where it is less concentrated (that is, diluted by solutes) may be very great and may require very high osmotic pressure to overcome the tendency to flow. Thus the pressure in the roots of a very tall tree may well be of the order of several atmospheres because of the tall column of liquid in the trunk. This pressure is not sufficient, however, to prevent the net flow of water into the roots for the concentration of water on the outside of the root membrane is sufficiently greater than the concentration of water in the root sap to overcome the pressure of the trunk water. Surrounding a fresh water plant (say a dandelion) with salt water reverses the normal difference in water concentration gradient and the plant dies of desiccation.

The principle of osmosis, that is flow through barriers with a net flow from regions of higher concentration to those of lower concentration, is equally important in the distribution of food throughout the living organism and in the disposal of wastes. A particular carbohydrate molecule has no intention of proceeding to any given spot in the body when it is taken into the mouth. As it travels through the alimentary tract the large molecule is broken up into smaller aggregates which can penetrate the small pores in the intestine and get into the body circulatory system. They then travel through the circulatory system, entering various cells from time to time. Diffusion is continually occurring back and forth through all cell walls but in a particular cell molecules may either be converted into bigger molecules which cannot leave, or they may be consumed. The waste products then diffuse out of the cell into the circula-

268   GENERAL CHEMISTRY

tory system until they are finally eliminated, again through osmosis. This picture is oversimplified—superimposed on osmosis in living cells in which active metabolism is occurring is a building up of the concentrations of some diffusible substances. However, when metabolism stops the osmotic processes again determine the direction of flow (see Chapter 39, page 650).

Osmosis appears also in the operation of the respiratory system. Inhaled oxygen crosses the lung membrane into the blood stream faster than it diffuses back because the escaping tendency (partial pressure) of the oxygen in the air is higher than that in the blood stream. The oxygen then diffuses back and forth between cells and blood until at last it is utilized in a cell. The waste carbon dioxide also diffuses from cell to blood and back many times before it comes to the lungs. The rate of flow of carbon dioxide from blood to lung is much higher than the reverse process since the escaping tendency (vapor pressure) of the carbon dioxide in the blood is much higher than that in the inhaled air. We have already pointed out in an earlier chapter that elimination of carbon dioxide in the lungs may be inhibited if the inhaled air has a high carbon dioxide content and that suffocation may result even though plenty of oxygen is available. Corresponding depletion of the carbon dioxide content of the blood if the carbon dioxide concentration in the lungs is too low has been pointed out as being equally bad (see page 71).

OSMOSIS AND MEASUREMENT OF CONCENTRATION

In the laboratory, osmosis may be used to determine the molality of a solution. For example, if pure solvent is placed on one side of a semipermeable membrane and a solution on the other the pressure one must impose on the solution to make the escaping tendency of the solvent equal on both sides of the membrane (the osmotic pressure) may be measured. From this value the molality of the solution can then be calculated. If the weights of solute and solvent used to make up the solution were measured the molar weight of the solute can also be calculated. Or, a solution of unknown molality may be separated by a semipermeable membrane from solutions of known molality. When any pair of solutions is found for which there is no net diffusion of solvent between the two sides of the membrane, these solutions have the same molal concentrations of solute. Again the molar weight of the solute can be calculated from the molality (compare examples on page 265). Practical difficulties arise with solutes of low molar weights because it is almost impossible to prepare a membrane permeable to a solvent and at the same time absolutely nonpermeable to small solute molecules. However, membranes may be made which are nonpermeable to large molecules such as the molecules of polymers and osmotic pressure measurements can then be carried out successfully. In this way the molar weights of polymers can be measured.

We thus have four experimental ways of counting the number of solute particles in a liquid solution. The molalities (or the molar weights) can be calculated from: (1) the lowering of the vapor pressure of the solvent, (2) the rise in boiling point of the solvent, (3) the lowering in freezing point of the solvent, and (4) the osmotic behavior of the solvent. For ionic solutions the additional method of determining the electrical conductivity may be used. Other methods are available for detecting the concentration of particular substances but the ones listed here are general for any of a large class of substances. If one knows the relative numbers of particles present in a solution, and also the total weight of the particles, he can calculate the molar weights.

DISTRIBUTION OF SOLUTE BETWEEN TWO IMMISCIBLE SOLVENTS

In speaking of solution equilibria thus far our chief examples have been those in which the escaping tendency of a substance from a pure phase is equal to its escaping tendency from a solution. Thus, we have spoken of pure gases dissolving in liquids and pure solids dissolving in liquids. (Pure liquids come to osmotic equilibrium with a solution only when the solution is under pressure.) It is just as possible, however, to study the distribution of a solute between two different solvents as to study its distribution between its pure phase and one solvent. Here again equilibrium will be attained when the escaping tendency of the solute is the same in every phase. Iodine (a nonpolar substance) is considerably more soluble in carbon tetrachloride (a nonpolar liquid) than it is in water (a polar liquid). If a solution of iodine in carbon tetrachloride is shaken with water, some of the iodine will dissolve in the water and the concentration of iodine in water will increase until its rate of escape from the water to the carbon tetrachloride exactly equals its rate of escape from the carbon tetrachloride into the water. Since the solubility of iodine in the nonpolar liquid is much greater than its solubility in water, its escaping tendency from the carbon tetrachloride will be less than from a water solution of the same concentration and the water solution will be considerably less concentrated at equilibrium than the carbon tetrachloride layer. (Note that the existence of this equilibrium depends on the fact that water and carbon tetrachloride are almost insoluble in each other. There is some mutual solubility, however, so that we have distribution of water and of carbon tetrachloride between both layers as well as distribution of iodine between both layers.) The ratio of the iodine concentrations in the two layers is independent of the concentration in either layer, for decreasing one of the concentrations by half will lower the escaping tendency from that phase by half and necessitate a similar decrease in the escaping tendency of the iodine from the other layer. This would mean a lowering of the concentration there to one half its former value also. Thus, the ratio of the two concentrations stays unchanged.

SUMMARY

We may summarize this chapter by saying that equilibrium is attained in any system when the escaping tendency of a substance is the same in every phase available to it. The escaping tendency is determined by the concentration (or pressure), the temperature, and the strength of the bonding forces. In general, an increase in either of the first two increases the escaping tendency and an increase in the last decreases the escaping tendency.

Ideal solutions, solutions in which the escaping tendency is proportional to the concentrations, are rare, but dilute solutions are close enough to ideal in many cases to allow a simple correlation between properties of solvent, solute, and concentrations.

Problem 17.1. Arrange the following in order of *decreasing* freezing point: 0.01 f hydrochloric acid, 0.05 f sugar, 0.02 f barium chloride, 55.5 f water, 0.01 f sulfuric acid.

Problem 17.2. Give five experimental proofs that a solution of sodium chloride contains Na^+ and Cl^- ions.

Problem 17.3. Give the approximate freezing points of the following aqueous solutions:
 a. 0.1 molal glycerine ($C_3H_8O_3$).
 b. 0.05 molal barium chloride.
 c. 1.00 g. of sodium hydroxide in 100 g. of water.

Problem 17.4. Describe three experimental methods of showing whether sulfurous acid is a strong or weak electroyte, i.e., is completely or only partially ionized in water.

Problem 17.5. Fill in the blanks: 0.200 moles of ammonia contains _____ molecules, weighs _____ grams, would occupy _____ liters at 0°C. and 1 atm., would occupy _____ liters at 50°C. and 1.5 atm. This amount of ammonia could neutralize _____ equivalents of sulfuric acid or _____ moles of sulfuric acid. This ammonia could neutralize _____ ml. of 0.06 f sulfuric acid and yield _____ grams of ammonium sulfate. If sparked in a vessel of 40.0 liters capacity until it had all decomposed into hydrogen and nitrogen, it would give a pressure of _____ atm. at 30°C. This quantity of ammonia could be produced from _____ grams of calcium cyanamide, formula $CaCN_2$, by the reaction: $CaCN_2 + 3H_2O = CaCO_3 + 2NH_3$.

Problem 17.6. 300 ml. of hydrogen chloride gas are dissolved in 400 ml. of water. The hydrogen chloride gas was measured at 2.00 atm. and 20°C. What is the formality of the resulting solution?

Problem 17.7. The equivalent weight of a certain acid is 50.0 g. What volume of 0.100 f sodium hydroxide would exactly neutralize 0.456 g. of it?

Problem 17.8. 28.3 ml. of 0.187 f sodium hydroxide is exactly neutralized by 16.4 ml. of sulfuric acid. What is the formal concentration of the sulfuric acid used?

Problem 17.9. In the neutralization of 100 ml. of 1 f hydrochloric acid by 100 ml. of 1 f sodium hydroxide a temperature rise of 6.2°C. was observed. Calculate the number of calories evolved when one mole of water is formed by the reaction.

$$H^+ + OH^- = H_2O$$

Assume all heat effects are due only to this reaction.

Problem 17.10. Suggest methods you could use to determine whether a given sample of water was "pure." Arrange them in approximate order of sensitivity.

Problem 17.11. Calculate the apparent molar weight of a substance, 1.24 g. of which in 100 ml. of water gave a solution which began to freeze at -0.202°C.

Problem 17.12. When 0.112 g. of a polymer was dissolved in 5.00 ml. of water the osmotic pressure was the same as in a 0.001 molal sucrose ($C_{12}H_{22}O_{11}$) solution. Calculate the average molar weight of the polymer.

18 CHEMICAL EQUILIBRIUM

IN CHAPTER 17 we found that equilibria among phases are dynamic; materials are entering and leaving each phase at the same rate. Thus liquid-vapor equilibrium is attained when the liquid vaporizes at exactly the same rate at which the vapor condenses to liquid. Solubility equilibrium is attained when the rate at which solute enters the solution is exactly equal to the rate at which solute leaves the solution. In this chapter we shall establish and utilize the fact that the equilibria in chemical reactions are attained when the "reagents" are reacting to give the "products" of the reaction at exactly the same rate at which the "products" are reacting to re-form the "reagents."

Dynamic equilibria may be viewed as the inevitable result of the fact that, at any given temperature, molecules do not all have the same kinetic energy (see Figure 10.2). There are always some molecules present, though perhaps only a minute number, which have enough kinetic energy to break the bonds holding them in the combination in which they would be most stable at the temperature of the bulk of the material. Conversely, these fragments, once formed, will eventually lose this extra energy and return to the original state—the one which is most stable at the temperature in question. When two possible states are equally stable, the substance will distribute itself equally between the two states. When the states are not identical in stability, the substance will be more commonly found in the more stable state, and this state will comprise the bulk of the system. Thus chlorine gas at room temperature contains primarily diatomic molecules, Cl_2, but about 1 molecule in every billion is monatomic, Cl. At 2000°K. about one half of the molecules are monatomic due to the higher kinetic energy.

The dynamic nature of chemical equilibrium is inherent in the competitive nature of chemical reactions. Thus substance A may form a more stable compound with substance B than with substance C. If substance C predominates, however, there will be more collisions between A and C than between A and B and the formation of the AC combination will be encouraged. This consequence will be most pronounced when the inherent stabilities of the two products AB and AC are not grossly different, but it will exist in all systems because of the kinetic energy effect. A typical example is the previously discussed reaction between carbon, oxygen, carbon monoxide, and carbon dioxide (see pages 87–90). In the presence of a large amount of oxygen, carbon dioxide is formed predominantly when hot carbon and oxygen are in contact. When less oxygen is present carbon monoxide can be detected. As the amount of oxygen present decreases that of carbon monoxide becomes more and more prevalent, compared to that of carbon dioxide, since there is less chance for a carbon monoxide molecule to meet an oxygen molecule and react with it to form carbon dioxide.

PRINCIPLE OF LE CHATELIER

The relative concentrations of substances present in a dynamic equilibrium system will depend on the relative stabilities of the substances involved, on the relative probabilities of collisions between the molecules which can react, and on the temperature of the system. A change in any one of these will cause a shift in the relative concentrations of the substances present at equilibrium, or, as it is commonly put, a shift in the equilibrium. Such shifts may be summarized qualitatively in the statement that an equilibrium will always shift in that direction which tends to undo the change being made. An increase in pressure, for instance, on a system at equilibrium will always cause that reaction to occur which will tend to decrease the pressure. Thus, increasing the pressure of carbon dioxide over water will cause more carbon dioxide to dissolve in the water since this process tends to decrease the total pressure.

An increase in the temperature of a system at equilibrium will always cause that reaction to occur which absorbs energy since the absorption of energy tends to lower the temperature. Heating gaseous water to a high temperature causes it to dissociate into hydrogen and oxygen since the dissociation process absorbs energy and tends to lower the temperature.

An increase in the concentration of one of the substances involved in an equilibrium always causes that reaction to occur which tends to use up the added substance. Addition of oxygen to an equilibrium system containing carbon, oxygen, carbon monoxide, and carbon dioxide leads to the formation of more of both the monoxide and the dioxide and the increase in the dioxide concentration is the greater since the oxygen is used up more effectively in this molecule containing two atoms of oxygen as compared to only one atom of oxygen in the monoxide.

This *principle* that any equilibrium system tends to shift, or react, in such a way as to undo any changes made upon it was first enunciated by Le Chatelier in 1888. The principle has as far-reaching applications as any in chemistry, for it can be applied equally well to any of the physical or life sciences and in many cases to the fields of economics and human relations as well. We have already applied it to some equilibria (see pages 140 and 257). The limitation of the principle to systems in dynamic equilibrium must always be borne in mind. Static systems and nonequilibrium systems may not follow the principle of Le Chatelier.

THE QUANTITATIVE TREATMENT OF EQUILIBRIA

The reaction between gaseous iodine and gaseous hydrogen to produce gaseous hydrogen iodide has been much studied in attempts to determine the quantitative relationships between the concentrations of substances at equilibrium and the effect of temperature changes on these concentrations. When gaseous hydrogen iodide is heated, part of it decomposes into hydrogen and iodine. When iodine and hydrogen are heated together, part of them combine to form hydrogen iodide. These facts indicate that it is indeed possible for this reaction to proceed in either "direction," as in equations 18.1 and 18.2 read from left to right.

$$HI_{(g)} + HI_{(g)} = H_{2(g)} + I_{2(g)} \tag{18.1}$$

$$H_{2(g)} + I_{2(g)} = HI_{(g)} + HI_{(g)} \tag{18.2}$$

Yet, at about 700°K., neither of these reactions goes to "completion"; measurable amounts of the reagents are always left. The rates of both reactions are slow (see page 88) but after some hours at a constant temperature the concentration of the mixture becomes constant and undergoes no further change with time. An equilibrium state has been reached. Our concept of dynamic equilibrium interprets the equilibrium state in terms of a continual reaction between the hydrogen and iodine to produce hydrogen iodide and a simultaneous decomposition of the hydrogen iodide into hydrogen and iodine. The rates of the two reactions are identical at equilibrium so that no net change in the concentrations occurs with passing time.

A simple picture of the situation would indicate that the rate of reaction of hydrogen and iodine at any temperature would be determined by the number of times per second hydrogen molecules collide with iodine molecules, for without such collisions reaction would be impossible. Any increase in the concentration of hydrogen would enhance the possibility of such a collision and thus increase the rate of reaction with the iodine. Similarly, any increase in the concentration of the iodine would enhance the possibility of a collision with hydrogen and increase the rate of the reaction. Trebling the concentration of either hydrogen or iodine, for instance, would treble the number of collisions and thus treble the rate. If one also trebled the concentration of the other gas the rate would increase by another factor of three, or a total factor of nine (3 × 3). Thus, at any given temperature the rate of reaction is proportional to the product of the concentrations of the reagents, or, in the present case

$$\text{the rate of reaction of hydrogen and iodine} = k_1[H_2] \times [I_2] \tag{18.3}$$

where $[H_2]$ represents the concentration of hydrogen in terms of moles of hydrogen per liter of gas, $[I_2]$ the concentration of iodine gas, and k_1 the proportionality constant.

In like manner the rate of reaction of hydrogen iodide is determined by the number of collisions between hydrogen iodide molecules. Thus, we obtain the rate of reaction of hydrogen iodide = $k_2[HI] \times [HI]$, (18.4)

quite analogous to equation 18.3.

But, under the condition of a dynamic equilibrium, these two rates of reaction become the same so that we may combine equations 18.3 and 18.4

$$k_1[H_2] \times [I_2] = k_2[HI] \times [HI] \quad (18.5)$$

which may be transposed to give

$$\frac{[H_2] \times [I_2]}{[HI] \times [HI]} = \frac{k_2}{k_1} \quad (18.6)$$

Since k_1 and k_2 are both constant terms at any given temperature, they may be combined in a single K, or K_{eq}, called the *equilibrium constant*, as in equation 18.7.

$$\frac{[H_2] \times [I_2]}{[HI] \times [HI]} = K_{eq} \quad (18.7)$$

Equation 18.7 is defined as the expression for the equilibrium constant for the reaction represented by the equation 18.8.

$$HI_{(g)} + HI_{(g)} = H_{2(g)} + I_{2(g)} \quad (18.8)$$

In this instance, as in all instances, it will be noted that the equilibrium constant expression is a fraction containing in its numerator the product of the concentrations of the substances on the right side of the equation and in its denominator the product of the concentrations of the substances on the left side of the equation. One can show that, for equilibrium systems at constant temperature in which concentrations measure escaping tendencies, such a fraction will always have a constant value even though the reactions proceed by much more complicated mechanisms than the one we attributed to this reaction. Furthermore, one need not know the mechanism in order to set up the expression for the equilibrium constant.

Equations 18.8 and 18.7 can be written in the simpler forms

$$2HI_{(g)} = H_{2(g)} + I_{2(g)} \quad (18.9)$$

and

$$\frac{[H_2] \times [I_2]}{[HI]^2} = K_{eq} \quad (18.10)$$

Note that the concentration of the hydrogen iodide is raised to the power represented by its coefficient in the chemical equation.

The first experimental proof that the course of reactions depends quantitatively on the concentrations of the reacting substances was obtained by two Norwegian chemists, Guldberg and Waage, in 1863. Since they expressed their results in terms of "active masses" (for concentrations) the equilibrium principle is often called the *law of mass action*, and the equilibrium constant the *mass action constant*.

We may test the validity of equation 18.10 by applying it to some experimental data on the hydrogen-iodine system, given in Table 18.1, from the work of Taylor and Crist. The agreement between the values in the last column indicates that dynamic equilibrium was attained (the systems were held at constant temperature from ten to thirty hours) and that equation 18.10 is a quantitative means of relating the equilibrium concentrations.

Table 18.1
Hydrogen, Iodine, and Hydrogen Iodide Equilibrium at 698.6°K.

$[H_2]$ (moles/liter)	$[I_2]$ (moles/liter)	$[HI]$ (moles/liter)	$K = \dfrac{[H_2][I_2]}{[HI]^2}$
1.8313×10^{-3}	3.1292×10^{-3}	17.671×10^{-3}	1.835×10^{-2}
2.2423×10^{-3}	2.3360×10^{-3}	16.850×10^{-3}	1.853×10^{-2}
2.9070×10^{-3}	1.7069×10^{-2}	16.482×10^{-3}	1.827×10^{-2}
3.5600×10^{-3}	1.2500×10^{-3}	15.588×10^{-3}	1.831×10^{-2}
4.5647×10^{-3}	0.7378×10^{-3}	13.544×10^{-3}	1.835×10^{-2}
0.4789×10^{-3}	0.4789×10^{-3}	3.531×10^{-3}	1.840×10^{-2}
0.4953×10^{-3}	0.4953×10^{-3}	3.655×10^{-3}	1.832×10^{-2}
1.1409×10^{-3}	1.1409×10^{-3}	8.410×10^{-3}	1.840×10^{-2}

Average 1.837×10^{-2}
or 0.01837

The first five lines give data on equilibrium systems obtained by heating hydrogen and iodine together. The last three lines give data on equilibrium systems obtained by heating pure hydrogen iodide. Note that the same constant is obtained by each method, indicating the dynamic nature of the system.

Because of the general validity of the expression for the equilibrium constant one need not derive it for every new reaction. If one knows the equation for the reaction he may write the equilibrium constant expression directly by forming a fraction whose numerator contains the product of the concentrations of the substances on the right hand of the equation (each concentration being raised to a power corresponding to the coefficient of that substance in the reaction) and whose denominator contains the product of the concentrations of the substances on the left side of the equation (with the appropriate powers again). Some typical examples are given below. Note that even complicated equations yield expressions for K in a straightforward manner.

Ionization of a poorly ionized acid in water

$$HCN = H^+ + CN^-$$

$$K_{eq} = \frac{[H^+][CN^-]}{[HCN]} \tag{18.11}$$

Reaction between substances in solution

$$Fe^{+++} + I^- = Fe^{++} + \tfrac{1}{2}I_2$$

$$K_{eq} = \frac{[Fe^{++}][I_2]^{\frac{1}{2}}}{[Fe^{+++}][I^-]} \tag{18.12}$$

$$2H^+ + HAsO_2 + 2NO_3^- = H_3AsO_4 + 2NO_2$$

$$K_{eq} = \frac{[H_3AsO_4][NO_2]^2}{[H^+]^2[HAsO_2][NO_3^-]^2} \tag{18.13}$$

EQUILIBRIA IN WHICH SOME CONCENTRATIONS REMAIN UNCHANGED

Certain equilibrium systems include substances whose concentrations do not change even though some of the substances are used up, or formed. The dissolving of some solid in water, for instance, leaves the concentration of solid in the solid phase unchanged. There is merely less solid present at equilibrium than at the beginning. Since the volume of the solid has decreased at exactly the same rate as the weight of solid, its concentration in moles per liter of solid is unchanged. Thus in the reaction

$$BaSO_{4(s)} = Ba^{++} + SO_4^{--} \tag{18.14}$$

the equilibrium constant could be written

$$K = \frac{[Ba^{++}] \times [SO_4^{--}]}{[BaSO_{4(s)}]} \tag{18.15}$$

But the term $[BaSO_{4(s)}]$ is, in reality, a constant for it represents the moles of barium sulfate per liter of solid barium sulfate. It is, therefore, convenient to transpose equation 18.15 to read:

$$K \times [BaSO_{4(s)}] = [Ba^{++}] \times [SO_4^{--}] \tag{18.16}$$

A further simplification is possible by defining $K \times [BaSO_{4(s)}] \equiv K_{sp}$ where K_{sp} is known as the *solubility product constant* or the *solubility product*. Thus

$$K \times [BaSO_{4(s)}] \equiv K_{sp} = [Ba^{++}] \times [SO_4^{--}]. \tag{18.17}$$

In general, therefore, the concentrations of solids, since they do not change during reaction, are included in the value of K as being part of the equilibrium constant itself.

Most of the reactions of chemistry in a beginning course are carried out in dilute water solutions. In many instances, if not all, the water is a participant in the reaction and may even be used up or formed during the reaction. It certainly affects the rate of the reactions occurring in it. On the other hand, its concentration remains unchanged for all practical purposes since it is present in such overwhelming concentration. For this reason, the concentration of water is included in the value of K for those reactions in which water is involved, not because the concentration of water is really constant but because its changes in concentration are so small as to have an inappreciable effect on the equilibrium. For example, pure water is somewhat ionized according to the equation

$$HOH = H^+ + OH^-$$

$$K = \frac{[H^+] \times [OH^-]}{[HOH]} \tag{18.18}$$

CHEMICAL EQUILIBRIUM 277

In any dilute solution, however, the [HOH] term is practically constant and is, therefore, included in the value of K_w as in

$$K \times [HOH] \equiv K_w = [H^+] \times [OH^-] \tag{18.19}$$

In the same manner, in each of the following equilibrium constant expressions the concentrations of solids and/or water are included in K.

$$Cu^{++} + Zn_{(s)} = Cu_{(s)} + Zn^{++}$$

$$K = \frac{[Zn^{++}]}{[Cu^{++}]} \tag{18.20}$$

$$2Cl^- + 2NO_3^- + 4H^+ = Cl_2 + 2NO_2 + 2H_2O$$

$$K = \frac{[Cl_2][NO_2]^2}{[Cl^-]^2[NO_3^-]^2[H^+]^4} \tag{18.21}$$

$$AgCl_{(s)} + 2NH_3 = Ag(NH_3)_2^+ + Cl^-$$

$$K = \frac{[Ag(NH_3)_2^+][Cl^-]}{[NH_3]^2} \tag{18.22}$$

$$CaCO_{3(s)} + 2H^+ = Ca^{++} + H_2O + CO_2$$

$$K = \frac{[Ca^{++}][CO_2]}{[H^+]^2} \tag{18.23}$$

PARTIAL PRESSURES AND EQUILIBRIUM CONSTANTS

For reactions in gases it is common practice to use the partial pressures of the gases rather than the concentration in moles per liter in the equilibrium constant expression. This practice is satisfactory since the partial pressure is directly proportional to the molar concentration. For instance, doubling the partial pressure doubles the molar concentration. However, the actual numerical values of the constants will depend on the units used to calculate them so that these units should always be stated clearly.

Similarly, the concentration of a substance in solution is, according to Henry's law (see page 258), proportional to its partial pressure in the gas phase. For this reason the partial pressure of a gas is commonly used as a measure of the concentration of the substance in solution. Again one must be careful to state the terms in which the equilibrium constant is given.

Consider, for example, the reaction represented in equation 18.23. The equilibrium constant is given as

$$K = \frac{[Ca^{++}] \times [CO_2]}{[H^+]^2} \tag{18.24}$$

where the various formulas in brackets represent molar concentrations in solution. If the hydrogen ion concentration is kept constant and the concentration of carbon dioxide is doubled, the concentration of calcium ion will decrease by one half, for the value of the whole fraction must remain constant and equal to K. But the concentration, $[CO_2]$, of dissolved carbon dioxide is directly proportional to its partial pressure, P_{CO_2}, above the solution and doubling its concentration in solution requires that this partial pressure also double. Thus, an equally useful value for the equilibrium constant would have been obtained if it had been written

$$K_1 = \frac{[Ca^{++}] \times P_{CO_2}}{[H^+]^2} \tag{18.25}$$

K and K_1 are not, of course, equal, but differ by the proportionality factor which relates the concentration of dissolved carbon dioxide to its partial pressure above the solution.

The effect of a change in partial pressure on an equilibrium is only that which one would expect from the change in concentration which accompanies such a change in partial pressure. An increase in partial pressure increases the concentration, and a decrease in partial pressure decreases the concentration of any given substance. The equilibrium shifts accordingly to compensate for any such change.

EFFECT OF TEMPERATURE CHANGES ON EQUILIBRIA

According to Le Chatelier's principle an increase in temperature in a system at equilibrium will always favor that reaction which absorbs energy. Table 18.2 lists some values for the equilibrium constant of the hydrogen-iodine

Table 18.2
Change of an Equilibrium Constant with Temperature

$$K = \frac{[H_2][I_2]}{[HI]^2}$$

T(°K.)	666.8	698.6	730.8	763.8
K	1.672×10^{-2}	1.837×10^{-2}	2.048×10^{-2}	2.203×10^{-2}

The fact that K increases with rising temperature indicates that hydrogen and iodine become more and more stable with respect to hydrogen iodide as the temperature rises.

reaction. It is apparent that the equilibrium constant increases with temperature. This means that the numerator of the equilibrium constant increases faster than the denominator as the temperature rises which in turn means that the formation of hydrogen and iodine from hydrogen iodide is favored at higher temperatures. It must be, therefore, that the reaction of hydrogen iodide to give hydrogen and gaseous iodine is an endothermic one, for it is the reaction which absorbs energy which is most favored by an increase in temperature.

The effect of rise in temperature may be viewed in terms of an increase in kinetic energy of the molecules, with more energy available for breaking of bonds (see pages 256–257). All bonds will be broken more readily but the fraction of the stronger bonds broken increases at a faster rate than the fraction of the weaker bonds broken since the number of molecules with very high kinetic energy rises more rapidly than the number of molecules with lower kinetic energy (see Figure 10.2). Hence the endothermic reactions increase in rate more rapidly than the exothermic reactions.

We might add that even the strongest bonds are destroyed by sufficiently high temperatures so that the simpler states of aggregation are found more commonly at high than at low temperatures, but these are only different ways of saying the same thing: The reactions which occur with the absorption of energy will be favored by a rise in temperature.

STABLE CHEMICAL SYSTEMS

Equilibria may be shifted by the addition of ingredients which react with some of the substances involved in the equilibrium. The effect will be particularly great when added ingredients form very stable combinations with the reacting substances. In reactions carried out in solution stable products generally become apparent in one of four ways: (1) The stable substances which form are electrically neutral but insoluble in the solution and a new phase is formed; (2) the stable substances are electrically neutral but soluble in the solution and weak electrolytes are formed; (3) The stable substances are electrically charged (and hence stay in solution since no new phase can have a net electrical charge) and complex ions are formed; (4) The stable substances have different oxidation numbers than their parent materials and hence oxidation-reduction has occurred. Since all chemical reactions start with materials previously at equilibrium and bring them to a new equilibrium condition (assuming that sufficient time is available), one can generalize the above four criteria by stating that that reaction will occur which will form (a) the most insoluble substances, (b) the least ionized substances, (c) the most tightly bound complex ions, or (d) the most stable oxidation-reduction products. In many cases two or more of these criteria will be operating simultaneously, perhaps in conflict, so that the competitive nature of the reactions must always be remembered.

The above four criteria are actually not very profound insights into chemical reactions but are, rather, merely convenient classifications into which chemical reactions may be divided. They are convenient because they involve ideas directly related to experiment and are based on experimental determinations of solubility, degree of ionization, dissociation of complex ions, and ease of oxidation and reduction, all of which may be correlated in terms of electronic structure and positions within the periodic system.

SOLUBILITY EQUILIBRIUM

One of the most apparent evidences of reaction in a chemical system is the appearance of a new phase due to the formation of a substance insoluble in the reaction mixture. Addition of a solution of silver nitrate to a solution of sodium chloride leads to the formation of a white precipitate which proves to be silver chloride. Both silver nitrate and sodium chloride are ionized in water solutions, as is also sodium nitrate so that one may write an equation for the reaction as follows:

$$Ag^+ + NO_3^- + Na^+ + Cl^- = AgCl_{(s)} + Na^+ + NO_3^- \quad (18.26)$$
$$\text{white}$$

It should be noted, however, that neither the sodium ion nor the nitrate ion has undergone any apparent change according to the equation written. Each is still an ion surrounded by water just as it was in the initial solution. Since the Na^+ and NO_3^- ions are not changed they have not participated in the over-all, or net, reaction. They may then be omitted from the equation for the net reaction which becomes

$$Ag^+ + Cl^- = AgCl_{(s)} \quad (18.27)$$
$$\text{white}$$

This equation indicates that silver ions and chloride ions have united to give a white, insoluble solid, silver chloride.

From our concept of dynamic equilibrium we draw the conclusion, however, that this reaction does not really go to completion. Rather, some silver chloride dissolves in the solution to give silver ions and chloride ions, which, in the equilibrium state, recombine at the same rate to form the solid silver chloride.

$$AgCl_{(s)} = Ag^+ + Cl^-$$
$$K_{sp} = [Ag^+] \times [Cl^-] = 1.7 \times 10^{-10} \quad (18.28)$$

Examination of the equilibrium constant expression, K_{sp}, shows that any increase in the chloride concentration at equilibrium must result in a corresponding decrease in the silver ion concentration, for the product of the two concentrations must remain constant. This is, of course, consistent with Le Chatelier's principle, which states that any increase in the chloride concentration at equilibrium will lead to the occurrence of that reaction which tends to remove the added chloride. The only possible such reaction here is the one with silver ion to give the silver chloride. Whenever this reaction occurs silver ion is used up, thus lowering its concentration.

These ideas will apply in general to solubility equilibrium. Increasing the concentration of any one of the substances participating in the equilibrium will tend to cause that reaction to occur which will use up the added material. Conversely, decreasing the concentration of one of the substances participating in the equilibrium will cause that reaction to occur which will tend to replace the substance being removed.

Addition of excess chloride ion to a saturated solution of silver chloride will cause the formation of more of the solid as the ionic concentrations adjust themselves so that the product of their concentrations remains equal to K_{sp}. Conversely, any process which removes chloride ion (or silver ion) from the solution will lead to the dissolving of some of the solid silver chloride. As long as any of the solid silver chloride remains in contact with the solution, the K_{sp} value will determine the silver and chloride concentrations with respect to one another.

CHEMICAL EQUILIBRIUM

The numerical value for this solubility product constant, $K_{sp} = ([Ag^+] \times [Cl^-])$, may be obtained as follows: If one shakes pure silver chloride with water the solid will dissolve somewhat to produce a saturated solution which is 1.3×10^{-5} molar in silver chloride. There are equal concentrations of silver ion and chloride ion—they have the value $[Ag^+] = [Cl^-] = 1.3 \times 10^{-5} M$. Therefore

$$K_{sp} = [Ag^+] \times [Cl^-] = (1.3 \times 10^{-5}) \times (1.3 \times 10^{-5}) = 1.7 \times 10^{-10} \quad (18.29)$$

Suppose one now dissolves sufficient sodium chloride in the solution to bring the chloride concentration up to $1 M$. (The sodium ion concentration will also be about $1 M$, of course, but the sodium ion does not participate in this equilibrium and can be neglected in the considerations.) This great increase in the chloride concentration will increase the chances of collisions between silver ions and chloride ions (according to the kinetic theory) and more silver chloride will precipitate. It will cause that reaction to occur which will tend to use up the added chloride ions (Le Chatelier's principle) and more silver chloride will precipitate. It will raise the chloride concentration to $1 M$ and according to the value $K_{sp} = 1.7 \times 10^{-10}$ (equilibrium constant reasoning) lower the silver ion concentration to 1.7×10^{-10} by precipitating more silver chloride. Note that all these three lines of reasoning lead to the same conclusion, more silver chloride is formed and the silver ion concentration falls to a lower value. This agreement is inevitable, of course, for equilibrium reasoning and Le Chatelier's principle are both firmly linked to the kinetic theory. The effect, on equilibria involving ions, produced by an addition of a compound which furnishes more of one of the reacting ions is called the *common ion effect*. In the above example Cl^- ion is the common ion furnished by the added salt.

Later on we shall discuss the factors which determine whether a substance will dissolve in water or not. Then we can correlate solubility behaviors with structural features. For the present, however, you will need to remember the solubility observations made or reported in class and laboratory, and to apply these observations to other chemical systems as you meet them.

WEAK ELECTROLYTE EQUILIBRIA

Compounds of elements which differ somewhat but not greatly in electronegativity are not primarily ionic in nature but are covalent. However, the bonds are polar, and, when dissolved in polar solvents, polar substances may ionize appreciably. Then they are called *weak electrolytes*. The more polar the bond the higher the fraction of the molecules which will be ionized at any one time. A substance which ionizes completely in solution is called a *strong electrolyte*, whereas a nonpolar substance which gives practically no ions is called a *nonelectrolyte*.

Our most common solvent is water. Its electrical conductivity, though small, is appreciable. Water must contain ions and be a weak electrolyte. It is electrically neutral. Hence it must contain an equivalent number of positive and negative ions. The conductivity and many other properties of water may be interpreted in terms of equal concentrations of hydrogen ions and hydroxyl ions. At 25°C. the concentration of each is 10^{-7} M. The concentration of oxide ions is negligible, being about 10^{-36} M. Thus the principal ionization equilibrium in water is

$$H_2O = H^+ + OH^-, \quad K_i = \frac{[H^+] \times [OH^-]}{[H_2O]} \qquad (18.30)$$

But the concentration of water, $[H_2O]$, is so large, 55.51 M, as to be unaffected by recombination of even all the ions. Hence we define a new constant

$$K_w = [H^+] \times [OH^-] = K_i \times [H_2O] \qquad (18.31)$$

Substitution of the experimental values for $[H^+]$ and $[OH^-]$ gives

$$K_w = [H^+] \times [OH^-] = 10^{-7} \times 10^{-7} = 10^{-14} \qquad (18.32)$$

Addition of the strongly ionized base, sodium hydroxide, to the water increases the hydroxide concentration. This increases the probability of reaction of hydroxide with hydrogen ions and leads to a decrease in the hydrogen ion concentration. If we know the final equilibrium concentration of either hydroxide or hydrogen ion we can calculate the other, for their product must equal 10^{-14}. Suppose that $[OH^-]$ becomes $0.01M = 10^{-2}M$. Then $[H^+] \times [OH^-] = [H^+] \times 10^{-2} = 10^{-14}$, and $[H^+] = 10^{-12}M$. Thus, in any aqueous solution one can calculate either $[H^+]$ or $[OH^-]$ if he knows the other one.

The concentration of hydrogen ion is referred to in so many connections, including biological systems, that a special unit, pH, is used. The pH of a solution is the negative logarithm of the hydrogen ion concentration. Thus a pH of 7 means $[H^+] = 10^{-7}M$, a pH of 3 means $[H^+] = 10^{-3}M$. Or, a 10^{-12} M hydrogen ion solution is said to have a pH of 12, etc.

Acetic acid, formula HOAc, and hydrocyanic acid, formula HCN, are other typical examples of weak electrolytes.

$$HOAc = H^+ + OAc^-; \quad K = 1.8 \times 10^{-5} = \frac{[H^+] \times [OAc^-]}{[HOAc]} \qquad (18.33)$$

$$HCN = H^+ + CN^-; \quad K = 4 \times 10^{-10} = \frac{[H^+] \times [CN^-]}{[HCN]} \qquad (18.34)$$

Note that the values of the ionization constants indicate that water is the least ionized, hydrocyanic acid next, and acetic acid is the most ionized of these three substances.

In a 1 M solution of hydrogen cyanide in water the concentration of hydrogen ion will equal that of cyanide ion, each being $2 \times 10^{-5}M$. (Show that this is true, using the value for the equilibrium constant.) If one now adds enough sodium cyanide to increase the cyanide concentration to 0.1 M (10^{-1} M) the hydrogen ion concentration will drop to $4 \times 10^{-9}M$. (Show that this result is consistent with the equilibrium constant for the reaction.) At the same time the $[OH^-]$ becomes $2.5 \times 10^{-6}M$.

Salts and bases (except ammonia in water) are usually strongly ionized electrolytes since they contain atoms of metallic elements which tend to form ions. Compounds containing only nonmetallic elements, however, tend to be weak electrolytes. It is for this reason that so many acids are weak electrolytes (called weak acids). As a matter of fact, the only common strong acids are the halogen acids (except hydrofluoric acid which is weak), nitric acid, perchloric acid, sulfuric acid, and phosphoric acid. And in the last two named, sulfuric and phosphoric, only the first hydrogen ion ionizes almost completely; the rest are weakly ionized.

HYDROLYSIS OF IONS

The existence of so many weak acids indicates that most negative ions have a strong attraction for hydrogen ions. The bond between the potential negative ion and the hydrogen is so strong that ionization seldom occurs, hence the acids are weakly ionized. One might well deduce from this that negative ions will tend to attract hydrogen ions from neighboring molecules to form these weakly ionized acids. Such a prediction is born out by experiment.

An aqueous solution of sodium acetate in water is basic. So is a solution of sodium cyanide or sodium carbonate. A solution of sodium chloride or nitrate, on the other hand, is neutral. These facts may be interpreted in terms of the following equations:

$$OAc^- + H_2O = HOAc + OH^-$$
$$CN^- + H_2O = HCN + OH^-$$
$$CO_3^{--} + H_2O = HCO_3^- + OH^-$$
but $Cl^- + H_2O =$ no reaction (HCl is a strongly ionized acid)
or $NO_3^- + H_2O =$ no reaction (HNO$_3$ is a strongly ionized acid)

In a similar way one interprets the acidity found in solutions of aluminum chloride or cupric nitrate in terms of the equations:

$$Al^{+++} + H_2O = AlOH^{++} + H^+$$
$$Cu^{++} + H_2O = CuOH^+ + H^+$$

Such reactions between anions and water to give weak acids and basic solutions, or between cations and water to give weak bases and acidic solutions are called *hydrolysis* reactions. They are essentially the result of competition between the anions and hydroxide ion for the hydrogen (or between the cation and the hydrogen ion for the hydroxide). The weaker the acid (or the weaker the base) which is formed the greater the extent of the hydrolysis and, hence, the more basic (or acidic) the solution becomes. Also, of course, the more concentrated the salt the greater the hydrolysis.

It may be noted that these hydrolysis reactions are the reverse of the reactions occurring when weak acids are titrated by weak bases or vice versa.

We shall discuss hydrolysis in greater detail on page 425.

ACID-BASE INDICATORS

Since hydrogen and hydroxyl ions are always present in any water solution it is advantageous to have methods of determining the concentration of each. We have already shown that a knowledge of the concentration of one of them allows the calculation of the concentration of the other from the relationship

284 GENERAL CHEMISTRY

$[H^+] \times [OH^-] = 10^{-14}$. A particularly easy method of determining these concentrations is to use certain colored materials whose color in water solution depends on the concentration of hydrogen ion in the solution. Such dyes are said to be acid-base indicators. Litmus is a well-known example. It is red in solutions containing more hydrogen ions than hydroxyl ions, and blue in solutions containing more hydroxyl ions than hydrogen ions. Table 18.3 shows some indicators with their colors in solutions of various acidities.

COMPLEX ION EQUILIBRIA

Substances need not react to give insoluble materials nor to form neutral soluble ones. Very often the reaction products are charged. When these charged particles contain more than one atom they are called complex ions. It has been customary, however, to separate these ions into two classes depending on their stabilities. Some polyatomic ions are so stable that they go through many types of chemical reaction unchanged. Sulfate ion, nitrate ion, phosphate ion, hydroxyl ion, and ammonium ion are typical examples. These very stable polyatomic ions are called *radicals*. Other polyatomic ions are not so stable but dissociate into smaller particles appreciably under laboratory conditions. It is to these less stable polyatomic ions that the term *complex ion* is usually applied.

Ferrous ions, for instance, in the presence of cyanide ions form the complex ion, $Fe(CN)_6^{----}$, which is in turn in equilibrium with the ferrous and cyanide ions.

$$Fe(CN)_6^{----} = Fe^{++} + 6CN^-; \quad K = \frac{[Fe^{++}][CN^-]^6}{[Fe(CN)_6^{4-}]} \qquad (18.35)$$

The tendency to form complexes may be interpreted in terms of the electronic structures of the various ions. Thus

Fe^{++} has the electron structure, 2, 8, 14, and needs twelve electrons to become 2, 8, 18, 8, an inert gas structure.

CN^- has the structure $:C:::N:$, and has an unshared pair of electrons at each end.

$Fe(CN)_6^{4-}$ has six CN^- groups surrounding the iron atom, each sharing two electrons with the iron which thus attains the 2, 8, 18, 8 structure.

In a similar fashion

$$Cu(NH_3)_4^{++} = Cu^{++} + 4NH_3; \quad K = \frac{[Cu^{++}][NH_3]^4}{[Cu(NH_3)_4^{++}]} \qquad (18.36)$$

Cu^{++} has the electron structure 2, 8, 17, which can change to 2, 8, 17, 8 when four ammonia molecules,

$$H-\underset{H}{\overset{H}{N}}: , \text{ share electron pairs, to give } H_3N:\underset{\underset{H_3}{N}}{\overset{\overset{H_3}{N}}{Cu}}:NH_3 \equiv Cu(NH_3)_4^{++}$$

Table 18.3
Colors of Some Indicators at Various Acidities

pH [H^+] [OH^-] INDICATOR	0 1 10^{-14}	1 10^{-1} 10^{-13}	2 10^{-2} 10^{-12}	3 10^{-3} 10^{-11}	4 10^{-4} 10^{-10}	5 10^{-5} 10^{-9}	6 10^{-6} 10^{-8}	7 10^{-7} 10^{-7}	8 10^{-8} 10^{-6}	9 10^{-9} 10^{-5}	10 10^{-10} 10^{-4}	11 10^{-11} 10^{-3}	12 10^{-12} 10^{-2}	13 10^{-13} 10^{-1}	14 10^{-14} 1
							COLOR									
Methyl Violet	yellow	aqua	dark blue	violet											
Bromphenol Blue		yellow			red violet	blue-violet									
Methyl Red			red			rose	buff	yellow							
Bromthymol Blue				yellow				blue green							
Thymol Blue		red	buff			yellow			tan	dark blue					
Phenolphthalein				colorless							red				
Alizarin Yellow R				colorless								yellow		orange	
Indigo Carmine					blue									green	yellow

The most common complex ions are those between the ions of the metallic elements in the central portion of the periodic table (for these ions do not have inert gas structures) and substances such as cyanide ions, ammonia molecules, chloride ions, and water, which have unshared pairs of electrons in their valence shells. In the complex ions these previously unshared pairs of electrons are shared.

OXIDATION-REDUCTION EQUILIBRIA

Many chemical reactions occur because more stable states can be attained if the atoms change oxidation states, by, for instance, gaining and losing electrons. Thus sodium reacts with water to form hydrogen gas, sodium ions, and hydroxide ions.

$$Na_{(s)} + H_2O = Na^+ + OH^- + \tfrac{1}{2}H_{2(g)}; \quad K = [Na^+][OH^-][H_2]^{\tfrac{1}{2}} \qquad (18.37)$$

The sodium is oxidized and the hydrogen reduced, as is evident from the changes in oxidation number of the sodium and the hydrogen. We shall have much more to say later about oxidation-reduction reactions but shall only mention them here for the sake of completeness.

THE APPROACH TO EQUILIBRIUM AND CATALYSTS

While it is true that chemical systems will come to a dynamic equilibrium in which each reaction is opposed by its reverse occurring at exactly the same rate, it is not true that this state is reached with equal rapidity in all instances. If all rates of reaction were rapid much of the universe as we know it would not exist. Coal would burn as soon as it was exposed to the atmosphere, and iron would dissolve rapidly upon contact with water. Life itself would be impossible, for all living matter depends on the slowness of chemical reactions in its metabolic processes. On the other hand, it should be clear that if all rates of reaction were very slow there would be just as profound differences in the universe as if all were very fast.

There is, as a matter of fact, a wide range of rates at which chemical systems approach equilibrium. One of the fields of chemistry, known as *kinetics*, devotes itself to the studies of these rates and to interpreting them in terms of the detailed changes which each atom undergoes as reaction proceeds.

It has been known for a long time that the rate of achievement of equilibrium can be changed in many ways. A rise in temperature almost always leads to a quicker reaction by increasing the kinetic energy and, hence, the probability of reacting, of each molecule. Since the effect of increased temperature is seldom uniform on all ingredients participating in an equilibrium, the relative amounts of substance present in the final equilibrium state varies with the temperature in a manner consistent with the Le Chatelier principle.

Intimate mixing, fine subdivision, and higher concentrations of the reactants also hasten reactions.

The speed of many reactions may also be changed by adding substances known as catalysts. Each reaction will have its own set of catalysts which may or may not catalyze other reactions. The term catalyst refers to a substance which is not used up but is regenerated during the reaction which it speeds, though it should be clear that the catalyst must enter into the course of the reaction if it is to have any effect on the rate.

Addition of manganese dioxide to molten potassium chlorate or to a solution of hydrogen peroxide greatly accelerates the evolution of oxygen, yet the weight of manganese dioxide after the reaction is the same as before. Platinum gauzes may be used to speed the reaction between sulfur dioxide and oxygen to give sulfur trioxide, formula SO_3. The gauze becomes very rough as its use is continued, indicating an active participation in the reaction, but the weight of platinum remains the same after as before the reaction.

Many industrial processes depend for their success on the use of catalysts to increase the rate of some reaction to a level where the daily plant output becomes sufficient to justify commercial production. The search for suitable and ever better catalysts enlists a large share of the research budget of many companies.

But it should be clearly remembered that the catalyst merely hastens the attainment of equilibrium. In the commercial synthesis of sulfur trioxide the equilibrium concentration of sulfur trioxide may be 95 per cent. This figure will remain the same regardless of the presence or absence of any catalyst or of the nature of the catalyst. The function of the catalyst is to reduce the reaction time from a matter of hours or days to a matter of seconds. The catalyst can have no effect whatsoever on the equilibrium concentrations. On the other hand, rise in temperature or increase in concentration of reagents, not only speeds the approach to equilibrium; they also affect the concentrations at equilibrium in a manner predictable from the principle of Le Chatelier.

SUMMARY

Chemical reactions in general achieve a state of dynamic equilibrium in which the "reagents" react to give "products" at exactly the same rate at which the "products" react to give "reagents." In many equilibria the equilibrium concentrations of all the participants in the reactions can be measured. This fact allows a thorough experimental check to be made of the equilibrium constant expressions derived from kinetic theory considerations. Experiments confirm the theory at every point. For each equilibrium one can write down directly a mathematical expression, the equilibrium constant expression, which quantitatively relates the concentrations of all the substances involved in the reactions. Equilibria can be shifted by changes in concentrations or temperatures, but the equilibrium constant itself changes only when temperature changes.

The rate of approach to equilibrium can be increased by increased concentrations or temperature. Rates may also be increased by more intimate mixing of reagents or by introduction of catalysts but these last two changes have no effect on the concentrations present in the final equilibrium state.

The principle of Le Chatelier allows a qualitative correlation between shifts in equilibria and imposed changes: An established dynamic equilibrium will always shift in such a direction as to counteract any change in the equilibrium conditions.

The classification of chemical reactions as producing: (1) new phases, (2) weak electrolytes, (3) complex ions, and (4) oxidation-reduction products allows a rather simple correlation of a great deal of information concerning stability and chemical equilibrium.

Problem 18.1. What substance(s) is(are) present at high concentration in the first of each pair of the following solutions that is(are) not present at high concentration in the second?
 a. 1 f ammonium chloride and 1 f ammonia.
 b. 1 f sodium chloride and 1 f hydrochloric acid.
 c. A saturated solution of rubidium chloride and a saturated solution of silver chloride.

Problem 18.2. Write the equation for the net (ionic) reaction which occurs when the following solutions are mixed in equivalent amounts. If no reaction occurs write "none."
 a. Sodium hydroxide and hydrochloric acid.
 b. Nitric acid and sodium chloride.
 c. Acetic acid and ammonia.
 d. Silver nitrate and sodium chloride.
 e. Nitric acid and potassium hydroxide.

Problem 18.3. Write the equation for the net reaction when solutions of the following are mixed in equivalent amounts. If no reaction occurs write "none."
 a. Hydrochloric acid and calcium hydroxide.
 b. Ammonia and nitric acid.
 c. Barium hydroxide and sodium sulfate.
 d. Sodium acetate and hydrochloric acid.

Problem 18.4. A saturated solution of silver acetate, formula AgOAc, in water is about 0.06f.
 a. What is the approximate concentration of Ag^+ ion in this solution?
 b. What is the approximate concentration of OAc^- ion in this solution? (Neglect the fact that OAc^- ion hydrolyzes.)
 c. What is the solubility product of silver acetate?

Problem 18.5. What is the effect upon the solubility of silver acetate of adding small amounts of (a) sodium nitrate, (b) nitric acid, (c) silver nitrate?

Problem 18.6. The rate at which hydrogen iodide is formed from hydrogen and iodine in the gaseous phase, i.e., the total number of moles formed per second, depends on the frequency of collision between hydrogen and iodine and also on the force per collision. What would you deduce from the kinetic theory regarding the initial effect on the rate of formation of hydrogen iodide of each of the following changes: (a) volume and temperature constant, amount of hydrogen decreased, (b) temperature increased, volume constant, (c) temperature constant, pressure doubled, (d) neon added, temperature and volume constant, (e) volume doubled, temperature constant.

Problem 18.7. Calculate the OH^- ion concentration in a 1 M solution of an acid, formula HX, which is 1 per cent ionized. Calculate the equilibrium constant for ionization of the acid.

Problem 18.8. Suggest two methods of assuring as complete precipitation of manganous sulfide as possible by hydrogen sulfide in the reaction: $Mn^{++} + H_2S = MnS_{(s)} + 2H^+$.

Problem 18.9. List the effect of the following factors on the solubility and on the rate of solution of sodium acetate. Give your reason in each case.

	DECREASE IN PARTICLE SIZE	INCREASE IN TEMPERATURE	STIRRING	ADDITION OF MORE SOLID SALT
SOLUBILITY				
RATE OF SOLUTION				

Problem 18.10. In a 1 f solution the acid, formula HX, is 0.1% ionized. Calculate the hydrogen ion concentration. Calculate the value for the ionization constant of the acid.

Problem 18.11. Hydrogen cyanide is a weak acid which ionizes in water according to the equation

$$HCN = H^+ + CN^-$$

What is the effect on the hydrogen ion concentration in a hydrocyanic acid solution when each of the following changes is made:
 a. Addition of a solution of 1 f hydrochloric acid
 b. Addition of a solution of 1 f sodium cyanide
 c. Addition of a solution of 1 f sodium hydroxide
 d. Addition of a solution of 1 f sodium chloride

Explain your answer to part (b) in terms of the kinetic theory.

Problem 18.12. The equilibrium constant for the reaction $HCN = H^+ + CN^-$, is 4×10^{-10}. What is the concentration of H^+ ion in a 0.01 f solution of this acid? What is the OH^- ion concentration in the solution?

Problem 18.13. The solubility of anhydrous sodium sulfate in water decreases as the temperature is raised. (a) Does the process of solution of this salt in water absorb energy or release energy? How do you know? (b) Is the process exothermic or endothermic? (c) If it were necessary to dissolve a small amount of this salt rapidly should hot or cold water be used? Why?

Problem 18.14. Give the amounts and concentrations of each of the species present at equilibrium when 0.02 moles of hydrogen chloride and 0.10 mole of ammonia are mixed in a liter of water. The so-called "ionization constant" for "ammonium hydroxide" is 1.8×10^{-5}.

Problem 18.15. How do you account for the fact that copper hydroxide dissolves in ammonia water? Write an equation and set up an expression for K for the reaction.

Problem 18.16. Some silver chloride is treated with ammonia water to give a solution containing $Ag(NH_3)_2^+$ ion and Cl^- ion. Write an equation and set up an expression for K for the reaction. How do you account for the fact that addition of zinc sulfate to this solution causes precipitation of solid silver chloride?

19 THE SULFUR FAMILY

THE ALCHEMISTS and early chemists observed that metals heated in air produce a friable ash or calx. The calxes usually were the oxides of the metals. Since the other elements of the sulfur family share with oxygen the forming of ashlike compounds from the metals, the members of the family are called the chalcogens (calx-formers). The chalcogens, Group 6a in the periodic table, have atomic numbers smaller by two units than those of the corresponding inert gases. Hence each of the chalcogens has six valence electrons and can achieve the electronic structure of an inert gas by acquiring two extra electrons to form an ion with charge $2-$. All the chalcogens are strongly electronegative, oxygen being the most electronegative and polonium the least. This regular decrease in electronegativity (increase in electropositivity) with increase in atomic size is characteristic of many groups in the periodic system (see Figure 15.2).

THE ELEMENTS

The stable molecules of the elements of the sulfur family, oxygen, sulfur, selenium, tellurium, and polonium, contain strong covalent bonds. But these tend to become more metallic in the element (and more ionic in the compounds) as the atomic number of the chalcogen increases.

We have already seen that oxygen is gaseous, consisting of diatomic molecules. It is paramagnetic, showing the presence of unpaired electrons. It condenses to liquid or solid only at very low temperatures (see Table 19.1). Ozone is also gaseous, consisting of triatomic molecules, probably with the structure

$$\overset{..}{\underset{..}{O}} = \overset{..}{O} \diagdown \\ \qquad\quad :\overset{..}{\underset{..}{O}}:$$

Each of the dashes, —, represents a bonding pair of electrons.

The boiling point of ozone is higher than that of oxygen, showing larger van der Waals forces than for oxygen, but its melting point is lower than that of oxygen—the lack of symmetry of the molecule makes it harder for ozone to crystallize from the liquid.

The other chalcogens are solids at room temperature. Sulfur has two crystalline forms, both yellow: the rhombic form stable below 95.4°C. and the monoclinic form stable above that temperature. Selenium crystallizes in a red, transparent form, the form most commonly produced, or as a gray, opaque, dense form, semimetallic in appearance. Since both sulfur and red selenium are somewhat soluble in organic solvents their molar weights may be determined by well-known methods, such as by their effect on the freezing points of the solvent. The observed molar weights correspond to the molecular formulas

Table 19.1
Melting and Boiling Points of the Chalcogens

ELEMENT	FORMULA	TRANSITION POINT IN °C.	MELTING POINT IN °C.	BOILING POINT IN °C.
Oxygen	O_2		−218.77	−182.97
	O_3		−249.5	−110.51
Sulfur				
rhombic	S_8		113	
		95.4		
monoclinic	S_8		119	444.60 (S_2 in vapor at high temperatures)
Selenium				
red	Se_8			
		150		
gray	(chains)		217.4	684.8 (Se_6 and Se_2 in vapor)
Tellurium	(chains)		450	1087.2 (Te_2 in vapor)

S_8 and Se_8. These same formulas are found for the gases at low temperatures but above 900°C. S_2 and Se_2 molecules predominate. Since tellurium is not soluble in solvents that do not react with it, its molar weight and its formula can not be determined from the solution laws. Above its boiling point, 1087.2°C., the vapor density corresponds to the molecular formula Te_2. Compare O_2, S_2, and Se_2. Gray selenium and tellurium are composed of atoms joined in infinite spiral chains packed parallel to one another in the crystals, hence the isomorphic relation between them.

Although tellurium is metallic in appearance it does not have the high electrical conductivity characteristic of the metals. It, like gray selenium, has a very small conductivity which increases somewhat when light shines on it. The effect of light shining on gray selenium is to increase the conductivity a thousand-fold; this effect is used in apparatus to throw electrical switches when the intensity of the incident light varies. Both sulfur and selenium may be prepared as "amorphous" (non-crystalline) solids, and, at higher temperatures, as plastic, rubbery forms.

Problem 19.1. Sulfur boils at 444.6°C. at standard pressure. Outline an experimental method for determining the molar weight and the formula of sulfur vapor.

Problem 19.2. Outline an experimental method for finding the molar weight of sulfur in solution.

THE FORMS OF SULFUR

When sulfur is heated slowly it undergoes a striking series of changes, which, when understood, throw light on the behavior of the other members of the family. Rhombic sulfur, the stable form found in nature, changes on heating to the monoclinic crystalline form with characteristic needlelike crystals at a transition temperature of 95.4°C. However, the transition of rhombic to monoclinic sulfur is slow enough to enable us to carry the rhombic form by rapid heating to a melting point at 113°C. Monoclinic sulfur melts at 119°C. Since the transition of monoclinic sulfur to the rhombic form is slower than the reverse transition, the monoclinic crystals may be cooled to room temperature. There, however, they change, over a period of days, to the stable, rhombic form. Thus, when transitions are slow enough, forms essentially unstable may persist for long periods of time. Such forms, existing at temperatures or pressures outside their range of stability, are called *metastable* forms. Diamond is a metastable form of carbon.

Sulfur at temperatures just above the melting points is a straw-colored, fluid liquid, with a viscosity not greatly different from those of the common liquids. However, when its temperature is raised slowly it darkens gradually to a red-brown color. At the same time its viscosity increases enormously, beginning at about 160°C., until, in the range 200 to 250°C., it becomes a plastic substance that barely flows. Thereafter, as it is heated to the boiling temperature the viscosity decreases gradually so that the mass becomes fluid again. At the boiling point, 444.6°C., the liquid changes to a gas whose molecular formula is S_8. The molecules of this gas appear to be stable to about 800°C. Above this temperature the diatomic molecules, S_2, are more stable. There is, of course, a temperature range in which S_8 and S_2 molecules are in equilibrium with one another in appreciable concentrations. Above 2000°C. appreciable amounts of monatomic molecules, S, are found. The same phenomena are found for selenium vapor, though the temperatures at which the simpler molecules appear are somewhat lower, as is to be expected from the larger atomic size of selenium. On cooling slowly, all the transformations of sulfur are reversed—monatomic, to diatomic, to octatomic vapor, dark liquid of moderate viscosity to liquid of very high viscosity, to fluid, straw-colored liquid, then monoclinic to rhombic sulfur crystals—showing that the changes are reversible and subject to the equilibrium principle. On the other hand, if the highly viscous liquid is quenched by pouring into cold water it becomes a rubbery, plastic substance which stretches and contracts like natural rubber. On repeated manipulation the plastic becomes granular and brittle as crystals.

appear in it. Similar quenching of hot sulfur vapor yields a purple solid, formula probably S_2, stable indefinitely at 100°K. but transforming in a few seconds to yellow sulfur at room temperature.

X-ray diffraction experiments show that the S_8 molecule consists of eight sulfur atoms joined in a puckered ring so that each sulfur atom is bonded to two other sulfur atoms, the bond angle being 105°, slightly less than the tetrahedral angle. These molecules exist in both rhombic and monoclinic crystals but arranged somewhat differently. Liquid sulfur, at the melting point, still contains these S_8 rings primarily, but when it is heated some of the rings break and form chains of eight atoms each. The atoms at the ends of the chains then have unpaired electrons, so that the ends of different chains can combine to form longer chains. The chain or fiber molecules characterize the plastic or rubbery sulfur called the μ form. They are so entangled in the plastic mass obtained by quenching that when the material is stretched the chains uncoil and elongate without movement of molecules past one another. When the tension is released the plastic returns to its relaxed shape.

The development of the dark color in the liquid, showing strong absorption of light, is concurrent with the forming of chains. The electrons formerly engaged in completing the ring structure are now free to move along the chain and can absorb the incident light. As the liquid is heated progressively, the increased kinetic energy tends to break the chains into shorter segments, explaining the decrease in viscosity and the deepening of the color near the boiling temperature. Since the ring molecules are the ones that escape as gas molecules, and since the ring and chain forms are in equilibrium with one another, the liquid boils away as S_8 molecules. When the plastic liquid is chilled, the sulfur μ molecules (chains) do not have time to rearrange into the rings and hence they persist at room temperature giving the plastic sulfur its rubbery properties. Fluid sulfur containing S_8 rings is known as sulfur λ.

SULFUR MINING

Rhombic sulfur, found in volcanic regions, has been known since ancient times. Called brimstone (burning stone) because it burns freely, it was regarded as the fuel of the infernal regions, including hell. For many years Sicily was the chief source of pure sulfur. However, drillings showed that large sulfur deposits existed under "salt domes" in the Gulf states, notably Louisiana and Texas. Conventional mining methods, such as the sinking of shafts to the beds, could not be used to procure the sulfur because poisonous vapors (hydrogen sulfide) and quicksands interfered. Herman Frasch, a petroleum engineer and chemist, devised a method of securing the sulfur from wells, an ingenious method that was made to work only after great difficulty. The method was to drill wells to the sulfur beds, pass water heated under pressure into the beds to melt the sulfur, and then to pump the melted sulfur to the surface. The first attempts to bring melted sulfur to the surface failed because sulfur is twice as dense as water. However, when air was blown into the sulfur its effective

294   GENERAL CHEMISTRY

density was decreased so that it could be brought to the surface as a foamy liquid. In practice, concentric pipes are sunk to the sulfur beds, hot water being sent down one pipe and air down another, forcing the liquid sulfur to the surface through a third pipe. The liquid sulfur flows into large bins where it separates from the air and water and crystallizes as masses of rhombic sulfur of high purity (more than 99.5 per cent). The mass is then broken into fragments by explosives for shipment by car or barge to the users.

Problem 19.3. In the Frasch process why is the water for melting heated under pressure? How hot should the water be? From your knowledge of the properties of common substances explain why the sulfur obtained is so pure. Through which of the three concentric pipes would you introduce the hot water? The air? Why? Diagram the arrangement of the pipes at the bottom of the well.

THE OXIDATION STATES OF THE CHALCOGENS

From their position in the periodic table, their relative electronegativities (shown in Figure 15.2) and the values of their covalent radii and ionic radii (shown in Table 14.1) we are able to derive many of the chemical properties of the chalcogens. We expect them to form covalent bonds with atoms of their own kind or with atoms of elements not too dissimilar in electronegativity. We expect them to form ionic bonds with the more electropositive of the metallic elements. We expect all the chalcogens except oxygen to have negative or positive oxidation numbers in compounds, depending on whether they combine with elements more electropositive or negative than themselves. Oxygen, being, after fluorine, the most electronegative of the elements, always has a negative oxidation number in its compounds (except those with fluorine), the usual number being $2-$. Only in peroxy-compounds is the oxidation other than $2-$, being $1-$ in peroxides and $\frac{1}{2}-$ in superoxides. In hydrogen peroxide, for example, the two oxygen atoms are joined by a covalent, nonpolar bond; each oxygen is also bonded to a hydrogen atom. The structure may be represented as H—O—O—H, though the molecule is not linear because the bond angles are much nearer the tetrahedral angle than the straight angle (180°). In metallic peroxides, such as sodium or barium peroxides, the oxygen pair exists as a diatomic ion, $(O_2)^{--}$ with charge $2-$. Therefore, in sodium and barium peroxide, formulas Na_2O_2 and BaO_2, the charges on sodium and barium are the normal $1+$ and $2+$ charges while each atom in the peroxide ion has an oxidation number of $1-$. In potassium superoxide, formula KO_2, the oxidation number of oxygen is $\frac{1}{2}-$.

Sulfur, selenium, and tellurium may, like oxygen, exist as doubly charged negative ions or be covalently bonded to more positive elements; then the oxidation number of the chalcogen is $2-$. However, some compounds exist in which sulfur is bonded to sulfur, for example, and then the oxidation number of the chalcogen becomes less negative than $2-$. (Compare oxygen.) Sulfur, selenium, and tellurium, unlike oxygen, may also have positive oxidation numbers, common values being 2+, 4+, and 6+. A glance at Figure 15.2 shows that sulfur is equal to carbon in electronegativity, only bromine, chlorine, nitrogen, oxygen, and fluorine being more negative. Consequently, sulfur has a positive oxidation number in compounds with the latter elements. Selenium is equal to iodine in electronegativity and follows sulfur and carbon directly. Tellurium is equal in electronegativity to hydrogen and phosphorus, and this group follows selenium. Thus, it is chiefly in compounds with oxygen and with the halogens that the chalcogens have their positive oxidation numbers. Table 19.2 summarizes some of the properties of the chalcogen atoms.

Table 19.2
Properties of Chalcogen Atoms

ELEMENT	ELECTRON STRUCTURE	COVALENT * RADIUS IN Å.	IONIC * RADIUS FOR X^{--} IONS IN Å.	RELATIVE † ELECTRO-NEGATIVITY
Oxygen	2, 6	0.66	1.40	3.5
Sulfur	2, 8, 6	1.04	1.84	2.5
Selenium	2, 8, 18, 6	1.17	1.98	2.4
Tellurium	2, 8, 18, 18, 6	1.37	2.21	2.1
Polonium	2, 8, 18, 32, 18, 6	—	—	—

* From Table 14.1.
† Compare Figure 15.2.

METALLIC SULFIDES

Metallic sulfides are interesting for several reasons: (1) a number of the commercially important metals are obtained from their naturally occurring sulfide ores, (2) most sulfides are extremely insoluble in water, and (3) many of them show marked metallic properties, such as luster and electrical conductivity.

In the various ores used as important sources of the corresponding metals are the following compounds (and formulas): copper sulfides, Cu_2S and CuS; lead sulfide, PbS; mercuric sulfide, HgS; nickel sulfide, NiS; silver sulfide, Ag_2S, and zinc sulfide, ZnS. Lead, nickel, and zinc sulfides are among those showing high luster and electrical conductivity of the metallic type. Iron pyrites, formula FeS_2, popularly called "fool's gold," has the color of gold and also some electrical conductivity. In the sulfides first listed, the metallic elements have their usual oxidation numbers and sulfur the oxidation number of 2−, but in pyrites the structure is somewhat different—the sulfur atoms are joined in pairs, as in $Fe^{++}(S_2)^{--}$. (Compare $Ba^{++}[O_2]^{--}$.) However, not all sulfides have compositions that can be expressed in simple formulas, for in some the proportions of sulfur and metal atoms may vary, somewhat as in alloys of the metals.

We have already mentioned the extreme insolubility of most metallic sulfides in water. Even though they may be prepared by mixing solutions containing the metallic ions and sulfide ions, most metallic sulfides are not ionic in character. The bonding is essentially covalent so that the sulfides in water furnish only minute concentrations of metallic ions and sulfide ions simultaneously. As we shall see, the concentration of sulfide ions can be controlled, so that the differences in solubility of the sulfides, though small, can be used to separate the sulfides into different groups in qualitative analysis. The sulfides of the alkali metal elements and of ammonium are saltlike in appearance and behavior. The crystals are ionic and are as soluble as the usual salts of the Group 1a elements. Sodium sulfide, formula Na_2S, and potassium sulfide, formula K_2S, are commonly used as sources of sulfide ion. The sulfides of the Group 2a and Group 3a elements are also ionic in character and soluble in water. However, sulfide ions react with water as shown by the equation

$$S^{--} + HOH = HS^- + OH^- \tag{19.1}$$

so that the solution is strongly basic and contains many OH^- ions. As a result the hydroxides of the Group 2a and Group 3a elements precipitate before the solubilities of the corresponding sulfides are equaled.

Sulfur combines directly with nearly all the elements. The only metallic elements with which sulfur does not combine directly to form sulfides are tellurium, gold, platinum, and iridium. The only other elements with which sulfur does not combine directly are the inert gases, iodine, and nitrogen but binary compounds of sulfur and nitrogen have been prepared by other means. Many metals combine with sulfur at room temperature. The black tarnish on silver is silver sulfide. It forms when sulfur or sulfur-containing compounds in the air or in foods come into contact with silver.

HYDROGEN SULFIDE, HYDROGEN SELENIDE, AND HYDROGEN TELLURIDE

Hydrogen and sulfur combine directly to form hydrogen sulfide.

$$H_{2(g)} + \tfrac{1}{8}S_{8(s)} \underset{\text{yellow}}{=} H_2S_{(g)} \tag{19.2}$$

The reaction is an equilibrium one. All the substances are present. A convenient method for preparing hydrogen sulfide is to treat a metallic sulfide such as ferrous sulfide, formula FeS, with a strong acid so that, after the solution is saturated, the hydrogen sulfide formed escapes as a gas. Hydrogen selenide and hydrogen telluride may be prepared in a similar way, aluminum selenide and aluminum telluride being commonly used.

$$\begin{aligned} FeS_{(s)} + 2H^+ &= Fe^{++} + H_2S_{(g)} \\ \text{black}& \\ Al_2Se_{3(s)} + 6H^+ &= 2Al^{+++} + 3H_2Se_{(g)} \\ Al_2Te_{3(s)} + 6H^+ &= 2Al^{+++} + 3H_2Te_{(g)} \end{aligned} \tag{19.3}$$

Hydrogen sulfide, unlike water, forms a nonpolar liquid. It is less stable with respect to the elements than is water, and the instability increases through hydrogen selenide to hydrogen telluride. Hydrogen sulfide is poisonous and has a vile odor. Hydrogen selenide is more poisonous and has a worse odor. Hydrogen telluride is most offensive of all in odor and is as poisonous as hydrogen selenide. Table 19.3 lists some of the properties of the hydrogen compounds.

Table 19.3
Properties of the Hydrogen Chalcogenides

FORMULA OF COMPOUND	MELTING POINT °C.	BOILING POINT °C.	$K_1 = \dfrac{[\text{H}^+][\text{HX}^-]}{[\text{H}_2\text{X}]}$	$K_2 = \dfrac{[\text{H}^+][\text{X}^{--}]}{[\text{HX}^-]}$
H_2O	0	100	1.8×10^{-16}	10^{-36}
H_2S	−85.53	−60.31	1.15×10^{-7}	10^{-15}
H_2Se	−65.7	−41.3	1.88×10^{-4}	10^{-10}
H_2Te	−51.	2.3	2.3×10^{-3}	10^{-5}

(header spans: EQUILIBRIUM CONSTANTS)

All the hydrogen chalcogenides are soluble in water and are weak acids. The acid strength increases from water to hydrogen telluride. A saturated water solution of hydrogen sulfide in equilibrium with hydrogen sulfide gas at one atmosphere pressure contains about 0.1 mole of hydrogen sulfide per liter. The strength of the several acids can be best stated in terms of the equilibrium constants for the ionizations. For the ionization of pure water we have, from equation 18.18

$$H_2O = H^+ + OH^-; \quad K_1 = \frac{[H^+] \times [OH^-]}{[H_2O]} \tag{19.4}$$

For pure water $[H^+] = [OH^-] = 10^{-7}$ moles per liter and $[H_2O] = 55.5$ moles per liter so that

$$K_1 = \frac{10^{-7} \times 10^{-7}}{55.5} = 1.8 \times 10^{-16} \tag{19.5}$$

The ionization of hydroxide ions to form hydrogen ions and oxide ions is much smaller. The ionization equation and the equilibrium constant equation are

$$OH^- = H^+ + O^{--}; \quad K_2 = \frac{[H^+] \times [O^{--}]}{[OH^-]} = \text{about } 10^{-36} \tag{19.6}$$

Since the values for the concentrations of hydrogen ion and hydroxide ion are approximately 10^{-7} moles per liter in pure water it appears that the concentration of the oxide ion, O^{--}, is about 10^{-36} moles per liter.

Problem 19.4. Write the equations for the reactions that occur when the following are treated with a solution of hydrochloric acid: aluminum sulfide, sodium sulfide, ferrous sulfide, sodium telluride.

Problem 19.5. From your knowledge of the Avogadro number calculate the number of oxide ions per liter of pure water. Repeat for sulfide ion.

The ionization constants for the other hydrogen chalcogenides are shown in Table 19.3. For all of them the primary ionization of the type, $H_2X = H^+ + HX^-$, for which the K_1 values are listed, predominates greatly over the ionization of the second hydrogen according to the reaction $HX^- = H^+ + X^{--}$, for which the K_2 values are given. This means that in a water solution of hydrogen sulfide, there is some ionization to produce H^+ and HS^- ions but that the HS^- ions ionize only slightly to yield S^{--} ions (and a very few additional hydrogen ions). So great is the attraction of sulfide ions for protons that, when a sulfide such as potassium or sodium sulfide is placed in water, most of the sulfide ions accept protons from water to form HS^- ions and OH^- ions, as shown in equation 19.1.

POLYSULFIDES

The tendency of sulfur to form sulfur-to-sulfur bonds is greater than that of oxygen to form oxygen-to-oxygen bonds, though the peroxide ion, $(O_2)^{--}$, is reasonably stable. When a solution of a sulfide salt, such as sodium or potassium sulfide, is heated with some elementary sulfur, one, two, three, or more sulfur atoms may attach themselves to a sulfide ion to form polysulfide ions having the charge 2−. The number of sulfur atoms added per sulfide ion depends on the relative amounts of sulfide and sulfur used. In terms of electronic structures the reactions are

$$: \!\overset{..}{\underset{..}{S}}\! :^{--} \; + \; : \!\overset{..}{\underset{..}{S}}\! : \;=\; : \!\overset{..}{\underset{..}{S}}\!-\!\overset{..}{\underset{..}{S}}\! :^{--} \tag{19.7}$$

sulfide ion   sulfur atom   disulfide ion

The reaction may continue to form trisulfide, tetrasulfide, and pentasulfide ions. Apparently all the polysulfide ions are chain ions. Remember the chains in elementary sulfur.

Polysulfides are not limited to the ions. Hydrogen disulfide, formula H_2S_2, and hydrogen trisulfide, formula H_2S_3, have been prepared. Sulfur-to-sulfur bonds are also present in some important organic compounds.

THE OXIDES

The other chalcogens react with oxygen to form oxides in which the oxygen has the oxidation number of 2− and the other elements have the appropriate positive oxidation numbers. Sulfur forms a series of different oxides but the most common and by far the most important are sulfur dioxide and sulfur trioxide. Sulfur dioxide is the oxide formed when sulfur or sulfur compounds are burned in air in the absence of a catalyst. Since most coals contain some organically combined sulfur, coal burners discharge sulfur dioxide as well as carbon dioxide into the air. In the winning of metals from their sulfide ores the ores are often "roasted" (heated in air). In the process the metallic sulfides are converted to the oxides and the sulfur converted to sulfur dioxide. A typical reaction is shown by the equation

$$\text{PbS}_{(s)} + \tfrac{3}{2}\text{O}_{2(g)} = \text{PbO}_{(s)} + \text{SO}_{2(g)} \qquad (19.8)$$
$$\text{black} \qquad\qquad\qquad \text{yellow}$$

Usually the sulfur dioxide is diluted by the air but on several occasions the air in industrial valleys under unusual atmospheric conditions has remained stagnant for several days until the sulfur dioxide reached toxic concentrations. In the air the sulfur dioxide is oxidized in a very slow reaction to sulfur trioxide.

$$\text{SO}_{2(g)} + \tfrac{1}{2}\text{O}_{2(g)} = \text{SO}_3 \qquad (19.9)$$

The sulfur trioxide, boiling point, 44.5°C., reacts with water vapor in the air to form sulfuric acid. When the acid is not neutralized by alkaline dust in the air, it descends as a mist to the earth. All vegetation in surrounding areas may be killed when ore smelters discharge large amounts of sulfur dioxide into the air.

The principal industrial use of sulfur dioxide is to make sulfuric acid. The dioxide is made most commonly by burning sulfur in air, but large quantities also come from roasting metallic sulfides, particularly iron pyrites. More and more is being made by reducing calcium sulfate.

Sulfur dioxide is a gas with a characteristic choking odor. Its electronic structure is

$$:\!\ddot{\text{O}}\!-\!\ddot{\text{S}}\!\cdot \qquad \text{or} \qquad \ddot{\text{O}}\!=\!\ddot{\text{S}}\!\cdot$$
$$\qquad \diagdown\!\ddot{\text{O}}\!: \qquad\qquad\qquad \diagdown\!\ddot{\text{O}}\!:$$

(Compare with ozone, page 290.) Since both oxygen atoms appear to be identical in behavior, the double bond is believed to be present equally in the two bond positions, a phenomenon known as *resonance*. We may generalize the concept of resonance to include all those instances in which we can write several equivalent or nearly equivalent electron structures for substances. The actual structure will be intermediate among the various resonant structures and more stable than any one of them. This means that our pictures of electron structure are oversimplified—the actual structures can be described only approximately by our present methods.

Selenium dioxide and tellurium dioxide are formed by burning the respective elements. The oxides are crystalline solids rather than gases. Table 19.4 lists some of their properties.

Sulfur trioxide forms very slowly in the reaction shown in equation 19.8

Table 19.4
Properties of Chalcogen Oxides

FORMULA OF COMPOUND	MELTING POINT °C.	BOILING POINT °C.
SO_2	−75.46	−10.02
SeO_2	340 (under pressure)	322 (sublimation point)
TeO_2	452	"bright red heat"
SO_3	16.8	43.3

unless a catalyst is present, and then the reaction proceeds at reasonable speed if the temperature is raised to 400 or 500°C. as in the "contact process" for making sulfuric acid (see page 302). Since sulfur trioxide decomposes into sulfur dioxide and oxygen to an appreciable extent at 500°C. the reaction temperature is kept as low as possible without undue sacrifice of speed of reaction.

The oldest method of preparing sulfur trioxide is one used by the alchemists in the fifteenth century—the heating of ferric sulfate.

$$Fe_2(SO_4)_{3(s)} = Fe_2O_{3(s)} + 3SO_{3(g)} \qquad (19.10)$$
$$\text{yellow} \qquad \text{red}$$

Other metallic sulfates may be used. Note that the salt is decomposed into a basic oxide and a volatile acidic oxide.

There is no strong evidence for the existence of selenium trioxide. Tellurium trioxide cannot be prepared by oxidation of the dioxide but is obtained when telluric acid, formula H_6TeO_6, is heated to drive out the water.

SULFUROUS ACID AND SULFITES

Sulfur dioxide is rather soluble in water; about 1.5 moles dissolve in 1000 g. of water at room temperature when the gas pressure is one atmosphere. A substantial fraction of the dissolved sulfur dioxide reacts with the water to form sulfurous acid.

$$SO_{2(g)} + H_2O = H_2SO_3 \qquad (19.11)$$

The electronic structure of sulfurous acid shown in a plane is

$$H-\overset{..}{\underset{..}{O}}-\overset{..}{\underset{|}{S}}-\overset{..}{\underset{..}{O}}-H$$
$$:\overset{..}{O}:$$

The oxygen atoms are arranged at the corners of the base of a triangular pyramid at whose apex is the sulfur atom. Sulfurous acid is a diprotic acid, having two replaceable hydrogen ions. The first ionizes moderately well according to the reaction

$$H_2SO_3 = H^+ + HSO_3^-; \quad K_1 = 1.7 \times 10^{-2} \qquad (19.12)$$

And the second ionizes to a much smaller extent

$$HSO_3^- = H^+ + SO_3^{--}; K_2 = 1 \times 10^{-7} \tag{19.13}$$

Sulfurous acid cannot be isolated but it forms two series of salts, one the hydrogen sulfites (sometimes called the bisulfites) in which the anion is the HSO_3^- ion and the other the sulfites in which the anion is the SO_3^{--} ion. The salts can be prepared conveniently by mixing the appropriate bases (as hydroxides or oxides) with sulfurous acid solutions.

Problem 19.6. In what molar ratios would you mix sodium hydroxide and sulfurous acid if you wished to prepare sodium sulfite? Sodium hydrogen sulfite?

Selenious acid, formula H_2SeO_3, is a crystalline solid, very soluble in water. It forms when selenium dioxide is treated with water. It is a much weaker acid than sulfurous acid. Tellurous acid, formula H_2TeO_3, has not been isolated as the pure compound but its salts, the tellurites, are known (see Table 20.5, page 327 for values of K_1).

SULFURIC ACID

Sulfur trioxide reacts vigorously with water, including water vapor, to form sulfuric acid. When the gas (the liquid boils at 43°C.) meets air it "fumes," that is, it forms a mist of tiny sulfuric acid droplets. Sulfuric acid is an oily liquid which reacts further with water (liquid or vapor) to form hydrates with formulas such as $H_2SO_4 \cdot H_2O$ and $H_2SO_4 \cdot 2H_2O$ which may be isolated as crystalline solids. Much heat is evolved in the reactions so that sulfuric acid must be added to water with caution to avoid spattering. The equation for the reaction between sulfur trioxide and water

$$SO_3 + H_2O = H_2SO_4 \tag{19.14}$$

may be expressed in terms of the electronic structures as

$$\overset{..}{\underset{..}{\text{O}}}\!=\!\overset{|}{\underset{|}{\text{S}}}\!+\!:\!\overset{..}{\underset{..}{\text{O}}}\!-\!\text{H} \quad = \quad \text{H}\!-\!\overset{..}{\underset{..}{\text{O}}}\!-\!\overset{\overset{..}{\underset{..}{\text{O}}}}{\underset{\underset{..}{\underset{..}{\text{O}}}}{\text{S}}}\!-\!\overset{..}{\underset{..}{\text{O}}}\!-\!\text{H} \tag{19.15}$$

The oxygen atoms in the acid occupy tetrahedral positions around the sulfur atom.

Sulfuric acid is a diprotic acid, ionizing in two steps

$$H_2SO_4 = H^+ + HSO_4^- \tag{19.16}$$

$$HSO_4^- = H^+ + SO_4^{--}; K_2 = 10^{-2} \tag{19.17}$$

In dilute water solutions the ionization in the first step is almost complete and that in the second step is substantial so that both HSO_4^- and SO_4^{--} ions are present in the solutions. There are two series of salts, the hydrogen sulfates (sometimes called the bisulfates) containing the HSO_4^- ion, and the normal sulfates containing the SO_4^{--} ion. The hydrogen sulfate salts are often used as solid acids. The calcium, strontium, and barium sulfates are important ores of these alkaline earth elements; the latter two sulfates are rather insoluble.

Sulfuric acid is widely used for three distinct properties:
  a. It is the cheapest strong acid.
  b. The concentrated acid is a dehydrating agent.
  c. The concentrated acid is an oxidizing agent.

Concentrated sulfuric acid reacts with many organic compounds containing hydrogen and oxygen. It removes these elements in the ratio 2H and O to form the hydrated acid and leave a carbonaceous residue. With sugar

$$C_{12}H_{22}O_{11(s)} + 11H_2SO_4 = 12C_{(s)} + 11H_2SO_4 \cdot H_2O \quad\quad (19.18)$$
$$\text{black}$$

In many organic reactions in which the water produced would interfere with the desired reaction, concentrated sulfuric acid is added to remove the water.

Selenic acid and telluric acid cannot be prepared from the corresponding oxides for these are not stable. They are obtained when selenous acid and tellurous acids are oxidized. Selenic acid has the formula H_2SeO_4 but telluric acid the formula H_6TeO_6, which may also be written $(HO)_6Te$. This compound is an example of one in which an atom is attached to more than four other atoms, the tellurium atom being bonded to six oxygen atoms. The tellurium atom shares its six valence electrons with the six different oxygen atoms. The tellurium atom is large enough to permit this many bonds without interference and has d orbitals available for the bonding electrons. Try writing an electronic structure for this acid.

COMMERCIAL PREPARATION OF SULFURIC ACID

In the United States alone about 10,000,000 tons of sulfuric acid are produced per year. Two commercial methods are used. The newer process, the *contact process*, depends on the use of finely divided platinum, or vanadium salts, as catalysts to promote the oxidation of sulfur dioxide according to equation 19.9. A mixture of sulfur dioxide and air is passed over the solid catalysts at 400° to 500°C. Since the reaction is exothermic the heat produced must be removed in order to keep the reaction mixture at the desired temperature. Some of the heat of reaction is used to preheat the gases to the reaction temperature. Since the reaction is reversible the temperature must be kept as low as possible if the maximum conversion of the dioxide to the trioxide is to be achieved. The gaseous sulfur trioxide, mixed with the unused air (mostly nitrogen) is bubbled through 98 per cent sulfuric acid, water being added to maintain this concentration. If the trioxide is bubbled through water, the water vapor evaporating into the gas bubbles reacts with the sulfur trioxide to form a mist which is absorbed only very slowly. "Fuming sulfuric acid" containing an excess (up to 65 per cent) of sulfur trioxide dissolved in sulfuric acid is also prepared by the contact process. As may be expected it is a very powerful dehydrating agent.

Of historical interest as well as of practical importance is the *lead chamber process*. In the last part of the eighteenth century, oxides of nitrogen were found to catalyze oxidation of sulfur dioxide by air. The actual mechanism of the reaction is still obscure but the reaction may be summarized in the equations

$$SO_{2(g)} + NO_{2(g)} = SO_{3(g)} + NO_{(g)} \quad (19.19)$$
(brown)

$$NO_{(g)} + \tfrac{1}{2}O_{2(g)} = NO_{2(g)} \quad (19.20)$$
(brown)

Steam is added to react with the sulfur trioxide to form the sulfuric acid. Since the reactions involve gases, from three to five large chambers are required. These are lead lined for lead becomes covered with lead sulfate, which is insoluble in the "chamber acid" (60–70 per cent sulfuric acid) produced. More concentrated sulfuric acid dissolves the lead sulfate, forming HSO_4^- ions in solution. If the exhaust gases—spent air (mostly nitrogen), some unreacted sulfur dioxide, and the oxides of nitrogen—were then discharged into the air the relatively expensive catalyst would be lost. An exhaust tower, called the Gay-Lussac tower, was introduced in 1827 to capture the catalyst. Concentrated sulfuric acid, brought in at the top of the exhaust tower, trickles down over broken tile and comes into contact with the exhaust gases rising in the tower. The oxides of nitrogen react with this acid to form water and "nitrosyl" sulfuric acid according to the equation

$$NO_{(g)} + NO_{2(g)} + 2H_2SO_4 = H_2O + 2(NO)HSO_4 \quad (19.21)$$
(brown)

The "nitrosyl" sulfuric acid is then brought to the top of another tower, called the Glover tower, where it is mixed with dilute sulfuric acid. The reaction shown in equation (19.21) is reversed when the water (present in the dilute acid) is added. This results in the release of the oxides of nitrogen. In the Glover tower these meet the incoming sulfur dioxide and air from the sulfur burners to produce some sulfuric acid. The gases are then swept from the Glover tower into the lead chambers.

The hot gases from the sulfur burners evaporate some of the water so that relatively concentrated acid is collected at the bottom of the Glover tower. The principal product of the lead chamber process is the chamber acid which is of proper concentration for the fertilizer industry. Pure sulfuric acid is usually made by the contact process, the sulfur dioxide being made by burning sulfur from Frasch wells. When sulfur dioxide from the burning of pyrites is used, impurities such as selenium dioxide "poison" the platinum catalyst by combining permanently with it so that it becomes unavailable. However, vanadate

304   GENERAL CHEMISTRY

catalysts have the advantage of being less readily poisoned. Sulfur dioxide from the burning of metallic sulfides may be used in the lead chamber process since impurities do not interfere with the nitrogen oxide catalysts and do no harm in the impure chamber acid.

Problem 19.7. On the basis of the kinetic theory, explain why sulfur trioxide is not absorbed as rapidly when the gas bubbles pass through water as when they pass through 98 per cent sulfuric acid.

Problem 19.8. Summarize the various reactions occurring in the lead chamber process.

Problem 19.9. Outline the apparatus used in the lead chamber process. Indicate what reactions occur in each part. Why not eliminate the Gay-Lussac tower and introduce the exhaust gases into the Glover tower? Does the acid used to make the nitrosyl sulfuric acid decrease the amount of daily product that can be sold?

PERSULFATES (PEROXY SULFATES)

When solutions containing bisulfate ions, HSO_4^-—for example, from potassium or ammonium bisulfates, formulas $KHSO_4$ and NH_4HSO_4—are electrolyzed between platinum electrodes a strongly oxidizing solution results. The oxidizing strength can be shown to be due to the ion, $S_2O_8^{--}$. On dilution with water the ion SO_5^{--} forms in the solution. The ions are called persulfate ions and the corresponding acids, formulas, $H_2S_2O_8$ and H_2SO_5, are known as persulfuric acids. Their systematic names are peroxydisulfuric acid and peroxysulfuric acid respectively. The structures of the ions are

$$\begin{array}{cc} \text{O} \quad\quad\quad \text{O} \\ | \quad\quad\quad\quad | \\ \text{O}-\text{S}-\text{O}-\text{O}-\text{S}-\text{O} \\ | \quad\quad\quad\quad | \\ \text{O} \quad\quad\quad \text{O} \end{array}^{--} \quad \text{and} \quad \begin{array}{c} \text{O} \\ | \\ \text{O}-\text{S}-\text{O}-\text{O} \\ | \\ \text{O} \end{array}^{--}$$

Both contain peroxide groups. Hydrogen peroxide, formula H_2O_2, may be distilled from the solution containing the H_2SO_5 species; this is the common commercial method for preparing hydrogen peroxide. Persulfates are unstable in aqueous solution since they give off oxygen on standing, reverting to sulfates.

THIOSULFATES

When the salts of sulfurous acid, the sulfites, are exposed to air they are gradually oxidized to sulfates. In this way a sulfite such as sodium sulfite becomes contaminated with sulfate. The reaction is fairly rapid in water solution. The solutions will be somewhat alkaline because of the hydrolysis reaction

$$SO_3^{--} + HOH = HSO_3^- + OH^- \tag{19.22}$$

in which the sulfite ion captures a proton from water. Sulfites in alkaline solution also react with sulfur to form thiosulfates. The reactions with oxygen and with sulfur may be schematically written as

$$\text{sulfite ion} + :\!\ddot{\underset{\cdot\cdot}{O}}\!: \;=\; \text{sulfate ion} \qquad (19.23)$$

$$\text{sulfite ion} + :\!\ddot{\underset{\cdot\cdot}{S}}\!: \;=\; \text{thiosulfate ion} \qquad (19.24)$$

Note that the sulfur atom which forms the coordinate bond with the sulfite ion occupies the same position as the fourth oxygen atom in the sulfate ion. In general, compounds in which a sulfur atom replaces an oxygen atom are called *thio*-compounds, the prefix, thio-, being placed before the name of the corresponding oxygenated compound. Thiosulfuric acid is not stable; in the presence of hydrogen ions sulfur and sulfurous acid are formed.

$$2H^+ + S_2O_3^{--} = \underset{\text{yellow}}{S_{(s)}} + H_2SO_3 \qquad (19.25)$$

Thiosulfate ions are readily oxidized and hence serve as reducing agents. They also form stable complex ions with Ag^+ ions so that, when added to silver bromide or silver chloride, they "dissolve" them. Solutions of sodium thiosulfate ("hypo") are used to "fix" photographic plates, films, and papers by removing the unreacted silver salts.

$$\underset{\text{yellow}}{AgBr_{(s)}} + 2S_2O_3^{--} = Ag(S_2O_3)_2^{---} + Br^- \qquad (19.26)$$

In solution, thiosulfate is oxidized by iodine to give tetrathionate ions as shown in the equation

$$\underset{\text{brown}}{I_2} + \underset{\substack{\text{thiosulfate}\\\text{ion}}}{2S_2O_3^{--}} = \underset{\substack{\text{tetrathionate}\\\text{ion}}}{S_4O_6^{--}} + 2I^- \qquad (19.27)$$

The tetrathionate ion has a structure comparable to that of the persulfate ion but is not a powerful oxidizing agent.

tetrathionate ion

Sulfur-to-sulfur bonds are more stable than oxygen-to-oxygen bonds.

OTHER THIO-ANIONS

Many other anions in addition to thiosulfate ions are known in which sulfur can be considered to have "replaced" oxygen. This is not surprising in view of the group similarities within the periodic arrangement. The series of ions—AsO_3^{3-}, AsO_2S^{3-}, $AsOS_2^{3-}$, and AsS_3^{3-}—is possible. The first member is the arsenite ion and the last the thioarsenite ion. Similar "substitutions" are known in the arsenates (AsO_4^{3-}, AsS_4^{3-}), stannates (SnO_3^-, SnS_3^{2-}), and antimonates (SbO_4^{3-}, SbS_4^{3-}). Some thiocompounds are known whose corresponding oxy- compound is unstable, the thiomercurate ion, formula HgS_2^{2-}, for instance. The tendency of the four elements, mercury, arsenic, tin, and antimony, to form thio-anions is commonly used in analytical chemistry to dissolve the sulfides of these elements selectively in a mixture of sulfides which may also include the sulfides of lead, copper, bismuth, and cadmium. The latter group of sulfides do not dissolve in a solution containing a high concentration of sulfide ion, since the thio-anions of these four elements are not stable (see page 384).

Problem 19.10. Try to draw an electron structural formula for $Ag(S_2O_3)_2^{---}$.
Problem 19.11. Diagram a possible geometric and electronic structure for the thioarsenite and thioarsenate ions.

OXIDATION-REDUCTION REACTIONS

The most common oxidation states of sulfur are

$$\begin{array}{cccc} 2- & 0 & 4+ & 6+ \\ H_2S & S_8 & SO_2 & SO_3 \\ S^{--} & & H_2SO_3 & H_2SO_4 \end{array}$$

We shall consider some of the oxidation-reduction reactions through which sulfur is brought from one oxidation state to another. The equations for the reactions may be derived by the method of half-reactions (as in Chapter 16) or by the method of oxidation numbers, commonly used for nonionic substances. Both methods rest on the principle that, in a reaction, the sum of all the electron gains must equal the sum of all the electron losses.

Sulfur and water are produced when hydrogen sulfide is burned in a limited amount of air. On comparing the products with the reactions we see that only the sulfur and the oxygen change in oxidation number. Each sulfur atom changes in oxidation number from $2-$ to 0 and each oxygen atom from 0 to $2-$:

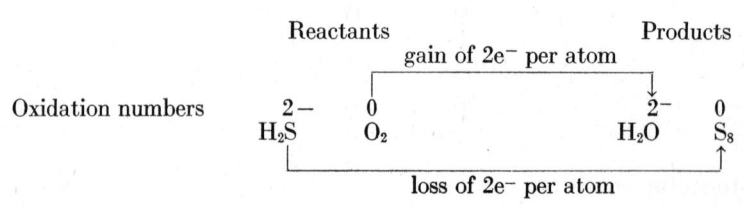

	Reactants		Products	
		gain of $2e^-$ per atom		
Oxidation numbers	$2-$	0	$2-$	0
	H_2S	O_2	H_2O	S_8
		loss of $2e^-$ per atom		

Therefore the reacting ratio of sulfur atoms to oxygen atoms is 1 to 1 and the equation is

$$H_2S_{(g)} + \tfrac{1}{2}O_2 = H_2O + \tfrac{1}{8}S_{8(s)} \quad \text{(yellow)} \tag{19.28}$$

with loss of $2e^-$ by sulfur and gain of $2e^-$ by oxygen.

When an excess of air is used, sulfur dioxide rather than sulfur is produced. Then the sulfur changes in oxidation number from $2-$ to $4+$. This means a loss of six electrons per sulfur atom, each oxygen atom gaining two electrons as before.

Oxidation numbers:
$$\underset{H_2S}{2-} \quad \underset{O_2}{0} \quad \underset{H_2O}{2-} \quad \underset{SO_2}{4+\;2-}$$

loss of $6e^-$ per atom; gain of $2e^-$ per atom

Three oxygen atoms, each gaining two electrons, are required per sulfur atom. The equation is, therefore

$$\underset{H_2S_{(g)}}{2-} + \underset{\tfrac{3}{2}O_{2(g)}}{0} = \underset{H_2O}{2-} + \underset{SO_{2(g)}}{4+\;2-} \tag{19.29}$$

loss of $6e^-$; $3(\text{gain of } 2e^-)$

Gaseous hydrogen sulfide and sulfur dioxide react to form water vapor and sulfur. Here the sulfide sulfur changes from $2-$ to 0 and the sulfur dioxide sulfur changes from $4+$ to 0. The oxygen and hydrogen do not change in oxidation number. Hence two molecules of hydrogen sulfide are required for each molecule of sulfur dioxide if the electron gains and losses are to be equal.

Oxidation numbers:
$$\underset{2H_2S_{(g)}}{2-} + \underset{SO_{2(g)}}{4+} = 2H_2O + \underset{\text{yellow}}{\tfrac{3}{8}S_{8(s)}} \quad 0 \tag{19.30}$$

$2(\text{loss of } 2e^-)$; gain of $4e^-$

For reactions in aqueous solution, either the method of oxidation numbers or the method of half-reactions may be used to derive oxidation-reduction equations. Sulfuric acid, when moderately concentrated, oxidizes hydrogen sulfide to sulfur, the sulfuric acid being reduced to sulfur dioxide. The equations for the half-reactions are

$$H_2S_{(g)} = \tfrac{1}{8}S_{8(s)} + 2H^+ + 2e^- \quad \text{(yellow)} \tag{19.31}$$

$$H_2SO_4 + 2H^+ + 2e^- = 2H_2O + SO_{2(g)} \tag{19.32}$$

Note that it is not necessary to use oxidation numbers to balance half-reactions. Note also that in half-reaction 19.31 hydrogen ions are produced and in half-reaction 19.32 hydrogen ions are consumed. Since, in this example, the electron gains and losses for the equations as written are equal, we may add the half-equations to obtain the equation for the reaction. Note that the hydrogen ions drop out upon addition of 19.31 and 19.32.

$$H_2S_{(g)} + H_2SO_4 = 2H_2O + SO_{2(g)} + \tfrac{1}{8}S_{8(s)} \text{ (yellow)} \tag{19.33}$$

In many reactions in which nitric acid acts as oxidizing agent the equation for the half-reaction is

$$HNO_3 + 3H^+ + 3e^- = 2H_2O + NO_{(g)} \tag{19.34}$$

When nitric acid is added in moderate concentration to a solution of hydrogen sulfide, the sulfide is oxidized to sulfur. If equation 19.31 is tripled and equation 19.34 is doubled, the electron gain and loss becomes equal so that on adding

$$3H_2S_{(g)} = \tfrac{3}{8}S_{8(s)} \text{ (yellow)} + 6H^+ + 6e^-$$

$$2HNO_3 + 6H^+ + 6e^- = 4H_2O + 2NO_{(g)}$$

$$\overline{3H_2S_{(g)} + 2HNO_3 = 4H_2O + 2NO_{(g)} + \tfrac{3}{8}S_{8(s)} \text{ (yellow)}} \tag{19.35}$$

Hot, concentrated sulfuric acid oxidizes a number of substances, including sulfur and metals such as copper, and is reduced to sulfur dioxide in the process. For the oxidation of sulfur to sulfur dioxide the equation for the half-reaction is

$$\tfrac{1}{8}S_{8(s)} \text{ (yellow)} + 2H_2O = SO_{2(g)} + 4H^+ + 4e^- \tag{19.36}$$

Equation 19.36, when added to equation 19.32 (multiplied by two), gives for the over-all reaction between sulfur and concentrated sulfuric acid

$$\tfrac{1}{8}S_{8(s)} \text{ (yellow)} + 2H_2SO_4 = 2H_2O + 3SO_{2(g)} \tag{19.37}$$

Concentrated nitric acid oxidizes hydrogen sulfide or sulfur up to the sulfate as in the half-reaction

$$\tfrac{1}{8}S_{8(s)} \text{ (yellow)} + 4H_2O = SO_4^{--} + 8H^+ + 6e^- \tag{19.38}$$

For the oxidation of copper the equation for the half-reaction is

$$Cu_{(s)} \text{ (red)} = Cu^{++} \text{ (blue)} + 2e^- \tag{19.39}$$

Copper reduces sulfuric acid to sulfur dioxide so that on combining half-equations 19.32 and 19.39 we have

$$Cu_{(s)} \text{ (red)} + H_2SO_4 + 2H^+ = Cu^{++} \text{ (blue)} + 2H_2O + SO_{2(g)} \tag{19.40}$$

In this reaction sulfuric acid functions in two ways—part acts as oxidizer and part as a source of the hydrogen ions consumed in the reaction. Sulfate ions or hydrogen sulfate ions will be present in the final solution to balance the charge of the Cu^{++} ions. In this reaction not more than half the sulfuric molecules can be reduced since four times as many hydrogen ions are used up as the sulfate ions. Though we have written S_8 as the formula of elementary sulfur it is common practice to write it as S.

Problem 19.12. Derive equations 19.33, 19.35, and 19.40, using the method of oxidation numbers.

Problem 19.13. Using the method of oxidation numbers derive the equations for the oxidation-reduction reactions of the following. Repeat using half equations.
  a. Sulfur and hydrogen
  b. Oxidation of thiosulfate to sulfate by nitric acid
  c. Oxidation of iron pyrites to sulfur dioxide and ferric ion by nitric acid
  d. Lanthanum and selenium

Problem 19.14. Calcium sulfate is common in minerals. How would you go about trying to make sulfur or sulfur dioxide from it? Do not try to be highly specific; merely discuss the types of reagents and reactions you would test.

20 THE HALOGENS

JUST AS the elements of Group 6a in the periodic table are known as chalcogens from their property of forming a "calx" when combined with a metal, so the elements of Group 7a are known as halogens since they form a "salt" when combined with a metal. (The Greek word for salt may be transliterated as "hals.")

The halogens are as nearly perfect an example as exists of a family in the periodic table; the properties of the elements and of their compounds change in an orderly way as atomic weight (or atomic number) increases. Some properties of the elements are listed in Table 20.1. Astatine has been prepared in small quantities only but enough is already known about its properties to indicate that they are consistent with those to be expected from an extrapolation of the properties of the other halogens. We shall, therefore, discuss only the properties of the other four halogens.

All halogen atoms have one less than the number of electrons of the nearest inert gas atom. Thus each has seven valence electrons. It is not surprising that the halogens exist as diatomic molecules in the solid, liquid, and gaseous phases even at rather high temperatures, for, by forming diatomic molecules each atom can achieve the inert gas structure of four pairs of electrons in its outer energy level, as in $:\overset{..}{X}:\overset{..}{X}:$, where X is any halogen kernel. Similarly each atom of the diatomic molecule may gain a single electron to form a monatomic ion, charge 1−, by reacting with an electropositive element. The salts, which give these elements the name "halogen," may be formed in this way:

$$M + \tfrac{1}{2}X_2 = M^+ + X^- = M^+X^- \equiv MX \qquad (20.1)$$

M represents any Group 1a element.

Most of the properties of the halogens differ much more for fluorine and chlorine than for chlorine and bromine, the difference for bromine and iodine being intermediate. This generalization is apparent in the properties listed in Table 20.1. A corresponding statement also applies to the chalcogens, the differences between oxygen and sulfur being greater than those between sulfur and selenium. The magnitude and rate in change of the various properties may in many cases be interpreted in terms of the size of covalent radius of the elements. The radii increase from fluorine to iodine but the increase is not regular. The largest increase is between fluorine and chlorine (a change of 0.35 Å.) and the next largest between bromine and iodine (0.19 Å.), whereas that between chlorine and bromine (0.15 Å.) is the smallest. Now it is true that we do not know what causes this irregular rate of increase but we can use

Table 20.1

Some Properties of the Halogen Elements

HALOGEN	AT. NO.	COLOR	PHASE AT 25°C. 1 ATM.	M.P. (°C.)	ELECTRICAL CONDUCTIVITY OF LIQUID (MHOS)	B.P. (°C.)	IONIZATION POTENTIAL (ELECTRON-VOLTS)	COVALENT RADIUS (Å.)	IONIC RADIUS (X^-) (Å.)
Fluorine	9	Light-yellow	Gas	−223	—	−187.9	18.6	.64	1.36
Chlorine	17	Yellow-green	Gas	−101.4	10^{-16}	−34.11	13.0	.99	1.81
Bromine	35	Red-brown	Liquid	−7.3	10^{-9}	58.8	11.8	1.14	1.95
Iodine	53	Violet	Solid	113.7	10^{-4}	187	10.4	1.33	2.16
Astatine	85	—	Solid	—	—	—	—	—	—

the radii very successfully to interpret the other properties and their change. Thus the increase (and the rate of increase) in intensity of color, melting point, electrical conductivity, and boiling point all reflect the fact that the electrons are becoming less and less tightly held to their "own" atoms as the atomic radius increases, and thus are freer to absorb light (to give color), to interact with neighboring atoms (to raise the melting and boiling points), and even to allow the formation of charged particles, either free electrons and ions or ions alone (to raise the electrical conductivity of the liquid). The luster of solid iodine also indicates the beginning of semi-metallic properties in iodine. The variation in ionization potentials follows a regular pattern also and is readily interpreted in terms of the atomic radius.

COVALENT AND IONIC RADII

Table 20.1 indicates that the radius of a negative ion is always larger than the covalent radius of the atom. (The difference for both the chalcogens and the halogens is almost constant at about 0.8 Å.) Two reasons for this increase are readily apparent: (1) there are more electrons per atom than before, thus there should be more mutual electron repulsion and the atom should increase in size; (2) the nuclear charge has not increased although the number of electrons held solely by the atom has, and each electron will, therefore, be attracted to the nucleus somewhat less strongly, again making the ion larger than the covalent atom. Neither of these factors is the principal reason for the observed increase which is here more apparent than real. The difference in size is based

312   GENERAL CHEMISTRY

primarily on the definitions in terms of which covalent and ionic sizes are expressed. Ions are spherically symmetrical and thus have the same radius in all directions, but atoms which are sharing electrons with other atoms may not behave as spheres as shown in Figure 20.1 where a typical diatomic molecule such as one of the halogens is illustrated. The molecule has the general appearance of two spheres which have been overlapped and this is a fair picture of the situation when covalent bonds form as they do in the halogen molecules. The "radius" to the outside of the spherical surface is considerably greater than the "radius" to the plane half way between the two atomic nuclei within the molecule. Yet it is this latter distance, half the distance between adjacent nuclei in the molecule, which is the covalent radius. It is sometimes loosely identified as the atomic radius. The other radius, that to the spherical portion of the atom which is not covalently bonded to another atom, is known as the van der Waals radius, and is always the longer of the two. In most cases the ionic radius is approximately the same as the van der Waals radius, though slightly longer for the two reasons listed above. Thus one can consider the reaction of a covalently bonded atom gaining electrons to form an ion, as one in which the atom fills out its shape to a complete sphere as compared to the truncated spherical shape it has when covalently bonded.

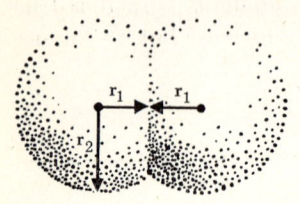

Figure 20.1. Covalent and van der Waals radii in a diatomic molecule. r_1 = covalent radius, r_2 = van der Waals radius.

TYPES OF BONDING BY THE HALOGENS

The simplest reaction of the halogens is the formation of the simple 1− ion from the element by gain of an electron from an electropositive, metallic element to form a salt. Fluoride, F⁻, chloride, Cl⁻, bromide, Br⁻, and iodide, I⁻, ions may all be formed in this way. Fluorine, having the smallest atoms, has the greatest tendency to form the ion, iodine the least. Most natural deposits containing the halogens (except iodine) consist of ionic, metallic halides.

The halogens may also attain four pairs of electrons in the outer energy level by sharing electrons with elements which do not differ much from themselves in electronegativity. Pure hydrogen fluoride, formula HF, hydrogen chloride, formula HCl, hydrogen bromide, formula HBr, and hydrogen iodide, formula HI, are typical covalent substances. They are colorless gases at room temperature and condense to liquids of low electrical conductivity. A typical reaction for the formation of such a covalent halide would be

$$\tfrac{1}{2}\text{H} - \text{H} + \tfrac{1}{2}\left[:\overset{..}{\underset{..}{\text{Cl}}} - \overset{..}{\underset{..}{\text{Cl}}}:\right] = \text{H} - \overset{..}{\underset{..}{\text{Cl}}}: \qquad (20.2)$$

Both the simple halide ions and the covalently bonded halide atoms have pairs of electrons which are not engaged in bonding, that is, they have unshared pairs. These unshared pairs of electrons may form a covalent bond with an electronegative element which has empty energy levels into which the unshared pairs of the halogen atom may enter. <u>Such covalent bonds in which both electrons of the pair come from the same atom are often called coordinate-covalent bonds.</u> Thus there is a whole series of chlorine compounds containing various amounts of oxygen bonded to the halogen based on this ability (see Table 20.2). Similar bromine and iodine compounds are also known but their series are not complete. No analogous fluorine compounds containing oxygen are known.

Table 20.2
Structures of Some Chlorine Compounds

H—Cl:	H :O: :Cl:	:O: :Cl—O—H	:O: :Cl—O: :O:H	:O: H—O—Cl—O: :O:
hydrochloric acid	hypochlorous acid	chlorous acid	chloric acid	perchloric acid
:Cl:⁻	:O:⁻ :Cl:	:O:⁻ :Cl—O:	:O:⁻ :Cl—O: :O:	:O:⁻ :O—Cl—O: :O:
chloride ion	hypochlorite ion	chlorite ion	chloric ion	perchlorate ion
(chlorides)	(hypochlorites)	(chlorites)	(chlorates)	(perchlorates)

Oxidation Number of Chlorine: 1−, 1+, 3+, 5+, 7+

No reason is known for the absence of a bromine oxidation state of 7+ (perbromate) and probably 3+ (bromite) as well, and of an iodine oxidation state of 3+ (iodite), but the absence of all fluorine states save the 1− (fluoride) state is explicable in terms of the very high electronegativity of fluorine (see page 220). There just isn't any element which is more electronegative, so that fluorine must always be negative with respect to the other elements in its compounds. Fluorine will thus always either gain one electron to form fluoride ion or share one electron to form covalent fluorides. There seems to be no current evidence that fluorine can form two covalent bonds at once.

The tendency of the simple halogen ions to use their unshared electron pairs to form covalent bonds leads to the existence of many weak electrolytes.

Examples are mercury and zinc chlorides, formulas $HgCl_2$ and $ZnCl_2$, and numerous complex ions such as $ZnCl_4^{--}$ and $AgCl_2^-$.

Problem 20.1. Draw a feasible electron structure for $ZnCl_4^{--}$ ion. For $AgCl_2^-$ ion. Can you deduce any reason for Zn^{++} ion holding four chlorides whereas Ag^+ ion holds only two? Draw formulas which are geometrically correct for the five acids listed in Table 20.2.

NATURAL OCCURRENCE OF THE HALOGENS

Practically all of the compounds of chlorine, bromine, and iodine with the common elements are soluble in water with the exception of some of the mercury, lead, and silver halides. Thus, while scattered halide deposits of these last three metals are found in nature, the bulk of these three halogens on the earth's surface has become concentrated in the oceans, or in beds which were the sites of ancient salt seas. Calcium fluoride, on the other hand, is rather insoluble in water and is found (as fluorite) in large beds which are the principal source of fluorine.

Fluorite, being insoluble in water, must be mined by blasting and loading methods. The solid deposits of the other halogens may also be mined in this way, or water may be pumped into the deposit and the brine removed for chemical treatment. In many parts of the world large brine deposits are already present beneath the surface of the ground (that at Midland, Michigan, is a famous example) and may be mined by pumping the brine to the surface.

Sodium chloride is so commonly found both as rock salt and in the oceans as to make it inconceivable that its sources will become seriously depleted in the foreseeable future. As far as exhaustion of natural supplies goes, the same statement applies to bromine compounds, now that they can be removed from sea water economically. But the situation is not really comparable since the low concentration of bromide in the water makes its extraction difficult. Thus real bromine shortages can develop. Calcium fluoride is now in limited but adequate supply and phosphate mines exploited for fertilizers may contribute large quantities soon. The iodine situation is more serious as far as potential supply goes for there is too small a concentration in the ocean water to make recovery appear feasible even though the total amount in the oceans is ample for an indefinite time. Fortunately some forms of seaweed concentrate iodine by a factor of as much as 10^5 over its concentration in the water and their ashes may contain as much as 3 per cent of iodine. A currently more attractive source, however, is the large deposit of Chilean saltpeter, formula $NaNO_3$, which contains about 1 per cent of iodine as iodate. The geological origin of this deposit is not known but its present continuance in spite of the high solubility of both sodium nitrate and iodate in water is due to the very low rainfall in that part of Chile.

That an ample supply of raw materials is not sufficient to insure an ample supply of a chemical is well attested by the periodic shortages of chlorine. Over

2,000,000 tons are produced annually in this country but the demand has risen more rapidly than the supply. The limiting factors are electric power and plants for producing the chlorine.

PREPARATION OF IODINE

In order to prepare iodine (oxidation state, 0) from iodate (oxidation state of the iodine, 5+) it is clearly necessary to use a reducing agent. Furthermore, the reducing agent should not be so strong that it will reduce the iodine all the way to iodide (oxidation state, 1−). Many suitable reducing agents are available but an aqueous solution of sulfur dioxide is used commercially, the sulfur dioxide being oxidized to sulfate ion in the process.

$$4H_2O + 2IO_3^- + 5SO_{2(g)} = 5SO_4^{--} + I_{2(s)} + 8H^+ \quad\quad (20.3)$$
$$\text{violet}$$

Problem 20.2. Justify in terms of change in oxidation numbers the ratios of iodate ion and sulfur dioxide used in equation 20.3.

Problem 20.3. Write equations for the half-reactions—the oxidation of iodate and the reduction of sulfur dioxide—and combine them to obtain equation 20.3.

The iodine precipitates from the solution and is purified by distillation. The vapor pressure of solid iodine is so high that it is possible to distill it below its melting point. This direct transformation from solid to gas is called *sublimation*.

PREPARATION OF FLUORINE

Other halogens than iodine occur primarily as halide ions, X^-. In order to prepare free halogen from them an oxidation process is necessary—electrons must be removed from the halide ions. The problem is to find something which "wants" the electrons more than the halide ion does. There are a few very specialized chemical reactions in which fluorine is evolved from its compounds, but in each case the compound itself has to be prepared from pure fluorine so that these processes could never constitute a primary source of the gas. As one would deduce from the electronegativity of fluorine there will be no other element able to oxidize fluoride ion to fluorine for there are no other reactive atoms which hold onto electrons as strongly as do fluorine atoms. One cannot prepare fluorine from a fluoride using only chemical substances for it is impossible to generate sufficient energy to remove the electron from the ion by direct chemical action. An electrical dynamo, or generator, is not so limited in its capabilities. It can furnish almost unlimited electrical energy at a high enough potential to transfer electrons. Fluorine is, therefore, prepared by electrolysis of a molten salt bath. A mixture of potassium fluoride and hydrogen fluoride make up the usual bath. The fluoride ion is discharged (relieved of its electron) at the anode and gaseous fluorine formed. Gaseous hydrogen is evolved at the cathode.

316 GENERAL CHEMISTRY

The problem here is one of finding a vessel which will hold the fluorine. All of the metals are, of course, attacked, as are also glass and other common structural materials. The storage problem is actually solved by the very simple device of confining the fluorine in a metal container and allowing the metal fluoride to form. In several metals, such as steel, nickel, copper, and platinum, the fluoride which forms adheres tightly and forms a tough coating which protects the rest of the metal from corrosion. (Remember the lead sulfate coating in the lead chamber process for making sulfuric acid.) Other fluorides, such as calcium fluoride, may be used to line the vessel on the same principle that fluorine cannot oxidize fluoride ions though it can oxidize almost any other negative ion or neutral atom.

In the electrolysis cell the fluoride ion must be the only potential negative ion present. If the fluoride were dissolved in water, oxygen rather than fluorine would be formed at the anode. Even at the low concentrations (10^{-36} moles per liter) at which oxygen ions, O^{--}, are present in water, the oxide ion (from the water) would be relieved of its electrons (to form gaseous oxygen) more readily than fluoride ions. The actual mechanism may well be the oxidation of water molecules rather than of oxide ions.

The very poisonous nature of fluorine coupled with its great reactivity and tendency to explode when it meets any reducing agent make fluorine one of the most difficult elements to handle. (Recall the long time interval between the "discovery" of fluorine in its compounds and its isolation as an element.)

PREPARATION OF CHLORINE

One could, of course, prepare chlorine from chlorides by treating a chloride with elementary fluorine. The fluorine "wants" electrons more than chloride ion does and thus will oxidize the chloride to chlorine, the fluorine being reduced to fluoride. Bromine could be produced in the same way from bromide, and iodine from iodide, consistent with the oxidizing powers of the elements in this family.

$$\tfrac{1}{2}F_2 + Cl^- \text{ (or } Br^- \text{ or } I^-) = F^- + \tfrac{1}{2}Cl_2 \text{ (or } \tfrac{1}{2}Br_2 \text{ or } \tfrac{1}{2}I_2) \tag{20.4}$$

This method is never used, however, partly because fluorine costs more than any of the other halogens, but more importantly because fluorine is hard to handle and simpler methods are available.

Many oxidizing agents are known which will convert chloride into elementary chlorine, particularly in acid solution. Common laboratory ones are manganese dioxide, lead dioxide, potassium permanganate, potassium chlorate, and potassium dichromate. The acid serves to remove, or tie up, the oxygen present in the oxidizing agent. Sulfuric acid is normally used since the sulfate ion is unreactive under these circumstances and does not complicate the reaction. With manganese dioxide the reaction is

$$2Cl^- + MnO_{2(s)} + 4H^+ = Cl_{2(g)} + Mn^{++} + 2H_2O \tag{20.5}$$
$$\text{black} \qquad\qquad \text{yellow-green}$$

The only naturally occurring oxidizing agent cheap enough to be used in the commercial preparation of chlorine is oxygen, the cheapest oxidizing agent available to the chemist. A glance at Figure 15.5, page 220, will show that oxygen is more electronegative than chlorine and thus might be expected to be able to oxidize the latter. In order to obtain appreciable rates of reactions the gas phase reaction between hydrogen chloride and oxygen is used. This insures high concentrations of the two reagents compared to those attainable in solution and also insures intimate contact of the reagents. The hydrogen chloride is obtained by treating sodium chloride with concentrated sulfuric acid. At low temperatures only one hydrogen of the sulfuric acid is sufficiently acidic and mobile to participate in the reaction, but at higher temperatures the sodium bisulfate melts and its hydrogen also reacts with the chloride. The gaseous hydrogen chloride is then mixed with air and the chlorine removed by a condensation process.

$$NaCl_{(s)} + H_2SO_4 = NaHSO_{4(s)} + HCl_{(g)}$$
$$NaHSO_4 + NaCl_{(s)} = Na_2SO_{4(s)} + HCl_{(g)}$$
$$2HCl_{(g)} + \tfrac{1}{2}O_{2(g)} = H_2O_{(g)} + Cl_{2(g)}$$
(20.6)

The process using oxidation by air, known as the Deacon process for preparing chlorine and of historical importance, is almost obsolete, for, though air is cheap, sulfuric acid is not and is increasingly in short supply due to sulfur shortages. Furthermore, other processes produce salable chemicals in addition to the chlorine, which is, indeed, often a by-product.

For many years the principal method of making chlorine has been the electrolysis of an aqueous solution of sodium chloride with the simultaneous production of gaseous hydrogen and a solution of sodium hydroxide.

$$(Na^+) + Cl^- + H_2O = (Na^+) + OH^- + \tfrac{1}{2}Cl_{2(g)} + \tfrac{1}{2}H_{2(g)}$$
(20.7)
$$\text{yellow-green}$$

The process was actually designed to produce the hydroxide, and the hydrogen and chlorine were often burned to form hydrogen chloride. Now the chlorine is in greater demand. The concentration of chloride in the solution must be kept high because in more dilute solutions of chloride ion (more concentrated in water) it is easier to oxidize the water to oxygen than it is to oxidize the chloride to chlorine. (Compare with fluorine.) The cells are designed to operate continuously with sodium chloride brine flowing in, sodium hydroxide solution flowing out, and hydrogen and chlorine gases being evolved in the carefully separated cathode and anode compartments. The great reactivity of chlorine complicates the cell design and limits the structural materials which can be used. Another problem is to collect the sodium hydroxide produced as free as possible from the salt brine fed into the cell. Commercial cells, such as the Hooker Type S cell, have an asbestos diaphram adjacent to the cathode (where the hydroxide ion and hydrogen gas are formed. The small amount of salt seeping through the diaphragm is later crystallized from the sodium hydroxide solution (see Figure 20.2).

It was, indeed, the great reactivity of chlorine, particularly at high temperatures, which contributed to the lack of a method of electrolyzing molten sodium chloride instead of its aqueous solution. The situation was further complicated by the difficulty of reclaiming the gaseous sodium which was formed simultaneously at these high temperatures (about 800°C.). Clearly needed was some method of lowering the temperature at which it would be possible to electrolyze

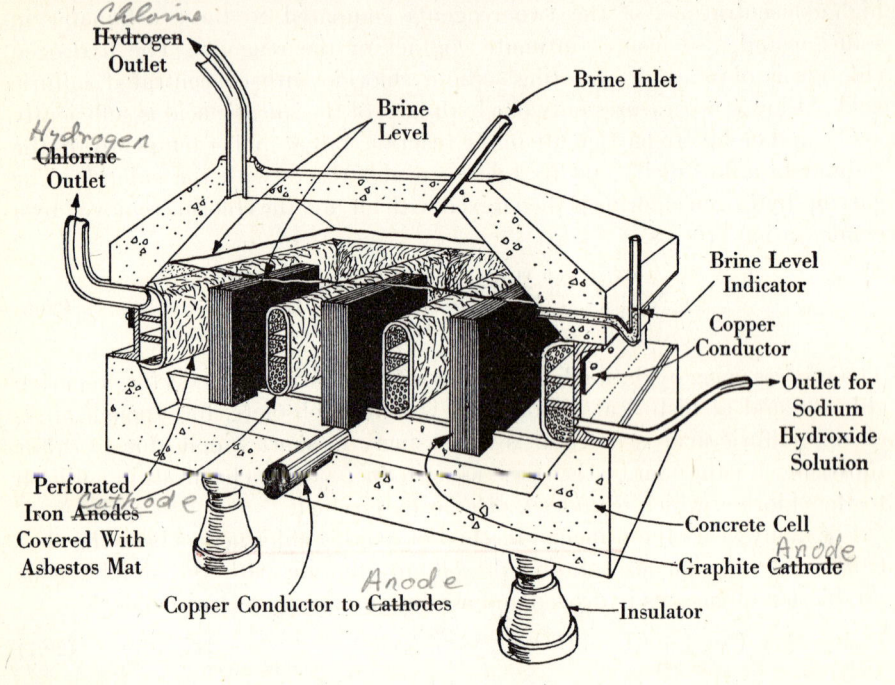

Figure 20.2.
Diagram of a Hooker Type S cell for the production of chlorine and a solution of sodium hydroxide from an aqueous solution of sodium chloride.

the molten sodium chloride. The Downs cell now operates to produce liquid metallic sodium and gaseous chlorine by electrolysis of a molten bath containing sodium chloride with some added salt, such as sodium carbonate, to lower the melting temperature (to about 600°C.) (see Figure 20.3).

$$NaCl_{(liq)} = Na_{(liq)} + \tfrac{1}{2}Cl_{2(g)} \quad\quad (20.8)$$
$$\text{yellow-green}$$

PREPARATION OF BROMINE

Bromine may also be produced by electrolytic processes but it is much simpler to oxidize bromides to bromine with chlorine gas, as in the commercial reclamation of bromine from brines and ocean water.

Bromine and iodine may both be prepared in the laboratory by the oxidation of bromides and iodides with manganese dioxide in acid solution, or similar oxidizing agents, or they may be prepared by using chlorine as the oxidizing agent. Iodine, of course, could be prepared from iodides with bromine as an oxidizing agent.

Problem 20.4. Write the equation for the oxidation of bromide ion by manganese dioxide in acid solution.

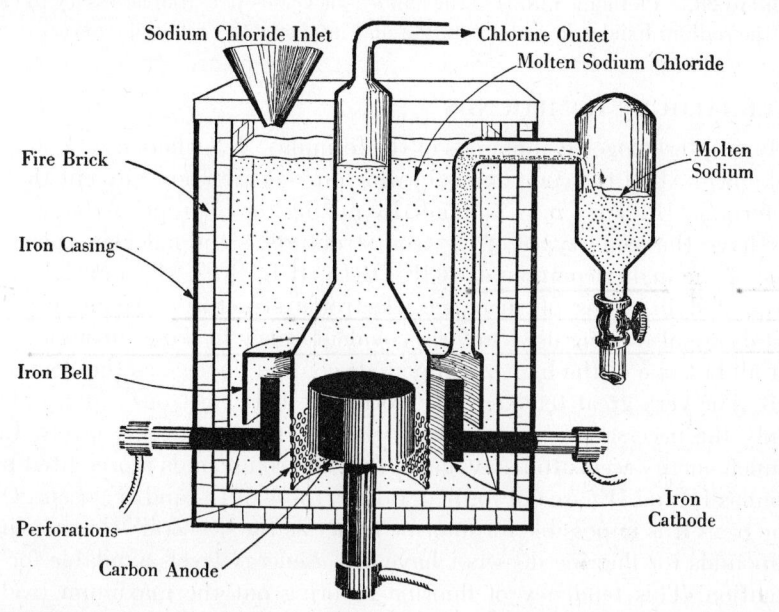

Figure 20.3.
Diagram of Downs cell for the production of sodium (and chlorine) from a molten bath of sodium chloride.

ELECTROLYSIS OF AQUEOUS HALIDE SOLUTIONS

The ease of electrolysis of aqueous solutions of sodium chloride, sodium bromide, and sodium iodide furnishes a further example of a consistent and readily interpretable trend in the halogen family. Electrolysis of approximately 1 M solutions of many of these salts in water gives hydrogen gas and a sodium hydroxide solution at the cathode and the halogen at the anode. Any differences in the voltage and in electrical work necessary to perform the electrolyses must then be largely due to differences involved in removing an electron from a halide ion and forming the neutral molecule in a water solution. The minimum voltages are: 0.5345 for the iodide, 1.087 for the bromide, and 1.3583 for the chloride. Thus the chlorine requires the most work (and highest voltage) and the iodide the least, consistent with the idea that the larger size of the iodide ion makes the removal of an electron easier. As was stated earlier, one cannot electrolyze an aqueous solution of sodium fluoride and obtain fluorine. If this is attempted, oxygen is produced at the anode rather than fluorine because the oxygen in the water is more readily oxidized. It is possible by an indirect method to calculate the voltage which would be required to electrolyze the fluoride if it were not for the water complication. This value is 2.85 volts, quite in line with the above series.

Problem 20.5. Plot ionic radius of the halide ions versus potential necessary to electrolyze the sodium halides in water solution and interpret the resulting curve.

INTERHALOGEN COMPOUNDS

Many interhalogen compounds of the formula XX_n' where n = 1, 3, 5, or 7, are known. All of the compounds in which n = 1 are known except that with the formula IF. They may be made by mixing the appropriate halogens and they have the same types of electron structure as the halogens themselves. None of the higher compounds (ClF_3, BrF_3, ICl_3, BrF_5, IF_5, and IF_7) can be represented in terms of inert gas electronic structures. Apparently the d orbitals are also being used to form covalent bonds in these substances. Note that all but one of the higher compounds contain fluorine as the "outer" element. The very great tendency of fluorine to share electrons could quite well supply the necessary energy to raise the electrons into the d levels. In fact so much energy seems to be available that the compounds represented by the formulas IF and IF_3 are not formed, rather, those of IF_5 and IF_7 occur. On the same basis it is impossible for fluorine to act as the "central" element in such compounds for fluorine does not have any d energy levels available for bond formation. This tendency of fluorine to bring out the maximum oxidation number and maximum number of bonds of an element is well known, as in the compounds with the formulas OsF_8 and SF_6. The highest corresponding chlorides known have the formulas $OsCl_4$ and SCl_4. The only higher interhalogen compound not containing fluorine is iodine trichloride, but here too the difference in electronegativity of the elements is sufficient to get the electrons into the d levels.

REACTIONS OF THE HALOGENS WITH WATER

Fluorine is such a powerful oxidizing agent that it cannot be kept in contact with water for any length of time; it reacts immediately to give oxygen, ozone, hydrogen peroxide, and other unidentified oxidizing agents. Chlorine, bromine, and iodine are more mild in their behavior and dissolve in water, bromine to a greater extent than chlorine, iodine being least soluble. Chlorine and bromine will slowly oxidize the water to oxygen, particularly in the light, but iodine will not. Each of these hologens does undergo an interesting set of reactions in aqueous solution, however, quite apart from the formation of oxygen.

Experimentally one notes that an aqueous solution of a halogen is always acidic, indicating the presence of H^+ (and hence of an equivalent quantity of negative ions). The presence of extra halide ions in solution markedly increases the amount of halogen which will dissolve, suggesting the formation of a complex ion. Addition of a base renders the solution almost colorless and increases the amount of halogen that will dissolve. Addition of an acid favors formation of the free halogen as evidenced both by the return of color and by the lessened amount of halogen that will dissolve. All of these facts may be interpreted quantitatively in terms of the following equilibria:

a. A strong acid and a weak acid are formed

$$\underset{\text{colored}}{X_2} + H_2O = H^+ + \underset{\text{colorless}}{X^-} + \underset{\text{colorless}}{HOX} \tag{20.9}$$

b. The halogen forms complex ions with the halide ion produced or with extra halide ions present

$$X^- + \underset{\text{colored}}{X_2} = \underset{\text{deeply colored}}{X_3^-} \tag{20.10}$$

$$X_3^- + \underset{\text{colored}}{X_2} = \underset{\text{deeply colored}}{X_5^-}$$

c. The weak acid ionizes somewhat and can be neutralized by a strong base

$$HOX = H^+ + \underset{\text{colorless}}{OX^-} \tag{20.11}$$

When a strong base is added, H^+ ions (see equations 20.9 and 20.11) are removed almost completely. Consequently the equilibria shift until few free halogen molecules or complex ions remain—the solution becomes almost colorless.

In a water solution saturated with bromine the various molecular and ionic species have the concentrations given in Table 20.3.

Table 20.3

Concentration of Various Chemical Species in Water Saturated with Bromine (25°C.)
(Bray)

SPECIES	Br_2	H^+	Br^-	$HOBr$	Br_3^-	Br_5^-	OBr^-
MOLARITY	0.2068	.00171	.00037	.00171	.00121	.00013	2×10^{-9}

Problem 20.6. Calculate the equilibrium constants for the four reactions (20.9, 20.10 and 20.11) in an aqueous bromine solution, using the data in Table 20.4 to obtain numerical values for the constants.

The above equilibria are attained rapidly in aqueous solutions, but two other reactions proceed to equilibrium much more slowly. For the hypobromous acid, as an example, they are

$$5\text{HOBr} = \text{H}^+ + \text{BrO}_3^- + 2\text{H}_2\text{O} + 2\underset{\text{brown}}{\text{Br}_2} \qquad (20.12)$$

$$4\text{HOBr} = \text{O}_2 + 2\text{H}_2\text{O} + 2\underset{\text{brown}}{\text{Br}_2} \qquad (20.13)$$

The rate of reaction of the type 20.12 increases greatly in the order: chlorine, bromine, iodine compound. Hypoiodous acid disappears almost completely within an hour after it is freshly prepared.

Problem 20.7. Account for the fact that the interhalogen compounds all contain an even number of atoms whereas the complex halide ions contain an odd number.

NONAQUEOUS SOLUTIONS OF THE HALOGENS

The nonpolar nature of the halogens prevents any of them from being very soluble in water, a polar solvent. On the other hand they are rather soluble in nonpolar solvents such as carbon tetrachloride and carbon disulfide, and in weakly polar solvents such as chloroform and ethanol (ethyl alcohol). Hence, one can extract rather completely the free halogen dissolved in water by shaking the solution with some solvent such as carbon tetrachloride, not itself soluble in water (see page 269). Since iodine, for instance, is about 100 times as soluble in carbon tetrachloride as in water, shaking carbon tetrachloride with an aqueous solution of iodine will produce a concentration of iodine in the carbon tetrachloride layer roughly one hundred times that which remains in the water layer. If only a small quantity of the carbon tetrachloride is used, the iodine concentration may be sufficient to color that layer even though the water layer originally appeared quite colorless. The same redistribution will occur with bromine and chlorine, but the chlorine color is so feeble that it may well not be detectable even after it has been concentrated.

Solutions of iodine in liquids of different polarity show an interesting variation in color. In nonpolar liquids the color is violet as is pure iodine vapor, but in polar liquids the color is brown as in the common tincture of iodine (a solution of iodine in ethanol). Intermediate colors may be obtained in liquids of only slight polarity. It was once thought that the solvent, when polar, must be interacting with the iodine molecules in such a way as to change the electronic fields within the molecule, so changing the ability to interact with light and producing color, and that this was a clear-cut example of the forces which polar molecules can exert on their neighbors and an indication of the magnitude of solvation phenomena. Recently, however, it has been suggested that the brown color is due to the I_3^- ions which can exist only in polar solvents.

The deep blue color of iodine in the presence of starch is an undisputed example of molecular interaction. The color is so intense as to constitute a very sensitive test for the presence of iodine molecules. The magnitude of the color change here is based on the fact that the starch molecules are formed into long coils spiraling about a central hole much as morning glories spiral about a string. The diameter of this central hole inside the starch coil is almost exactly the same as the van der Waals diameter of the iodine molecule and the hole is lined with hydroxyl groups (OH) of the starch molecule. These highly polar hydroxyl groups are thus brought into very close juxtaposition with an iodine molecule which diffuses into the hole and they interact strongly with the iodine electron field changing the color absorption of the iodine until only the deep blue color remains unabsorbed.

OXYGEN COMPOUNDS OF THE HALOGENS

Many binary compounds between oxygen and the halogens are known but they are of very little interest or application save in the field of structural chemistry and a study of the nature of the chemical bond. The application of chlorine dioxide, formula ClO_2, as a bleach and disinfectant is the principal exception. Contrast this with the importance of the oxides of sulfur.

The definitely known oxides have the formulas: F_2O, F_2O_2; Cl_2O, Cl_2O_2, ClO_2, ClO_3 (Cl_2O_6), Cl_2O_7; Br_2O, Br_3O_8, BrO_2; I_2O_4, I_4O_9 ($I(IO_3)_3$), I_2O_5. Many of these, it will be noted, have odd molecules (which have an uneven number of electrons). This formation of odd molecules and unusual oxidation states with oxygen may well recall the unique nature of the oxygen molecule itself, with its two unpaired electrons, and should underline the limitations of our ideas which relate bond formation to the pairing of electrons, particularly the accenting of groups of four pairs of electrons in the outer s and p energy levels.

THE HYDROGEN HALIDES

The hydrogen halides, with the formulas HF, HCl, HBr, and HI, are all covalent substances. Some of their properties are listed in Table 20.4. Certain trends are apparent. All are poor conductors of electricity as pure liquids and all but hydrogen fluoride have simple diatomic molecules in the gas, liquid, and solid phases. At low pressures and high temperatures hydrogen fluoride gas has a density corresponding to the formula HF, but at higher pressures and lower temperatures the average molecular weight in the gas increases as shown by gas density data. Electron diffraction studies also show that hydrogen fluoride polymerizes into zigzag chain molecules and even into ring molecules. The distance from a hydrogen nucleus to a fluorine nucleus in the HF molecule is 1.00 Å, and the distance between two fluorine nuclei (with a hydrogen atom between them) in the polymers is 2.7 Å. Thus it might appear that the hydrogen is probably closer to one of the adjacent fluorines than to the other in the chain structure. Chains have also been found in liquid and solid hydrogen fluoride. In the solid they are lined up parallel to one another and have the dimensions shown in Figure 20.4.

The surprisingly high melting point and boiling point of hydrogen fluoride listed in Table 20.4 are readily explicable in terms of its tendency to form polymers, for considerably more energy is required to separate polymers, as in melting or boiling, than for simple molecules.

The tendency to form polymeric chains is evidence for the very polar nature

324 GENERAL CHEMISTRY

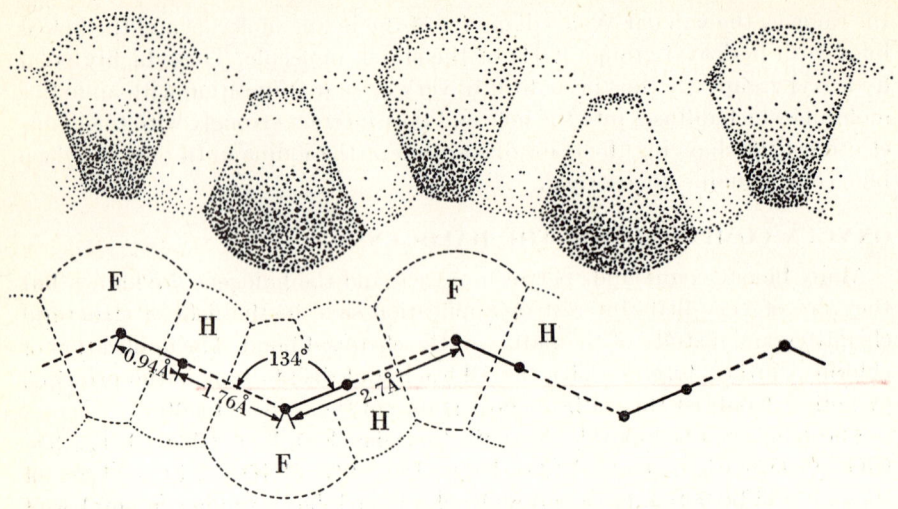

Figure 20.4.
Section of a chain molecule (polymer) of hydrogen fluoride in the crystalline state.

of the H—F bond, providing optimum conditions for the formation of hydrogen bonds between the molecules. The hydrogen bonds between fluorine and hydrogen are, as a matter of fact, the strongest hydrogen bonds known. An excellent additional example of such bonding is the very stable HF_2^- ion. Here the bonding is so strong to both fluorine atoms that the hydrogen atom

Table 20.4
Properties of Hydrogen Halides

FORMULA	M.P. °C.	B.P. °C.	PER CENT OF DISSOCIATION INTO ELEMENTS AT 1000° K.	ACID STRENGTH
HF	−83.7	+19.54		weak
HCl	−114.2	−85.0	0.00134	strong
HBr	−81.6	−66.7	1	strong
HI	−50.8	−35.4	28	very strong

takes up a position halfway between the two fluorine atoms and is equally strongly bonded to each. One need not say however that the hydrogen has formed two covalent bonds, a statement which cannot be made consistent with our current pictures of the available energy levels for bonding in the hydrogen atoms. It is probably more correct to state that the bonding in FHF^- is principally ionic, the hydrogen ion being between two fluoride ions.

The decrease in bond strength in the series hydrogen fluoride to hydrogen iodide is apparent from the data on degree of dissociation of the gaseous halides presented to Table 20.4.

All four of the hydrogen halides may be made from metallic halides by treatment with a strong, nonvolatile acid. Calcium fluoride, sodium chloride, sodium bromide, and potassium iodide are usually used. The hydrogen halides are all volatile and may be distilled from the reaction mixture. It is, of course,

$$MX_{(s)} + H^+ = HX_{(g)} + M^+ \qquad (20.14)$$

necessary in each case to use an acid which is not a good enough oxidizing agent to convert the halide to the halogen. For example, one should not use concentrated sulfuric acid on a bromide or iodide (which are more readily oxidized than fluoride or chloride) if the hydrogen halide is desired, since sulfuric acid will oxidize either of these to the corresponding halogen.

$$2Br^- + 3H_2SO_4 = \underset{\text{brown}}{Br_2} + SO_{2(g)} + 2H_2O + 2HSO_4^- \qquad (20.15)$$

$$6I^- + 7H_2SO_4 = \underset{\text{violet}}{3I_{2(s)}} + \underset{\text{yellow}}{S_{(s)}} + 4H_2O + 6HSO_4^- \qquad (20.16)$$

Phosphoric acid may be used in these cases or some more specific method such as the hydrolysis of the phosphorus halide, or the reaction between hydrogen sulfide and iodine in water solution may be used.

$$PX_3 + 3HOH = 3HX + HPO(OH)_2 \qquad (20.17)$$

$$H_2S + \underset{\text{violet}}{I_2} = 2HI + \underset{\text{yellow}}{\tfrac{1}{8}S_{8(s)}} \qquad (20.18)$$

Even phosphoric acid is hardly satisfactory for preparing hydrogen iodide, which dissociates into the elements appreciably at the reaction temperature.

There are few large scale uses of hydrogen bromide and hydrogen iodide. Hydrogen fluoride is used industrially as an acid catalyst and also is applied to the etching and frosting of glass, though much frosted glass is now made by sandblasting. The reactions between hydrogen fluoride and glass occur because of the great stability of silicon tetrafluoride, formula SiF_4. This compound is even more stable than silicon dioxide (silica) and the silicates, principal constituents of glasses.

$$SiO_{2(s)} + 4HF = SiF_{4(g)} + 2H_2O \qquad (20.19)$$

$$Na_2SiO_{3(s)} + 6HF = SiF_{4(g)} + 2NaF_{(s)} + 3H_2O \qquad (20.20)$$

Silicon tetrachloride, formula $SiCl_4$, is also a well-known compound but it is unstable with respect to silicon dioxide in the presence of water and hence the reverse of reaction 20.19 occurs in this case.

$$SiCl_4 + 2H_2O = SiO_{2(s)} + 4HCl \qquad (20.21)$$

Hydrogen chloride, particularly in its aqueous solution as hydrochloric acid (commercially called muriatic acid), finds widespread application in chemical laboratories and in industry. It is a cheap, strong acid, not readily oxidized, forms soluble salts with most metallic elements, and serves as an easily handled intermediate in the formation of many compounds of chlorine. It is probably the most commonly used acid in a chemistry laboratory for the same reasons, so that, when directions call for the addition of "an acid," hydrochloric acid is almost always considered first.

Problem 20.8. Which is the cheaper, sulfuric acid or hydrochloric acid?

STRENGTH OF ACIDS IN WATER

Most hydrogen-containing acids, when pure, are weak electrolytes and typical covalent compounds. This is true of sulfuric, phosphoric, and the halogen acids. Yet these same substances in water often ionize almost completely to become strong acids in aqueous solution. The explanation is the ability of water to hydrate the hydrogen ion and the negative ion of the acid, thus allowing the ions to coexist. One should remember, however, that this process involves competition between a water molecule and the negative ion of the acid for the proton. The process may be presented as

$$HX + H_2O = H_3O^+ + X^- \qquad (20.22)$$

where H_3O^+ indicates a hydrated proton and X^- a hydrated negative ion. Any factor tending to strengthen the H—X bond will decrease the strength of the acid dissolved in water. Hydrogen fluoride, for instance, is a weak acid in water but the other hydrogen halides are strong acids. The small fluorine atom, or fluoride ion, has, as a result of its size, a very high charge density compared with the chloride, bromide, and iodide atoms or ions. This high charge density results in a strong bond between hydrogen and fluorine and a low dissociation of hydrogen fluoride into ions in water solution. The same phenomenon accounts for the progressive weakening of the acid ionization in the series hydrogen telluride to water (see Table 19.3), and in other such series.

Many acids contain oxygen in addition to hydrogen and some "central" element. In fact, it was originally thought that all acids contained oxygen, a name which means acid producer. In most of these oxygen-containing acids the hydrogen is bonded to the oxygen which is in turn bonded to the central atom. Thus these acids contain M—O—H groups, where M stands for the central atom. Note that this grouping is also characteristic of many of the substances we have called bases [formulas NaOH, Ca(OH)$_2$, etc.]. Whether such an M—O—H group will actually be acidic or basic depends on which bond can be ionized more readily, the O—H bond, or the M—O bond. The former substances will be acidic in water, the latter basic (see also pages 239, 244).

When the element M in a compound containing M—O—H groups is strongly electropositive, the compound will be composed of M$^+$ and OH$^-$ ions even in the solid phase. The water solutions of these are strong bases. The alkali and alkaline earth hydroxides are examples.

On the other hand, when the element, M, in a compound containing

M—O—H groups is strongly electronegative, strong covalent bonds will be formed with the oxygen making it unlikely that the M—O bond will ionize in water solution. Under such conditions the ionization of the O—H bond becomes more likely and acids, even strong acids, are found in water solution. It is inherent in the nature of the bonds, however, that acids will not ordinarily be ionized in the pure liquid state whereas bases will be. Hence, also, in water solution one is apt to find a larger percentage of metallic hydroxides which are strong bases than of nonmetallic hydroxides which are strong acids. There are, thus, relatively few strong acids. The common ones, in rough order of decreasing acidic strength, are those with the formulas: $HClO_4$, HI, HBr, HNO_3, HCl, H_2SO_4, and H_3PO_4. Only the first hydrogen is largely ionized in aqueous

Table 20.5

Variation of Acid Strength for Two Series of Acids
(See also Table 19.3)

ACID FORMULA	K_1	ACID FORMULA	K
H_2SO_3	1.7×10^{-2}	HOCl	3.5×10^{-8}
H_2SeO_3	3×10^{-3}	HOBr	2×10^{-9}
H_2TeO_3	6×10^{-6}	HOI	5×10^{-13}

solutions of sulfuric and phosphoric acid; the second and third hydrogens find it increasingly harder to escape (ionize) as the consequent charge on the negative ion increases.

The strength of the hydrogen halide acids increases as the halogen ion becomes larger and the charge density smaller for it becomes easier for the hydrogen ion to escape from the negative halide ion. The trend is reversed in the hydroxy acids. As the M atom becomes smaller, or as its charge (as indicated for instance by its oxidation number) becomes larger its own positive charge density increases and its hold on the neighboring oxygen atoms increases. The bond becomes stronger between M and O. Simultaneously the O—H bond weakens as the electrons are pulled more strongly toward the M atom. It thus becomes easier for the hydrogen to ionize and the acid is stronger the more positive the oxidation number of M becomes and the smaller its atomic radius is. Sulfuric acid is a stronger acid than sulfurous acid largely because of the higher oxidation number of the sulfur in the former. Selenous acid is a weaker acid than sulfurous acid and tellurous acid is still weaker primarily because of the increase in atomic radius in the series S, Se, Te, accompanied by a consequent decrease in charge density, a weakening of the M—O bond and a strengthening of the O—H bond. These effects are well illustrated in Table 20.5, which lists the ionization constant, K_1 or K, for two series of acids.

There are numerous exceptions, particularly as the acids become stronger. Selenic acid is slightly stronger than sulfuric for instance. But the concept of the effect of charge density of the central atom on the acid strength serves as a useful guide in correlating trends.

Problem 20.9. Predict whether or not the substance with the formula $HPO(OH)_2$ (equation 20.17) is ionized in the pure state and whether its water solution will be basic or acidic. Draw a possible geometric and electronic structure for the compound.

POSITIVE OXIDATION STATES OF THE HALOGENS

A summary of the known positive oxidation states of the halogens, not including those which exist only in the halogen oxides previously discussed, is presented in Table 20.6.

Table 20.6
Positive Oxidation States of the Halogens in Acids and Ions

HALOGEN SYMBOL	OXIDATION STATE			
	1+	3+	5+	7+
F	No positive oxidation states known			
Cl	HOCl, OCl$^-$	HOClO, ClO$_2^-$	HOClO$_2$, ClO$_3^-$	HOClO$_3$, ClO$_4^-$
Br	HOBr, OBr$^-$	———	HOBrO$_2$, BrO$_3^-$	———
I$_2$	HOI, OI$^-$	———	HOIO$_2$, IO$_3^-$	H$_5$IO$_6$, IO$_6^{5-}$, I$_2$O$_{11}^{8-}$, IO$_5^{3-}$, I$_2$O$_9^{4-}$, IO$_4^{1-}$
	weak acids, good oxidizing agents	weak acid, powerful oxidizing agent	strong acids, good oxidizing agents	strong acids, powerful oxidizing agents

All of these substances are made by oxidation of the appropriate halide. The higher oxidation states may be achieved by electrolytic oxidation. Many of the substances listed in Table 20.6 are highly unstable in the pure state (as is common for such potent oxidizing agents) and may explode with little triggering. All are extremely dangerous in the presence of reducing agents, particularly in hot, concentrated, acid solution. In 1947 in Los Angeles a vat containing about 60 gallons of perchloric acid, with some water and organic material present so that the perchloric acid constituted perhaps half of the total solution, blew up and caused 17 deaths, 150 injuries, and $1,500,000 in property damage. Apparently the explosion was precipitated by overheating in the bath when the refrigerating system which held the temperature below 85°F. (30°C.) was shut off. Many other explosions of perchlorates have occurred. These chemicals, which are powerful oxidizing agents, should be treated with care.

Advantage is taken of these oxidizing powers commercially in the use of perchlorates in fireworks and flares as a source of oxygen, in sodium chlorite and sodium hypochlorite solutions as bleaches and disinfectants, and in bleaching powder. Bleaching powder is a solid of somewhat variable composition prepared by passing chlorine over calcium hydroxide, but it contains primarily the substances with formulas Ca(OCl)$_2$, Ca(OH)$_2$, and CaCl$_2$ in various intermolecular compounds more or less hydrated. The active bleaching ingredient is the hypochlorite. Sodium hypochlorite solution may be made by bubbling chlorine into aqueous sodium hydroxide. Note that chlorine is both oxidized and reduced in this reaction. The chlorine may be regenerated by acidifying the solution. The basic solution is used as a medical antiseptic, Dakin's solution.

$$\underset{\text{yellow}}{Cl_{2(g)}} + 2OH^- = H_2O + OCl^- + Cl^- \qquad (20.23)$$

Problem 20.10. Explain the generation of chlorine from a commercial solution of sodium hypochlorite in terms of the kinetic theory of chemical equilibrium.

The existence in water solution of periodic acid, formula H_5IO_6 rather than HIO_4, is reminiscent of telluric acid, formula H_6TeO_6. The large atoms, I and Te, have ample space around them to allow the octahedral coordination of six groups rather than the limit of four found in the molecules $HClO_4$ and H_2SO_4. The atoms with higher atomic numbers also have d energy levels readily available for forming extra bonds as was shown for the interhalogen compounds. Periodate ions with a lower coordination number of oxygen are also known and are listed in Table 20.6.

Problem 20.11. Draw feasible geometric and electron structural formulas for the periodate ions listed in Table 20.6.

Problem 20.12. Write equations for the reactions that occur when:
  a. Chloride ion (as a reducing agent) and perchlorate ion (as an oxidizing agent) are mixed in acid solution.
  b. Chlorine is dissolved in hot, slightly acid solution to give chlorate and chloride ions. (Would this reaction be more or less apt to occur if the acidity were increased?)
  c. A solution of nitric acid and hydrochloric acid is heated to give nitric oxide, (formula NO) and chlorine.
  d. Chlorine is bubbled into a solution of calcium iodide.
  e. Iodine is added to a solution of lithium bromide.
  f. Solutions of ferric chloride and potassium iodide are mixed to give iodine.
  g. Thiosulfate ions are mixed with iodine to give iodide ions and tetrathionate ions ($S_4O_6^=$).

ANALYTICAL TESTS FOR THE HALOGENS AND HALOGEN COMPOUNDS

Analytical methods to determine the kind and amount of halogen-containing species in a mixture of substances are available, but such methods may become very involved when the mixtures are complicated. It is generally much easier to see whether any halogen compounds are present, and if so, of which halogens, than it is to identify the particular form in which the halogen is combined.

Thus a reducing agent such as metallic tin or iron will reduce an acid solution of any form of common, inorganic, halogen-containing compound to simple halide ions. Our problem then becomes one of distinguishing between F⁻, Cl⁻, Br⁻, and I⁻ in the presence of one another. We shall assume in the following that no other negative ions are present in the solution. This would not be true in the general case and allowance would have to be made for the possibility of their reaction.

Fluoride ion may be detected in the presence of the other three halides by adding a solution of calcium nitrate to a slightly acidified (with nitric acid) solution of the halides. White calcium fluoride will precipitate but the calcium salts of the other halides are very soluble. It is necessary to acidify before adding the calcium solution to prevent the precipitation of either calcium hydroxide or calcium carbonate, both of which are soluble in acid solution. (Carbonate ion forms when the carbon dioxide of the air dissolves in water.) Why use nitric acid to acidify the solution? Why not acidify strongly with nitric acid?

The three halides—chloride, bromide, and iodide—all form insoluble compounds with silver ion, the formulas (and colors) being AgCl (white), AgBr (pale yellow), and AgI (bright yellow). All are insoluble in the dilute acid

$$Ag^+ + X^- = AgX_{(s)} \qquad (20.24)$$

added to prevent silver hydroxide from precipitating. Thus any formation of precipitate when a solution of silver nitrate is added to a solution known to contain any or all of the halide ions, but no other negative ions, indicates the presence of at least one of these three. They may be differentiated by their color when separated, but the formation of any colored solid may conceal the presence of a less highly colored substance, making it necessary to separate the halides for further tests.

The three silver halides differ appreciably in their solubility in water, the iodide being least soluble and the chloride most soluble of the three. (Compare the solubility of silver fluoride.) Thus there will be a higher concentration of silver ions in equilibrium with silver chloride than silver iodide. Or one may say that the iodide ions hang on to the silver more tightly than do the bromide ions or the chloride ions. If we can find some reagent which hangs on to silver ion more tightly than chloride, but less tightly than bromide or iodide it should be possible to dissolve the silver chloride and leave the bromide and iodide as solids. A solution of ammonia in water (3 f) does just this by forming a complex ion with the silver, as in equation 20.25. In a 3 f ammonia solution there

$$Ag^+ + 2NH_3 = Ag(NH_3)_2^+ \qquad (20.25)$$

is enough ammonia to tie up the silver more effectively than would chloride ion but not as effectively as do bromide and iodide ions. The net reaction which occurs is

$$AgCl_{(s)} + 2NH_3(3f) = Ag(NH_3)_2^+ + Cl^- \qquad (20.26)$$
white

If one then decants this solution containing the ammonia complex and dissolved chloride ion from the residual silver bromide and silver iodide solids one can reprecipitate the silver chloride, practically free from bromide or iodide, by acidifying the solution and obtaining white silver chloride. What acid would you use?

$$Ag(NH_3)_2^+ + Cl^- + 2H^+ = AgCl_{(s)} + 2NH_4^+ \qquad (20.27)$$
$$\text{white}$$

In other words, the ammonia forms a stronger bond with the hydrogen ion than with the silver ion under these conditions so that the silver ion is freed and again reacts with the chloride ion.

Whereas $3f$ ammonia solution will appreciably dissolve only silver chloride, a $7f$ ammonia solution (having a higher concentration of ammonia) will dissolve silver bromide (as well as silver chloride). The silver iodide is again practically insoluble. Thus, treatment of the mixture of silver bromide and iodide with $7f$ ammonia solution extracts the silver bromide and leaves a bright yellow residue containing the silver iodide.

$$AgBr_{(s)} + 2NH_3(7f) = Ag(NH_3)_2^+ + Br^- \qquad (20.28)$$
$$\text{yellow}$$

The solution when decanted and acidified yields a light-yellow precipitate of silver bromide practically free from chloride or iodide. If fluoride, chloride, bromide, and iodide—all four—were present in the original solution, one will now have the four separate precipitates, the formulas (and colors) being CaF_2 (white), AgCl (white), AgBr (pale yellow), and AgI (bright yellow). The absence of one of the precipitates indicates, of course, the absence of that halide ion in the original solution.

Bromide and iodide may be tested for in the presence of one another and the other halogens by a quite different method based on the oxidizing power of chlorine toward bromide and iodide ions. Addition of a small quantity of chlorine water to a solution containing both bromide and iodide will result in the oxidation of some of the iodide to iodine. Any bromide which is momentarily oxidized will immediately react with iodide to form iodine, and will

$$Cl_2 + 2I^- = 2Cl^- + I_2 \qquad (20.29)$$
$$\text{yellow-green} \qquad \text{brown or violet}$$

itself revert to bromide. If this solution is now shaken with a small quantity of

$$Br_2 + 2I^- = 2Br^- + I_2 \qquad (20.30)$$
$$\text{red-brown} \qquad \text{brown or violet}$$

carbon tetrachloride, the tetrachloride will extract the free iodine from the water and attain the characteristic violet color of iodine in nonpolar solvents. Further slow addition of chlorine water with continued shaking will lead to the disappearance of the violet color. This is because the chlorine oxidizes the iodine in the water layer to iodate ion which is colorless. The iodine in the nonpolar layer redissolves in the water to attempt to maintain the distribution equilibrium, and is there oxidized, thus eventually exhausting the violet color. Once the iodine is all oxidized to iodate, further addition of chlorine water

$$6H_2O + 5Cl_2 + I_2 = 10Cl^- + 2IO_3^- + 12H^+ \qquad (20.31)$$
$$\text{yellow-green} \quad \text{violet}$$

oxidizes the bromide to bromine and shaking produces the brownish-red color

$$Cl_2 + 2Br^- = 2Cl^- + Br_2 \qquad (20.32)$$
$$\text{yellow-green} \qquad \text{red-brown}$$

of bromine in the carbon tetrachloride layer due to concentration of the bromine there. This test can be run even more quickly than the silver halide separation and is, of course, specific for the iodide and bromide ions.

A further very sensitive test for iodine is the blue color which it forms with starch. This test is also highly specific so that the presence of other substances, so long as they are not too highly colored themselves, does not interfere with it.

Such analytical methods, which tell whether or not a substance is present, belong to the field of qualitative analytical chemistry. Methods which allow one to decide accurately how much of a given substance is present belong to the field of quantitative analytical chemistry. It should be seen that most of the above methods could, at least in principle, be applied to the quantitative analysis of a halide mixture if measured quantities were used throughout.

Problem 20.13. Outline a method of testing for iodide ion in solution based on obtaining the blue color of the starch-iodine complex.

Problem 20.14. Outline a method for showing that ClO_4^- ions are present in solution if one knows that there are no other halogen-containing substances present. Write equations for each reaction.

Problem 20.15. List at least ten properties of the halogens, or of halogen compounds, which vary in a systematic manner in the order, fluorine to iodine. Interpret each of these variations in terms of atomic radii, nuclear charges, and electronic structures.

Problem 20.16. Predict some properties of astatine and its compounds.

Problem 20.17. Solutions of the following substances are mixed. Select those in which an appreciable reaction occurs. Write equations for the net reaction in these cases.
   a. bromine and potassium iodide.
   b. iodine and sodium bromide.
   c. sodium iodate, sodium bromide, and perchloric acid.
   d. chlorine and sodium iodide.

Problem 20.18. Which of the halogens (a) has the lowest melting point, (b) the largest atomic number, (c) is the weakest oxidizing agent, (d) is present in bleaching powder, (e) is obtained commercially in large quantities from sea water, (f) is easiest to oxidize, (g) has two complete shells of electrons below the valence shell, (h) decomposes water with the evolution of ozone, (i) gives a weak acid when its hydrogen compound is dissolved in water, (j) has the most extensive and varied commercial uses.

Problem 20.19. Monel metal is an alloy of copper and nickel. What advice can you give concerning its use as a container for fluorine?

Problem 20.20. Write the electronic structure of (a) each of the halogen atoms, (b) hypochlorous acid, (c) water, (d) sodium chloride, (e) chlorine.

Problem 20.21. Write the chemical formulas of the following commonly mentioned chemicals:
- a. Table salt.
- b. Oil of vitriol.
- c. Hypo.
- d. Brimstone.
- e. Diamond.
- f. Dakin's solution.
- g. Heavy water.
- h. Dry ice.
- i. Muriatic acid.
- j. Ozone.

Problem 20.22. Select the formula for the atom, molecule, or ion having the stated characteristic under comparable conditions. Give reasons for each choice.
 a. Largest radius: Na, Mg, Li, Al, Al^{+++}.
 b. Largest number of valence electrons: Al, Ca, Ba, Mg, K.
 c. Strongest oxidizing agent: Cu^{++}, Zn^{++}, K$^+$, Al^{+++}, Fe^{++}.
 d. Lowest density: O$_3$, H$_2$S, SO$_2$, CO, NH$_3$.
 e. Molecule which in the gaseous phase at 20°C. has the highest velocity: O$_2$, H$_2$S, SO$_2$, N$_2$, Ne, A.
 f. Strongest reducing agent: Mg, Ca, Al, Cl$_2$.

Problem 20.23. Which formula represents the strongest acid in each of the following sets: (a) HF, HBr, HI, (b) H$_2$O, H$_2$S, H$_2$Se, (c) NH$_3$, H$_2$O, HF, (d) HClO$_3$, HBrO$_3$, HIO$_3$, (e) Ca(OH)$_2$, Cr(OH)$_2$, Zn(OH)$_2$?

21 NUCLEAR CHEMISTRY

WE HAVE now considered the chemistry of the halogen and chalcogen elements in terms of the electron structures of the atoms. Under this picture the outer electron structures of an atom may vary but its nuclear charge (and mass) do not. Since it is the nuclear charge which identifies an atom as being of a particular element we can use Dalton's idea of indestructible atoms to interpret chemistry.

But we already know from Chapters 3 and 13 that nuclei themselves may undergo changes known as radioactive changes. During radioactive processes it is common for the nuclear charge to change and so to transform or transmute an atom from one element to another. These radioactive processes, which result in changes within the atomic nucleus, will be discussed in terms of a neutron-proton structure of the nucleus.

NATURAL RADIOACTIVITY

The early researchers in radioactivity soon identified the mass and charge of alpha particles, beta particles, and gamma particles as summarized in Table 21.1. Recent work has shown that certain other particles are emitted in radioactive processes occurring in nature, that is, in natural radioactivity. These

Table 21.1
Particles Found in Natural Radioacitivity

PARTICLE	CHARGE	ATOMIC WEIGHT	IDENTITY IN TERMS OF FUNDAMENTAL PARTICLES
alpha, α	2+	4	$2p + 2n$
beta, β	1−	$\frac{1}{1840}$	electron
gamma, γ	0	0	energy

other radiations were found only after they had been first identified in processes induced in the laboratory so that we still classify natural radioactivity as including only the emission of α, β and γ radiation by ores and rocks.

All the naturally occurring isotopes of all elements beyond bismuth in the periodic system are radioactive. This is to say that the nucleus of each isotope is unstable and emits α, β, or γ particles. Some of the isotopes have very short half lives (see page 172), yet all are found in nature. These short-lived isotopes exist because new atoms of these isotopes form continually from other atoms by radioactive processes. Thus each naturally radioactive isotope of the heavy elements is a member of a disintegration series of isotopes. The first member of each series emits an alpha ray, changing into the second member of the series, the second member then disintegrates into the third, etc. These relations lead to the terminology which refers to parent isotope, daughter isotope, grand-daughter isotope, etc.

If appreciable quantities of naturally radioactive isotopes are to be found, the parent isotope of each series must be reasonably common and, just as importantly, must have a long half life in order still to be present after the passage of geologic time. As a matter of fact we shall soon show that the ages of rocks may be estimated rather accurately from the content of radioactive isotopes and that these ages run as high as two to three billion years. Thus, only parent isotopes with half lives of about a billion years or longer would still be in existence today to keep the series alive. One series of naturally radioactive isotopes is listed in part in Table 21.2, together with the half life of each isotope and the particle each emits. Note the long half life of the parent isotope U^{238} compared to those of the other members of the series. The gamma rays are not listed in the table for, though they often accompany the emission of alpha or beta particles, they are never emitted by themselves in natural radioactivity.

Three series of naturally radioactive isotopes are known but only one, the uranium series, is listed in Table 21.2. A thorium series beginning with Th^{232} and an actinium series beginning with U^{235} are also known. The mass numbers in the thorium series are exactly divisible by 4, and this series is known as the "$4n$" disintegration series. The uranium series is known as the "$4n + 2$" series, since division of the isotopic masses by 4 leaves a remainder of 2 in each case. Similarly, the actinium series is the "$4n + 3$" series. The "$4n + 1$" series has been sought in nature for a long time but not found. It is now possible to prepare the isotopes in this series in the laboratory. The longest half life in the $4n + 1$ series is that of Np^{237}, 2×10^6 years, not long enough to insure current existence of the series even though the series may have been present earlier in the earth's history. In the same way, other isotopes once present on earth have disappeared, leaving stable isotopes as products.

We may note in passing that the early workers in radioactivity were not familiar with the concept of isotopes. They often named daughter elements after the parent. Thus the first four members of the uranium series were known as uranium I (U_I), uranium X_1 (UX_1), uranium X_2 (UX_2), and uranium II (U_{II}). The fourth member, you will see, was correctly identified as a kind of uranium. These notations are still used by research men but their use is disappearing.

Table 21.2
A Naturally Occurring Uranium (4n + 2) Radioactive Disintegration Series

Pb^{206} Stable ←α 140d← Po^{210} ↑β 22y ↑ Pb^{210} ←α 10⁻⁶s← Po^{214} ↑β 27m ↑ Pb^{214}		Bi^{210} Bi^{214}		Po^{218} ↑α 3m ↑		Rn^{222} ↑α 4d ↑		Ra^{226} ↑α 2×10³y ↑	↑α 8×10⁴y ↑	Th^{230} ↑α 2×10⁵y ↑ Th^{234}	Pa^{234} ↑β 25d ↑ ↑α 4×10⁹y ↑	U^{234} ↑β 1m ↑ U^{238}

ATOMIC NUMBER	82	83	84	85	86	87	88	89	90	91	92
FAMILY IN PERIODIC SYSTEM	4a	5a	6a	7a	0	1a	2a	3b			

Each isotope in the series from U^{238} to Pb^{206} is shown together with the particle (α or β) emitted by each isotope, and the half life of the isotope. Key to half lives: y = years, d = days, h = hours, m = minutes, s = seconds.

Known naturally occurring radioactive isotopes of five other elements are listed in Table 21.3. The rest of the isotopes occurring in nature are presumed to be stable, but it should be clearly noted that this may mean only that their radioactive half lives are so long that the occasional radioactive emission escapes detection. For instance, a half life of 10^{12} years, such as Re^{187} possesses, means that in one mole of rhenium less than 1000 atoms would be disintegrating per second. Any feasible method of measuring these radiations deals with such a small sample (less than 0.001 mole) that there would be less than one disintegration per second to detect, illustrating the fact that the determination of a long half life is a very difficult experiment. For instance, recent work indicates that no stable isotopes of indium exist, yet the half lives, about 10^{14} years, are so long that it is not yet possible to identify the radioactive changes definitely.

Table 21.3
Some Known Naturally Occurring Radioactive Isotopes

PARENT	HALF LIFE	DAUGHTER
K^{40}	$2 \times 10^8 y$	Ca^{40}
Rb^{87}	$6 \times 10^{10} y$	Sr^{87}
Sm^{152}	$1 \times 10^{12} y$	Nd^{148}
Lu^{176}	$2 \times 10^{10} y$	Hf^{176}
Re^{187}	$3 \times 10^{12} y$	Os^{187}

Short half lives are also difficult to measure. The 10^{-11} second half life of Po^{212} means that half of the Po^{212} nuclei present at any time disintegrate within one-hundred billionth of a second.

Measurement of radioactivity is thus limited in practice to nuclei with half lives between about 10^{-12} seconds and 10^{12} years. Longer lived nuclei are said to be stable. Shorter lived nuclei are said to have only transitory existence since they can not be identified experimentally.

GEOLOGIC CLOCKS

The problem of the age of the earth, which has long fascinated man, can be attacked through accurate estimates of the ages of naturally radioactive ores. If one assumes that a given uranium ore originally contained no Pb^{206} isotope then any of this isotope of lead found in the ore must have originated from the radioactive decay of the uranium. The accuracy of the assumption may be determined from the present isotopic composition of the lead in the rock since the uranium disintegration series produces only the Pb^{206} isotope (see Table 21.2). Other sources of lead contain a mixture of isotopes. A simple determination of the ratio of the weight of lead (Pb^{206}) to weight of uranium (U^{238}) allows a calculation of the time elapsed since the rock solidified. Since half of the uranium is converted to lead every 4×10^9 (4 billion) years, a sample of rock containing equal numbers of moles of U^{238} and Pb^{206} would be approximately 4 billion years old.

Similar methods can be applied with varying degrees of success to rocks containing any of the naturally radioactive materials. The results depend on the geologic history of the rocks (metamorphosis, degree of leaching by water, etc.) and the validity of the underlying assumptions of the method. The methods are not much good for rocks less than a few hundred million years old, but they indicate that the very oldest rocks known are about 2.2 billion years old. Other independent methods give ages up to about 5×10^9 years for the universe. Thus we may use a time of about 5 billion years ago as that when the universe began to take its present form.

RADIOACTIVE PROCESSES

Today one is not limited to naturally occurring radioactive materials—at least one radioactive isotope is known for every element in the periodic system. Altogether, more than 800 unstable isotopes have now been discovered and the number grows. In terms of a proton-neutron structure of the nucleus all the isotopes of an element have the same number of protons—they differ only in the number of neutrons. An isotope whose mass number is greater than the chemical atomic weight of its element has more neutrons than the average atom of the element and one with lower mass number has fewer neutrons. These relations allow us to interpret the types of radioactive processes found for the unstable synthetic isotopes.

A few, but only a few, of the unstable isotopes emit neutrons. This fact is somewhat surprising in view of the assumed presence of neutrons in all nuclei except that of the prevalent isotope of hydrogen. When an isotope has too many neutrons to be stable it is evidently harder for it to emit a neutron than it is to convert the neutron into a proton through the process of negative beta particle emission. Whatever the reason, isotopes with a neutron excess char-

$$_0n^1 = {_1p^1} + {_{-1}\beta^0} \tag{21.1}$$

acteristically emit negative beta particles when they undergo radioactive change. As a result the nucleus gains a proton and now belongs to the element of next higher atomic number. It may not be too heavy to be a stable isotope of this element. An example is

$$_{11}Na^{24} = {_{12}Mg^{24}} + {_{-1}\beta^0} \tag{21.2}$$

The nuclei that are too light to be stable have too many protons rather than too many neutrons. Yet protons have never been detected in radioactivity. It must be even harder for a nucleus to release a proton than to release a neutron. This fact is particularly surprising because the positive charge on the proton might be expected to make its escape from the nucleus rather easy. Instead, loss of positive charge on the nucleus may be accomplished by emission of a particle having a mass identical with that of an electron but bearing unit positive charge rather than unit negative charge. This particle, called a *positron*, is often called a *positive beta particle*, symbol β^+, for this reason. The negative beta particle is then given the symbol β^-. Emission of a positron may be considered as originating in the transformation of a proton into a neutron through positron emission.

$$_1p^1 = {_0n^1} + {_1\beta^0} \tag{21.3}$$

Emission of positrons is usual for the unstable isotopes that have too light masses. The resulting isotope has fewer protons and more neutrons

$$_{29}Cu^{58} = {_{28}Ni^{58}} + {_1\beta^0} \tag{21.4}$$

Overabundance of protons in an isotope may also be a cause for alpha particle emission. However, alpha particles are emitted only from isotopes of the elements of highest atomic numbers, (Sm^{152} is an outstanding exception; see Table 21.3).

Another type of radioactivity also is found for some isotopes lighter than the average for the element. Certain unstable nuclei are able to capture electrons from the lowest (the 1s or K) energy level of the atom. This process, called *K capture*, results in the conversion of a proton into a neutron, so reducing the proton excess (neutron deficiency).

$$_{96}Cm^{241} + {_{-1}e^0} = {_{95}Am^{241}} \tag{21.5}$$

The factor which will finally limit the number of transuranium elements that can be synthesized may turn out to be the great probability of K capture in elements of high atomic number, whose K electrons are very close to the nucleus. X-rays are emitted immediately following K capture as other electrons fall into the lowest energy level left vacant by the capture process. K capture processes are also interesting in that their half lives are affected appreciably by alteration of the chemical bonds of the active atom. No other nuclear transformations are affected by the nature of the chemical bonding.

In Table 21.4 are listed the types of radioactive process, their interpretation in terms of nuclear changes, and the types of isotopes which may be expected to undergo each change. The most common processes are electron and positron emission. Alpha emission is next most common. Neutron emission and K capture are uncommon. Simple gamma emission is also uncommon but the emission of a gamma ray simultaneously with an electron, positron, or alpha is very common, the gamma ray carrying off some of the energy of the reaction.

NUCLEAR BOMBARDMENTS

A study of radioactive processes, summarized in Table 21.4, does not exhaust the possible types of nuclear reactions. Radioactive processes are those which proceed with a definite and measurable half life. Many nuclear reactions are known which are practically instantaneous, occurring only when a nucleus is supplied with a large amount of energy from an outside source. These are called *bombardment reactions*. Bombardment reactions are occurring in nature

340   GENERAL CHEMISTRY

continuously as the particles emitted by naturally occurring radioactive materials impinge on neighboring nuclei, or as cosmic rays strike atomic nuclei. These bombardments may cause transmutations in the struck nuclei. The number of such changes occurring in any given volume in a small time interval is not great. An average human is penetrated by only a few cosmic rays per second. Most of the rays pass through the body with no effect on it. Yet the evidence is slowly building up that these bombardments do have a measurable and permanent effect, particularly on genetic materials.

Table 21.4
Types of Radioactive Processes

| PARTICLE EMITTED |||TYPES OF ISOTOPE EMITTING PARTICLE|CHANGE IN NUCLEUS|
NAME	SYMBOL	OTHER IDENTIFICATION		
alpha	α	helium nucleus	usually atomic number greater than 80	loss of 2 protons and 2 neutrons
negative beta	β^-	electron	mass number greater than average for element	neutron to proton
gamma	γ	energy	———	loss of energy
positive beta	β^+	positron	mass number less than average for element	proton to neutron
neutron	n	———	mass number greater than average for element	loss of neutron
K capture	K	orbital electron capture with x-ray emission	mass number less than average for element	proton to neutron

The idea has even been advanced that a large fraction of the mutations of living organisms stem from the chemical effects resulting when a cosmic ray causes a nuclear transmutation in a gene and so alters the chemical nature of the gene. Since there is little which can be done to regulate the cosmic rays, there seems to be small chance that these mutations can be appreciably diminished. It is clear, on the other hand, that other radiation impinging on living matter will increase the mutation rate. This fact has been established without question in laboratory experiments. Since most mutations are bad in the sense that they lead to deficiencies in the offspring, it is clear that adequate precautions should always be taken to prevent any more than the minimum dose of radiation on genetic material. (It should be mentioned here for completeness that the effect of penetrating radiation on orbital electrons may lead to the breaking of chemical bonds and so cause even more widespread chemical changes than the occasional nuclear bombardment would yield.)

Man now has at his disposal various devices which are millions of times more powerful in total dosage than any conceivable natural source of radiation. X-ray machines, Van de Graff generators, cyclotrons, betatrons, synchrotrons, linear accelerators, atomic piles, and atomic bombs are only a few examples. Most of these devices act on the principle of using electrical energy to accelerate charged particles to very high velocities. At these high velocities the particles will have correspondingly high energies and often prove effective in initiating nuclear reactions upon collision with nuclei.

Before proceeding to a discussion of some of these devices and the uses to which they may be put, let us examine the experimental problem of trying to bombard nuclei. In the first place nuclei are tiny, less than one out of every million billion parts of a given volume of supposedly solid material contains an atomic nucleus. The problem of hitting atomic nuclei has been compared to that of standing outside a barn with a 22-caliber rifle and trying to shoot a rat inside without knowing where he is. The usual solution to the problem, as far as nuclei are concerned, is to use as intense a beam of radiation as possible and as thick a piece of target material as possible in order to get as many nuclei in the path of the beam as is feasible.

The second problem involves the electrical nature of the atom and the nucleus. Each nucleus is surrounded by negative electrons which will repel any negative projectiles aimed at the nucleus. The nucleus itself is positive in charge and will repel any positively charged projectiles as they approach. Only the most energetic negative or positive projectiles will be able to penetrate into the nucleus. A neutral particle will not be so repelled and we shall find that neutrons are, in many ways, better bombarding particles than are the charged particles.

The third problem involves the detection of any changes which may occur. If the product of the reaction is stable or has a very long half life, it will be necessary to let the reaction forming it proceed long enough to make a great many atoms so that they may be isolated and detected. If the half life of the product is short it will be necessary to work very rapidly with the bombarded material in order to test for the product before it has all undergone its normal radioactive disintegration.

BOMBARDING DEVICES

Devices for bombarding nuclei may be conveniently divided into three classes: radioactive sources, particle accelerators, and atomic piles.

Radioactive sources may be used for the radiations they produce directly. Radium, for instance, is often used as a source of high energy alpha particles and cobalt 60 as a source of negative beta particles. Or the radioactive source may be combined with some other substance which, when bombarded by it, produces a secondary radiation. A mixture of radium and beryllium serves as a neutron source in this way. The neutrons may then be used to bombard still other material.

$$_{88}Ra^{226} = {}_{86}Rn^{222} + {}_{2}\alpha^4 \tag{21.6}$$

$$_{2}\alpha^4 + {}_{4}Be^9 = {}_{6}C^{12} + {}_{0}n^1 \tag{21.7}$$

Particle accelerators utilize electrical energy to produce x-rays (neutral photons), high-energy electrons (negative particles), or high-energy protons, deuterons, tritons, or alphas (positive particles). The protons themselves are obtained by ionizing ordinary hydrogen gas (nuclei containing one proton), deuterons by ionizing "heavy" hydrogen, H^2 (nuclei containing one proton and one neutron), tritons by ionizing hydrogen gas rich in tritium, H^3 (nuclei containing one proton and two neutrons), and alphas by ionizing helium gas (nuclei containing two protons and two neutrons). Heavier nuclei have been used occasionally and their use will become more common as the particle accelerators are perfected. The principal bombarding particles, other than neutrons, are the low weight, positive, atomic nuclei, particularly of hydrogen and helium. Most of the newer machines are designed to accelerate these positive particles. Energies of tens of millions of electron volts are readily obtainable, hundreds of millions are common, and billions are now possible. These energies begin to approach the highest known in nature, those of the cosmic rays, and far surpass anything in the realm of natural radioactivity where energies of the order of tens of millions of electron volts are maximum.

The atomic pile works on a very different principle from the particle accelerators. It was discovered in 1939 that uranium 235 when bombarded with neutrons splits up into two nuclei approximately equal in weight plus some 2.5 additional neutrons on the average. This splitting process induced by neutrons is known as "nuclear fission accompanied by secondary neutron emission." By 1942 it was demonstrated that the secondary neutrons could be used to decompose more U^{235} and so to continue a chain reaction. Since only 1 of the 2.5 neutrons produced on the average need be used to continue the reaction there is an excess of 1.5 neutrons to allow for those which escape from the pile or react with impurities and to use in bombarding other materials. An atomic pile consists in essence of a large "pile" of uranium and auxiliary equipment in which secondary neutrons maintain the fission process and as many of the "extra" neutrons as feasible are used for bombardment purposes. Many atomic piles are now in operation in this country and abroad. The larger ones can produce neutron beams far more intense than the particle beams obtained in any other way. Fortunately the neutron is also a better bombarding particle for many purposes than any other, so that nuclear transmutations can now be produced on a very large scale. In fact, tons of material have been transmuted in these piles over a period of years.

BOMBARDMENT REACTIONS

Many types of nuclear bombardment reactions are known and new ones are continually being discovered. They all have in common the property of occurring almost instantaneously so that no half life for any intermediate product is determinable. This may mean that the reactions really are instantaneous or only that the half lives of the intermediates are so short as to be outside the range of measurement. On the other hand, the nuclei produced by such bombardments are ordinarily radioactive and have measurable half lives. Thus the bombardment reactions may be used to synthesize radioactive nuclei not found in nature from the stable nuclei which are present.

Table 21.5 lists some of the more common types of nuclear reactions. The

Table 21.5

Some Bombardment Reactions

(The particle most commonly expelled by each bombarding particle is set first in boldface.)

BOMBARDING PARTICLE	EXPELLED PARTICLE	EXAMPLE
n	**γ**, α, p, 2n, n, He^3	$_{48}Cd^{115} + {_0}n^1 = {_{48}}Cd^{116} + {_0}γ^0$
d	**p**, α, 2n, n, γ, t	$_{23}V^{51} + {_1}d^2 = {_{23}}V^{52} + {_1}p^1$
p	**n**, α, p, γ	$_{25}Mn^{55} + {_1}p^1 = {_{26}}Fe^{55} + {_0}n^1$
α	**n**, α, p, d, 2n	$_9F^{19} + {_2}α^4 = {_{11}}Na^{22} + {_0}n^1$
γ	**n**, p	$_{35}Br^{81} + γ = {_{35}}Br^{80} + {_0}n^1$
e$^-$(β$^-$)	e$^-$(β$^-$)	$_{34}Se^{81} + {_{-1}}β^0 = {_{34}}Se^{81*} + {_{-1}}β^0$
He^3	p	$_{14}Si^{28} + {_2}He^3 = {_{15}}P^{30} + {_1}p^1$

* The second form of the Se^{81} isotope has higher nuclear energy than the first. Its neutrons and protons are in higher energy levels, or at least one of them is.

particle most commonly expelled by each of the bombarding particles is given first. It is interesting to note that the most commonly expelled particle is a neutron. We have already mentioned the α,n (α particle in, neutron out) reaction between radium and beryllium as a source of neutrons (equation 21.7).

The d,p (deuteron in, proton out) reaction is interesting, for the evidence on this reaction indicates that the deuteron generally does not actually enter the nucleus but loses its neutron to the nucleus on the fly so to speak, the proton within the deuteron being repelled by the target nucleus and so continuing on its path.

The probability of a given reaction occurring will vary with the energy of the bombarding particle and the nature of the target nucleus, particularly its charge. In many cases several reactions occur simultaneously, making the experimental identification of the products rather difficult. The identification of the particular reaction occurring is also complicated by the fact that most targets contain more than one isotope. It may be quite difficult to determine just which isotope is undergoing reaction. For this reason a target, such as natural gold, which has only one stable isotope, is particularly nice to work with. As an example, bombardment of gold with neutrons (an n,γ reaction, followed by β^- emission) leads to the formation of mercury 198 as a single

$$_{79}Au^{197} + {_0}n^1 = {_{79}}Au^{198} + \gamma \qquad (21.8)$$

$$_{79}Au^{198} = {_{80}}Hg^{198} + {_{-1}}\beta^0 \qquad (21.9)$$

pure isotope. Arc lights made of this single isotope of mercury emit very sharply defined wave lengths of light and are now serving as the most accurately known standard of length.

All of the bombardment reactions listed in Table 21.5 involve the emission of a single particle, or at most two particles, per bombardment. Two additional types of reaction are known in which more than two particles are emitted. Bombardment of nuclei with very high energy alpha particles sometimes smashes the nucleus into five or six or more fragments, some of them simple particles and some nuclei of elements higher than lithium in the periodic system. This process in which large fragments of the nucleus are knocked off on bombardment is known as *spallation*, by analogy to the geologic process of rock weathering or glacial action in which large shell-like fragments of rock break away from a massive formation.

A few isotopes are known which break approximately in half when bombarded with neutrons, gamma rays, or other particles. This process is known as *nuclear fission*. For three isotopes—U^{235}, Pu^{239}, and U^{233}—the process of neutron fission assumes much more than scientific interest. These three isotopes, only the first of which is commonly found in nature, not only undergo fission when bombarded with neutrons. They also release an average of better than two neutrons per fission. These neutrons are then available to cause further fission if they enter nuclei which are capable of this reaction.

The uniqueness of these neutron fission reactions lies in the fact that they can be self-perpetuating reactions which will proceed until the fissionable material in the vicinity has been used up. For all other known nuclear bombardments it is necessary to supply, from outside the system, a new bombarding particle for each nucleus which is to be changed. Supplying these particles requires the expenditure of great amounts of energy because only a small fraction of the bombarding particles are effective. Even though the reacting nuclei may release relatively large quantities of energy, more energy must always be put into the system than is released by it. The neutron fission of U^{235}, Pu^{239}, and U^{233}, on the other hand, releases a billion billion times as much energy as is used in triggering the reaction. Furthermore this energy can be released slowly, in a controlled fashion, to furnish power for an engine, or can be released in a ten-thousandth of a second to produce a devastating explosion. The speed of release of the energy can be easily controlled and readily changed from time to time.

A few bombardment reactions are known in which the bombarding particles merge with the target nuclei to give relatively stable products. *Fusion reactions* are of this type. The main source of the energy evolution in the sun, for instance, appears to be adequately described by the series of equations in Table 21.6. These reactions, known as the Bethe cycle, describe the net conversion of

Table 21.6
The Solar Reaction for the Production of Atomic Energy

	Δm
$_1H^1 + {_6}C^{12} = {_7}N^{13}$	-0.00210
$_7N^{13} = {_6}C^{13} + {_1}e^0$	-0.0018
$_1H^1 + {_6}C^{13} = {_7}N^{14}$	-0.00828
$_1H^1 + {_7}N^{14} = {_8}O^{15}$	-0.0077
$_8O^{15} = {_7}N^{15} + {_1}e^0$	-0.00247
$_1H^1 + {_7}N^{15} = {_6}C^{12} + {_2}He^4$	-0.00515
Net: $4\,_1H^1 = {_2}He^4 + 2\,_1e^0$	-0.02750

hydrogen atoms (protons) to helium atoms (alpha particles).

$$4\,_1H^1 = {_2}He^4 + 2\,_1\beta^0 \tag{21.10}$$

Hydrogen bombs supposedly operate in a similar fashion, possibly using reactions such as

$$_1H^3 + {_1}H^3 = {_2}He^4 + 2\,_0n^1 \tag{21.11}$$

$$_1H^2 + {_1}H^3 = {_2}He^4 + {_0}n^1 \tag{21.12}$$

$$_3Li^7 + {_1}H^2 = 2\,_2He^4 + {_0}n^1 \tag{21.13}$$

All these reactions 21.10, 21.11, 21.12, and 21.13 involve a considerable loss in mass, hence a large evolution of energy per unit of reacting mass. Thus all are efficient energy sources.

NUCLEAR ENERGY—"ATOMIC ENERGY"

Most nuclear reactions release energies of the order of several million electron volts per reacting nucleus. The nuclear fission reaction, on the other hand, releases more than one hundred million electron volts per nucleus. This, in itself, is a very tiny amount of energy. When considered in terms of energy per mole of atoms, however, the true immensity of the energy change becomes apparent. Nuclear fission of one mole, about ½ pound, of U^{235} produces as much energy as the combustion of 4 million pounds of coal. Furthermore, the process of fission, once started, is self continuing, for it uses part of the products of the reaction (the neutrons) to maintain the fission process in additional nuclei. In this respect it is analogous to the combustion of coal in which some of the emitted energy is used to warm up more coal to the combustion temperature. Just as the rate of combustion of coal can be controlled by adjusting the amount of coal present and the rate at which it comes to combustion temperature, so also can the rate of uranium fission be controlled by adjusting the amount of fissionable material present and the rate at which neutrons enter it. And just as a single piece of coal will quickly stop burning as it radiates so much energy that it cools below the combustion temperature, so a small piece of fissionable material will quickly stop undergoing fission for the neutrons will escape from the material before striking a fissionable nucleus. This behavior leads to the concept of *critical size* in self-sustaining fission reactions. The critical size is the minimum size of fissionable material which will just support a continuous reaction. The criterion determining this critical size is that, on the average, at least one of the secondary neutrons must hit a fissionable nucleus rather than escape from the block of fissionable material. Too high a fraction of the neutrons escape from a smaller piece to maintain the reaction. In a larger piece the reaction accelerates with time since more than one secondary neutron causes fission on the average. If the size is exactly equal to the critical size the reaction will proceed at a constant rate.

When more than the critical size of fissionable material is present as purified U^{235}, Pu^{239}, or U^{233}, the fission reaction will proceed with great and increasing rapidity once a neutron enters the material. The great rapidity arises from the fact that the secondary neutrons are emitted at high speeds and will, in purified materials, quickly strike another fissionable nucleus to continue the reaction. The increasing rate of reaction with passing time stems from the fact that more than two secondary neutrons are emitted in each fission process. Each of these detonates two more nuclei. The neutrons from these detonate four more nuclei, then eight, sixteen, and so on, in ever increasing profusion. The fission reaction is so rapid and the rate of neutron travel so high that the whole reaction in a moderate sized piece of material will be over in about one hundred-thousandth of a second. Such sudden energy release inevitably results in an explosion.

Atomic bombs are typical of such a fast nuclear fission reaction. A single fission bomb, containing perhaps fifty pounds of fissionable material and exploding in a small fraction of a second, will cause as much damage to a city as a one thousand plane raid with conventional high explosives and fire bombs. Practically complete destruction will be wrought over a radius of some two miles from the point under which the bomb explodes. In addition to the explosive force of the bomb one must contend with the incendiary effect. The temperature at the center of the exploding bomb is of the order of ten million degrees and the heat radiated is sufficient to create surface temperatures of more than one thousand degrees at distances greater than one mile. This surface temperature is quite adequate to start fires which, with those started from broken electrical wiring and gas mains, lead to a fire storm to complete the destruction near the target center. The third destructive effect of atomic bombs, which is much less widespread than the other two, lies in the nuclear radiation initiated at the instant of explosion. Only the neutron and x-radiation are apt to penetrate the atmosphere far enough to cause serious casualties. These radiations cause about ten per cent of the human casualties following an atomic bomb explosion.

Defense against an atomic bomb is similar to defense against other weapons, the only effective defenses being distance and barriers. The chief difference lies in the great increase in distance necessary for a fair degree of safety (if in the open, four miles or more) and the much thicker and stronger barriers required at short distances. To be completely adequate against any type of A-bomb attack a barrier would have to be about one mile thick, but, for most purposes, several feet of concrete or even of packed dirt would be fairly effective.

Hydrogen bombs may well have a range five times or more that of atomic bombs, and their radiation effects will become relatively more important due to the very great production of neutrons. Blast and heat will probably still be the most destructive features of the explosions, however.

Atomic piles are operated by assembling a critical mass of material and regulating the concentration and velocity of neutrons so that a steady reaction is maintained. Just as much energy is produced per pound of fissionable material in the pile as in the bombs, but the energy is produced over a longer time interval and is controlled. The regulation is attained by introducing into the pile bars of materials such as boron or cadmium. These elements absorb neutrons and remove them so that they cannot continue the fission chain. By inserting the bars a greater or lesser distance it is possible to control the system so that exactly one secondary neutron on the average goes on to cause fission of a nucleus. This leaves about 1.5 neutrons (see page 342) on the average which must be prevented from causing fission if the pile is to operate at a steady level. Some of these will inevitably escape from the pile and be lost and some will react with impurities but great advantages can be attained by utilizing the remaining neutrons for bombardment purposes rather than by merely absorbing them in cadmium or boron rods.

PRODUCTION OF FISSIONABLE MATERIALS

The only fissionable material useful for power production of energy and found in nature is U^{235}. The U^{235} constitutes about 0.7 per cent of natural uranium, the rest being mostly U^{238}. Metallic uranium and uranium compounds containing this isotope ratio may be used directly in power production but the critical sizes are very large. Smaller critical sizes may be attained if enriched or pure U^{235} is used. Separating this isotope from the other uranium isotopes is a tedious, but possible, process. It may be done most readily in a large mass spectrograph or in a diffusion apparatus. The diffusion apparatus, such as in the large plants at Oak Ridge, takes advantage of the difference in average molecular velocity between gaseous uranium hexafluoride made from U^{235} and the same compound made from the common U^{238} isotope. The lighter molecules diffuse faster through the barriers. By use of acres and acres of barrier space, many barriers in series, and several months of time it is possible to produce practically pure U^{235}.

Two other isotopes, U^{233} and Pu^{239}, have already been mentioned as also being fissionable. Neither of these occurs in nature to any extent. Both, however, may be made by bombarding fairly common isotopes with neutrons as shown in the following sequences:

$$Th^{232} + n = Th^{233} = Pa^{233} + \beta^- \qquad (21.14)$$
$$Pa^{233} = U^{233} + \beta^- \qquad (21.15)$$
$$U^{238} + n = U^{239} = Np^{239} + \beta^- \qquad (21.16)$$
$$Np^{239} = Pu^{239} + \beta^- \qquad (21.17)$$

Here we have a real use for the extra secondary neutrons formed in an atomic pile operating with U^{235} as fuel. The secondary neutrons in the pile may be used to form either U^{233} or Pu^{239}. These processes of neutron absorption will then compete with the fission process for the neutrons present. The desired balance between the two processes can be most readily obtained by using fairly small pieces of uranium embedded in a lattice of graphite. The small pieces of uranium insure that most of the emitted secondary neutrons will escape from the uranium into the graphite before they strike any nuclei. Carbon nuclei do not react readily with neutrons but do slow them down, from their high emission velocities, to velocities comparable with those of ordinary gaseous molecules. The slowed down neutrons will wander through the pile and eventually enter a piece of uranium again to give either fission (if they collide with U^{235}) or Pu^{239} formation (if they collide with U^{238}). The trick is to design the pile so that the first process occurs with just enough frequency to keep the pile operating and the second process uses as many of the other neutrons as possible. It will be seen that, with 2.5 neutrons being emitted per fission on the average, 1 of these must be used to continue the fission process and the other 1.5 are available for Pu^{239} (or U^{233}) formation. If, on the average, more than one of these 1.5 neutrons is actually captured, it is possible to increase the content of fissionable nuclei in the pile with continued operation. It is thus theoretically possible to convert all the U^{238} in the world into fissionable material, as well as all the Th^{232}, merely by continuing pile operation in the above way. An atomic pile which produces more fissionable material during operation than is actually used up is known as a "breeder pile," the operation being called "breeding." By breeding it will be possible to increase the amount of material in the world which can be used in fission reactions by a factor of perhaps 100.

It should be clearly noted that atomic piles generate great amounts of energy as they operate. They can therefore be used as power plants, either stationary or mobile. Since the weight of fuel they use—one-millionth of the amount of coal to generate the same power—is so small, a plant can be operated in any location in which it can be built, with no concern for other sources of power to run the plant. Furthermore an atomic engine could have sealed within itself sufficient fuel to operate, without refueling, for a very long period of time. It is for this reason that atomic powered submarines (first launched in 1954), atomic powered ships (supposedly available by 1960), and atomic powered airplanes (supposedly available in the not too distant future) are so eagerly sought.

USES OF RADIOISOTOPES

Unstable nuclei are characterized by the half life of the isotope to which they belong. At some instant each will emit a particle and be transformed into another isotope or even another element. Up to this instant, however, the atom acts as would any other isotope of the element. It undergoes the same chemical reactions and exhibits the same chemical properties as do the stable isotopes. At the instant in which it undergoes the nuclear reaction, the atom undergoes several changes. Just as firing a gun not only ejects the bullet but also kicks the gun in the opposite direction, so the expulsion of a nuclear particle kicks the remainder of the nucleus in the opposite direction. This recoil energy is almost always sufficient to break the chemical bonds of the atom and to move it several atomic diameters away from its former site. There the atom will come to rest and may react with other atoms in the vicinity. It will now react as determined by its atomic number after emission of the radioactive particle and it may well belong to a different element than formerly, with different chemistry. Nuclear processes, therefore, can cause widespread chemical changes in their vicinity.

Usually the chemical changes accompanying transmutations are of minor interest, but if they occur in a living system they may be of great import. It is becoming common practice, for instance, to imbed radioactive materials in cancers and tumorous growths. The chemical changes accompanying the radioactive changes tend to break down the neighboring molecules necessary to the continued growth of the cancer or tumor and thus arrest its growth, or even destroy it. It should be clear, of course, that great care must be taken not to cause too severe damage to neighboring, healthy tissue.

Most applications of radioisotopes utilize the emitted particles to identify the spot at which the radioactive change occurred. Radioactive sodium chloride introduced into the blood stream, for instance, allows a rapid determination of the effectiveness of the circulatory system and of the extent to which it is damaged in a crushed limb. Some phosphorus compounds are selectively concentrated in brain tumors. Hence these can be located by feeding a patient substances containing compounds of radioactive phosphorus. The tumor can then be located by the direction from which the emitted beta particles come. Thus the surgeon can be sure of the location of the tumor without operating. Or the metabolism of iodine in the body may be studied by feeding iodine compounds containing some radioactive iodine atoms and following their passage through the body by means of external Geiger counters. The speed of assimilation by various parts of the body, the length of retention there, and the rate of elimination may all be determined without surgical technics.

The speed and the detailed mechanisms of many chemical reactions can be found by using radioactive isotopes. Minute quantities of materials may be traced through complicated processes by use of radioisotopic methods. The atomic age may not be as rosy as some have painted it, but, for the first time, scientists now have a tool which allows study of changes involving only a small number of molecules.

The possible uses of radioisotopes are limitless. In medicine they will be used more and more in diagnosis, therapy, and research. In industry they will find wider and wider application in control, tracer technics, and research. It is not overstating the case to claim that radioisotopes rank with the great discoveries of all time in the potentialities they show for increasing our knowledge of the physical universe and our ability to control it to some extent.

Problem 21.1. Write equations for the following. Discuss each change in terms of the neutron-proton theory of the nucleus.
  a. Fluorine 17 is radioactive.
  b. Fluorine 20 is radioactive.
  c. Plutonium 239 emits an alpha particle.
  d. Sodium 22 emits a β^+ particle.
  e. Neptunium 238 undergoes K capture.
  f. Fluorine undergoes a d-t reaction.
  g. Gold undergoes an α-2n reaction.
  h. Plutonium 239 undergoes fission to give lanthanum 145, 4 neutrons, and another nucleus. Both daughter nuclei are radioactive. What will they emit?

Problem 21.2. Francium 223 has been found in nature. Can you account for this fact? Its half life is 21 minutes.

Problem 21.3. Plutonium 239, half life 24,000 years, is found in nature in minute amounts. Can you account for this fact?

Problem 21.4. Thorium 232 undergoes neutron fission, and bismuth 209 undergoes fission with deuterons. Why can't these reactions be used in a nuclear engine?

Problem 21.5. For how many nights would it be necessary to send out one thousand plane raids with conventional explosives to duplicate the damage done by one thousand atomic bombs delivered in a single night?

Problem 21.6. Is the material stored as atomic bombs capable of any use except military?

Problem 21.7. Uranium contains 0.7 per cent of uranium 235. Sources which will readily yield approximately ten thousand tons of uranium are known. How many bombs could be made? How many tons of coal could this replace in terms of available energy? How many years would this atomic fuel last if it were used at the same rate of energy production which is now found for coal? See page 92. How will these figures be changed as breeding becomes widespread?

Problem 21.8. Indicate how you would use radioisotopes to tackle the problem of vitamin usage in the body.

Problem 21.9. Only some three thousand atoms of the element curium (half life 2.5 hours) were originally made. How was it possible to prove that the element existed at all?

Problem 21.10. A uranium ore sample is found to contain 1.19 g of uranium 238 and 1.03 g of lead 206. What weight of helium has escaped from the ore sample? How many alpha particles does this represent? How old is the ore?

22 THE NITROGEN FAMILY

GROUP 5a of the periodic system contains the elements whose atoms have five valence electrons, three less than the number (eight) in the atoms of the corresponding inert gas elements. It is called the *nitrogen family* after the first element in the family or the *phosphorus family* after the most typical element. Sulfur and chlorine, like phosphorus lying in the third period of the periodic system, are also more typical elements than the first members of the chalcogen and halogen families. As may be deduced from the numbers of electrons in their atoms, the members of the nitrogen family have odd atomic numbers.

OCCURRENCE OF NITROGEN AND PHOSPHORUS

The most abundant elements of the nitrogen family, nitrogen and phosphorus, do not rank particularly high in the list of abundance of elements on the earth (see Table 7.1) but they are essential to living organisms. They, together with potassium, are the primary constituent elements in commercial fertilizers. Although nitrogen is abundant in stars and in the sun's atmosphere and comprises four fifths of the earth's atmosphere it is rather scarce in the hydrosphere and lithosphere of the earth. There it is found in the form of nitrates, nitrites, and ammonium salts, all of which are water-soluble, and in proteins which are products of living organisms. Because its inorganic compounds are so soluble they tend to leach out of soils and so be lacking in sufficient amounts for the synthesis of the proteins in growing plants. Large beds of sodium nitrate are found in arid regions of Chile. They were the world's chief commercial source of nitrogen compounds between the time of their discovery, in the early part of the nineteenth century, and the twentieth century, when methods were devised for obtaining nitrogen compounds from the nitrogen of the air. Substantial amounts, though a minor fraction of the present world production of nitrogen compounds, are still obtained from these beds. Potassium nitrate, saltpeter, known to the alchemists, has been found in small beds but it is usually made from sodium nitrate, which is called Chilean saltpeter.

Phosphorus in the lithosphere is found mainly in the insoluble calcium salts, calcium phosphate, formula $Ca_3(PO_4)_2$ and apatite, formula $CaF_2 \cdot 3Ca_3(PO_4)_2$.

352   GENERAL CHEMISTRY

Calcium phosphate is the principal inorganic constituent of teeth and bones but phosphate groups are constituents of complex organic compounds (see Chapter 39) found in all cells and in body fluids. The element phosphorus was first prepared by the alchemist, Brandt, in 1669 from urine by a complicated procedure. The phosphorus compounds in most soils are low enough in abundance to be limiting factors to the growth of plants when crops are removed.

ELEMENTS OF THE NITROGEN FAMILY

The elements of the nitrogen family with their valency shell of two s and three p electrons can form three covalent bonds per atom, the three p electrons pairing with electrons from other atoms to form the three bonds. However, the tendency to form covalent bonds and the electronegativity of the elements decrease from nitrogen to bismuth. Nitrogen, a typical nonmetallic element, does not form a monatomic positive ion, but bismuth can lose its three p electrons to strongly electronegative groups to form bismuth ions, Bi^{+++}. Nitrogen forms very stable diatomic molecules, N_2, with a triple bond between the atoms, $:N\equiv N:$. It is a gas with very low melting and boiling points (see Table 22.1), indicating little residual attraction between the molecules. On the other hand bismuth is a crystalline metal with much higher melting and boiling points. Above the boiling point, 1560°C., the vapor consists of a mixture of Bi_2 and Bi molecules. The other elements, phosphorus, arsenic, and antimony, each form several types of solids, the more voluminous type being translucent, distinctly nonmetallic, and soluble in organic solvents, and the denser type being opaque and more or less metallic, showing metallic conduction, and being insoluble in organic solvents.

Phosphorus vapor from any of its solid forms has a density corresponding to P_4 molecules at temperatures below 800°C. and even at 1700°C. only about half the molecules have the formula P_2. Arsenic vapor also consists mostly of As_4 molecules below 800°C., although the proportion of As_2 molecules increases more rapidly with temperature than for phosphorus. Antimony vapor, with its Sb_4 molecules, dissociates only slightly more than arsenic vapor. The structures of these tetratomic molecules are of the type in which each atom is bonded by a single electron pair to three other atoms to form a regular tetrahedral pyramid, the bond angles being 60 degrees. The liquids have tetratomic molecules corresponding to those in the vapors. See Figure 22.1 for a diagram of the P_4 molecule. The corresponding As_4 and Sb_4 molecules are larger (see Table 22.2 for values of the respective covalent radii).

In white phosphorus (and the corresponding yellow arsenic and yellow antimony) the packing unit in the crystalline solid is the tetratomic molecule. As Table 22.1 shows, the melting and boiling points correspond to those of simple molecular crystals. White phosphorus is soluble in organic solvents, again indicative of its simple molecular structure. It is poisonous. When finely divided and exposed to air it bursts into flame spontaneously, hence it is customarily stored under water.

Table 22.1
Properties of Elements of the Nitrogen Family

ELEMENT	FORMULA OF GAS	SOLID FORMS	MOLECULAR FORMULA OF SOLID	DENSITY OF SOLID g/ml	MELTING POINT °C.	BOILING POINT °C.	OTHER PROPERTIES
Nitrogen	N_2		N_2		-208	-195.8	
Phosphorus	P_4, P_2	white (yellow)	P_4	1.83	44.1	280	Soluble in organic solvents.
		red (violet)	——	2.34	sublimes (1 atm.) at 416°		Insoluble in organic solvents.
		black	——	2.69			
Arsenic	As_4, As_2	yellow	As_4	1.97			Soluble in organic solvents.
		black	——	4.73			
		gray	——	5.73	sublimes (1 atm.) at 633°		Shows metallic conduction.
Antimony	Sb_4, Sb_2	yellow	Sb_4		unstable		Soluble in organic solvents.
		black	——	5.3			
		gray	——	6.67	630	1,325	Shows metallic conduction.
Bismuth	Bi_2, Bi	metallic (slightly red)	——	9.80	273	1,560	Metallic.

Red (or violet) phosphorus, on the other hand, is not poisonous or especially inflammable and is not soluble in organic solvents. When heated it sublimes at 416°C. to give P_4 vapor at one atmosphere pressure. At its melting point, 590°C. at 43.1 atmospheres, the liquid consists of P_4 molecules. These facts

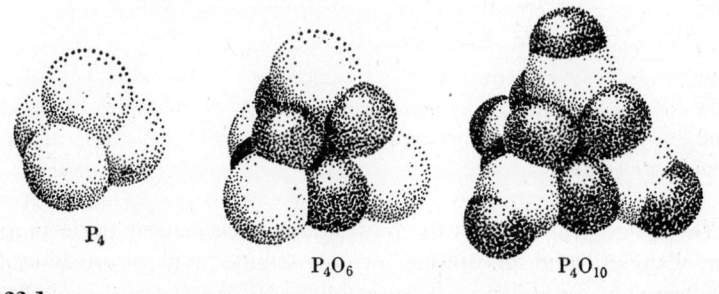

P_4 P_4O_6 P_4O_{10}

Figure 22.1.
Molecular structures of white phosphorus, phosphorus "trioxide," and phosphorus "pentoxide."

indicate that red phosphorus consists of large molecules which must be broken down to form the simpler liquid and gaseous molecules. White phosphorus may be converted to the stabler red form on heating to 260°C. in an inert atmosphere, or at lower temperatures in the presence of catalysts such as iodine.

Black phosphorus, a still denser crystalline form, is produced under high pressures (12,000 to 35,000 atmospheres).

Corresponding crystalline forms are found for arsenic and antimony. Yellow arsenic and yellow antimony correspond to white phosphorus although they are less stable. They are soluble in organic solvents, showing the presence of small molecular units. Gray arsenic and gray antimony show increasing metallic character, between that of red or black phosphorus and of metallic bismuth. They are insoluble in organic solvents.

THE HYDROGEN COMPOUNDS

As may be expected, the elements of the nitrogen family combine with hydrogen to form compounds of the type MH_3. The electronic structure is represented in a plane by

$$H:\overset{..}{\underset{H}{M}}:H, \text{ or } H—\underset{H}{\overset{..}{M}}—H$$

Because of the tetrahedral symmetry of the electron distribution, the ammonia molecule has the three-dimensional configuration shown in Figure 22.2. In the nitrogen hydride, ammonia, the nitrogen is electronegative to the hydrogen (see Table 22.2) but the polarity of the bonds is much less for the other mem-

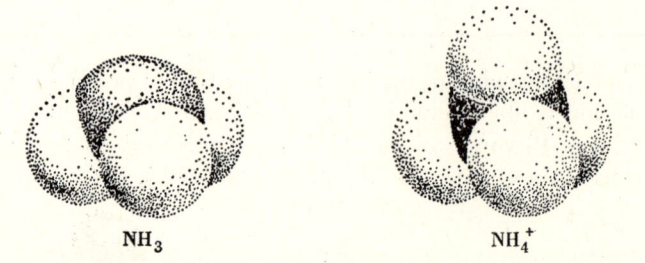

NH_3 NH_4^+

Figure 22.2.
Molecular structures of ammonia and of ammonium ion. Note that the ammonium ion differs only by the addition of a proton to the unshared pair of electrons at the apex of the ammonia molecule.

bers of the series. Ammonia is the most stable with respect to decomposition into the elements and phosphine, arsine, stibine, and bismuthine show a steadily decreasing stability. All the compounds are gases at room temperature. Inspection of the melting and boiling points of the compounds shows that ammonia has higher melting and boiling points than the trend of the other members of the series would indicate. (Compare with the abnormalities of water and hydrogen fluoride among the hydrogen compounds of the chalcogen and halogen series.) The high boiling points and melting points indicate strong hydrogen bonding in these substances (see page 222). Ammonia has distinctive basic properties whereas the other members of the series do not. The special properties of ammonia will be discussed more completely in a later section.

Table 22.2
Hydrogen Compounds of the Nitrogen Family

ELEMENT	RELATIVE ELECTRO- NEGATIVITY	COVALENT RADIUS, (Å.)	HYDROGEN COMPOUND	FORMULA	MELTING POINT °C.	BOILING POINT °C.
Nitrogen	3.0	0.70	Ammonia	NH_3	−78	−33.5
Phosphorus	2.1	1.10	Phosphine	PH_3	−135.5	−87
Arsenic	2.0	1.21	Arsine	AsH_3	−113.5	−54.8
Antimony	1.8	1.41	Stibine	SbH_3	−88	−18
Bismuth		1.46	Bismuthine	BiH_3		ca. +20
Hydrogen	2.1	0.30				

Nitrogen is the only element of the family electronegative enough to form the negative ion, charge 3−. Metallic nitrides are ionic in character. Metallic compounds of the other elements in the family exist but their bonds are covalent or metallic. These compounds, when treated with acids, yield the hydrogen compounds. Some of the metallic nitrides react even with as weak an acid as water.

$$Na^+{}_3N^{---}{}_{(s)} + 3HOH = NH_{3(g)} + 3Na^+ + 3OH^- \quad (22.1)$$

The nitrides of Group 2a also react with water or acids to yield ammonia.

The hydrogen compounds of the other members of the nitrogen family are formed when their metallic compounds are treated with acid.

$$AlP_{(s)} + 3H^+ = PH_{3(g)} + Al^{+++} \quad (22.2)$$

$$Zn_3As_{2(s)} + 6H^+ = 2AsH_{3(g)} + 3Zn^{++} \quad (22.3)$$

Phosphine may also be prepared by heating white phosphorus with a solution of an alkaline hydroxide.

$$P_{4(liq)} + 3OH^- + 3H_2O = PH_{3(g)} + 3H_2PO_2^- \quad (22.4)$$

In this reaction the hypophosphite ion, $H_2PO_2^-$, in which phosphorus has an oxidation number of 1+, is also formed. Arsine also results when such arsenic compounds as oxides, arsenites, or arsenates are reduced in a vessel in which zinc is treated with acid. It is not known whether the reducing action is accomplished by hydrogen atoms not yet combined to form diatomic molecules of hydrogen or hydrogen adsorbed on the surface of the metal, or whether the zinc itself reduces the arsenic.

356 GENERAL CHEMISTRY

$$As_4O_6 + 12H_2 = 4AsH_{3(g)} + 6H_2O$$

or

$$As_4O_6 + 12Zn_{(s)} + 24H^+ = 4AsH_{3(g)} + 12Zn^{++} + 6H_2O \qquad (22.5)$$

The arsine, being gaseous, is carried along by the stream of hydrogen gas from the generator. If passed through a hot glass tube the arsine decomposes and the arsenic is deposited as a "mirror" of metallic arsenic in the colder parts of the tube.

$$AsH_{3(g)} = As_{(s)} + \tfrac{3}{2}H_{2(g)} \qquad (22.6)$$

Reactions 22.5 and 22.6 form the basis of the Marsh test for the presence of arsenic compounds, most of which are poisonous.

AMMONIA

Ammonia is made industrially in large quantities by the Haber process (invented in 1909) from nitrogen of the air and hydrogen gas.

$$\tfrac{1}{2}N_{2(g)} + \tfrac{3}{2}H_{2(g)} = NH_{3(g)} + 11{,}000 \text{ cal.} \qquad (22.7)$$

Although the reaction is exothermic, relatively high temperatures are needed if the reaction is to proceed at an appreciable rate. The extraordinarily large amount of energy, 171,000 cal. per mole, required to form nitrogen atoms from the diatomic molecules

$$171{,}000 \text{ cal.} + N_{2(g)} = 2N_{(g)}$$

is a measure of the strength of the bond between the two nitrogen atoms in the molecule. High temperatures result in increased reaction rates with nitrogen gas because more N—N bonds are broken. On the other hand ammonia also becomes less stable at higher temperatures, the net result being that the equilibrium mixture contains less ammonia at higher temperatures. The per cent by volume of ammonia in equilibrium with a mixture containing three moles of hydrogen to one of nitrogen at a pressure of 1 atmosphere is 98.5 at 27°C., 8.7 at 327°C. and 0.21 at 627°C. At higher pressures (greater concentrations of the reacting gases) the equilibrium percentages of ammonia increase in accordance with the principle of Le Chatelier and the mass action law. In present practice, iron containing small amounts of aluminum and potassium oxides is used as a catalyst and the reaction is carried out at temperatures of 550–600°C. and pressures of several hundred atmospheres. Pressures up to one thousand atmospheres have been used but the steel reaction vessels may fail at the high temperatures and pressures. Even though only part of the equilibrium gases (say ten per cent) are ammonia, the ammonia can be removed and the unreacted nitrogen and hydrogen repassed through the reaction vessel until most of the original gases are converted to ammonia. The American production of synthetic ammonia from nitrogen of the air is about one million tons per year and most of this is made by the Haber process.

An ancient method of preparing ammonia was to heat nitrogenous organic material (rich in protein) such as horns and hoofs in the absence of air to form "spirits of hartshorn." This old process has its modern counterpart. Coal, a substance of organic origin, contains combined hydrogen and small amounts of combined nitrogen (see Table 8.1). When the coal is heated to form coke (see page 93), ammonia is one of the gases driven off. In the United States about 250,000 tons of such "by-product" ammonia are produced per year. The ammonia is removed from the other distillation products by dissolving it in water and is then treated with sulfuric acid to form ammonium sulfate. The ammonium sulfate, a salt, is mostly used in agricultural fertilizers.

$$2NH_3 + H_2SO_4 = (NH_4)_2SO_4 \qquad (22.8)$$

A third commercial source of ammonia is less used. When nitrogen is passed over calcium carbide at 1000°C. (in the absence of oxygen) calcium cyanamide is formed. When this substance is treated with steam, ammonia is formed.

$$CaC_{2(s)} + N_{2(g)} = CaCN_{2(s)} + C_{(s)} \qquad (22.9)$$
calcium   calcium
carbide   cyanamide

$$CaCN_{2(s)} + 3H_2O_{(g)} = 2NH_{3(g)} + CaCO_{3(s)} \qquad (22.10)$$

Ammonia under pressure can be liquefied at room temperature. As may be guessed from its abnormal freezing and boiling points, ammonia is an associated liquid, the molecules being bound together with hydrogen bonds. It is an excellent solvent for many substances, including a number of salts. It is available commercially in steel cylinders. Ammonia finds increasing use as a cheap small-scale source of hydrogen, for when heated it decomposes almost completely according to the reaction (see also equation 22.7).

$$2NH_{3(g)} = N_{2(g)} + 3H_{2(g)} \qquad (22.11)$$

Problem 22.1. Calculate the weight of nitrogen in one cu. mi. of air at 20°C. and 750 mm. pressure. Express the weight in metric tons. What weight of ammonia could be prepared from this nitrogen? Compare with the annual production of synthetic ammonia in the United States. (1 metric ton = 1000 kilogram; 1 cubic foot = 28.3 liters; 1 mile = 5280 feet; 1 kilogram = 2.2 pounds.)

AMMONIA WATER

Ammonia is very soluble in water. Water solutions are sold commercially as *aqua ammonia* (ammonia water) or as *ammonium hydroxide*. Household ammonia is a dilute water solution. Water solutions of ammonia exhibit an interesting set of equilibrium reactions. They include equilibria between the liquid phase and the gas phase, and between molecules and ions in the solution.

$$H_2O \text{ (in solution)} = H_2O_{(g)}$$
$$NH_3 \text{ (in solution)} = NH_{3(g)}$$

In the solution

$$NH_3 + xH_2O = NH_3 \cdot xH_2O$$
$$NH_3 + HOH = NH_4^+ + OH^-$$
$$NH_3 \cdot xH_2O = NH_4^+ + OH^- + (x-1) H_2O$$
$$HOH = H^+ + OH^-$$

It has been customary in chemistry to assume that ammonia forms a definite hydrate with water, x being one, and to write the formula for the hydrate in the form NH_4OH. However, in both ammonia and water molecules there is a complete octet of electrons so that any definite bond holding the neutral molecules together would probably be a hydrogen bond. Such a bond would be weak. The electronic formulation is

$$\underset{\text{ammonia}}{\overset{H}{\underset{H}{H-N}}\!:\,} + \underset{\text{water}}{\overset{H}{H-\overset{..}{\underset{..}{O}}\!:\,}} = \underset{\text{"ammonium hydroxide"}}{\overset{H}{\underset{H}{H-N}}\!:\,H-\overset{H}{\underset{..}{O}}\!:\,} \quad (22.12)$$

One may assume that this "molecule" ionizes rather weakly according to the reaction

$$NH_4OH = NH_4^+ + OH^- \quad (22.13)$$

On the other hand, many chemists, in the absence of direct evidence that molecular NH_4OH actually exists in solution or in the gas phase, prefer to regard the ion-producing reaction as

$$\underset{\text{ammonia}}{\overset{H}{\underset{H}{H-N}}\!:\,} + \underset{\text{water}}{\overset{H}{H-\overset{..}{\underset{H}{O}}\!:\,}} = \underset{\text{ammonium ion}}{\overset{H}{\underset{H}{H-\overset{+}{N}-H}}} + \underset{\text{hydroxide ion}}{:\overset{..}{\underset{..}{O}}-H^-} \quad (22.14)$$

In an acid solution, there being an abundance of hydrogen ions, the reaction would be

$$\overset{H}{\underset{H}{H-N}}\!:\, + H^+ = \overset{H}{\underset{H}{H-\overset{+}{N}-H}} \quad (22.15)$$

Later we shall consider many other examples of reactions in which ammonia, whether in solution or as a gas, combines with positively charged ions. Because the formulation according to equation 22.14 and 22.15 is more direct than that based on the hypothetical molecular ammonium hydroxide we shall use it almost exclusively.

Equilibrium constant expressions for the ionization reactions 22.13 and 22.14 are written in the respective forms

$$K = \frac{[NH_4^+] \times [OH^-]}{[NH_4OH]} = 1.8 \times 10^{-5} \quad (22.13a)$$

$$K = \frac{[NH_4^+] \times [OH^-]}{[NH_3]} = 1.8 \times 10^{-5} \tag{22.14a}$$

where $[NH_4OH]$ in equation 22.13a and $[NH_3]$ in equation 22.14a represents the concentration of *all* the original ammonia, whether unhydrated or hydrated, except that appearing in the ammonium ions. The value of the ionization constant shows that in a $1 f$ solution of ammonia water the concentration of the ammonium ions, and hydroxide ions, is 0.0043 molar. Thus, ammonia water is weakly basic.

Problem 22.2. Calculate the concentration of OH^- ions (and NH_4^+ ions) in a $0.1 f$ solution of ammonia water.

Problem 22.3. What is the hydrogen ion concentration of the solution in Problem 22.2? The pH?

COORDINATION OF AMMONIA

We have already noted in equations 22.13 and 22.14 the tendency of ammonia to share protons with water (hydrogen bonding) or to capture them completely even though ammonia has its quota of eight valence electrons. In either case ammonia shares its unbonded electron pair with a proton. The covalent bond formed when both electrons of the bonding pair are contributed by one of the atoms is sometimes called a *coordinate covalent* or a *coordinate* bond. The atom furnishing the electron pair is called the *donor* atom and the other atom is called the *acceptor* atom.

Ammonia has an unusual tendency to exhibit coordinate covalency. It combines vigorously with protons from acids to form the ammonium ion as in equation 22.15. It cannot react with neutral hydrogen atoms or molecules in this way because ammonia already has its full quota of electrons. The ammonium ion has a tetrahedral symmetry so that the four hydrogen atoms are indistinguishable even though only one of them came from the acid. Consequently the positive charge on the ion must be associated with the whole ion and not with any particular hydrogen atom (see Figure 22.2).

Even as a gas, ammonia has basic properties. When gaseous ammonia meets gaseous hydrogen chloride it coordinates the proton to form a "smoke" of tiny particles of crystalline ammonium chloride, a salt. It is interesting that this and many other gas phase reactions occur only in the presence of water vapor. The absolutely dry gases do not react.

$$NH_{3(g)} + HCl_{(g)} = NH_4^+Cl^-_{(s)} \tag{22.16}$$
$$\text{ammonium chloride}$$

In general, ammonia reacts with acids in water solution to form typical salt solutions consisting of ions. The ammonium ion has the same charge as and about the same size as the rubidium ion and is not much larger than the potassium ion. Ammonium salts have about the same solubilities as the corresponding potassium salts and are usually isomorphous with them. Attempts

360   GENERAL CHEMISTRY

have been made to prepare neutral "ammonium" but the compound with its nine electrons is unstable. Temporary alloys of ammonium with mercury have been prepared by electrolyzing ammonium salts with a mercury cathode but the "ammonium" decomposes to give ammonia and hydrogen.

In the presence of strong bases, ammonium ion loses a proton and neutral ammonia is formed.

$$NH_4^+ + OH^- = NH_3 + HOH \qquad (22.17)$$
$$\text{ammonium ion} \quad \text{ammonia}$$

When the solution is heated or boiled, ammonia gas appears in the vapor. Since ammonia is the only common gaseous base, its presence in the vapor detected by wet red litmus turning blue serves as a test for ammonium ion in the solution. Note that the ammonium ion is destroyed in the testing process.

Ammonia also coordinates other cations. A number of cations of the elements in the middle of the long periods of the periodic table form coordination compounds by acting as acceptors to donor molecules such as ammonia. A proton coordinates only a single ammonia molecule, but a silver ion, Ag^+, coordinates two ammonia molecules and a cupric ion, Cu^{++}, coordinates four ammonia molecules. With silver ion the reaction is

$$Ag^+ + 2 : \underset{H}{\overset{H}{N}}{-}H = H{-}\underset{H}{\overset{H}{N}} : Ag : \underset{H}{\overset{H}{N}}{-}H \qquad (22.18)$$

Equation 22.18 represents an equilibrium reaction, subject to the mass action law. At equilibrium the concentration of uncoordinated silver ion decreases as the concentration of ammonia increases. We have already shown (page 330) that, through this equilibrium, ammonia water may be used to distinguish between the presence of chloride, bromide, and iodide ions.

The reaction of ammonia with copper ions and other colored ions can be followed because of the resulting change in color. Anhydrous copper ions are colorless. When anhydrous copper sulfate (colorless) is added to water it dissolves and a light-blue color appears, the color of the hydrated copper ion. This ion results because water may also be coordinated by ions.

$$Cu^{++} + 4H{-}\underset{H}{\overset{..}{O}}: = \underset{\underset{\underset{H}{\overset{H}{\diagdown}}{\overset{..}{O}}}{\diagup}}{\overset{\overset{H\diagdown\,\,\diagup H}{\overset{..}{O}}}{\diagdown}}\underset{}{Cu}\underset{\overset{..}{O}\diagdown H}{\overset{\diagup O:}{\diagup}}\qquad (22.19)$$
colorless
light-blue

If ammonia is now added, the ammonia, being more strongly coordinated than the water, replaces the water and a deep-blue ion results:

THE NITROGEN FAMILY

$$Cu(H_2O)_4^{++} + 4 :NH_3 = \begin{array}{c} H\ H\ H \\ \backslash | / \\ H\ N\ H \\ \backslash\ | \ / \\ H-N-Cu-N-H \\ / \ | \ \backslash \\ H\ N\ H \\ / | \backslash \\ H\ H\ H \end{array}^{++} + 4H-\ddot{O}: \qquad (22.20)$$

light-blue (left); deep-blue (right)

Such ions as $Ag(NH_3)_2^+$, $Cu(NH_3)_4^{++}$, and $Ag(CN)_2^-$ are typical complex ions (see page 284). The latter complex ion carries a negative charge because it is formed from a positive silver ion, Ag^+, and two negative cyanide ions, CN^-.

Ammonia also coordinates with certain neutral molecules which are electron deficient, boron trifluoride for instance.

$$\begin{array}{c} F\ \ \ F \\ \backslash / \\ B \\ | \\ F \end{array} + :N\begin{array}{c}H \\ -H \\ H\end{array} = \begin{array}{c} F\ \ \ H \\ \backslash / \\ F-B-N-H \\ / \ \backslash \\ F\ \ \ H \end{array} \qquad (22.21)$$

Problem 22.4. Write the equation for the net reaction between a solution of ammonium chloride and one of calcium hydroxide.

Problem 22.5. Outline an electronic structure for the cyanide ion, CN^-; for the complex ion, $Ag(CN)_2^-$.

THE HALOGEN COMPOUNDS

From the number of valence electrons of the atoms in the nitrogen family we may expect them to form halides of the type MX_3 where X stands for any halogen. Nitrogen forms such compounds but only the fluoride, formula NF_3, is stable. The chloride has been prepared but is unstable and decomposes explosively according to the reaction

$$2NCl_{3(g)} = N_{2(g)} + 3Cl_{2(g)} + 110{,}800 \text{ cal.} \qquad (22.22)$$
yellow-green

There is some question as to whether the bromide has been prepared and the iodide, isolated only as an ammonia complex, formula $NI_3 \cdot NH_3$, is also explosive.

As the electropositive character of the nitrogen family increases with increasing atomic number the stability of the positive oxidation states, and, hence, that of the halide compounds, increases also. All the trihalides of phosphorus exist. They are hydrolyzed by water to form the hydrogen halide and phosphorous acid according to the reaction

$$PX_3 + 3HOH = 3HX + HPO(OH)_2 \qquad (22.23)$$
phosphorous acid

Arsenic trihalides are also covalent compounds but they are less completely hydrolyzed than the corresponding phosphorus trihalides. Antimony trihalides show some ionic character but the concentration of Sb^{+++} is low. In water solution there is partial hydrolysis so that the *antimonyl* ion SbO$^+$ appears. The reaction for the trichloride is

$$\text{SbCl}_3 + 2\text{HOH} = 2\text{H}^+ + 2\text{Cl}^- + \underset{\text{white}}{\text{SbOCl}_{(s)}} \tag{22.24}$$

the antimonyl chloride appearing as a precipitate. Bismuth is electropositive enough to form the trivalent ion, Bi^{+++}; bismuth trifluoride is ionic but the other trihalides have some covalent character. Bismuth trichloride hydrolyzes to form the insoluble bismuthyl chloride, formula BiOCl, analogous to the reaction shown for antimony trichloride in equation 22.24.

In Chapter 19 we found that sulfur can form the hexafluoride, formula SF$_6$, in which sulfur is surrounded by six electron pairs rather than the customary four pairs. Phosphorus by sharing five electron pairs in a similar way can form pentahalides; those with formulas PF$_5$, PCl$_5$, and PBr$_5$ are known. Antimony also forms these pentahalides, and arsenic and bismuth form the pentafluorides, formulas AsF$_5$ and BiF$_5$. The phosphorus pentahalides are hydrolyzed by excess water to form the hydrogen halides and phosphoric acid.

$$\text{PX}_5 + 4\text{HOH} = 5\text{HX} + \underset{\text{phosphoric acid}}{\text{H}_3\text{PO}_4} \tag{22.25}$$

Phosphorus pentachloride exists as PCl$_5$ molecules in the gas and liquid phase but as alternate PCl$_4^+$ and PCl$_6^-$ ions in the crystal. This is an excellent example of the effect crystal forces can have on the relative stability of alternative structures. It also illustrates the danger of drawing conclusions concerning structures in one phase from data observed on another phase.

Problem 22.6. Hydrogen bromide is sometimes made in the laboratory by the following method: (1) red phosphorus is treated with liquid bromine, (2) the product is treated with water, (3) the hydrogen bromide is freed from any unreacted bromine vapor by passing the gas from step (2) over hot copper. The hydrogen bromide does not react with copper. Which of the reactions are oxidation-reduction reactions? Write the equations for the reactions, balancing the oxidation-reduction reactions by the oxidation-state method or the half-reaction method.

THE OXIDES OF NITROGEN

Nitrogen forms an unusual series of oxides and also forms peroxides. The oxides are shown in Table 22.3. Their molecular shapes are diagrammed in Figure 22.3. Of these the starred oxides with formulas NO and NO$_2$ contain a single odd-numbered atom and hence the molecules have an odd number of electrons. Such stable molecules with an uneven number of electrons are very rare. At low temperatures the dioxide polymerizes to form the dimer, N$_2$O$_4$, in which the number of electrons is even.

$$\underset{\text{brown}}{2\text{NO}_2} = \underset{\text{colorless}}{\text{N}_2\text{O}_4} \tag{22.26}$$

THE NITROGEN FAMILY 363

N₂O

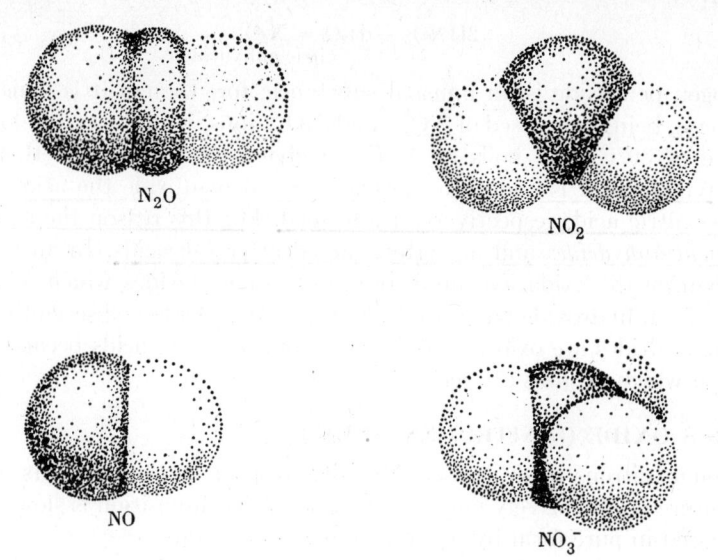

NO₂

NO

NO₃⁻

Figure 22.3.
Molecular structures of nitrous oxide, nitric oxide, nitrogen dioxide, and nitrate ion.

The two species are in equilibrium with one another, the fraction in the dimer form decreasing as the temperature increases.

Except at low temperatures dinitrogen trioxide exists only in equilibrium with appreciable quantities of nitric oxide and nitrogen dioxide. Dinitrogen pentoxide is made by treating nitric acid with strong dehydrating agents such as phosphorus pentoxide.

Table 22.3
Oxides and Acids of Nitrogen

OXIDATION NUMBER	1+	2+	3+	4+	5+
FORMULA	N₂O	NO *	N₂O₃	NO₂*	N₂O₅
COMMON NAME	nitrous oxide	nitric oxide	(di)nitrogen trioxide	nitrogen dioxide	(di)nitrogen pentoxide
COLOR			green	brown N₂O₄ nitrogen tetroxide	
ELECTRON STRUCTURE	:N=N=O:	:N=O:	:Ö: N—O—N: :O:	:O: :O=N—O: :O:	:O: N—O—N (gas) :O: :O:
CORRESPONDING ACID AND NAME	H—O—N=N—O—H hyponitrous acid		H—O—N=O nitrous acid		H—O—N :O: :O: nitric acid

* ODD NO. OF ELECTRONS

$$2HNO_3 - H_2O = N_2O_5 \quad (22.27)$$
nitric anhydride

Dinitrogen pentoxide is an unusual substance, for, though it is ionic in the solid phase, being composed of NO_2^+ and NO_3^- ions, it melts at the low temperature of 30°C. and boils at 47°C. to give N_2O_5 molecules. (Remember PCl_5.) When water is added to the trioxide and pentoxide the acids nitrous acid and nitric acid, respectively, are formed. For this reason the oxides are called *acid anhydrides* and are often named after the acids. In an acid and its anhydride the oxidation numbers are the same. Oxides which react with water to form hydroxide bases are called basic anhydrides. Observe that acids whose anhydrides are oxides contain OH groups but are acids because of the ease with which protons are released.

NITROUS OXIDE (DINITROGEN OXIDE)

Although nitrous oxide is unstable with respect to the elements at room temperature it is relatively inert for the rate of decomposition is slow. It may be prepared in pure form by heating ammonium nitrate.

$$NH_4NO_{3(s)} = N_2O_{(g)} + 2H_2O_{(g)} \quad (22.28)$$

The temperature must be carefully controlled; otherwise the reaction may proceed explosively to form nitrogen, oxygen, and water. Nitrous oxide is used as an anaesthetic. Wood, phosphorus, and sulfur burn readily in it, nitrogen gas being released. On the other hand, nitrous oxide may be oxidized to nitric oxide by a strong oxidizer such as permanganate.

NITRIC OXIDE

Nitric oxide is a gas resembling nitrogen, oxygen, and carbon monoxide in its general properties. Although the molecule contains an odd number of valence electrons it is not colored and it shows little tendency to polymerize into double molecules. It is unstable with respect to molecular nitrogen and oxygen but the large amounts of energy needed to break the N—O bond are responsible for its inertness to decomposition. In one commercial method of preparation, the *arc process*, air is passed through an electric arc. At the temperature of the arc small amounts of nitric oxide are formed from the nitrogen and oxygen of the air and these remain when the air is very rapidly cooled.

$$N_{2(g)} + O_{2(g)} = 2NO_{(g)} \quad (22.29)$$

Nitric oxide may also be made by passing air over a very hot "pebble bed," then rapidly chilling the product gases.

The most important commercial method of making nitric oxide is to burn ammonia in air, using platinum gauze as a catalyst. The reaction is

$$4NH_{3(g)} + 5O_{2(g)} = 4NO_{(g)} + 6H_2O_{(g)} \quad (22.30)$$

The chief use of nitric oxide is to make nitrogen dioxide and nitric acid. At ordinary temperatures the colorless nitric oxide combines rapidly with oxygen to form the brown nitrogen dioxide.

$$NO_{(g)} + \tfrac{1}{2}O_{2(g)} = \underset{\text{brown}}{NO_{2(g)}} \qquad (22.31)$$

Nitric oxide is formed when nitric acid is reduced by a metal such as copper which does not have the power to reduce hydrogen ions to gaseous hydrogen. With somewhat diluted nitric acid the principal reaction is

$$\underset{\text{red}}{3Cu_{(s)}} = \underset{\text{blue}}{3Cu^{++}} + 6e^-$$

$$2NO_3^- + 8H^+ + 6e^- = 2NO_{(g)} + 4H_2O \qquad (22.32)$$

$$\underset{\text{red}}{3Cu_{(s)}} + 2NO_3^- + 8H^+ = \underset{\text{blue}}{3Cu^{++}} + 2NO_{(g)} + 4H_2O \qquad (22.33)$$

However, other reduction products of the nitric acid are nitrogen and nitrogen dioxide so that the nitric oxide produced is not pure. More powerful reducing agents, zinc, for example, reduce some of the nitrate ion all the way to ammonium ion.

NITROGEN DIOXIDE

At room temperature nitrogen dioxide is mostly polymerized to nitrogen tetroxide according to the reaction shown in equation 22.26. The equilibrium mixture is a liquid below 21.3°C. The equilibrium changes with temperature so that the dissociation of nitrogen tetroxide to nitrogen dioxide is almost complete at 135°C. Above 150°C. nitrogen dioxide begins to dissociate to nitric oxide and oxygen, and this equilibrium also changes with temperature so that the dissociation is almost complete at 620°C.

$$\underset{\text{colorless}}{N_2O_{4(g)}} \text{ (Below 140°C.)} = \underset{\text{brown}}{2NO_{2(g)}} \text{ (Between 140 and 620°C.)} = \underset{\text{colorless}}{2NO_{(g)} + O_{2(g)}}$$

$$(22.34)$$

Nitrogen dioxide is a product of decomposition of nitric acid and is responsible for the yellow or brown color in nitric acid or its concentrated water solutions.

$$2HNO_3 = \underset{\text{brown}}{2NO_2} + H_2O + \tfrac{1}{2}O_{2(g)} \qquad (22.35)$$

Equilibrium between nitric oxide and nitrogen dioxide and with nitrous and nitric acid exists in water solution. When nitrogen dioxide is dissolved in cold water the principal reaction is

$$\underset{\text{brown}}{2NO_{2(g)}} + HOH = \underset{\substack{\text{nitrous}\\\text{acid}}}{HNO_2} + H^+ + NO_3^- \qquad (22.36)$$

In the dioxide the oxidation number of the nitrogen is $4+$, in the nitrous acid it is $3+$ and in the nitrate it is $5+$. However, nitrous acid decomposes according to the reaction

$$3HNO_2 = H^+ + NO_3^- + H_2O + 2NO_{(g)} \qquad (22.37)$$

the rate of decomposition increasing with temperature. Consequently, when nitrogen dioxide is dissolved in warm water the principal reaction is

$$3NO_{2(g)} + HOH = 2H^+ + 2NO_3^- + NO_{(g)} \quad (22.38)$$
$$\text{brown}$$

When nitrogen dioxide is passed into an alkaline solution, nitrite, and nitrate ions are formed and when an equimolar mixture of the monoxide and dioxide is used almost pure nitrite is formed

$$2NO_{2(g)} + 2OH^- = NO_2^- + NO_3^- + H_2O \quad (22.39)$$
$$\text{brown}$$

$$NO_{2(g)} + NO_{(g)} + 2OH^- = 2NO_2^- + H_2O \quad (22.40)$$
$$\text{brown}$$

If the mixture of the monoxide and the dioxide is cooled, it condenses to a green liquid and freezes to a solid at $-102°C$. In the solid the molecular formula is N_2O_3 but in the liquid and in the gas phases there is substantial dissociation according to the equilibrium reaction

$$N_2O_3 = NO + NO_2 \quad (22.41)$$
$$\text{green} \quad\quad \text{brown}$$

At room temperature the dissociation is almost complete. The nitrogen trioxide is the anhydride of nitrous acid.

Nitrogen dioxide mixed with oxygen but free from nitric oxide may be made by heating a heavy metal nitrate salt such as lead nitrate

$$Pb(NO_3)_{2(s)} = PbO_{(s)} + 2NO_{2(g)} + \tfrac{1}{2}O_{2(g)} \quad (22.42)$$
$$\text{brown}$$

NITROUS ACID AND NITRITES

Nitrous acid is stable only in solution. It is a weak acid. Its ionization constant has the value, $K = 4.5 \times 10^{-4}$. It is, therefore, slightly stronger than acetic acid. It forms stable salts with the elements of the alkali and alkaline earth families. These are very soluble in water. They remain stable at high temperatures. Indeed, nitrites may be prepared by heating the nitrates of the alkali and alkaline earth elements

$$NaNO_{3(s)} = NaNO_{2(s)} + \tfrac{1}{2}O_{2(g)} \quad (22.43)$$
$$Ca(NO_3)_{2(s)} = Ca(NO_2)_{2(s)} + O_{2(g)} \quad (22.44)$$

The nitrates of the heavier metals decompose to the oxide, nitrogen dioxide and oxygen as in equation 22.42.

NITRIC ACID

Pure nitric acid may be prepared as a colorless liquid. It boils at 86°C. Its vapor pressure is, therefore, relatively high so that it fumes in air. Since it decomposes slowly according to equation 22.35, the liquid when boiled finally contains water as well as nitric acid. The concentrated acid of commerce is the constant boiling solution containing about 70 per cent nitric acid (about 18 formal in nitric acid) and is colored by the presence of nitrogen dioxide.

Some nitric acid is still prepared by the older method of heating Chilean saltpeter with concentrated sulfuric acid, and distilling off the nitric acid.

$$NaNO_{3(s)} + H_2SO_4 = HNO_{3(g)} + NaHSO_{4(s)} \qquad (22.45)$$

Most nitric acid is now made by oxidation of ammonia according to equation 22.30 and further reaction of the nitrogen oxides with water according to equations 22.31 and 22.38. In Norway the arc process is used to make nitric oxide and nitric acid. This reaction is of practical interest also because some nitric oxide is made in the air during thunderstorms. By the above processes nitric acid is formed and washed into the soil. This reaction may be the predominant way in which nitrates are added to the soil naturally to maintain its fertility.

Nitric acid is a powerful and commonly used oxidizing agent. The reactions are complicated by the fact that the reduction products may be those with the formulas NO_2, NO_2^-, NO, N_2O, N_2, or NH_4^+, or mixtures of these depending on the concentration of the acid, the temperature of the reaction, and the nature of the reducing agent. In the above series the oxidation number of the nitrogen changes from $5+$ to $4+$, $3+$, $2+$, $1+$, 0, and $3-$, respectively. With warm, concentrated acid on copper, nitrogen dioxide is a principal product, the equation for the half-reaction being

$$2H^+ + NO_3^- + e^- = \underset{\text{brown}}{NO_{2(g)}} + H_2O \qquad (22.46)$$

With more dilute acid, nitric oxide is a principal product as in equation 22.33.

Problem 22.7. Outline the electronic structure of nitrous acid, nitric acid, the nitrite ion, the nitrate ion. In which of these do you expect to find resonance? See page 299.

Problem 22.8. Using the method of half-reactions, derive the equation for the reaction of hot, concentrated nitric acid on copper; on silver.

Problem 22.9. When zinc is added to a dilute solution of nitric acid some ammonium ions are produced. Their presence may be detected by treating the solution with sodium hydroxide and heating. What are the reactions producing these results?

NITRIC ACID AND EXPLOSIVES

Among the oldest of explosives is *gunpowder* or *black powder* made from potassium nitrate, sulfur, and charcoal. An intimate mixture of these, when ignited, burns with the evolution of much heat to form gaseous products, nitrogen, carbon dioxide, carbon monoxide, and sulfur dioxide. These gases, confined to the original volume of the solid mixture, develop enormous pressures and expand rapidly with great force. Some of the ash, formula K_2O, appears as smoke. Many modern explosives are organic nitrogen compounds which can burn more completely to form wholly gaseous products. They are usually made with nitric acid.

One type of explosive compounds is made by treating hydrocarbons with nitric acid or a mixture of nitric and sulfuric acids. One mole of benzene will react with three moles of nitric acid according to the reaction

$$C_6H_6 + 3HONO_2 = C_6H_3(NO_2)_3 + 3HOH \qquad (22.47)$$
$$\text{benzene} \qquad\qquad \text{trinitrobenzene}$$

Observe that the oxygen in the water comes from the hydroxyl group of the nitric acid. Trinitrotoluene [TNT, formula $CH_3C_6H_2(NO_2)_3$] made from toluene and nitric acid is a compound of similar type.

Other organic compounds contain hydroxyl groups which react with nitric acid. An example is glycerine for which the reaction is

$$C_3H_5(OH)_3 + 3HONO_2 = C_3H_5(ONO_2)_3 + 3HOH \qquad (22.48)$$
$$\text{glycerine} \qquad\qquad \text{glyceryl trinitrate}$$

Glyceryl trinitrate, commonly but wrongly called "nitroglycerine," is a liquid explosive somewhat dangerous to handle. When absorbed in a porous solid, usually combustible, it is safer. In this form it is called *dynamite*. Cellulose materials such as cotton and starch also contain hydroxyl groups and can be nitrated to form explosives. Less highly nitrated organic compounds are used to make plastics, lacquers, and dyes. Most of the nitric acid made is used to form nitro or nitrated derivatives of organic compounds.

Problem 22.10. Write an equation for the explosion of TNT; of nitroglycerine. Which explosion is more apt to be smoky and which smokeless?

OXIDES OF THE PHOSPHORUS GROUP

All the elements of the phosphorus group form "trioxides" with the typical empirical formula, M_2O_3. In these the oxidation state is 3+. Molar weights in the gas phase and crystal structure data indicate that the molecular units correspond to the doubled formulas, P_4O_6, As_4O_6, and Sb_4O_6. The structure of bismuth trioxide is not known. The structures of the "trioxides" (and "pentoxides") may be derived from those of the tetrahedral M_4 molecules of the elements (see Figure 22.1). In the phosphorus compounds an oxygen atom rests between each two phosphorus atoms. In the "pentoxide," with the empirical formula, P_2O_5, and molecular formula, P_4O_{10}, four more oxygen atoms are present per molecule, one oxygen being attached to each phosphorus atom. Phosphorus "pentoxide" may be made by heating the "trioxide" with excess oxygen.

$$P_{4(g)} + 3O_{2(g)} = P_4O_{6(s)} \qquad (22.49)$$
$$\text{"trioxide"}$$

$$P_4O_{6(s)} + 2O_{2(g)} = P_4O_{10(s)} \qquad (22.50)$$
$$\text{"pentoxide"}$$

The "pentoxides" of arsenic and antimony cannot be made by direct action of oxygen but may be made by action of concentrated nitric acid on the elements. The "tetroxides," with the general formula M_4O_8, may be regarded as compounds of the "trioxides" with the "pentoxides" (see Table 22.4).

The "trioxides" are the anhydrides of the compounds, $P(OH)_3$, $As(OH)_3$, $Sb(OH)_3$ and $Bi(OH)_3$. The first, orthophosphorous acid, is a weak acid, the second, orthoarsenious acid is still weaker and the third, orthoantimonous acid is the weakest acid. The fourth, bismuth hydroxide, appears to have few acid properties, but is, rather, basic, yielding OH^- ions. Phosphorous acid appears to have only two ionizable hydrogen atoms, the third hydrogen being attached directly to phosphorus as in the formula

$$\ddot{\text{O}}:$$
$$\text{H}-\ddot{\text{O}}-\overset{|}{\underset{|}{\text{P}}}-\ddot{\text{O}}-\text{H}$$
$$\text{H}$$

Table 22.4
Common Oxides and Acids of Phosphorus, Arsenic, Antimony, and Bismuth

OXIDATION NUMBER	NAME	PHOSPHORUS	ARSENIC	ANTIMONY	BISMUTH
	Oxides—				
3+	"Trioxide"	P_4O_6	As_4O_6	Sb_4O_6	(Bi_2O_3)
4+	"Tetroxide"	P_4O_8	As_4O_8	Sb_4O_8	——
5+	"Pentoxide"	P_4O_{10}	(As_2O_5)	(Sb_2O_5)	(Bi_2O_5)
	Acids—				
3+	Ortho—ous	$H_2(HPO_3)$	H_3AsO_3	H_3SbO_3	$Bi(OH)_3$
	Meta—ous	$(HPO_2)_n$	$(HAsO_2)_n$	$(HSbO_2)_n$	——
5+	Ortho—ic	H_3PO_4	H_3AsO_4	$HSb(OH)_6$	——
	Pyro—ic	$H_4P_2O_7$	$H_4As_2O_7$	——	——
	Meta—ic	$(HPO_3)_n$	$(HAsO_3)_n$		

With alkalies it forms salts of the type NaH_2PO_3 and Na_2HPO_3. Arsenious and antimonous acids also form salts of the type Na_3AsO_3 and Na_3SbO_3. Arsenic "trioxide," commonly called "arsenic," arsenious acid, and arsenites are poisonous. Their chief uses are as insecticides.

PHOSPHORIC, ARSENIC, AND ANTIMONIC ACIDS

Phosphorus "pentoxide" is noted as being among the most effective of drying agents. It reacts vigorously with water until it is completely converted to orthophosphoric acid.

$$P_4O_{10(s)} + 6H_2O = 4H_3PO_{4(liq)} \quad (22.51)$$
$$\text{orthophosphoric acid}$$

370 GENERAL CHEMISTRY

The structure of the acid is

$$\text{H}-\text{O}-\overset{\overset{\displaystyle :\text{O}:}{|}}{\underset{\underset{\displaystyle \text{H}}{|}}{\underset{\displaystyle :\text{O}:}{\text{P}}}}-\text{O}-\text{H}$$

Orthoarsenic acid, H_3AsO_4, has a similar structure. It may be made by oxidizing arsenious acid with nitric acid.

We have already seen that orthosulfuric acid (H_2SO_4) has the structure $(HO)_2SO_2$, but orthotelluric acid has the structure $(HO)_6Te$. In both, the oxidation state is 6+. Similarly, the antimony atom in its 5+ oxidation state may be surrounded by six oxygen atoms (six OH groups) whereas the phosphorus atom in its 5+ oxidation state may be surrounded by only four oxygen atoms (including three OH groups) as in $(HO)_3PO$. Thus orthoantimonic acid has the formula $HSb(OH)_6$, sometimes written as $H_3SbO_4 \cdot 2H_2O$, but the first formula shows the presence of the octahedral $Sb(OH)_6^-$ ion and of one easily ionizable hydrogen ion.

Other phosphoric acids than the ortho acid are known. They are the pyrophosphoric acid with the formula, $H_4P_2O_7$, and the metaphosphoric acid with the empirical formula HPO_3. The latter corresponds to nitric acid, HNO_3, in form but it tends to polymerize to form large molecules represented by $(HPO_3)_n$, where n is 2, 3, or some larger number. The polymeric forms of different acids will be discussed in a later chapter.

These oxides and acids are summarized in Table 22.4.

Orthophosphoric acid, a solid at room temperature, is very soluble in water. The molecule can ionize to yield three hydrogen ions according to the steps

$$H_3PO_4 = H^+ + H_2PO^-; \quad K_1 = 1.1 \times 10^{-2} \quad (22.52)$$

$$H_2PO_4^- = H^+ + HPO_4^{--}; \quad K_2 = 5.6 \times 10^{-8} \quad (22.53)$$

$$HPO_4^{--} = H^+ + PO_4^{---}; \quad K_3 = 1.2 \times 10^{-12} \quad (22.54)$$

but, as the values for the equilibrium constants show, only the first ionization reaction occurs to an appreciable extent. Salts of all three of the indicated ions are in common use. Examples are sodium dihydrogen phosphate, formula NaH_2PO_4, disodium hydrogen phosphate, formula Na_2HPO_4, and trisodium phosphate, formula Na_3PO_4. Water solutions of the latter are strongly basic because of the tendency of the triply charged phosphate ions, PO_4^{---}, to take protons from water.

$$PO_4^{---} + HOH = HPO_4^{--} + OH^- \quad (22.55)$$

Problem 22.11. Write equations for the hydrolysis and for the ionization of HPO_4^- and of $H_2PO_4^-$. Which of the reactions, hydrolysis or ionization, has the greater tendency to occur for each ion? Interpret in terms of the structure and charge of the ions.

PHOSPHORUS FROM PHOSPHATES

Because the mineral phosphorite from which phosphorus and its compounds are prepared industrially is insoluble in water and stable with respect to its elements except at very high temperatures, special methods must be employed to make usable compounds. The mineral is calcium phosphate, formula $Ca_3(PO_4)_2$. We observed in reaction 22.55 the tendency of the phosphate ion to reduce its negative charge by combining with protons. With acids the $H_2PO_4^-$ ion is readily formed. This reaction is used to convert calcium phosphate to calcium dihydrogen phosphate, which is much more soluble in water. With sulfuric acid the reaction is

$$Ca_3(PO_4)_{2(s)} + 2H_2SO_4 + 4H_2O = Ca(H_2PO_4)_{2(s)} + 2CaSO_4 \cdot 2H_2O_{(s)} \quad (22.56)$$

The product is sold in commercial fertilizers as *superphosphate*. The calcium sulfate in the mixture usually has no special value. In modern practice there is a tendency to make richer fertilizers by using phosphoric acid instead of sulfuric acid. Then the reaction is

$$Ca_3(PO_4)_{2(s)} + 4H_3PO_4 = 3Ca(H_2PO_4)_{2(s)} \quad (22.57)$$

This product, being better than "super," is called *triple superphosphate*. Nitric acid is also being used, thus introducing nitrogen into the phosphate fertilizer.

Phosphorus is made by heating the phosphate rock with carbon and sand in an electric furnace at temperatures above 1000°C. According to Franck and Füldner, who studied the various possible equilibria, the important steps are: (1) action of carbon on the calcium phosphate to form calcium phosphide and carbon monoxide, (2) reaction of the calcium phosphide with more calcium phosphate to form calcium oxide and phosphorus (gas), (3) reaction of the calcium oxide with silicon dioxide to form calcium silicate, formula $CaSiO_3$. The sand increases the yield by combining with the lime, one of the substances produced in step 2. The over-all equation for the reaction may be written as

$$Ca_3(PO_4)_{2(s)} + 3SiO_{2(s)} + 5C_{(s)} = 3CaSiO_{3(s)} + 5CO_{(g)} + \tfrac{1}{2}P_{4(g)} \quad (22.58)$$

The phosphorus vapor is condensed under water.

When the phosphorus vapor from the furnace is burned in excess air, "phosphorus pentoxide" is formed. This oxide, or phosphorus itself, is used to make the other desired compounds. White phosphorus, though poisonous, was once used in the manufacture of matches. The trisulfide, formula P_4S_3, has now replaced it. Red phosphorus is not poisonous, apparently because it is not soluble and because it has a very low vapor pressure.

Problem 22.12. In commercial fertilizers the nitrogen content is expressed in terms of *per cent of ammonia* What is the value for the per cent of ammonia in pure ammonium sulfate? By-product ammonium sulfate analyzes about 22 per cent. What is the "per cent ammonia" in pure sodium nitrate? Assume that you could convert the nitrate to ammonia.

Problem 22.13. In commercial fertilizers the phosphorus content is expressed in terms of *per cent of phosphorus pentoxide*. What is the value for the "per cent of phosphorus pentoxide" in superphosphate? In triple superphosphate? In orthophosphoric acid?

Problem 22.14. In commercial fertilizers the potassium content is expressed in terms of *per cent of potash* (formula K_2O). What is the "per cent of potash" in potassium chloride, the compound usually used in fertilizers?

SUMMARY

Nitrogen and phosphorus are of special interest because their compounds are important, biologically, and because they are limiting factors in the growth of foodstuffs. Nitrogen compounds are also important as explosives for peaceful use as well as for war. Among inorganic compounds of this group the ammonium compounds and the nitrates are most common. The ammonium compounds are salts containing ammonium ions, NH_4^+, together with the common negative ions. The inorganic nitrates are also salts containing the negative ion, NO_3^-, together with the common positive ions. In water solution the salts have the properties of their constituent ions.

Because nitrogen compounds have a tendency to decompose with evolution of large amounts of energy into substances of low molar weight and because these substances are gases, nitrogen compounds are usually well fitted for use as explosives. The salt, ammonium nitrate, is usually regarded as a harmless compound but under proper (or improper) conditions it decomposes explosively as in the Texas City disaster in which a ship loaded with this salt took fire and exploded in 1946.

Problem 22.15. Give the amounts and concentrations of the products when the following solutions are mixed:
 a. 0.01 mole of hydrogen chloride and 0.10 mole of ammonia in 1 l. of water.
 b. 500 ml. of water containing 0.17 mole of silver nitrate and 2 l. of water containing 0.10 mole of hydrogen chloride.

Problem 22.16. Intrepret the following facts in terms of position of elements in the periodic table: (a) sodium arsenite solution is more alkaline than sodium nitrite, (b) phosphorous trichloride is more completely hydrolyzed than arsenic trichloride, (c) arsine is more easily decomposed into its elements than ammonia.

Problem 22.17. State uses for any five of the substances having the following formulas: (a) P_2O_5, (b) P_4S_3, (c) Sb, (d) $PbHAsO_4$, (e) $CaHPO_4$, (f) N_2O, (g) HNO_3.

Problem 22.18. Correlate the following facts with the position of the elements in the periodic system: (a) arsenious sulfide is more easily dissolved than antimonous sulfide by ammonium sulfide to give ions of the type MS_3^{---} (b) nitrogen trichloride is explosive, whereas phosphorous trichloride is not, (c) bismuth hydride is more unstable with respect to the elements than is ammonia.

Problem 22.19. Give the formulas of the following: (a) arsenious sulfide, (b) orthophosphoric acid, (c) stibine, (d) bismuth oxide, (e) sodium nitrite, (f) hypophosphorous acid, (g) thioarsenite ion.

23 PRINCIPLES OF QUALITATIVE ANALYSIS

WE DISCUSSED, on pages 329–332, some analytical methods of testing a solution for the presence of the various halide ions F^-, Cl^-, Br^-, and I^-. The methods used to differentiate the four ions involved selective precipitation of the fluoride ion with calcium ion, differences in solubilities in water and ammonia water of the silver salts of the other three halides, and differences in the ease of oxidation of the halide ions. Such methods of testing for the presence of substances come under the heading of qualitative analysis. The analyses are qualitative in the sense that they do not give information as to the exact amount of each ingredient present; they only tell whether it is present in sufficient amount to give the test. However, qualitative results become semi-quantitative if one notes the relative amounts of the various precipitates formed and the relative intensities of the various colors used as identification.

Since each element is different from the rest, one may, in principle, design special methods which will allow the detection of any element or any of its compounds in the presence of any others. Such a procedure is actually not feasible because the reagents used usually can react with more than one substance. For example, if sulfide ions are present with the halide ions in the solution to which silver ions are added, the dark silver sulfide precipitated conceals any of the silver halides that may also be precipitated and so makes this reaction useless as a specific test for the halide ions. Only a few of the known tests may be used without regard to the possible total composition of the material to be tested. In testing for ions one must generally use a series of reactions to separate the ions present in the original solution into restricted groups of ions and then test for the individual ions in the presence of only the others in that group.

Many systematic schemes of analysis for ions are known in inorganic chemistry. Generally they are divided into two classes: Schemes for detecting the negative ions (anions) present in a given substance, and schemes for detecting the positive ions (cations) present. Since nonmetallic elements usually appear in the negative ions or anions, while metallic elements usually appear in the positive ions or cations, it is common to refer to anion analysis and cation analysis as the two branches of qualitative analysis for determining the presence of the nonmetallic and metallic elements, respectively.

Although it is possible to develop a complete scheme of analysis for all the anions and all the cations that might conceivably be present in a substance to be tested, a student can learn the general methods and principles of such a scheme without going through the complexity required for a completely inclusive one. We shall, therefore, limit ourselves to a systematic scheme of cation analysis and shall further limit ourselves to a fairly small number of cations, some 25 in all.

SCOPE OF THE SCHEME OF ANALYSIS

The scheme of analysis we shall develop in this chapter will cover the detection of any or all of the following elements (listed in order of increasing atomic number) in a substance from which the ions may be derived: sodium, magnesium, aluminum, potassium, calcium, chromium, manganese, iron, cobalt, nickel, copper, zinc, arsenic, strontium, silver, cadmium, tin, antimony, barium, mercury (we shall distinguish between mercuric and mercurous ions), lead, and bismuth. Most of these will be identified in solutions in which they occur as cations, or positive ions. We shall also include in the scheme the detection of ammonium ions and of hydrogen ions.

We shall presume for the moment that the unknown is in the form of an aqueous solution and shall defer consideration of the treatment needed to prepare a solid unknown for analysis. Analysis of gases is highly specialized and we shall not deal with it at all.

Many schemes may be developed for the separation and identification of the cations we have selected. We might first precipitate all those cations which form insoluble sulfates in acid solution. Addition of sulfuric acid to the unknown solution would result in practically complete precipitation of the sulfates of any strontium, barium, and lead present and partial precipitation of calcium as the sulfate. These sulfates could then be removed from contact with the solution by filtration or centrifugation. We would no longer need to concern ourselves with the above cations, except calcium, now that they have been removed, and might next precipitate those among the remaining ions which form hydroxides insoluble in a strongly basic solution containing ammonia. Magnesium, manganese, iron, and mercury hydroxides would precipitate under these conditions and could be removed. Or we might first precipitate the insoluble chlorides, or the insoluble carbonates, or the insoluble phosphates, etc.

Among the many possible schemes of separation there will be some giving groups which are not amenable to further treatment, but several schemes equally applicable to laboratory analysis are currently used. From the available schemes we shall select only one for formal discussion, but the student is strongly urged to invent modifications or amplifications which will better the scheme or which will allow a more rapid analysis once the absence of certain ions has been established. It is foolish to use the regular and complete scheme when one knows ahead of time that certain ions are definitely absent and do not need to be removed.

SPECIFIC TESTS ON THE UNKNOWN SOLUTION

The simplest test to perform on an unknown in solution is to note the color of the solution. All the ions containing copper (cupric), chromium, cobalt, and nickel, are highly colored and the ions of iron and manganese generally have enough color to be seen. Common colors due to cations are: bright blue for cupric copper, bluish-violet for chromium, green for nickel, chromium, or copper, bright pink for cobalt, pale pink for cobalt or manganese, and yellow-brown for iron. The colored anions most commonly met are: yellow $CrO_4^=$, orange $Cr_2O_7^=$, and purple MnO_4^-. Absence of color indicates that none of these ions is present in large concentration. Other colors may be met and identified but the above are the most common ones.

Specific tests for each of the 25 elements, valid in the presence of any of the others, would be very appealing. Then small portions of the unknown could be put in each of 25 test tubes, and to each test tube be added one of the 25 specific reagents. Certain tubes would give reactions constituting the expected positive identification while other tubes would not give a test reaction. One would then know which elements were present and which were absent. A number of rather specific tests for the cations are known but they are, in general, used only by the experts who understand the special conditions and limitations of the tests. All agree that beginning students learn more about the principles of qualitative analysis, including laboratory operation, observation, and the drawing of conclusions from the experimental data, by performing qualitative separations without using the specific (usually organic) reagents. All agree also that qualitative analysis offers to the beginning student an excellent opportunity to apply scientific method to a laboratory problem within his powers.

Several specific tests will be made. They use common reagents and they show the potentialities of the method. If hydrogen ions, H^+, and ammonium ions, NH_4^+, are to be tested for, the tests must be made on the original solution because both of these ions are added to the unknown in later steps. Therefore any tests to be made for these ions must be specific tests. Manganese ions may also be readily tested for in the original solution even though all other cations are present.

A drop of the unknown on a piece of litmus paper quickly tells whether the unknown solution is acidic or basic and the use of other indicators will identify the concentration of hydrogen ions and hydroxide ions (see page 285). This test is very valuable since many ions cannot exist in basic solutions, and others cannot exist in neutral solutions. Silver, cobalt, nickel and copper ions are not soluble in a basic solution unless some complexing material such as ammonia is present (compare pages 284, 330), and the ions of magnesium, calcium, manganese, iron, and mercury, are insoluble in all common basic solutions. Similarly aluminum, chromium, iron, tin, antimony, and bismuth ions are insoluble in approximately neutral solutions. They only remain in solution if the hydrogen concentration is above about 10^{-4} M. In neutral solutions they precipitate as the hydroxides but if concentrated base is added some of these redissolve. Some of the other ions also precipitate in neutral solution but the ones mentioned require the most acid to remain in solution.

One may test for ammonium ion, NH_4^+, or ammonia, NH_3, by taking advantage of the fact that ammonia is the only common volatile base. The unknown solution is made basic (to convert NH_4^+ to NH_3), if it is not already so, and warmed gently. Some of the ammonia present in the basic solution will evaporate and may be detected with a piece of wet red litmus or a drop of 6 f hydrochloric acid suspended in the gas phase in the mouth of the test tube.

It should be noted that the three tests, color, acidity, and presence of ammonia, allow one to derive a great deal of information about the possible contents of the unknown solution, information which simplifies the interpretation of further tests.

Problem 23.1. A clear, colorless, unknown solution has a strong odor of ammonia. What ions in our list of twenty-five may be present, and what are known to be absent?

Problem 23.2. An unknown solution is light-brown. What can you say about the acidity of the solution and the ions which are known to be absent?

Problem 23.3. An unknown solution has a very deep blue color and is basic. Would you expect to find ammonia in the unknown? What ions are certainly absent?

The test for manganese in the original unknown is another typical specific test even in the presence of all the other possible cations. The test depends on the fact that powerful oxidizing agents convert manganese, no matter what its original compound, into permanganate ion. The permanganate ion has an intense purple color which covers any other color in the solution and so is apparent regardless of the presence of other colored substances. Certain reducing agents, such as chloride ion, may interfere with the test but they may be readily eliminated if present. The reaction usually used is the oxidation of the manganese by lead dioxide in the presence of hot 6 f nitric acid.

$$2Mn^{++} + 5PbO_{2(s)} + 4H^+ = 2MnO_4^- + 5Pb^{++} + 2H_2O \quad (23.1)$$
$$\text{pink} \quad \text{violet} \qquad\qquad \text{purple}$$

GENERAL APPROACH TO A SYSTEMATIC METHOD OF ANALYSIS

All systematic methods of analysis, as opposed to specific tests, separate the ions in the original unknown solution into smaller groups of ions by using some common property of each group of ions to remove this group from the rest of the ions not having that property. The property usually used is solubility, since precipitated solids may readily be removed from contact with a solution by filtration or, more rapidly, by centrifugation.

Only three of the twenty-five ions listed form chlorides insoluble in hydrochloric acid solution. Therefore, addition of hydrochloric acid to an unknown will cause the precipitation of these three ions, Ag^+, Pb^{++}, and Hg_2^{++} (mercurous ion), but no others. The resulting solid chlorides may then be filtered, or centrifuged, free of the other ions still in solution. Since part of the solution containing the other ions still wets the solids one must wash the solids with more of the hydrochloric acid solution used to cause the precipitation to remove the other ions completely. Why do you suppose that water is not used to wash the solids? In general, how would one select the reagent to be used to wash a freshly precipitated solid free of other materials? These three ions—silver, lead, and mercurous—constitute *Group I* of our qualitative scheme of analysis. *Group I* is known as the group of cations which form insoluble chlorides.

In the scheme we shall follow, *Group II* consists of ions of those remaining elements which form sulfides insoluble in slightly acidic solution, 0.4 M in H^+ ion to be exact. These elements and their oxidation states are Cu^{++}, Cd^{++}, Bi^{+++}, Hg^{++} (mercuric ion), As^{3+} or $^{5+}$, Sb^{3+} or $^{5+}$, and Sn^{2+} or $^{4+}$. Any lead ion which did not precipitate completely in *Group I* will precipitate in this group of sulfides insoluble in acids.

Group III is composed of those ions (other than those already removed) forming hydroxides insoluble in a weakly basic solution in the presence of ammonia. These are the 3+ ions of iron, aluminum, and chromium. The hydroxides of the other ions present, all of which have a charge of only 2+ or 1+, are soluble under these conditions.

Group IV contains the ions (again other than those already removed) which precipitate as sulfides in basic solution. The doubly charged ions of zinc, nickel, cobalt, and manganese precipitate in this group of sulfides, soluble in acids but insoluble in bases.

Group V contains those of the remaining ions which precipitate as insoluble carbonates in a slightly basic solution. The alkaline earth ions, Ca^{++}, Sr^{++}, and Ba^{++}, precipitate in *Group V*.

Group VI, the final group, contains Na^+, K^+, and Mg^{++}. Few of the compounds of these ions are insoluble in water, a fact which accounts for their remaining until this final group.

Each of the analytical *Groups* with the exception of *Group II* contains three or four of the original possible ions. Specific tests may now be made either in the presence of the other two or three ions, or, if necessary, further separation may be made before the final confirmatory tests are used. These further separations and tests we shall discuss later. In *Group II*, however, there are cations of seven different elements, or eight counting lead. This group is much too large for convenient work and is ordinarily split in half, into *Groups II A* and *II B*.

Group II is separated into *Groups II A* and *II B* by taking advantage of the different solubilities of the precipitated sulfides in an aqueous, basic solution of sulfide ion and polysulfide ion, commonly known as the *sodium sulfide*

378 GENERAL CHEMISTRY

reagent. The sulfides of mercuric mercury, arsenic, antimony, and tin are soluble in this reagent. The sulfides of copper, cadmium, bismuth, and lead are not.

We have thus obtained seven groups or sub-groups of ions, each such group containing three or four different cations.

Problem 23.4. Using colored pencils, or different types of cross-hatching, mark the periodic table on page 153 to show the positions of each of the analytical groups. For instance, mark the positions of analytical *Group I* elements in red, those of *II A* in light blue, those of *II B* in dark blue, etc., throughout the whole analytical scheme. Are any regularities apparent either within the analytical groups or in the sequence in which the *Groups* follow one another when considered in terms of the periodic system?

TYPES OF REACTIONS USEFUL IN QUALITATIVE ANALYSIS

Reactions, in general, occur until a state of dynamic equilibrium is attained. However the reagents will react almost completely if the concentrations in the solution of any of the substances produced in the reaction can be kept low by formation of:

a. a precipitate,
b. a gas,
c. a weak electrolyte,
d. a complex ion,
e. an oxidized and a reduced product,

or any combination of these. We said "almost completely" rather than "completely" because:

a. all precipitates are somewhat soluble,
b. all gases are somewhat soluble,
c. all weak electrolytes are somewhat ionized,
d. all complex ions are somewhat dissociated, and
e. all oxidation-reduction reactions are somewhat reversible.

Consequently no reaction could go to completion unless one of the reagents could be completely removed from the reaction system, as, for instance, by pumping off the gas that is formed in a reaction.

Examples of each of the above equilibrium types are:

a. $Ag^+ + Cl^- = AgCl_{(s)}$ white   (23.2)

b. $2H^+ + CO_3^{--} = H_2O + CO_{2(g)}$ (23.3)

c. $2H^+ + S^{--} = H_2S$ (23.4)

d. $Ag^+ + 2NH_3 = Ag(NH_3)_2^+$ (23.5)

e. $2Fe^{+++} + H_2S = 2Fe^{++} + S_{(s)} + 2H^+$ (23.6)
    brown   light   yellow
                  green   or
                             white

PRINCIPLES OF QUALITATIVE ANALYSIS 379

All of the above reactions occur when our scheme of analysis is followed and many more of each type will also be found.

It is not enough to have the various substances undergo reaction in an analytical scheme; the reactions must result in some observable change if they are to serve for identifications. The only readily observable types of reactions are those which produce an insoluble substance (gas, solid, or liquid) and/or a color change. Reactions 23.4 and 23.5 do neither of these and hence, would be unobservable and useless of themselves for identifying substances in the unknown. For this reason it is very important to notice the relative solubilities of the various substance produced and to observe the colors which are characteristic of each substance. These characteristics are, after all, the experimenter's only method of correlating most of the observed changes with the substances causing them.

THE EQUILIBRIUM CONSTANT

Chapter 18 on chemical equilibrium (pages 271–277) developed the idea of dynamic equilibrium and pointed out that equilibria could be treated quantitatively in terms of equilibrium constants and equilibrium constant expressions.

The equilibrium constant for equation 23.2 is

$$K = \frac{[AgCl_{(s)}]}{[Ag^+][Cl^-]} \tag{23.7}$$

or since $[AgCl_{(s)}]$ is a constant (see page 276) we may rearrange equation 23.7 to give

$$[Ag^+][Cl^-] = \frac{[AgCl_{(s)}]}{K} = K_{sp} \tag{23.8}$$

where the product $[Ag^+][Cl^-]$, or K_{sp}, is called the *solubility product* or *solubility product constant* for silver chloride. Before silver chloride will precipitate from a solution, the concentration of the silver ion and the chloride ion must be such that the product of the two concentrations exceeds the numerical value of the solubility product. Only the excess of silver ions and chloride ions over that necessary to maintain these concentrations can precipitate. Conversely, if one has solid silver chloride in equilibrium with a saturated solution of the ions, any reaction which lowers the concentration of either ion in the solution will allow more of the silver chloride to dissolve. The solution process will occur until the product of the concentrations of the silver and chloride ions again equals the solubility product in numerical value or until the silver chloride is completely dissolved, whichever happens first.

The value of the solubility product of silver chloride is

$$[Ag^+][Cl^-] = 1.7 \times 10^{-10} \tag{23.9}$$

If a solution is 0.1 M in Cl^- ion the Ag^+ ion concentration cannot exceed $1.7 \times 10^{-9}\ M$, though it may be less if there is no solid silver chloride present.

Thus

$$[Ag^+][Cl^-] = [Ag^+] \times (0.1) = 1.7 \times 10^{-10} = K_{sp}$$
$$[Ag^+] = 1.7 \times 10^{-9} M \qquad (23.10)$$

Addition of enough Cl⁻ ion to make a solution 0.1 M in Cl⁻ ion would, therefore, rather efficiently remove the Ag⁺ ion from solution. Note that the concentrations of ions are expressed in moles per liter (molarities). Other concentration units would result in different numerical values for the equilibrium constants.

The numerical value for the dissociation constant of $Ag(NH_3)_2^+$ ion as in the reaction $Ag(NH_3)_2^+ = 2NH_3 + Ag^+$, is

$$K = \frac{[NH_3]^2[Ag^+]}{[Ag(NH_3)_2^+]} = 6 \times 10^{-8} \qquad (23.11)$$

If the value of [NH₃] in a solution containing Ag⁺ ion were made 3 M then

$$\frac{(3)^2 \times [Ag^+]}{[Ag(NH_3)_2^+]} = 6 \times 10^{-8}, \text{ or } \frac{[Ag^+]}{[Ag(NH_3)_2^+]} = \frac{6 \times 10^{-8}}{9} = 7 \times 10^{-9}$$

which indicates that practically all the silver is present in the form of $Ag(NH_3)_2^+$ ion. If, for instance, the value of $[Ag(NH_3)_2^+]$ is 0.1 M when the value of [NH₃] is 3 M we obtain

$$6 \times 10^{-8} = \frac{[NH_3]^2 \times [Ag^+]}{[Ag(NH_3)_2^+]} = \frac{(3)^2 \times [Ag^+]}{(0.1)}$$

$$[Ag^+] = \frac{0.1}{(3)^2} \times 6 \times 10^{-8} = 7 \times 10^{-10} M \qquad (23.12)$$

Comparison of the concentrations of silver ion obtained in equations 23.10 and 23.12 leads to an interesting conclusion. We found from equation 23.10 that the silver ion concentration in equilibrium with 0.1 M Cl⁻ ion could be as high as 1.7×10^{-9} M. In equation 23.12 we found that the silver ion concentration in equilibrium with 3 M ammonia would be only 7×10^{-10} M if the concentration of $Ag(NH_3)_2^+$ is 0.1 M. Clearly the concentration of silver ion in the presence of 3 M ammonia is less than it can be in the presence of 0.1 M chloride. In other words the ammonia forms a more stable combination with the silver ion than does the chloride under these conditions. In the competition between the chloride ion and the ammonia for the silver ion the ammonia has a greater tendency to react with the silver than does the chloride. Thus, if the species shown in equation 23.13 are present

$$AgCl_{(s)} + 2NH_3 = Ag(NH_3)_2^+ + Cl^- \qquad (23.13)$$

the reaction which forms the substances on the right will predominate and silver chloride will dissolve in 3 M ammonia water.

Show that the equilibrium constant corresponding to equation 23.13 is algebraically equal to the solubility product of equation 23.9 divided by the equilibrium constant of equation 23.11. Calculate the numerical value of the equilibrium constant corresponding to equation 23.13.

Problem 23.5. Show that a solution 0.1 M in Cl$^-$ ion will precipitate silver chloride from a solution containing 0.1 M Ag(NH$_3$)$_2^+$ which is 1 M in ammonia but not from 3 M ammonia solution.

Equilibrium constant expressions and numerical values may be used in similar fashion to predict the tendency of other reactions to occur under specific conditions and we shall make frequent use of this method to determine the concentration of reagents which should be used in order to accomplish desired separations and identifications in the analytical scheme.

PRECIPITATION OF ANALYTICAL GROUP I—THE INSOLUBLE CHLORIDES

Table 23.1 lists the solubilities and the solubility product constants of some of the compounds met in the separation and analysis of *Group I*. All of the chlorides are white, so the group precipitate should be white.

It will be noted that the solubilities and the solubility products do not seem consistent for every substance. For example, a solubility of lead chloride of 0.039 M might indicate concentrations of lead ion equal to 0.039 M and of chloride ion equal to 2 × 0.039 M = 0.078 M in the saturated solution. The solubility product for the reaction PbCl$_{2(s)}$ = Pb^{++} + 2Cl$^-$ is expressed as

$$K_{sp} = [\text{Pb}^{++}][\text{Cl}^-]^2 \tag{23.14}$$

which would give

$$K_{sp} = [\text{Pb}^{++}][\text{Cl}^-]^2 = (0.039)(0.078)^2 = 2.4 \times 10^{-4} \tag{23.15}$$

This value of 2.4 × 10^{-4} is considerably greater than the published value of 1.7 × 10^{-5}. The apparent discrepancy lies in assuming that all ions which form when lead chloride dissolves in water remain as simple lead ions or simple chloride ions. The chloride ions do remain simple chloride ions but the lead ions react with the water to produce PbOH$^+$ ions to a considerable ex-

Table 23.1
Solubility of Some Salts of *Group I* Cations

SALT FORMULA	COLOR	SOLUBILITY IN MOLES PER LITER	SOLUBILITY-PRODUCT CONSTANT, K_{sp}
AgCl	white	1.3 × 10^{-5}	[Ag$^+$] × [Cl$^-$] = 1.7 × 10^{-10}
Hg$_2$Cl$_2$	white	9 × 10^{-7}	[Hg$_2^{++}$] × [Cl$^-$]^2 = 1.1 × 10^{-18}
PbCl$_2$	white	0.039	[Pb^{++}] × [Cl$^-$]^2 = 1.7 × 10^{-5}
PbI$_2$	yellow	0.00165	[Pb^{++}] × [I$^-$]^2 = 8.7 × 10^{-9}
PbCrO$_4$	yellow	2 × 10^{-7}	[Pb^{++}] × [CrO$_4^{--}$] = 1.8 × 10^{-14}
PbSO$_4$	white	1.5 × 10^{-4}	[Pb^{++}] × [SO$_4^{--}$] = 1.8 × 10^{-8}

tent. This hydrolysis (reaction with water) lowers the concentration of simple Pb^{++} ions.

$$Pb^{++} + H_2O = PbOH^+ + H^+ \qquad (23.16)$$

Since the chloride ion concentration ion is 0.078 M we may calculate the Pb^{++} ion concentration from the solubility-product constant:

$$1.7 \times 10^{-5} = [Pb^{++}][Cl^-]^2 = [Pb^{++}](0.078)^2$$

$$[Pb^{++}] = \frac{1.7 \times 10^{-5}}{(0.078)^2} = 0.0028 M \qquad (23.17)$$

The concentration of $PbOH^+$ ions is the difference between the total lead dissolved, 0.039 moles per liter, and the amount present as Pb^{++} ion, 0.0028 moles per liter. The concentration of $PbOH^+$ is, then, 0.036 M and approximately ninety per cent of the lead has hydrolyzed. Calculation will show that the silver ion is less hydrolyzed than the lead ion. It should be noted in passing that the use of hydrochloric acid as a precipitating agent will diminish the extent of the hydrolysis of the positive ions by keeping the acidity of the solution high (see equation 23.16).

It should be clear from the data listed in Table 23.1 that lead chloride is the most soluble of the three chlorides in *Group I* and will be the hardest to precipitate quantitatively or completely. One may be tempted to add a large excess of chloride ion to encourage precipitation. The higher the chloride ion concentration rises, the lower the lead ion concentration will fall in order to maintain the constancy of the solubility product, and the state of dynamic solubility equilibrium. Unfortunately, although the added chloride will increase the precipitation of the lead ion, it decreases the precipitation of the silver. At high concentrations of chloride ion a new equilibrium becomes important (equation 23.18) and the silver chloride dissolves

$$\underset{\text{white}}{AgCl_{(s)}} + Cl^- = AgCl_2^- \qquad (23.18)$$

due to the formation of a complex ion with the excess chloride. For this reason one is limited to a total chloride ion concentration of about 1 M.

Complications which arise upon adding excess reagent are common in analytical work so that it is often very important to add a carefully measured amount of reagent, neither more nor less. The good analyst learns which steps are critical as to concentration of reagents and which are not, and thus greatly lessens the time which must be spent on an analysis. This learning can only come, however, if the student understands what each reagent does, and the theory behind its use.

PRECIPITATION OF ANALYTICAL GROUP II—THE SULFIDES INSOLUBLE IN ACID

Hydrogen sulfide ionizes according to the equations

$$H_2S = H^+ + HS^- \qquad (23.19)$$
$$HS^- = H^+ + S^{--} \qquad (23.20)$$

which may be added to give an over-all equation

$$H_2S = 2H^+ + S^{--} \tag{23.21}$$

The ionization constants, K_1, K_2, and K, for the equilibria represented by equations 23.19, 23.20, and 23.21 are

$$K_1 = \frac{[H^+] \times [HS^-]}{[H_2S]} = 10^{-7} \tag{23.22}$$

$$K_2 = \frac{[H^+] \times [S^{--}]}{[HS^-]} = 10^{-15} \tag{23.23}$$

$$K = K_1 K_2 = \frac{[H^+]^2 \times [S^{--}]}{[H_2S]} = 10^{-22} \tag{23.24}$$

In a saturated solution of hydrogen sulfide at one atmosphere pressure the concentration of hydrogen sulfide is about 0.1 M, so that the sulfide ion concentration becomes

$$[S^{--}] = \frac{(0.1)}{[H^+]^2} \times 10^{-22} = \frac{10^{-23}}{[H^+]^2} \tag{23.25}$$

If the solution is made acid with hydrochloric acid so that the concentration of H^+ ion becomes 0.4 M the sulfide ion concentration becomes

$$[S^{--}] = \frac{10^{-23}}{(0.4)^2} = 6 \times 10^{-23} M \tag{23.26}$$

It is evident that only extremely insoluble sulfides will precipitate with this low concentration of sulfide ion. From Table 23.2 select those which may be expected to precipitate.

Table 23.2
Solubility of Some Sulfides

SULFIDE FORMULA	COLOR	SOLUBILITY IN MOLES PER LITER	SOLUBILITY-PRODUCT CONSTANT K_{sp}
CdS	yellow	3.1×10^{-10}	$[Cd^{++}] \times [S^{--}] = 7.1 \times 10^{-28}$
CuS	black	2.2×10^{-17}	$[Cu^{++}] \times [S^{--}] = 3.5 \times 10^{-42}$
PbS	black	2.2×10^{-10}	$[Pb^{++}] \times [S^{--}] = 3.4 \times 10^{-28}$
HgS	black	2.1×10^{-23}	$[Hg^{++}] \times [S^{--}] = 3 \times 10^{-54}$
FeS	black	1.3×10^{-6}	$[Fe^{++}] \times [S^{--}] = 3.7 \times 10^{-19}$
ZnS	white	3.1×10^{-9}	$[Zn^{++}] \times [S^{--}] = 6.9 \times 10^{-26}$
NiS	black	4×10^{-10}	$[Ni^{++}] \times [S^{--}] = 1.1 \times 10^{-27}$

The sulfides actually precipitated in *Group II* in the presence of 0.4 M H^+ ion are, in rough order of increasing solubility, mercuric sulfide (black), copper sulfide (black), arsenic sulfides (yellow), antimony sulfides (orange), tin sulfides (yellow or brown), bismuth sulfide (dark brown), lead sulfide (black), and cadmium sulfide (yellow). If the hydrogen sulfide is bubbled slowly into the solution the sulfides will precipitate roughly in the order given, the most insoluble ones precipitating first, and layers of different colored sulfides may actually be obtained in the bottom of the test tube. This simplifies the identification problem somewhat since the colors of the sulfides alone are sometimes sufficient to identify them. Only antimony, for instance, forms an orange sulfide. Precipitation of any of the dark sulfides—those of mercury, copper, stannous tin, bismuth, or lead—may hide the colors of the less intensely colored ones, but the appearance of a clear yellow sulfide clearly indicates that none of the darker ones are present and simplifies the tests from that point on.

Group II is ordinarily precipitated by bubbling hydrogen sulfide into a solution which was made 0.4 M in hydrochloric acid. It should be noted, however, that the precipitation reactions cause a simultaneous increase in the acidity of the solution. For example,

$$Cd^{++} + H_2S = CdS_{(s)} + 2H^+ \quad (23.27)$$
$$\text{yellow}$$

The consequent increase in acidity to a value above 0.4 M leads to a decrease in the sulfide ion concentration and diminishes the effectiveness of precipitation of the sulfides, particularly the more soluble ones such as cadmium sulfide. It is, therefore, necessary after precipitation seems complete, to dilute the solution until the acidity returns to 0.4 M and then to bubble in more hydrogen sulfide to insure precipitation of cadmium sulfide.

SEPARATION OF GROUPS II A AND II B—THE SODIUM SULFIDE REAGENT

The sodium sulfide reagent is prepared from sodium sulfide (formula Na_2S), sulfur, and sodium hydroxide. The sodium sulfide furnishes S^{--} ions. However, many of these ions react with water according to the reaction

$$S^{--} + HOH = HS^- + OH^- \quad (23.28)$$

unless an excess of OH^- ions are present. The number and concentration of S^{--} ions will be increased if sodium hydroxide is added to the solution.

The sulfide ions from the sodium sulfide combine with some of the sulfides of *Group II B* to form soluble complex ions according to the reactions.

$$As_4S_{6(s)} + 6S^{--} = 4AsS_3^{---} \quad (23.29)$$
$$\text{yellow} \qquad\qquad \text{thioarsenite ion}$$

$$Sb_4S_{6(s)} + 6S^{--} = 4SbS_3^{---} \quad (23.30)$$
$$\text{orange} \qquad\qquad \text{thioantimonite ion}$$

$$HgS_{(s)} + S^{--} = HgS_2^{--} \quad (23.31)$$
$$\text{black} \qquad\qquad \text{thiomercurate ion}$$

However, the thio-ite ions, especially the thiostannite ion, are not as stable as the corresponding thio-ate ions. Therefore some free sulfur is added in making the reagent to change some of the sulfide ions, formula S^{--}, to polysulfide ions, formula S_2^{--}, which, in turn, oxidize the -ites to the -ates. Thus

$$\underset{\text{yellow}}{AsS_3^{---}} + S_2^{--} = \underset{\substack{\text{thioarsenate} \\ \text{ion}}}{AsS_4^{---}} + S^{--} \tag{23.32}$$

$$\underset{\text{yellow}}{SbS_3^{---}} + S_2^{--} = \underset{\substack{\text{thioantimonate} \\ \text{ion}}}{SbS_4^{---}} + S^{--} \tag{23.33}$$

$$\underset{\text{brown}}{SnS_{(s)}} + \underset{\text{yellow}}{S_2^{--}} = \underset{\substack{\text{thiostannate} \\ \text{ion}}}{SnS_3^{--}} \tag{23.34}$$

Observe that all these sulfides except mercuric sulfide can be oxidized by the polysulfide. An excess of OH^- ions must be present to keep the sulfide ion concentration high enough to dissolve the mercuric sulfide as HgS_2^{--} ions (see equations 23.28 and 23.31).

Thus, addition of the sodium sulfide reagent to the mixture of sulfides precipitated in *Group II* leads to the solution of the mercury, arsenic, antimony, and tin sulfides. The copper, cadmium, bismuth, and lead sulfides remain as solids and may be separated from the solution.

The sodium sulfide separation of *Group II* is based on the differences in acidity of the sulfides. Mercury, arsenic, tin, and antimony are more electronegative elements than copper, cadmium, bismuth, and lead. The former, therefore, are more prone to share electrons in their compounds. Their compounds are more acidic, the atoms more apt to form complex anions such as the "thio" ions above. The *Group II A* elements have a greater tendency to form simple cations. They are more electropositive in nature. They do not have as great a tendency to form anions such as the "thio" complexes, and their sulfides are insoluble in excess sulfide ion. Note that the split between the two groups corresponds to position in the periodic table.

REPRECIPITATION OF GROUP II B

When an acid is added to the thio-ate ions the H^+ ions combine with the S^{--} ions in equilibrium with the "thio" complex ions to form hydrogen sulfide. As a result the complex ions are decomposed and the sulfides are reprecipitated. Thus,

$$4AsS_4^{---} + 12H^+ = \underset{\text{yellow}}{As_4S_{10(s)}} + 6H_2S \tag{23.35}$$

$$SnS_3^{--} + 2H^+ = \underset{\text{yellow}}{SnS_{2(s)}} + H_2S \tag{23.36}$$

$$HgS_2^{--} + 2H^+ = \underset{\text{black}}{HgS_{(s)}} + H_2S \tag{23.37}$$

$$2SbS_4^{---} + 6H^+ = \underset{\text{orange}}{Sb_2S_{4(s)}} + 3H_2S + \underset{\substack{\text{yellow or} \\ \text{white}}}{S_{(s)}} \tag{23.38}$$

Observe that the higher oxidation state sulfides are precipitated but note particularly that the antimony sulfide has the formula Sb_2S_4. This formula might better be written SbSbS$_4$ and the compound named antimonous thioantimonate. Half the antimony atoms are in the 3+ oxidation state and half in the 5+ state.

Finely divided sulfur, usually white, also is precipitated, because an excess of the sulfide reagent was used. The reaction is

$$S_2^{--} + 2H^+ = H_2S_{(g)} + S_{(s)} \quad (23.39)$$
$$\text{usually white}$$

Problem 23.6. Why may lead appear in *Group II* since it was already tested for in *Group I*?
Problem 23.7. Is copper sulfide soluble in hydrochloric acid? Is cadmium sulfide? Why?
Problem 23.8. Why is the solubility of a sulfide greater than would be calculated from the solubility product alone?
Problem 23.9. Why is "sodium sulfide reagent" used? Why is sodium sulfide insufficient? Why is sodium hydroxide added?
Problem 23.10. If mercuric sulfide does not dissolve in the sulfide reagent, where will it appear?
Problem 23.11. When the sulfide reagent solution supposed to contain *Group II B* is acidified what conclusion may be drawn if: (a) Only a white precipitate appears? (b) A black precipitate appears? (c) A yellow precipitate appears?
Problem 23.12. Note that the formula of the arsenic sulfide precipitated from the sulfide reagent is As$_4$S$_{10}$ but that of the antimony sulfide is Sb$_2$S$_4$. How is the instability of the sulfide with formula Sb$_4$S$_{10}$ compared to that with formula As$_4$S$_{10}$ consistent with the more metallic nature of the antimony?
Problem 23.13. 9 f hydrochloric acid will dissolve antimony tetrasulfide and stannic sulfide, but not arsenic pentasulfide and mercuric sulfide; ammonia water will dissolve arsenic pentasulfide but not mercuric sulfide. Interpret in terms of acidity of the sulfides and metallic nature of the elements.

PRECIPITATION OF ANALYTICAL GROUP III—HYDROXIDES INSOLUBLE IN AMMONIA

Ammonia reacts with water according to the equation

$$NH_3 + H_2O = NH_4^+ + OH^- \quad (23.40)$$

(See page 358.) The equilibrium constant (here called the ionization constant) is

$$K = \frac{[NH_4^+] \times [OH^-]}{[NH_3]} = 1.8 \times 10^{-5} \quad (23.41)$$

If the concentration of the ammonia is 0.1 M, the concentration of OH$^-$ ion is

$$[OH^-] = \frac{[NH_3]}{[NH_4^+]} \times 1.8 \times 10^{-5} = \frac{0.1}{[NH_4^+]} \times 1.8 \times 10^{-5} = \frac{1.8 \times 10^{-6}}{[NH_4^+]} \quad (23.42)$$

In pure ammonia water [OH$^-$] = [NH$_4^+$] so from equation 23.42

$$[OH^-] \times [NH_4^+] = [OH^-]^2 = 1.8 \times 10^{-6}; [OH^-] = 1.3 \times 10^{-3} = 0.0013 M \quad (23.43)$$

But if the NH_4^+ ion concentration is made $3M$ by addition of solid ammonium chloride, we find from equation 23.42 that

$$[OH^-] = \frac{0.1}{3} \times 1.8 \times 10^{-5} = 6 \times 10^{-7} = 0.0000006M \qquad (23.44)$$

Hydroxide ions of this concentration will cause precipitation of only the more insoluble hydroxides.

Table 23.3
Solubility of Some Hydroxides

HYDROXIDE FORMULAS	COLOR	SOLUBILITY IN MOLES PER LITER	SOLUBILITY-PRODUCT CONSTANT, K_{sp}
$Fe(OH)_3$	brown	4.4×10^{-10}	$[Fe^{+++}] \times [OH^-]^3 = 4 \times 10^{-38}$
$Fe(OH)_2$	light green	1.7×10^{-5}	$[Fe^{++}] \times [OH^-]^2 = 1.65 \times 10^{-15}$
$Mg(OH)_2$	white	4.6×10^{-4}	$[Mg^{++}] \times [OH^-]^2 = 5.5 \times 10^{-11}$
$Mn(OH)_2$	pink	2.1×10^{-5}	$[Mn^{++}] \times [OH^-]^2 = 4.5 \times 10^{-17}$
$Co(OH)_2$	pink	No data	$[Co^{++}] \times [OH^-]^2 = 2 \times 10^{-16}$
$Ni(OH)_2$	green	1.4×10^{-4}	$[Ni^{++}] \times [OH^-]^2 = 1.6 \times 10^{-14}$

The concentration of ferric ion in equilibrium with the OH^- ion whose concentration is calculated above as $6 \times 10^{-7} M$, is obtained from Table 23.3 as

$$[Fe^{+++}] = \frac{4 \times 10^{-38}}{[OH^-]^3} = \frac{4 \times 10^{-38}}{(6 \times 10^{-7})^3} = 2 \times 10^{-19}M. \qquad (23.45)$$

It is evident that the ferric iron is practically completely precipitated. The chromic (Cr^{+++}) ions and aluminum, (Al^{+++}) ions also precipitate. But if the iron is present as ferrous ions, we find from Table 23.3

$$[Fe^{++}] = \frac{1.65 \times 10^{-15}}{[OH^-]^2} = \frac{1.65 \times 10^{-15}}{(6 \times 10^{-7})^2} = 0.0047M \qquad (23.46)$$

Thus ferrous iron would not precipitate quantitatively in *Group III*. The hydrogen sulfide added for *Group II* reduced any ferric ions to ferrous ions; these ions must therefore be oxidized back to ferric ions by nitric acid so that the iron will precipitate quantitatively in *Group III*.

To keep any manganese hydroxide from precipitating, excess ammonia is boiled off. This reduces the concentration of OH^- ions. Cobalt and nickel hydroxides might be expected to precipitate but they form stable complex ions, such as the $Co(NH_3)_4^{++}$ ion, with ammonia, so that the concentration of the free Co^{++} and Ni^{++} ions are cut down.

Before ammonia is added to the filtrate from *Group II*, the hydrogen sulfide must be boiled off or oxidized with $16 f$ nitric acid. If it is not, the sulfide ions from the reaction

$$2NH_3 + H_2S = 2NH_4^+ + S^{--} \qquad (23.47)$$

would precipitate the sulfides of *Group IV* with the hydroxides of *Group III*.

AMPHOTERIC HYDROXIDES

Aluminum and zinc hydroxides are called "amphoteric" because they dissolve in both acids and bases. The solubility in acids is explained by the reactions

$$Al(OH)_{3(s)} + 3H^+ = 3HOH + Al^{+++} \qquad (23.48)$$
white

$$Zn(OH)_{2(s)} + 2H^+ = 2HOH + Zn^{++} \qquad (23.49)$$
white

The solubility in bases may be explained in terms of formation of complex ions with the hydroxyl ion. Thus,

$$Al(OH)_{3(s)} + OH^- = Al(OH)_4^- \text{ (aluminate ion)} \qquad (23.50)$$
white

$$Zn(OH)_{2(s)} + 2OH^- = Zn(OH)_4^{--} \text{ (zincate ion)} \qquad (23.51)$$
white

The aluminum hydroxide is separated from the ferric hydroxide as the soluble aluminate ion, and the zinc hydroxide is separated from manganous hydroxide in *Group IV* as the soluble zincate ion.

Problem 23.14. Why is sodium hydroxide solution not used to precipitate the hydroxides of *Group III*? Give three reasons.

Problem 23.15. Why is care taken to avoid an excess of ammonia before separating *Group III*?

Problem 23.16. Why is the hydrogen sulfide boiled off before *Group III* is precipitated?

Problem 23.17. Why is ammonium chloride added before *Group III* is precipitated? Why added as solid and not as solution?

Problem 23.18. Why is the nitric acid added before *Group III* is precipitated? Why added after the hydrogen sulfide is boiled off?

PRECIPITATION OF ANALYTICAL GROUP IV—THE SULFIDES SOLUBLE IN ACID BUT INSOLUBLE IN BASIC SOLUTION

Zinc, cobalt, nickel, and manganese ions are precipitated as the sulfides if the concentration of sulfide ions is great enough. A basic sulfide solution, such as that of ammonium sulfide, formula $(NH_4)_2S$, has a sulfide ion concentration high enough to exceed the solubility products of the *Group IV* sulfides (see Table 23.2). Had the acidity been too low at the time of the precipitation of the *Group II* sulfides, some of these sulfides would have precipitated with them.

PRECIPITATION OF ANALYTICAL GROUP V—THE INSOLUBLE CARBONATES OF THE REMAINING CATIONS

Calcium, strontium, and barium ions are precipitated as the carbonates by adding ammonium carbonate to a solution of carefully regulated basicity. If the solution is too basic, magnesium ion will also precipitate in this group as a basic magnesium carbonate. On the other hand, the solution cannot be made acidic because the hydrogen ion concentration is then great enough to remove the carbonate ion by the following reactions:

$$CO_3^{--} + H^+ = HCO_3^- \tag{23.52}$$

$$HCO_3^- + H^+ = H_2O + CO_2 \tag{23.53}$$

$$CO_2 \text{ (in solution)} = CO_{2(g)} \tag{23.54}$$

In acid solution the concentration of carbonate ion becomes so low that the *Group V* ions will not precipitate.

ANALYTICAL GROUP VI

Analytical *Group VI* contains those ions—sodium, magnesium, and potassium—which have not precipitated in any preceding group. Most of the compounds of these ions are soluble so that it is not surprising to find them in this last group. In fact, no error of the analyst can be great enough to precipitate the sodium or potassium with any preceding group, although sloppy work may lose the magnesium in either *Group IV* or *V*, more likely the latter.

IDENTIFICATION OF EACH ELEMENT

The "separation reactions" outlined above give seven separated groups of cations. Each group may contain as many as three or four different compounds if carried through reactions we have discussed. The *Group I* cations will be present in their solid chlorides, the *Group II A* and *II B* cations in their solid sulfides, the *Group III* cations in their solid hydroxides, the *Group IV* cations in their solid sulfides, the *Group V* cations in their solid carbonates, and the *Group VI* cations as ions in solutions.

Further tests require that most of the substances be taken back into solution, and one reason for selecting the scheme outlined is that it yields group precipitates which may be dissolved readily. The detailed steps in the further analysis we shall leave to the laboratory, but we shall discuss some of the confirmatory tests when we study the various elements in later chapters. Some further separations of the ions in the groups are accomplished by using still other equilibria than the ones we have mentioned, but no new principles are involved. The qualitative scheme you use in the laboratory may differ in detail from the one outlined above; it may even be one which does not use sulfides as a means of separating ions into groups. Nevertheless, common principles are applied in all schemes. You will find it worth while to discover how and why the two schemes differ.

PREPARING A SOLID UNKNOWN FOR ANALYSIS

Often one must analyze a solid rather than a solution. Occasionally examination of the solid alone is sufficient particularly if it be pure. In the general case, however, the first step is to dissolve the solid, and then to carry the resulting solution through the regular scheme of analysis.

The usual technic is to try a series of solvents and note how much, and, if possible, what part, of the solid dissolves in each. Water is always tried first, followed by hydrochloric acid (dissolves many metals, hydroxides and oxides, sulfides, carbonates), sodium hydroxide (dissolves amphoteric oxides and hydroxides, some metals), ammonia water (dissolves many compounds of elements which can form ammonia complexes), nitric acid (dissolves most metals, many sulfides by oxidizing the sulfide to sulfur, in addition to those substances dissolved by hydrochloric acid), and finally aqua regia made up of 3 volumes of concentrated hydrochloric acid to 1 volume concentrated nitric acid (dissolves all metals and sulfides, plus those substances dissolved by nitric acid and those dissolved by hydrochloric acid). An experienced analyst will have a pretty good idea of the content of the unknown by this time; he will have noted what each solvent accomplished and the color changes which occurred. The only common compounds of the twenty-five cations we have discussed which would be insoluble in all of these solvents would be strontium or barium sulfate, particularly the latter. These are dissolved after a carbonate treatment (see page 480).

If the unknown dissolves completely in one of the solvents, that solution may be carried into the regular scheme directly. If not the solutions may be combined or each may be carried through the scheme separately in order to take advantage of any preliminary separations. The former method usually involves less work and time.

Problem 23.19. A colorless unknown solution gives no precipitate in *Group I*, but gives a yellow precipitate in *Group II*. It is known to contain no ions of the other groups. What substances are definitely absent and what may be present in the original solution?

Problem 23.20. A colorless unknown solution gives a white precipitate with $1\ f$ hydrochloric acid. This precipitate is centrifuged free of the supernatant liquid and is found to be completely soluble in ammonia water. The centrate (solution from which solid was centrifuged) is made $0.4\ M$ in hydrogen ion, and hydrogen sulfide is bubbled into it. A black precipitate forms. On the basis of this information state what substances are definitely absent and what may be present in the original unknown.

Problem 23.21. An unknown solution is colorless. What substances are definitely absent?

Problem 23.22. Precipitation of *Group III* gives a white precipitate. What can you deduce about the presence or absence of the substances in this group?

Problem 23.23. Precipitation of *Group IV* gives a white precipitate. What can you deduce about the presence or absence of the substances in this group?

Problem 23.24. How would you get the following solids into solution for the purposes of qualitative analysis: (a) barium carbonate, (b) zinc sulfide, (c) copper (d) mercurous sulfate, (e) nickel nitrate, (f) ferric oxide.

Problem 23.25. Use the solubility of ferrous hydroxide and its K_{sp} to calculate the percentage of ferrous ions hydrolyzed in a saturated aqueous solution of the hydroxide.

24 SOLUBILITY OF SALTS AND CRYSTAL STRUCTURES

RATHER COMPLETE theoretical discussions are now available of the factors which determine the solubility of nonelectrolytes in one another. An organic chemist, dealing primarily with hydrocarbons modified by functional groups of known polarity, finds that the simple rule "like dissolves like" covers the majority of cases very satisfactorily. Thus, polar compounds such as ethanol form solutions in all proportions with water (a polar liquid) but have a limited solubility in hydrocarbons (nonpolar liquids) such as gasoline. The nonpolar organic liquids mix with each other in all proportions but have limited solubility in polar liquids.

Solid compounds below their melting points always have a limited solubility in a liquid solution. If the crystalline phase of a substance A is the stable one at the experimental temperature and pressure, the escaping tendency of the molecules of A from the crystalline solid is less than that from the pure liquid phase. Hence, the escaping tendency of the molecules of A from a liquid phase becomes equal to that from the solid phase when the concentration of the molecules of A in the liquid phase is less than it is in pure liquid A, that is, when there are some foreign molecules present as in a solution. The effects are predictable for many systems of organic compounds. The solubility of salts in water is more difficult to interpret, requiring special consideration. There is no known theory which allows one to calculate the solubility relations of salts.

EMPIRICAL SOLUBILITY RULES

Because he lacks the necessary theoretical knowledge, the inorganic chemist depends on empirical rules for the solubility of salts in water. The more common salts are covered by the following rules: All nitrates are soluble. All chlorides, bromides, and iodides except those of silver, lead, and mercurous mercury are soluble. All sulfates except those of calcium, strontium, barium, mercury, lead, and silver are soluble. All salts of the alkali elements are soluble. All sulfides except those of the alkali and alkaline earth elements are insoluble.

All phosphates except those of the alkali elements are insoluble. All hydroxides except those of the alkali elements are insoluble. (Hydroxides are not salts, strictly speaking, but many of them form ionic crystals, and hydroxide solubilities depend on factors similar to those for salts.)

Here the summary rests. Even so, the terms soluble and insoluble cover broad categories. The salts called *soluble* range in solubility from 0.1 to about 30 molal (moles of salt per 1000 g. [55.5 moles] of water). The "insoluble" salts are often divided into two classes: those with solubilities between 10^{-1} and 10^{-3} molal, called *slightly soluble*, and those with solubilities below 10^{-3} molal, called *insoluble*. Even the most insoluble salts yield some ions to the solution. Solubility data on which the rules rest are given in Table 24.1.

Table 24.1
Approximate Molal Solubilities of Some Salts (and Hydroxides)
The numbers represent the approximate exponent of ten for the molal solubilities of the respective compounds: 1 means approximately 10^1, or 10 molal, 0 means approximately 10^0, or 1 molal, -2 means approximately 10^{-2}, or 0.01 molal, etc. The symbol ——— indicates that the compound is not stable in contact with water. A blank space indicates lack of data.

IONS	F$^-$	Cl$^-$	Br$^-$	I$^-$	NO$_3^-$	IO$_3^-$	BrO$_3^-$	ClO$_3^-$	ClO$_4^-$	CO$_3^{--}$	SO$_4^{--}$	CrO$_4^{--}$	PO$_4^{3-}$	S^{--}	OH$^-$
Li$^+$	-1	1	1	1	1			1	1	-1	0	1	-3		0
Na$^+$	0	1	1	1	1	-1	0	1	1	0	0	0	0	0	1
K$^+$	1	0	1	1	0	-1	-1	1	-1	1	0	0	1		1
Rb$^+$	1	1	1	1	0	-1	-1	1	-1	1	0	0			1
Cs$^+$	1	1	1	0	0	-1	-1		-2	1	1	0			1
NH$_4^+$		1	1	1	1	-1			0	1	1	0		———	———
Be^{++}										-2	0				-5
Mg^{++}	-3	1	1	1	1	-1		1	0	-3	0	1	-3	———	-4
Ca^{++}	-4	1	1	1	1	-3		1	1	-4	-2	0	-3		-2
Sr^{++}	-3	0	0	1	0	-3	0	1	1	-4	-3	-3			-1
Ba^{++}	-2	0	0	1	-1	-4	-2	0	1	-4	-4	-5			-1
Al^{+++}	-1	1									0			———	-5
Cr^{+++}											0			———	
Mn^{++}	-1	1	1		1					-3	0			-5	-5
Fe^{++}		1	0		1					-3	0			-6	-5
Fe^{+++}	-2	1		———	1						1			———	-10
Co^{++}		0	1	1	0	-2	0	1			0				
Ni^{++}	-1	1	1	0	1	-2	-1	1	1	-3	0			-10	-4
Cu^{++}		1			1	-2		1			0			-17	
Zn^{++}	-1	1	1	1	1	-2	0	1		-4	1			-9	-5
Ag$^+$	1	-5	-6	-9	1	-5	-2	0	1	-4	-2	-4	-6	-16	———
Cd^{++}	-1	1	0	0			0	1			0			-10	-5
Hg$_2^{++}$		-6	-11	-10							-3			———	
Hg^{++}		0	-1	-5	1		-3	0			-5			-23	
Sn^{++}		1		-1							0				-5
Pb^{++}	-3	-2	-2	-3	0	-4	-2	0		-5	-4	-7	-7	-10	-3

THE SPECIAL PROBLEM OF SALTS IN WATER

A solubility equilibrium is not inherently different from other equilibrium processes. Its attainment is the result of competitive processes, there being a net reaction until equilibrium is reached. When the solute species passes from the solution phase to its pure phase at the same rate as it leaves the pure phase for the solution a saturation equilibrium obtains.

SOLUBILITY OF SALTS AND CRYSTAL STRUCTURES

These principles apply to the solubility of salts in water but some special effects influence the final equilibrium state. Water has a well-organized structure of its own but the dissolved salts disrupt this structure. Salts, also, have well-organized structures which are disrupted on solution. Salts are relatively high melting, showing that their solid phases at room temperature are much more stable than their own liquid phases. From this fact alone one would expect their escaping tendency at room temperature to be very low. Their low vapor pressures corroborate this view. The ions they produce are quite unlike water and might therefore be expected not to dissolve in water at all. Yet salts do dissolve in water. There must be powerful interactions between ions and water to form "complexes" from which the ions have low escaping tendencies and the complexes must be enough like water to mingle freely with it. These ideas help to explain solubility of salts in water but they do not differentiate between salts which, we have already seen, vary enormously in their solubilities.

Since much of inorganic chemistry deals with salts in water solution, and most of qualitative analysis is concerned with equilibrium between salts and their aqueous solutions, we have practical as well as theoretical reasons for considering the factors which help to determine the final equilibrium states. The known factors which influence salt solubility occur together, inextricably interwoven. However, we shall study these factors separately in order to evaluate their relative importance in explaining solubilities and the mechanism of solution of salts in water. In some instances the correlations turn out to be fairly simple and straightforward. We shall consider first the factors contributing to the stability of the crystal phase and second those contributing to stability of the solution phase.

THE STRUCTURE OF SALTS

Although salts furnish excellent examples of ionic crystal lattices (for that of sodium chloride, see Figure 15.3), many substances called salts conform to other types of crystal structure. For historical reasons salts have been defined in other terms than of their crystal structure. Oxides and hydroxides, many of which form ionic crystals, were not called salts, whereas sulfides and iodides, for example, are called salts even though many do not form ionic crystals. We shall not argue the point but merely call attention to the fact so that the actual structures may be understood.

The fact that the halogen ("salt-former") atoms can form either ionic or covalent bonds leads to some interesting structural situations in solid halides. They may be arranged into four classes based on the structural units within the crystal: (1) discrete molecules of low molecular weight (Al_2Br_6, Fe_2Cl_6, Au_2Cl_6, hydrogen halides), (2) chain molecules of "indefinite" length, that is, extending from one face of the crystal to another ($PdCl_2$), (3) planar molecules "indefinite" in length and width, leading to a layer lattice similar to graphite (see Figure 7.2) with strong bonding within the layer but only weak van der

Waals forces between the layers (HgI_2, $CdCl_2$, $CrCl_3$, BiI_3, $MgCl_2$, CdI_2), and (4) <u>three-dimensional arrangements "infinite"</u> in length, width, and height, with strong bonding between neighboring atoms extending in all directions throughout the whole crystal so that each crystal is a single molecule, the type of bonding varying from highly ionic (alkali halides) to largely covalent (cuprous halides).

The four types of arrangement are illustrated (in two dimensions) in Figure 24.1. Note that for all four types the halogen atoms, designated by open circles are arranged in the same pattern. The other atoms, designated by dark circles, are placed within the halogen lattice in different patterns, leading to the different types of structure.

We do not know all the reasons for particular ions (or atoms) forming one type of lattice rather than another but one reason is the relative sizes of the cations and anions (or atoms). Inspection of Figure 12.3 shows that the halide ions are considerably larger than most of the positively charged ions. For this reason the structure of a crystal containing a halide is often determined largely by how the halogen atoms can pack most closely together, for they are the bulkiest part of the substance. When the halogen atoms do pack as closely together as possible there will always be small holes between them into which the smaller nonhalogen atoms must fit. The holes between the halogen atoms must, of course, be large enough to hold the second kind of atom. The larger the cation the more loosely the halide ions must pack in order to leave large enough holes. Conversely, the smaller the cation the more closely the halide ions can pack. An amazing thing, however, is that halides containing the same halogen but different second elements may crystallize in different structural arrangements even though the atoms of the second elements are practically identical in size and charge. No complete interpretation of this is known.

MACROMOLECULAR CRYSTALS AND SOLUBILITY

Before considering the influence of the other structural factors on solubility we shall discuss here only the relation between bond type and solubility. It is well known that water is a much better solvent for polar and ionic substances than nonpolar ones. The salts (Type 1 above) having discrete molecules held together in the crystal by van der Waals forces are soluble in water. On the other hand, macromolecular substances held together by covalent bonding (diamond and silicon carbide, for example) are insoluble. The low solubility of the chlorides, bromides, and iodides of silver, lead, and mercurous mercury (and most other salts of these elements) may be attributed to the tendency of their atoms to form covalent bonds with the halide ions and form macromolecular crystals. The more electropositive elements have less tendency to share electrons in this way, hence their halides are more highly ionic and are rather soluble in water. Further evidence for the great effect of macromolecular covalent crystals on solubility is furnished by the sulfides. Only the most highly electropositive (alkali and alkaline earth) elements form soluble

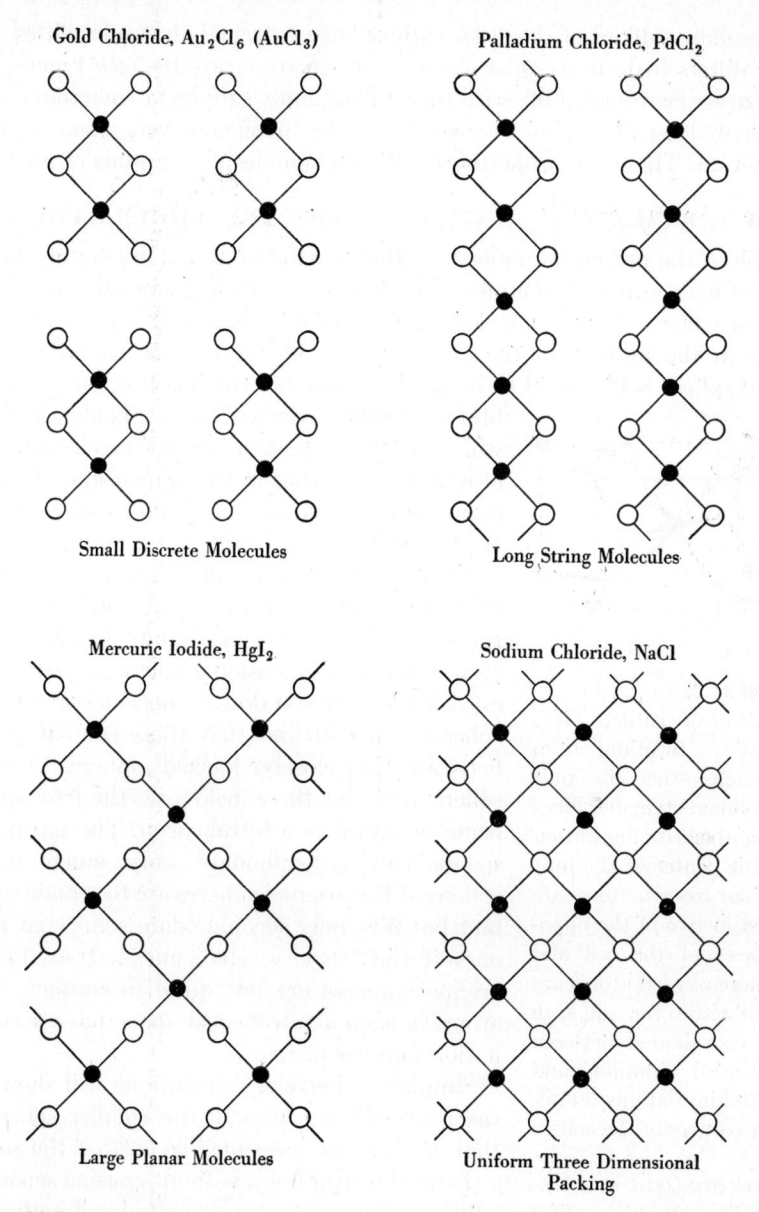

Figure 24.1.

Several structures derived from the same initial packing lattice. Note that the arrangement of the open circles (halogen atoms) is identical in each case. Only the distribution of the filled-in circles (metal atoms), and the bonds differ.

395

sulfides. The sulfides of the other cations have extremely low solubilities. Now sulfur differs little from most elements in electronegativity (see Figure 11.1) and shares electrons readily with them. That many sulfides are macromolecular is indicated by their high degree of metallic luster and very good electrical conduction. These are properties of the macromolecular crystals of metals.

ATOM ARRANGEMENT IN CRYSTALS AND THE RADIUS RATIO

Some of the principles underlying the packing of atoms in crystals may be clarified by a series of examples. The closest geometrically possible packing of uniform spheres is one in which twelve spheres are in contact with any one sphere in the interior of the arrangement. The *coordination number* of the central sphere is then said to be twelve. You may confirm this fact with marbles, or, crudely, even with coins. Six identical coins will exactly fill the area around the circumference of a seventh, so that in two dimensions the maximum closeness of packing leads to six neighbors. If identical layers of coins are now placed above and below the first you will find that you can have three coins below and three above the original central one to attain the maximum possible coordination in three-dimensional packing, twelve nearest neighbors. If you do this more accurately with spheres you will find that there are small holes between the closely packed spheres where a sphere rests on three below it, the four spheres being arranged in a tetrahedron. The tetrahedral spaces can accommodate only much smaller spheres if the original spheres are to remain in contact but they may accommodate somewhat larger ones if the lattice swells somewhat so that the original spheres are not quite in contact. Small atoms in such a tetrahedral space have a coordination number of four.

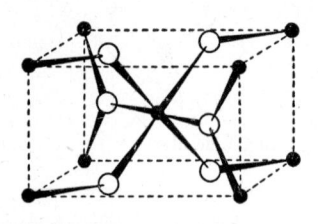

● Titanium ○ Oxide

Figure 24.2.
Structure of rutile, TiO$_2$. In rutile a titanium atom is at each corner of a unit cell having rectangular faces and another titanium atom is at the center of the unit cell. Four oxygen atoms are located in two of the opposite faces of the cell and two more oxygen atoms are located within the cell, each being coordinated between the central titanium and two titanium atoms on adjacent corners of the cell.

Simple geometrical calculations will show that the ratio of the radius of the smaller spheres to that of the larger ones must be 0.225 if the smaller spheres are to fit exactly into the tetrahedral holes without causing separation of the larger spheres. Different types of packing may be considered in the same way and the limiting ratio of the radii calculated for each type. In general, the larger the smaller atom the greater will be the number of a given size of larger atoms that surround it to form a stable crystal. The ratio of the radius of the positively charged ion (cation) to that of the negatively charged atom (anion) is defined as the *radius ratio*. In the above example, if the smaller atom is the cation, the radius ratio is 0.225.

Two common types of crystal structure are the rutile structure, Figure 24.2, (named from rutile, formula TiO_2) and the fluorite structure, Figure 24.3, (named from fluorite, formula CaF_2). In these there are two anions for every cation. Six large atoms (anions) surround each smaller one (cation) in rutile, while eight large atoms are around each smaller one in fluorite. It can be shown that the critical radius ratio for the transition from one structure to the other is 0.73, the fluorite structure being stable if the radius ratio is greater than and the rutile being stable if the radius ratio is less than 0.73. Some typical substances crystallizing in each system are listed in Table 24.2, together with the radius ratio for each substance. Note the agreement with the theory.

These structural ideas are not limited to the halides but apply to all crystals. In Table 24.3 is listed a more complete sequence of oxides in which the number of oxygen atoms around a given positive atom varies all the way from 3 to 12 as the radius ratio changes. The excellent concurrence between theory and experiment should be noted.

The general relationship between coordination number and radius ratio is summarized in Table 24.4 for simple types of packing. The radius ratios given in Table 24.4 should be considered as the minimum for each type of packing since any lower value would allow the big negative ions to come into direct contact and give rise to large repulsive for-

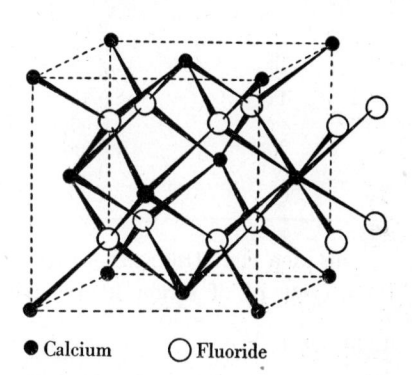

● Calcium   ○ Fluoride

Figure 24.3.
Structure of fluorite, CaF_2. In fluorite a calcium ion is present at each corner of the cubic unit cell and another calcium is at the center of each cube face. The fluoride ions are arranged at the corners of a cube smaller than the unit cell but concentric with it. The smaller cube has an edge length half that of the unit cell.

Table 24.2

Radius Ratios of Some Difluorides
(Based on radius of F^- ion equal to 1.36Å.)

FLUORITE STRUCTURE COORDINATION NUMBER OF CATION = 8	Cation	Cu^{++}	Ca^{++}	Sr^{++}	Ba^{++}	Cd^{++}	Hg^{++}
	Radius Ratio	0.71	0.73	0.76	0.99	0.71	0.81
RUTILE STRUCTURE COORDINATION NUMBER OF CATION = 6	Cation	Mg^{++}	Ni^{++}	Co^{++}	Zn^{++}	Fe^{++}	Mn^{++}
	Radius Ratio	0.48	0.51	0.53	0.54	0.55	0.59

398   GENERAL CHEMISTRY

ces. Such a crystal should be unstable with respect to some other form of packing in which the negative atoms were not in contact.

Table 24.3

Coordination Number (CN) of Some Cations in Oxides as a Function of the Radius Ratio
(Based on radius of O^{--} ion = 1.40 Å.)

CATION	RADIUS RATIO	THEORETICAL CN	OBSERVED CN
B^{+++}	0.20	3 or 4	3, 4
Be^{++}	0.22	4	4
Al^{+++}	0.36	4 or 6	4, 5, 6
Ti^{++++}	0.55	6	6
Zr^{++++}	0.62	6 or 8	6, 8
Na^+	0.68	6 or 8	6, 7, 8, 9, 10, 12
K^+	0.95	8 or 12	6, 8
Cs^+	1.2	12	12

The idea that the radius ratio will determine the over-all packing is based on a concept of larger atoms packed as closely as possible consistent with

Table 24.4

Theoretical Relationship between Coordination Number and Radius Ratio

MINIMUM RADIUS RATIO	0.225	0.414	0.732	1.000
COORDINATION NUMBER	4	6	8	12
GEOMETRY	Tetrahedral	Octahedral	Simple Cubic	Closest packed

leaving holes of sufficient size for the smaller atoms to fit into them. The "sufficient size" will then determine the coordination number of larger atoms around the smaller ones as we have already shown. Once this coordination number is known the coordination number of smaller atoms around the larger ones may be obtained from an examination of the stoichiometric ratio in the substance. The ratio of the two coordination numbers must be the same as the ratio of the two kinds of atoms in the stoichiometric formula. Thus in rutile (formula TiO_2) the coordination number of the titanium is six (each titanium atom is surrounded by six oxygen atoms) while that of oxygen is three (each oxygen atom is surrounded by three titanium atoms) as shown in Figure 24.2. Note that the ratio of the two coordination numbers, 6 and 3, is the same as the ratio of the number of oxygen atoms to titanium atoms, 2 to 1, in the compound. Similarly, in fluorite the coordination numbers are 8 and 4, being in the same ratio, 2 to 1, as the number of fluorine atoms and calcium atoms.

EFFECT OF RELATIVE SIZE OF IONS

The halides of the alkali elements are a particularly good group of ionic substances to use in studying principles of solubility. Because of the large differences in electronegatively between the alkali elements and the halogens

SOLUBILITY OF SALTS AND CRYSTAL STRUCTURES

the crystals are ionic with almost no contribution of covalent bonding. All the ions have the inert gas structure tending to give spherical symmetry to the ions. All ionic charges are unity. There is one positive ion for every negative ion so that the coordination numbers of both are identical.

Yet, as may be noted in Table 24.1, there are differences in solubility. That of the fluorides increases in the order, lithium to cesium fluoride, that of the chlorides (and that of the bromides if accurate data are used) passes through a minimum, and that of the iodides decreases in the order lithium to cesium iodide. Similarly, both the lithium and the sodium salts become more soluble in the order fluoride to iodide, both the potassium and the rubidium salts show a minimum, and the cesium salts become less soluble in the order fluoride to iodide. The common crystal form of most of the halides of the alkali elements is the *sodium chloride structure* in which the coordination numbers are 6, though the common crystal structure of cesium chloride, bromide, and iodide is somewhat different (*cesium chloride structure* with coordination numbers of 8). The ions in all these salts are remarkably similar in most respects but they differ greatly in size. The effect of difference in size is reflected in differences in stability of the crystals (leading finally to a different coordination number) and differences in solubility resulting from the changes in stability.

In Figure 24.4 is shown a portion of a face of each of the crystals (assuming the sodium chloride structure) with the ionic sizes drawn to scale. For each the

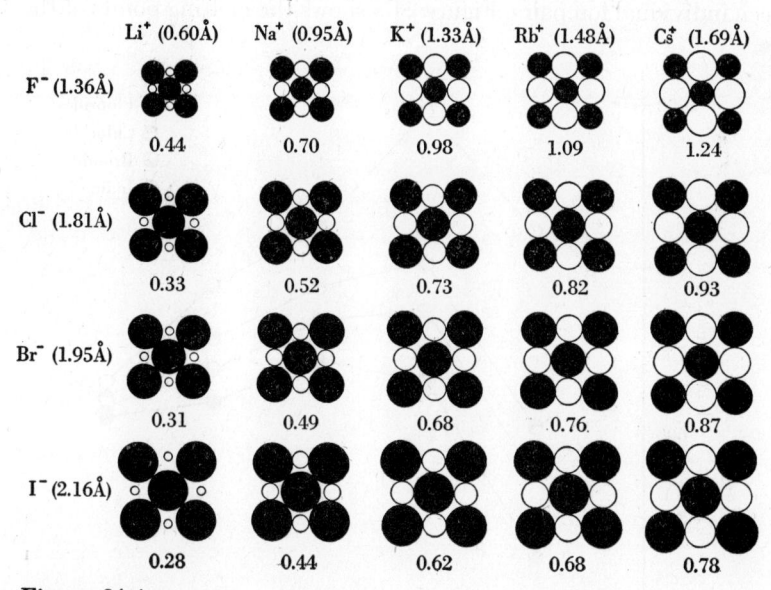

	Li⁺ (0.60Å)	Na⁺ (0.95Å)	K⁺ (1.33Å)	Rb⁺ (1.48Å)	Cs⁺ (1.69Å)
F⁻ (1.36Å)	0.44	0.70	0.98	1.09	1.24
Cl⁻ (1.81Å)	0.33	0.52	0.73	0.82	0.93
Br⁻ (1.95Å)	0.31	0.49	0.68	0.76	0.87
I⁻ (2.16Å)	0.28	0.44	0.62	0.68	0.78

Figure 24.4.
Effect of relative ionic sizes on the contact of ions in the alkali halide crystals. The numbers below the diagrams indicate the radius ratio. (Cesium chloride, cesium bromide, and cesium iodide have a somewhat different crystal structure at room temperature than that indicated in the figure.)

value of the radius ratio, r^+/r^-, is also given. A reason for the stability and solubility trends is apparent—there are important differences in the nearness to which ions of like charge can approach one another in the crystal. In lithium iodide, where the iodide ions can actually be in contact, large repulsive forces arise in the solid, decreasing the stability of the crystal and increasing the solubility. As the size of the negative ions decreases, the lithium ions become more effective in keeping them separated, the stability increases, and the solubility decreases, being least for the fluoride. Conversely, in the cesium salts the fluoride ions are too small to keep the cesium ions separated whereas the iodide ions are more effective. As a result cesium fluoride is more soluble than cesium iodide. This effect of the value of the ratio between the radii (or diameters) of the ions will explain the minimum solubility values found in some of the series. It is interesting to note that minimum solubility does not occur when the value of the radius ratio is unity, that is, when the oppositely charged ions have the same size. Rather, solubility minima occur when the ratio is about 0.75, though other factors may change the value in other series of salts.

Both the melting and the boiling points of the series of alkali halides reflect the effect of the radius ratio. Abnormally low values mean that less energy is needed to break up the regular crystal structure to form liquid and to separate the particles of the liquid to form gas than is to be expected from the forces between individual ion pairs. Figure 24.5 shows the melting points of the alkali

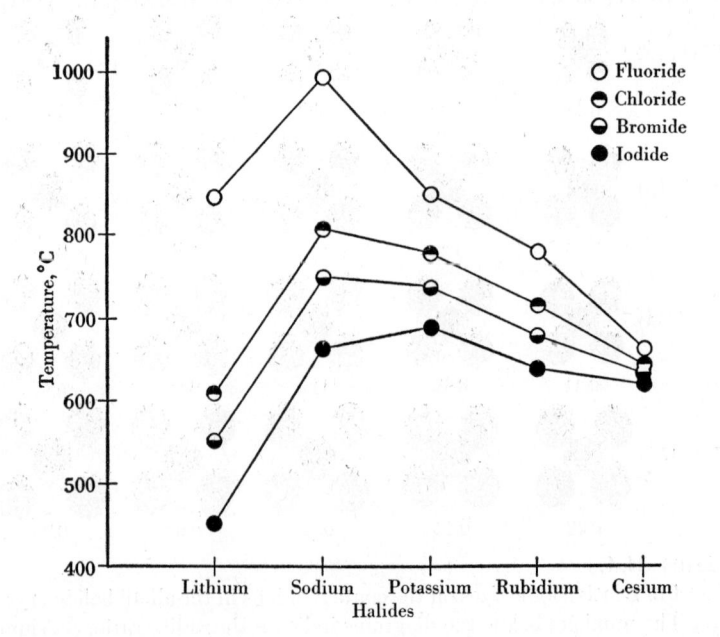

Figure 24.5.
Melting points of the alkali halides.

halides. The four lithium halides, and sodium chloride, bromide, and iodide have melting and boiling points considerably lower than would be expected. Lithium iodide shows the maximum effect with a melting point 250° lower and a boiling point 500° lower than the interatomic bonding forces would predict. This is the compound with ratio of ionic radii farthest from the most stable ratio.

EFFECT OF CHARGE DENSITY

The actual sizes of the ions also influence the stability of the crystal. The small ions, such as lithium or fluoride ions, have a relatively high charge density since their charge is concentrated on a fairly small sphere. These ions attract their neighbors very strongly and their salts are in general less soluble (and have higher melting and boiling points) than one would predict from radius ratio alone. The very low solubility of lithium fluoride in particular and of all fluorides in general is indicative of this effect. The generally high solubilities of iodides, nitrates, chlorates, and perchlorates is partially due to their low charge density, coupled with a correspondingly low radius ratio.

The effect of charge density becomes evident when one compares the alkali halide salts, in which both ions have unit charge, to such substances as the alkaline earth carbonates in which each ion has a double charge. The drop in solubility is very great. For the same reason the double charge on the sulfate ion might be expected to render sulfates insoluble also but the large size of the sulfate ion leads to small values of the radius ratio so that most sulfate solubilities remain rather appreciable, though mostly lower than those of the alkali halides. The only insoluble sulfates other than silver sulfate are those of $2+$ ions in which the radius ratio is relatively large (Sr^{++}, Ba^{++}, Hg^{++}, and Pb^{++}).

The very low solubilities of the phosphates can be attributed largely to the high charge density of the phosphate ion. The same explanation applies to the silicates. Likewise, the general insolubility of oxides and hydroxides may, in many instances, be explained by the high charge density on the oxide and hydroxide ions.

EFFECT OF RELATIVE NUMBERS OF POSITIVE AND NEGATIVE IONS

The data in Table 24.1 show that many salts with an equal number of positive and negative ions (such as the alkali halides or calcium carbonate known as 1—1 salts from the stoichiometric ratio between the ions) have appreciably lower solubilities than corresponding salts having an unequal number of the two ions. Compare the solubility of calcium carbonate, a 1—1 salt, with those of calcium chloride, a 1—2 salt, sodium carbonate, a 2—1 salt, or aluminum chloride a 1—3 salt, for example.

It is generally easier to pack ions into a crystal if they can be alternated as in sodium chloride so that each ion is completely surrounded by unlike ions and is well shielded from ions of its own charge. A very stable packing is more difficult to achieve when there are more of one kind of ion than another. How-

402 GENERAL CHEMISTRY

ever, radius ratio effects can be very important in affecting solubilities of crystals other than those of the 1—1 type as is well shown by the solubilities of the alkaline earth halides. The iodides (large negative ion) are much more soluble than the fluorides (small negative ion).

EFFECT OF IONIC SHAPE

Ions have shapes as well as charges and sizes (see Figure 24.6). Halide, oxide, and sulfide ions are spherical; nitrate and carbonate ions have the atomic nuclei in a flat triangle; iodate, bromate, and chlorate ions are triangular pyramids, and perchlorate, sulfate, chromate, and phosphate ions are

Sulfate, $SO_4^=$ Sulfite, $SO_3^=$ Nitrate, NO_3^-

Hydroxide, OH^- Oxide, $O^=$ Nitrite, NO_2^-

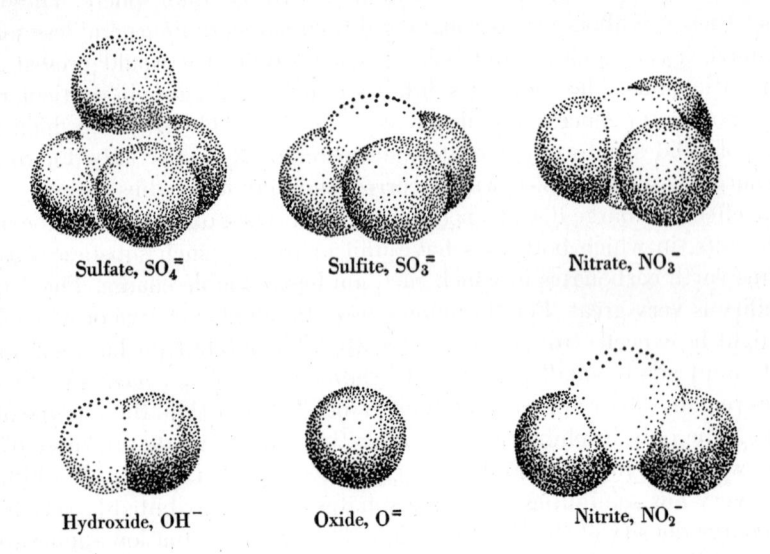

Figure 24.6.
Symmetries (shapes) of some common anions.

tetrahedral pyramids (but approach a spherical shape). Hydroxide ions are slightly elongated along the bond axis, but are close to being spherical. These shapes influence the packing in crystals and affect solubility but no clear-cut generalization can be drawn. It may well be, however, that it is the planar shape of the nitrate ion coupled with its low charge density which renders the nitrates of silver, lead, and mercury soluble (in contrast to the spherical halide ions which form insoluble salts with these cations).

The shape of the hydroxide is of outstanding importance in causing the low solubility of most hydroxides. Here we have an elongated ion which is strongly dipolar, the hydrogen end being positive. As a result strong hydrogen bonds are formed in the crystal, greatly stabilizing it. Only in the hydroxides of the alkali elements (1—1 compounds) are the hydroxide ions separated from one another sufficiently to prevent hydrogen bonding between the ions.

EFFECT OF HYDRATION

So far we have discussed only those effects which increase or decrease the stability of the crystal with respect to disintegration. The situation in the solution is equally important in determining the final equilibrium. The fact that ionic materials dissolve in water at all indicates that strong attractions must exist between the ions and the water molecules and that these attractions must be comparable in magnitude to those between oppositely charged ions in the crystal. Since water is a polar substance negative ions strongly attract the positive hydrogen atoms of the water around themselves and positive ions similarly attract the negative oxygen atoms of the water. Both kinds of ions become hydrated. The higher the charge density on the ion the stronger its tendency to hydrate and so to dissolve. But high charge densities also lead to strong attractive forces in the crystals. As a matter of fact the charge density effect is much greater inside a crystal than in a solution since an ion of opposite charge can be attracted more strongly by a given ion than can a molecule which is merely polar in nature. Furthermore, hydration bonding varies little from ion to ion and does not serve to differentiate appreciably among them. The notable exception is hydrogen ion—very large solubilities of acids in water may be attributed directly to the very strong hydration bonds which form between the hydrogen ion and the water molecules. As a matter of fact, all acids in a solid or pure liquid state are very poorly ionized. They are, rather, essentially covalent. The tendency of hydrogen ion to hydrate is so strong, however, that several acids become almost completely ionized and many are highly soluble in aqueous solution.

Bonding effects between water and individual ions can be appreciable for those ions having available empty orbitals with which the water molecule can form covalent bonds by using the unshared electrons of its oxygen atom. The solubilities of many of the transition ions such as those of copper, zinc, iron, etc., may be enhanced in this way.

Hydration enters into solubility relationships in other ways than through direct attractions between the ions and the water. Extensive hydration ties up a substantial fraction of the water on individual ions so that the insulating effect of the water between ions of opposite charge decreases. Ionic attractions tending to re-form the solid become appreciable. At the same time the concentration of "free" water decreases and a practical limit to salt solubility of about 30 molal is reached even for the most soluble salts.

EFFECT OF THE STRUCTURE OF WATER

We have considered the stabilities of the crystal and of the solution. We must also consider the effect of the stability of pure water itself on solubilities. The principal intermolecular force in liquid water arises from hydrogen bonding in which each hydrogen atom tends to be between two oxygen atoms, and each oxygen atom tends to be surrounded tetrahedrally by four hydrogen atoms. A rise in temperature, of course, tends to break down this structure to a more random one (Le Chatelier's principle) and this may be one of the principal reasons for the usual increase in solubility of a salt with rising temperature, for it is certainly true that the introduction of most ions into water disturbs the hydrogen bonding already present. The hydrogen bonds in liquid water are similar to those in solid ice so that this disturbance by added ions has been called the "snowplow" effect inasmuch as the ions tend to break up the ice-like structure.

Some few ions can enter into the water structure with minimum disturbance since they, too, are capable of forming hydrogen bonds. Ammonium ion is noteworthy in this connection since it forms strong hydrogen bonds with the water, tending to encourage the existence of an ice-like structure. This action has been called the "iceberg" or "snowball" effect, as contrasted to the "snowplow" effect of most ions. It will be noted that ammonium compounds are generally more soluble than the corresponding potassium ones even though these two ions are very similar in charge and size.

SUMMARY FOR WATER SOLUTIONS

Most of the effects outlined above (there are other minor effects we have not mentioned) may be related to the sizes and charges of the individual ions. Often some of the effects work to increase while others work to decrease the solubility of a substance at the same time (for example, charge density as it affects both hydration and ionic attractions in the crystal). It is, therefore, understandable why a simple, generally applicable theory for the solubility of electrolytes is not available. Few beginning students will be able to evaluate the relative contribution of each factor in a particular case. Yet many trends are readily seen and simply interpreted, and most of the formal rules can be based on a physical interpretation. Charge and size are the fundamental variables but the dozen or so factors discussed above are recapitulated in Table 24.5. The principal factors which differentiate salts as to their solubility

Table 24.5

Factors Influencing the Solubilities of Salts in Water

Crystal stability enhanced by:	Covalently-bonded macromolecules High charge densities on ions Radius ratio near 0.75 1–1 stoichiometry Hydrogen bonding in solids (hydroxides) Symmetrical shapes of ions
Solution stability enhanced by:	Hydration of ions Covalent bond formation, complexes Insulation effect of water "Snowball effect" of NH_4^+ and NO_3^- ions
Solution stability decreased by:	Removal of water through hydration "Snowplow effect"

in water are those factors which determine the stability of the crystal; solution effects are secondary. But to interpret solubilities intelligently one must remember the competitive nature of solution processes.

NONAQUEOUS SOLVENTS

There is no solvent equal to water in dissolving so many salts at room temperatures. The alcohols and some other organic substances do dissolve appreciable quantities of some salts, and, in certain cases, dissolve more of a given salt than would water. Inorganic solvents such as liquid sulfur dioxide, ammonia, hydrogen sulfide, hydrogen cyanide, and a host of others have been only partially investigated, yet water excels all in its extensive solvent powers, though the other solvents are often used in special cases where the presence of water is undesirable.

In these other solvents the same factors determine the stabilities of the crystals and the same factors affect the solutions. The principal differentiating factor, which makes water a generally better solvent than any of the others, is the marked ability of water to hydrate (a more general term is "solvate") the ions due to its own highly polar nature. Liquid hydrogen fluoride, which might be expected to be even more polar than water (see Figure 11.1), does show promise as a solvent for special applications, but even it is apparently not as good as water as an all around solvent. Hydrogen fluoride has not been investigated thoroughly as a solvent, however, for it is highly corrosive to most materials, is very poisonous, and is expensive. Its tendency to polymerize with itself (see page 324) will also interfere with its acting as a solvent for salts.

The role of water as the nearest approach to a universal solvent for salts thus seems safe for the future. Water is the only substance, liquid near room temperature, having the requisite polarity to furnish the high degree of solvation bonding which can compete with the strong interionic attractions in the salt crystals and dissolve such a large number of salts.

Problem 24.1. How do you account for the trend in solubility: zinc sulfide, cadmium sulfide, mercuric sulfide?

Problem 24.2. How do you account for the trend in solubility of the alkaline earth sulfates in the order beryllium to barium sulfate?

Problem 24.3. How do you account for the trend in solubility of the alkaline earth hydroxides in the order beryllium to barium hydroxide?

Problem 24.4. How do you account for the low solubility of silver compounds (radius of Ag^+ ion is 1.26 Å) as contrasted with the high solubility of potassium compounds (radius of K^+ ion is 1.33 Å) even though the ionic charges are identical and the ionic radii are almost equal?

Problem 24.5. How do you account for the trend in solubility: silver iodate < silver bromate < silver chlorate < silver perchlorate?

Problem 24.6. State which of the following solids are "soluble" to a considerable extent (that is, disappear as solids and leave no residue) in: (a) water, (b) $1f$ hydrochloric acid solution, (c) 6 f sodium hydroxide solution, (d) 6 f ammonia solution. The solids are: (1) copper metal, (2) cupric hydroxide, (3) aluminum metal, (4) aluminum hydroxide, (5) magnesium hydroxide, (6) zinc hydroxide, (7) sodium chloride, (8) silver chloride, (9) aluminum chloride, and (10) cupric sulfate. Note that some of the solids may be "soluble" in more than one of the reagents. Write an equation for each "solution" process.

25 OXIDES AND THEIR REACTIONS WITH WATER

THE OXIDES and hydroxides of the elements deserve special attention for a number of reasons. Oxygen atoms are more abundant in the lithosphere than the atoms of all other elements combined, 63 per cent of them being oxygen. Oxides of all the elements (except the noble gas elements) exist in nature or can be prepared in the laboratory. Most elements react directly with atmospheric oxygen and some of the others react when the temperature is raised. Even the noble metals, stable in air, form oxides under proper conditions. Very thin layers of oxides coat the usual commercial metals, separating the underlying metal from the air and thus retarding further corrosion.

We have already found that many elements form series of compounds representing different oxidation states of the elements. It is, therefore, not surprising that most elements form two or more oxides. Some oxides represent characteristic oxidation states of the elements. Historically, these oxides were invaluable guides to the chemists who established the periodic table of the elements. Other oxides, however, have formulas not representative of the chemical families, a fact which delayed the grouping of the elements into families for many decades. The atomic weights of the elements were necessary for final clarification.

Except in the oxide of fluorine, formula F_2O, the oxygen in an oxide or in the corresponding hydroxide is in the 2− oxidation state. In peroxides, with typical formulas H_2O_2, Na_2O_2, BaO_2, etc., the oxidation state of the oxygen is 1−, and in superoxides, such as that of potassium, formula KO_2, the oxidation state of the oxygen is $\frac{1}{2}$−. These appear to be the only stable oxidation states of oxygen: 2−, 1−, $\frac{1}{2}$−. In consequence, the other element in oxides is in some positive oxidation state. This fact permits us to consider only the positive oxidation states of the elements in this chapter.

RELATIONSHIPS ALONG DIAGONALS IN THE PERIODIC TABLE

Hitherto the relations in the periodic table we have emphasized were those between the elements in the same vertical column, containing the elements in the same group or family. In vertical columns the unifying principle is the number of valence electrons. We shall, in later chapters, consider relations between elements in the same period or horizontal row. In these the unifying principle is the electronic structure in the levels underlying the valence shell. In this chapter we shall need to consider some relations along diagonals.

In each column the size of atoms, whether expressed in terms of volume or covalent radius, increases with increasing atomic number. On the other hand, in the second and third periods and in the parts of the long periods shown in Table 25.1 the atomic size decreases with increasing atomic number. It appears that in oxides (and other compounds) the size of the central (positive) atom helps determine the nature of the compound. In many instances the atomic size is approximately constant along diagonals running from upper left to lower right in the periodic table. This constancy in size (see Figure 12.3) leads to similarities in properties, hence our need to consider relations between elements along the diagonals.

MOLECULAR OXIDES

The oxides of the typical nonmetallic elements are molecular. The formulas are relatively simple and those of the gases and liquids rest on molar weights determined experimentally in the usual ways. At room temperature the oxides with lighter, smaller molecules are gases, those with somewhat larger molecules are liquids and those with the largest molecules are crystalline solids. Table 25.1 lists these oxides, together with the bordering oxides which are not molecular but consist of macromolecules (for example, silicon dioxide and selenium dioxide). For macromolecular substances a formula such as SiO_2 represents only the ratio between numbers of atoms (here silicon and oxygen

Table 25.1

Formulas of Some Molecular Oxides at Room Temperature and of Some Bordering Macromolecular Oxides
(Macromolecular oxides indicated by *)

PERIOD	4a	5a	6a	7a
I					$H_2O_{(liq)}$
II	$CO_{(g)}$ $CO_{2(g)}$	$N_2O, NO, NO_{2(g)}$ $N_2O_3, N_2O_{4(liq)}$ $N_2O_{5(s)}$		$F_2O_{(g)}$
III	$(SiO_2)_{n(s)}$*	$P_4O_{6(liq)}$ $P_4O_{10(s)}$ or $(P_2O_5)^*_{n(s)}$	$SO_{2(g)}$ $SO_{3(liq)}$ or $(SO_3)_n$*	$Cl_2O, ClO_{2(g)}$ $Cl_2O_{7(liq)}$
IV		$(As_2O_3)_{n(s)}$* or $As_4O_{6(s)}$	$(SeO_2)_{n(s)}$*	Bromine oxides, Br_2O and BrO_2, unstable at room temperature. $Br_3O_{8(s)}$
V		$(Sb_2O_3)_{n(s)}$*	$(TeO_2)_{n(s)}$* $(TeO_3)_{n(s)}$*	$I_2O_{4(s)}$ $I_4O_{9(s)}$ $I_2O_{5(s)}$

(Note: $H_2O_{(liq)}$ appears in Period I under Group 7a area)

atoms); the subscript n indicates that an indefinite, often very large number, are present in the macromolecule. Note that the line between the molecular and the macromolecular oxides follows a diagonal across the periodic table.

REACTION OF MOLECULAR OXIDES WITH WATER

From our knowledge of solution equilibrium we are able to make some predictions about the expected solubility of molecular oxides in water. On the assumption that there is no specific reaction between water and the oxides one would expect that the gaseous oxides with low boiling points (examples, carbon monoxide, and nitric oxide) would be but slightly soluble and that those gases more easily liquefied (examples, carbon dioxide, nitrous oxide, and sulfur dioxide) would be appreciably soluble. The more polar liquid oxides might be expected to mix with water without limit and solid oxides, like all solids, would be expected to have a limited solubility. Observations of the actual solubilities and especially of the unusual heat effects observed in the solution processes show that more is involved than a simple dissolving. Many of the oxides react with water to form new molecular species which can often, but not always, be separated from the solutions and identified as pure substances. The solutions are acidic and the new substances formed are hydroxide-containing acids. A few examples will illustrate the kinds of reactions.

Carbon monoxide and nitric oxide do not react with water and their solubilities correspond to those of nitrogen and oxygen and other gases with similar boiling points. Carbon dioxide and sulfur dioxide react with water to form acid solutions. The reactions are typical of acidic oxides, those electron-deficient in the Lewis sense (see page 243). The type reaction is

$$R::O + :O:H = R:O:H$$
$$H :O:$$
$$H \tag{25.1}$$

or

$$R{=}O + O{-}H = R{-}O{-}H$$
$$\phantom{R{=}O + }| \phantom{= R{-}}|$$
$$\phantom{R{=}O + }H \phantom{= R{-}}O$$
$$\phantom{R{=}O + = R{-}O{-}}|$$
$$\phantom{R{=}O + = R{-}O{-}}H$$

Note that by the reaction the double bond is exchanged for two single bonds. The resulting hydroxide is acidic when the R—O bond is stronger than the O—H bond. Then ionization occurs according to the usual mechanism.

$$R{-}O{-}H + H{-}\overset{..}{O}: \ = \ R{-}O^- + H{-}\overset{..}{O}{-}H^+$$
$$\phantom{R{-}}| \phantom{{-}H + }| \phantom{= R{-}}| \phantom{+ H{-}}|$$
$$\phantom{R{-}}O \phantom{{-}H + }H \phantom{= R{-}}O \phantom{+ H{-}}H \tag{25.2}$$
$$\phantom{R{-}}| \phantom{{-}H + H \ = R{-}}|$$
$$\phantom{R{-}}H \phantom{{-}H + H \ = R{-}}H$$
$$\phantom{R{-}O{-}H + H{-}\overset{..}{O}: \ = R{-}O^- + }\text{hydronium ion}$$

Or, if we do not indicate the hydration of the proton

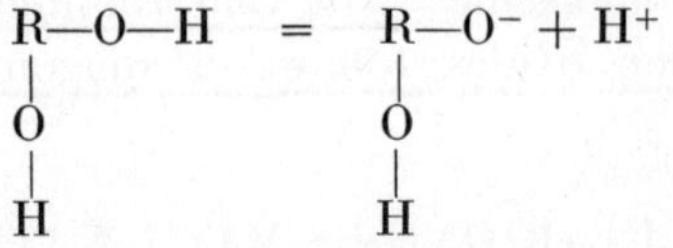

$$\begin{array}{c} \text{R—O—H} \\ | \\ \text{O} \\ | \\ \text{H} \end{array} \quad = \quad \begin{array}{c} \text{R—O}^- \\ | \\ \text{O} \\ | \\ \text{H} \end{array} + \text{H}^+ \quad (25.3)$$

Note that none of these reactions involve oxidation-reduction.

The rate of reaction and the strength of acid formed depend on the nature of the radical R. The influence of structure on rate is illustrated by the reactions of carbon dioxide and sulfur dioxide

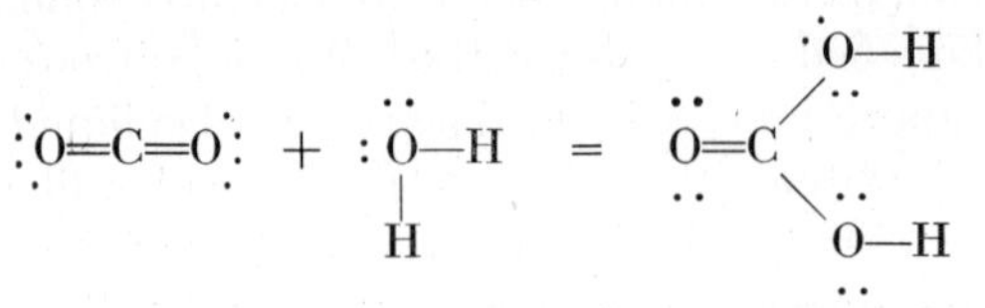

$$:\!O\!=\!C\!=\!O\!: \;+\; :\!\underset{H}{O}\!-\!H \;=\; O\!=\!C\!\!\diagdown\!\!\begin{array}{c}O\!-\!H\\O\!-\!H\end{array} \quad (25.4)$$

carbonic acid

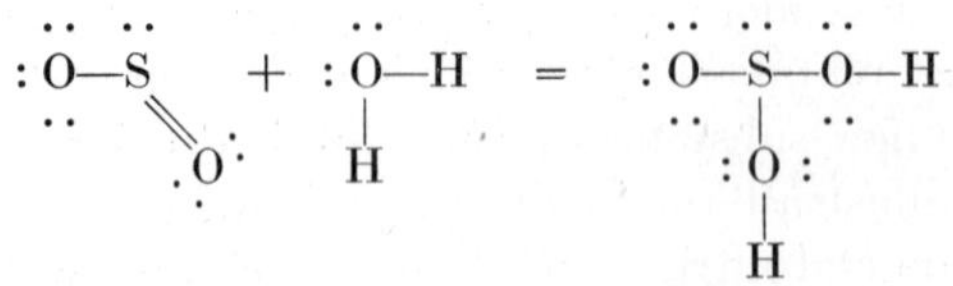

$$:\!O\!=\!\underset{\underset{\cdot O\cdot}{\diagdown}}{S} \;+\; :\!\underset{H}{O}\!-\!H \;=\; :\!O\!-\!\underset{\underset{H}{\overset{:O:}{|}}}{S}\!-\!O\!-\!H \quad (25.5)$$

sulfurous acid

Carbon dioxide has a linear molecule but sulfur dioxide has a bent molecule, with the oxygen atoms more nearly in the positions found in the acid molecule. Experimentally we find that when carbon dioxide and sulfur dioxide gases are bubbled into separate vessels containing water, the solution into which the sulfur dioxide is bubbled becomes acid more quickly, showing that the hydration of the sulfur dioxide proceeds more rapidly. This fact is consistent with the less drastic change in molecular geometry when sulfur dioxide reacts with water.

When nitrogen dioxide is bubbled into water it also produces an acid solution but the reaction is not of the type shown in equation 25.3. It involves oxidation-reduction (see page 365, equations 22.36 and 22.37).

Liquid and solid oxides may also react with water to form acids. For liquid "phosphorus trioxide" and sulfur trioxide, and for solid nitrogen pentoxide the reactions are

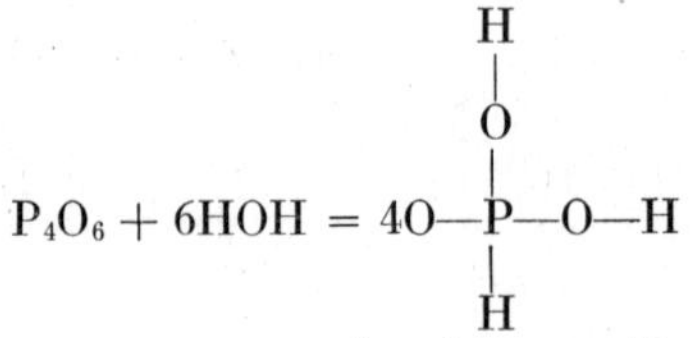

$$P_4O_6 + 6HOH = 4O\!-\!\underset{\underset{H}{|}}{\overset{\overset{H}{|}}{\underset{|}{O}}}\!P\!-\!O\!-\!H \quad (25.6)$$

phosphorous acid

$$SO_3 + HOH = \begin{matrix} H \\ O \\ O\,S\,O\,H \\ O \end{matrix} \quad \text{sulfuric acid} \tag{25.7}$$

$$N_2O_{5(s)} + HOH = 2O\,N\,O\,H \atop O \quad \text{nitric acid} \tag{25.8}$$

These reactions proceed vigorously.

Oxides which react with water without change in oxidation state to form acids are called *acid anhydrides*. The name is appropriate because most acid anhydrides may be made by removing the elements of water from the corresponding acids. Indeed, some acid anhydrides, especially those representing the higher oxidation states, cannot be made by direct union of the elements but must be made by removing water from the acids (example, tellurium trioxide). Table 25.2 shows the formulas of some acid anhydrides and of the corresponding acids (see also Table 22.4, page 369).

Table 25.2

Formulas of Some Hydroxy Acids and Acid Anhydrides

PERIOD	4a	5a	6a	7a
II		N_2O_3, HNO_2 nitrous		
	CO_2, H_2CO_3 carbonic	N_2O_5, HNO_3 nitric		
III	$(SiO_2)_n$, $(H_2SiO_3)_n$ metasilicic	P_4O_6, H_3PO_3 ortho-phosphorous	SO_2, H_2SO_3 sulfurous	Cl_2O, $HClO$ hypochlorous
				— $HClO_2$ chlorous
	H_4SiO_4 orthosilicic	P_4O_{10}, $(HPO_3)_n$ meta-phosphoric	SO_3, H_2SO_4 sulfuric	
				— $HClO_3$ chloric
		H_3PO_4 ortho-phosphoric		Cl_2O_7, $HClO_4$ perchloric

GROUP

Note that some of the anhydrides may be hydrated to different degrees to form more than one acid. Comparison with Table 25.1 will show that some oxides are not acid anhydrides and that some acids exist for which there are not stable anhydrides. This lack of agreement between the list of stable oxides and the list of stable acids is not surprising because the factors making for stability in oxides and acids are different.

When acid anhydrides are added to an excess of water the acids exist in water solution. Many acids cannot be isolated from solution. Examples are carbonic acid, sulfurous acid, and hypochlorous acid. Attempts to remove the water in the solution lead to dehydration of the acid itself so that the oxide is formed. Even for an acid as stable as sulfuric acid small amounts of water (probably combined with protons from the sulfuric acid) and sulfur trioxide are present at equilibrium with the acid. In so-called "pure" 100 per cent sulfuric acid the molecular species present are predominantly H_2SO_4, but there are appreciable amounts of H_3O^+, HSO_4^-, and SO_3. On the other hand, when the acids are weak, that is, poorly ionized, there is good evidence for the existence of acid molecules in solution, even though the acid cannot be isolated. Nitrous acid is such an acid. Measurements of the hydrogen ion concentration in the solution and of the total acid concentration show that most of the acid must be in the molecular form. When an alkali is added the acid is neutralized

$$OH^- + \underset{\substack{\text{nitrous} \\ \text{acid}}}{HONO} = HOH + \underset{\substack{\text{nitrite} \\ \text{ion}}}{NO_2^-} \tag{25.9}$$

and the nitrite ion is formed. Salts containing this ion may be crystallized from the solution and these nitrites are stable even though the pure acid cannot be prepared.

STABILITIES OF ACIDS AND THEIR IONS

General statements may be made about the hydroxy acids of the elements in the last groups of the periodic table. The acids and ions of the Period II elements, carbon and nitrogen, have at most three atoms of oxygen surrounding the central atom, as in carbonic and nitric acids and their anions. In nitrous acid there are only two oxygen atoms around the central atom. In general, the acid in which the central atom is in a lower oxidation state has fewer oxygen atoms than the acid in which the oxidation state is higher. The maximum number of atoms around the central atoms is related to the size of the central atom. Thus, the phosphorus atom (Period III), being larger than the nitrogen atom, has four oxygen atoms as the maximum number in the 5+ acid and three oxygen atoms in the 3+ acid. The elements in Period III are generally characterized by a maximum coordination number toward oxygen of 4.

A phosphoric acid (5+ oxidation state) also exists in which the central phosphorus atoms might appear to have a coordination number of 3, the acid being called metaphosphoric acid, formula HPO_3. Later we shall show that this acid polymerizes to increase the coordination number to 4. (Contrast nitric acid.) The acid with the formula H_3PO_4 is called orthophosphoric acid. The prefix *ortho-* is used to designate the most highly hydrated (hydroxylated) acid, and the prefix, *meta-*, the least highly hydrated acid of an element in a particular oxidation state. Table 25.2 illustrates the usage. In later periods, the maximum coordination number for oxygen may increase to 6. In Period V, for example, the coordination number of the central atom in orthoantimonic acid, formula $HSb(OH)_6$, orthotelluric acid, formula H_6TeO_6, and orthoperiodic acid, formula H_5IO_6, is 6.

The salts precipitated from acid solutions depend on the nature of the acid molecules present. For example, metaphosphate or orthophosphate salts may be prepared from phosphoric acid solutions. Since the hydration of metaphosphoric acid or of metaphosphate ion is very slow

$$\left(\begin{array}{c} \text{O} \\ \text{H O P} \\ \text{O} \end{array}\right)_n + n\,\text{HOH} = n\,\begin{array}{c} \text{H} \\ \text{O} \\ \text{H O P O H} \\ \text{O} \end{array} \qquad (25.10)$$

metaphosphoric acid (polymer)   orthophosphoric acid

precipitation of the corresponding salts would indicate the ratio in which the two acids were present. Where equilibrium is reached rapidly as in some ortho-meta acid solutions the salt precipitated may be entirely that of one of the ion forms regardless of the relative amounts present before precipitation occurred.

A third type of phosphoric acid (5+ state) with intermediate hydration (hydroxylation) may be prepared. When the ortho-salt, disodium hydrogen phosphate, formula Na_2HPO_4, is heated above its melting point, water is driven off and a new type of anion, the pyrophosphate ion, is formed.

$$2\,\begin{array}{c} \text{O} \\ \text{O P O H} \\ \text{O} \end{array}^{--} = \text{HOH}_{(g)} + \begin{array}{c} \text{O} \quad \text{O} \\ \text{O P O P O} \\ \text{O} \quad \text{O} \end{array}^{----} \qquad (25.11)$$

hydrogen phosphate ion   pyrophosphate ion

In the presence of hydrogen ions, pyrophosphoric acid, formula $H_4P_2O_7$, and the anions, $H_3P_2O_7^-$, $H_2P_2O_7^{--}$, etc., are formed. In a similar way the pyrosulfate ion, $S_2O_7^{--}$, may be obtained by heating a salt containing the hydrogen sulfate ion, HSO_4^-, to drive out water. However, the pyrosulfate ion rehydrates immediately to form bisulfate when added to water. The hydration of pyrophosphate is much slower.

IONIZATION OF HYDROXYACIDS

The hydroxides of the nonmetallic elements in water solution yield hydrogen ions by transfer of protons from the acid molecules to the water, as shown in equation 25.2. The anions produced are stable because of the very strong bonds between the oxygen atoms and the central atom. The acids with but one hydroxyl group per molecule can yield but one hydrogen ion (hydronium ion, sometimes called oxonium ion) per molecule of the acid. These *monoprotic acids* range in strength from those weaker than hypochlorous to perchloric acid which is the strongest (see page 326, *et. seq.*).

Diprotic acids, those that can yield two hydrogen ions per molecule, ionize in steps. For sulfuric acid, if we neglect the water necessary to form the hydronium ion, the steps may be written

$$H_2SO_4 = H^+ + HSO_4^- \qquad (25.12)$$
$$HSO_4^- = H^+ + SO_4^{--} \qquad (25.13)$$

414   GENERAL CHEMISTRY

The ionization in the first step is so extensive that we do not ordinarily write an equilibrium constant expression for it. For the second step, equation 25.13, the ionization constant expression is

$$K_2 = \frac{[H^+] \times [SO_4^{--}]}{[HSO_4^-]} = 1.2 \times 10^{-2} \tag{25.14}$$

Because the ionization according to equation 25.12 predominates, the concentrations of hydrogen ion and bisulfate ion, HSO_4^-, will be approximately equal. Then, from equation 25.14, we deduce that in a sulfuric acid solution greater than 0.1 M, $[SO_4^{--}] = 1.2 \times 10^{-2}$ almost independently of the total sulfuric acid concentration.

The different degrees of ionization of sulfuric acid in the two steps help explain why sodium bisulfate rather than sodium sulfate remains when nitric acid is distilled from a mixture of sodium nitrate and sulfuric acid. The acid strength in the still drops rapidly as soon as the hydrogen ions from the first ionization step have been removed (with nitrate ions) in the form of nitric acid vapor. Since sulfuric acid solutions contain both bisulfate and sulfate ions, the salts precipitated when cations are added depend on the relative solubilities of the salts as well as on the concentrations of the bisulfate and sulfate ions. Thus, when barium ions are added, barium sulfate precipitates even though sulfate ions are less abundant than bisulfate ions. The solution becomes progressively more acidic because of the reaction

$$Ba^{++} + HSO_4^- = BaSO_{4(s)} + H^+ \tag{25.15}$$

Orthophosphoric acid, a *triprotic acid*, ionizes in three steps, but the ionization for the last step is very weak. The equations and the ionization constants were given on page 370.

Problem 25.1. Write the equilibrium constant expressions for K_1, K_2, and K_3 for the three ionization steps for phosphoric acid. Write the equilibrium constant expression for the over-all equation $H_3PO_4 = 3H^+ + PO_4^{---}$, and show that its equilibrium constant, K, equals $K_1 \times K_2 \times K_3$.

Problem 25.2. Indicate the valence electrons for the substances whose formulas appear in equations 25.10 and 25.11. Interpret the tendency of metaphosphoric acid to polymerize in terms of these electron structures. Why does nitric acid not polymerize?

ACID STRENGTH AND THE PERIODIC TABLE—A REVIEW

In general, the acid strength of the hydroxy acids representing different oxidation states of a single element increases with increasing oxidation state. Table 25.3 gives some characteristic examples.

For the elements in the same periodic group and the same oxidation state the acid strength of the hydroxy acids decreases with increasing atomic number (and atomic size). When the central atom is smallest the attachment of oxygen to it is strongest because of the high charge density. Then the attachment of

Table 25.3
Increase in Acid Strength with Oxidation State
(Arrow indicates increasing order)
(The numerical values represent K_1, the constant for the ionization of one hydrogen)

OXIDATION STATE Group	1+	2+	3+	4+	5+	6+	7+
7a	HClO (3.5×10^{-8})		HClO$_2$		HClO$_3$ (>1)		HClO$_4$ $(>>1)$
6a				H$_2$SO$_3$ (1.7×10^{-2})		H$_2$SO$_4$ (>1)	
5a			H$_3$PO$_3$ (1.6×10^{-2})		H$_3$PO$_4$ (1.1×10^{-2})		

(→ INCREASING ACID STRENGTH)

the oxygen to hydrogen is weakest. These effects are shown in Table 25.4 where the arrows show the order of generally increasing acid strength. See also the discussion on page 117.

Table 25.4
Increase in Acid Strength with Position in the Periodic Table
(Arrows indicate increasing order)
(Numerical values are for K_1)

OXIDATION STATE	1+	2+	3+	4+	5+	6+	7+
Period II			HNO$_2$ 4×10^{-4}		HNO$_3$ >1		
III	HOCl 3.5×10^{-8}		H$_3$PO$_3$ 1.6×10^{-2}	H$_2$SO$_3$ 1.7×10^{-2}	H$_3$PO$_4$ 8×10^{-3}	H$_2$SO$_4$ >1	HClO$_4$ $>>1$
IV	HOBr 2×10^{-9}		H$_3$AsO$_3$ 6×10^{-10}	H$_2$SeO$_3$ 3×10^{-3}	H$_3$AsO$_4$ 5×10^{-3}	H$_2$SeO$_4$	
V	HOI 5×10^{-13}		H$_3$SbO$_3$	H$_2$TeO$_3$ 6×10^{-6}	H$_7$SbO$_6$	H$_6$TeO$_6$ 6×10^{-7}	H$_5$IO$_6$ 2.3×10^{-2}

POLYMERIC ACIDS AND IONS

The formula HPO$_3$ for metaphosphoric acid is an empirical formula. The evidence shows that the molecular formula is some multiple, (HPO$_3$)$_n$, where n may have different integral values. Metaphosphoric acid is an example of a *polymer*. It consists of molecules composed of repeating units of the *monomer* HPO$_3$. The simplest polymers are *dimers* and *trimers*, composed of two and three units, respectively, of the simple monomer, but polymers are known whose molar weights show that they are made of hundreds of thousands of monomeric units of small molar weight. When the polymer metaphosphoric acid is treated with water it dissolves and ionizes to form hydrogen ions and large metaphosphate ions corresponding in molar weight to the polymeric acid. Such large polymeric ions are often called *polyions*, and the acids themselves, *polyacids*.

That metaphosphoric acid is a polymer may be deduced from the following facts. When "phosphorus pentoxide," molecular formula P_4O_{10}, is treated with ice water only metaphosphoric acid is formed. On long standing at higher temperatures pyrophosphoric acid and finally orthophosphoric acid are formed. But in the pyrophosphoric acid the phosphorus atoms are joined in pairs through oxygen atoms whereas in the orthophosphoric acid each phosphorus atom exists in a separate molecule or ion. In the tetrahedral P_4O_{10} molecules the P—O—P bonds are present to the greatest extent, there being six such bonds. On hydration these bonds will be broken progressively until none exist. The inference is that more P—O—P bonds exist in metaphosphate than in the other acids. A structural diagram in two dimensions will indicate possible linear structures of the dimer and trimer of metaphosphoric acid and metaphosphate ions.

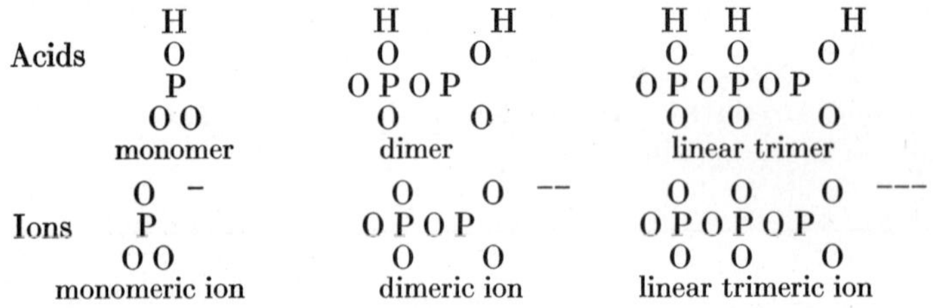

```
                H                H   H            H   H       H
   Acids        O                O   O            O   O       O
                P                O P O P          O P O P O P
                O O              O   O            O   O       O
              monomer              dimer            linear trimer

                O    -           O   O   --       O   O       O   ---
   Ions         P                O P O P          O P O P O P
                O O              O   O            O   O       O
            monomeric ion        dimeric ion        linear trimeric ion
```

Metaphosphate ions with long chains are known. The end phosphorus may coordinate a water molecule for its fourth oxygen or may form a ring (cyclic) structure by coordinating one of the oxygen atoms in its own polyacid or polyion (see Figure 25.1).

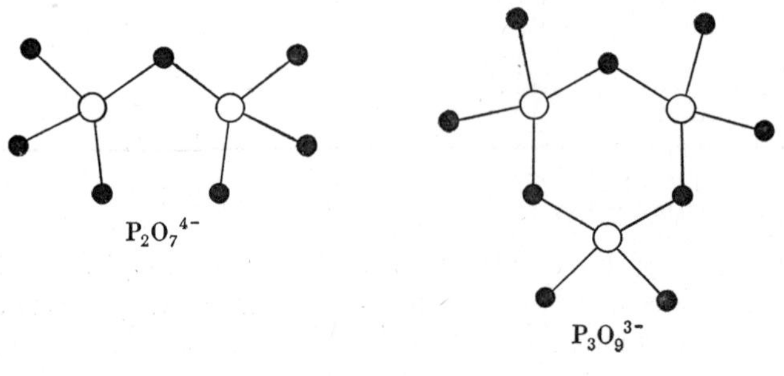

$P_2O_7^{4-}$

$P_3O_9^{3-}$

Figure 25.1.
Structures of two polyphosphate ions.

When salts such as sodium metaphosphate are melted and cooled they do not crystallize but, instead, form glassy solids. Crystals form readily only when the units, whether atoms, ions, or molecules forming the crystal lattice, are small enough or regular enough in size and shape to fit easily into the crystal pattern. Appearance of glasses rather than crystalline solids is additional evidence for the large polyions.

We have considered the metaphosphate system in some detail because the acids of the elements lying between the typical nonmetallic and metallic elements act in this way. Boron, preceding carbon in Period II, forms the macromolecular boron sesquioxide with the empirical formula, B_2O_3. Boron oxide reacts with water to form metaboric acid, empirical formula HOBO, and orthoboric acid, empirical formula $B(OH)_3$. Both are weak acids that can be separated from the solution. At room temperature boric acid and its polymers appear to be in measurable equilibrium with one another (unlike the phosphoric acids which are transformed almost completely into the more stable orthophosphates.) Only in crystalline salts with triply charged cations, as in the formula $ScBO_3$, does the orthoborate ion appear as the anion. In other crystalline salts, such as those of the alkali and alkaline earth cations, the anions are hydrated chain, ring or tetrahedral polymeric ions, the monomer being the BO_2^- or the $H_2BO_3^-$ ion. The naturally occurring salt, borax, has the empirical formula $Na_2B_4O_7 \cdot 10H_2O$. The polymerizing tendencies of the borate ion makes it a useful constituent of special glasses, such as Pyrex.

Silicon dioxide, a macromolecular oxide, occurs in several forms, one of which is quartz. It is rather insoluble in water but the metasilicic and orthosilicic acids with the empirical formulas H_3SiO_3 and H_4SiO_4 may be prepared by other means. These acids occur in highly polymerized forms and the great majority of the salts have polymerized anions that extend to the surfaces of the crystals. Only the alkali silicates are soluble in water and these form glasses rather than crystalline solids when separated from solution.

THE IONIC OXIDES

The elements of the alkali family form oxides with typical salt structures. This fact is not surprising because Group 1a is the most electropositive family; all its members have a strong tendency to lose electrons to become singly charged cations. All form oxides of the type $(M^+)_2O^{--}$ and the resulting ions have stable inert gas structures. The cations themselves have unusually large diameters. Consequently those larger than lithium ion also form stable crystals with the doubly charged peroxide ion, O_2^{--}. The resulting peroxides (sometimes incorrectly called dioxides) give the typical peroxide reactions. The larger cations, beginning with potassium ion, form superoxides with the structure $M^+O_2^-$ in which the superoxide group is a singly charged ion, O_2^-. The "trioxides" may be crystalline solutions of the peroxide and the superoxide. Table 25.5 lists the various oxides. Note that the smaller cations do not form stable solid peroxides and superoxides, persumably because these small cations cannot hold the large anions apart and so prevent them from reacting. Thus lithium superoxide may be stable in ammonia solution (probably as Li^+ and O_2^-) but is unstable as a solid.

Table 25.5
Ionic Oxides of the Alkali and Alkaline Earth Elements

	ALKALINE OXIDES					ALKALINE EARTH OXIDES	
Type	Oxide	Peroxide	"Tri-oxide"	Super-oxide	Ozonides	Oxide	Peroxide
EMPIRICAL FORMULA STRUCTURE	M_2O $(M^+)_2O^{--}$	M_2O_2 $(M^+)_2(O_2)^{--}$	M_2O_3 ?	MO_2 $M^+(O_2)^-$	MO_3 $M^+(O_3)^-$	MO $M^{++}O^{--}$	MO_2 $M^{++}(O_2)^{--}$
Period II	Li_2O	Li_2O_2 (indirectly)	—	—		(BeO) macro-molecular	—
Period III	Na_2O	Na_2O_2	—	NaO_2 (at 300 atm.)	NaO_3	MgO	—
Period IV	K_2O	K_2O_2	K_2O_3	KO_2	KO_3	CaO	CaO_2 (indirectly)
Period V	Rb_2O	Rb_2O_2	Rb_2O_3	RbO_2	?	SrO	SrO_2
Period VI	Cs_2O	Cs_2O_2	Cs_2O_3	CsO_2	CsO_3	BaO	BaO_2

In the alkaline earth group, Group 2a, beryllium is the exception in forming a macromolecular oxide rather than an ionic oxide. This behavior is explained by the small size and resulting high charge density of the beryllium ion. All the other elements in the group form ionic oxides of the type $M^{++}O^{--}$. As a family, the alkaline earth metals form large doubly charged cations but they are smaller than the alkali cations in the same period. One consequence is that only Ca^{++}, Sr^{++}, and Ba^{++} form stable peroxides, $M^{++}(O_2)^{--}$, and calcium peroxide must be formed indirectly, not by the direct action of oxygen gas on calcium metal. The larger cations can form the peroxide directly. Table 25.5 lists these also. In both alkali and alkaline earth families only the monoxides are anhydrides of the corresponding basic hydroxides. No alkaline earth superoxides are known.

REACTION OF IONIC OXIDES WITH WATER

The typical reaction of ionic oxides with water is expressed by the equation

$$O^{--} + HOH = 2OH^- \qquad (25.16)$$

The oxide ion is stable in the ionic crystalline lattice but can be present only to an infinitesimal extent (10^{-36} molar) in water solution. The charge density on the oxide ion is reduced when it accepts a proton from water to form two singly charged hydroxide ions. Ionic oxides react vigorously with water to form the corresponding hydroxides.

The hydroxides of the alkali elements are very soluble in water and the solutions are strongly basic. Lithium hydroxide is the least soluble, the saturated solution being about 5 molar.

The alkaline earth ionic oxides also react vigorously with water to form hydroxides, but the resulting hydroxides, unlike those of the alkali elements, are not very soluble in water. As a result the crystalline oxides, when in contact with water, are converted to hydroxides most of which then precipitate. The remaining water solution contains M^{++} and OH^- ions. Table 25.6 lists the solubility of the hydroxides in water. Note that the solubility increases in the order magnesium to barium hydroxide. Magnesium hydroxide is insoluble enough to occur naturally as the mineral, brucite.

Table 25.6

Solubility of the Basic Hydroxides and Anhydrides of Groups 1a and 2a

GROUP 1A			GROUP 2A		
Oxide Formula $(M^+)_2O^{--}$	Hydroxide Formula M^+OH^-	Solubility of Hydroxide (moles per 1000 g·H_2O)	Oxide Formula $M^{++}O^{--}$	Hydroxide Formula $M^{++}(OH^-)_2$	Solubility of Hydroxide (moles per l.)
Li_2O	LiOH	6	BeO	$Be(OH)_2$	5×10^{-9}
Na_2O	NaOH	27	MgO	$Mg(OH)_2$	3×10^{-4}
K_2O	KOH	21	CaO	$Ca(OH)_2$	0.022
Rb_2O	RbOH	18	SrO	$Sr(OH)_2$	0.065
Cs_2O	CsOH	25	BaO	$Ba(OH)_2$	0.22

When these hydroxides are heated they dissociate according to the reaction

$$M(OH)_{2(s)} = MO_{(s)} + H_2O_{(g)} \qquad (25.17)$$

The reaction is reversible and endothermic so that the equilibrium pressure of water vapor increases with increasing temperature. The temperatures at which the vapor pressure of water equals 10 mm. are: $Mg(OH)_2$, 300°C.; $Ca(OH)_2$, 390°C.; $Sr(OH)_2$, 466°C.; $Ba(OH)_2$, 700°C. Thus, the stability with respect to thermal decomposition is greatest for barium hydroxide but the stability with respect to formation of the ions in water solution is least for barium hydroxide. In the solution all the hydroxides are almost completely ionized so that differences in basicity do not influence the solubility in water greatly. On the other hand, differences in basicity do govern the energy with which the oxides hydrate to form the hydroxides. Barium oxide is the most basic of the alkaline earth oxides, hence holds on to the weak acid, water, the most.

The crystalline oxides or hydroxides of the alkaline earth elements, or water suspensions (slurries) of the solid hydroxides, are among our cheapest bases. All have the ability to neutralize acids according to the reactions

$$MO_{(s)} + 2H^+ = M^{++} + HOH \qquad (25.18)$$
$$M(OH)_{2(s)} + 2H^+ = M^{++} + 2HOH \qquad (25.19)$$

Milk of magnesia (a slurry of magnesium hydroxide), quicklime, formula CaO, slaked lime, formula $Ca(OH)_2$, or lime water, a saturated solution of calcium hydroxide, are often used for this purpose.

420 GENERAL CHEMISTRY

Beryllium oxide and hydroxide were included in Tables 25.5 and 25.6 to fill out the elements in Group 2a and not because their properties are like those of the other members of the group. Beryllium oxide is a very hard substance existing as macromolecules. It is insoluble in water but when treated with acids it reacts slowly to form a solution of a beryllium salt.

$$BeO_{(s)} + 2H^+ = Be^{++} + H_2O \tag{25.20}$$

The beryllium ion is highly hydrated. When hydroxide ions are added to the solution a gelatinous precipitate of $Be(OH)_2 \cdot xH_2O$ forms. (See Table 25.6 for its solubility in water.) This hydroxide may be dehydrated to form the oxide.

BASIC STRENGTH AND THE PERIODIC TABLE

For the hydroxides of the metallic elements the order of increasing basic strength with respect to position in the periodic table *is opposite* in direction to the order of increasing acid strength shown in Tables 25.3 and 25.4. In each group studied basic strength increases with atomic number and in each period basic strength decreases with atomic number. Since the elements in Groups 1a and 2a have unique oxidation states they do not illustrate the effect of oxidation state. However, in later groups in which elements may have more than one oxidation number, we shall find that for each element the hydroxides corresponding to the lower oxidation state are more basic (less acidic) than the hydroxides in the higher oxidation states, for example, 2+ chromium hydroxide, basic; 3+ chromium hydroxide, amphoteric; 6+ chromium hydroxide, acidic (see also pages 326 and 327).

The oxides and hydroxides in Group 3b continue the trends of Group 1a and Group 2a (see Table 25.7). Within the group the basic strength increases with atomic number and the solubility of the hydroxides increases. Aluminum hydroxide is extremely insoluble but the higher members of the group become less insoluble. Within each period the hydroxide becomes less basic and less soluble with increasing atomic number.

Table 25.7

Increase in Basic Strength with Position in the Periodic Table (Increasing order shown by arrows)

GROUP	1A	2A	3A
OXIDATION STATE	1+	2+	3+
FORMULAS FOR HYDROXIDE	LiOH NaOH KOH RbOH CsOH	$Be(OH)_2$ $Mg(OH)_2$ $Ca(OH)_2$ $Sr(OH)_2$ $Ba(OH)_2$	$Al(OH)_3$ $Sc(OH)_3$ $Y(OH)_3$ Rare earth hydroxides

The rare earth group of elements, atomic numbers 57 to 71, follow the general rule that, within a period, basicity decreases with increasing atomic number. Element number 57, lanthanum (Period VI), the first of the rare earth elements, is more basic than yttrium (Period V) as the general rule requires, but, since basicity decreases with atomic number in a given period, element number 71, lutetium, is more acidic than lanthanum and is also more acidic than yttrium. This behavior is explained by the fact that the lanthanum ion, La^{+++}, is larger than the yttrium ion, Y^{+++}, but the lutetium ion, Lu^{+++}, is smaller (see Table 14.2, pages 180–181; also Chapter 29).

THE MACROMOLECULAR OXIDES

The oxides of the elements lying between the molecular oxides on the right and the ionic oxides on the left side of the periodic table are macromolecular. With few, but important, exceptions they are "insoluble" in water, that is, they do not react with water to form small molecular units. This fact is not surprising in view of the bonding in the macromolecular crystals. We have already discussed the molecular acid oxides on the right side of the periodic table, the ionic basic oxides on the left side, and some of the macromolecular oxides bordering on these. In this section we shall consider the intermediate oxides, those for the elements in Groups 4b to 4a.

The elements of Groups 4b to 4a are metallic and all of them lose electrons to form cations. However, these cations, unlike those of the Group 1a, 2a, and 3b elements, do not have the inert gas structure. One result is that the cations are able to coordinate molecules and ions to form complexes which may be cationic or anionic. Furthermore, most of the elements in Groups 4b to 4a exist in more than one oxidation state. Since acidity generally increases with atomic number in each period and with oxidation state for a single element, we find that the lower oxide of an element may be basic and the higher oxide acidic.

Most of the macromolecular oxides do not dissolve in water or react appreciably with it. Two exceptions are: chromium trioxide, formula CrO_3, which gives soluble chromic acid, formula H_2CrO_4, and thallous oxide, formula Tl_2O, which gives soluble thallous hydroxide, formula $TlOH$.

REACTION OF INSOLUBLE OXIDES WITH ACIDS

Many macromolecular oxides, insoluble in water, react with acids to produce dissolved salts. For some reactions hot, concentrated acids are necessary. The charge on the cation produced and its relation to the charge density are important factors in the reactions, for the ions with high charge density react with water in ways which reduce the charge density.

Beryllium oxide reacts with acids according to the reaction

$$BeO_{(s)} + 2H^+ = Be^{++} + HOH \qquad (25.21)$$

The beryllium ion formed is very small and has a high charge density. If the acid concentration is low, the ion may reduce its charge by reacting with water as follows:

$$Be^{++} + HOH = Be(OH)^+ + H^+ \qquad (25.22)$$

Increase in concentration of acid, in accordance with the equilibrium principle, will decrease the concentration of the $Be(OH)^+$ ion. Aluminum oxide also reacts with strong acids

$$Al_2O_{3(s)} + 6H^+ = 2Al^{+++} + 3HOH \qquad (25.23)$$

The aluminum ion, a small triply charged ion, also reduces its charge density by reacting with water

$$Al^{+++} + HOH = Al(OH)^{++} + H^+ \qquad (25.24)$$
$$Al(OH)^{++} + HOH = Al(OH)_2^+ + H^+ \qquad (25.25)$$
$$Al(OH)_2^+ + HOH = Al(OH)_{3(s)} + H^+ \qquad (25.26)$$

Hence, as the acidity of the solution is decreased the hydrolysis reactions proceed. Aluminum hydroxide will precipitate while the solution still remains slightly acid. Titanium dioxide is even more difficult to "dissolve" in acids and any resulting Ti^{++++} ions hydrolyze very extensively. On reduction of the acidity a polymerized jelly-like hydroxide forms. Silicon dioxide does not "dissolve" in acids. Even $Si(OH)_3^+$ ions are apparently unstable.

For many of the oxides, solution in acids may be correlated with the charge density on the cations produced in the solution process. When the oxidation state of the metallic element in the oxide is 1+ or 2+ the oxides tend to dissolve readily but when the oxidation state is higher they are often much more difficult to dissolve. High concentrations of acid are needed to diminish hydrolysis and so prevent precipitation of the hydroxides. For example, stannous oxide, formula SnO, reacts readily with acids to produce Sn^{++} ions, but these hydrolyze. In neutral solutions the hydroxide precipitates. On the other hand stannic oxide is not readily soluble in strong acids; the Sn^{++++} ion would have too high a charge density.

REACTION OF OXIDES TO FORM ANIONS IN WATER SOLUTIONS

Many of the transition elements, especially in their higher oxidation states, have such a great tendency to hydroxylate that they form stable anions, particularly in basic solutions. When the oxidation number of the central atom is 4+ or less the anions are stable only in basic solution; in neutral solutions of such substances the hydroxides precipitate. When the oxidation number is higher the anions may be stable in neutral or even acid solutions.

The oxide of manganese (Group 7b) in the 7+ oxidation state is a molecular oxide and has the acidic properties associated with such oxides. It is an explosive, oily liquid with the formula Mn_2O_7. With water it reacts to form a strong acid, permanganic acid.

$$\underset{\text{manganese heptoxide}}{Mn_2O_{7(liq)}} + HOH = 2H^+ + \underset{\text{permanganic acid}}{MnO_4^-} \qquad (25.27)$$

Note that the bond between the central atom and the oxygen atom is strong enough to produce a stable anion. Similarly, the 6+ oxide of chromium (Group 6b) is a solid but with a low melting point which indicates some weak bonds in the solid. It reacts readily with water to form a strong acid (compare with sulfur trioxide) which consists of an equilibrium mixture of acid chromate and dichromate ions.

$$2CrO_{3(s)} + HOH = 2H^+ + \underset{\underset{\text{dichromate ion}}{O\ \ \ O}}{\overset{O\ \ \ \ O}{O\ Cr\ O\ Cr\ O}}{}^{--} \quad (25.28)$$

$$\underset{O\ \ \ O}{\overset{O\ \ \ \ O}{O\ Cr\ O\ Cr\ O}}{}^{--} + HOH = 2\underset{\underset{\text{acid chromate ion}}{O}}{\overset{O}{O\ Cr\ OH}}{}^{-} \quad (25.29)$$

Note that the permanganate and chromate ions, in which the central atom has a coordination number of 4, are stable in neutral or acid solutions as well as in basic solutions. The chromate ion present in basic solution is CrO_4^{--}. When manganese and chromium are in lower oxidation states the oxides are more basic.

We have already seen that stannous oxide reacts with acids to form stannous ion, Sn^{++} (which may be hydroxylated) but that stannic oxide does not. However, stannic oxide reacts with bases or solutions of strong base to form a stable anion, the stannate ion.

$$SnO_{2(s)} + 2HOH + 2OH^- = Sn(OH)_6^{--} \quad (25.30)$$

When the solution is neutralized with acid, a highly polymerized (colloidal), hydrated stannic hydroxide, usually called "stannic acid," precipitates.

$$Sn(OH)_6^{--} + 2H^+ = 2HOH + \underset{\text{polymerized}}{Sn(OH)_{4(s)}} \quad (25.31)$$

In strong hydrochloric acid the precipitate "dissolves" to form a solution containing the chloride complex of the stannic ion.

$$Sn(OH)_{4(s)} + 4H^+ + 6Cl^- = SnCl_6^{--} + 4HOH \quad (25.31)$$

The oxides and hydroxides of the Group 4b elements, titanium, zirconium, and hafnium are more basic than those of Groups 5b, *et seq*. The 4+ cations have the inert gas structure and have less tendency to hydroxylate to form anions. As is to be expected, titanium is the most acidic of the group. It forms titanates when the oxide is treated with molten alkalies, but zirconium oxide does not react readily even with this treatment. Nevertheless, in some minerals the polymerized forms of the titanate ion $(TiO_3^{--})_n$ and the zirconate ion $(ZrO_3^{--})_n$ occur.

AMPHOTERIC HYDROXIDES

The hydroxides insoluble in water which react both with acids to form cations and with strong bases to form anions are called *amphoteric*. Only hydroxides of the metallic elements are included in the category for only these have the ability to yield cations in water solution. On the other hand, an atom must have a relatively high coordinating ability for oxygen atoms if it is to form a stable oxy- or hydroxy anion.

Both beryllium hydroxide and aluminum hydroxide are amphoteric. The action of hydroxide ions on the cations in producing first the insoluble hydroxide and then a stable anion may be better understood if we represent the Be^{++} as a hydrated form, $Be(H_2O)_4^{++}$. Then, on treatment with hydroxide ions in increasing concentration, the following series of substitutions of hydroxide ion for water take place:

$$Be(H_2O)_4^{++} + OH^- = Be(H_2O)_3OH^+ + HOH \qquad (25.33)$$

$$Be(H_2O)_3OH^+ + OH^- = \underset{\text{beryllium hydroxide}}{Be(H_2O)_2(OH)_{2(s)}} + HOH \qquad (25.34)$$

$$\underset{\text{beryllium hydroxide}}{Be(H_2O)_2(OH)_{2(s)}} + OH^- = \underset{\text{metaberyllate ion}}{Be(H_2O)(OH)_3^-} + HOH \qquad (25.35)$$

$$Be(H_2O)(OH)_3^- + OH^- = \underset{\text{orthoberyllate ion}}{Be(OH)_4^{--}} + HOH \qquad (25.36)$$

Sodium salts of the metaberyllate ion and the orthoberyllate ions have been prepared. In writing the equations it is conventional to use formulas without the water of hydration. The water is included in equations 25.33 to 25.36 to illustrate the constancy in coordination number of beryllium during the process. For the reactions of aluminum ions, the water of hydration being neglected, we have

$$Al^{+++} + 3OH^- = Al(OH)_{3(s)} \qquad (25.37)$$

$$Al(OH)_{3(s)} + OH^- = \underset{\text{metaaluminate ion}}{Al(OH)_4^-} \qquad (25.38)$$

$$Al(OH)_4^- + 2OH^- = \underset{\text{orthoaluminate ion}}{Al(OH)_6^{---}} \qquad (25.39)$$

Because of its high charge the orthoaluminate ion is stable only when the concentration of hydroxide ion is high.

Problem 25.3. Write equations corresponding to 25.37, 25.38, and 25.39, but including the water of hydration of the ions. Write equations for the reactions that occur when hydrogen ions are added gradually to a solution of sodium orthoaluminate.

The list of amphoteric hydroxides includes those with the following formulas: $Be(OH)_2$, $Al(OH)_3$, $Cr(OH)_3$, $Zn(OH)_2$, $Sn(OH)_2$, $Sn(OH)_4$, $Pb(OH)_2$, $As(OH)_3$, and $Sb(OH)_3$. Note the diagonal relationship in the periodic table. Vanadium pentoxide, formula V_2O_5, also reacts both with acids and with bases, forming the vanadate ion, VO_4^{---}, with the latter. In acids the cations VO_2^+ and VO^{+++} are possible.

There are, of course, no sharp breaks from basic to amphoteric to acidic hydroxides. The general tendency is for oxides to become less basic (more acidic) as the atomic number increases in each row of the periodic table.

When the acidity and basicity approximately balance the oxide is said to be amphoteric, but it must be remembered that the borderline is arbitrary and related to the acid-base properties of water. In general, all oxides (except the most acidic or the most basic) may show either acidic or basic properties, depending on the other reagents present. Single experiments will reveal only one possible behavior.

HYDROLYSIS OF SALTS

Most salts when dissolved in pure water form solutions that are not neutral —the solutions are either acidic or basic. If the solution is to remain neutral, the salt ions must not react with the water, or if they do they must remove hydrogen and hydroxide ions in equal amounts. The cations of Group 1a and Group 2a elements (except beryllium) do not combine appreciably with hydroxide ion in solution but most other cations do. Then the solution becomes acidic because of reactions of the type

$$M^{++} + HOH = M(OH)^+ + H^+ \tag{25.40}$$

Similarly the anions from strong acids do not combine appreciably with hydrogen ion in the solutions. The common anions in this group are nitrate, chloride, chlorate, perchlorate, and permanganate, all of which are singly charged. The doubly charged sulfate ion combines only weakly with hydrogen ions. Other anions, HCO_3^-, CO_3^{--}, HPO_4^{--}, PO_4^{---}, and acetate ion combine with hydrogen ions from the water to form a basic solution through reactions of the type

$$X^- + HOH = HX + OH^- \tag{25.41}$$

A solution of sodium carbonate is rather strongly basic because the carbonate ions combine with hydrogen ions to form bicarbonate ions. A solution of copper sulfate is acidic because the copper ion combines with hydroxide ions until the basic sulfate, formula $(CuOH)_2SO_4$, precipitates. The degree of hydrolysis, hence the weakness of the base or acid formed, may be measured by determining the concentration of hydrogen or hydroxide ions developed in the solution. The weaker the base and/or acid formed the greater the hydrolysis of the salt.

The hydrolysis of ammonium acetate is interesting for its water solution is neutral. Yet the degree of hydrolysis is large. This situation occurs because ammonia is as weak a base ($K_b = 1.8 \times 10^{-5}$) as acetic acid is as an acid ($K_a = 1.8 \times 10^{-5}$). Consequently both ammonium ion and acetate ion hydrolyze extensively but equally, yielding a neutral solution.

DIRECT REACTION OF ACIDIC AND BASIC OXIDES

Acidic and basic oxides may react directly to form salts, but high temperatures are necessary if the oxides are macromolecular. Then the oxides fuse (melt) and permit continuing contact between the reactants. The reaction

$$CaO + SiO_2 = CaSiO_3 \tag{25.42}$$

is important in many metallurgical processes as a method for removing sand, formula usually SiO_2, from the ore.

The ionic oxides react directly with gaseous carbon dioxide and water vapor. Quicklime exposed to air forms "air-slaked lime," a mixture of calcium carbonate and calcium hydroxide.

$$CaO_{(s)} + CO_{2(g)} = CaCO_{3(s)} \tag{25.43}$$
$$CaO_{(s)} + H_2O_{(g)} = Ca(OH)_{2(s)} \tag{25.44}$$

Oxides in which the oxidation number of the metallic element is fractional may be regarded as salts formed from two oxides of the same element having differing basicity. Thus, red lead, formula Pb_3O_4 (apparent oxidation number of the lead $\frac{8}{3}$), may be regarded as plumbous plumbate, formula $Pb_2(PbO_4)$, the 2+ lead being present in the cations and the 4+ lead in the anion. Similarly the black iron oxide, formula Fe_3O_4, is better represented by the formula Fe_2FeO_4.

Direct reaction between oxides to form salts is uncomplicated by the question of solubility in water and of the stability of ions in water solution. In fused oxides and their mixtures we find highly charged cations and anions too reactive with water to be stable in water solution.

Problem 25.4. Prepare an expanded form of the periodic table and on it draw lines (zigzag if necessary) in different colors dividing the elements into the following classes:
  a. The metallic and the nonmetallic elements.
  b. Those forming molecular oxides, macromolecular oxides, and ionic oxides.
  c. Those forming water-soluble hydroxides and water-insoluble hydroxides.
  d. Those forming acidic hydroxides only, basic hydroxides only, both acidic and basic hydroxides, and amphoteric hydroxides.

Use reference books if necessary to get the facts for deciding doubtful cases.

SUMMARY

Some classes of substances formed by the different elements are separated by diagonal lines sloping from upper left to lower right across the periodic table. The line separating the metallic elements from the nonmetallic elements is such a line. When this line is drawn on the basis of the usual definitions of metals in terms of the bulk properties of luster, high thermal and electrical conductivities, ductility, and malleability, it coincides almost completely with the line separating those elements whose atoms lose electrons to form simple cations from those elements whose atoms do not. According to a current view of the metallic state, metals have crystalline lattices in which the atoms are cations and the electrons resulting from the ionization are mobile and belong to the entire metal crystal.

The lines separating the elements which form ionic oxides, those which form macromolecular oxides, and those which form molecular oxides are also definite. The transitions from one kind of bonding to another are fairly sharp.

On the contrary, the decrease in basicity of the oxides (and corresponding increase in acidity) is gradual from element to element and without abrupt change. The element at the lower left of the periodic table has the most basic oxide and the elements at the upper right (excluding the inert gases) the most acidic oxides. Comparison of the intermediate oxides is complicated by the fact that oxidation states of the elements in the long periods do not increase steadily but show maxima and minima near the middle of the periods. This fact is particularly important because the acidity of the oxides of a single element increases with increasing positive oxidation number.

Only a few oxides react with water to form soluble acids or bases. All the ionic oxides form strongly basic hydroxides but the solubilities decrease rapidly as the basic strength decreases. All the molecular oxides form acidic hydroxides and all are fairly soluble in water. The line separating the elements forming soluble acids from those forming insoluble acids agrees rather well with the line separating those forming the molecular from those forming the macromolecular oxides, and with the line separating the nonmetallic from the metallic elements.

In general, the basic hydroxides, even though insoluble or only slightly soluble, react with strong acids to form salt solutions, the metallic element appearing in the cation. The acidic hydroxides react with strong bases to form salt solutions in which the central element, though having a positive oxidation number, appears in the anions. The latter statement applies to the acidic oxides of the metallic elements as well as to the oxides of the nonmetallic elements. There remains a group of insoluble hydroxides of the metallic elements bordering the nonmetallic elements. These react with acids to form soluble salts in which the metallic element forms the cation. They also react with strong bases to form soluble salts in which the metallic element is in the anion. This group is called the amphoteric hydroxides.

For some of the transition elements the oxides are more resistant to attack by acids (or bases) than the corresponding hydroxides, a fact not surprising in view of the strong bonding forces present in the macromolecular crystals. Some oxides are attacked only by hot acids or fused alkaline hydroxides. In the absence of water the anion may be different from the corresponding ion in water solution. For that matter cations are also different. In anhydrous copper sulfate, the copper ion, Cu^{++}, is colorless but in water solution it is hydrated and blue.

Most of these facts and trends can be interpreted in terms of charge density. As the charge density of atoms increases their tendency to form strong bonds with oxygen also increases hence their compounds are less basic (release OH^- ions less readily) but more acidic, for example, remove OH^- from H_2O more readily releasing H^+ ions in the process. The tendencies to be more or less metallic, to form ionic or covalent bonds, and to exist as soluble or insoluble compounds may be similarly interpreted in terms of size, charge, and electron structure of the constituent atoms.

Problem 25.5. What are the formulas for the anhydrides of the substances represented by the following formulas: (a) Ca(OH)$_2$, (b) NaOH, (c) H$_2$SO$_3$, (d) H$_3$PO$_4$, (e) Al(OH)$_3$, (f) H$_2$S$_2$O$_7$?

Problem 25.6. The substances with the following formulas are dissolved in water. Indicate whether the solution is acidic, basic, or neutral.

a. KHSO$_4$
b. NH$_4$Cl
c. K$_2$CO$_3$
d. NaOAc
e. Cd(NO$_3$)$_2$
f. NH$_4$OAc
g. FeCl$_3$
h. KCl
i. ZnSO$_4$

State your reason for each decision.

Problem 25.7. Arrange the following solutions in order of decreasing hydrogen ion concentration: (a) 0.1 f sodium chloride, (b) 1 f sodium hydroxide, (c) 1 f sodium acetate, (d) 1 f ammonium chloride, (e) 0.1 f hydrochloric acid, (f) 0.5 f sodium carbonate, (g) 0.01 f sulfuric acid, (h) 1 f acetic acid, (i) 0.1 f ammonia solution.

Problem 25.8. Why does a baking powder containing aluminum sulfate and sodium bicarbonate release carbon dioxide when wet?

Problem 25.9. Name five commercial preparations whose usefulness depends on hydrolysis and list the function of hydrolysis in each case.

Problem 25.10. Account for the fact that most sulfates (including those as insoluble as barium sulfate and lead sulfate) are more soluble in acid solution than in water alone.

Problem 25.11. Account for the nonexistence of alkaline earth superoxides.

26 ELECTROCHEMISTRY AND ELECTRICAL CELLS

ELECTROCHEMISTRY DEALS with the relationships among electrical currents, electromotive forces, and chemical substances. Electrical currents are charged particles, either electrons or ions, in motion, and the electromotive forces are the "forces" causing the motion. Large currents mean large numbers of electrons or ions passing through a given area per unit time. The forces producing the movement of the electrical particles are expressed in the electromotive force (EMF) unit, the volt. The work that may be done by a given quantity of moving charge varies directly with the force causing the flow. Large voltages mean large amounts of work. Similarly, the work that may be done at a given voltage varies directly with the number of charged particles moving. Large numbers mean large amounts of work.

We have already discussed the nature of electrical conductivity (page 209) and a typical electrochemical process, electrolysis (pages 209–212).

In this chapter we shall consider methods of using chemical reactions as sources of electrical energy (in electrical cells or batteries), and shall predict the direction of chemical reactions both inside and outside of cells from the voltages.

HALF-REACTIONS AND OXIDATION-REDUCTION

If one suspends a copper penny in a solution of mercurous nitrate, the solution becomes blue and the penny becomes coated with a shiny, silvery, liquid film. The blue color is due to copper ions and the silvery liquid is mercury. An oxidation-reduction reaction has evidently occurred in which the copper atoms lose electrons and the mercurous ions gain electrons as in equation 26.1.

$$Cu_{(s)} + Hg_2^{++} = Cu^{++} + 2Hg_{(liq)} \qquad (26.1)$$
$$\text{red} \qquad \text{blue}$$

Mercury clearly must have a greater tendency to hold electrons than does copper metal, for, in the competition between the mercurous ions and the cupric ions for the electrons, it is the mercury which gains them.

In the same way, one may observe that a piece of metallic lead immersed in a solution of copper ions quickly becomes coated with metallic copper.

Simultaneously, the blue solution loses its color. The reaction is represented by the equation

$$Pb_{(s)} + Cu^{++} = Cu_{(s)} + Pb^{++} \qquad (26.2)$$
$$\phantom{Pb_{(s)} + Cu^{++} = } \text{blue} \text{red}$$

Apparently copper has a greater tendency to hold electrons than does lead, hence cupric ions take the electrons from the metallic lead.

On the basis of logic, one might reason that, if mercury holds electrons more tightly than copper does and copper more tightly than lead, mercury will hold electrons more tightly than lead does. Then mercurous ions will take electrons from metallic lead. Equation 26.3 should represent the reaction.

$$Pb_{(s)} + Hg_2^{++} = Pb^{++} + 2Hg_{(liq)} \qquad (26.3)$$

The reaction does occur, justifying the conclusion. Or one could have concluded that, since mercury has the greater tendency to retain electrons, metallic mercury will not react appreciably with lead ions. This, too, is a correct conclusion.

$$Pb^{++} + Hg_{(liq)} = \text{no reaction}$$

Each of the above equations may be written as the sum of two partial equations, or half-reaction equations, as outlined on page 228, *et seq.*

From equation 26.1:

$$Cu_{(s)} = Cu^{++} + 2e^-$$
$$2e^- + Hg_2^{++} = 2Hg_{(liq)} \qquad (26.1a)$$
$$\text{or } e^- + \tfrac{1}{2}Hg_2^{++} = Hg_{(liq)}$$

From equation 26.2:

$$Pb_{(s)} = Pb^{++} + 2e^-$$
$$2e^- + Cu^{++} = Cu_{(s)} \qquad (26.2a)$$

From equation 26.3:

$$Pb_{(s)} = Pb^{++} + 2e^-$$
$$2e^- + Hg_2^{++} = 2Hg_{(liq)} \qquad (26.3a)$$
$$\text{or } e^- + \tfrac{1}{2}Hg_2^{++} = Hg_{(liq)}$$

These half-reaction equations show clearly that reaction 26.3 involves no changes not already observed in reactions 26.1 or 26.2. The changes are merely paired in a different way so that one can, from a knowledge of the reactions for 26.1 and 26.2, predict the reaction for 26.3.

The six partial equations as paired in equations 26.1a, 26.2a, and 26.3a and read from left to right show that mercurous ions gain electrons more readily than cupric ions do, and cupric ions gain electrons more readily than lead ions. Hence mercurous ions gain electrons more readily than lead ions do. The whole set of six partial equations may be readily summarized in a set of three if all the half-equations are written for the gaining of electrons, and are then arranged in order of increasing tendency of the oxidizing agent to gain electrons. Lead ion gaining electrons will be at the top of the list, cupric ion next, and mercurous ion at the bottom.

ELECTROCHEMISTRY AND ELECTRICAL CELLS 431

$$\text{Least tendency to occur} \quad 2e^- + Pb^{++} = Pb_{(s)} \quad (26.4)$$
$$2e^- + Cu^{++} = Cu_{(s)} \quad (26.5)$$
$$\text{Greatest tendency to occur} \quad e^- + \tfrac{1}{2}Hg_2^{++} = Hg_{(liq)} \quad (26.6)$$

Which way we write these half-reaction equations, whether for the gaining of electrons or yielding of electrons is quite arbitrary. The fact that lead ion, of the three ions listed, has the least tendency to gain electrons means conversely that lead metal has the greatest tendency to lose electrons, with copper next, and mercury least in this respect. In the list of half-equations 26.4, 26.5, and 26.6, the oxidizing agents (Pb^{++}, Cu^{++}, and Hg_2^{++} ions) are in one column, and the reducing agents (lead, copper, and mercury) in another. The best oxidizing agent (Hg_2^{++} ion) is at the bottom of its column. The best reducing agent (lead) is at the top of its column.

One may make an extensive table of oxidation-reduction half-reactions by continuing experiments of the above type, observing whether or not reaction occurs, and writing half-reaction equations for those reactions which do occur. The half-reaction equations can then be arranged in an order of increasing tendency of the half-reaction to use up electrons. An abbreviated form of such an arrangement is given in Table 26.1. All the reactions are for water solutions

Table 26.1

Equations for Some Oxidation-Reduction Half-Reactions in Water Solution

HALF-EQUATION NUMBER	OXIDIZING AGENTS / REDUCING AGENTS	STANDARD VOLTAGE (E°)
1	$e^- + Na^+ = Na_{(s)}$	-2.712
2	$2e^- + Mg^{++} = Mg_{(s)}$	-2.24
3	$3e^- + Al^{+++} = Al_{(s)}$	-1.67
4	$e^- + H_2O = \tfrac{1}{2}H_{2(g)} + OH^-$	-0.828
5	$2e^- + Zn^{++} = Zn_{(s)}$	-0.7620
6	$e^- + \tfrac{1}{2}Ag_2S_{(s)} = Ag_{(s)} + \tfrac{1}{2}S^{--}$	-0.71
7	$2e^- + Fe^{++} = Fe_{(s)}$	-0.440
8	$e^- + H^+(10^{-7} M) = \tfrac{1}{2}H_{2(g)}$	-0.414
9	$2e^- + Sn^{++} = Sn_{(s)}$	-0.136
10	$2e^- + Pb^{++} = Pb_{(s)}$	-0.126
11	$e^- + H^+ = \tfrac{1}{2}H_{2(g)}$	0.0000
12	$2e^- + 2H^+ + S_{(s)} = H_2S_{(g)}$	0.141
13	$2e^- + Cu^{++} = Cu_{(s)}$	0.3448
14	$e^- + \tfrac{1}{2}I_{2(s)} = I^-$	0.5345
15	$e^- + Fe^{+++} = Fe^{++}$	0.771
16	$e^- + \tfrac{1}{2}Hg_2^{++} = Hg_{(liq)}$	0.7986
17	$e^- + Ag^+ = Ag_{(s)}$	0.7995
18	$2e^- + 2H^+(10^{-7} M) + \tfrac{1}{2}O_{2(g)} = H_2O$	0.815
19	$3e^- + 4H^+ + NO_3^- = NO_{(g)} + 2H_2O$	0.96
20	$3e^- + AuCl_4^- = Au_{(s)} + 4Cl^-$	1.00
21	$e^- + \tfrac{1}{2}Br_{2(liq)} = Br^-$	1.087
22	$2e^- + 2H^+ + \tfrac{1}{2}O_{2(g)} = H_2O$	1.229
23	$e^- + \tfrac{1}{2}Cl_{2(g)} = Cl^-$	1.3583
24	$3e^- + Au^{+++} = Au_{(s)}$	1.42
25	$5e^- + 8H^+ + MnO_4^- = Mn^{++} + 4H_2O$	1.52
26	$e^- + \tfrac{1}{2}F_{2(g)} = F^-$	3.03

of the ions. The poorest oxidizing agent listed is sodium ion and the best oxidizing agent listed is gaseous fluorine. Similarly, the best reducing agent listed is sodium metal, and the poorest reducing agent listed is fluoride ion. The oxidation-reduction reaction with the greatest tendency to occur would be that between the best oxidizing agent and the best reducing agent. For this list the reaction would be that between gaseous fluorine and metallic sodium. In general, any oxidizing agent listed will react only with those reducing agents above it in the table. Cu^{++} ion, for instance, will oxidize hydrogen, lead, tin, etc., but will not oxidize Fe^{++} ion, mercury, or silver, etc.

The voltages listed in the column at the far right are a numerical measure of the tendency of the reactions to occur as written from left to right when each reactant is in the standard state defined on page 443. We shall now see how these numbers are determined, and how cell voltages vary with concentration changes of the reactants.

Problem 26.1. The reactions represented by the following equations are known to proceed. Separate each into its component half-reaction equations and arrange the half-equations, as much as the data permit, in order of increasing tendency of oxidizing half-reactions to occur, as in Table 26.1.

$$Ga_{(s)} + 3Cr^{+++} = 3Cr^{++} + Ga^{+++}$$
$$\text{violet} \quad \text{blue}$$

$$2Cr^{++} + Ni^{++} = 2Cr^{+++} + Ni_{(s)}$$
$$\text{blue} \quad \text{green} \quad \text{violet}$$

$$Ni_{(s)} + 2V^{+++} = Ni^{++} + 2V^{++}$$
$$\text{green} \quad \text{green} \quad \text{violet}$$

What can you predict about the reaction according to the equation

$$Ga_{(s)} + 3V^{+++} = 3V^{++} + Ga^{+++}?$$
$$\text{green} \quad \text{violet}$$

Problem 26.2. Follow the directions in Problem 26.1 for the following:

$$Cd_{(s)} + Sn^{++++} = Cd^{++} + Sn^{++}$$
$$2H^+ + Pb_{(s)} + O_{2(g)} = Pb^{++} + H_2O_2$$
$$Pb^{++} + Cd_{(s)} = Pb_{(s)} + Cd^{++}$$
$$Sn^{++++} + Pb_{(s)} = Pb^{++} + Sn^{++}$$

What can you deduce about the tendency of hydrogen peroxide to reduce Cd^{++} ion to cadmium using only the above data?

Problem 26.3. Write equations for oxidation-reduction reactions between the following, applying the information in Table 26.1. If no reaction occurs, write "none." (a) Sn^{++} ion and iron, (b) Sn^{++} ion and copper, (c) iodine and bromide ion, (d) chlorine and bromide ion, (e) sodium ion and bromide ion, (f) lead, hydrogen ion, and nitrate ion, (g) Fe^{++} ion, hydrogen ion, and MnO_4^- ion.

ELECTRIC CELLS

When metallic lead is immersed in a solution of cupric ions long fronds of metallic copper grow out from the lead surface. Close examination of these fronds shows that they grow at their edges by the accretion of copper, rather than grow out from the base where they are attached to the lead. In other words, the lead atoms are converted to lead ions at the surface of the metallic lead. The electrons produced by this process move through the metallic lead and the copper fronds until they meet a cupric ion somewhere along the edge of the frond, unite with the cupric ion, and form metallic copper (see Figure 26.1). It is clearly not necessary to have the reducing agent, lead in this in-

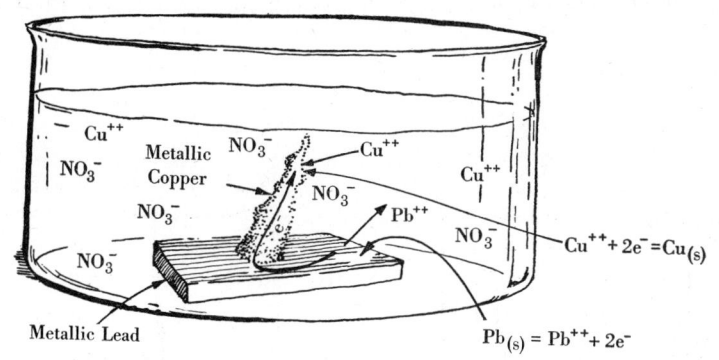

Figure 26.1.
Reduction of cupric ion by metallic lead (schematic).

stance, and the oxidizing agent, cupric ion in this instance, in contact as long as the electrons can move from one to the other and as long as the ions can move to the proper surfaces. The electrons must move because of an electromotive force and as they move they constitute an electric current. Ions of opposite charge in the solution must move simultaneously, but in opposite directions. If one can get the electrons to flow as a current through a wire external to the system their tendency to flow under the electrical "pressure" can be harnessed as a source of energy to light a lamp, run a motor, or do other useful work. Electric cells or batteries are designed to do work.

The reaction, a source of electrical energy, is represented by equation 26.2

$$Pb_{(s)} + Cu^{++} = Cu_{(s)} + Pb^{++} \qquad (26.2)$$
$$\text{blue} \quad \text{red}$$

The essential ingredients for the chemical reaction are metallic lead and cupric ions in water solution. However, one cannot have cupric ions without having some negative ion in the solution at the same time, for instance, nitrate ion. Thus, for a cell, we need metallic lead and a water solution of a copper salt such as cupric nitrate. Since our aim is to make the electrons flow through an external wire in going from the metallic lead to the cupric ions, we might put metallic lead and liquid water in one beaker, a water solution of cupric nitrate in a neighboring beaker, and connect the metallic lead to the cupric nitrate solution with a wire through which the electrons could flow. As the lead atoms give up their electrons to form lead ions the electrons would be driven through

434 GENERAL CHEMISTRY

the wire until they meet cupric ions in the other beaker. The electrons and cupric ions could then react to form metallic copper, as in Figure 26.2. Unfortunately for our simple theory, the apparatus as outlined in Figure 26.2 will not operate. Neither electrical voltage nor electrical current will be observed in the connecting wire. Wherein does this experiment differ from that shown in Figure 26.1?

A physicist or electrical engineer would diagnose the difficulty in the setup of Figure 26.2 as being due to an "open circuit," for it is a fundamental

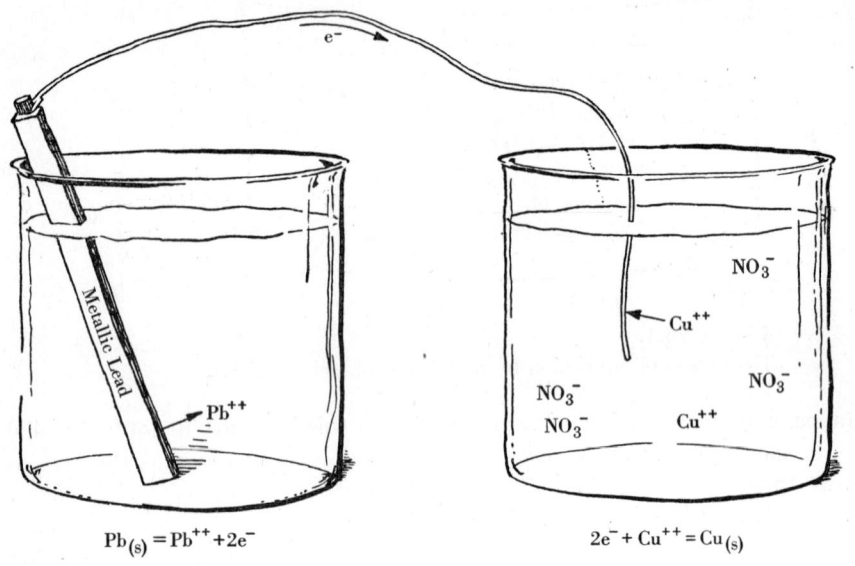

$Pb_{(s)} = Pb^{++} + 2e^-$ $\qquad$ $2e^- + Cu^{++} = Cu_{(s)}$

Figure 26.2.
Partially connected half-cells—not a functioning cell.

principle of electricity that every circuit must be a closed one, that the current must be able to follow a complete circle, not just flow one way as Figure 26.2 has it doing. If the apparatus diagrammed in Figure 26.2 were to operate as an electric cell it would be analogous to having the lights in a room stay on regardless of whether the light switch were in the on or off position.

A chemist diagnoses the problem similarly but in somewhat different terms. If the apparatus in Figure 26.2 were to operate, we can see that the solution in the beaker at the left would accumulate positively charged lead ions while the beaker at the right would be losing more and more positively charged copper ions with no change in the number of negatively charged nitrate ions. The beaker on the left would acquire a large positive charge and the beaker on the right an equally large negative charge, contrary to the principle that ionic solutions must remain electrically neutral, which means they must contain equivalent numbers of positive and negative ions. Thus the operation would cease as soon as the net positive charge on the beaker at the left, and the net negative charge on the beaker at the right were sufficient to overcome the tendency of the negative electrons to move from left to right. For all practical purposes this means that the operation of the cell would never begin. Actually a few lead ions would form and a few cupric ions be reduced, but the net charges created by these changes would then stop the flow of electrons. The problem now reduces to finding a method of keeping the number of negative and positive ions balanced in each of the two beakers even though positive ions are being produced in one beaker and removed from the other. Note that this problem does not arise for the apparatus in Figure 26.1 since the entire reaction occurs in a single container within which the ions are free to move.

From our previous discussion of electrolysis you may remember that ions, as well as electrons, can move and constitute an electric current. If we provide a means whereby the ions can move from one beaker to the other they will do so and maintain the electric neutrality of the two solutions. Figure 26.3 indicates three possible ways of providing paths for the ions. The physicist and

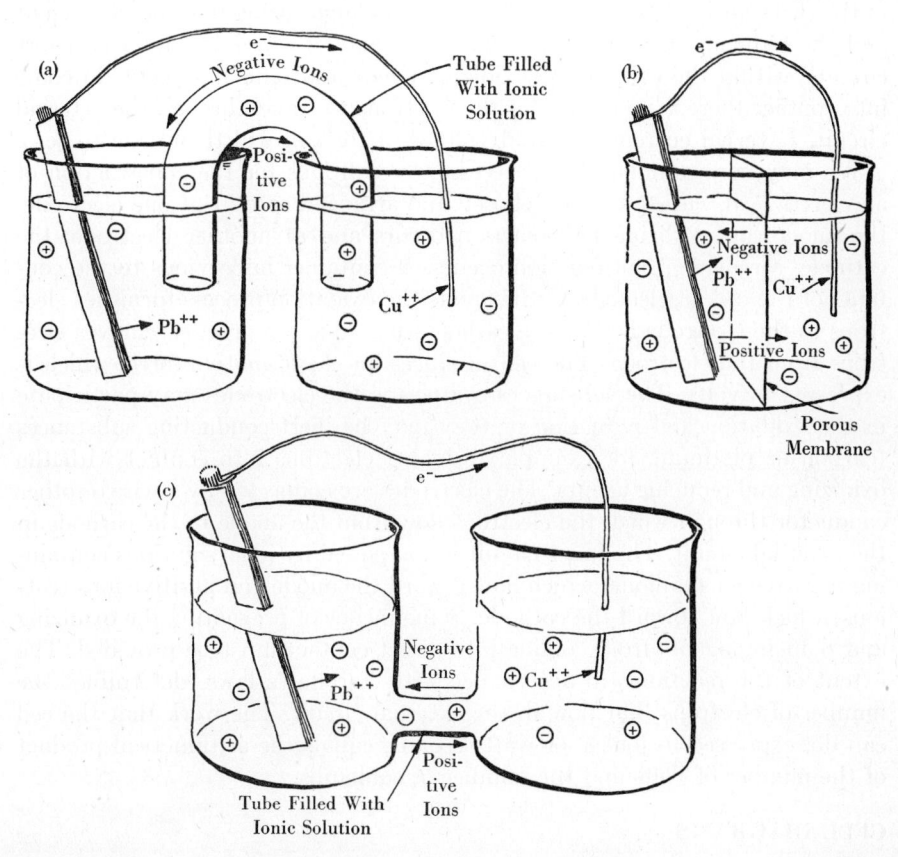

Figure 26.3.
Some typical cell arrangements.

electrical engineer would now point out that the circuit is complete so that electrons can move in an uninterrupted path. The chemist points out that positive ions may now move from the anode beaker, where they tend to be in excess, to the cathode beaker where they tend to be deficient, and that the negative ions may move from the cathode beaker, where they tend to be in excess, to the anode beaker, where they tend to be deficient. The electrical circuit is complete and the electric neutrality of the ionic solutions is maintained. Figure 26.3 gives the essential components for an electric cell and illustrates the changes which occur therein.

Figure 26.3b is the simplest diagram to draw and corresponds to many cells which are met so we shall use this type of diagram to illustrate cells. The porous membrane may be an unsintered clay barrier of perhaps 1 to 3 mm. thickness. Such a barrier is full of millions of tiny channels through which the hydrated ions will move under the influence of the electrical potentials of the cells. The barrier will, however, prevent gross convection currents and mixing of the two solutions. Such convection currents might bring the oxidizing agent and the reducing agent into direct contact and so cause an "internal short circuit" within the cell. If the oxidizing agent and reducing agent do come into contact there is no reason for the electrons to travel through the external circuit. External current flow and voltage of the cell will then drop to zero.

We may now summarize the necessary conditions for the construction of an electric cell. Substances are chosen and arranged so that at one electrode, the anode, an oxidizing half-reaction occurs and at another electrode, the cathode, a reducing half-reaction occurs. A container impervious to the contents of the cell is selected. At the anode the oxidation process furnishes electrons to the electrode and at the cathode the reduction process removes electrons from the electrode. The cell produces an electromotive force, which is expressed in volts. The substances composing the electrodes may participate in the oxidation and reduction or they may be inert conducting substances (carbon or platinum, for example) bringing electrons into contact with the oxidizing and reducing agents. The electrodes are connected by a wire or other conductor through which the electrons flow from the anode to the cathode in the external circuit. The inner circuit is completed by ionic solutions containing negative ions (anions) which flow toward the anode and positive ions (cations) which flow toward the cathode. Some means of preventing the oxidizing and reducing agents from coming into direct contact must be provided. The extent of the reactions, in accordance with Faraday's laws, determines the number of electrons that flow in the external circuit. The work that the cell can do, expressed in joules, or watt-seconds, equals the arithmetical product of the number of volts and the number of coulombs.

CELL DIAGRAMS

A complete diagram of a cell utilizing the reaction between hydrogen and iodine according to the equation

ELECTROCHEMISTRY AND ELECTRICAL CELLS   437

$$\tfrac{1}{2}H_{2(g)} + \tfrac{1}{2}I_{2(s)} = H^+ + I^- \tag{26.7}$$
$$\text{violet}$$

is shown in Figure 26.4. Many differences from Figure 26.3 will be noted, but similarities are also apparent.

Equation 26.7 may be separated into the half-reaction equations

$$\tfrac{1}{2}H_{2(g)} = H^+ + e^- \tag{26.8}$$
$$e^- + \tfrac{1}{2}I_{2(s)} = I^- \tag{26.9}$$

The oxidizing agent is solid iodine and the reducing agent is gaseous hydrogen. A glass vessel will be a suitable container since it does not react with the cell

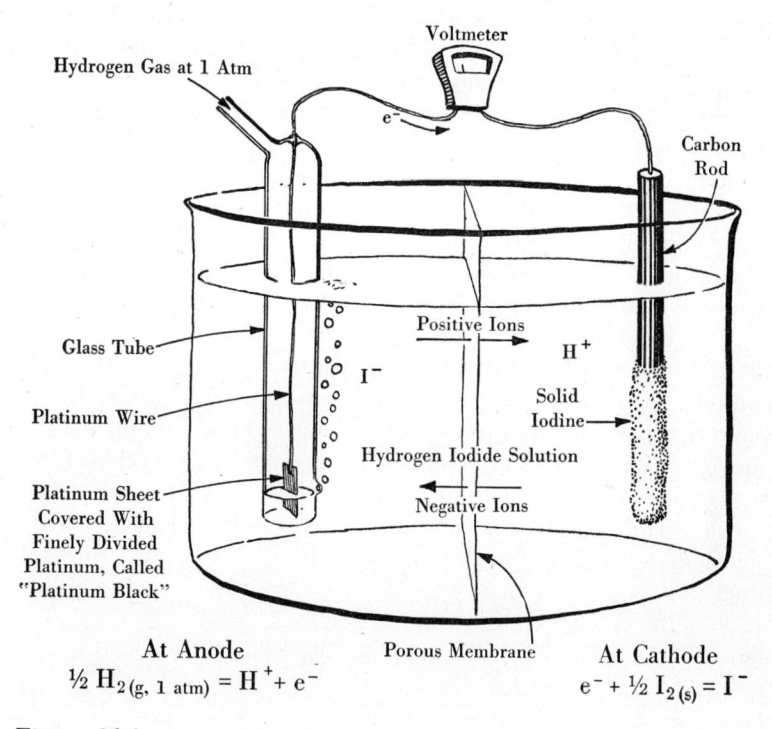

Figure 26.4.
Cell with hydrogen electrode and iodine electrode.

chemicals. The electrodes constitute a special problem, however, since neither solid iodine nor gaseous hydrogen is a sufficiently good conductor of electricity to serve as the electrode proper. This problem is solved for the iodine by coating a graphite electrode, which is a good conductor of electrons and is chemically inert to the cell contents, with solid iodine. The graphite supports the iodine mechanically and conducts the electrons to it from the external circuit. The hydrogen electrode is fashioned by coating a piece of platinum with very finely divided platinum, known as platinum black, and bubbling hydrogen over its surface. The platinum black becomes coated with hydrogen, supports it, and conducts electrons away from it to the external circuit. The large area of the platinum black provides ample surface at which oxidation of the hydrogen to hydrogen ions can proceed. In this cell the platinum anode and the carbon cathode are inert chemically and serve only to support the reducing and oxidizing agents, respectively, and to conduct the electrons to and from the external circuit.

A solution of hydrogen iodide would probably be used as electrolyte, or conducting solution, in the cell, but since neither H^+ ions or I^- ions are consumed in the cell reaction any ionic solution whose ions did not react with either the oxidizing agent or the reducing agent would be satisfactory. Sodium chloride or potassium nitrate would work well. However, certain properties of the cell are easier to define and measure if the electrolyte is made up of known concentrations of the ions produced in the reaction.

It might be thought that in this cell no porous barrier would be necessary—the iodine is solid and should remain on its electrode and the hydrogen is gaseous and will bubble out of the solution only about its electrode. If both materials were really insoluble in the electrolyte no barrier would be needed for they could not come into contact. Actually the solubility of iodine is high enough to make a barrier desirable. You may remember that iodine is even more soluble in an iodide solution than in pure water (see page 321).

As the cell diagrammed in Figure 26.4 operates, electrons flow in the external circuit from the anode to the cathode. Negative iodide ions are produced at the cathode, tending to cause an excess of negative ions about the cathode. To counteract this effect positive ions move toward the cathode and the iodide ions move away from it. At the same time positive hydrogen ions form at the anode, so that negative ions move toward this electrode and positive ions move away. The net effect is shown in Figure 26.4 where the net motion of negative ions toward the anode and of positive ions toward the cathode is indicated.

Problem 26.4. Diagram cells that can operate according to the equations

a. $Sn_{(s)} + 2Ag^+ = 2Ag_{(s)} + Sn^{++}$

b. $Pb_{(s)} + 2Fe^{+++} = 2Fe^{++} + Pb^{++}$
   yellow

c. $Cl^- + Au_{(s)} + \frac{3}{2}Cl_{2(g)} = AuCl_4^-$
   yellow   yellow-green   yellow

Indicate the direction of electronic and ionic current flows and identify the anode and cathode of each cell.

Problem 26.5. Would it be possible to use a platinum rather than a carbon anode in the cell diagrammed in Figure 26.4?

ELECTRIC CELL VOLTAGES

The electromotive force, or EMF, causing the flow of an electric current through a cell is usually expressed in volts and measured with a voltmeter.

Some idea of the magnitude of a volt may be obtained from the following: The customary voltage for household currents in America is 110 volts, the EMF of the three-cell lead storage battery in an automobile is about 6 volts, and the usual dry cell or flashlight cell has an EMF of about 1.5 volts. The storage battery and the dry cell use chemical reactions directly as sources of electrical energy.

A certain amount of work must always be done in an electric cell to move the ions through the electrolyte and the electrons through the wire. Some of the electromotive force of the cell will be used to maintain the current so that the actual voltage of a cell in operation will always be less than that of the cell when no current is flowing. The dimming of a car's lights when the starter button is depressed results from the lowering of the EMF of the battery when it is delivering current. Special devices are available for measuring the EMF of a cell under conditions of no current flow. The measured voltages are then the maximum which a cell can generate. The instrument usually used is the potentiometer.

SOURCES OF EMF IN ELECTRIC CELLS

Electric cells can generate electromotive force only as long as some net reaction proceeds within the cell. When chemical equilibrium is attained, the EMF drops to zero. The farther from equilibrium a particular cell is, the higher the value of the voltage. We must look to the existence of nonequilibrium situations within the cell as sources of EMF.

When a substance is immersed in water, a few of the atoms may dissolve as ions. Then the substance becomes charged, but it soon has a charge of such magnitude that the ions are attracted back to the substance just as often as they leave it. Equilibrium between the substance, its ions in water, and the electric charge is attained. The resultant charge on the substance is a source of electric potential, usually known as its *solution potential*. The solution potential may be either negative or positive depending on whether electrons are left on the electrode or are taken from it in the solution process. No method is known for determining the absolute magnitude of the solution potentials but it is certain that they differ from substance to substance because of the varying tendency of substances to hold electrons.

Another source of EMF is the junctions between the conductors in the external part of the circuit. Electrons tend to leave different metals, but at different rates. Hence, when two metals are joined there will be a net flow of electrons from the metal with lesser to the metal with greater retentiveness for electrons. The resultant difference in charge is a source of potential called the *contact potential*. There is evidence that contact potentials are generally larger than the differences between solution potentials and so constitute a major part of the over-all EMF of the cell.

A third source of EMF arises out of differences in the diffusion rate of ions. If the concentrations of ions in the solution varies from place to place the

440 GENERAL CHEMISTRY

ions will move in greater numbers from the regions of high concentration to regions of low concentration than in the opposite direction. This net migration is called diffusion. The positive ions and the negative ions must diffuse at equal rates if the different parts of the solution are to remain electrically neutral. When their diffusion rates differ, the resulting local charges are a source of potentials called *concentration* or *diffusion potentials*.

As long as the different parts of a cell are isolated, equilibrium will be maintained in the parts and no current will flow. If the different parts of the cell are now joined so that electrons and ions can flow, the contact potentials, the solution potentials, and the diffusion potentials lead to a continuing current. The EMF of a cell is the result of all potentials in the cell.

CONCENTRATION CELLS

We have seen that the EMF of a cell depends on the nature of the electrode reactions. But we know that the extent of reaction depends on the concentrations of the reacting substances as well as on their nature. How does the EMF of a cell depend on concentrations?

A particularly simple type of cell is one with identical electrodes immersed in solutions differing only in the concentrations of their ions. Figure 26.5 diagrams such a cell. Note that for identical electrodes there is no contact potential. The equation for the anode reaction for this cell is

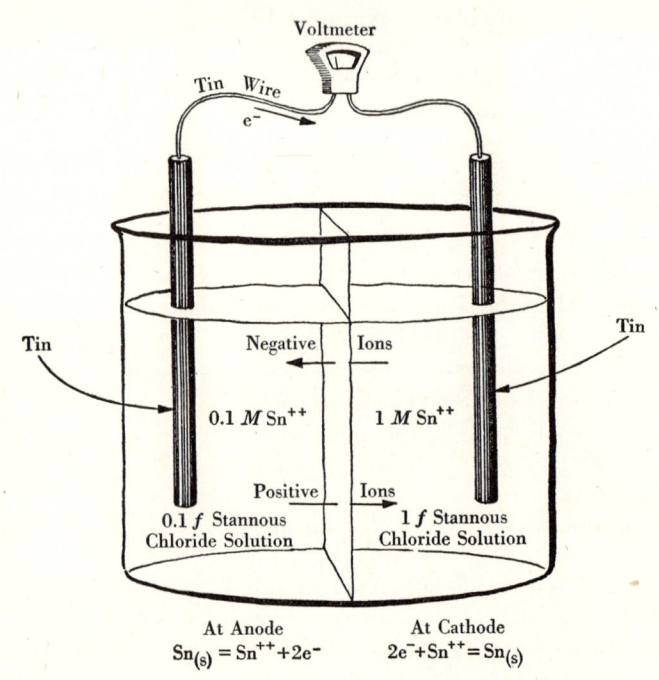

At Anode
$Sn_{(s)} = Sn^{++} + 2e^-$

At Cathode
$2e^- + Sn^{++} = Sn_{(s)}$

Figure 26.5.
Concentration cell—electrolytes of differing concentrations.

$$Sn_{(s)} = Sn^{++} + 2e^-$$

and that of the cathode reaction is

$$2e^- + Sn^{++} = Sn_{(s)}$$

the reverse of the anode reaction. In other words, tin is dissolving to form stannous ions at the anode and stannous ions are plating out at the cathode to form tin. This process is readily explicable in terms of the equilibria involved. Since the concentration of stannous ions around the cathode is ten times that around the anode, stannous ions hit the cathode and acquire electrons from it ten times as often as they do at the anode. Electrons are removed from the cathode more rapidly than from the anode and an EMF develops. Tin plates out on the cathode, using up electrons which are replaced through the external wire as the tin on the anode dissolves. The process will continue until the concentration of stannous chloride is the same around each electrode or until the anode has completely dissolved, whichever occurs first.

A similar effect is obtained if the cell diagrammed in Figure 26.6 is set up.

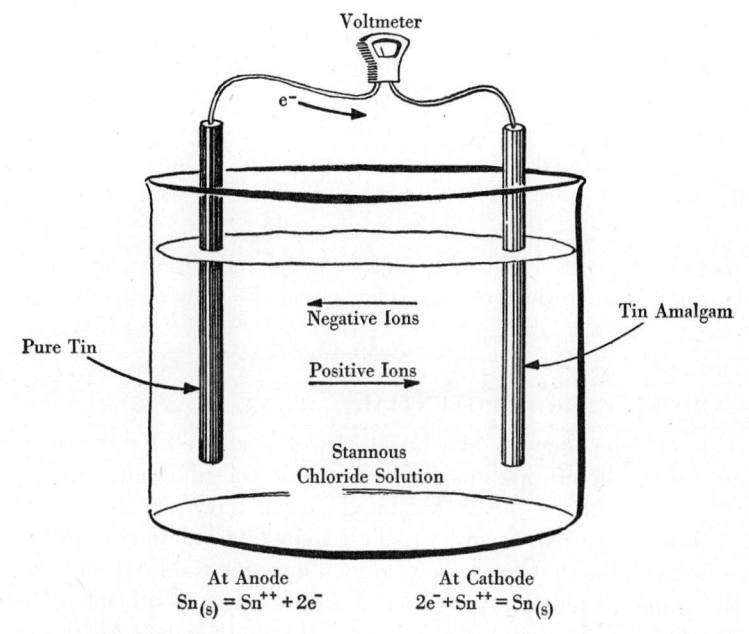

Figure 26.6.
Concentration cell—electrodes of differing concentrations.

In this cell there is a single electrolyte of uniform concentration and thus no concentration potential, but the two electrodes are slightly different. Hence there is a contact potential. One electrode is pure tin, the other is a tin amalgam, that is, tin dissolved in mercury. The concentration of tin in the second electrode is less than in the first. Since the tin concentration in the amalgam

442   GENERAL CHEMISTRY

is less, its tendency to dissolve as stannous ions will be less than that of pure tin. The net effect is that the pure tin will go into solution as stannous ion and stannous ions will plate out on the amalgamated electrode as tin atoms.

Concentration cells always involve transfer of some substance from a region where it is more concentrated (for example, pure tin) to a region where its concentration is less (for example, tin amalgam). Such transfers are inherent in all spontaneous flow processes and may be stated in terms of the ideas of escaping tendency which we developed on pages 255 and 269. The escaping tendency of pure tin is greater than that of tin dissolved in mercury, just as the escaping tendency of stannous ions from a more concentrated solution is greater than from a dilute one. These differences in escaping tendency lead to nonequilibrium situations such as those diagrammed in the cells of Figures 26.5 and 26.6 with the result that definite potentials are generated.

One would reach the same conclusions by applying the equilibrium principles discussed in Chapter 18 to the half-equation

$$2e^- + Sn^{++} = Sn_{(s)} \tag{26.10}$$

An increase in concentration of stannous ions increases the tendency of the reaction to occur as read from left to right. Similarly, a decrease in the concentration of tin (as by formation of the amalgam) decreases the reverse process and increases the tendency of the reaction to occur. The cathode, at which these processes occur, acquires a more negative potential; the EMF of the cell increases.

Problem 26.6. Which would have the higher EMF, the cell diagrammed in Figure 26.5, or a similar cell in which the two stannous chloride concentrations were $1\,f$ and $0.01\,f$?

STANDARD ELECTRODE POTENTIALS

One cannot determine the absolute EMF of a half-cell for the same reason that one cannot determine absolute values for the different potentials contributing to the EMF of a cell. As stated earlier, however, the over-all EMF of cells can be measured. If now we select some half-reaction as standard and set up a half-cell for that reaction we may determine the EMF of cells formed when the standard half-cell is combined with a series of other half-cells. The EMF of a cell will be the algebraic sum of the EMF values for the two half-cells, being the result of the standard electrode half reaction plus the reaction in the other half-cell.

The half reaction of the hydrogen electrode, represented by the half-equation, or its reverse, respectively,

$$\left. \begin{array}{l} e^- + H^+ = \tfrac{1}{2}H_{2(g)};\ E° = 0.0000 \\ \tfrac{1}{2}H_{2(g)} = H^+ + e^-;\ E° = 0.0000 \end{array} \right\} \tag{26.11}$$

is, by agreement, selected as the standard half-cell reaction. An arbitrary value of 0.0000 volts is assigned to it. Hence, in a cell containing the standard hydrogen electrode, the over-all voltage value for the cell is assigned to the other half-cell. For example, for the cell for which the equation for the reaction is

$$\tfrac{1}{2}Zn_{(s)} + H^+ = \tfrac{1}{2}Zn^{++} + \tfrac{1}{2}H_{2(g)} \tag{26.12}$$

the EMF is 0.7620 volts. Since the EMF of the hydrogen electrode is arbitrarily set at 0.0000, (see equation 26.11) that for the zinc electrode for which the half-equation is

$$\tfrac{1}{2}Zn_{(s)} = \tfrac{1}{2}Zn^{++} + e^-$$

becomes 0.7620 volts. The EMF for the reverse reaction, for which the half-equation is

$$e^- + \tfrac{1}{2}Zn^{++} = \tfrac{1}{2}Zn_{(s)}$$

is the negative of the above value, or -0.7620 volts, the negative sign indicating that it is more difficult for Zn^{++} ions to gain electrons than for H^+ ions (see equation 5, Table 26.1).

Similarly, the over-all EMF of 0.7995 volts found for the cell for which the equation for the reaction is

$$\tfrac{1}{2}H_{2(g)} + Ag^+ = Ag_{(s)} + H^+; E = 0.7995 \text{ volts} \tag{26.13}$$

leads to a value of 0.7995 volts for the EMF of the half-cell for which the half-equation is

$$e^- + Ag^+ = Ag_{(s)}$$

The positive value indicates that it is easier for Ag^+ ions to gain electrons than for H^+ (see equation 17, Table 26.1). The method may be extended to other cells with other desired half-reactions. Then, by the logic used in obtaining equation 26.3 from equations 26.1 and 26.2, one may calculate the EMF values of new cells from those of the half-cells.

Since changes in concentrations of the reacting substances in cells change the values of the EMF it is apparent that the concentrations must be defined if standard electrodes and half cells are to have reproducible values for their EMF. For standard electrodes the concentrations of pure liquids and solids are those at 1 atmosphere pressure and at 25°C. For gases the partial pressure is set at 1 atmosphere. Temperature must be specified, since cell reactions, like other reactions, are influenced by the temperature. The usual standard temperature is 25°C. The concentrations of ions is 1 molal, unless otherwise specified. These conditions lead to the standard, E°, values (sometimes called *standard single electrode potentials*) for the electrode reactions in Table 26.1. Since the difference between molalities and molarities of ions is not important for our present purposes, we will represent ion concentrations in terms of their molarities.

CELL VOLTAGES FROM STANDARD ELECTRODE POTENTIALS

Some typical calculations of over-all cell voltages based on the $E°$ values listed in Table 26.1 are made below. The cell voltage is the algebraic sum of the standard half-reaction potentials for the cathode reaction and the anode reaction.

$$
\begin{array}{lllr}
& & & E° \\
\text{A. Cathode:} & e^- + Ag^+ & = Ag_{(s)} & +0.7995 \\
\text{Anode:} & \tfrac{1}{2}H_{2(g)} & = H^+ + e^- & +0.0000 \\
\hline
\text{Cell:} & Ag^+ + \tfrac{1}{2}H_{2(g)} & = Ag_{(s)} + H^+ & 0.7995 \text{ volts} \\
\\
\text{B. Cathode:} & 2e^- + 2Ag^+ & = 2Ag_{(s)} & +0.7995 \\
\text{Anode:} & Fe_{(s)} & = Fe^{++} + 2e^- & +0.440 \\
\hline
\text{Cell:} & Fe_{(s)} + 2Ag^+ & = 2Ag_{(s)} + Fe^{++} & +1.239 \text{ volts}
\end{array}
$$

Note that since the equation for the anode reaction is the reverse of that found in Table 26.1, the sign of the EMF must also be reversed. Anode reactions are always the reverse of the cathode reactions, for which the equations are indicated in Table 26.1. Note also that multiplying a half-reaction equation by a factor, such as 2, does not change the EMF of the reaction. See the cathode equation in "B."

$$
\begin{array}{lllr}
\text{C. Cathode:} & e^- + \tfrac{1}{2}Br_2 & = Br^- & +1.087 \\
\text{Anode:} & Fe^{++} & = Fe^{+++} + e^- & -0.771 \\
\hline
\text{Cell:} & Fe^{++} + \tfrac{1}{2}Br_2 & = Br^- + Fe^{+++} & +0.316 \text{ volts}
\end{array}
$$

Note that in every instance the cathode reaction is lower in Table 26.1 than the anode reaction, consistent with the fact that the best oxidizing agents (those substances gaining electrons from the cathode) are lowest in the table (see page 431). Note also that if the anode and cathode are correctly identified, the over-all cell voltage is always positive. A negative cell voltage indicates that the electrodes have been incorrectly identified and that the cell reaction does not proceed as represented, but in the opposite direction.

QUANTITATIVE EFFECT OF CHANGE IN CONCENTRATION ON ELECTRODE POTENTIALS

We have seen that the tendency of a particular oxidation or reduction to occur at an electrode depends on the concentration of the substances involved. We shall now consider a few specific examples quantitatively.

The standard hydrogen electrode, as already stated, has hydrogen gas at a partial pressure of 1 atmosphere and is immersed in a solution in which the hydrogen ion concentration is $1\,M$ (actually 1 molal). Then

$$e^- + H^+ = \tfrac{1}{2}H_{2(g)} \qquad E° = 0.000 \text{ volts}$$

If the concentration either of hydrogen ion or of hydrogen gas changes the EMF changes. This fact is indicated by equation 8 in Table 26.1.

$$e^- + H^+_{(10^{-7}\,M)} = \tfrac{1}{2}H_{2(g)} \qquad E° = -0.414 \text{ volts}$$

If a cell is set up with two hydrogen electrodes, one having a hydrogen ion concentration at 1 M and the other at 10^{-7} M, as in pure water or neutral salt solution, the difference in electrode potential is 0.414 volts. Such a cell is diagrammed in Figure 26.7. The decrease in electrode potential is consistent

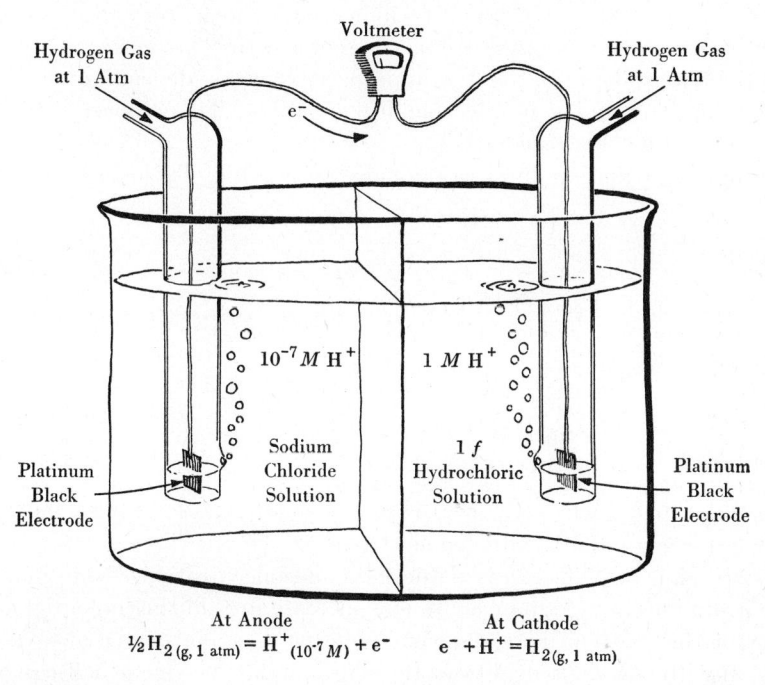

Figure 26.7.
Cell for measurement of hydrogen ion concentrations.

with the diminished tendency of hydrogen ions to combine with electrons to form hydrogen gas when their concentration is decreased.

In the same way, equations 18 and 22 in Table 26.1

$$2e^- + 2H^+ + \tfrac{1}{2}O_{2(g)} = H_2O \qquad E° = 1.229 \text{ volts}$$
$$2e^- + 2H^+_{(10^{-7} M)} + \tfrac{1}{2}O_{2(g)} = H_2O \qquad E° = 0.815 \text{ volts}$$

show a decrease of 0.414 volts resulting from a change in the hydrogen ion concentration from 1 M to 10^{-7} M.

The fact that both sets of reactions happen to give the same difference in EMF, -0.414 volts, for a change in concentration of the hydrogen ion concentration from 1 M to 10^{-7} M should not lead to the conclusion that this will be true for any reaction involving hydrogen ions, but the constant value is more than coincidental.

The formula which, at 25°C., does relate EMF to concentrations for the general reaction $aA + bB = cC + dD$ is

$$E = E° - \frac{0.0592}{n} \log \frac{[C]^c[D]^d}{[A]^a[B]^b} \qquad (26.14)$$

where E° is the voltage for standard concentrations, n is the number of electrons involved in the oxidation-reduction of a moles of A and b moles of B, and the symbols [A], [B], [C], and [D] indicate the molar concentrations of the respective substances (or their partial pressures if they are gases). These concentrations must be raised to the appropriate powers, depending on the coefficients a, b, c, and d in the chemical equation. The "concentration" of electrons need not be considered.

On applying equation 26.14 to the half-reaction 8 in Table 26.1

$$e^- + H^+{}_{(10^{-7}\,M)} = \tfrac{1}{2}H_{2(g,\,1\text{ atm.})}$$

we calculate

$$E = E° - \frac{0.0592}{n} \log \frac{P_{H_2}^{\frac{1}{2}}}{[H^+]}$$

$$= 0.0000 - \frac{0.0592}{1} \log \frac{(1)^{\frac{1}{2}}}{10^{-7}} = -0.0592 \log 10^7$$

$$= -0.0592 \times 7$$

$$= -0.414 \text{ volts}$$

On the other hand, when $[H^+] = 1$ rather than $10^{-7}\,M$, $E = E° = 0.0000$, as it should for a standard hydrogen electrode.

Examination of Table 26.1 in the light of concentration effects indicates why nitrate ions and permanganate ions increase in oxidizing potential as the acidity of the solution increases while chlorine does not change in oxidizing potential with change in acidity of the solution. The pertinent half-equations are

$$3e^- + 4H^+ + NO_3^- = NO_{(g)} + 2H_2O \qquad E° = 0.96 \text{ volts}$$
$$5e^- + 8H^+ + MnO_4^- = Mn^{++} + 4H_2O \qquad E° = 1.52 \text{ volts}$$
$$e^- + \tfrac{1}{2}Cl_{2(g)} = Cl^- \qquad E° = 1.3583 \text{ volts}$$

Both nitrate ions and permanganate ions react with hydrogen ions when they act as oxidizing agents, but chlorine does not. As a result chlorine will oxidize nitric oxide to nitrate ion in dilute acid, whereas nitrate ion will oxidize chloride ion to chlorine in concentrated acid, even though chlorine is a better oxidizing agent than nitrate ion in $1\,M$ acid to the extent of 0.398 volts.

$$3Cl^- + 4H^+ + NO_3^- \underset{\text{dilute acid}}{\overset{\text{concentrated acid}}{\rightleftharpoons}} NO_{(g)} + 2H_2O + \tfrac{3}{2}Cl_{2(g)} \qquad (26.16)$$

THE LEAD STORAGE BATTERY

One of the most common electrical cells uses the reaction shown by the equation

$$\underset{\text{brown}}{PbO_{2(s)}} + Pb_{(s)} + 4H^+ + 2SO_4^{--} = 2PbSO_{4(s)} + 2H_2O \qquad (26.17)$$

as a source of electrical energy. For the anode reaction the half-equation is

$$Pb_{(s)} + SO_4^{--} = PbSO_{4(s)} + 2e^- \tag{26.18}$$

and for the cathode reaction the half-equation is

$$2e^- + \underset{\text{brown}}{PbO_{2(s)}} + SO_4^{--} + 4H^+ = PbSO_{4(s)} + 2H_2O \tag{26.19}$$

The EMF for the over-all cell reaction is about two volts, the usual six volt automobile battery being made up of three of these cells connected in series so that the total voltage is the sum of those of the three separate cells. Cells connected in series are known as "batteries."

The lead storage battery has the very desirable property of being readily "recharged," when, after continued use, either the lead dioxide oxidizing agent, the sulfuric acid electrolyte, or the lead reducing agent has been used up. The charging process involves connecting the battery to an electrical source with higher voltage than the battery and "running the battery backward." Thus electrons are forced onto the electrode formerly covered with lead and the lead sulfate is reduced to metallic lead. Note that the reaction involves a reversal of equation 26.17, which represents the change at the anode when the battery is discharging. The charging process simultaneously removes electrons from the plate formerly covered with lead dioxide, thus oxidizing the lead sulfate to lead dioxide. This charging reaction involves a reversal of equation 26.18, which occurs on discharge at the cathode. In other words, the lead storage battery is readily reversible. It may be recharged many times and used over and over again.

The discharge process uses up the lead dioxide, the lead, and also the sulfate and hydrogen ions present in the electrolyte. This removal of sulfuric acid from the solution lowers the density of the solution. Thus the density of the electrolyte is a rough measure of the state of the battery, a low density indicating that the battery should be recharged.

Batteries and cells usually have positive and negative signs indicated on their connecting posts. These are established by convention consistent with the flow of electricity in the external current. Thus the electrode at which negative current, electrons, leaves the cell to enter the external circuit is called negative. (It is also the anode of the cell.) The electrode at which electrons enter the cell is, similarly, called positive. (It is the cathode.)

THE DRY CELL

Another very common source of electrical energy is the "dry cell." Actually there are several types of dry cells, but one particular kind is so common that it has almost pre-empted the name. This cell is the one usually found in flashlights. The older models consist of a metallic zinc can, packed with a black, moist powder (primarily manganese dioxide and ammonium chloride with a little water) and having a carbon electrode down the center. The carbon electrode is insulated from the zinc can, which serves as the other

448 GENERAL CHEMISTRY

electrode, by a wax plug at one end of the battery. The cell reaction here is much more complicated than that in the lead storage battery but may be approximated by the equation

$$Zn_{(s)} + 2MnO_{2(s)} + 2NH_4^+ = Zn^{++} + 2MnOOH_{(s)} + 2NH_3 \qquad (26.20)$$
$$\text{black} \hspace{6em} \text{brown}$$

The zinc can is the anode and the carbon rod the cathode in this cell. In newer models the zinc anode is the center rod and the carbon cathode is a coating on the plastic can of the cell. Consistent with convention the carbon cathode is called positive. Here electrons enter the cell during discharge. Contrary to the lead storage battery, the dry cell is not reversible and cannot be recharged. Its chief advantages over the lead storage battery are lighter weight, lower initial cost, and no fluid electrolyte to spill. Many other storage batteries, dry cells, and nonreversible wet batteries are known and used commercially but the lead storage battery and the zinc-manganese dioxide dry cell are typical.

Problem 26.7. A used dry cell does not smell highly of ammonia when it is opened. How do you account for this fact in the light of the products of the reaction in equation 26.19?

Problem 26.8. Lead storage batteries have been known to freeze when a heavy current is drawn from them in very cold weather. What does this indicate about the cell reaction? Why don't the batteries freeze in below zero weather since the electrolyte is largely water?

Problem 26.9. Diagram the lead storage battery, showing direction of motion of all currents both on charge and discharge.

Problem 26.10. The Edison storage battery operates on the reaction

$$Fe_{(s)} + NiO_{2(s)} + 2H_2O = Fe(OH)_{2(s)} + Ni(OH)_{2(s)}$$
$$\hspace{4em}\text{black} \hspace{6em} \text{green} \hspace{3em} \text{green}$$

Write equations for the anode and cathode reactions. What electrolyte do you think is used in this battery? Diagram the cell and show the direction of current flow as it operates.

Problem 26.11. Calculate the concentration of Au^{+++} ion in equilibrium with $1\ M$ $AuCl_4^-$ ion when the chloride ion concentration is also $1\ M$. Use the data in Table 26.1.

Problem 26.12. For the cell reactions represented by the following equations calculate the over-all EMF of the cells when all the solids are pure, all the gases have a partial pressure of one atmosphere, and all ions are $1\ M$ in concentration:

a. $Sn_{(s)} + Pb^{++} = Pb_{(s)} + Sn^{++}$
b. $Hg_{(liq)} + Ag^+ = Ag_{(s)} + \frac{1}{2}Hg_2^{++}$
c. $Cu_{(s)} + Cl_{2(g)} = Cu^{++} + 2Cl^-$
   red   yellow-green   blue
d. $2AuCl_4^- + 3Fe_{(s)} = 2Au_{(s)} + 8Cl^- + 3Fe^{++}$
   yellow   yellow

Problem 26.13. A cell is operating with a zinc anode in zinc sulfate solution and a cadmium cathode in cadmium sulfate solution. Equal concentrations of ammonia are added to each side. The cell voltage increases. Which ammonia complex, that with zinc ion or that with cadmium ion, is more stable? Interpret your answer in terms of the sizes and charges of the two ions.

Problem 26.14. Decide whether or not the reactions represented by the following equations will occur. Use the data in Table 26.1.

a. $Fe^{++} + 2Ag_{(s)} = 2Ag^+ + Fe_{(s)}$
b. $Fe^{+++} + I^- = Fe^{++} + \frac{1}{2}I_{2(s)}$
   yellow   violet
c. $Fe^{+++} + Ag_{(s)} = Ag^+ + Fe^{++}$
   yellow
d. $Fe_{(s)} + 2Fe^{+++} = 3Fe^{++}$
            yellow

Problem 26.15. Arrange the following substances in the order of increasing tendency to take up electrons. Mark your series to show for which substance this tendency is smallest: (a) chlorine, (b) Ag^+ ion in water, (c) Na^+ ion in water, (d) fluorine, (e) Cu^{++} ion in water, (f) Zn^{++} ion in water.

Problem 26.16. How could you decide from a single experiment whether tin or silver is the stronger reducing agent?

Problem 26.17. What constituents of an electric cell is it essential to keep out of direct contact with each other?

Problem 26.18. Complete the following to form equations representing net reactions: (a) $Fe^{+++} + I^- = Fe^{++} + I_2$ (in acid solution); (b) $NO_3^- + Zn = Zn^{++} + NH_4^+$ (in acid solution); (c) $Cu(OH)_2 + NH_3 = Cu(NH_3)_4^{++}$ (in basic solution); (d) $OCl^- + AsO_2^- = AsO_4^{---} + Cl^-$ (in basic solution).

Problem 26.19. What new substances will be formed, and in what approximate amounts when the following are mixed? All ions are in water solution. (a) Ag^+ ion (1 mole), copper (1 mole), and zinc (1 mole); (b) chlorine (1 mole), bromine (1 mole), and I^- ion (4 moles); (c) 100 ml. of 0.1 f silver nitrate and 500 ml. of 0.05 f hydrochloric acid.

Problem 26.20. Solely on the basis of the following observations, arrange as far as possible in order of increasing oxidizing power (i.e., with the strongest oxidizing couple at the bottom of the list) the oxidizing and reducing couples represented in the following: (a) Sn^{++} ion reduces Fe^{+++} ion; (b) $Cr_2O_7^{--}$ ion in 1 M acid oxidizes Fe^{++} ion to Fe^{+++} ion; (c) Cr^{+++} ion in 1 M acid reduces MnO_4^- ion to manganese dioxide; (d) Sn^{++} ion does not reduce Zn^{++} ion.

Problem 26.21. Write half-reaction equations for the processes which take place when dilute solutions of the following salts are electrolyzed: (a) silver nitrate, (b) copper sulfate, (c) potassium nitrate, (d) sodium peroxide (which hydrolyzes giving HO_2^- ion, and OH^- ion).

27 METALS FROM ORES; METALLURGY

IN PRECEDING chapters we have discussed the occurrence, preparation, and properties of many of the nonmetallic elements and the chemistry of some compounds of the metallic elements, particularly their oxides. In this chapter we shall deal with some of the problems one meets in starting with the raw materials found in nature and obtaining the metals from them.

MINERALS AND ORES

The general sources of raw materials available to us are three: the atmosphere (see Chapter 6), the hydrosphere, and the lithosphere. None of the metallic elements, however, forms a volatile compound stable enough to be present in the atmosphere in appreciable amounts. A few form water-soluble compounds with the common anions and are found in appreciable concentrations in the oceans and landlocked seas such as the Dead Sea, the Caspian Sea, the Great Salt Lake, etc. The majority form insoluble compounds with the anions present in the earth's crust and are found as solid deposits. When these solids, thousands of which are known, are homogeneous, and when they approximate pure substances in composition, they are called *minerals*. Deposits of minerals worth commercial development are known as *ores*. In common practice the term ore may include the heterogeneous mass of minerals associated with the ore desired. In this sense "iron ore" includes whatever the power shovel scoops up from the ore bed.

For a very few elements no minerals are known. Such elements are found only as replacements for other elements in minerals of the latter. Rubidium, for instance, is never found as a pure rubidium compound in nature but only in potassium minerals, in which it occupies random crystal sites in place of potassium ions. This replacement is possible because of the similar sizes and identical charges of rubidium and potassium ions. In general the ratios of two such elements in minerals is variable.

METALS FROM ORES: METALLURGY   451

Table 27.1
Some Natural Sources of the Elements in Terms of the Periodic Table

He * gas wells	Ne * atm.	A * atm.	Kr * atm.	Xe * atm.	Rn * uranium ores	
H water, natural gas	F CaF$_2$	Cl NaCl, ocean	Br ocean	I iodate		
	O * atm.,	S * sulfide	Se with S	Te gold telluride		
	N * atm., nitrates	P phosphate	As sulfide	Sb sulfide	Bi * sulfide	
	C coal, oil	Si silicate	Ge sulfide	Sn sulfide, oxide	Pb sulfide	
	B Na$_2$B$_4$O$_7$	Al oxide	Ga sulfide	In sulfide	Tl sulfide	
			Zn sulfide, oxide	Cd sulfide, oxide	Hg sulfide	
			Cu * sulfide	Ag * sulfide	Au * telluride	
			Ni sulfide	Pd *	Pt *	
			Co sulfide	Rh *	Ir *	
			Fe oxide	Ru *	Os *	
			Mn oxide		Re with Mo	
			Cr oxide	Mo sulfide	W oxide	U oxide
			V oxide	Cb oxide	Ta oxide	
			Ti oxide	Zr silicate	Hf with Zr	Th phosphate, **oxide**
			Sc silicate	Y phosphate	Rare Earths phosphate	
	Be oxide, silicate	Mg ocean, carbonate	Ca carbonate, sulfate	Sr carbonate, sulfate	Ba carbonate, sulfate	Ra uranium ores
	Li phosphate, silicate	Na chloride, ocean, sulfate	K chloride, sulfate	Rb with K	Cs silicate	

* Elements which commonly occur uncombined in nature.

The great majority of minerals are of no commercial importance as sources of the elements, either because of their rarity or because of the difficulty of obtaining the pure element from them. Usually only a few minerals of each element are found as ores. The most common ores of the various elements are listed in Table 27.1 in the form of a periodic table. Note the consistent variation of ore types with position in the table and the correlation with the electropositive nature of the elements. Examination of the table will show that the great majority of ores contain sulfides, oxides, or the metallic elements themselves. Chlorides, sulfates, silicates, and phosphates constitute most of the rest except for a few special substances such as gold telluride.

Table 27.1 should not be interpreted to mean that the commercial ores, or the minerals they contain, correspond to the pure compounds found in the laboratory. Not only are impurities almost inevitably present, but the principal compounds themselves may be of a kind not usually prepared in laboratory practice. Chromium, for instance, is listed as occurring in an oxide ore. The actual mineral approximates the composition $FeCr_2O_4$, which may also be written $FeO \cdot Cr_2O_3$. This latter formulation does not intimate that the mineral is a heterogeneous mixture containing ferrous oxide and chromium sesquioxide. Rather, it represents the mineral as a compound between these two oxides. Actually the compound is a macromolecular substance in which the oxygen atoms occupy positions in the crystal lattice between those positions occupied by iron and chromium atoms. The latter crystal positions can also be occupied by $2+$ ions of some elements other than iron, or by $3+$ ions of some elements other than chromium if the substituent ions have approximately the same size as the iron or chromium ions they replace. Such substitution is common in nature and is one reason why few minerals have compositions corresponding exactly to those of the pure substances prepared in the laboratory. The majority of minerals then, are, not pure compounds, and the details of the metallurgy, or "winning of the metal" from its ore will depend on what the total constituency of the ore is.

GEOLOGICAL FORMATION OF ORE BODIES

Most theories of the geological structure of the earth agree in stating that the earth was once a hot fluid body. They differ markedly in their detailed interpretation of the present distribution of minerals and ore bodies in terms of the changes which have since occurred. It is possible, however, to obtain considerable insight into these processes without committing one's self to any particular geological theory. The processes of differentiation may be divided into four groups: (1) separation of mutually insoluble liquid substances during the early stages of cooling, (2) fractional crystallization of solid substances upon further cooling of the separate liquids originally formed, (3) weathering of the primary crystallizate (mainly by water) once the surface temperature of the earth dropped to the neighborhood of 100°C. and below, and (4) biological action which started at a still later date.

Most of the present ore bodies owe their relatively pure state and their localization within narrow confines (both necessary attributes of an ore body) to weathering action on the primary crystallizates, often coupled with biological action. Continual weathering by rain, wind, and temperature changes, for instance, wears away the primordial materials. The debris is carried down stream toward the ocean. The stream current gradually slackens as the mouth of the river broadens and the suspended solids settle out, the most dense settling out most rapidly. It is for this reason, a high density, that the platinum metals, thorium phosphate (monazite), gold, etc., are commonly found concentrated in alluvial deposits. At the same time soluble materials, such as the alkali halides, remain in solution and make the oceans "salty." An average composition of ocean water is given in Table 27.2. Much calcium ion also enters the oceans dissolved in river water, slightly acid because of the carbon

Table 27.2

An Average Composition of Ocean Water Disregarding Dissolved Gases

The elements are present in the form of various ions. Those in **bold-face type** are removed from ocean on a commercial scale. The pH of ocean water is 8.

ELEMENT	PARTS PER MILLION (MG/KG)	ELEMENT	PARTS PER MILLION (MG/KG)
chlorine	18980	copper	0.001–0.01
sodium	10561	zinc	0.005
magnesium	1272	lead	0.004
sulfur	884	selenium	0.004
calcium	400	cesium	0.002
potassium	380	uranium	0.0015
bromine	65	molybdenum	0.0005
carbon	28	thorium	0.0005
strontium	13	cerium	0.0004
boron	4.6	silver	0.0003
silicon	0.02–4.0	vanadium	0.0007
fluorine	1.4	lanthanum	0.0003
nitrogen	0.01–0.7	yttrium	0.0003
aluminum	0.5	nickel	0.0001
rubidium	0.2	scandium	0.00004
lithium	0.1	mercury	0.00003
phosphorus	0.001–0.10	gold	0.000006
barium	0.05	radium	$0.2\text{–}3 \times 10^{-10}$
iodine	0.05	chromium	trace
arsenic	0.01–0.02	cobalt	trace
iron	0.002–0.02	cadmium	trace
manganese	0.001–0.01	tin	trace

H. U. Sverdrup, M. W. Johnson, and R. H. Fleming, *The Oceans, Their Physics, Chemistry, and General Biology* (Copyright, 1942, by Prentice-Hall, Inc., New York), pp. 176, 177. Reprinted by permission of the publisher.

dioxide content. Shell fish reduce the acidity of the water with their body fluids and precipitate the calcium ion as calcium carbonate to build their shells. Much of this calcium carbonate ends up in sedimentary limestone deposits in the course of geological history. The geological history of many ore bodies may be traced through similar weathering and biological cycles.

ENRICHMENT OF ORES

A few ores, iron ore for instance, may be pure enough to be fed directly into the process for preparing the metal. Most ores, however, require preliminary steps to concentrate the desired mineral and remove from it impurities which would interfere in later stages of the metallurgical process. The enrichment steps may be merely sorting operations in which the various impurities are removed mechanically, or they may be very complicated chemical procedures which convert the ore to another compound quite different from that found in the ore.

Copper sulfide is often separated from the non-copper-bearing portion of the ore, known as gangue, by *flotation*. Separation by flotation is based on the fact that certain detergents make it possible for water, or other fluids, to wet some surfaces without wetting others. When the water wets a surface it sticks to the surface and tends to carry the wetted material along with it. The water may be beaten into a froth, which presents a greatly increased surface for wetting the desired material. Use of a detergent causing water to wet copper sulfide but not the gangue results in the copper sulfide being concentrated in the froth. This rises to the top of the flotation bath, and is skimmed off. The solid copper sulfide is recovered by allowing the froth to collapse and the copper sulfide to settle out. Ores containing less than 1 per cent of copper become industrially useful because of flotation. Flotation processes have been worked out in great detail for many systems; the range of available detergents is so wide that it is possible for instance, to float potassium chloride selectively away from sodium chloride or to float sodium chloride selectively away from potassium chloride by choosing the proper combination of detergent and froth. This is an amazing feat when one considers the great similarity in the crystals of these two salts.

Magnetic separation is becoming important in the metallurgy of iron as the Mesabi range of iron ore becomes depleted. Other ores, containing a lower percentage of iron, are known in which the iron compound is magnetic whereas the gangue is not. If such ore is dropped through a magnetic field the iron compound may be deflected into a different receiving bin than the gangue and a good separation obtained. A similar electrostatic separation, relying on the fact that the gangue retains an electrical charge better than stannic oxide does, is used in tin metallurgy.

Ferric oxide and various silicates are major impurities in aluminum oxide ores (bauxite). These must be removed before the ore can be reduced to aluminum if one is to obtain pure aluminum. Only the aluminum oxide is soluble in bases. Remember the amphoteric nature of this oxide. Treatment of the bauxite with a hot sodium hydroxide solution dissolves the aluminum as aluminate ion leaving the iron oxide and the silicate impurities as solids. The solution is filtered, cooled, and sometimes made neutral. Then aluminum hydroxide of very high purity precipitates. The hydroxide is heated to form the oxide and sent to the final step of the process in which it is reduced to metallic aluminum. This is a typical *selective solution* process; others are sometimes used to enrich ores. The following equations summarize the process for aluminum oxide.

Selective solution:
$$Al_2O_{3(s)} + Fe_2O_{3(s)} + 2OH^- + 3H_2O = 2Al(OH)_4^- + Fe_2O_{3(s)} \quad (27.1)$$
white ... red ... red

On cooling or neutralization:
$$Al(OH)_4^- = Al(OH)_{3(s)} + OH^- \quad (27.2)$$
white

Calcining:
$$2Al(OH)_{3(s)} = Al_2O_{3(s)} + 3H_2O_{(g)} \quad (27.3)$$
white ... white

Magnesium chloride, a raw material used as a source of metallic magnesium, may be obtained from the mineral, magnesite, formula $MgCO_3$. The magnesium carbonate is heated and converted to magnesium oxide. The magnesium oxide is then treated with hydrogen chloride or chlorine to give magnesium chloride. Magnesium oxide may also be obtained, and more cheaply, by precipitating the magnesium ions in sea water as the hydroxide, filtering out the hydroxide, and heating it to give magnesium oxide. Ocean water contains approximately 0.13 g. of magnesium ion per 100 g. of solution (see Table 27.2), or about 0.1 per cent magnesium. Few commercial ores contain such a small percentage of the desired material, yet the magnesium ion is simply and quantitatively precipitated from the ocean water. The precipitant is a calcium hydroxide slurry, made by mixing calcium oxide (obtained by heating calcium carbonate either from limestone or sea shells) with water. Practically pure magnesium hydroxide is obtained in this way. The effluent from the plant is returned to the ocean in such a manner that it does not become mixed with the plant intake waters and so dilute them. This process is an example of *selective precipitation* also used to enrich ores.

Other enrichment procedures are used but flotation, selective solution, and selective precipitation are the most common.

WINNING OF METALLIC ELEMENTS FOUND FREE IN NATURE

Enrichment processes are further illustrated in the metallurgy of the metallic elements found free in nature. Table 27.1 shows that all such elements are found in the middle of the long periods of the periodic table. Thus, all have high densities (because of their small and massive atoms) and may be separated from the surrounding materials by very simple flotation methods which require no added detergent but merely a rapidly flowing stream of water. The gold miners' panning methods, and sluice boxes with cleats along the bottom to catch the heavy metals as they settle, are typical of the simplicity of the separations. The effectiveness of the sluice for the recovery of silver and gold is increased if its bottom is covered with mercury. Mercury will readily dissolve gold and silver but not the accompanying rocks. This process captures even the tiniest metal particles which otherwise might wash down the sluice. The mercury solution is removed from time to time and the mercury distilled, leaving the gold and silver which may be separated by further chemical treatment. This amalgamation method (mercury solutions of metals are called amalgams) is essentially a selective solution method; it cannot be used with platinum, which mercury does not dissolve.

Another example of selective solution is the Parkes process for removing the silver present in many lead ores. The ore is smelted to produce the liquid metals dissolved in one another, and about 2 per cent of zinc metal is stirred into the melt. Zinc and lead are mutually insoluble, but silver is much more soluble in zinc than in lead. The silver thus concentrates in the zinc phase which rises to the top of the lead layer when agitation ceases. The zinc layer solidifies first upon cooling and is broken up and removed from the still molten lead layer. The zinc and silver are separated by distilling the zinc, leaving solid silver. Note that *selective distillation*, as applied here and in the amalgamation methods, is also useful in enriching substances.

The prices of silver and gold, fixed by governments for currency and other reasons, are now so high that it is economically feasible to utilize ores containing such minute amounts of the metals that settling, amalgamation, and similar methods do not work. One method used on such highly dilute ores is treatment with a sodium cyanide solution in the presence of air. Both gold and silver ions form very stable complex ions with cyanide ion. The cyanide thus decreases still further the minute concentrations of gold and silver ions, normally formed by the oxidizing action of air (oxygen) on the metals, and allows the air oxidation process to proceed until practically all the gold and silver have been converted into the cyanide complexes. The gold and silver are precipitated from the complexes when metallic zinc is added. Equations 27.4 and 27.5 illustrate the reactions for silver.

$$2Ag_{(s)} + \tfrac{1}{2}O_2 + 4CN^- + H_2O = 2Ag(CN)_2^- + 2OH^- \qquad (27.4)$$

$$2Ag(CN)_2^- + Zn_{(s)} = Zn(CN)_4^{--} + 2Ag_{(s)} \qquad (27.5)$$

If the content of free metal in an ore is high, one can often separate the metal from the gangue by heating the ore above the melting point of the metal. The gangue usually has a higher melting point than the metal so that the pure metal may be run off and cast into ingots. Bismuth is commonly separated from its ores in this way.

GENERAL PROBLEM OF REDUCING A MINERAL TO THE METAL

We have already discussed the fact that the metallic elements form compounds in which the atoms assume positive oxidation numbers. These compounds may be ionic, molecular, or macromolecular in nature as pointed out in the discussion of the oxides in Chapter 25. In any case, the winning of the metal from these compounds must involve the use of a reducing agent which will change the oxidation number of the element from its positive value in the compound to an oxidation number of zero. Electrons must be supplied. Metallurgy of this type involves finding the cheapest reducing agent and the

METALS FROM ORES: METALLURGY   457

best conditions for its action on each enriched ore. The more electropositive the metal, the more powerful the reducing agents needed.

The reducing agents may be divided into four general classes: (1) The anion or anions present in the mineral may reduce the cation, usually at high temperatures. This method is particularly applicable to sulfide ores of the least electropositive metallic elements; when heated in air (roasted) they give the metal plus sulfur dioxide. The metal almost always contains some dissolved oxide and sulfide. (2) Carbon, in the form of coke, may be used as a reducing agent. Carbon is the cheapest reducing agent other than the anion of the mineral. However, since carbon is solid at feasible temperatures, it is usually converted to gaseous carbon monoxide which is then the active reducing agent. The gas can make good contact with the solid mineral and give a high rate of reaction. Some air is usually introduced into the system to help convert the carbon to the monoxide just as air is used in the roasting of sulfide ores to convert the sulfide to the dioxide. (3) More powerful chemical reducing agents, such as hydrogen, aluminum, or sodium, may be used if their expense can be covered by the cost of the product. (4) Electrolytic cells may be used to reduce the most electropositive cations, such as those of the alkali and alkaline earth elements, aluminum, etc. Electrolysis can be used only if the molten compound or its solution in some solvent is ionic.

METAL PRODUCTION BY ROASTING OF ORES IN AIR

Many minerals, particularly the sulfides, when heated in a limited supply of air, react to give a metal and a volatile product containing the material formerly present in the anion of the ore. For a sulfide ore this reaction may be represented by equation 27.6.

$$MS_{(s)} + O_{2(g)} = M_{(liq) \text{ or } (g)} + SO_{2(g)} \qquad (27.6)$$

It should be clear that the air supply must be carefully regulated so that oxides are not formed instead of the metal. This regulation is not difficult for the less electropositive metals such as mercury, copper, silver, and lead. The mercury produced by condensing its vapor formed in a reaction of this type is pure enough for immediate sale. When lead sulfide is roasted the more electropositive metals present as impurities in the lead are oxidized to their oxides by a slight excess of air. These oxides, being insoluble in the molten lead, can be skimmed off. The silver may be removed by the Parkes process.

The oxides of lead, silver, and copper are all somewhat soluble in their respective metals and are always produced to a slight extent in the roasting process, the copper being most seriously contaminated. When the liquid copper is stirred with green wood poles, the vapor released from these poles reduces most of the oxide to the metal. Further purification of the copper, or the lead or silver, may be accomplished by electrolytic refining which we shall discuss shortly.

Roasting of compounds of elements more electropositive than copper, mercury, lead, and silver leads to the formation of oxides as the end product plus sulfur dioxide gas. Equation 27.7 represents a typical reaction

$$MS_{(s)} + \tfrac{3}{2}O_{2(g)} = MO_{(s)} + SO_{2(g)} \tag{27.7}$$

These oxides must then be reduced if the metal is to be obtained. The sulfides of molybdenum, cobalt, nickel, zinc, cadmium, tin, arsenic, and antimony are commonly roasted to the corresponding oxide in this way. Occasionally sulfates as well as oxides are formed in the roasting process.

METAL PRODUCTION BY REDUCTION WITH CARBON (COKE)

All of the oxides produced by roasting of the above mentioned sulfides in air can be reduced to the metal by carbon in the form of coke. In addition, the oxides of iron, manganese, chromium, and tungsten are commonly reduced with coke. Tungsten is formed as a pure powder by this method but the iron, chromium, and manganese metals contain considerable quantities of dissolved carbon. When their usual minerals are reduced, chromium and manganese are produced as alloys with iron. Tungsten, molybdenum, cobalt, nickel, zinc, cadmium, tin, arsenic, and antimony are produced in a form pure enough for sale. However, it is occasionally profitable to separate traces of other metals by fractional distillation or electrolytic refining. Thus, cadmium may be distilled from the zinc metal, and arsenic from antimony.

The mechanism of the roasting reaction in sulfide ores is essentially interaction between gaseous oxygen and the ore; for carbon reduction of ores the mechanism can not be so simple since both the ore and coke are solids and hence are unable to come into intimate enough contact. Reactions between solids are known but they are always very slow. Industrial reactions must be rapid in order to produce profitable quantities of product per unit of time and of apparatus. Reduction of an oxide with carbon, therefore, almost invariably proceeds through a series of reactions typified by the equations

$$C_{(s)} + O_{2(g)} = CO_{2(g)} + 94{,}000 \text{ cal.} \tag{27.8}$$
$$41{,}000 \text{ cal.} + C_{(s)} + CO_{2(g)} = 2CO_{(g)} \tag{27.9}$$
$$CO_{(g)} + \underset{\text{ore}}{MO_{(s)}} = CO_{2(g)} + M_{(liq)} \tag{27.10}$$

The carbon dioxide produced in reactions such as 27.10 may again be reduced to carbon monoxide by the excess coke and so reduce still more ore. All the equations listed here describe reactions between gases and solids to give at least one gaseous product. Such reactions can proceed rapidly since the gas can make excellent contact with the solid, readily reach the reacting solid surface, and the gaseous product can readily diffuse away after reaction. See pages 87–90 for a discussion of the reactions between carbon and oxygen.

In most metallurgical processes the metal is produced at temperatures above its melting point as a liquid which separates from the solids and gases. It can then be tapped off from time to time and cast into ingots. The temperature may even be high enough so that appreciable amounts of metal can be condensed from the flue gases. Tungsten, with its very high melting point, is a notable exception and is produced as a powder. This powder is compacted into bulk metal by passing a heavy electric current through the powder, sintering it together. The bars so produced are then hammered, or cold worked, into a malleable product.

REDUCTION OF IRON ORE IN THE BLAST FURNACE: PRODUCTION OF PIG IRON

By far the largest scale metallurgical process using coke as a reducing agent is the blast furnace conversion of iron ore to pig iron. Enough ore is treated in this way to produce 10^9 tons of steel per year. The major component of steels is iron.

The principal iron ores are partly hydrated oxides containing varying quantities of impurities, mostly silicates. The ores are commonly referred to as "ferric oxide," though always more or less hydrous in nature. Their composition, as regards water content, lies between that of ferric oxide and that of ferric hydroxide.

The problem posed is to reduce the ore to metal, and to do it in such a way that the metal formed may be separated from the silicates which are less readily reduced by hot carbon. Unfortunately the silicates form a viscous, glassy substance at the optimum temperature for the reduction of the ore by coke. This viscous glass would coat the inside of the furnace and the molten iron produced by the reduction process, and so make it impossible to remove the molten contents of the furnace with any ease. Some silicates, as a matter of fact, do not even melt at blast furnace temperatures and would thus accumulate as solids within the furnace. Their periodic removal would be difficult to accomplish. Calcium oxide, however, lowers the melting points and increases the fluidity of these silicates so that they can form a layer of molten "slag" on the iron in the bottom of the furnace. The slag is less dense than the molten iron and floats on it. The molten slag is run off from time to time. It may be dumped as useless, dropped through a tall tower filled with water to granulate it into slag rock, or, in some cases, used in making cement.

Calcium carbonate (limestone) is added with the charge of coke and iron ore and is converted into calcium oxide at the blast furnace temperatures according to the equation

$$CaCO_{3(s)} = CaO_{(s)} + CO_{2(g)} \tag{27.11}$$

The calcium oxide then reacts with such substances as silica (sand), as in equation 27.12, to form the fluid slag.

$$CaO_{(s)} + SiO_{2(s)} = CaSiO_{3(liq)} \tag{27.12}$$

The reduction of the ore is accomplished through a series of reactions which may be represented by the equations

Major
$$\begin{cases} C_{(s)} + O_{2(g)} = CO_{2(g)} + 94{,}000 \text{ cal.} & (27.8) \\ C_{(s)} + CO_{2(g)} = 2CO_{(g)} - 41{,}000 \text{ cal.} & (27.9) \\ 3CO_{(g)} + Fe_2O_3 \cdot xH_2O_{(s)} = 2Fe_{(liq)} + 3CO_{2(g)} + xH_2O_{(g)} & (27.13) \\ \quad \text{red} \end{cases}$$

Minor
$$\begin{cases} C_{(s)} + H_2O = CO_{(g)} + H_{2(g)} & (27.14) \\ 3H_{2(g)} + Fe_2O_3 \cdot xH_2O_{(s)} = 2Fe_{(liq)} + (x+3)H_2O_{(g)} & (27.15) \\ \quad \text{red} \end{cases}$$

Minute $\quad \tfrac{3}{2}C_{(s)} + Fe_2O_3 \cdot xH_2O_{(s)} = 2Fe_{(liq)} + CO_{2(g)} + xH_2O_{(g)} \quad (27.16)$
$\qquad\qquad\qquad \text{red}$

Most of the reactions occurring in the blast furnace are endothermic. Thus energy must be supplied if the reaction temperatures are to be maintained. Equation 27.8 is exothermic (see page 87) so air is introduced near the bottom of the furnace to burn enough coke to keep the over-all temperatures at the desired level. It is highly desirable to minimize the amount of coke and air used for this purpose since no iron is produced directly by this reaction. Hence, the blast furnace is designed to conserve thermal energy and to use it as efficiently as possible. The air to burn the coke is introduced just above the slag level in the bottom of the furnace and the combustion zone, where the highest temperatures are attained, is just above this point. The hot gaseous products are removed at the top of the furnace. The crushed limestone, ore, and coke are introduced through ports at the top of the furnace and become preheated as they descend through the rising gas. Preheating of the solid charge uses up much of the thermal energy in the gases and brings the solids to high enough temperatures to permit reduction of most of the ore with formation of liquid iron in the region well above the combustion zone. An excess of carbon is always used and the last vestiges of oxide are reduced in the pool of molten iron and slag at the bottom of the furnace.

The gases leaving the top of the furnace are still hot. Their energy is conserved by passing them through towers, known as hot stoves, filled with a brick checker work which is thus heated. When the temperature of the interior of a given stove is nearing that of the exhaust gases, the gases are diverted to another stove. Air, on its way to the bottom of the blast furnace, is now run through the recently heated stove, so that the air is preheated before it enters the bottom of the furnace. In many instances a further economy is achieved by burning the cooled blast furnace gases, which contain appreciable quantities of carbon monoxide and hydrogen, under steam-generating boilers.

The types of *counter-current flow* used in blast furnace design to preheat the falling charge by cooling the escaping gases, and to preheat the entering air by further cooling the escaping gases, are typical of thousands of counter-current processes used in industry. It is always more efficient to have two reacting materials flowing in opposite directions as they react than it is merely to mix them or to have them flow in the same direction. In a counter-flow process the most completely reacted materials always meet the most concentrated reactants. The more concentrated the reactants the more the equilibria are shifted toward complete reaction, hence the greater the yield of the reaction. In the

METALS FROM ORES: METALLURGY 461

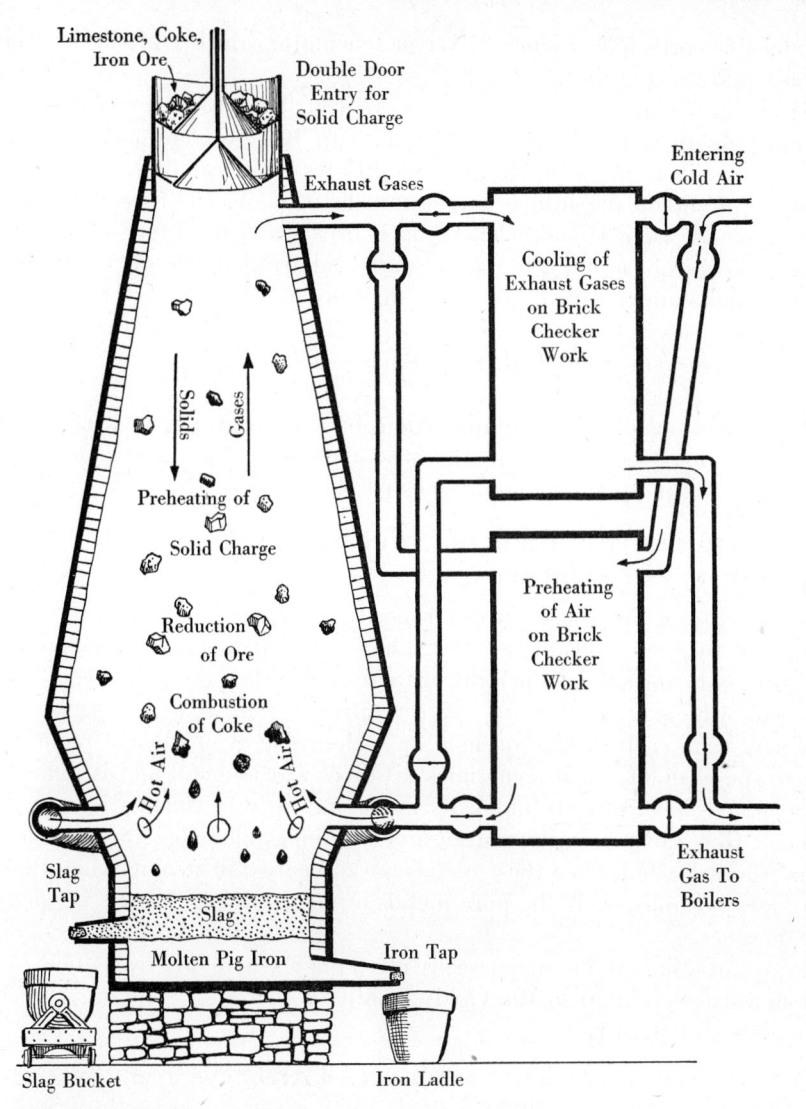

Figure 27.1.
Blast furnace for the production of iron (schematic).

blast furnace the reactant we have been discussing is thermal energy, but the same arguments hold for chemical reactants.

The tapering interior of the blast furnace is also an integral part of the design, the cross section being greatest where the temperature is highest, and, hence, where the gases occupy the most volume. Above and below this level the bore is smaller since the gases are progressively cooler. Such construction minimizes turbulence within the furnace and insures even operation of the counter-flow principle. Figure 27.1 is a schematic drawing of the iron blast furnace and its operation.

The blast furnace does not produce pure iron. The product, called *pig iron*, contains about 92 to 94 per cent of iron, 3 to 4 per cent of carbon, up to 2 per cent of silicon (from reduction of the silicates), and usually some sulfur and phosphorus. Some pig iron is recast into articles of commerce and is then known as cast iron. However cast iron is brittle and has limited uses. Practically all pig iron is refined to remove undesirable impurities and the iron then used to make alloys called steels. We shall discuss the alloys of iron and the making of steels in Chapter 32 where we shall consider the behavior of metals and alloys. Actually, very little pure iron is produced and then not in the blast furnace.

The reductions of other metallic oxides by carbon, while not performed on the tremendous scale found in the steel industry, follow the same general principles and methods as those discussed above.

METAL PRODUCTION BY REDUCTION WITH HYDROGEN, ALUMINUM, AND SODIUM

We have seen that the least electropositive elements may be reduced from their ores by the anions in the ores. The somewhat more electropositive elements may be formed by the reducing action of carbon on the oxide ores. The elements which are still more electropositive require reducing agents more powerful than carbon. Carbon may be undesirable even when it reduces the ore to the element, for it sometimes dissolves in the metal and is difficult to remove. We have already noted its dissolving in iron. Carbon is even more difficult to remove from its solution in chromium, manganese, and vanadium than from iron, but when these metals are to be used in steel making, the carbon does not matter. If the pure metals are desired they cannot be made in this manner.

Pure chromium and manganese are often made, therefore, by reducing their oxides with aluminum in the Goldschmidt, or thermite, reaction. For chromium the equation is

$$Cr_2O_{3(s)} + 2Al = 2Cr + Al_2O_{3(s)} \qquad (27.17)$$
$$\text{green}$$

These reactions are highly exothermic and produce liquid metals which may be run into molds. Columbium and tantalum may also be prepared in this way but not vanadium since some dioxide always remains in the vanadium. Aluminum cannot be used with titanium or zirconium to give pure metals directly because these metals dissolve appreciable quantities of the aluminum but the aluminum can be distilled from the zirconium alloy to give pure zirconium.

Hydrogen can reduce all the oxides reduced by carbon, but is more expensive than coke. The additional cost may be more than offset, however, by a more desirable product. Hydrogen can also reduce vanadium chloride, and columbium and tantalum oxides. It is the usual reducer for tungsten oxide. With some elements it forms undesirable hydrides.

Metallic sodium, a still more powerful reducing agent, is sometimes used to reduce the chlorides of titanium and zirconium, though metallic magnesium is now the commercial reducer. Sodium has been used in the past to prepare aluminum and the alkaline earth metals, but these very highly electropositive elements are now prepared almost entirely by electrolysis of molten salts.

METAL PRODUCTION BY ELECTROLYSIS OF FUSED SALTS

The most electropositive elements can be produced from their compounds with the use of only the most powerful reducing agents, but none of these powerful reducing agents exists in nature. For this reason the isolation of the alkali metals, the alkaline earth metals, aluminum, and the other fairly electropositive elements had to be antedated by Galvani's discovery of the electric battery. The subsequent discovery of the electric generator made the preparation of these elements commercially feasible, for generators can supply the high currents needed. A 10-ampere current (10 coulombs per second) common in households requires 9,650 seconds, or nearly 3 hours, for the passage of one faraday, which will produce one equivalent of metal: 23 grams of sodium, 12 of magnesium, or 9 of aluminum. The limiting factor in commercial metal production by electrolysis (in addition to cost) is the design of cells and cell conditions which give the desired products at sufficient rates and in such a way that they can be isolated.

For many years the electrolysis of fused sodium chloride was not commercially feasible. The Downs method solved the problem as outlined on page 319. The older Castner process of electrolyzing the low-melting sodium hydroxide, which had to be prepared from sodium chloride, is now obsolete. A good process for the production of metallic potassium is still badly needed.

Practically all the magnesium now made is produced by electrolysis of a fused bath of magnesium chloride containing some added solutes to lower the temperature and increase the over-all efficiency of the process. This process was discussed on pages 210 and 211. The other alkaline earth metals are produced in a similar fashion.

Problem 27.1. Why electrolyze chlorides rather than oxides? After all, the alkaline earth oxides are much more readily attainable, magnesium oxide for instance.

PRODUCTION OF METALLIC ALUMINUM BY ELECTROLYSIS

The problem of aluminum production by electrolysis is somewhat different from that of the alkali metals and the alkaline earth metals. The common ore, bauxite, is an oxide of very high melting point, and most molten aluminum compounds do not conduct an electric current. Aluminum forms a macromolecular oxide and molecular halides rather than ionic compounds. Since the liquids are either very hard to obtain, as with the oxide, or are nonconductive, as with the halides, electrolysis of aluminum seems out of the question. True, water solutions of its compounds are conducting but aluminum is too reactive a metal to be deposited from water solution. Hydrogen is formed instead.

The problem of the reduction of aluminum by electrolysis of its fused ores was originally solved by Hall in 1886. The identical process was discovered some weeks later by Heroult in France. It is interesting to note that the priority of Hall's discovery was settled in court on the basis of the testimony of Professor Jewett of Oberlin College. Jewett testified that Hall showed him the aluminum in Jewett's office in the chemistry building and, by a great coincidence,

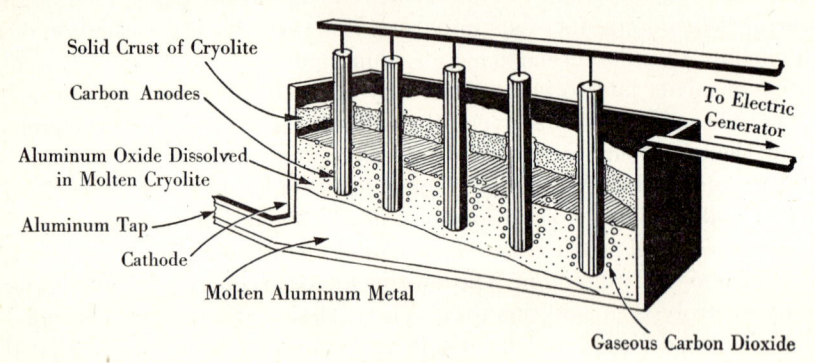

Figure 27.2.
Cell for producing aluminum from a fused salt bath.

the chemistry building was torn down in the interval between Hall's discovery and Heroult's. The phenomenon of simultaneous discovery, so well illustrated in the Hall process, is common in science and necessitates careful dating of experiments if priority is to be claimed.

Previous to Hall's work, aluminum was prepared by reducing its chloride, originally with potassium, then later with sodium. An electrolytic process would obviously be cheaper since the sodium itself had to be made by electrolysis. The problem was to find a molten salt bath in which aluminum compounds could be electrolyzed, preferably one in which aluminum oxide, the common ore of aluminum, could be dissolved and electrolyzed. Using batteries made of fruit jars and a blacksmith's forge to keep the salt baths molten, Hall tried to electrolyze many systems before he discovered that the aluminum mineral, cryolite, with the formula Na_3AlF_6, had the desired property of dissolving aluminum oxide at relatively low temperatures to give a conducting bath from which aluminum could be reduced. The method used today is essentially that of 70 years ago; it is interesting to note that the mechanism and theory of the process are still only partially understood.

In the modern electrolysis cell, liquid aluminum is deposited on a layer of retort coke covering the iron cell wall to form the cathode. The aluminum sinks

METALS FROM ORES: METALLURGY

to the bottom of the cell and is periodically removed. Bauxite and small amounts of cryolite are added to maintain the level of the electrolyte. The bath is kept molten (about 1200°C.) by the heating effect of the electrical current. Oxygen and carbon dioxide and carbon monoxide are produced at the carbon anodes, the carbon oxides predominating since the electrode reacts with the oxygen at the elevated operating temperatures. The electrode is slowly fed into the cell to replace the part burned away. The cell is diagrammed schematically in Figure 27.2.

ELECTROLYTIC REFINING

Many of the metals produced by the processes we have discussed contain small amounts of impurities. Even traces of impurities may be harmful for

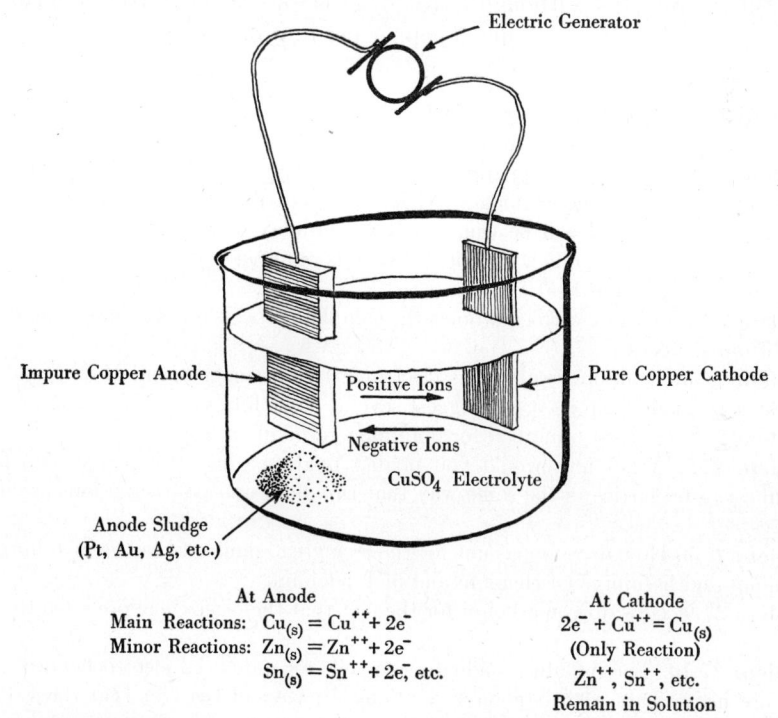

At Anode
Main Reactions: $Cu_{(s)} = Cu^{++} + 2e^-$
Minor Reactions: $Zn_{(s)} = Zn^{++} + 2e^-$
$Sn_{(s)} = Sn^{++} + 2e^-$, etc.

At Cathode
$2e^- + Cu^{++} = Cu_{(s)}$
(Only Reaction)
Zn^{++}, Sn^{++}, etc.
Remain in Solution

Figure 27.3.
Cell for purifying copper by electrolysis (schematic).

some uses. The conductivity of copper, for instance, is very markedly decreased by traces of certain elements such as arsenic, hence copper for electrical conductors must be very pure. Electrolytic refining can produce very pure metals.

Electrolytic refining involves the oxidation of a metal from an impure anode and its redeposition on a cathode of high purity. A solution of a salt of the

466 GENERAL CHEMISTRY

metal serves as electrolyte. The cell is an example of a concentration cell (see page 440) having electrodes with slightly different concentrations. The voltage applied to the cell is adjusted so that the more electronegative impurities are not oxidized at all but collect below the anode as an "anode sludge." This anode sludge, containing such elements as silver, gold, and platinum, often has sufficient worth to offset all of the cost of electrolysis. The more electropositive impurities in the anode are, of course, oxidized even more readily than the metal to be purified, but the voltage is kept low so that they are not reduced at the cathode but remain in solution.

In the electrolytic refining of copper, for instance, elements below copper in Table 26.1 are deposited in the anode sludge while those above copper in the table remain in solution as their ions. A schematic diagram for this process is given in Figure 27.3. Although the voltage is low, heavy currents must pass through the cell to transfer much copper per unit of time.

Problem 27.2. Summarize the principal metallurgical processes in terms of the electropositive nature of the element to be manufactured.

Problem 27.3. Diagram an apparatus for the electrolytic refining of nickel. What elements may be in the anode sludge? What elements will remain in solution as their ions? How much nickel will be transferred per faraday of electricity. If the voltage of the cell is 1 volt how much electrical energy is required per gram of nickel refined. (This energy appears as heat.)

Problem 27.4. Outline, with equations, the complete process for obtaining magnesium metal from the ocean.

Problem 27.5. Uranium is about as electropositive as magnesium. How would you suggest it be made from its ores? Suggest several possibilities.

Problem 27.6. Suggest a method for obtaining germanium from its ore.

Problem 27.7. What ions would you predict might be interchangeable with ferric ions in a crystal lattice in the same way that rubidium and potassium ions are interchangeable?

Problem 27.8. How do you account for the *very* great similarity in the metallurgy of zirconium and hafnium? Of rhenium and molybdenum?

Problem 27.9. How do you account for the fact that the bronze age preceded the iron age?

Problem 27.10. The metallic conductors to cells for industrial electrochemical processes are heavy bars with large cross sections. In view of the fact that the voltages used are low (on the order of a few volts) and that copper is expensive why do the builders of the cells use so much copper in this way?

Problem 27.11. In the Hall electrolytic cell the carbon electrodes are oxidized to carbon dioxide. What weight of carbon anode will be consumed for each mole of aluminum produced? For each pound of aluminum produced?

Problem 27.12. In the Hall electrolytic cell how many faradays of electricity are required to produce one pound of aluminum? If 12 kilowatt hours of electrical energy is required, what is the cell voltage?

Problem 27.13. Explain briefly the chemical basis of the "cyanide process" for extracting gold from low-grade ores.

METALS FROM ORES: METALLURGY   467

Problem 27.14. If 1 ml. of sea water contained 9×10^{11} atoms of gold, what would be the weight of the gold in a liter of sea water? A plant is to be built to extract this gold from sea water. It is expected that the plant will be obsolete and of no value twenty years from its construction date. During this twenty-year period 50,000,000 gal/day of sea water will be processed with 90 per cent removal of the gold. What must the total twenty-year budget of the company be if the average value of the gold obtained is $600 a pound? Would you invest in such a company?

28 THE HIGHLY ELECTRO-POSITIVE ELEMENTS

WE HAVE found the most highly electropositive elements to be those along the left side of the periodic table. The various criteria we have used—the ionic character of most of their compounds, including their oxides, the low values for the ionization potentials of the gaseous atoms, and the highly negative values for the single electrode potentials—all are aspects of the tendencies of the atoms of these elements to lose valence electrons and become cations. As groups the Group 1a elements are the most electropositive, the Group 2a elements less, and the Group 3 elements still less positive. However, electropositivity is one of the relationships following diagonals in the periodic table because the position of maximum electropositivity is in the lower left hand corner and the electropositivity of the elements decreases as they lie upward and to the right of this position. The effects are shown in the chemistries of the elements.

The Group 1a elements, the *alkali elements*, receive their name from the very strong bases, historically called alkalies, which they form. The Group 2a elements are called *alkaline earth elements*. The name "earth elements" is not commonly used for Group 3 except as it appears in the name, *rare earth elements*, which is applied to fourteen elements, cerium through lutetium, usually classed as a subgroup of Group 3. We shall discuss lanthanum and the rare earth subgroup in Chapter 29. The third elements from the left in each row of the periodic table are boron and aluminum, usually classified in Group 3a, and scandium, yttrium, and lanthanum, usually classified as Group 3b. These elements appear in our tabulations.

All the elements in these groups, except boron, crystallize as metals. Boron is not highly electropositive and does not form cations. It is included in the tabulations for completeness and to show how the border elements between the metallic and nonmetallic elements differ in properties from their neighbors. In Table 28.1 the elements are arranged in block form at the top and the properties are listed in a corresponding arrangement. This form of table permits direct comparison of numerical values with respect both to group and to period (row) in the periodic table. The student should study Table 28.1 in connection with the following discussion to see to what degree the data in the table support the general conclusions that are drawn and to see the relative magnitudes of differences.

THE ELEMENTS

The elements listed in Table 28.1 show wide variations in properties. The melting points range from room temperature to about 2000°C. The densities

Table 28.1

Properties of the Elements of Groups 1a, 2a, and 3

PERIOD	II	III	IV	V	VI
1. Elements: Group 1a Group 2a Group 3	Lithium Beryllium Boron	Sodium Magnesium Aluminum	Potassium Calcium Scandium	Rubidium Strontium Yttrium	Cesium Barium Lanthanum
2. Atomic number and symbol	3 Li 4 Be 5 B	11 Na 12 Mg 13 Al	19 K 20 Ca 21 Sc	37 Rb 38 Sr 39 Y	55 Cs 56 Ba 57 La
3. Atomic radius (covalent) in Å.	1.52 1.11 0.88	1.86 1.60 1.43	2.31 1.97 1.60	2.44 2.15 1.80	2.62 2.17 1.88
4. Ionic (+) radius (++) in Å. (+++)	0.60 0.31 —	0.95 0.65 0.50	1.33 0.99 0.81	1.48 1.13 0.93	1.69 1.35 1.15
5. Atomic weight	6.9 9.0 10.8	23.0 24.3 27.0	39.1 40.1 45.1	85.5 87.6 88.9	132.9 137.4 138.9
6. Density of element in grams per cm.^{3}	0.53 1.73 2.45	0.97 1.74 2.71	0.86 1.55 2.5	1.53 2.6 5.57	1.90 3.78 6.15
7. Melting point in °C.	180 1283 2040	98 650 660	63 850 1400	39 770 1500	29 704 880
8. Boiling point in °C.	1326 — —	889 1120 2327	757 — 3900	679 1384 4100	690 1638 —
9. Ionization potential (1st electron) in electron-volts	5.4 9.3 8.3	5.1 7.6 6.0	4.3 6.1 6.6	4.2 5.7 6.5	3.9 5.2 5.5
10. Single electrode potential in volts	−3.045 −1.85 —	−2.714 −2.37 −1.66	−2.925 −2.87 −2.08	−2.925 −2.89 −2.37	−2.923 −2.90 −2.52

range from a value one half that of water to a value six times that of water. The values of the ionization potentials for the removal of single electrons from the gaseous atoms show that the valence electrons for boron and aluminum are arranged differently than those for the atoms of the Group 3b elements.

All the elements in Group 1a crystallize as metals in the body-centered cubic system. In this crystal arrangement each atom is so situated that it has eight nearest neighbors, that is, eight other atoms with which it is in contact and to which it is bonded. This arrangement is slightly less compact than the face-centered cubic crystal system and the close-packed hexagonal system which have the closest possible packing of atoms all of one size. In these systems each atom has twelve nearest neighbors. The elements of Groups 2a and 3 crystallize in one or the other of these two closest-packed systems. Each of the atoms of the Group 2a and 3 elements have two or three valence electrons available for bonding with their twelve neighbors, but the atoms of the alkali elements have only one for bonding eight neighbors. The Group 3 elements have melting points somewhat lower, though not much lower, than those of the majority of elements in the middle of the long periods but the Group 2a elements with only two valence electrons per atom have melting points much lower than the average. The Group 1a elements have unusually low melting points for metals, and they are usually soft. These properties correlate with the weakness of the bonding in the crystals.

ATOMIC AND IONIC RADII

The volume occupied by a mole of substance depends primarily on the volumes attributable to the individual molecules or atoms but it also depends on the way these molecules or atoms are packed. The more loosely they are packed the more "free space" will be present in the mole of substance. We may avoid some of the difficulties in deciding how large atoms or molecules are by emphasizing the distances between atom centers. In a metal crystal the distances between the equilibrium positions of the atom centers (nuclei) may be measured precisely from observations on the diffraction of x-rays of known wave length. If the atoms are regarded as spheres the distance, d, between the centers of adjacent atoms is twice the radius, r, of each. The values of the atomic radii in part 3 of Table 28.1 were derived in this way. They represent one half the distance between the centers of atoms closest to one another in the crystal.

When metallic crystals are evaporated to form gaseous atoms, the centers of the latter, on collision, are farther apart than they were in the crystal. The van der Waals radii, calculated from the distance of closest approach of the gaseous atoms, are always larger than the atomic or covalent radius derived from distances between centers of bonded atoms. See also the discussion on page 312.

The calculation of ionic radii is somewhat more complicated. In potassium chloride crystals the internuclear distance between the potassium ions and the

THE HIGHLY ELECTRO-POSITIVE ELEMENTS 471

chloride ions is measured as 3.14 Å (see Figure 28.1). If, as is true, the potassium ion is smaller than the chloride ion we cannot divide the value, 3.14, by two to obtain the ionic radii. However, if we measure the interatomic distances for all the potassium halides and assume that the radius of the potassium ion remains constant, the differences in distance will represent the differences in radius of the halide ions. Similarly, the differences in the interatomic distances of the ions in the series LiCl, NaCl, KCl, RbCl, and CsCl will measure the differences in radius of the alkali ions. With such data, tables of the relative radii of the different ions can be calculated, and absolute values can be obtained if the radius of one ion can be fixed. The tables of relative radii give consistent values except for those obtained using lithium iodide, bromide, and chloride. Presumably the anions are actually in contact in these salts and the lithium ion does not "fill" the holes between the halide ions (see Figure 24.1). If the iodide ions are in contact in lithium iodide half the distance between iodide nuclei in the crystal can be taken as the radius of iodide ion. The radii of chloride and bromide ions are calculated similarly. Other ionic radii are then calculated from data on other crystals to give a consistent set. On the basis of wave mechanics Pauling calculated values for ionic radii which agree very well with those derived from measurements on crystals. Values for ionic radii are given in part 4 of Table 28.1.

Because the ionic radii represent the values for ions packed in crystals, they may not represent the radii of the ions in solution where the ions are separated from one another. We should not think of ions or atoms as rigid spheres with definite surfaces but rather as electronic systems whose range of influence depends on the nature of the other atoms surrounding them. You will observe that the ionic radii of the alkali elements are about 0.9 Å smaller than the atomic radii, which correspond to the covalent radii. Because the van der Waals radii, covalent radii, and

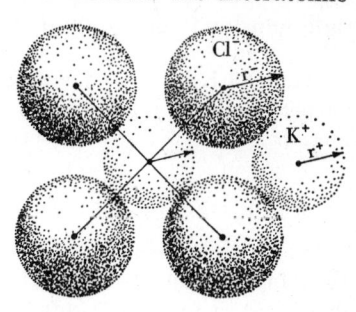

Figure 28.1.
Internuclear distance and ionic radii in potassium chloride (sodium chloride lattice). Radius, r^+, of potassium ion is 1.33 Å. Radius, r^-, of chloride ion is 1.81 Å.

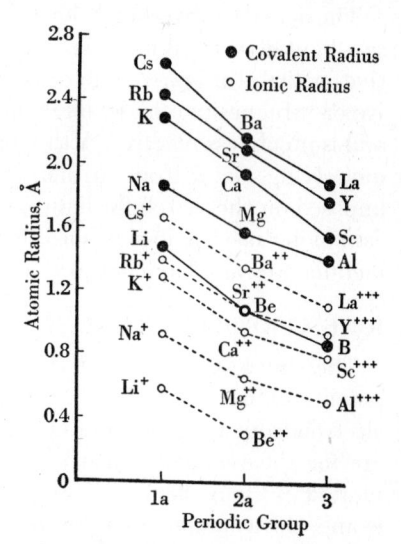

Figure 28.2.
Covalent and ionic radii of the highly electropositive elements.

472 GENERAL CHEMISTRY

ionic radii of the atoms of any element differ we must know what the nature of the bonding is before we can use the radii to calculate the effective volume of atoms in different types of compounds. Values for the metallic or covalent radii and for the ionic radii are plotted in Figure 28.2.

Problem 28.1. Using the known internuclear distances and the geometric arrangement for potassium chloride shown in Figure 28.1, calculate the shortest internuclear distance between chloride ions; between potassium ions.

DENSITY OF THE ELEMENTS

We have seen that the molar volumes of pure substances depend on the way the molecules and atoms are packed as well as on the radius of each atom. The density, the mass per unit volume, is influenced in the same way. For the alkali metals, all of which crystallize in the same crystal system, the densities of the bulk material are directly proportional to those of the individual atoms. Although the atomic volume increases for the series: lithium, sodium, potassium, rubidium, cesium, and the atomic weight increases in the same order (part 5, Table 28.1), the densities show a minimum for potassium (see part 6 of Table 28.1). This means that the increase in atomic radius of potassium over sodium more than compensates for the increase in atomic weight. For the higher elements in the series the atomic radius does not increase greatly so that the density must increase. The minimum in density found in the Group 1a series is found also in Groups 2a and 3, the minima occurring for the elements in Period III.

The density table shows the weight advantage of magnesium over aluminum as a light structural material. Calcium would be still lighter but it is too reactive in the atmosphere. Its oxide is soluble and reacts vigorously with water vapor. Magnesium oxide, like aluminum, forms an oxide which is less soluble and is much less reactive. A thin oxide film on the metal therefore protects the underlying metal from further corrosion. The table shows the natural limit imposed on the search for light structural materials among the metals. Metals cannot be used if lower densities are required but plastics made from non-metallic atoms of low density are now available.

IONIZATION POTENTIAL AND SINGLE ELECTRODE POTENTIAL

The simplest measure of the hold of atoms for electrons is the ionization potential, the value (in electron-volts) of the energy needed to remove an electron from a gaseous atom of the element. The values in part 9 of Table 28.1 are for the removal of a single electron from the gaseous atoms. They are plotted in Figure 28.3. For the Group 1a and 2a elements the electron removed is an s electron and the listed potentials are measures of the hold of the atom for such electrons, the $6s$ electron of cesium being least strongly held. For the Group 3 elements there are three valence electrons only two of which can be s electrons. The third electron of boron and aluminum (Group 3a) must be a p

electron ($2p$ or $3p$). Such an electron is more easily removed than an s electron, as the ionization potentials show. The third electron of scandium, yttrium, and lanthanum (Group 3b) is a d electron in a lower energy level. The electron assignments were given in the periodic table on pages 192–193, and on pages 189 and 190.

The single electrode potentials in part 10 of Table 28.1 are obtained from suitable electrochemical cells. For the Group 2a elements the order of values is what we expect from the ionization potentials of the gaseous elements, barium having the greatest tendency to give off electrons and beryllium the least. However, for the Group 1a elements the order is not regular. We would expect lithium to have the least tendency to form the ion but it has the greatest. The reason may be found in the high degree of hydration of the lithium ion. The hydrated ions have a lower tendency to accept electrons than might be expected from the known ionization potentials. They are stabilized by the strong hydration.

IONIC HYDRIDES

The strongly electropositive elements, those which form ionic oxides, also are the ones that form hydrides, saltlike in character. Examples are lithium hydride, formula LiH, and calcium hydride, formula CaH_2. In the hydrides, the electropositive elements form the cations and the hydrogen the anion. The electronic structure of the negative hydrogen ion, H^-, will be that of neutral helium. The ionic hydrides are colorless, crystalline compounds with high melting points. When the molten hydrides are electrolyzed hydrogen is evolved at the anode in the quantity predicted by Faraday's law. The hydrides of Group 1a crystallize according to the sodium chloride lattice. Each cation is surrounded by six H^- ions and each H^- ion by six cations. In water the hydrides decompose to form hydroxides and hydrogen

$$M^+H^-_{(s)} + HOH = H_{2(g)} + M^+ + OH^- \tag{28.1}$$

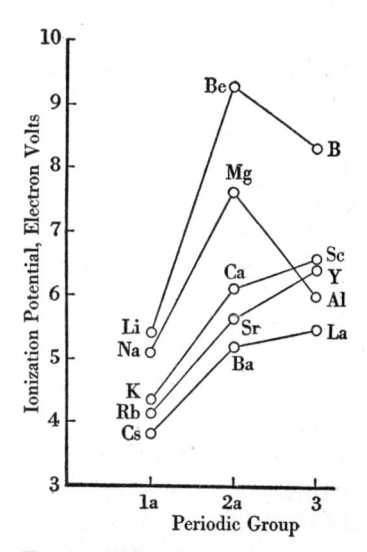

Figure 28.3. Ionization potentials of the highly electropositive elements.

Problem 28.2. Write half-reaction equations for the reaction in equation 28.1. What is the oxidizing agent? The reducing agent?

Lithium hydride is the most stable of the alkali hydrides and cesium hydride the least. Sodium hydride decomposes somewhat at its melting point and the higher hydrides, those of potassium, rubidium, and cesium, decompose below their melting points. Sodium hydride is used as a very effective reducing agent to remove scale (oxide) from fabricated metal parts.

$$MO_{(s)} + NaH = M_{(s)} + NaOH \tag{28.2}$$

The sodium hydroxide can then be washed from the metal leaving a clean surface for plating or polishing.

Although lithium hydride is the most stable of the Group 1a hydrides, beryllium and magnesium hydrides (Group 2a) are not stable. Evidently these cations are too small to give stable crystals with hydride anions. Calcium hydride is the most stable hydride of the alkaline earth group, followed by strontium hydride and barium hydride in decreasing order of stability. Recently an interesting compound, lithium aluminum hydride, with the formula $LiAlH_4$, has been prepared. It is a very effective reducing agent, useful in nonaqueous solvents for reducing organic compounds.

Problem 28.3. Diagram a possible electron structure for lithium aluminum hydride.
Problem 28.4. Predict how lithium aluminum hydride will react with water. Write the equation.

SALTS OF THE ALKALI ELEMENTS

Most of the chemistry of the alkali elements is the chemistry of the cations Li^+, Na^+, K^+, Rb^+, and Cs^+. Almost all the salts of these cations are water soluble. In water solution the salts furnish the anions and cations characteristic of the salt, and these ions hydrate or hydrolyze in their own characteristic ways. Although sodium and potassium are almost equally abundant in the earth's crust, deposits of sodium salts are more available, so that sodium salts are usually cheaper than the corresponding potassium salts. Therefore, when one wants some anion in solution one usually selects the sodium salt as the source. However, for analytical work requiring very pure reagents, potassium salts are often selected. The reason is to be found in the degree of hydration of the ions Na^+ and K^+. The former cation, being smaller, is more apt to be highly hydrated. Consequently, when the anhydrous sodium salt is exposed to air it is more likely to be hygroscopic than the corresponding potassium salt. In fireworks, for example, potassium nitrate is preferred to sodium nitrate as the solid oxidizer because it is less likely to become damp when exposed to air.

Because sodium chloride is the most available sodium mineral, most other sodium salts are ultimately prepared from it. Some may be prepared from sodium carbonate but the sodium carbonate is itself usually prepared from sodium chloride. Borax, sodium tetraborate, is "mined" directly as a mineral and source of borate ion, boric acid, boric oxide, and boron itself.

SODIUM CARBONATE

Although sodium carbonate is crystallized from the water of some desert lakes in California and Africa, most sodium carbonate, an important industrial

THE HIGHLY ELECTRO-POSITIVE ELEMENTS

chemical, is made according to the method of the Solvays of Belgium. The starting materials are sodium chloride and calcium carbonate. The products are sodium carbonate and calcium chloride. If the latter are dissolved in water and mixed, calcium carbonate precipitates, leaving a solution of sodium chloride. Consequently, it is obvious that the desired products cannot be made directly from the starting materials. However, by a roundabout method using acid-base reactions, one may obtain the desired products. In the Solvay process a salt brine is saturated, first with ammonia gas and then with carbon dioxide gas. When the solution is cooled to remove the heat of neutralization, sodium bicarbonate precipitates.

$$NH_{3(g)} + CO_{2(g)} + H_2O = NH_4^+ + HCO_3^- \tag{28.3}$$
$$Na^+ + Cl^- + NH_4^+ + HCO_3^- = NaHCO_{3(s)} + NH_4^+ + Cl^- \tag{28.4}$$

The solid sodium bicarbonate, when removed and heated, yields gaseous carbon dioxide and water and solid sodium carbonate.

$$2NaHCO_{3(s)} = Na_2CO_{3(s)} + CO_{2(g)} + H_2O_{(g)} \tag{28.5}$$

Limestone is a source both of the necessary carbon dioxide and of the base required to regenerate ammonia from the ammonium ion formed (see equation 28.3) and remaining after the precipitation (see equation 28.4).

$$CaCO_{3(s)} = CaO_{(s)} + CO_{2(g)} \tag{28.6}$$
$$CaO_{(s)} + H_2O = Ca(OH)_{2(s)} \tag{28.7}$$
$$Ca(OH)_{2(s)} + 2NH_4^+ + 2Cl^- = 2NH_{3(g)} + 2H_2O + Ca^{++} + 2Cl^- \tag{28.8}$$

Calcium chloride may be crystallized from the final solution and sold as a by-product.

Problem 28.5. Add the equations for the various steps in the Solvay process and find the resulting equation for the over-all reaction.

Anhydrous sodium carbonate is sold as *soda ash*. The name survives from the early method of extracting sodium carbonate from the ashes of sea plants. The carbonate may be used to neutralize strong acids because of the reaction

$$CO_3^{--} + 2H^+ = H_2O + CO_{2(g)} \tag{28.9}$$

carbon dioxide gas being evolved. In water, the carbonate ion hydrolyzes to form a basic solution

$$CO_3^{--} + HOH = HCO_3^- + OH^- \tag{28.10}$$

For domestic use the crystalline decahydrate, formula $Na_2CO_3 \cdot 10H_2O$, known as *washing soda*, is the usual form.

Potassium carbonate may not be prepared from potassium chloride by the Solvay process because potassium bicarbonate, the intermediate product, is not insoluble enough. A double salt of potassium bicarbonate with magnesium carbonate may be precipitated and the potassium carbonate recovered from

SODIUM BICARBONATE

Sodium bicarbonate, also called *baking soda*, is used as a mild base for neutralizing acids, and as a source of carbon dioxide in baking or in the soda-acid type of fire extinguisher. A water solution of bicarbonate is slightly basic because the hydrolysis reaction proceeds to a greater extent than the ionization of bicarbonate ion. Compare the corresponding phosphate solutions described on page 370.

$$HCO_3^- + HOH = H_2CO_3 + OH^- \qquad (28.11)$$

With an acid the reactions are represented by the equations

$$HCO_3^- + H^+ = H_2CO_3 \qquad (28.12)$$
$$H_2CO_3 = CO_{2(g)} + H_2O \qquad (28.13)$$

If baking soda is to be used as a source of carbon dioxide for leavening, the acid chosen must be rather weak. Otherwise, the carbon dioxide that is to make the bread or pastry light and porous is evolved before the structure is established in the baking process. Baking powders are mixtures of baking soda and some solid, weak acid. The acid must be solid and dry if it is not to react with the bicarbonate in the baking powder can. "Cream of tartar," potassium hydrogen tartarate with the formula $KHC_4H_4O_6$ was one of the first acids to be used in baking powder. Lactic acid, a liquid acid present in sour milk, is also an effective acid (but not proper in baking powder itself). "Phosphate" baking powders contain solid calcium dihydrogen phosphate, formula $Ca(H_2PO_4)_2$, as the acid. The $H_2PO_4^-$ ion is a weak enough acid for the purpose. In "alum" baking powders the acid is sodium aluminum sulfate, formula $NaAl(SO_4)_2$. At baking temperatures hydrolysis occurs extensively because water is ionized more extensively to form H^+ and OH^- ions than at room temperature. This produces hydrogen ions in sufficient concentration, through such reactions as

$$Al^{+++} + 3HOH = Al(OH)_{3(s)} + 3H^+ \qquad (28.14)$$

(Compare equations 25.24, 25.25 and 25.26, page 422.) Commercial baking powders often contain mixtures of the above acids.

THE ALKALI HALIDES

Sodium chloride and potassium chloride are the only alkali halides abundant enough as minerals to be prepared by crystallization from water solutions of the minerals. As we have already noted, they serve as starting compounds for the preparation of other salts. The fluorides may be prepared by action of hydrogen fluoride on the carbonates. For sodium fluoride the equation is

$$Na_2CO_{3(s)} + 2HF = 2NaF + H_2O + CO_{2(g)} \qquad (28.15)$$

Problem 28.6. What is a good commercial method for preparing hydrogen fluoride?

For the bromides and iodides a number of methods are available. Bromine and iodine, usually prepared as the free elements from sea water or from salt brines, according to the methods discussed in Chapter 20, are sources of the halogens.

Problem 28.7. Outline two methods for preparing sodium bromide from bromine.

SODIUM HYDROXIDE AND POTASSIUM HYDROXIDE

Several methods may be used to prepare sodium hydroxide from salt:
1. The sodium metal made from sodium chloride in a Downs cell may be treated with water vapor to produce a water solution of pure sodium hydroxide.

$$Na + HOH = Na^+ + OH^- + \tfrac{1}{2}H_{2(g)} \quad (28.16)$$

The method represented by equation 28.16 is restricted to laboratory preparation and is seldom used even there.

2. When a water solution of sodium chloride is electrolyzed, sodium hydroxide and hydrogen are produced at the cathode (see page 317). In the Hooker cell a mixture of sodium hydroxide and sodium chloride drip from the cathode. Most of the sodium chloride is separated by precipitation, but the sodium hydroxide made in this way is contaminated with chloride. About half of the commercial sodium hydroxide is made in this way.

3. In the Castner process, concentrated salt solutions are electrolyzed with a mercury cathode. Sodium produced at the mercury cathode dissolves in it to make a dilute amalgam. The amalgam may then be treated with water to form a water solution of sodium hydroxide. (Compare method 1.) This process makes pure sodium hydroxide.

$$Hg_{(liq)} + Na^+ + e^- = Hg(Na)_{(liq)} \quad (28.17)$$
$$Hg(Na)_{(liq)} + HOH = Hg_{(liq)} + Na^+ + OH^- + \tfrac{1}{2}H_{2(g)} \quad (28.18)$$

4. About half of the sodium hydroxide of commerce is prepared by an older method. A water solution of sodium carbonate is treated with a calcium hydroxide slurry, calcium carbonate being precipitated.

$$2Na^+ + CO_3^{--} + Ca(OH)_{2(s)} = CaCO_{3(s)} + 2Na^+ + 2OH^- \quad (28.19)$$

In all the methods 1 to 4 sodium chloride was the original source of the sodium ion in the hydroxide. The methods described may also be applied to making potassium hydroxide.

Problem 28.8. Since reaction 28.19 is commercially feasible, what may you deduce about the relative costs of sodium carbonate and sodium hydroxide as commercial bases?

THE ALKALI NITRATES

In connection with nitrates in Chapter 19 we noted that potassium nitrate was once mined in small beds as saltpeter and that sodium nitrate is still mined in Chile as Chile saltpeter. However, some sodium nitrate is now prepared synthetically by treating sodium carbonate with nitric acid made from atmospheric nitrogen and oxygen. Potassium nitrate is prepared from sodium nitrate and potassium chloride by a simple method based on the fact that sodium chloride, especially at high temperatures is much less soluble in water than potassium nitrate, sodium nitrate, or potassium chloride. When hot concentrated solutions of sodium nitrate and potassium chloride are mixed, sodium chloride precipitates.

$$Na^+ + NO_3^- + K^+ + Cl^- = NaCl_{(s)} + K^+ + NO_3^- \qquad (28.20)$$

Most of it can be separated from the solution by evaporation before potassium nitrate begins to precipitate.

THE ALKALI SULFATES

Although the sulfates of sodium and potassium occur in minerals and are isolated to some extent from these sources, they are also prepared from other sources. For example, sodium sulfate is the by-product, "salt cake," remaining when hydrogen chloride is made by heating sodium chloride with sulfuric acid.

REACTIONS OF THE ALKALI CATIONS IN ANALYSIS

The common salts of the alkali elements are so soluble that the cations remain in solution after the cations of the other analytical groups have been precipitated in the group reactions. There is no anion that will precipitate all the cations of the alkali elements quantitatively. Lithium ions may be precipitated with fluoride ions, phosphate ions, or carbonate ions (see Table 24.1), but not quantitatively, for the salts are appreciably soluble. Sodium ions may be precipitated as the antimonate, formula $NaSb(OH)_6$, the precipitating ion being obtained from the more soluble potassium antimonate. Sodium ions are also precipitated in a triple acetate, the other cations being the uranyl ion UO_2^{2+} and a doubly charged cation such as magnesium ion or zinc ion. The formula of the sodium zinc uranyl acetate is $NaZn_2(UO_2)_2(C_2H_3O_2)_9 \cdot 6H_2O$.

A greater number of relatively insoluble salts of potassium, rubidium, and cesium are known and their solubilities follow a regular series as a function of cation radius. The ammonium ion behaves similarly to the potassium ion. This fact is important because, in analytical separations, ammonium chloride is often added so that ammonium ions will be present. Chloroplatinic acid, formula H_2PtCl_6, gives a yellow precipitate with K^+ ions

$$2K^+ + PtCl_6^{--} = K_2PtCl_{6(s)} \qquad (28.21)$$
$$\text{yellow}$$

About 1 gram of the potassium chloroplatinate is soluble in 100 grams of water but the precipitate is practically insoluble in a 75 per cent alcohol solution. Cesium chloroplatinate is less soluble than potassium chloroplatinate and rubidium chloroplatinate has an intermediate solubility. In general, no single reagent would enable one to separate K^+, Rb^+, and Cs^+ ions quantitatively in a single precipitation. Other salts of these ions (and ammonium ion) that are relatively insoluble are the perchlorates and the cobaltinitrites (with sodium ion). For K^+ ions the equations are

$$K^+ + ClO_4^- = KClO_{4(s)} \quad \text{white} \tag{28.22}$$

$$2K^+ + Na^+ + Co(NO_2)_6^{---} = K_2NaCo(NO_2)_{6(s)} \quad \text{yellow} \tag{28.23}$$

The sodium ions will be present because sodium cobaltinitrite is the reagent used.

Because it is so difficult to find satisfactory precipitating agents for the alkali cations and because these ions when heated in a flame emit characteristic colors, the cations are often identified by the flame colors. The light from the flame may be passed into a spectroscope which separates the light of different wave lengths so that the images of the slit appear in different colors as separate lines. With a modern "flame spectrophotometer" one can measure the intensities of different lines produced by standard solutions containing known concentrations of the ions and compare them with the intensities produced by the "unknown" solution. In this way one may rapidly analyze solutions containing sodium and potassium ions, for example. The characteristic flame colors are: lithium, red; sodium yellow; potassium, violet; rubidium, bluish red; and cesium, blue. The yellow flame test for sodium is very delicate. Almost all substances in a laboratory, including distilled water kept in glass vessels, contain enough sodium ions to give the test. One must take this fact into account when testing for sodium ions in higher concentrations.

OCCURRENCE OF THE ALKALINE EARTH ELEMENTS

Calcium is the fifth most abundant element in the lithosphere and magnesium the seventh. (See Table 7.1.) The other elements of the Group 2a elements are much less abundant but are widespread. They are found in some silicates, for example. Among the more important minerals serving as sources of the elements are the following with their formulas: beryl, $3BeO \cdot Al_2O_3 \cdot 6SiO_2$; magnesite, $MgCO_3$, dolomite, $MgCO_3 \cdot CaCO_3$; limestone, $CaCO_3$; gypsum, $CaSO_4 \cdot 2H_2O$; strontianite, $SrCO_3$; celestite, $SrSO_4$; and barite, $BaSO_4$. Magnesium chloride is present in appreciable quantities in sea water. The calcium minerals fluorite, formula CaF_2, and calcium phosphate are used as commercial sources for the anions.

THE ALKALINE EARTH METALS

A general method for preparing the alkaline earth elements is electrolysis of their molten chlorides or fluorides, sometimes mixed with alkali halides to lower the melting temperatures. Large amounts of metallic magnesium are prepared in this way from magnesium chloride. The largest use of magnesium is in light alloys. The metals of the group are used as "getters" in vacuum tubes to remove the last traces of gases such as oxygen, nitrogen, and water vapor. They are also used as reducers to remove the last traces of oxides from other metals.

THE SALTS OF THE ALKALINE EARTH CATIONS

The cations of the alkaline earth elements, all doubly charged, form the usual salts with anions. In general, the salts formed with singly charged anions such as Cl^- and NO_3^- ions are fairly soluble but those with the doubly charged or triply charged anions are rather insoluble. Beryllium and magnesium ions are somewhat exceptional. Their sulfates are soluble, hydrated magnesium sulfate, formula $MgSO_4 \cdot 7H_2O$, being sold as Epsom salts. Calcium sulfate hemihydrate, formula $CaSO_4 \cdot \frac{1}{2}H_2O$, made by heating gypsum to drive out water, is known as plaster of Paris. When mixed with water it sets slowly as the crystalline dihydrate is re-formed.

We have already found that beryllium and magnesium hydroxides are insoluble. When Be^{++} and Mg^{++} ions are treated with a carbonate solution, alkaline because of hydrolysis, the basic carbonate rather than the carbonate is usually precipitated. The magnesium compound has the formula $Mg(OH)_2 \cdot 3MgCO_3$. The carbonates of calcium, strontium, and barium are more insoluble, and the hydroxides are appreciably soluble so that Ca^{++}, Sr^{++}, and Ba^{++} ions are precipitated as the carbonates. The solubilities of the carbonates are comparable to those of the corresponding sulfates. Consequently, when the crystalline sulfates are treated with a concentrated solution of carbonate ion they are partially converted to the carbonates. When fused with sodium carbonate they are converted quantitatively to carbonates.

$$BaSO_{4(s)} + CO_3^{--} = BaCO_{3(s)} + SO_4^{--} \tag{28.24}$$

The carbonates may then be washed free of sulfate and dissolved in hydrochloric acid.

The soluble salts of the alkaline earth cations may be prepared by treating the carbonates or hydroxides with the acids furnishing the appropriate anions. Even as weak an acid as carbonic acid will attack the carbonates. For example, when ground waters containing some dissolved carbon dioxide trickle over limestone or dolomite they react to form somewhat soluble bicarbonates

$$CaCO_{3(s)} + H_2CO_3 = Ca^{++} + 2HCO_3^- \tag{28.25}$$

In this way calcium and magnesium ions enter the water, making it "hard." Limestone caves, some of them large and spectacular, were made by this process.

Barium sulfate is converted commercially into barium sulfide by heating with coke. Any desired barium salt may then be prepared by treating the barium sulfide with the appropriate acid.

THE HIGHLY ELECTRO-POSITIVE ELEMENTS 481

$$BaSO_{4(s)} + 4C_{(s)} = BaS_{(s)} + 4CO_{(g)} \quad (28.26)$$
$$\text{black}$$
$$BaS_{(s)} + 2HX = Ba^{++} + 2X^- + H_2S_{(g)} \quad (28.27)$$

SOFTENING OF WATER

The undesirable ions found in hard waters are commonly Ca^{++}, Mg^{++}, SO_4^{--}, and HCO_3^- ions. Hard waters are considered undesirable for two principal reasons: (1) When the usual soaps—sodium or potassium salts of certain fatty acids—are added to hard waters, the calcium or magnesium soaps, which are insoluble, precipitate. In this way soap is wasted and an undesirable curdy precipitate remains. (2) When hard waters are heated, bicarbonate ions are decomposed into carbonate ions and carbon dioxide, which is driven off, and calcium or magnesium carbonates are precipitated.

$$2HCO_3^- \xrightarrow{\text{heat}} CO_3^{--} + H_2O + CO_{2(g)} \quad (28.28)$$
$$Ca^{++} + CO_3^{--} = CaCO_{3(s)} \quad (28.29)$$

The precipitate coats the heating pipes, filling them and cutting down heat transmission from the heater to the water. The hardness removed by heating, as in equations 28.28 and 28.29, is called *temporary hardness*. In a boiler, the water, when evaporated, leaves behind as hard residues any calcium or magnesium sulfates that were present in the water. Furthermore, calcium sulfate is less soluble in hot than cold water so it precipitates, forming "scale," when its solution is heated.

Because sodium salts and sodium soaps are soluble it it usually sufficient in a water softening process to replace the calcium and magnesium ions with sodium ions. Two types of processes are in common use.

1. The Lime-Soda Process

Let lime be added in sufficient quantity to change bicarbonate ion to carbonate ion and to precipitate the magnesium ions as the hydroxide.

$$Ca(OH)_{2(s)} + Ca^{++} + 2HCO_3^- = 2CaCO_{3(s)} + 2HOH \quad (28.30)$$
$$Ca(OH)_{2(s)} + Mg^{++} = Mg(OH)_{2(s)} + Ca^{++} \quad (28.31)$$

Then let sodium carbonate be added to precipitate the remaining calcium ions as calcium carbonate.

$$Na_2CO_{3(s)} + Ca^{++} = CaCO_{3(s)} + 2Na^+ \quad (28.32)$$

The softened water will contain the added sodium ions, the original sulfate ions, and the very small concentrations of calcium ion and magnesium ion that are in equilibrium with solid calcium carbonate and magnesium hydroxide, respectively.

2. The Ion Exchange Process

Certain naturally occurring silicates, called zeolites, and some synthetic resins are porous solids containing large polymeric anions together with sodium ions. When hard waters are trickled through the zeolites or resins the calcium and magnesium ions are held more strongly than the sodium ions. They displace the sodium ions so that the effluent water contains Na^+ ion rather than Ca^{++} or Mg^{++} ions. If R^- represents a monomeric unit of the polymeric anion the reactions may be represented by the equation

$$2NaR_{(s)} + Ca^{++} = CaR_{2(s)} + 2Na^+ \tag{28.33}$$

The reactions are reversible. Therefore the zeolite or resin can be regenerated by passing a salt brine through it, sweeping out the calcium and magnesium ions and replacing them with sodium ions. When the brine is washed out and discarded the softener is ready for reuse. For the regeneration, equation 28.33 is read from right to left.

Some modern resins are called acid exchangers, and others base exchangers. The acid exchanger combines with the cations of salts, replacing them with H^+ ions. The base exchanger replaces the anions of salts with OH^- ions. When hard water is passed in sequence through the two types of exchangers, the H^+ and OH^- ions neutralize one another, forming water. In this way "demineralized," or ion-free, water is made. It can be almost equal to the best distilled water in freedom from ions.

ANALYTICAL REACTIONS OF THE ALKALINE EARTH CATIONS

Sodium and ammonium sulfides do not precipitate the alkaline earth cations because their sulfide ions are hydrolyzed too extensively to exceed the concentrations allowed by the solubility product constants of the alkaline earth sulfides. The cations, therefore, remain in solution after Analytical *Group IV* has been precipitated. Ammonium carbonate precipitates the carbonates of calcium, strontium, and barium, and sometimes the basic carbonate of magnesium, formula $Mg(OH)_2 \cdot 3MgCO_3$. The latter does not precipitate if a high concentration of ammonium ions is present to decrease the concentration of hydroxide ions. Then the Mg^{++} ions appear in Analytical *Group VI* and only calcium, strontium, and barium carbonates are precipitated in Analytical *Group V*. Differences in solubilities of the chromates permit isolation of barium chromate, formula $BaCrO_4$. Calcium ions may be separated from strontium ions by adding oxalate ions.

$$Ca^{++} + \underset{\text{oxalate ion}}{C_2O_4^{--}} = \underset{\text{white}}{CaC_2O_{4(s)}} \tag{28.34}$$

Calcium oxalate is often separated for quantitative determinations. Barium sulfate is the usual barium compound weighed in quantitative analysis. Magnesium ions are precipitated quantitatively in the phosphate, formula $MgNH_4PO_4 \cdot 6H_2O$, and beryllium ions in the hydroxide.

The chlorides or other volatile compounds of calcium, strontium, and barium when heated in a flame give colors characteristic of the cations. The colors are: calcium, dull red; strontium, bright red; barium, green. In a spectroscope the characteristic lines are separated so that quantitative determination of the amounts present can be made.

THE GROUP 3 ELEMENTS

The properties of the third elements from the left end of each row in the periodic table on page 153 vary a great deal more than those of Groups 1a and 2a. The element of lowest atomic number, boron, forms no simple positive ions, existing only in anions and molecular structures in its compounds. Boron is essentially nonmetallic in nature, preferring to share electrons rather than to lose them to form ions, which would have to have a very large charge density. We shall not discuss its chemistry here for boron is not a highly electropositive element. On the other hand, actinium, the element in Group 3 with highest atomic number, is as electropositive as calcium.

The very wide use of metallic aluminum (or its alloys) in structural materials exposed to severe weathering conditions might lead one to the conclusion that aluminum is not highly electropositive. Actually the ionization potential of its gaseous atoms is lower than that of magnesium and about equal to that of potassium. (See Table 28.1.) Its single electrode potential in water (see Table 28.1) is also high. Aluminum is, therefore, a highly electropositive element in spite of its apparent inertness to chemical reaction.

The elements in Group 3b—scandium, yttrium, lanthanum and the rare earth subgroup, and actinium—are even more electropositive than aluminum, but we shall discuss them in the next chapter. We shall not discuss the Group 3a elements: gallium, indium, and thallium. Many of their properties can be deduced from their positions in the periodic table.

ALUMINUM

Aluminum exhibits only one oxidation state, 3+, which is characteristic of its position in the periodic system. Its chemistry in water solution is primarily the chemistry of aluminum hydroxide and the ions obtainable from it as the acidity of the solution varies. Most of this chemistry has already been discussed on pages 422 and 424 where the amphoteric nature of the hydroxide was interpreted in terms of the aluminum-containing substances which exist in acid, neutral, and basic solutions. The hydroxide itself is very insoluble in neutral water and even in slightly acid and basic solutions, such as those found in rain water and tap water. Furthermore the hydroxide and the oxide adhere very strongly to an aluminum surface once they form there. It is for this reason that aluminum appears to be so chemically inert. The surface which is actually exposed, and which is inert, is one of aluminum oxide, or hydroxide, or an intermediate composition. Aluminum itself reacts rapidly with water and oxygen, even when cold, and immediately becomes covered by an oxide layer.

The reaction of metallic aluminum with water may be demonstrated by placing a drop of mercury on an aluminum surface. Eventually the mercury will work its way through the oxide coat. Scraping away the oxide beneath the mercury greatly accelerates the process. In contact with the aluminum, the mercury forms an amalgam to which aluminum oxide does not adhere. Thus metallic aluminum, dissolved in mercury, will be exposed to chemicals in contact with the amalgam. If the amalgamated surface is held under water, bubbles of hydrogen will form on the surface. Even in ordinary moist air the rate of reaction is rapid. Long "whiskers" of aluminum hydroxide grow on the surface of the amalgam and hydrogen gas is formed as in equation 28.35

$$Al_{(s)} + 3H_2O = Al(OH)_{3(s)} + \tfrac{3}{2}H_{2(g)} \tag{28.35}$$

It is well known that aluminum pots become shiny when beets, apple sauce, or fruit juices are heated in them. The juices of all these foods are acid. The acid removes part of the oxide layer from the aluminum pan and the underlying aluminum is dissolved by the water. Fortunately, all food acids are sufficiently weak so that the complete solution of the pan takes a very long time. In the early days of aluminum cooking utensils some claims were made that the dissolved aluminum had deleterious, not to say poisonous, effects on human beings. The falsity of this statement has been well attested by millions of people who refuse to show the expected symptoms, but the charge is still heard occasionally.

Even the metallurgy of aluminum is essentially concerned with the chemistry of aluminum oxide as discussed on pages 455 and 463.

THE ALUMS

The alums are a set of common compounds often containing aluminum. They have the type formula $M'Q'''(SO_4)_2 \cdot 12H_2O$. Here M' can be any of a number of singly charged positive ions such as sodium, potassium, ammonium, thallium, rubidium ions, etc., and Q''' can be any of a large number of triply charged positive ions. Alums containing 3+ aluminum, chromium, iron, titanium, vanadium, manganese, cobalt, gallium, indium, ruthenium, and iridium are known. All of the possible combinations do not occur since the relative sizes of the singly and triply charged ions must be complementary. They must fit into the single crystal structure which is characteristic of all alums. No lithium alums, for instance, are known. The position of the water molecules in the alums has been definitely established by x-ray diffraction. Six of the water molecules are coordinated to the singly charged positive ion, and six to the triply charged positive ion. This fact may account for the lack of a lithium alum since the normal maximum coordination number of the small lithium ion is four.

ALUMINUM HALIDES

Aluminum chloride, whose formula is often written $AlCl_3$, sublimes at 180°C. and has a gas density corresponding to the formula Al_2Cl_6 at low temperatures. Its molecular weight in nonpolar solvents also indicates the formula Al_2Cl_6. In this interesting molecule each aluminum atom is coordinated to

THE HIGHLY ELECTRO-POSITIVE ELEMENTS 485

four chlorine atoms, two of the chlorine atoms being shared in common by the aluminum atoms. These two chlorine atoms form a planar, four-membered ring of atoms with the two aluminum atoms. (See Figure 28.4.) The other four chlorine atoms, two bonded to each aluminum atom, lie in a single plane at right angles to that of the four-membered ring. The bromide and iodide are similar, but the fluoride is a high melting (1290°C.), macromolecular substance.

The tendency of aluminum to coordinate the halogens is also shown by the existence of the very stable complex ion, $AlCl_4^-$. Higher complexes are also known as in cryolite, which has the AlF_6^{---} ion. The stability of the chloride complex accounts for the rapid corrosion of metallic aluminum in salt water. The surface layer of oxide reacts with the chloride ion to form $AlCl_4^-$ ion. Some of the early aluminum alloys failed to stand up structurally because of this corrosion.

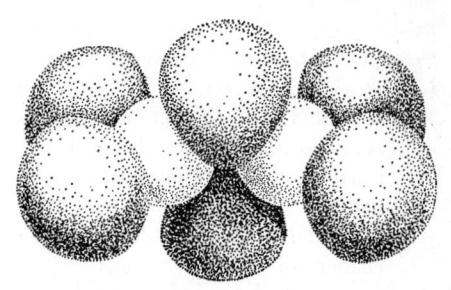

Figure 28.4.
Structure of aluminum chloride, Al_2Cl_6.

Problem 28.9. Interpret the tendency of aluminum chloride to exist as a dimer rather than as a monomer in terms of the electron structures of the monomer and dimer.

Problem 28.10. Crystallization of aluminum chloride from water gives a product of composition, $AlCl_3 \cdot 6H_2O$. Aluminum oxide forms when this is heated. Write an equation for the reaction. How would you prepare anhydrous aluminum chloride?

Problem 28.11. Explain why sodium bicarbonate is baking soda and sodium carbonate is washing soda and not vice versa.

Problem 28.12. Which of the elements in Group 1a (a) is most abundant, (b) has the largest atomic radius, (c) is a constituent of ordinary soap, (d) is important in commercial fertilizers? Compare lithium and potassium as to (e) atomic number, (f) colors imparted to flames, (g) ease of removal of an electron from the gaseous atom, (h) single electrode potential.

Problem 28.13. Outline the Solvay process for preparing sodium carbonate by writing net reactions for each step in the process. There are four or five steps. Why is potassium bicarbonate not prepared by the Solvay process?

Problem 28.14. Give two methods for testing for the presence of potassium ion in solution.

Problem 28.15. From top to bottom of Group 2a, how do the following properties change: (a) atomic weight, (b) solubility of chlorides, (c) solubility of hydroxides, (d) solubility of sulfates, (e) atomic radius, (f) ease of loss of electrons, (g) density of solid elements?

Problem 28.16. On a certain day Oberlin raw water contained 2.5 millimoles of calcium bicarbonate, 1.1 millimoles of calcium sulfate, and 0.4 millimoles of magnesium sulfate per liter. How many moles of lime and soda ash were required to soften one liter of this water? How many grams of each were required for 1000 cubic feet of water?

Problem 28.17. Which of the following pairs can exist together in the same solution at 0.01 M concentration without appreciable chemical combination? If chemical combination occurs, list the products formed: (a) Ba^{++} and SO_4^{--} ions, (b) Mg^{++} and OH^- ions, (c) Sr^{++} and Cl^- ions, (d) Ca^{++} ion and carbonic acid, (e) OAc^- and CO_3^{--} ions.

Problem 28.18. State very briefly the distinction between "temporary hardness" and "permanent hardness" in water. For each kind, give two methods that may be used for softening the water.

Problem 28.19. State what may be observed in each experiment below. Interpret all observations, write equations for any net reactions, and interpret any differences.
  a. Carbon dioxide is bubbled through a solution of calcium hydroxide until no further change will occur.
  b. Carbon dioxide is bubbled through a solution of calcium chloride until no further change will occur.

Problem 28.20. Explain very briefly the mechanism of formation of limestone caves and the relation to "hard water."

Problem 28.21. How would you prepare (a) pure solid calcium sulfate from solid calcium carbonate, (b) pure solid calcium carbonate from solid calcium sulfate, (c) solid calcium chloride from solid calcium sulfate?

Problem 28.22. How could you decide whether solutions of each of the following contains the impurity named: (a) sodium carbonate in sodium hydroxide solution, (b) potassium chloride in sodium chloride solution, (c) barium chloride in barium nitrate solution?

Problem 28.23. Give a practical use for each of the following: (a) calcium sulfate hemihydrate, (b) barium sulfate, (c) magnesium oxide, (d) metallic calcium, (e) calcium carbide.

Problem 28.24. If you wish to use a large quantity of sodium carbonate in water solution and find that the price per pound of washing soda is half that of soda ash which would you buy? Give your reasons.

29 THE RARE EARTH ELEMENTS, AND SCANDIUM AND YTTRIUM

MENDELEEFF'S FIRST periodic table, based on many incorrect atomic weights, listed the element erbium as following calcium, and the elements cerium, lanthanum, and dysprosium as following strontium. He knew of no analogous elements to follow barium and left spaces there for future elements. In the years since Mendeleeff proposed the periodic table, the atomic weights of the above four elements have been shown to be slightly greater than that of barium, so that they must immediately follow it in the periodic arrangement. Furthermore eleven more elements, making fifteen in all, have been discovered whose chemistry is very similar to the first four and whose atomic weights also put them in the sequence immediately following barium. Mendeleeff's original table left room for four elements between barium and what we now call hafnium, but his improvements and those of others cut this space to leave room for only one element (see page 153). The work of Moseley proved, however, that there were fifteen elements which indubitably belonged between barium and what we now call hafnium in the periodic arrangement, not just one.

Much effort was wasted in trying to force the rare earth elements into early forms of the table, and in decrying their "eruption" as spoiling the symmetry of the early tables. Since much of their chemistry is almost identical regardless of the element, it became customary to put all fifteen elements in one place in the periodic table, to treat them almost as a vagary of nature, and to neglect them as unimportant either to theory or practice. The rise of the electronic and nuclear theory of the elements since 1920 at last gave a reasonable interpretation of the occurrence of these elements and their relationship to the other elements. The atomic energy project gave great impetus to intensive research into their chemistry since they are among the most common of the fission products in neutron chain fission processes. Furthermore it is now realized that a study of these elements gives an unparalleled opportunity to study the effect

488 GENERAL CHEMISTRY

of gradual changes in atomic properties—such as size and electron structure—on the gross chemical and physical properties of elements and their compounds.

OCCURRENCE IN NATURE

The name "rare" earth elements attached to elements 57 through 71 is somewhat of a misnomer. Cerium, for instance, is more abundant than the well-known elements: cadmium, mercury, tin, tungsten, antimony, or bismuth.

All of the rare earth elements are highly electropositive, so that they are difficult to prepare as metals. The most common raw material source is monazite, formula $CePO_4$, and the alluvial sands in which monazite tends to concentrate with other rare earth compounds. Fluoride, carbonate, and silicate minerals are also known. The rare earth elements are listed in Table 29.1 together with their relative abundance and the number of stable isotopes of each found in nature. The actual abundance of each in the earth's crust may be calculated from the fact that cerium constitutes about 0.001 per cent of the crust. The greater rarity of the elements of odd atomic number and the small number of their isotopes, never more than two stable ones, is consistent with the trend throughout the periodic table (see page 173).

ELECTRONIC STRUCTURE AND OXIDATION STATES

The electronic structures of the rare earth elements are very difficult to determine since the various energy levels available lie close together (see page 191). Table 14.5, page 190, summarizes the most recent determinations for the gaseous atoms.

Table 29.1
The Rare Earth Elements

ATOMIC NUMBER	ELEMENT	SYMBOL	RELATIVE ABUNDANCE	NO. OF STABLE ISOTOPES
57	Lanthanum	La	7	1
58	Cerium	Ce	31	4
59	Praseodymium	Pr	5	1
60	Neodymium	Nd	18	7
61	Promethium	Pm	0	0
62	Samarium	Sm	7	6 *
63	Europium	Eu	0.2	2
64	Gadolinium	Gd	7	7
65	Terbium	Tb	1	1
66	Dysprosium	Dy	7	6
67	Holmium	Ho	1	1
68	Erbium	Er	6	6
69	Thulium	Tm	1	1
70	Ytterbium	Yb	7	7
71	Lutetium	Lu	1.5	2

* Samarium also has an isotope, Sm^{148}, which is a naturally occurring alpha ray emitter with a half life of 1.4×10^{11} years.

It is apparent from Table 14.5 that the rare earth elements occur where they do in the periodic system because the $4f$ energy level begins to fill with electrons at atomic number 58. The fourteen elements following lanthanum, atomic number 57, correspond to the number of electrons, 14, necessary to fill the $4f$ level completely. This complete filling is achieved with lutetium, atomic number 71, and elements of higher atomic number have the $4f$ level completely filled with electrons. Lanthanum is sometimes said not to be a rare earth element, since it contains no $4f$ electrons. However, its chemistry is so similar to the next fourteen elements that chemists usually include lanthanum with them. All fifteen elements form the *lanthanide series*.

The electron structures in Table 14.5 are for the gaseous atoms. For the solid elements some evidence indicates that all, except europium and ytterbium, use three electrons to form bonds. The three electrons would be the $6s$ electrons plus a $5d$ electron for lanthanum, gadolinium, and lutetium, or a $4f$ electron for each of the others. The atomic radii of europium and ytterbium are much higher than would be expected from comparison with the other lanthanides, suggesting weaker bonding in the solid elements. The ionic radii show no such irregularities. Weak bonding in europium and ytterbium in their solids is consistent with the idea that an exactly half-full energy level (europium) and a completely full level (ytterbium) are very stable configurations from which it is hard to remove an electron. Thus europium and ytterbium may use only two electrons (and no $4f$ electrons) to bond in the solid elements whereas the other elements use three.

In compounds each of the rare earth elements exists most commonly as cations in a 3+ oxidation state. All the ions have similar sizes. See Table 29.2. Hence there is little difference in their chemical behavior. Further evidence for the stability of exactly half-full energy levels and exactly full energy levels is given by the occurrence of 2+ ions of europium and ytterbium (compare the situation in their solids) and of 4+ ions of cerium. The existence of 2+ ions of samarium indicates that it is not impossible to deviate from these stable levels. These ions and the 3+ ions are the only rare earth ions that exist in water solution.

Problem 29.1. Write the electron structures of 2+ ions of samarium, europium, and ytterbium, and of 4+ ions of cerium. Why are these stable? Why should you not expect to find a 2+ ion of gadolinium?

ACIDITY OF THE RARE EARTH IONS

The principal difference between the 3+ ions of the different rare earth elements is their radius. The smaller the radius, the higher the charge density, and the greater the tendency to attract negative ions. In other words, the ions of higher atomic number, and smaller size, will be more electron deficient and more acidic, in the sense of the Lewis theory of acids and bases. In practice one must also consider the negative ion and the crystal structure of the product but it is well established that the acidity of the rare earth ions increases in a regular order. The increase is consistent with the trend in other parts of the periodic table, but it is more readily studied here since ionic size is the only important variable for these 3+ ions and it changes only slightly. The second column in Table 29.2 lists the ratio of the solubility product constant of each of the rare

Table 29.2
Acidity of the Rare Earth 3+ Ions

Element M	Atomic Radius of Element in Å	Radius of 3+ Ion in Å	$\dfrac{K_{M(OH)_3}}{K_{Gd(OH)_3}}$	MCl₃	MBr₃	MI₃
La	1.87	1.15	480	850	783	761
Ce	1.81	1.01	71	800	732	752
Pr	1.82	1.00	129	770	693	733
Nd	1.82	.99	9.0	760	684	775
Pm	—	.98	—	—	—	—
Sm	—	.98	3.2	678	664	820
Eu	2.04	.97	1.6	623	—	—
Gd	1.79	.96	1.0	609	765	926
Tb	1.77	.95	—	588	—	—
Dy	1.77	.94	—	654	881	955
Ho	1.76	.93	—	718	914	1010
Er	1.75	.92	0.062	774	950	1020
Tm	1.74	.91	0.016	821	—	1015
Yb	1.93	.89	0.014	854	940	—
Lu	1.74	.89	0.012	892	—	1045

(Columns: RELATIVE SOLUBILITY PRODUCT OF HYDROXIDES; MELTING POINTS OF HALIDES °C.)

earth hydroxides, represented by the formula $M(OH)_3$, to that of gadolinium hydroxide. Note the regular decrease in the solubility product constants with increasing atomic number. The solubility product of gadolinium hydroxide equals 2.1×10^{-22} so that the value of each of the others may be calculated. The melting points of the halides are also listed in the table. A similar trend appears except that there is a minimum melting point within each series, the minimum moving toward lower atomic numbers as the atomic number of the halide increases. Note that in every case the lutetium compound forms the most stable solid.

MAGNETIC PROPERTIES OF RARE EARTHS AND THEIR COMPOUNDS

The property of magnetism correlates with the existence of unpaired electrons within atoms (see page 187). Ferromagnetic substances, such as metallic iron, are those from which permanent magnets can be made. Metallic gadolinium is ferromagnetic. Substances which are attracted into a magnetic field, but are not themselves permanent magnets, are said to be paramagnetic. The salts of all of the rare earth elements except lanthanum and lutetium (whose ions contain only paired electrons) are paramagnetic. This fact is evidence for the existence of unpaired electrons in these ions. See Table 29.3. The

THE RARE EARTH ELEMENTS, AND SCANDIUM AND YTTRIUM

intensity of the magnetic effect is proportional to the number of unpaired electrons and to the strength of their interaction. The actual data for the 3+ ions of the rare earths are plotted in Figure 29.1. Note the minimum magnetic moment in those ions (Sm^{+++} and Eu^{+++}) in which the $4f$ level is almost

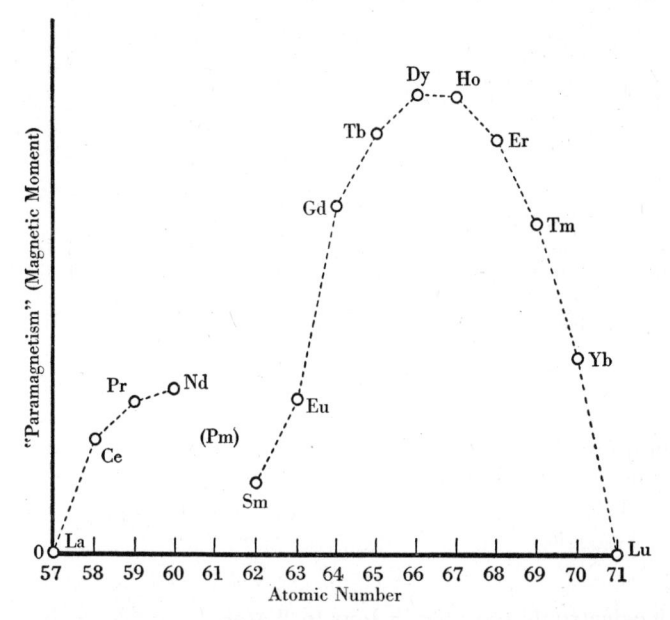

Figure 29.1.
Paramagnetism of the 3+ rare earth ions.

exactly half full and the maxima in the curve corresponding to those ions whose energy levels are farthest removed from the half full or completely full state.

COLOR OF THE RARE EARTH IONS

The colors of the 3+ ions of the rare earths in water solution are listed in Table 29.3. Color is due to the interaction of light with electrons and consequent absorption of light energy when electrons move to higher energy levels. Light in the visible part of the spectrum may be absorbed when atoms have loosely held electrons and closely spaced energy levels. We have seen in the past that substances with unpaired electrons are apt to satisfy these conditions and to be colored. Note (Table 29.3) that the ions with no unpaired electrons or with only one unpaired electron and those of Gd^{+++} ions with exactly half-full energy levels are colorless. The intensity of the color, or depth of color, is apparently related to the number of unpaired electrons, the most deeply colored ions being those most distant from electron configurations containing only full or half full levels. Compare the magnetic moment variation.

Table 29.3
Colors of the Rare Earth 3+ Ions

ION	COLOR	NUMBER OF 4F ELECTRONS	NUMBER OF UNPAIRED ELECTRONS IN THE IONS
La	colorless	0	0
Ce	colorless	1	1
Pr	yellow-green	2	2
Nd	red-violet	3	3
Pm	—	4	4
Sm	pale yellow	5	5
Eu	pale pink	6	6
Gd	colorless	7	7
Tb	very pale pink	8	6
Dy	pale yellow-green	9	5
Ho	brownish-yellow	10	4
Er	rose	11	3
Tm	pale green	12	2
Yb	colorless	13	1
Lu	colorless	14	0

Interpretation of color is actually somewhat more complicated than this simple picture would indicate. Note the colors of the isoelectronic ions of the rare earths (Table 29.4). Isoelectronic ions contain the same number of elec-

Table 29.4
Colors of Isoelectronic Rare Earth Ions in Water

NUMBER OF 4F ELECTRONS	ION	COLOR	ION	COLOR
0	La^{+++}	colorless	Ce^{++++}	orange-red
6	Eu^{+++}	pale pink	Sm^{++}	deep red-brown
7	Gd^{+++}	colorless	Eu^{++}	pale straw color
14	Lu^{+++}	colorless	Yb^{++}	green

trons, and, perhaps, similar electron structures. The implication is clear that the electron structures are not really identical in these isoelectronic ions.

SEPARATION OF THE RARE EARTH ELEMENTS AND COMPOUNDS

The rare earth compounds are almost always found together and are never found in separated pure minerals. The Ce^{+++} ion may be readily separated by oxidizing it to the 4+ ceric ion (with sodium hypochlorite) and precipitating it as the hydroxide, formula Ce(OH)$_4$. Samarium, europium, and ytterbium 3+ ions may be removed by electrolysis of a sulfate solution. The three ions are reduced to the 2+ state—samarous, europous, and ytterbous, respectively—and precipitate as insoluble sulfates. They may be separated from one another by taking advantage of the differences in ease of oxidation and reduction of their compounds. Lanthanum may be separated from the other 3+ ions by precipitation of the hydroxides with ammonia water. The lanthanum ion is so much larger, and so much less acid, than the rest that it stays in solution. See the solubility product ratios in Table 29.2.

Problem 29.2. Which ions are most apt to stay in solution with the lanthanum during an ammonia precipitation? How could you detect their presence? Give two methods.

The separation of the other nine rare earths is tedious and costly. Prior to 1940 the only feasible process was fractional crystallization. Thousands and hundreds of thousands of sequential fractional crystallizations and redissolving of the salts were required to accomplish appreciable separations. Some samples have been worked on for upwards of twenty years in attempts to obtain highly purified materials. The great number of steps in the process is a result of the very slight differences in the solubilities of the salts, due, of course, to the very similar ionic sizes.

Since 1940 numerous solid materials have been found which selectively adsorb ions from solutions. These *ion exchange resins* (see page 481) when in contact with a solution containing several kinds of ions, will absorb one of them more strongly than any of the rest, partially removing this ion from solution. If there is an insufficient concentration of this ion to saturate the resin, the ion which is next most readily adsorbed will also be removed from the solution. The process will continue until all the sites on the resin which can hold ions are filled. The ions least tightly adsorbed by the resin will remain in the solution. By adjusting the relative amounts of resin and solution one can remove the various ions from the solution selectively and obtain good separations.

Ion exchange resins have proved effective in separating the rare earth ions, for only slight differences in acidity of the ions are needed to give considerable differentiation in adsorption on the resin. Unfortunately this method is not capable at present of large scale use so that only small samples of the purified rare earth compounds can be prepared. The method has, however, greatly facilitated work with the rare earths, since it allows rapid preparation of samples of high purity. In actual practice the solution containing the lanthanide ions is usually poured into the top of a long tube packed with the resin. As the solution flows down the tube the various ions are adsorbed. Lutetium, being most acidic is adsorbed most strongly and stays near the top of the tube at the adsorption sites there. Ytterbium, if present, is adsorbed next, and so on down the series with lanthanum being adsorbed last since it is least tightly held.

Problem 29.3. How would you remove the adsorbed rare earth ions from the adsorption column and obtain each rare earth in a solution relatively free from the others?

THE ACTINIDE SERIES

The lanthanide series occurs in the sixth period of the periodic table. In this series the $4f$ energy levels are filled. In a similar way one might expect a second "rare earth" series, following actinium, in which the $5f$ levels fill. See pages 192 and 193. There is considerable evidence that the elements beyond actinium in atomic number correspond in many ways to the lanthanide rare earths. Fortunately for the ease of separation of this second series, called the actinide series, the ions are much more readily oxidized and reduced than those of the lanthanide series and have, for the most part, several oxidation states. If it were not for this fact the separation of plutonium from uranium would be much more difficult than it is.

There is already considerable evidence that the actinide elements with atomic numbers greater than 95 may exist only as $3+$ ions in their compounds and thus be very difficult to separate.

Problem 29.4. Account for the greater number of oxidation states in the actinide series, as contrasted with the lanthanide series, in terms of available energy levels.

Problem 29.5. Why is it easier to isolate pure ytterbium compounds than to isolate pure europium compounds?

Problem 29.6. Lanthanum hydroxide is more basic than lutetium hydroxide. Correlate this fact with the acidic nature of the cations.

THE RARE EARTH ELEMENTS AND THE PERIODIC SYSTEM

We now can see that the apparently anomalous occurrence of the rare earth elements following barium in the periodic system is readily interpreted in terms of the introduction of the $4f$ electrons. No lighter elements contained f electrons so that the previous symmetry of the table is lost. The occurrence of the actinide series following radium confirms this view.

Because of their identical charges and their almost identical sizes, the rare earth ions have almost identical chemistry. None of them can be reduced to the metal from an aqueous solution, all being about as electropositive as magnesium. Like aluminum, they are usually formed by electrolytic reduction of the oxide dissolved in the fluoride. All form very insoluble hydroxides (see Table 29.2), insoluble phosphates, and insoluble fluorides. The solubilities of any given compound of the elements, such as the nitrate for instance, differ little from element to element. In every case, however, the solubility varies in a fairly systematic manner through the series from lanthanum to lutetium. Sometimes the solubility increases with atomic number, sometimes it decreases, and sometimes it shows a minimum or maximum. Relatively few cases of transpositions of the order, or of erratic fluctuations are found.

The marked effect of ionic size on chemical behavior is well illustrated by the properties of the rare earth ions relative to those of scandium and yttrium ions. The scandium ion, Sc^{+++}, radius 0.81 Å., is considerably smaller than that of yttrium, Y^{+++} radius 0.93 Å., or of the rare earths, whose radii range from

1.15 Å. (La) to 0.89 Å. (Lu). See Table 29.2. A geochemical consequence is that yttrium is almost always found with the rare earth elements whereas scandium may not be. As a matter of fact, yttrium is so much like a rare earth element that the rare earth series is often split into two groups: the cerium group with atomic numbers 57 through 62, (La, Ce, Pr, Nd, Sm) and the yttrium group, with atomic numbers 63 through 71. This latter group is composed of ions closely similar to yttrium in size (see Table 29.2). The differentiations and similarities are so great that the second group of elements is almost always found concentrated in yttrium ores, whereas the first group concentrates in cerium ores.

Rare earth chemistry is not limited entirely to precipitation reactions, and the few oxidation-reduction possibilities already mentioned. The ions can also form complexes which may be complex ions or weak electrolytes. These complexes appear to arise primarily from the high charge density on the rare earth ions and to have ionic bonding rather than covalent bonding. There is some hope that the discovery of new complexing agents will eventually uncover some which can discriminate highly between the various rare earth ions. Then a rapid, large scale method of separating the rare earths could be based on their use.

Problem 29.7. The solubility product constant of yttrium hydroxide is 8.1×10^{-23}. Calculate the ratio of this constant to that of gadolinium hydroxide and compare this ratio with those in Table 29.4. Correlate this comparison with a comparison of the radii of the positive ions.

Problem 29.8. How would you separate a scandium compound from yttrium and rare earth compounds? Assume that the starting material is a mixture of the oxides.

Problem 29.9. What method would you use if you were asked to determine whether a given sample of material did or did not contain promethium, element 61?

30 ELEMENTS IN THE CENTRAL REGION OF THE PERIODIC TABLE—I

WE HAVE now discussed the properties of the elements on the left and the right sides of the periodic table; specifically, those lying in the three columns at the left and those in the four columns at the right. We have also dealt briefly with carbon and hydrogen. The chemistry of carbon and its compounds will be considered in greater detail when we discuss organic chemistry in the later chapters. Boron and silicon will be considered in connection with structural materials. This leaves for discussion the metallic elements in the fourth through fourteenth columns of the long rows in the table, Groups 4b, 5b, 6b, 7b, 8b, 9b, 10b, 1b, 2b, 3a, and 4a. Many of these elements are technically known as "transition elements," (Groups 3b, 4b, 5b, 6b, 7b, 8b, 9b, 10b, 1b, and 2b). This term has come to mean elements which differ from the adjacent elements in the number of d electrons they contain. (See the electron structures outlined on page 191, or pages 192 and 193.) Note that all the elements in the b families are transition elements.

The transition elements as isolated atoms usually have one or two valence s electrons, and occur where they do in the periodic table because of the filling of the d energy levels. Since d levels lie very close in total energy to the s levels of the next shell (see Figure 14.4, page 191) the transition elements customarily show more than one oxidation state in addition to the zero state. A further consequence of the small energy differences between their s and d electron energy levels, and the corresponding p levels for that matter, is the great tendency of the transition elements to form weak electrolytes and complex ions. These complexes often form when an atom uses its s, d, and p orbitals to share electrons with other atoms and so attempts to achieve an inert gas sturcture.

GENERAL TRENDS IN PROPERTIES

Some of the properties of the thirty-three central elements are listed in Table 30.1. Note that the atomic radii (part 2) are remarkably similar, as a glance at Figure 12.3, page 157, will corroborate. Since most of these elements crystallize in one of the close packed structures with twelve nearest neighbors, their densities (part 3) vary in an orderly fashion, increasing with increase in

Table 30.1
Properties of the Elements in the Central Region of the Periodic Table Group

	4B	5B	6B	7B	8B	9B	10B	1B	2B	3A	4A
1. Element—symbol and atomic number Period IV	Ti 22	V 23	Cr 24	Mn 25	Fe 26	Co 27	Ni 28	Cu 29	Zn 30	Ga 31	Ge 32
Period V	Zr 40	Nb 41	Mo 42	Tc 43	Ru 44	Rh 45	Pd 46	Ag 47	Cd 48	In 49	Sn 50
Period VI	Hf 72	Ta 73	W 74	Re 75	Os 76	Ir 77	Pt 78	Au 79	Hg 80	Tl 81	Pb 82
2. Atomic radius (covalent, in Å.)	1.46 1.57 1.57	1.31 1.43 1.43	1.25 1.36 1.37	1.29 1.35 1.37	1.26 1.33 1.34	1.25 1.34 1.35	1.24 1.38 1.38	1.28 1.44 1.44	1.33 1.49 1.55	1.22 1.62 1.71	1.22 1.4 1.75
3. Density of element (g. per cm.^{3})	4.5 6.4	5.96 8.4 16.6	7.1 10.2 19.3	7.2 21.4	7.85 12.3 22.5	8.8 12.1 22.4	8.8 11.5 21.4	8.92 10.5 19.3	7.14 8.6 13.5	5.9 7.3 11.9	5.40 7.31 11.34
4. Melting point (in °C.)	1725 1857 2227	1720 1950 3027	1800 2622 3380	1247 3137	1530 >1950 2500	1490 1966 2454	1455 1557 1774	1083 961 1063	419 321 −39	30 156 303	959 232 328
5. Boiling point (in °C.)			2660 5690 4830	2032				2310 1927 2200	906 764 357	1983 2100 1460	2700 2362 1755
6. Ionization potential (1st electron) (in electron-volts)	6.8 6.9	6.8	6.7 7.2 8.1	7.9 7.9	7.8 8.7	7.8	7.6 8.3 8.9	7.7 7.5 9.2	9.4 9.0 10.4	6.0 5.8 6.1	8.1 7.3 7.4
7. Single electrode potential (in volts)	−1.75 −1.53 −1.68	−1.5 −1.1	−0.86 −0.2 −0.05	−1.05	−0.44 0.45 0.7	−0.28 0.6 1.0	−0.25 0.83 1.2	0.35 0.80 1.42	−0.76 −0.40 0.85	−0.52 −0.34 0.34	−0.4 −0.14 −0.13

atomic weight. Slight anomalies in the density reflect irregular changes in the electron structure (chromium, for instance) whereas gross anomalies reflect the existence of more loosely packed crystal structures. For instance, the value of 5.62 for the density of tin (not listed in Table 30.1) corresponds to a crystal form (gray tin) in which the coordination number of each atom is 4, whereas the listed density 7.31 corresponds to a crystal form (white tin) in which the coordination number of the tin is six.

The melting points of the elements in each family or column (part 4) increase in general with increasing atomic number, mercury and germanium being outstanding exceptions. In the rows, on the other hand, the melting points increase to a maximum with Group 6b and then decrease in a more or less regular fashion. Germanium and mercury are again out of line, but gallium is also.

Data on the boiling points of the elements (part 5) are fragmentary but the trends are similar to those shown by the melting points. However, all of Group 2b is now out of line. Note that the boiling point of gallium is approximately consistent with the position of the element, even though its melting point is low. The latter reflects the peculiar crystal structure of gallium in which each atom has only one nearest neighbor, indicating a tendency to form Ga_2 molecules in the crystal. Melting minimizes this tendency and the liquid behaves "normally." One consequence of this idiosyncracy of gallium is that there is a longer temperature interval between its melting and boiling points than for other substances liquid near room temperature. Gallium is sometimes used as the indicating liquid in thermometers for this reason.

The ionization potentials of the gaseous atoms (part 6) are also remarkably constant, although those of Groups 2b and 3a are high and low respectively. We have stated on pages 229 and 230 that electron structures in which the two outer levels hold eighteen, and two electrons respectively are unusually stable. This structure—18,2—is said to contain an *inert pair* of electrons. Such an electron arrangement is difficult to break into to remove an electron, hence the high ionization potential for Group 2b whose neutral atoms have this structure. The ionization potentials for Group 3a are low since their 1+ ions have the stable structure. The constancy of the rest of the ionization potentials is a reflection of a similar constancy in atomic radii and number of valence electrons. The low boiling points (small interatomic attraction in the liquid state) of the Group 2b elements is also attributable to the inertness of the electron structure—18,2—with a correspondingly small tendency to form interatomic bonds.

The single electrode potentials of the elements (part 7) show much more variation than any other listed property. Regular trends are present, however. It is particularly noteworthy that the ease of oxidation of the elements *decreases* with increasing atomic number in these groups as contrasted with the behavior in the families near the sides of the periodic table where the most readily oxidized element in any group was always that of highest atomic number. Compare those for the group potassium to cesium or bromine to iodine, with those for zinc to mercury, for instance. The potentials listed are those between the metal and whichever of its ions can exist in equilibrium with it at room temperatures, for example, Fe—Fe^{++}, Cu—Cu^{++}.

Problem 30.1. Which is the densest of the elements? Explain.

Problem 30.2. Will iron float or sink in mercury? How about platinum?

OXIDATION STATES OF THE ELEMENTS

The elements of the "a" groups have, as we have seen, the maximum oxidation states of 1+, 2+, 3+, 4+, 5+, 6+, and 7+ respectively, corresponding to the group number of the element. The group number indicates the *group oxidation state*. The maximum oxidation states of the "b" groups, with the notable exception of Group 1b and Groups 8b, 9b, and 10b, are also the group oxidation states. The group number of an element, which represents the number of electrons (valence electrons) beyond a completed shell of 8 or of 18, shows the number of electrons available for bonding. Thus, chromium in Group 6b has six electrons more than the nearest inert gas, argon, and has a maximum oxidation number of 6+, and indium, in Group 3a has 3 electrons in excess of a shell of eighteen and has a maximum oxidation number of 3+. The Group 1b elements—copper, silver, and gold—do exhibit the group oxidation number of 1+, but this number is not the maximum for any of them. We shall consider this fact when we discuss this group.

For most elements the group oxidation number is the most common oxidation number and for some—for example, the elements of the alkali, alkaline earth, and aluminum families—it is the only oxidation number other than zero. However, all thirty-three of the elements we are considering, except hafnium, zinc, and cadmium, show more than one oxidation state. Table 30.2 lists the known oxidation states and their relative occurrence, together with the outer electron structure of the neutral atoms, for the elements in Groups 4b, 5b, 6b, 7b, 8b, 9b, 10b, 1b, 2b, 3a, and 4a lying in Periods IV, V, and VI. See also Table 25.8 for the known oxides of these elements. Note that for some elements the most common state is not the group oxidation state and that for iron, cobalt, nickel, rhodium, palladium, iridium, and platinum, all oxidation states are lower than the group states.

Several further generalizations may be drawn. The most common oxidation states other than the group states are the 2+ and 3+ states. All these "central" elements show one or the other and most of them show both of these states. We have already indicated that oxidation states greater than 3+ are not attained by monatomic ions in water solution because of the high charge density in such ions. The higher oxidation states exist only in complex ions or in crystals. Thus, 7+ manganese is found in MnO_4^- ions both in crystals and in aqueous solution.

A further generalization is that within each group the higher oxidation states become more stable and the lower oxidation states less stable as the atomic number increases. The only real exception to this rule is found in Group 4a where the 4+ state is most common for germanium whereas the 2+ state is most common for tin and lead. Apparently the stability of an inert pair of *s* electrons (see page 498 and Table 16.2) is enhanced as the atomic number increases. The 1+ oxidation state for mercury is an interesting example of the influence of an inert electron pair. Mercury atoms, with the electron structure of 2, 8, 18, 32, 18, 2, contain an inert pair in themselves and are

Table 30.2
Oxidation States of the Elements in the Central Region of the Periodic Table

PERIODIC GROUP	PERIOD IV Element Symbol	Outer Electron Structure	Oxidation States	PERIOD V Element Symbol	Outer Electron Structure	Oxidation States	PERIOD VI Element Symbol	Outer Electron Structure	Oxidation States
4b	Ti	10, 2	4, 3, 2	Zr	10, 2	4, 3, 2	Hf	10, 2	4
5b	V	11, 2	5 4, 3, 2	Nb	12, 1	5, 3	Ta	11, 2	5, 3, 2
6b	Cr	13, 1	6, 4, 3, 2, 1	Mo	13, 1	6, 5, 4, 3, 2	W	12, 2	6, 5, 4, 3, 2
7b	Mn	13, 2	7, 6, 4, 3, 2, 1	Tc	13, 2 (?)		Re	13, 2	7, 6, 5, 4, 3, 2
8b	Fe	14, 2	6, 3, 2	Ru	15, 1	8, 7, 6, 5, 4, 3, 2, 1	Os	14, 2	8, 6, 4, 3, 2
9b	Co	15, 2	4, 3, 2	Rh	16, 1	3	Ir	17	6, 4, 3, 2, 1
10b	Ni	16, 2	3, 2, 1	Pd	18	4, 3, 2	Pt	17, 1	4, 3, 2
1b	Cu	18, 1	2, 1	Ag	18, 1	2, 1	Au	18, 1	3, 1
2b	Zn	18, 2	2	Cd	18, 2	2	Hg	18, 2	2, 1
3a	Ga	18, 3	3, 2	In	18, 3	3, 2, 1	Tl	18, 3	3, 1
4a	Ge	18, 4	4, 2	Sn	18, 4	4, 2	Pb	18, 4	4, 2

Triply underlined oxidation states are most common ones. Amount of underlining indicates commonness of states. Doubtful states are not listed.

ELEMENTS IN THE CENTRAL REGION—I 501

relatively stable and inert. But the 1+ state for mercury exists and is fairly stable even in water solution. However, the mercurous ion is found experimentally to have the formula Hg_2^{++}. The explanation is that an inert electron pair is shared by two 1+ atoms to form the diatomic ions. The great stability of the inert pair is indicated by the fact that the mercurous ion is the only known example of two atoms both having positive oxidation numbers being directly joined together.

COMPOUNDS CONTAINING ELEMENTS WITH ZERO OXIDATION NUMBER

Some of the transition elements form compounds in which their oxidation number as calculated by the usual conventions is zero. The carbonyls with formulas $Ni(CO)_4$ and $Fe(CO)_5$ are typical. They form when carbon monoxide gas is passed over the metal at high pressures and moderate temperatures. Their existence may be readily interpreted in terms of electron structure. Iron atoms, with the structure 2, 8, 14, 2, need ten more electrons and nickel atoms, with the structure 2, 8, 16, 2, need eight more electrons to achieve the inert gas structure, 2, 8, 18, 8. The carbon monoxide molecule has the structure : C≡O : so that it can share two of its electrons with an acceptor atom, such as an iron or nickel atom, to form a covalent bond. The iron atom will accept electron pairs from five carbon monoxide molecules and the nickel atom from four, hence the molecular formulas $Fe(CO)_5$ and $Ni(CO)_4$. The existence of carbonyls with formulas $Cr(CO)_6$, $Mo(CO)_6$, $Ru(CO)_5$, $W(CO)_6$, and $Os(CO)_5$, can be explained similarly.

The odd numbered elements in Groups 7b and 9b do not form corresponding carbonyls containing only one of their atoms since their odd number of electrons makes it impossible for them to attain an inert gas structure in a simple carbonyl. However, the "odd" molecule of nitric oxide, formula NO, can donate three electrons for the sharing process. Hence we can account for compounds, both of odd and even numbered elements, as represented by the formulas $Co(CO)_3NO$ and $Fe(CO)_2(NO)_2$.

Problem 30.3. Outline the electron structures for the molecules represented by the formulas $W(CO)_6$, $Os(CO)_5$, $Co(CO)_3NO$, and $Fe(CO)_2(NO)_2$. Predict the shapes of these molecules.

EQUILIBRIA AMONG DIFFERENT OXIDATION STATES OF AN ELEMENT

When an element can exist in three different oxidation states there may be equilibrium among the three states. Equation 30.1 represents such an equilibrium involving simple ions in two states and the metal in a third.

$$M_{(s)} + 2M^{+++} = 3M^{++} \qquad (30.1)$$

The intermediate oxidation state, in this instance that of the M^{++} ion, may be most stable; then this ion is formed when the metal and the M^{+++} ion are in contact. Or, the M^{++} state may be less stable and change spontaneously to form the metallic and higher oxidation states. Such a spontaneous change is known as a *disproportionation*. Each of the Group 1b elements exhibits three oxidation states; the equilibria among them are shown in the equations

$$\underset{\text{red}}{Cu_{(s)}} + \underset{\text{blue}}{Cu^{++}} = 2Cu^+; \quad K = \frac{[Cu^+]^2}{[Cu^{++}]} = 10^{-6} \tag{30.2}$$

$$Ag_{(s)} + Ag^{++} = 2Ag^+ \tag{30.3}$$

$$\underset{\text{yellow}}{2Au_{(s)}} + \underset{\text{yellow}}{Au^{+++}} = 3Au^+ \tag{30.4}$$

The copper and gold equilibria favor disproportionation of the 1+ ions, cuprous and aurous, into the metal and the ions of higher oxidation state. On the other hand, argentous ions, Ag^+, are stable with respect to the lower and higher oxidation states. Hence, even in the presence of excess metal, copper and gold are ordinarily oxidized to Cu^{++} and Au^{+++} ions, respectively, but silver yields the Ag^+ ion.

Because of their low equilibrium concentrations the less stable oxidation states are usually formed by complexing their ions or by precipitating them in insoluble solids. These products reduce the concentration of the less stable ions in the solution still further and cause the equilibrium to shift. Thus, copper oxide and metallic copper treated with hydrochloric acid form insoluble cuprous chloride, cupric ion in the presence of iodide ion forms insoluble cuprous iodide and iodine, and cupric ion in the presence of cyanide ion forms the very stable cuprous cyanide complex ion, formula $Cu(CN)_2^-$, and cyanogen, formula $(CN)_2$.

$$\underset{\text{black}}{CuO_{(s)}} + \underset{\text{red}}{Cu_{(s)}} + 2H^+ + 2Cl^- = 2CuCl_{(s)} + H_2O \tag{30.5}$$

$$\underset{\text{blue}}{Cu^{++}} + 2I^- = \underset{\text{brown}}{CuI_{(s)}} + \underset{\text{violet}}{\tfrac{1}{2}I_2} \tag{30.6}$$

$$\underset{\text{blue}}{Cu^{++}} + 3CN^- = Cu(CN)_2^- + \tfrac{1}{2}(CN)_{2(g)} \tag{30.7}$$

When the ions of the elements listed in Table 30.3 are in contact with the metals in aqueous solution the 1+ ions of silver, mercury, and thallium are stable, the 2+ ions are stable for the elements in Period IV, titanium through zinc, and also for cadmium, tin, and lead, and the 3+ ions are stable for gallium, indium, and gold. The other elements seldom exist in water solution as simple ions since their tendency to form complexes is great. In the absence of the metal some of the ions indicated are unstable in water solution. For example, Ti^{++}, V^{++}, and Cr^{++} ions react with the water to form hydrogen and the more stable 3+ ions. Some ions (particularly Hg_2^{++}, Fe^{++}, and Sn^{++}) are readily oxidized by the oxygen of the air to higher states. Therefore water

CARBONATE $(CO_3)^=$

$$\frac{MW}{22.4} = \frac{W}{V_{S.T.P.}}$$

114

---
220 & 431 "ELECTRONEG"

PERMANGANATE $(MnO_4)^{-1}$

---
p 518 COMPLEXES

$v_s = \sqrt{\frac{\gamma P}{\rho}}$ $\gamma \cong \frac{5}{3}$

WATER
 BOILING PT $+0.52°C$ / MOLE IN $1000\,g\,H_2O$
 FREEZING PT $-1.86°C$ / MOLE IN $1000\,g\,H_2O$

$(BiO_3)^-$ BISMUTHATE   202-206

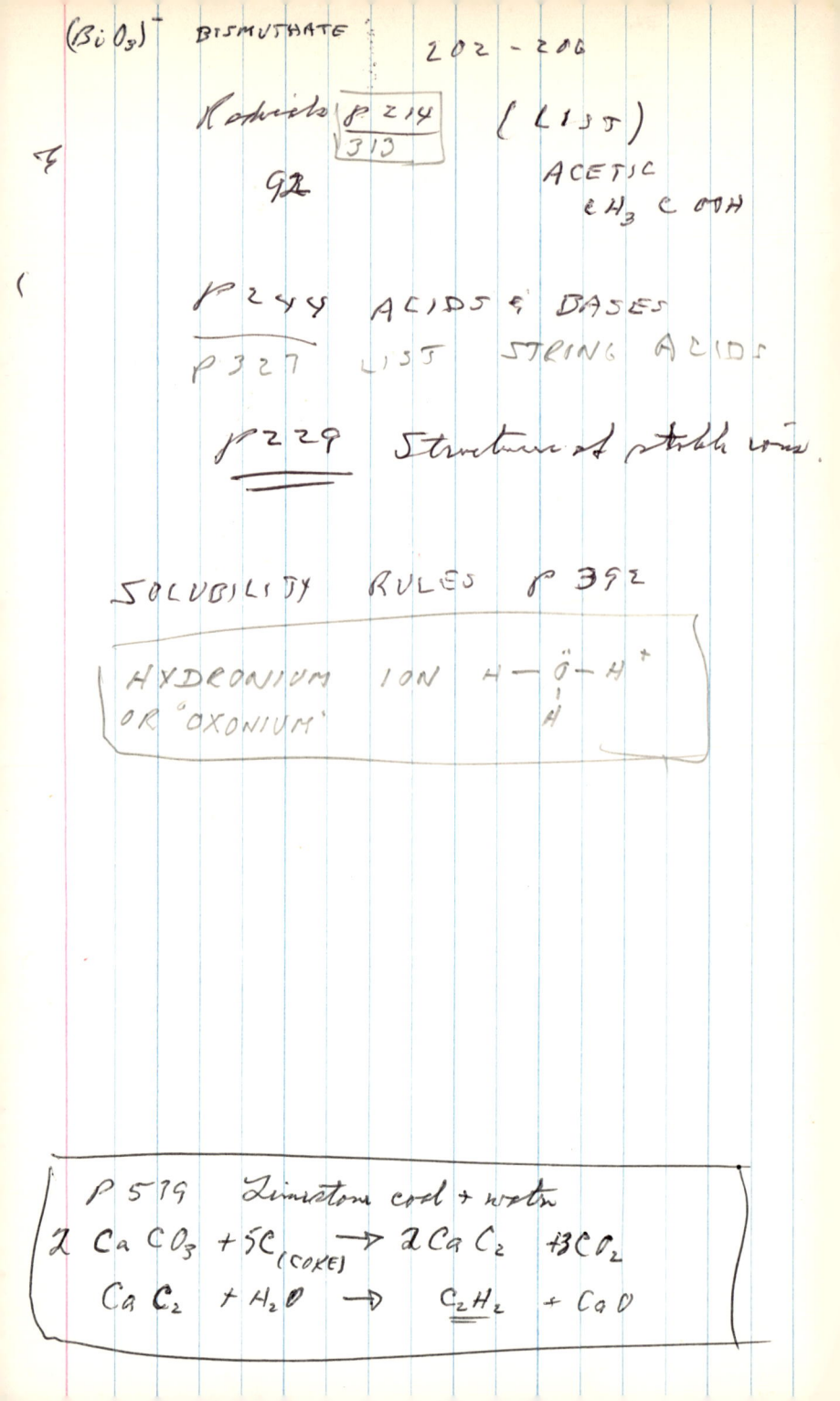

Kohich p 214   (LIST)
                313
        92   ACETIC
                           CH_3COOH

p 244 ACIDS & BASES
p 327 LIST STRING ACIDS

p 229 Structure of stable ions.

SOLUBILITY RULES p 392

HYDRONIUM ION $H-\ddot{O}-H^+$
OR "OXONIUM" $|$
                     H

p 579 Limestone coal + water
$2 CaCO_3 + 5C_{(COKE)} \rightarrow 2CaC_2 + 3CO_2$
$CaC_2 + H_2O \rightarrow C_2H_2 + CaO$

solutions of these must always be in contact with excess metal if the lower oxidation states are to be maintained.

Problem 30.4. How do you account for the fact that a strip of copper immersed in a solution of cupric chloride becomes coated with a layer of white precipitate but a strip of copper in a solution of cupric sulfate keeps its original bright surface?

EASE OF OXIDATION OF THE ELEMENTS

Within the "a" groups of the periodic table ease of oxidation of the elements generally increases with increasing atomic number. Within the "b" groups this trend is usually reversed, the most noble element in any group being that of highest atomic number. Thus cesium and iodine are much more readily oxidized than lithium and fluorine, respectively, whereas tungsten and gold are much more difficult to oxidize than chromium and copper.

The fact that chromium and nickel are commonly used as plating metals to preserve bright luster on metallic objects should not be attributed to resistance to oxidation. Both of these metals are readily oxidized by air even at room temperature but each forms a tightly adherent oxide coat which greatly impedes further oxidation by preventing the oxygen from reaching the metal. Platinum and gold, on the other hand, are truly inert, not merely protected by an oxide coating.

The reversal in ease of oxidation as a function of atomic number in "b" groups is readily explicable in terms of atomic radii. Within "a" groups the atomic radius usually increases appreciably with increasing atomic number. The distance of the valence electrons from the nucleus then increases so that, in spite of the increased nuclear charge, the valence electrons may be lost more readily by the larger atoms. In contrast, in the central region of the periodic table the increase in atomic radius within a group is usually much smaller. See Table 30.1, part 2. Then the increase in nuclear charge becomes the factor determining the ease with which electrons may be removed in an oxidation process; the elements of high nuclear charge (high atomic number) become more resistant to oxidation than those of lower nuclear charge but similar atomic radius. This effect is demonstrated by the single electrode potentials listed in Table 30.1, part 7. These show that the elements of higher atomic number in each group are usually less readily oxidized (have a more positive electrode potential in aqueous solution).

The single electrode potentials of many metals are plotted in Figure 30.1 against the covalent radius of the metals. The lines connect elements in the same period of the periodic system. Note that, in each period, the electrode potential falls as the atomic radius decreases, then rises again as the increase in size which occurs around Group 1b becomes sufficient to offset the continuous increase in nuclear charge. The decrease in size near the end of each long period is reflected in a marked decrease in electrode potential. Data are also

504 GENERAL CHEMISTRY

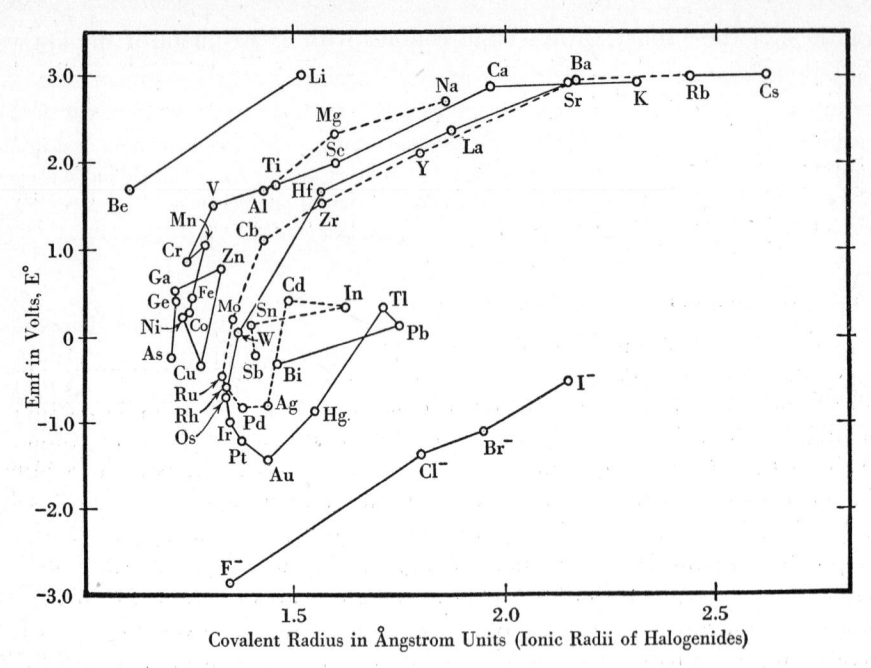

Figure 30.1.
Standard electromotive force as a function of the covalent radius of the elements.

included for the halide ions which show a very uniform relation between electrode potential and ionic radius.

ATOMIC RADIUS AND ELECTRON STRUCTURE; THE LANTHANIDE CONTRACTION

The fact that the atomic radii within a group do not increase with increasing atomic number as much in the center as at the ends of the rows of the periodic table may be interpreted in terms of interaction of nuclear charge with electron structure. You will note in part 2 of Table 30.1 that the atomic radius increases appreciably between the first and second row but increases very little between the second and third row. A glance at the atomic numbers of the elements will suggest a reason.

The elements in the second row (Period V) have atomic numbers 18 greater than those above them in the first row (Period IV), but atomic numbers 32 less than those below them in the third row (Period VI). Thus the atomic number change between Period IV and V is 18, but that between Period V and VI is 32. The difference arises, of course, because of the lanthanide series of elements just preceding hafnium. The abnormally low radii of the elements following lanthanum are said to be due to the lanthanide contraction, that is, to the extra 14 units of nuclear charge attracting the outer electrons. The effects of the lanthanide contraction are apparent also in the densities, melting points, and ionization potentials listed in Table 30.1. As would be expected, the effect gradually fades out as the atomic number continues to increase and becomes of minor importance in the elements just beyond lead in atomic number. Beyond Group 4a the element of highest atomic number is most readily oxidized, for instance.

The lanthanide contraction may also be used to account for the increase in stability of the higher oxidation states with increasing atomic number in this part of the periodic table. (Contrast this tendency with that in the nitrogen family, for instance, where lower oxidation numbers are favored by the high atomic number elements.) The lower oxidation states are customarily ionic in nature and are formed by elements which lose electrons fairly readily. The higher oxidation states are always more covalent, since ions of high charge density are unstable. Thus high oxidation states are more readily achieved by elements which tend to share rather than to lose electrons. Since the lanthanide contraction makes it relatively difficult for atoms to lose electrons it encourages the existence of high oxidation states, or at least discourages the existence of lower, ionic ones.

Problem 30.5. Why is gold more commonly used in jewelry than copper? Why is platinum more used in jewelry than tungsten?

RESEMBLANCES BETWEEN THE "a" AND "b" GROUPS IN THE PERIODIC TABLE

Many forms of the periodic table have been suggested. (See Chapter 12.) Three of these are shown on pages 153, 158, and 192 respectively. Those on pages 153 and 192 are known as "long form" tables, and those of the type on page 158 are known as "short form" tables. A comparison of Table 12.4 on page 158 and Table 12.3 on page 153 will show that the short form lists the elements in the same order as the long form, but differs primarily in that the short form places both the "a" and "b" groups of the long form in the same column rather than in separate columns. Since the elements in the same column in a periodic table are supposed to have similar properties, there must be similarities between the "a" and "b" groups of the long form table. That the two groups are not identical in properties is indicated in the short form tables by columns which split them into "a" and "b" "subgroups."

If similarity of properties is to be interpreted in terms of similar electron structures, it must be possible for "a" and "b" groups to have similar electron structures. On the other hand we have already pointed out that the elements in the central region of the periodic table differ from those at the ends of the periodic table in that they often use d electrons and d orbitals in forming bonds, whereas the elements near the ends generally use s and p electrons and orbitals in forming bonds. When different types of orbitals are used in bond formation the behaviors of the elements are apt to be quite different, but when similar orbitals are used the behaviors are similar.

All the Group 1a elements have an outer electron structure of 8, 1. The single electron is an s electron. It lies in a much higher energy level than the preceding eight electrons and is thus the only electron used in bonding the solid alkali elements. It is also the only electron lost when these elements are oxidized to form their compounds. On the other hand, all the Group 1b elements have an outer electron structure of 18, 1. The single electron is again an s electron. Its energy level, however, is only slightly higher than that of the preceding d electrons (see page 191). Both the s electron and some of the d electrons are, therefore, used in bonding the solid Group 1b elements (copper, silver, and gold). Similarly, it is common for these elements to lose one or two d electrons (when they are oxidized to Cu^{++}, Ag^{++}, or Au^{+++}, for instance). Clearly, the elements in such oxidation states will not show any great similarities to the alkali elements in oxidation state $1+$. On the other hand, the Group 1b elements can also lose the single s electron to achieve a $1+$ oxidation state. This state will differ in electron structure from that of the $1+$ oxidation state of the alkali elements in that the outer electron shell is one of 18 rather than 8. Thus compounds with the formulas KCl and CuCl, RbCl and AgCl, exist but their properties are quite different in spite of the similar formulas.

Chromium in Group 6b may be compared with sulfur in Group 6a in a similar fashion. Chromium atoms have an electron structure 2, 8, 13, 1. Sulfur atoms have an electron structure of 2, 8, 6. No similarities are apparent in the behavior of the pure elements. Both elements can exist in several oxidation states. Examination of the electron structures of each state shows that the kernel electron structures of the chromium and sulfur are similar only for the $6+$ oxidation state, and, as a matter of fact, the chemical behavior of the two when in this oxidation state is also similar. Chromates and sulfates have many properties in common. Both are good, but slow, oxidizing agents. The solubilities of their salts are similar. Both tend to polymerize to form poly-ions such as $S_2O_7^{--}$ and $Cr_2O_7^{--}$ in concentrated solutions of high acidity. They also show marked differences, the most apparent one being that the chromates are colored (yellow to orange) whereas the sulfates are colorless.

The most important single similarity between the "a" and "b" groups of the same group number is that, with the exception already discussed from Groups 1a and 1b, they show the same maximum oxidation number, a number equal to the group number. It is in this maximum oxidation state that the properties are most similar. The lower oxidation states and the elements themselves are generally dissimilar in behavior.

CAUSES OF COLOR

Practically all inorganic colored substances contain elements from the central portion of the periodic table. Conversely, practically none containing only elements from the end groups of the long form of the periodic table are colored. Thus all the halides of the alkali elements, the alkaline earth elements, and the Group 3 elements (but not the rare earths) are colorless. But many of the halides of the elements from Group 4b through Group 1b are colored. The colors of the sulfides follow the same generalization except that the colored sulfides extend through Group 6a. Other compounds behave analogously.

We have already pointed out that, according to our theory of atomic structure, color arises when white light falls on an object containing loosely held electrons and closely spaced energy levels. White light consists of photons of all possible energies lying in the range of visible light and those photons which have just enough energy to move the electrons into a higher energy level are absorbed on striking a "colored" material. Photons of other energies find no electrons which can absorb their energy and they are, therefore, reflected or transmitted. Since light photons of certain energies have been absorbed, one now sees not white light but colored light. Thus absorption of photons of energy corresponding to yellow light makes an object appear blue since photons of energy corresponding to blue light are not absorbed but are reflected or transmitted. In every case the observed color is the one complementary to the color which is absorbed.

The structural factors correlating with color formation may be summarized as: (1) closely spaced energy levels, (2) unpaired electrons, (3) deviations from completely full and exactly half-full d and f energy levels, (4) covalent rather than ionic bonding, and (5) presence in a substance of a single element in two different oxidation states.

The colorless nature of the ions of the alkali elements, the alkaline earth elements, and the Group 3 elements (excepting the rare earths) is explained by their lack of any of the features ordinarily leading to color. The color of certain of the rare earth ions, but not of others, is interpreted in terms of the presence or absence of factors 1, 2, and 3. The fact that most of the Group 4b through Group 1b elements in most of their oxidation states are colored rests on these same three factors. The absence of color in Ag^+, Zn^{++}, Cd^{++}, Hg^{++}, and Hg_2^{++} ions, and most $4+$ compounds of titanium may be attributed to the presence of full or exactly half-full energy levels in these substances. The colors of the ions, hydrated Cu^{++} (blue), Ni^{++} (green), Cr^{+++} (green), Co^{++} (pink), MnO_4^{--} (green), etc., may be interpreted in terms of the first three criteria for color.

The transition in color from silver fluoride (colorless), silver chloride (colorless), silver bromide (light yellow), to silver iodide (yellow-green) is not interpretable in terms of the first three factors. This transition is apparently due to a gradual transition from ionic bonding in the fluoride to a higher and higher degree of covalent bonding as one moves toward the iodide. Covalent bonding in a crystal leads to greater electronic mobility because each atom shares electrons with its neighbors. In the ionic substance each electron is restricted to its original ion. The increased electron mobility in the covalent state is accompanied by the introduction of different energy levels used to bond the atoms covalently, and it is common to have these energy levels so closely spaced that color results. This effect is particularly noticeable in the sulfides. The sulfides of Groups 1a, 2a, and 3b are all ionic and colorless. The sulfides which are highly covalent are black. Sulfides with intermediate bonding show color. Table 30.3 gives several examples of this behavior. In each group

Table 30.3
Changes in Color with Change from Ionic to Covalent Bonding in Sulfides

GROUP	1B	2B	3A	4A	5A
Formula and color of the sulfide	CuS black	ZnS white	Ga_2S_3 white	GeS white	As_2S_3 yellow
	Ag_2S black	CdS yellow	In_2S_3 yellow	SnS brown	Sb_2S_3 orange
	Au_2S black	HgS black	Tl_2S_3 black	PbS black	Bi_2S_3 black

the color deepens with increasing atomic number, consistent with the increasing tendency to form covalent bonds. The oxides show the same effect except that oxides are more apt to be ionic than sulfides, oxygen being more electronegative than sulfur. The series, lead oxide (light yellow), lead dioxide (brown), is typical.

There are, however, two other oxides of lead known, with empirical formulas Pb_3O_4 (red) and Pb_2O_3 (red-yellow). These compounds may be written Pb_2PbO_4 and $PbPbO_3$, respectively, indicating that the lead in the compound exists partly in the 2+ oxidation state (plumbous) and partly in the 4+ oxidation state (plumbic). These compounds may be named diplumbous plumbate and monoplumbous plumbate, respectively. The existence of two oxidation states of an element in such close proximity leads to color formation. Other examples are magnetic iron oxide, formula Fe_3O_4 (black), and potassium ferroferricyanide, formula $KFeFe(CN)_6$ (deep blue) made from the almost colorless ferrous ions and ferricyanide ions, plus colorless potassium ions.

Problem 30.6. What factor or factors account for the fact that ferric hydroxide is much more strongly colored than ferrous hydroxide?

COMPLEXES OF THE CENTRAL ELEMENTS

All of the elements in Groups 4b through 4a have some tendency to form complexes, both complex ions and weak electrolytes. This tendency may be attributed to the fact that they seldom can achieve inert gas electronic structures in any other way. The elements are electron deficient (with respect to the closest inert gas structure) in most of the known oxidation states. They are, therefore, able to act as electron acceptors when in contact with atoms or molecules having unshared pairs of electrons. The Cr^{3+} and Co^{3+} ions form by far the greatest number of complexes of high stability. They are joined in this respect by Pt^{4+} and Pt^{2+} ions. These three elements, in the oxidation states listed, form thousands of known complexes.

In general, complexing ability of a given element increases with increase in positive oxidation state due to the higher charge (compare 2+ and 3+ states for chromium, or cobalt, or iron). Complexing ability also generally increases with increasing atomic number within each group. Some of the higher atomic number elements have such a great tendency to form complexes that they form highly polymerized solids of very low solubility. The lower atomic number chromium and cobalt on the other hand form smaller, more soluble aggregates. Zinc forms a soluble complex, $Zn(NH_3)_4^{++}$, with ammonia for instance, but mercury forms an insoluble compound, formula $HgNH_2X$, where X is a halogen or hydroxide radical. The complexing ability also generally increases with increasing atomic number, within the rows, reaching a maximum in Groups 6b, 7b, 8b, 9b, and 10b and then decreasing again.

The electron donor atoms shown in Table 30.4 are carbon, nitrogen, oxygen, sulfur, and halogen. The reason is that only the more electronegative elements (see page 220) can act as electron donors. Some complexes, particularly those containing fluoride, are primarily ionic in nature rather than covalent. The ionic attraction is strong due to the small size and high charge density of the fluoride ion. Many complexes containing water are bound by the attraction of the ion for the dipolar water molecules, but the majority of complexes seem to be formed through the sharing of electron pairs by the donor and acceptor atoms. The electron structural formulas of some of the donor groups are given in Table 30.4.

In many instances it is possible to form a complex containing more than one kind of donor substance grouped around a single acceptor atom. It is common to indicate the shared electron pair by an arrow pointing toward the acceptor atom. For example

Diaquo-dichloro-dicuprous-dicarbonyl (a) is probably planar, whereas dichloro-tetrammino-cobaltic ion (b) or (c), has the four groups in a plane with the cobalt atom, and one group above and one below that plane. This latter configuration is known as octahedral (six apexes and eight sides). It

510 GENERAL CHEMISTRY

should be noted that there are two ways in which the six groups can be arranged about the cobalt atom. They are shown in (b) and (c). In the first, (b), the chlorine atoms are on opposite apexes of the octahedron. In the second, (c), they are on adjacent apexes. Substances, like these, containing the same atoms arranged in different geometrical ways are called *isomers*. Isomers may

Table 30.4
Structures of Some Electron Donors Which Form Complexes
(Donated electrons indicated by ⁰₀)

DONOR ATOM	ELECTRON STRUCTURE OF DONOR GROUP	COMPLEXES FORMED	EXAMPLES
C	⁰₀C≡N:⁻	cyanide complexes	$Fe(CN)_6^{4-}$ yellow
	⁰₀C=O:	carbonyl complexes	$Ni(CO)_4$
N	⁰₀N—H with H above and H below	ammines (ammonia complexes)	$Ni(NH_3)_4^{++}$ blue $Co(NH_3)_6^{+++}$ blue
	⁰₀N=O	nitroso complexes (one or three electrons)	$Mn(CN)_5NO^{3-}$
	⁰₀N with =O and —O:⁻	nitrito complexes	$Co(NO_2)_6^{3-}$ yellow
O	⁰₀O:⁻⁻	-yl ions (as cations)	VO^{+++} yellow
	⁰₀O—H⁻	-ites and -ates (as anions) hydroxide complexes	$Zn(OH)_4^{--}$
	⁰₀O—H with H below	aquo complexes	$Cu(H_2O)_4^{++}$ light blue
	oxalate structure (two C's with O's)	oxalato complexes (usually 4 electrons)	$VO(C_2O_4)_2^-$ $Fe(C_2O_4)_3^{3-}$
	carbonate structure C=O with two O's	carbonato complexes (2 or 4 electrons)	$Co(CO_3)_2^{--}$

Table 30.4—*Continued*

S			
	:S:⁻⁻	sulfide complexes	HgS_2^{--}
	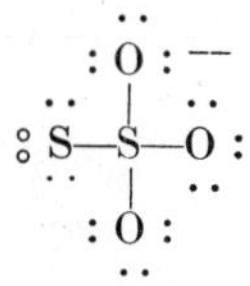 S—S—O with O above and O below	thiosulfate complexes	$Ag(S_2O_3)_2^{3-}$
	:S—C≡N:⁻	thiocyanate complexes	$Fe(CNS)_6^{3-}$ red
F, Cl, Br, I	:F:⁻, :Cl:⁻, :Br:⁻, :I:⁻	halide complexes	$CuCl_4^{--}$ green

be quite different in their properties such as melting point, boiling point, chemical stability with respect to various reactions, color, solubility, etc., depending on the differences in their geometries.

Problem 30.7. Are there any possible isomers of the cuprous carbonyl complex illustrated above? If so, diagram them and arrange them according to stability.

Problem 30.8. Cupric chloride dihydrate, formula $CuCl_2 \cdot 2H_2O$, crystallizes so that each copper ion is surrounded by two chloride ions and two water molecules lying in the same plane as the copper. How many isomers would be possible for this grouping? Which would be most stable?

Even coordination numbers are much more common than odd ones. A coordination number of 6 is most common, followed by 4, then 2, then 3, 1, and 5. The usual shape of a six-coordinated group is octahedral, of a four-coordinated group tetrahedral or square planar. A two-coordinated group may be either linear or bent, whereas one-coordination must obviously give a linear molecule. See Figure 15.1 and Table 15.5. Three-coordinated groups are usually either plane triangles or triangular pyramids with the "central" atom at the apex, whereas five-coordinated groups are usually trigonal bipyramids, meaning two triangular pyramids base to base with the "central" atom in the center of this common base and the 5 coordinated atoms at the 5 apexes of the bipyramid. The more common occurrence of the even numbered coordination groups is usually interpreted in terms of the higher degree of symmetry which is possible in an octahedron or tetrahedron compared to a trigonal bipyramid. All the bonds can be identical in the first two, allowing greater electron mobility, whereas it is impossible for all of the bonds in a bipyramid to be geometrically equivalent.

Both titanium and vanadium form cations which contain oxygen, TiO^{++}, VO^{+++}, and VO^{++} ions, respectively. Up to now we have discussed many complex anions containing oxygen—NO_3^-, SO_3^{--}, SO_4^{--}, PO_4^{---}, ClO_3^-, etc.—but not positively charged, oxygen containing ions. Oxygen containing cations are called -yl ions, example, titanyl ion, TiO^{++}. Unfortunately for simple nomenclature practice, both 5+ and 4+ vanadium exist in the oxygen containing cations, VO^{+++} and VO^{++}. Both are known as vanadyl ions but the suffix -ol has been suggested for the lower state. There are also compounds such as vanadyl monochloride, formula VOCl, in which the vanadium has an oxidation number of 3+. In such instances it is necessary to specify the oxidation number rather than just to say "vanadyl compounds." Uranyl ion, UO_2^{++}, is another common -yl ion, and UO_2^+, uranol, ions also are known. Note the high oxidation number of the uranium. All of the -yl cations exist, of course, for the same reason that the -ite and -ate ions exist, that is, the high charge density which would appear on atoms of high oxidation number if they were to exist as simple ions is greatly reduced when they form complex ions. Whether atoms of high oxidation numbers (higher than 3+) exist as cations or anions depends principally on the orbitals available for bonding. The atoms near the right end of the periodic table customarily attain an inert gas structure by forming anions containing oxygen, while those just left of center tend to form cations, the inert gas structure being too distant to be achieved by coordination with oxygen.

Problem 30.9. How do you account for the fact that silver forms the chloride complex ion $AgCl_2^-$ whereas copper forms the $CuCl_4^{--}$ ion?

Problem 30.10. How do you account for the fact that Fe^{+++} ion precipitates as ferric hydroxide when added to ammonia water but Zn^{++} forms the $Zn(NH_3)_4^{++}$ ion?

ACID-BASE RELATIONSHIPS

The acidity and basicity of the hydroxides of the elements in the central portion of the periodic table vary in the usual manner. The higher oxidation states of each element are more acidic than the lower oxidation states. With chromium and manganese the complete transition from basic (the 2+ states), through amphoteric (the 3+ states), to acidic (the highest states, 6+ and 7+, respectively) occurs.

The variations within the groups are consistent with the electronegative nature of the elements. Most of the groups in the central region show increasing electronegativity with increasing atomic number (contrary to the trends at the ends of the table). We have already considered this effect under "Ease of Oxidation" on page 503. A consequence is that the elements of higher atomic number in a group are more acidic for the same oxidation state than those of lower atomic number. Part of the trend in the solubilities of the sulfides in Group 2b may be interpreted in terms of this feature. (See also pages 243 and 414). Zinc sulfide dissolves in very dilute acid, cadmium sulfide dissolves in 3f acid, but mercuric sulfide is insoluble in the most concentrated acid. Mercuric sulfide does dissolve in a highly basic sulfide solution to form HgS_2^{--} ion, however. This behavior is consistent with the idea that zinc sulfide (and oxide) is basic, cadmium sulfide less basic and more acidic, and mercuric sulfide even more acidic.

The trend in each period, the oxidation number remaining constant, is to have a slow decrease in basicity and a corresponding increase in acidity of the oxides and hydroxides similar to the trend in the rare earths. The situation is complicated by the effect of increasing atomic number on the relative stabilities of the electron energy levels which lie close together in this region of the table. Numerous unaccountable anomalies occur, particularly in the higher oxidation states. The 2+ states from titanium to germanium show a rather regular increase in acidity, however. The 2+ hydroxides to the left of cupric hydroxide are of decreasing basicity as copper is approached. Cupric hydroxide is appreciably amphoteric and dissolves readily in acid and somewhat in base. Zinc hydroxide is completely amphoteric and is readily soluble in both acidic and basic solutions. Germanous hydroxide is acidic, though weaker than acetic acid.

Problem 30.11. Predict the relative acidity of the hydroxides with the formulas $Ge(OH)_2$, $Sn(OH)_2$, and $Pb(OH)_2$ from your knowledge of the relative electronegativity of the elements.

Problem 30.12. Predict the relative acidity of the hydroxides with the formulas $Ni(OH)_2$ and $Pd(OH)_2$.

CATALYSTS

One of the important applications of the transition elements and their compounds is in catalysis. There is, as yet, no general theory of catalysis which allows one to prejudge catalysts for given reactions with certainty or to interpret their action in detail. It is, however, generally conceded that the catalytic effects of these elements may be traced to their closely spaced energy levels. In some oxidation reactions, for instance, the oxides of elements having two oxidation states will catalyze the reaction whereas oxides of elements having only one oxidation state will not. This fact might be interpreted in terms of an alternation on the surface of the catalyst between the two oxidation states, the body of the catalyst serving as an energy source to activate the reactants when they strike the surface.

Some of the factors known to influence catalytic activity, in addition to the existence of several possible oxidation states, are the state of subdivision of the catalyst and the roughness of the surface (the more area the greater the catalytic effect), the interatomic distances in the catalyst (these should approximate the distances in the substances whose reaction is to be catalyzed so that the two—reactant and catalyst—fit together), "purity" of the catalyst (minute amounts of certain substances attack the catalyst and destroy or diminish its activity, probably by coating the surface), temperature (temperature must be high enough to activate the reactants without decomposing the products, and yet the catalytic effect of many substances is destroyed by sintering since this process diminishes the surface area), and last, the medium on which the catalyst is supported (many catalysts achieve a greatly enhanced activity when they are supported on certain surfaces or mixed with small amounts of substances—themselves not catalysts—called promotors). Many of these factors have the effect of adjusting the electronic energy levels in the catalyst so that they can interact properly with electronic energy levels of the substances whose reactions are to be catalyzed. The catalyst differs from the other reactants in that its energy levels and atomic arrangements are essentially the same after reaction as they were before, even though they certainly underwent changes during the actual reaction.

THE ELEMENTS AS METALS

The bulk properties of the elements in the central region of the periodic table are typical metallic properties: luster, high electrical and thermal conductivities, ductility, and malleability. All the common metals except aluminum and magnesium consist of elements from the central region. The pure transition elements have many excellent properties as metals but practically all commercial metals are alloys, that is, metals with more than one constituent element. We shall consider metals and alloys in Chapter 32 and shall only comment here that the extensive solubilities of the transition elements in one another is evidence for their similarities in atomic size and in electronic structure.

Problem 30.13. Without recourse to the data in the chapter, prepare a table for the zinc, cadmium, mercury group showing change in density, ease of oxidation, color of sulfide, hardness, boiling point, and basic nature of the hydroxide with increasing atomic number. Correlate each of these trends with atomic size, electronic structure, and nuclear charge trends in the group.

Problem 30.14. Repeat problem 30.13 for some of the other groups in the periodic table.

Problem 30.15. Discuss some of the changes in properties of the elements and their compounds as the atomic number increases within the rows of the periodic table. Correlate these changes with atomic size, electron structure, and nuclear charge variations.

Problem 30.16. How do you account for the general decrease in atomic size with increasing atomic number in the rows of the periodic table, followed by an increase in size beginning about Group 1b, then a subsequent decrease? See pages 157, 180, and 181 for the data on size.

Problem 30.17. Explain very briefly in terms of atomic structure (a) why copper can form a colored ion, and (b) why its ions can form ammonia complexes, whereas these properties are not observed for potassium and its ions.

Problem 30.18. From your knowledge of the properties of Fe^{++} and Cu^{++} ions compare (a) the solubility of nickelous (2+) sulfide and cupric sulfide, (b) the stability of the ammonia complexes of Ni^{++} ion, (c) the oxidizing power of ferric hydroxide and nickelic (3+) hydroxide.

Problem 30.19. Write in consecutive order the six elements in the periodic table beginning with chromium. Which of these elements has (a) the strongest tendency to change from M^{++} to M^{+++}, (b) the least soluble sulfide of the type MS, (c) the most stable complex ion, $M(NH_3)_4^{++}$, (d) atomic number 28?

Problem 30.20. Give the formulas of three "complex" ions or molecules no two of which contain the same complex-forming constituent (i.e., there must be three different donors and three different acceptors).

Problem 30.21. Vanadium is in Group 5 in the periodic table, being the fifth element in the row which starts with potassium, just as phosphorous is the fifth element in the row which starts with sodium. (a) Give two respects in which you expect vanadium to be similar to phosphorus. (b) Give two respects in which you expect vanadium to be different from phosphorus. (c) Explain briefly why you expect such differences and similarities.

Problem 30.22. What is the oxidation number of chromium in each of the substances or ions represented by the following formulas: $CrCl_2$, Cr_2O_3, $Cr_2(SO_4)_3$, CrO_2^-, CrO_4^{--}, $Cr_2O_7^{--}$, CrO_3, Cr.

Problem 30.23. From their position in the periodic table which would you expect to be the stronger acid, plumbic acid or stannic acid?

Problem 30.24. The atom of the element A has 2, 8, 8 electrons outside its nucleus, the atom of B has an atomic number 7 greater than A, the atom of C has an atomic number 3 less than A, and the atom of D an atomic number 19 greater than A. Which element: (a) is metallic, (b) has a gaseous hydride, (c) has an oxide in its highest valence state which is a base, (d) has the highest melting point?

Problem 30.25. Underline the formula for the substance or substances having the characteristic called for:

a. Lowest ionization potential	Cl_2	F_2	Mg	Au	
b. Highest valence, 7+	S	Te	I	Mn	Cr
c. Best reducing agent	Fe^{++}	Ni^{++}	Cr^{++}	Mn^{++}	
d. All shells up to 4s filled with electrons	Mn	Br	Cu	Hg	Zn

31 ELEMENTS IN THE CENTRAL REGION OF THE PERIODIC TABLE—II

IN THE last chapter we reviewed the general trends in properties of the elements in the central portion of the periodic table and of their compounds. We shall now take up the individual groups for a more detailed study of their chemistry.

TITANIUM, ZIRCONIUM, AND HAFNIUM—GROUP 4b

Titanium is the fourth most naturally abundant, structural, metallic element. Only aluminum, iron, and magnesium are more abundant. The metal has a lower density and a higher strength than stainless steel, and has much better corrosion resistance than the low-density magnesium and aluminum alloys. Its use in aircraft construction would be particularly desirable. Yet its chemistry is not widely known and its production is very limited due to its difficult metallurgy (see page 463). Only about 25,000 tons are produced annually in the U. S. A. Over 98 per cent of the cost of the metal (about $1.50 per pound) is incurred in processing the ore to obtain metal. The corresponding percentages for iron, aluminum, and magnesium are 50 per cent, 95 per cent, and 90 per cent respectively. The costs per pound for these three metals are about $0.03, $0.15, and $0.21. If the cost of processing titanium ore to the metal could be reduced to 90 per cent of the total, as with magnesium, the metal would cost about $0.30 per pound and could compete more than successfully with the present structural materials.

Hafnium is a very rare element but zirconium is more common in nature than copper, lead, and zinc combined. Its ores usually require enrichment and again have difficult metallurgies but the high corrosion resistance of the metal makes its manufacture appear to be desirable if the metallurgical problems can be solved. The chemistry of hafnium is almost identical to that of zirconium.

The largest current use of titanium appears to be in white paint pigments such as titanium oxide, formula TiO_2. The pigments are very white and have excellent covering power and permanence. Titanium tetrachloride is widely used in warfare as a smoke generator. The tetrachloride hydrolyzes with the water in the atmosphere to produce dense clouds of the dioxide. The reduction of titanium oxide with carbon in an electric furnace produces titanium carbide, formula TiC, a very hard substance much used for the cutting tips of high speed lathe tools.

Zirconium finds its biggest use as the oxide or silicate in refractories for lining high temperature furnaces. The oxide is also used in porcelains, vitreous enamels, and pottery glazes.

VANADIUM, NIOBIUM, AND TANTALUM—GROUP 5b

Vanadium is the most common member of this group but is seldom obtained as the pure metal. Its principal use is in steel-making where 0.1 or 0.2 per cent vanadium in the steel greatly increases the strength and toughness of the steel. Vanadium to be used in steel-making is prepared by reduction of ores containing both vanadium and iron, with carbon as the reducing agent. The product is known as ferro-vanadium. Some of the vanadates, compounds containing vanadium in the 5+ oxidation state, are excellent catalysts for the oxidation of sulfur dioxide to the trioxide. They rival platinum in this respect and have the great advantage of being more rugged, that is, less easily poisoned by impurities. Vanadium ores have achieved an added interest of late for they usually contain appreciable quantities of uranium.

Niobium is much more like tantalum than it is like vanadium. This behavior is characteristic of the trends in properties of the "b" groups. (Effect of the lanthanide contraction; see page 504.) There are few applications which use niobium (formerly also called columbium) or its compounds as a first choice.

Tantalum is most widely used when corrosion due to high acid concentrations is a problem. It is one of the few metals to resist corrosion in concentrated hydrochloric acid. It is customarily used as a thin sheet supported in a thicker vessel to add strength. It has a high thermal conductivity, as would be expected in a metal, and is often used in heat exchangers which must be immersed in a corrosive, highly acid solution.

Tantalum is also widely used as a bone replacement and suture material in surgery. It is inert to the surrounding flesh, is not absorbed, and is strong enough to serve as a substitute for pieces of the skull which have been removed, bases for new noses, artificial jawbones, etc. The sutures are much used in rejoining nerve tissue.

Few compounds of tantalum are used. The principal water-soluble salt of tantalum with the formula K_2TaF_7 shows the very unusual coordination number of 7 for tantalum.

CHROMIUM, MOLYBDENUM, AND TUNGSTEN—GROUP 6b

Chromium finds many uses in metal (chrome plate, stainless steel, and the very hard chrome steels), in chromic compounds containing 3+ chromium (the pigment, chrome green, formula Cr_2O_3), and in chromates and dichromates (leather tanning, strong oxidizing agents, the pigment, chrome yellow, formula $PbCrO_4$). Ferro-chrome may be prepared by the reduction of chromite, formula $FeCr_2O_4$, with carbon. Ferro-chrome has too high a carbon content to be useful in making low-carbon chrome steels, however, so that the Goldschmidt process is used to prepare chromium for making such steels.

In spite of the fact that water is more readily reduced to hydrogen at the cathode than is 3+ chromium to the metal, metallic chromium may be plated from aqueous solutions of chromic chloride to which some chromate has been added. The rate of chromium deposition is greater than that of hydrogen and the presence of the chromate prevents the hydrogen from pitting the plated surface. In commercial practice chromium trioxide is used as the source of chromium because it results in smoother deposits. It must be admitted that chromium plating from water solutions is more of an art than a science and that the theory of the operation is far from being understood. Chromium plate on iron is best if the iron is first plated with copper and then with nickel. The numerous "brightening agents" which are added to the bath to obtain a better plate have been discovered by the process of cut-and-try rather than by any prediction of their success on a theoretical basis.

Molybdenum and tungsten find their biggest applications as metals in circumstances in which their exceptionally high melting points permit their use whereas other metals would melt. The tungsten filament of an incandescent lamp is an outstanding example. Since both tungsten and molybdenum oxidize rapidly at elevated temperatures they may be used only in inert or reducing atmospheres. Any one using them as industrial "heating elements," electronic tube parts, arc electrodes, and electrical contacts must remember this fact. Both tungsten and molybdenum have about the same coefficient of thermal expansion as the glasses used in electronic tubes. They are wet readily by the molten glasses and form tight, leak-proof seals when cooled.

There is little use for the compounds of tungsten and molybdenum except as catalysts. Chromium compounds, on the other hand, are commonly used. We shall discuss some of them.

COMPOUNDS OF 2+ CHROMIUM

The chromous ion, Cr^{++}, pale blue, may be formed by electrolytic reduction of solutions of Cr^{+++} ions or by reducing these solutions with metallic zinc. The Cr^{++} ion is a strong enough reducing agent, however, to reduce water (slowly) to hydrogen and be oxidized to Cr^{+++} ion. Hence, few compounds of 2+ chromium in aqueous solutions are used.

COMPOUNDS OF 3+ CHROMIUM

Chromium in the 3+ state is one of the great complex formers. It is probable that the concentration of the simple Cr^{+++} ion is negligibly small in all its aqueous solutions and in most solids.

Chromic chloride, a violet solid prepared by passing chlorine over chromium, is very insoluble in water. If the water contains a small quantity of some reducing agent such as stannous ion, ferrous ion, sulfite ion, or chromous ion, the violet solid dissolves and a dark green solid of formula $CrCl_3 \cdot 6H_2O$ precipitates. This solid will dissolve in more water to give the ion $CrCl_2(H_2O)_4^+$. The formula of this ion is proved by x-ray diffraction and by the fact that only one third of the chloride in the chromium solution will precipitate when silver nitrate solution is added. If the dark green solution is diluted and boiled it turns dull violet. All the chloride may be precipitated from this solution, indicating that the ion $Cr(H_2O)_6^{+++}$ is now present. The intermediate ion $Cr(H_2O)_5Cl^{++}$ may also be prepared. It is light green. All three ions are present at equilibrium but the violet, fully hydrated complex is favored at low temperatures and high dilutions.

Problem 31.1. Are there any isomers of each of the chloro-aquo-chromic complexes?

Addition of a base to an aqueous solution of 3+ chromium gives a dark green precipitate soluble in excess of strong base, but not soluble in ammonia. The basic solution is bright green. The precipitate also dissolves in acid, indicating the amphoteric nature of the 3+ state. The formulas of the ions in basic solution have not been definitely established and there is some discussion as to whether true solutions or colloidal suspensions are obtained, but the following equations approximate the changes involved. Note the similarities to the corresponding aluminum equations, page 424.

$$\underset{\text{violet}}{Cr^{+++}} + 3OH^- = \underset{\text{dull green}}{Cr(OH)_{3(s)}} \qquad (31.1)$$

$$\underset{\text{dull green}}{Cr(OH)_{3(s)}} + OH^- = \underset{\text{bright green}}{Cr(OH)_4^-} \qquad (31.2)$$

The coordination number of the chromium is actually 6 in all of the above states, but the formulas shown are often used for simplicity. They neglect hydration of the ions.

Problem 31.2. How do you account for the fact that adding sodium hydroxide to a violet solution of chromic chloride in water until the solution is colorless and the chromium precipitated, and then adding hydrochloric acid to redissolve the precipitate gives a green solution rather than a violet one like the original? How would you proceed to test your explanation experimentally? Addition of the same quantity of hydrochloric acid to the original violet solution does not appreciably change its color.

Chromium sesquioxide, formula Cr_2O_3, may be prepared by heating the hydroxide, formula $Cr(OH)_3$, or by reduction of chromates and dichromates. It is often used as a green pigment. Chromium sesquisulfide, formula Cr_2S_3, can be made from the elements, but attempts to precipitate it from water solution give the hydroxide instead because of the great insolubility of the latter. Aluminum sulfide behaves similarly. Both these sulfides give a strong odor of hydrogen sulfide in contact with the atmosphere due to hydrolysis with water vapor.

$$Cr_2S_{3(s)} + 3H_2O_{(g)} = Cr_2O_{3(s)} + 3H_2S_{(g)} \quad (31.3)$$
$$\text{green} \qquad\qquad\qquad \text{green}$$

Chromium sesquioxide is isomorphous with aluminum oxide and can replace it in minerals such as the spinels, formula MAl_2O_4, where M can be magnesium or other dipositive ions. How do you account for these similarities in the chemistry of 3+ chromium and 3+ aluminum when they are not in the same periodic group?

COMPOUNDS OF 6+ CHROMIUM

Chromium in the 6+ state occurs in the trioxide, formula CrO_3, in some chromyl halides such as that with the formula CrO_2Cl_2, and in anions, the most common being CrO_4^{--}, $HCrO_4^-$, and $Cr_2O_7^{--}$ ions. More complicated anions such as $Cr_3O_{10}^{--}$, $Cr_4O_{13}^{--}$, etc., exist in concentrated solutions. Only the anions are stable in water solution. The equilibria among the common anions are given in the following equations together with their equilibrium constants.

$$Cr_2O_7^{--} + H_2O = 2HCrO_4^-; K_1 = \frac{[HCrO_4^-]^2}{[Cr_2O_7^{--}]} = 0.02 \quad (31.4)$$
$$\text{orange} \qquad\qquad \text{orange}$$

$$HCrO_4^- = H^+ + CrO_4^{--}; K_2 = \frac{[H^+][CrO_4^{--}]}{[HCrO_4^-]} = 3.70 \times 10^{-7} \quad (31.5)$$
$$\text{orange} \qquad \text{yellow}$$

Calculations will show that the yellow form, CrO_4^{--}, will exist almost to the exclusion of the others when the hydrogen ion concentration is less than 10^{-9} M, whereas the amount of $Cr_2O_7^{--}$ does not become preponderant until the hydrogen ion is greater than 10^{-5} M and the total chromium concentration exceeds about 0.1 M. Thus we see that basic solutions will contain the yellow CrO_4^{--}, dilute chromate in acid solutions will contain the orange $HCrO_4^-$, and more concentrated chromate in acid solutions will contain preponderantly the orange $Cr_2O_7^{--}$. Amazingly enough, the last two ions are almost identical in color.

The anions containing 6+ chromium may be prepared by oxidizing 3+ chromium compounds either in acidic solutions or in basic solutions. The half equations for the two processes are given in the following:

Acid solution—high chromium ion concentrations

$$2Cr^{+++} + 7H_2O = Cr_2O_7^{--} + 14H^+ + 6e^- \quad (31.6)$$
$$\text{violet} \qquad\qquad \text{orange}$$

Acid solution—low chromium ion concentrations

$$Cr^{+++} + 4H_2O = HCrO_4^- + 7H^+ + 3e^- \quad (31.7)$$
violet   orange

Basic solution

$$Cr(OH)_4^- + 4OH^- = CrO_4^{--} + 4H_2O + 3e^- \quad (31.8)$$
green   yellow

It can be seen from equations 31.6, 31.7, and 31.8 that the oxidation should proceed much more readily in basic than in acidic solution since the hydrogen ions appear among the products of the reaction while the hydroxide ions are among the reagents. This means that a high hydroxide concentration will favor reaction in equation 31.8 as written whereas a high hydrogen ion concentration will favor the reverse of reactions in equations 31.6 and 31.7. Experimentally we find that 6+ chromium is a powerful oxidizing agent in acidic solution, whereas 3+ chromium is a reducing agent in basic solution.

An interesting confirmation of the reasoning above may be obtained by adding sodium peroxide to a basic solution of chromite ion, $Cr(OH)_4^-$. The green color disappears and the solution turns yellow, indicating the presence of chromate ion CrO_4^{--}. If this solution is now acidified, it becomes orange ($HCrO_4^-$ and $Cr_2O_7^{--}$ ions), evolves gaseous oxygen (from oxidation of the peroxide still present), and turns violet indicating the presence of Cr^{+++}. Thus peroxide in basic solution oxidizes 3+ chromium to 6+ chromium but is itself oxidized in acidic solution by the 6+ chromium which changes back to the 3+ state. See equations 31.9 and 31.10.

In base: $3Na_2O_{2(s)} + 2Cr(OH)_4^- = 2CrO_4^{--} + 6Na^+ + 4OH^- + 2H_2O$ (31.9)
                                  green   yellow

In acid: $3H_2O_2 + 2HCrO_4^- + 8H^+ = 2Cr^{+++} + 3O_{2(g)} + 8H_2O$ (31.10)
                                orange   violet

Note that by applying equilibrium considerations and our knowledge of the influence of concentration on the equilibrium to reactions for which the half equations and equations indicate the actual reacting species we can often predict successfully the conditions under which reaction will occur. Of course the actual reacting species can be determined only by experiment. In the example used the known colors of the chromium-containing ions and well-known tests for acidity or basicity of the solution give us the necessary facts.

Problem 31.3. Prepare a table showing the formulas of the chromium-containing species in acidic, neutral, and basic solutions of 3+ chromium; of 6+ chromium.

When the alkaline peroxide solution containing chromate is first acidified, as mentioned above, a deep blue color is formed which quickly fades away leaving the orange of the acid chromate. The blue-colored substance is very soluble, and rather stable, in ether solutions and may be extracted by shaking the solution with ether as it is acidified. The blue substance is known to be a peroxy complex of 6+ chromium and may have the composition CrO_5. The formation of this peroxy compound is a delicate analytical test for 6+ chromium. A more common test for chromium in solution is to precipitate it as the 3+ hydroxide, formula $Cr(OH)_3$, and then oxidize it to CrO_4^{--} ion with sodium peroxide to separate the chromium from other ions also precipitated as hydroxides. One then boils the solution, acidifies it, and adds a solution containing lead or barium ions. The yellow chromate, formula $PbCrO_4$ or $BaCrO_4$, precipitates.

Problem 31.4. In preparing a solution to test it for chromium by the lead chromate precipitation, why boil the peroxide solution before acidifying it? Why acidify it?

MANGANESE, TECHNETIUM, AND RHENIUM—GROUP 7b

There are no stable isotopes of technetium, and rhenium is a very rare element so that manganese is the only member of this family of any great chemical importance. Manganese, like chromium, may be plated from an aqueous solution in spite of being more electropositive than the hydrogen in water and the purest manganese is made in this way. Most manganese is made as ferro-manganese, however, and is used in the steel and alloying industries.

The principal ore of manganese is pyrolusite, with the formula MnO_2. Manganese dioxide is the only common compound of 4+ manganese. It dissolves in concentrated hydrochloric acid to give the complex ion $MnCl_6^{--}$ (brown) but on standing these ions decompose, evolving chlorine. When purified, pyrolusite is used as the black oxidizer in the common dry cell (see page 447). Manganese dioxide is added to molten, raw glass to oxidize colored impurities, principally Fe^{++} ion (green) to Fe^{+++} ion (almost colorless).

The only monatomic ion of manganese found in aqueous solution is the Mn^{++} ion. It has a very light pink color and is stable to oxidation by air. However, the 2+ hydroxide, pink when freshly precipitated, changes quickly in air to the brown 3+ hydroxide, formula $Mn(OH)_3$. The 2+ state is more stable for the simple ion but the 3+ state becomes stabilized in complexes or precipitates (compare copper, page 527). Due to its higher charge the 3+ state also forms more complexes than the 2+ state. The high stability of the manganous ion may be explained in terms of exactly half-filled d orbitals. The same explanation accounts for the pale color as contrasted with the high colors of the ions in neighboring groups. Most manganous salts are soluble in water but the sulfide, also pink, precipitates from slightly basic solution.

The simplest test for manganese in compounds is to oxidize it to the 7+ state in the form of the highly colored, purple permanganate ion, MnO_4^-. Lead dioxide or sodium bismuthate in nitric acid is used as the oxidizer. The test is very sensitive since the color may be readily detected when the concentration of the permanganate ion is less than 10^{-6} M. Or the manganese compound may be dissolved in a fused borax bead with some sodium carbonate (to make the bead basic) and some nitrate (to serve as an oxidizing agent). In basic, strongly oxidizing solutions—either melts or aqueous solutions—the 6+ state of the manganate ion MnO_4^{--} (green) is formed rather than permanganate. Thus the bead turns green if it contains manganese.

Manganate ion may also be made by air oxidation of an aqueous alkaline solution of manganous ion, or of an alkaline suspension of manganese dioxide. The higher oxidation state, being more acidic than the lower ones, is stabilized by the basic solution. The 2− manganate ion is more stabilized by base than the 1− permanganate ion, but disproportionates into permanganate and manganese dioxide when the solution is acidified. Manganates are of little importance since they are stable only in strongly basic media, but permanganates are much used as powerful oxidizing agents. The strength of permanganate as an oxidizing agent increases rapidly with increasing acidity as equation 31.11 shows. Concentrated acids should not be added to permanganates since the compounds formed disproportionate explosively to give oxygen and manganese dioxide.

Potassium permanganate, in addition to being a very effective oxidizing agent, also serves as its own indicator. When the permanganate is dropped slowly into the reaction mix its violet color persists or not, depending on whether an excess has been added. It is, thus, very easy to add exactly enough permanganate to complete an oxidation, and no more. If the amount added was measured accurately, one can readily calculate the number of equivalents of oxidizable material originally present in the solution. Thus one mole of permanganate will react with exactly five moles of ferrous ion according to equation 31.11.

$$\underset{\text{purple}}{MnO_4^-} + \underset{\text{light green}}{5Fe^{++}} + 8H^+ = \underset{\text{yellow-brown}}{5Fe^{+++}} + \underset{\text{light pink}}{Mn^{++}} + 4H_2O \quad (31.11)$$

As the experiment is usually performed, all the ionic concentrations are so low that only the color of the permanganate ion is apparent. Thus the purple color of permanganate pervades the solution as soon as the first drop in excess is added.

Problem 31.5. Write equations: (1) for the disproportionation of manganate ion into permanganate ion and manganese dioxide; (2) for the air oxidation of manganese dioxide to manganate ion; (3) for the air oxidation of manganous hydroxide to manganic hydroxide; (4) for the solution of manganese dioxide in concentrated hydrochloric acid; (5) for the oxidation of manganous ion to manganate ion in a molten bead containing carbonate and nitrate ions; and (6) for the oxidation of manganous ion to permanganate by lead dioxide in acid solution.

IRON, COBALT, AND NICKEL

Iron, cobalt, and nickel do not constitute a vertical group in the periodic table but the properties are much more similar for the three than they are between any of them and the elements lying below them in the table. The other elements in Groups 8b, 9b, and 10b we shall treat under the heading, the platinum metals.

The alloys of iron, cobalt, and nickel are important structural metals. Nickel is also used as a bright plate to protect other metals, thanks to its highly adherent, transparent oxide coating. The alloy of nickel and copper known as Monel is important in its own right, but the bulk of the cobalt and nickel are used in steel-making. Monel is an unusual alloy in that it may be formed by direct smelting of an ore, found in Ontario, which already contains a desirable ratio of copper to nickel in the form of their sulfides.

Very pure iron and nickel may be prepared by passing carbon monoxide over the impure metal at high pressures and moderate temperatures (about 100°C.). Volatile carbonyls, formulas $Fe(CO)_5$ and $Ni(CO)_4$, form. They may be decomposed into the pure element and monoxide at higher temperatures and lower pressures. This is known as the Mond process. Cobalt with its odd number of electrons cannot form a simple carbonyl but the process can still be used since a carbonyl, formula $Co_2(CO)_8$, does form and distill. Its structure is not known, but may involve a cobalt-to-cobalt bond and two carbon monoxide bridges between the cobalt atoms.

The three elements exhibit 2+ (-ous) and 3+ (-ic) oxidation states. The stability of the 2+ state toward oxidation increases markedly from iron to cobalt to nickel; the stability of the 3+ state toward reduction decreases correspondingly. Very few 3+ compounds of nickel are known. The higher oxidation state of the elements is always stabilized by complex formation, the effect being particularly marked with cobalt. All of the complexes tend to show octahedral coordination.

The simple ions of the three may be precipitated as the hydroxides, insoluble in excess base. However the hydroxides of cobalt and nickel will dissolve in ammonia due to complex formation. The 2+ ions may also be precipitated as sulfides in a basic sulfide solution. Ferric ion may be precipitated with sulfide from a basic solution to give ferric sulfide (black), but this compound disproportionates into ferrous sulfide (black) and sulfur on standing. The sulfide concentration must be very high if ferric sulfide is to form, otherwise ferric hydroxide (red-brown) will precipitate, due to its very low solubility.

It is interesting to note that the compound ferric iodide cannot exist since ferric ion is too strong an oxidizing agent and iodide ion is too strong a reducing agent. Thus ferric ions and iodide ions react to give ferrous ions and iodine. (Compare with cupric iodide.)

$$\underset{\text{yellow}}{Fe^{+++}} + I^- = Fe^{++} + \underset{\text{violet}}{\tfrac{1}{2}I_2} \tag{31.12}$$

Problem 31.6. Explain the fact that ferric ion in water solution is much more highly colored than it is in glass.

THE RUSTING OF IRON

The rusting of iron is unquestionably one of the most important reactions in an industrial country. It is important because it weakens structural iron and leads to mechanical failure. Unfortunately, rust does not adhere to the underlying metal as do the oxides of chromium, nickel, aluminum, zinc, tin, and other metals. The rust flakes off readily and does little to protect the metal under it. Rust is a reddish-brown solid of widely variant composition. Liquid water is necessary for its formation. Freshly formed rust is soft and contains large amounts of water, either "bound" in hydroxide groups as in ferric hydroxide or "adsorbed" on the solid to give hydrous oxides and hydroxides. On standing, it loses water and becomes harder, finally approaching the formula Fe_2O_3 in composition. Iron rust may be represented by a formula, $Fe_2O_3 \cdot xH_2O$.

Though red iron oxide does not adhere to iron, black magnetic iron oxide, formula Fe_3O_4, does. This oxide is formed when iron is heated in air at high temperatures, and "black iron" is made in this way. It is resistant to rusting as long as the oxide layer is intact. Red iron oxide, on the other hand, is always formed in low-temperature oxidation processes in the presence of water, either as bulk liquid or a thin liquid film, and of atmospheric or dissolved oxygen. Acids also increase the corrosion rate.

Several mechanisms of rusting are known. One involves the action of carbon dioxide as an acid, oxygen as an oxidizing agent, and water. The possible steps in the process are summarized in equations 31.13 through 31.19.

Acid forming:
$$CO_2 + H_2O = H^+ + HCO_3^- \quad (31.13)$$

Initial oxidation:
$$2H^+ + Fe_{(s)} = Fe^{++} + H_{2(g)} \quad (31.14)$$

or

$$H^+ + Fe_{(s)} + \tfrac{1}{2}O_2 = Fe(OH)^+ \quad (31.15)$$

Final oxidation:
$$2Fe^{++} + \tfrac{1}{2}O_2 + 5H_2O = 2Fe(OH)_{3(s)} + 4H^+ \quad (31.16)$$
$$\text{red}$$

or

$$2Fe(OH)^+ + \tfrac{1}{2}O_2 + 3H_2O = 2Fe(OH)_{3(s)} + 2H^+ \quad (31.17)$$
$$\text{red}$$

Over-all reaction:

31.14 plus 31.16:
$$2Fe_{(s)} + \tfrac{1}{2}O_2 + 5H_2O = 2Fe(OH)_{3(s)} + 2H_{2(g)} \quad (31.18)$$
$$\text{red}$$

31.15 plus 31.17:
$$2Fe_{(s)} + \tfrac{3}{2}O_2 + 3H_2O = 2Fe(OH)_{3(s)} \quad (31.19)$$
$$\text{red}$$

Note that the acidity of the solution is unchanged by the rusting process, but that hydrogen ion acts as a catalyst in both methods of bringing about corrosion. This mechanism is one of the fastest for rusting and is the reason that distilled water containing dissolved air causes such rapid rusting. Distilled water is slightly acid due to the carbon dioxide content. Tap water, usually basic from the softening process, gives slower corrosion, and sodium hydroxide solutions give almost no corrosion on iron.

Another mechanism involves direct oxidation by oxygen dissolved in water, according to the following equations:

$$Fe_{(s)} + \tfrac{1}{2}O_2 + H_2O = Fe(OH)_{2(s)} \tag{31.20}$$

$$2Fe(OH)_{2(s)} + \tfrac{1}{2}O_2 + H_2O = 2Fe(OH)_{3(s)} \tag{31.21}$$
$$\text{red}$$

Over-all reaction: $$2Fe_{(s)} + \tfrac{3}{2}O_2 + 3H_2O = 2Fe(OH)_{3(s)} \tag{31.22}$$
$$\text{red}$$

This mechanism is much slower than the acid-catalyzed one, largely because the ferrous hydroxide coats the iron surface and slows down further corrosion. The presence of chloride ions in the solution (as in salt water) greatly enhances the corrosion rate partly by forming complex chloride-containing ions which remove the partially oxidized iron from the surface. This 2+ iron complex is then oxidized to the ferric state within the body of the solution.

Electrolytes in general also enhance corrosion through their role in electrolytic cells. Oxygen is reduced at the iron near the upper surface of the liquid where its concentration is highest and the iron lower in the container is oxidized to ferrous ions. These ions are later oxidized to the ferric state within the bulk liquid. The half-equations for these reactions differ from those for the preceding mechanisms because the oxidation reduction is now proceeding as a cell process with the anode and cathode processes separated, but the over-all reaction is the same. (Equations 31.19, 31.22, and 31.26 are identical.)

Near contact of air, solution, and iron: $$2e^- + \tfrac{1}{2}O_2 + H_2O = 2OH^- \tag{31.23}$$

Away from air at iron surface: $$Fe_{(s)} = Fe^{++} + 2e^- \tag{31.24}$$

In bulk of solution: $$2Fe^{++} + \tfrac{1}{2}O_2 + H_2O + 4OH^- = Fe(OH)_{3(s)} \tag{31.25}$$
$$\text{red}$$

Over-all reaction: $$2Fe_{(s)} + \tfrac{3}{2}O_2 + 3H_2O = 2Fe(OH)_{3(s)} \tag{31.26}$$
$$\text{red}$$

Electrolytic corrosion may also be very rapid when metals or alloys of different composition are in contact with the iron so that the iron acts as the anode in the cell.

Corrosion, in the sense of oxidation, of iron in particular and of metals in general, is stopped in one of two ways. The surface is either covered by a protective film such as a paint, a plated metal, a corrosion-resistant, adherent film such as an oxide or a phosphate, or the metal is charged to a negative electrode potential which is sufficiently high to reduce back to the metal any oxidation products which may form. Iron pipes passing through acid soil are frequently connected to blocks of magnesium (or zinc). The magnesium has a higher oxidation potential than the iron, and, as the magnesium corrodes, the iron pipe is maintained at a negative potential which prevents corrosion of the iron. Or iron is frequently dipped into phosphate (Parkerized), metallic zinc (galvanized), or metallic tin (tin plated) baths to coat it with a protective layer, though tin is now usually electrodeposited.

THE PLATINUM METALS

Ruthenium, rhodium, and palladium, and osmium, iridium, and platinum may be grouped together since much of their chemistry is similar. All are very noble metals, rare, and high priced. The use of platinum in jewelry is well known. Its great inertness and high melting point also make it useful in platinum resistance thermometers and platinum-platinum rhodium thermocouples used in measuring high temperatures. Special chemical apparatus to be used under highly corrosive conditions is sometimes made of platinum. Platinum reacts readily, however, with metals in the groups to the right of it in the periodic table, with selenium and tellurium, and with fused alkalies. It also should be kept out of reducing flames since it forms a brittle carbide. The most serious corrosion comes, however, when it is in simultaneous contact with chlorides and an oxidizing agent. The complexes between platinum and chloride are highly stable, hence the ready solubility of platinum in aqua regia.

$$Pt_{(s)} + 6Cl^- + 4NO_3^- + 8H^+ = \underset{\text{yellow}}{PtCl_6^{--}} + \underset{\text{brown}}{4NO_{2(g)}} + 4H_2O \qquad (31.27)$$

The other elements have relatively small-scale uses in pen points, dentistry, electrical contacts, and catalysts. Osmium and ruthenium are interesting in that they alone, of all the elements, can exhibit oxidation states of 8+ as in the compounds with the formulas OsO_4, OsF_8, and RuO_4.

COPPER, SILVER, AND GOLD—GROUP 1b

Group 1b is unique in many respects. We have already commented that each of its elements shows a maximum oxidation number greater than the group number, 1. The tendency of the elements in the higher oxidation states to form complexes may account for their existence. For example, the 3+ state for gold exists only in highly stable complexes; a stable simple auric ion, Au^{+++}, is never found. Cupric ions are also highly complexed—by water if not by other species. Simple cuprous ions may be more stable than simple cupric ions. At high temperatures cuprous halides and cuprous sulfide, respectively, are formed when the metal is heated with the halogens or sulfur. But in aqueous solution at low temperature cuprous ions disproportionate into cupric ions and metallic copper—water complexes the cupric ion more tightly than it does the cuprous ion. Similarly, aurous ions disproportionate into auric complexes and metallic gold in the presence of complexing agents. The reason for the instability of the higher oxidation state of silver is not known, but for most practical purposes silver exists only in the 1+ oxidation state, both as the simple ion and in complexes. The higher state is readily formed, however, by electrolysis of an aqueous solution of silver nitrate. Metallic silver forms at the cathode and the 2+ oxide, formula AgO (black), forms at the anode.

Most silver compounds are insoluble in water, the only notable exceptions being the nitrate and the fluoride which are very soluble. Cuprous salts have solubilities like those of silver. Most cupric salts are soluble, the outstanding exceptions being the sulfide, oxide-hydroxide, and phosphate. Cupric sulfide is insoluble in acids but reacts with oxidizing agents such as 3 f nitric acid which can oxidize the sulfide ion to sulfur or even to sulfate. The oxide and hydroxide are soluble in acids, and show enough amphoteric nature to be slightly soluble in strong bases; both are soluble in ammonia to give the deep blue tetra-ammino complex ion. This ion is so highly colored that its formation constitutes a sensitive test for cupric ions in solution, few other ions having a deep enough color to hide the blue of the complex.

Copper, silver, and gold are widely used in jewelry and in coinage. The metals are among the best conductors. Copper (and sometimes silver) is very important to the electrical industry. Several metals (sodium and aluminum) used commercially are better electrical conductors per unit weight than copper but none is better per unit of cross section of conducting wire or bar. Hence, long spans of cable such as high tension lines may use aluminum wire, but copper is always used in the fine windings of motors, dynamos, etc., where space rather than low weight is at a premium. The elements, especially copper, also find wide application in alloys. The brasses are alloys of copper and zinc, and the bronzes of copper, zinc, and tin with other metals added for special properties they impart. Except as metallic conductors, where minute traces of impurities very markedly decrease the conductivity of the metal, these elements are seldom used as the pure metals. Pure metals are too soft and malleable for most applications, including coinage and jewelry, and are almost always alloyed with one another or with other elements.

Cupric ions in low concentrations are highly toxic to many lower forms of life so that some cupric compounds are used in pesticides. The insecticide Paris green, formula $Cu_4(C_2H_3O_2)_2(AsO_3)_2$, also contains arsenate ion as an active ingredient. Bordeaux mixture, made from cupric sulfate and slaked lime, is a fungicide. Cupric sulfate itself is often dissolved in outdoor pools to kill algae and reptilian life. Yet traces of copper are required by many living organisms.

CHEMISTRY OF THE PHOTOGRAPHIC PROCESS

One of the largest uses of silver is in the photographic industry, primarily as silver chloride and silver bromide. Both of these compounds are *photosensitive*, being slowly decomposed into the elements by light. Most photographic films, plates, and papers contain small crystals of these halides suspended in gelatin ("emulsions") and supported on a tough base such as glass, plastic film, or paper. The detailed chemistry of the photographic process is not understood even after very extensive investigation but the general changes which occur are known.

Photographic emulsions exposed to light for short times show no visible image on the emulsion; it appears quite blank to the eye. The presence of a "latent image" is demonstrated however, when the emulsion is immersed in a weak reducing agent, known as the photographic "developer." The developer reduces to metallic silver those crystals of silver halide which have been struck by light and so forms a visible image. The unexposed silver halide is not affected by the developer and is later removed with sodium thiosulfate ("hypo"). The reactions may be summarized in the following equations, the formula $AgCl^*_{(s)}$ indicating light-struck halide:

Exposure: $$AgCl_{(s)} \text{ (white)} + light = AgCl^*_{(s)} \text{ (white)} \tag{31.28}$$

Development: $$AgCl^*_{(s)} \text{ (white)} + \begin{pmatrix} e^- \text{ from} \\ \text{reducing agent} \end{pmatrix} = Ag_{(s)} \text{ (black)} + Cl^- \tag{31.29}$$

Fixing: $$AgCl_{(s)} \text{ (white)} + 2S_2O_3^{--} = Ag(S_2O_3)_2^{---} + Cl^- \tag{31.30}$$

It should be clear that the reducing agent to be used as a developer must be chosen with great care for it must reduce only the light-struck halide and leave the rest unchanged.

ZINC, CADMIUM, AND MERCURY—GROUP 2b

The Group 2b family differs from the preceding ones in that zinc and cadmium resemble one another much more strongly than do cadmium and mercury. In the preceding groups the resemblances were most striking between the Period V and Period VI elements. The great stability of an inert pair of s electrons in mercury completely changes the picture for this group as a re-examination of Table 30.1 on page 497 will show. Zinc and cadmium exist only in the 2+ state in their compounds but mercury exhibits this state and a 1+ state as well. We have already discussed on page 498 an interpretation of this peculiarity. See Table 16.2 for electron structures of the ions.

Most common compounds of zinc and cadmium are soluble in water and hydrolyze to give acid solutions. An aqueous solution of zinc chloride, or even the solid hydrate itself, is often used as a flux in soldering metals. The flux dissolves the oxide coat on the metal and prepares and maintains a clean metallic surface to which the solder can adhere. Both zinc and cadmium hydroxides are amphoteric, the cadmium hydroxide being the less acidic of the two. Mercuric hydroxide is such a weak acid that it does not dissolve appreciably in basic solutions. Both zinc and cadmium ions readily form water-soluble ammonia complexes, but with mercuric ion the compound formed has the formula $HgNH_2OH$. It is insoluble, indicating the great tendency of mercuric ion to form insoluble, three-dimensional, solid complexes. At very high ammonia concentrations some $Hg(NH_3)_4^{++}$ ion is formed; its salts are soluble in water.

Many mercury compounds are highly colored. The crystal form of mercuric iodide stable at room temperature has a red color. When heated above a transition temperature of 127°C. it changes to a different crystal form, colored yellow, which is stable above the transition temperature. Hence this change in crystal forms is more spectacular, but not more important, than the transitions common for very many crystalline solids.

The two greatest uses of zinc are in alloys, particularly in brass, and in metal plating, particularly on iron. Zinc is a very electropositive metal but forms a tough, adherent, relatively inert, basic carbonate coating which protects the metal from corrosion except under acidic or basic conditions. The hydroxide is amphoteric, hence the limitation of corrosion resistance to approximately neutral solutions. The electropositive nature of the element allows it to protect underlying iron even though there may be holes in the zinc coat which permit the corrosive agent to reach the iron. The higher reducing potential of the zinc will keep the iron charged to a negative potential so that the zinc will be oxidized rather than the iron. Compare with the use of magnesium to prevent underground corrosion of iron pipe. Cadmium is also used in protective plating and is interchangeable with zinc in many such applications. Cadmium is less electropositive than zinc and so oxidizes more slowly and lasts longer, yet it also is more electropositive than iron and thus protects the latter.

Both cadmium and zinc compounds are used in pigments. Lithopone, a mixture of barium sulfate and zinc sulfide, is a common white pigment, and cadmium yellow, formula CdS, a common yellow one.

Many uses of mercury (thermometers, amalgams, manometers) depend on the fact that it is the only common metal which is liquid near room temperature, but its biggest single use is in the manufacture of fulminate, mercuric cyanate, formula $Hg(CNO)_2$. Fulminate is used as a detonator in many applications of high explosives, such as artillery shells. Since the demand for it fluctuates widely from time to time, depending on military as well as industrial use, the price of mercury, and the number of mercury mines which can operate economically also fluctuates, probably more widely than for any other metal.

The toxicity of the elements of Group 2b increases rapidly with increasing atomic number, as is characteristic with elements of most of the families of the periodic table. Some of this toxicity is due to the fact that the compounds of the elements of high atomic weight tend to be insoluble in the body fluids, causing precipitation of compounds of the elements within the tiny passages of the kidneys, for instance, and leading to the general effect of "heavy metal" poisoning. "Heavy metal" poisoning is, in general, cumulative due to its method of action and it may take years to build up a lethal dose within the body. Some of the elements also have more specific effects. Mercury is a particularly insidious poison because of the high volatility of the metal and its compounds and the cumulative poisoning effect, a fact not realized for many years. Mercury poisoning was endemic at one time in the hat industry (mercury compounds were used in the felting process) and in dentistry, when the dentist squeezed the excess mercury out of the filling amalgams in the palm of his hand rather than in a dish. (It is interesting to note that one of the symptoms of mercury poisoning is a falling out of the teeth.) Occasional serious cases of mercury poisoning still arise when someone confuses mercurous chloride, used in internal medicine as calomel, and mercuric chloride, a deadly poison called corrosive sublimate. Why do you suppose that one of these compounds may be administered internally with safety, whereas the other one is lethal?

Problem 31.7. What compounds would you mix to prepare lithopone?

Problem 31.8. Account for the fact that mercuric iodide changes color spontaneously from red to yellow when heated above 127°C. but maintains the yellow color indefinitely when again cooled below the transition temperature. It will revert to the red form if pressed, under a knife for instance.

Problem 31.9. How could you obtain separated, pure compounds of Zn^{++}, Cd^{++}, and Hg^{++} ions if ions of all three were originally present in the same solution?

GALLIUM, INDIUM, AND THALLIUM—GROUP 3a

These elements are all relatively rare and of no wide scale application. Their general properties are those which would be predicted from the regular trends in this region of the periodic table.

GERMANIUM, TIN, AND LEAD—GROUP 4a

Germanium compounds have limited use. In them the 4+ oxidation state for germanium is most common. The oxidation states of the Group 4a were discussed briefly on page 499. Most tin compounds are soluble in water but the salts are highly hydrolyzed. The stannic, 4+, state in water exists only in complex ions of the type, $SnCl_6^{--}$ and $Sn(OH)_6^{--}$. Stannous hydroxide, like stannic hydroxide, precipitates even from slightly acidic solutions but it redissolves in strongly basic solution. Lead commonly forms the 2+ ion but most of its salts are insoluble in water; the nitrate as usual is the outstanding exception. Lead acetate, known as sugar of lead because of its sweet taste, is soluble, and the soluble complex ion $Pb(C_2H_3O_2)_4^{--}$ is formed when lead sulfate, for example, is treated with a solution of acetate ion. In this group the order of increase in acidity—from 2+ lead to 2+ tin to 4+ tin—is characteristic of the end groups in the periodic table rather than of those in the central region.

Germanium has limited but important use in the electrical industry because it is a semi-conductor, that is, a conductor with fairly high resistance. In "transistors" its conductivity can be varied widely so that they can replace vacuum electronic tubes for many purposes. Tin and lead are widely used but are in very short supply. The known reserves of lead are about as small (some thirty years supply) as those of any element. Tin plate and alloys use most of the tin and storage batteries, white lead for paint, alloys, and gun projectiles use most of the lead. Another widespread use is reflected in the word, plumbing, derived from *plumbum*.

White lead is a basic lead carbonate, prepared by air oxidation of lead in the presence of acetic acid and carbon dioxide. Its formula approximates $Pb_3(OH)_2(CO_3)_2$. It is very white, and has excellent covering power. Unfortunately lead sulfide, black, is more stable than white lead so that leaded paints darken on long exposure to the air. Partly because of cost it is being replaced by other white pigments in paints. (Can you name two other white pigments and list the comparative advantages and disadvantages of each of the three for paints?)

Lead compounds are highly toxic and the effects of small doses are cumulative. Lead poisoning was serious for painters and others exposed to lead compounds until proper precautions were taken to prevent excessive intake. Lead, like the other "heavy metals," is eliminated only very slowly by the body.

Problem 31.10. How could you prepare the following in pure solid form: (a) lead sulfate from lead sulfide, (b) tin tetrachloride from stannous hydroxide, (c) plumbous hydroxide from lead, (d) stannic sulfide from a solution of stannous chloride, (e) lead chloride from lead dioxide, (f) lead nitrate from lead chloride?

Problem 31.11. How could you prepare in pure solid form: (a) ferrous hydroxide from ferrous sulfide, (b) ferric hydroxide from ferrous hydroxide, (c) ferrous hydroxide from ferric hydroxide, (d) ferrous chloride from ferric nitrate, (e) Prussian blue, formula $KFeFe(CN)_6$, from iron and potassium cyanide?

Problem 31.12. How would you prepare in pure solid form: (a) stannous chloride from stannic chloride, (b) lead chloride from lead sulfide, (c) mercurous chloride from mercuric chloride, (d) lead dioxide from lead, (e) stannic sulfide from SnS_3^{--} ions?

Problem 31.13. Compare the strengths as acids of (a) arsenious and antimonous acids, (b) arsenious and arsenic acids. Give reasons for your answer.

Problem 31.14. How would you get the following solids into solution for the purposes of qualitative analysis: (a) calomel, (b) cadmium yellow, (c) cinnabar, (d) cupric oxide?

Problem 31.15. When solutions of ferric chloride and sodium carbonate are mixed, ferric hydroxide is precipitated rather than ferric carbonate. Explain.

Problem 31.16. State a use for each of the following and the property utilized: (a) mercuric sulfide, (b) the iron sulfide, formula FeS_2, (c)–(e) ferric oxide (three uses), (f)–(h) mercury (three uses), (i) iron carbide.

Problem 31.17. To a solution prepared by mixing 100 ml. of $0.010\,f$ potassium iodide with 400 ml. of $0.1\,f$ sulfuric acid is added 1.74 g. of manganese dioxide. The mixture is stirred until reaction is complete. What are the approximate concentrations of (a) Mn^{++} ion, (b) iodine, and (c) I^- ion in the resulting solution?

Problem 31.18. Name reagents that will dissolve (a) silver oxide but not silver chloride, (b) zinc hydroxide but not cadmium hydroxide, (c) zinc but not copper, (d) silver carbonate but not calcium carbonate, (e) zinc bromide but not silver bromide, (f) zinc sulfide but not cupric sulfide.

Problem 31.19. What reagents would dissolve (a) cadmium sulfide but not mercuric sulfide, (b) mercuric oxide but not mercuric sulfide, (c) silver chloride but not mercurous chloride, (d) mercurous chloride but not silver chloride, (e) mercury but not mercuric sulfide, (f) ferrous sulfide but not silver sulfide, (g) cupric hydroxide but not ferrous hydroxide, (h) iron but not copper?

Problem 31.20. What would be present after reaction, and in what amounts, when the following are mixed:

a. 0.02 mole of mercury and 0.10 mole of mercuric nitrate in 5 l. of water.
b. 0.05 mole of mercuric chloride and 0.10 mole of stannous chloride, both in solution.
c. 0.4 mole of zinc, 0.4 mole of ferric chloride, and 0.1 mole of chlorine in 10 l. of water.

32 METALS AND ALLOYS

METALS WERE known to prehistoric man but not the pure elements. The metallic specimens, whether found as native metal or prepared from ores, contained elements other than the principal constituent. The minor constituents were sometimes present in the original ore and sometimes they were introduced in the smelting process. For whatever reasons, definite minor constituents are found in old metals. Archeological specimens of metals are often classified or dated on the basis of the minor elements present. Even today the source of metals may be deduced from the impurities that are present. Most of the present metals of commerce are not pure elements. Indeed, for most purposes the properties of the metals are better suited to the desired use when the metals are alloys.

Metals are recognized by certain properties called *metallic*. Common metallic properties are luster and good electrical and thermal conductivity. Workability, the ability to be deformed permanently without rupture, is another property of most metals. The majority of the pure chemical elements have these properties and are classified as metallic elements. The atoms of these elements have the ability to lose electrons to form cations, a fact we have already used to define the metallic elements. The bulk properties of metals—luster, conductivity, and workability—are related to the atomic structure of the metallic elements and to the ability of the atoms to form cations.

Metals are so important in our civilization that we shall consider them in some detail to see how the properties are related to their composition and structure.

ALLOYS

A metallic substance, that is, one with metallic properties is called an *alloy* if it consists of more than one chemical element. An alloy may be composed entirely of metallic elements (example, brass, an alloy of copper and zinc) or be composed of a metallic element together with a nonmetallic element (example, steel, an alloy of the metallic element, iron, and the nonmetallic element, carbon). An alloy may, of course, be composed of more than two elements. However, all known metallic substances have as their principal constituents one or more metallic elements. Apparently metallic elements must be present in dominating amounts if the substance is to have metallic properties. Boron, hydrogen, nitrogen, and silicon are among the other nonmetallic elements that may be present in minor amounts in alloys.

METALLIC PROPERTIES

We are already familiar with the fact that metals are the best conductors of electricity. Electrons are able to move freely from atom to atom in the metal so that when electrons are added to one end of a metal strip and removed from the other, a current of electrons flows through the strip. The explanation is that valence electrons are held in common by the atoms and are free to move. The electrical pressures required to produce a given flow of electrons varies from metal to metal and the current flowing under a given pressure (electrical conductivity) varies accordingly.

It is a significant fact that the metals are also excellent conductors of heat and that for most pure metals the thermal conductivity is proportional to the electrical conductivity. That is, the metals with the highest electrical conductivity have the highest thermal conductivity. Every student who has heated a glass rod to red heat in a flame learns that the glass rod a short distance from the hot section remains fairly cool whereas a metal rod held at an equal distance would have become unbearably hot. Aluminum and copper, both excellent conductors of electricity, are also excellent conductors of heat. Utensils of these metals placed over the burners of a kitchen stove conduct heat so well that their temperatures become fairly uniform. Iron utensils do not heat nearly as evenly. Because of the parallelism between thermal and electrical conductivity we conclude that the valence electrons of the metals act as the transporting medium for the thermal energy.

The workability of metals may be expressed in terms of ductility, malleability, and toughness. When a material may be drawn out permanently without rupture so that its length increases while its cross section decreases it is said to be *ductile*. If the material may be deformed permanently without rupture by applied pressure, as by hammering or by rolling, it is said to be *malleable*. A material is said to be *tough* (and not brittle) when it remains strong during deformation so that a large amount of energy must be expended to break it. *Hardness* is a measure of the resistance to permanent deformation. Deformability without rupture is one of the most interesting properties of metals.

PURE METALS

The surface of a piece of metal that appears homogeneous to the naked eye is seen under the microscope to consist of a mosaic of small intermingled grains. When the metal consists of a single metallic element the grains can be shown to be small crystals of the element. Within each grain the atoms are arranged in an orderly way characteristic of the crystal habit of the element. The majority of the metallic elements crystallize in the face-centered cubic system, though some crystallize in the hexagonal system and others in the body-centered cubic system. In the first two systems each atom is close packed and in contact with twelve neighbors and in the body-centered system each atom is in contact with eight neighbors. However, since the grain surfaces do not meet at regular angles there will be some atoms at the grain boundaries that are not full members of either grain and that must form the bonds between the grains.

If suitable precautions are taken, pieces of metal may be prepared that consist of but a single grain. Such a piece is called a *single crystal*. A single crystal has the maximum electrical and thermal conductivity for the element, there being the minimum of interference with the free passage of electrons. However, single crystals are softer than a polycrystalline mass of the same dimensions. In the single crystal there is the minimum resistance to the movement of the atoms of one crystal plane past those of an adjacent plane. Indeed, after the single crystal is bent it can no longer exist as a single crystal for the displaced atoms arrange themselves in new and smaller crystals. Then there is more resistance to deformation and the material becomes harder. A piece of pure metal becomes harder when it is bent, drawn, or hammered.

The reason a metal may be worked without rupture must be found in the fact that the atoms readily form strong bonds with new neighbors when they are displaced from old ones. Old grains may be reorganized into new ones without loss of strength so long as the grain boundaries remain bonded together. When the grain boundaries become separated on drawing or hammering the piece of metal breaks apart.

The metallic elements, like other pure substances, have definite melting and boiling points. However, their bulk properties, such as hardness and electrical conductivity, which depend on the size and orientation of the individual crystals vary slightly with the previous history of the sample of metal. Single crystals, of course, have definite and reproducible bulk properties.

TYPES OF ALLOYS

When an alloy is formed from two or more constituent elements the properties usually differ decidedly from those of the pure elements. We can understand the reasons more fully if we consider the possible structures of binary alloys, those containing two constituent elements. Let the two constituents be designated as A and B, respectively, and let us assume that A and B may be mixed in any ratios to form a liquid solution. Since most metals do form completely miscible liquid solutions we shall not lose much in the way of generality by this assumption. The temperature must, of course, be high enough to make the alloy melt completely to liquid. The temperature necessary will depend on the particular pair of elements in the alloy.

When the liquid alloy is cooled sufficiently, crystals begin to separate from

METALS AND ALLOYS 537

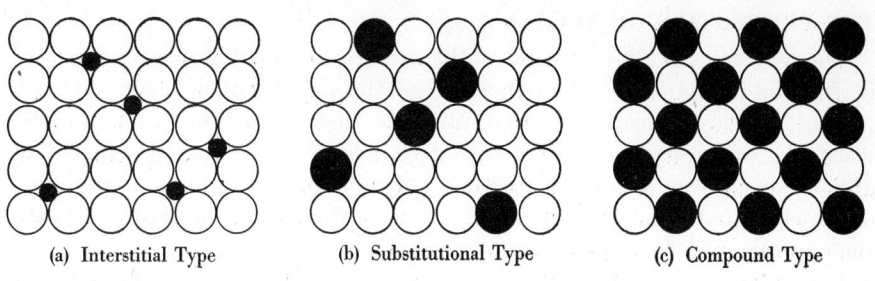

(a) Interstitial Type (b) Substitutional Type (c) Compound Type

Figure 32.1.
Alloy types (two dimensions).

the liquid solution. The nature of the separating crystals determines the classification according to the following four types. See Figure 32.1.

1. Simple Eutectic Type

When the atoms of A and B are sufficiently different, crystals of pure A or of pure B or some of pure A and some of pure B will form from the cooling melt. The familiar freezing-point-lowering effect is found in these alloys. See pages 263–264. The composition of the liquid solution having the lowest freezing temperature is called the *eutectic composition* and its freezing temperature is called the *eutectic temperature*.

2. Substitutional Solid Solution Type

When the atoms of A and B are not too different in size and somewhat similar chemically, and when atoms of A and atoms of B may crystallize out in the *same crystals*, the atoms of A and B become randomly distributed throughout the crystals at the regular lattice points. The resulting crystalline solid is called a solid solution. This type of solid solution in which one kind of atom may be substituted for another may be called the *substitutional solid solution* type.

3. Interstitial Solid Solution Type

When B is a nonmetallic element with small atoms, the atoms of B may enter empty spaces in the regular crystal of A. In this type the atoms of A crystallize in its regular crystal pattern and B is present in some of the available holes between the atoms of A. An *interstitial solid solution* is formed.

4. Compound Type

When atoms of A and B form crystals with definite composition and with definite melting points the crystalline solid is called a *compound*. Although these compounds have definite melting points they apparently exist only in the crystal phase and not in the liquid solution.

THE PROPERTIES OF ALLOYS

The properties of alloys depend on the ways the different atoms are arranged in the metal even more than they do on the particular elements that are present. We have already seen that most pure metals, including iron, are soft, workable, and tough, even though not especially strong, because planes of atoms can slip past one another without much hindrance to find new positions of almost equal strength. Alloys are stronger though less workable because the opportunities for slippage are decreased.

Actual description of an alloy is complicated by the fact that the different grains have different structure and composition. Plumber's solder made from tin and lead is of the eutectic type, but the separate grains are not pure tin or pure lead. The tin crystals have a small amount of lead dissolved in solid solution and the lead crystals have a somewhat larger amount of dissolved tin. The solubilities depend somewhat on temperature so that the actual composition depends on the temperature to which the solder is heated even when the solder remains solid. Nickel and copper, on the other hand, form an unbroken series of solid solutions but when the liquid is crystallized the first grains to form have relatively more nickel and the last to form have relatively more copper. However, when the mosaic mixture of crystals is heated below the melting points of the crystals the concentration in the different crystals tends to equalize by diffusion of the atoms.

In a particular alloy some of the crystal grains may be solid solutions and others metallic compounds. When first laid down at high temperatures the grains may have been at equilibrium with the liquid, but at room temperature the equilibrium conditions may be different. Then the properties of the alloy may change on aging, that is, with the passage of time. These facts explain why the "heat treatment" or the aging of an alloy subsequent to its original manufacture may change the properties drastically. The forming of new grains so small as to be below the resolving power of optical microscopes may change the properties greatly. The critical range of sizes lies between atomic dimensions, about 1 Å., to about 10^{-4} cm. or 10,000 Å. on an edge.

ELECTRICAL CONDUCTIVITY OF ALLOYS

The best electrical conductors are pure metals, though some metallic compounds have high electrical conductivities. When the structure is regular the resistance to the movement of the conducting electrons is at a minimum. Tiny amounts of impurities may decrease conductivity greatly, especially when the impurities form layers between the conducting crystals. When copper has 2 atomic per cent of tin, or one foreign atom in fifty, in solid solution the conductivity is halved. If 2 per cent of iron is present in solid solution the conductivity is reduced to one fifth. Gold, like copper, is an excellent conductor but a solid solution containing 50 per cent of each of gold and copper has only one fifth the conductivity of the separate pure metals. For these reasons copper wire and aluminum wire for electrical transmission purposes are made as pure as possible. The copper is refined by electrolysis for this purpose.

HARDNESS AND STRENGTH

Alloys are always used where hardness and strength are desired. Solid solutions are not as hard as other types of alloys but they are harder and stronger than the pure metals. Thus, the tensile strength of brass is about 50 per cent greater than that of pure copper or pure zinc. Interstitial solid solutions are much harder and stronger than pure metals. The interspersed atoms in the spaces of the regular crystal lattices are very effective in decreasing slippage. Pure iron has a tensile strength of about 40,000 pounds per square inch, but a steel containing some interstitial carbon and some manganese in solid solution in gamma iron has a tensile strength three times as great.

Intermetallic compounds are hard and strong, but are rather brittle. The atoms in their relatively fixed positions resist movement and do not form strong new bonds readily when displaced from their former position. Eutectic mixtures, though consisting of relatively soft grains, are also hard and brittle. The grains of different composition surround one another after slippage, but the grains tend to separate under stress. Thus, joints held together by plumber's solder separate when the metal is twisted or bent.

CORROSION OF ALLOYS

Many alloys are prepared and used because they resist corrosion. Although zinc is a fairly reactive metal it loses some of its ability to react when it is imbedded in a solid solution, as in brass. Although the zinc atoms at the surface may react leaving almost pure copper on the surface, those below the surface are protected and can continue to lend strength to the alloy. Some aluminum alloys, desirable because of their strength, hardness, and lightness, corrode rather rapidly because the products of the corrosion do not form a good protective film. Hence such alloys are often sandwiched between thin layers of pure aluminum in the fabrication process. The pure aluminum surfaces protect the alloy from corrosion and are themselves resistant because of the protective properties of aluminum oxide formed on the surface.

"Stainless steels" are, strictly speaking, not steels because they are not carbon alloys. A typical stainless steel contains 18 per cent chromium, and 8 per cent nickel by weight, the rest being iron. The oxidation products of the chromium and nickel form a protective coating effective under acid conditions or at high temperatures, conditions under which ordinary iron or steel fail quickly. Most corrosion-resistant alloys are rather expensive because of the high cost of the metals that confer the corrosion resistance.

CAST IRON

The molten iron in the blast furnace becomes saturated with carbon (about 4 per cent carbon) and it also contains some silicon (up to 2 per cent), sulfur, and phosphorus, which result from the reducing action of the carbon on the clays or salts present in the impure ore in the furnace. The resulting pig iron obtained from the furnace contains 92–94 per cent iron and melts at about 1150°C. (The melting point of pure iron is 1535°C.) Carbon has a limited solubility in solid iron so that when the melt crystallizes the excess carbon appears as graphite or in cementite, formula Fe_3C. The pig iron may be melted and cast in molds to form various objects. "White cast iron" is formed when the mold is chilled suddenly so that the carbon appears in cementite. The product is hard and brittle. "Gray cast iron" is formed on slower cooling so that much of the excess carbon appears as graphite. Gray iron is more ductile. Cast iron objects are rather cheap and resist corrosion well. Sewer pipe is an example.

WROUGHT IRON

Once made by hand, wrought iron is now made by machinery because of its special properties of toughness and durability. Pig iron is poured into molten slag and oxidized until most of the carbon and other nonmetallic impurities are removed. In the process the freezing point rises and the mass becomes more solid. Most of the slag is then squeezed out by hammering, but some of it remains in thin layers interspersed throughout the nearly pure iron. This slag acts as a coating to protect the pure iron, which in itself would not resist corrosion. The process is interesting as a modern adaptation of the oldest method for refining pig iron.

STEEL

Most pig iron finally appears as steel of which 10^9 tons are produced per year. The two principal methods for purifying the pig iron are the Bessemer process and the open-hearth process. In the Bessemer process molten pig iron is poured into an oval vessel and a blast of air forced through the melt to oxidize the undesired elements. After about 15 minutes the impurities have moved to the slag layer and the purified metal is poured into ingots for later use. In the blowing process most of the carbon is burned out so that more is added if high carbon steels are desired. Other metals such as manganese may be added before the pouring if they are wanted in the ingot steel. The Bessemer process is rapid, but cannot be controlled precisely enough to produce the best steels.

In the open-hearth process the pig iron is placed in a covered hearth and kept hot with a gas fuel while the impurities are oxidized by rusty scrap, by iron ore, or by oxygen gas. The process may take eight hours, but high quality steel can be produced under carefully controlled conditions. The desired alloying materials are added before the charge is poured.

Low carbon steel may contain up to 0.5 per cent carbon and high carbon steel may contain up to 1.5 per cent carbon. Manganese, tungsten, molybdenum, vanadium, chromium, and nickel may be added for special purposes.

HEAT TREATMENT OF STEEL

The properties of the iron-carbon alloys, called steels, depend on the way the constituent atoms are distributed in the alloy and this in turn depends on the amount of carbon and on the thermal treatment given to the steels. Pure iron has two crystalline forms. The first, called alpha iron, has the body-centered cubic structure and is ferromagnetic below 766°C. It is stable from room temperature up to 906°C. and iron of this crystal structure is also stable from 1400° to the melting point, 1535°C. In the range, 906° to 1400°, a face-centered cubic form, called gamma iron, is stable. This form is nonmagnetic. The carbon in the steel may be present as graphite, as interstitial carbon, or as cementite, depending on the amount of carbon and on the thermal treatment of the steel.

Above 906° the carbon is present, interstitially, in gamma iron crystals. Below 690° this system is not stable unless manganese is present and then it may be preserved to room temperature. Otherwise the iron-carbon solid solution changes to a eutectic mixture of cementite and alpha iron containing about 0.006 per cent carbon in solid solution. Or, if the carbon-gamma iron solution is quenched, the gamma iron changes to alpha iron, but the carbon forms a supersaturated interstitial solution in the alpha iron. Of course, some of these are unstable at room temperature or even at higher temperatures so that further changes take place when the steels are reheated. One of the functions of the other metals added to steel is to change the temperatures at which the changes take place.

SUMMARY

Most of the properties desired in commercial metals are best obtained in alloys. Alloys are metals having more than one kind of element. The mechanical and electrical properties of alloys differ decidedly from those of the constituent elements and in ways which depend on the arrangements of the atoms of different kinds in the alloys. One cannot understand the properties of alloys without understanding the structures of the metals and the effects of these structures on the metals. The chemical properties of alloys may be more accurately deduced from the properties of the constituent elements if one takes into account the fact that each element is less concentrated in the alloy than it is in the pure metal.

Problem 32.2. Steel is sometimes exposed at high temperatures to an atmosphere containing carbon (in methane), nitrogen (gaseous), or both (in sodium cyanide). This treatment, known as case hardening or nitriding, produces a very hard surface. How do you account for the change?

Problem 32.3. Why use "coin" silver or "sterling" silver rather than pure silver for the respective applications?

Problem 32.4. Long exposure of brass to soft, natural waters causes it to turn red and lose most of its strength. How do you account for this fact?

Problem 32.5. What advantages has cast iron over steel? What are its relative disadvantages?

Problem 32.6. Hard alloys to be used in bearings are often suspended in a soft alloy. Why is this practice desirable?

Problem 32.7. Identical metal surfaces are almost never allowed to rub as bearings. They tend to "seize" or bind one another. How do you account for this fact and why may dissimilar metals and alloys not "seize"? Under what conditions may they seize?

Problem 32.8. What are the constituents of the following alloys: (a) solder, (b) pewter, (c) type metal, (d) bronze, (e) fusible alloy (melting below 100°), (f) "18-8 stainless"?

Problem 32.9. Can you deduce any interpretation of the fact that gray cast iron is less brittle than white cast iron?

Problem 32.10. How would you go about deciding whether a given alloy of unknown composition is of the eutectic, substitutional solid solution, interstitial solid solution, or metallic compound type?

33 SILICATES

THE METALS have many desirable attributes as structural materials. They are strong and can be fabricated to proper shapes but even the most abundant of commercial metals, iron and its alloys, is too expensive and too scarce to be used for the greatest bulk of construction. One of the oldest structural materials is wood, an organic material whose strength is due to its cellulose structure. The plastics, newest of structural materials, are also made from organic substances. Overshadowing all of these for structural purposes are the silicates and silica. They appear in the natural building material, granite, and in the manufactured products, brick, cement, mortar, ceramics, and glass. Thus, silicates are of more than academic interest.

Silicates and silica form most of the lithosphere of the earth. Well over 90 per cent of the atoms in the average sample of earth are in silicates. The most abundant atoms in silicates, oxygen and silicon, represent the majority of atoms in the lithosphere; 62 per cent are oxygen atoms, 21 per cent are silicon atoms and 6 per cent are aluminum atoms. Only 2 per cent of the atoms of the lithosphere are iron atoms. The abundance of the nine most plentiful elements is shown in Table 33.1. (Carbon is the tenth in abundance. See Table 7.1.) These elements, together with limited amounts of others, form the great

Table 33.1
Most Abundant Elements in the Lithosphere

ELEMENT	ATOMIC PER CENT	VOLUME PER CENT
Oxygen	62.5	91.6
Silicon	21.0	0.80
Aluminum	6.4	0.76
Sodium	2.7	1.60
Calcium	1.9	1.48
Iron	1.9	0.68
Magnesium	1.8	0.56
Potassium	1.4	2.14
Titanium	0.3	0.22

544 GENERAL CHEMISTRY

variety of structures found in the rocks, clays, sands, and soils that form the earth's crust. In this chapter we shall consider the atomic arrangements in naturally occurring silicates and shall see how these arrangements are related to the structures of the bulk materials.

ATOMIC VOLUMES IN SILICATES

Although the oxygen atoms in the lithosphere comprise 62 per cent of the total number of atoms they furnish 92 per cent of the volume. There are only one third as many silicon atoms as oxygen atoms, 21 atomic per cent, and they

Table 33.2

Ionic Radii and Coordination Number of Atoms in Silicates

ELEMENT SYMBOL	IONIC CHARGE	IONIC RADIUS	COORDINATION NUMBER WITH OXYGEN
O	2−	1.40	
Be	2+	0.60	4
Li	1+	0.31	4
Si	4+	0.39	4
Al	3+	0.50	4, 6
Mg	2+	0.65	6
Ti	4+	0.7	6
Fe	2+	0.81	6
Na	1+	0.95	6, (8)
Ca	2+	0.99	8
K	1+	1.33	6 to 12
Ba	2+	1.35	6 to 12

furnish less than one per cent of the volume. These values and others are listed in Table 33.1. A consequence of the large atomic volume of the oxygen is that its atoms dominate the structure of silicates. The volume of the silicon atoms is small enough not to interfere with the packing of the oxygen atoms though the arrangements of silicon and oxygen atoms must conform to the coordination numbers of these elements. Silicon has a coordination number of four—each silicon atom is surrounded tetrahedrally by four oxygen atoms. When no oxygen atoms are bonded to more than one silicon atom at a time, each orthosilicate ion, SiO_4^{4-}, remains independent and four oxygen atoms are present for each silicon atom. Usually, one or more of the oxygen atoms in a SiO_4 tetrahedron are bonded to silicon atoms in neighboring tetrahedra. Then the ratio of oxygen atoms to silicon atoms becomes less than four. The lowest ratio of oxygen to silicon atoms is reached in silica, formula SiO_2, in which each oxygen atom is bonded to two silicon atoms and each silicon atom to four oxygen atoms.

In orthosilicates, each SiO_4 tetrahedron has a negative charge of 4− and is a separate anion. (Such highly charged ions are stable in crystals but not in water solution.) The appropriate number of positive ions must be present in the mineral to form a neutral compound, the number of cations required being dependent on the amount of charge on each ion. In pure silica there is no net charge and therefore no positive ions are present. In the natural silicates the number of cations required decreases as the ratio of the oxygen to silicon decreases from four toward two.

The most abundant cations in silicates are the singly charged ions, Na^+ and K^+, the doubly charged ions, Ca^{++}, Fe^{++}, and Mg^{++}, the triply charged ions, Al^{+++} and Fe^{+++}, and the quadruply charged ion, Ti^{++++}, though other cations are found in lesser amounts. The silicates of beryllium and zirconium, for example, are the usual commercial ores for these cations. The cations are found in positions in the silicate lattices in which they are surrounded by the oxygen atoms of the silicon tetrahedra. The arrangements are such that each cation coordinates a definite number of oxygen atoms. The atomic radii and the coordination numbers of the cations listed in Table 33.2 show how the prevailing coordination number increases with ionic radii and volumes of the cations. (See also page 398.)

SUBSTITUTION OF ATOMS IN SILICATES

One of the characteristics of silicate minerals is the ease with which atoms may be substituted for one another within the oxygen framework of the silicates. Size of atom or ion is more important than ionic charge in the substitutions, provided, of course, that total electrical neutrality of the mineral is maintained. Aluminum atoms may be present in two types of positions. Some atoms may be substituted for silicon atoms within the oxygen tetrahedra in the silicate anions. Then there is this important consequence—for every aluminum atom, oxidation number 3+, substituted for a silicon atom, oxidation number 4+, the negative charge of the anion is increased by one. Then the total positive charge of the cations associated with the anion in the crystal must be increased by one.

A second possible position of aluminum atoms in silicates is as a positive ion not in a "silicon position." When an aluminum ion, Al^{+++}, is substituted for a divalent cation such as Ca^{++} or Mg^{++} the total cationic charge increases. An aluminum ion substituted for a magnesium ion as cation compensates in electric charge for substitution of aluminum for silicon in the anion. In general, the cations, Mg^{++}, Fe^{+++}, and Al^{+++} have sizes similar enough to make them interchangeable, and Ca^{++} and Na^+ are also interchangeable with each other for the same reasons. Consider the silicate, diopside, with the formula, $CaMg(Si_2O_6)$. Isomorphous with it are the substances represented by the formulas $NaFe(Si_2O_6)$ and $NaAl(Si_2O_6)$. These represent substitution of a monovalent ion and a trivalent ion for two divalent ions. Also isomorphous with diopside are the substances in which aluminum is substituted for part of the silicon, typical formulas being $CaFe(AlSiO_6)$ and $CaAl(AlSiO_6)$. Then both anionic charge and cationic charge are increased. In the most general case the formula of the mineral augite, isomorphous with diopside, may be represented by a generalized formula

$$(Ca, Na)(Mg, Fe, Al)(Al, Si)O_6$$

in which the ions or atoms within the parentheses may be substituted freely for one another, the only restriction being that the electrical neutrality of the mineral is preserved. In some minerals, as in the previous example, the total number of positive ions remains fixed during the substitutions but in other minerals in which the total "holes" in the silicate lattice is greater than the number of positive ions needed to neutralize the charge, two sodium ions, for example, may be substituted for a calcium ion even though the relative number of positive ions is thereby increased.

TYPES OF SILICATES

A most instructive classification of the natural silicates is in terms of the structures of the silicate anions present in the minerals. In the following sections we shall discuss idealized silicates, it being understood that some substitutions are found in the natural minerals. When the fundamental silicate structures are understood, the substitution rules discussed in the preceding section may be applied where necessary. In our classification we shall proceed from the simplest anions to the most complicated polymeric anions. Drawings showing structures of some anions are shown in Figure 33.1.

1. Orthosilicate Type. Anion, SiO_4^{4-} [Garnets, $M_3^{II}M_2^{III}(SiO_4)_3$, where M^{II} is Ca^{++}, Mg^{++}, Mn^{++}, or Fe^{++}, and M^{III} is Al^{+++}, Cr^{+++}, or Fe^{+++}]

The SiO_4 tetrahedra crystallize as individual anion units and the appropriate number of cations occupy some of the positions between the oxygen atoms of the neighboring tetrahedra. (See Figure 33.1a.)

2. Disilicate Type. Anion, $Si_2O_7^{6-}$ (Rare) [Thortveitite, $Sc_2Si_2O_7$]

One oxygen atom is held in common as part of two SiO_4 tetrahedra. The anion is a disilicate ion with charge 6−. (See Figure 33.1b.) The Si—O—Si bridge is linear.

3. Cyclic Types. Anion, $(SiO_3)_n^{2n-}$ [Beryl (emerald), $Be_3Al_2Si_6O_{18}$]

Each SiO_4 tetrahedron shares two of its oxygen atoms, one atom with each of two neighboring tetrahedra to form a ring. The ring may involve three tetrahedra, in which case n = 3. (See Figure 33.1c.) Rings of six tetrahedra (n = 6) are also known. Cyclic, or ring, ions are examples of polymeric ions, the monomer unit being $SiO_3^=$ with charge 2−. The cations lie between and among the rings.

4. Single Chain Type. Anion, $(SiO_3)_n^{2n-}$ [Diopside, $CaMg(SiO_3)_2$]

Each tetrahedron (except the two end ones) shares an oxygen atom with each of its two neighbors to form an endless chain. The bonding of the tetra-

SILICATES 547

(a) Orthosilicate
SiO_4^{4-}

Oxygen Atom

Silicon Atom Tetrahedrally Surrounded By Four Oxygen Atoms

(b) Disilicate
$Si_2O_7^{6-}$

(c) Cyclic Trisilicate
$(SiO_3)_3^{6-}$

(d) Endless Single Chain
$(SiO_3)_n^{2n-}$
(Pyroxenes)

(e) Endless Double Chain
$(Si_4O_{11})_n^{6n-}$
(Amphiboles)

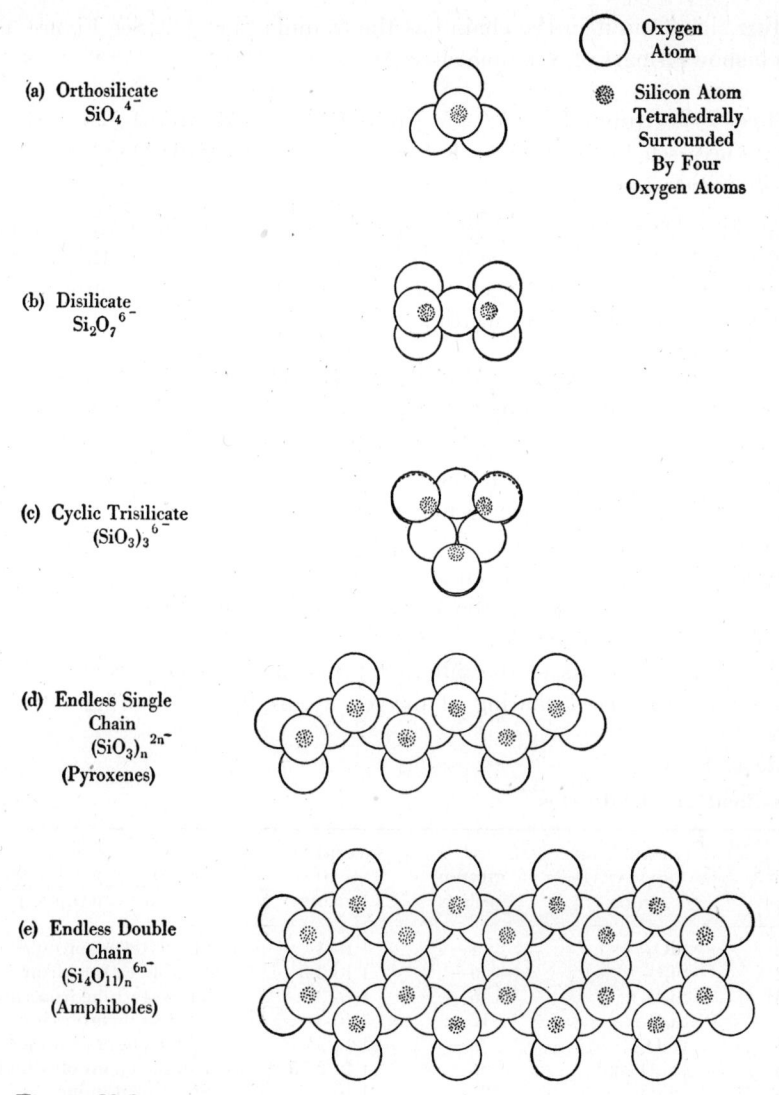

Figure 33.1.
Structures of some silicate anions.

hedra is like that in Type 3 except that the chains are longer and are not closed to form rings. Figure 33.1d shows part of a chain. The end tetrahedra in the chain may have OH groups to provide the quota of four oxygen atoms around each silicon atom.

5. Double Chain Type. Anion, $(Si_4O_{11})_n^{6n-}$ [Asbestos, $(OH)_6Mg_6Si_4O_{11}$]

Some of the tetrahedra share two oxygen atoms and others share three so that two single chains are linked together to form a double chain. The re-

548   GENERAL CHEMISTRY

peating silicate unit in the chain has the formula $Si_4O_{11}^{6-}$. (See Figure 33.1e, which shows a part of a double chain.)

6. **Sheet Type. Anion, $(Si_2O_5)_n^{2n-}$ [Mica, $(OH)_2(K, Na)Al_2(Si_3AlO_{10})$, negative silicate layers held together by K^+(or Na^+)ions; talc, $(OH)_2Mg_3Si_4O_{10}$, electrically neutral layers]**

The tetrahedra are crosslinked through commonly held oxygen atoms to form sheet ions extending indefinitely in two dimensions. Within the sheet each tetrahedron shares three oxygen atoms. The sheet ion is an indefinite extension of the double chain both in width and in length.

7. **Framework Type. Anion, $(AlSiO_4)_n^{n-}$ [orthoclase, $K(Si_3AlO_8)$; ultramarine, $Na_8(Si_6Al_6O_{24})(S_2)$, contains S_2^{--} ions]**

Framework ions, extending indefinitely in three dimensions, are possible only if some of the silicon atoms are replaced with aluminum atoms. Pure silica, for which the macromolecular formula is $(SiO_2)_n$, forms a three-dimensional framework in which each oxygen atom in each tetrahedron is shared with neighboring tetrahedra but such a framework is electrically neutral and contains no ions. However, the framework has a negative charge for each aluminum atom substituted for a silicon atom.

The structural units of the different types of silicates are summarized in Table 33.3. Increased sharing of oxygen atoms by neighboring tetrahedra

Table 33.3
Classification of Silicates

TYPE	FORMULA OF SILICATE ANION	CHARGE ON ION	RATIO OF SI TO O ATOMS	STRUCTURAL UNIT
1	SiO_4	4−	1 to 4	Single tetrahedron
2	Si_2O_7	6−	1 to 3.5	Double tetrahedron
3	Si_3O_9	6−	1 to 3	Three-tetrahedron ring
	Si_6O_{18}	12−	1 to 3	Six-tetrahedron ring
4	$(SiO_3)_n$	2n−	1 to 3	Single chain of n units
5	$(Si_4O_{11})_n$	6n−	1 to 2.75	Double chain of n units
6	$(Si_2O_5)_n$	2n−	1 to 2.5	Sheet of n units
7	$(SiAlO_4)_n$	n−		Three-dimensional framework of n units
	$(SiO_2)_m(AlO_2)_n$			
Silica	$(SiO_2)_n$	0	1 to 2	Three-dimensional framework with no charge

leads to an increased ratio of silicon atoms to oxygen atoms. The fourth column of the table shows how the ratio may be used to characterize the different types. With no sharing the ratio is 1 to 4. With complete sharing in a three-dimensional framework, the ratio is 1 to 2 as in silica. Then, only if aluminum is substituted for silicon in some of the tetrahedra can this framework be an ion. The charge of the ion will depend on the number of substitutions. As we have already mentioned, aluminum may be substituted for silicon in the other silicate types, the negative charge of the silicate ion being increased for each atom substituted.

LAYER SILICATES

Sheet ions, based on multiples of $Si_2O_5^{--}$, result from an indefinite extension in two dimensions of the double chain structure shown in Figure 33.1e. Most sheet ions are a network of rings of six tetrahedra but some are known which have alternate rings of four and eight tetrahedra. The negative charge per Si_2O_5 unit is only $2-$ but some of the silicon atoms may be replaced by aluminum ions to increase the negative charge of the sheets.

The micas can easily be split into thin layers because the positive ions binding the sheet ions together are K^+ ions which are large. The brittle micas, formula $(OH)_2CaAl_2(Si_2Al_2O_{10})$, are harder because the sheets are held together by Ca^{++} ions which are smaller and more highly charged than the K^+ ions. In talc magnesium ions are bound in such a way that the layers are not ions but are electrically neutral and held together by weak forces. Hence the talcs are very soft—the layers slip readily so that they may be used for their lubricating qualities. Kaolinite, a clay of formula $(OH)_4Al_2Si_2O_5$, also has electrically neutral layers. The chlorites are interesting because they are built of oppositely charged sheet ions. The negative sheets are of the mica type, formula $(OH)_2Mg_3(Si_3AlO_{10})^-$, and the positive sheets of the brucite type, formula $Mg_2Al(OH)_6^+$.

FRAMEWORK SILICATES

In the framework silicates every oxygen surrounding a silicon atom is bonded to another silicon (or aluminum) atom to produce the three-dimensional framework. Pure silica has the framework structure but it is not ionic. We shall discuss it in the next section. The framework acquires a negative charge when an aluminum atom substitutes for a silicon atom and it must then enclose the corresponding number of positive ions.

The feldspars are the most abundant of the silicates, forming 60 per cent of the igneous rocks. The constituents of granite are quartz, feldspar, and micas. Feldspars have two types of structure depending on whether the cations are K^+ and Ba^{++} (large) or Na^+ and Ca^{++} (smaller). The small cations (Fe^{++}, Mn^{++}, etc.) are not found in the feldspars.

The zeolites have more open frameworks than the feldspars with interesting consequences. The bound water can be removed or restored [as in chabozite, formula $Ca(Si_4Al_2O_{12}) \cdot 6H_2O$,] without appreciable effect on the framework structure and ions can be exchanged rather freely. Thus, half the calcium ions in thomsonite, formula $NaCa_2(Si_5Al_5O_{20}) \cdot 6H_2O$, can be exchanged reversibly with sodium ions. This exchange may be used to soften hard waters (see pages 481 and 493).

Ultramarines are colored framework silicates used as pigments. They contain negative ions such as S_2^{--}, Cl^-, or SO_4^{--} and these are exchangeable. The sodium ions are also exchangeable by ions such as Li^+, Tl^+, Ag^+, and Ca^{++} to produce variations in color.

SILICA

Silica in the form of quartz is a major mineral, comprising 12 per cent of igneous rocks. Quartz is the stable crystal form of silica at room temperature but two other crystal forms, tridymite and cristobalite, are stable at higher temperatures. The regions of stability are

$$\text{quartz} \rightarrow 870°C. \leftarrow \text{tridymite} \rightarrow 1470°C. \leftarrow \text{cristobalite} \rightarrow 1710°C.\overset{\text{melting point}}{}$$

The three forms differ in the way the tetrahedra are joined together to form the framework. Although only quartz is stable at ordinary temperatures, some tridymite and cristobalite are found in nature. The transition from one form to the other involves the breaking of silicon-oxygen bonds and the linking of tetrahedra in different ways. Transitions are slow even in the presence of catalysts. Quartz crystals occur in right-handed and left-handed forms, depending on right- or left-handed twist of the spirals of tetrahedra in the crystals. They have unusual stability because of the strength of the three-dimensional bonding.

Silica has a high melting point, 1710°C., and even at that high temperature does not flow readily, that is, it is highly viscous. Apparently silica does not lose its framework structure even above its melting temperature. To do so would involve rupture of many of its silicon-oxygen bonds. However, some of the regularity is lost, for when the liquid melt is cooled it does not recrystallize but becomes more and more viscous until, at about 1500°C., it hardens to a glassy solid. The melt is so viscous that, when sand is melted, the air from the spaces between the sand grains is trapped as bubbles in the viscous mass and is almost impossible to remove. Clear silica glass (often called *quartz glass*) is made by melting large quartz crystals in a vacuum so that no air remains to be trapped. Quartz glass transmits light of a wider range of frequencies than does ordinary glass. This property makes it useful for optical instruments in the ultraviolet range. Quartz glass expands and contracts only slightly with change in temperature—the red hot glass may be immersed in cold water without fracturing. Crystalline quartz expands and contracts much more.

OTHER POLYMERIC IONS

Earlier we discussed the ability of phosphorus to form long metaphosphate chains (see page 415). Each phosphorus atom tends to surround itself by four oxygen atoms even when this means sharing of oxygen with the phosphorus atom of another tetrahedron. Note the similarity to silicon. The result is a chain ion of variable length. The character and structure of the polymeric ions depends on the ratio of phosphorus to oxygen and thus to the linking of the tetrahedra. Germanium forms series of compounds analogous to the silicates but is not commercially important. We have already seen that aluminum can be substituted in silicate tetrahedra, but such substitution is limited because aluminum-oxygen tetrahedra do not form extensive crosslinked structures by themselves.

Boron trioxide and borates show crosslinked structures but the structures have not been identified in detail. Boron trioxide, empirical formula B_2O_3, readily forms a glassy solid and, like silica, is difficult to crystallize. It, therefore, appears to be highly structured. The naturally occurring borate salts are crystalline but readily form glassy solids when cooled from their melts. Some typical formulas, listed in Table 33.5, indicate that polymeric ions must be present.

Table 33.5
Formulas of Some Borate Minerals

MINERAL	FORMULA
Kernite	$Na_2B_4O_7 \cdot 4H_2O$
Borax	$Na_2B_4O_7 \cdot 10H_2O$
Ulexite	$NaCaB_5O_9 \cdot 8H_2O$
Colemanite	$Ca_2B_6O_{11} \cdot 5H_2O$
Boracite	$Mg_7B_{16}O_{30} \cdot Cl_2$

Many other polymeric ions analogous to the silicates are known. Their general behavior can be interpreted in terms of the factors we have discussed for the silicates.

STRUCTURE OF GLASSES

Experience shows that molten salts containing monatomic or small, highly symmetrical, complex ions form crystals and not glassy solids when cooled below their melting points. Such molten salts are not viscous. However, some melts are highly viscous. These can often be cooled far below their freezing points without crystallizing. As the temperature falls they harden slowly to form glassy solids. In the glassy solids the atoms and ions have the disordered and somewhat random distribution characteristic of liquids rather than the precise, repeating arrangements corresponding to crystalline solids. Crystalline solids when fractured tend to cleave along the surfaces of crystal planes whereas glassy solids do not fracture along planes but along curved surfaces, as in conchoidal fractures.

Viscosity at the melting point is related to tendency to form glassy rather than crystalline solids. When the units forming the crystal cannot move freely they are hindered in finding their orderly positions in a crystal structure. Complexity of the crystal unit is also an important factor. Large organic molecules with unsymmetrical structure are hard to crystallize and tend to harden

552   GENERAL CHEMISTRY

to solids having the irregular structure of glasses. Salts with large polymeric ions, as we have already indicated, often form glassy solids rather than crystalline solids.

COMMERCIAL GLASSES

Most commercial glasses have silica as the chief component and are classed as silicate glasses. One reason for their pre-eminence is their lack of solubility in water. Phosphate glasses are limited in application because water reacts with them to break down the polymeric ions to simpler, water-soluble ions. Silica glass has excellent chemical resistance but silica melts at too high a temperature to be handled and fabricated in ordinary industrial equipment. Addition of 25 per cent by weight of sodium oxide to silica lowers the melting point from 1710°C. to 793°C. (freezing-point-lowering effect). The resulting substance is water-soluble and hence unsuitable as a commercial glass. It is sold as *water glass*. When lime replaces some of the sodium oxide, resistance of the glass to water increases.

The ternary eutectic (see page 537) of the system sodium oxide-lime-silica is found to have the composition 21.3 per cent sodium oxide, 5.2 per cent lime, 73.5 per cent silica by weight. The eutectic temperature is at about 725°C. It is the lowest freezing temperature for a glass made from these components (soda lime glass). Glasses of the soda lime type were made by the ancients and they comprise about 90 per cent of all glass made today. Most soda lime glasses today have somewhat less soda and more lime than the eutectic ratio to decrease chemical reactivity of the glasses. A typical glass has the analysis in per cent by weight, sodium oxide, 16.9, lime, 10.2, silica, 72.9. The composition of this glass can be expressed by the formula $Na_2O \cdot 0.67CaO \cdot 4.52SiO_2$. Glass of this composition can be made by melting together 100 parts (by weight) of sand, 40 parts of soda ash, formula Na_2CO_3, and 25 parts of limestone, formula $CaCO_3$. What do you suppose happens to the carbonate ions?

Problem 33.1. Calculate a formula for water glass in terms of oxides as in the formula used for the typical soda lime glass.

Problem 33.2. From the formula given for a typical soda lime glass calculate the silicon to oxygen ratio and compare with the ratio for some silicates listed in Table 33.3.

Other oxides are used to make glasses for special purposes. Borax is a common source for boron trioxide (and sodium oxide), feldspar for alumina and potassium oxide (and silica), and dolomite for magnesium oxide (and lime). The "Pyrex" commonly used for chemical glass is a borosilicate glass. A typical analysis, in per cent by weight, is

FORMULA OF OXIDE	SiO_2	B_2O_3	Al_2O_3	Na_2O	K_2O
PER CENT BY WEIGHT	80.5	12.9	2.2	3.8	0.4

This glass has only about one third the thermal expansion of soda lime glass and therefore breaks much less readily when heated or cooled suddenly. It has excellent resistance to chemical reagents. All glasses resist water and acids much more than they do alkalies. The latter react to form soluble silicates.

From their compositions we see that the silicate glasses with their low oxygen-to-silicon ratios must be highly structured. They must, therefore, be difficult to crystallize. Nevertheless, many glasses, especially when aged, tend to crystallize (devitrify) when heated to their softening points. (Remember that the softening points are below the melting points.) Apparently, on aging some of the disordered silicate may, through slight movements over long periods of time, rearrange enough to start tiny crystals. These seed crystals can then grow when the glass is reheated. Soda lime glass can be softened and worked in a gas-air flame but Pyrex glass needs a gas-oxygen flame and quartz glass a hydrogen-oxygen flame to soften it for working.

Freshly made glass fibers have enormous tensile strength, much greater than metal wires of the same size. On aging and especially on weathering the tensile strength falls rapidly to low values. It appears that small cracks develop in glass which cause breaking under stress. The inherent instability of the glassy structure limits the use of glass for structural purposes where strength is required, but it finds increasing application particularly when the fibers are immersed (bonded) in certain plastics.

The "enamels" used to coat metals to make bath tubs and other objects are glasses. An indispensable property of an enamel is that it shall not separate from the underlying metal when the object cools during manufacture. Glasses of special composition are chosen, glasses that will contract at the same rate as the metal. Metallic oxides are used to color the enamel or to make it opaque.

CERAMICS

Bricks, chinaware, and porcelain are made by heating ("burning") molded objects made from suitable clays in kilns until some of the material melts. On cooling, the remaining material is found to be bound together. Use is made of the fact that the different minerals in clays have different melting points. Glazes are put on objects by coating the objects with some relatively low-melting clay and heating until the coating melts.

CEMENT

Portland cement is made by heating a mixture of clay and limestone in a kiln and grinding the "clinker" to a fine powder. The resulting mixture may be characterized by the formulas Ca_2SiO_4, Ca_3SiO_5, and $Ca_3Al_2O_6$. On treatment with water the calcium aluminate hydrolyzes to form the hydroxides of calcium and aluminum and these recrystallize with the calcium silicates to form a mosaic of crystals. Time is needed for the "setting" of cement. In construction, cement is mixed with sand and with gravel or crushed stone and limited amounts of water to form *concrete*. A mix with the ratios 1 part cement, 3 parts sand, and 5 parts gravel is common.

Problem 33.3. Account for the greater inertness of commercial glasses toward acids than toward bases in terms of the chemical composition of the glasses. Note the oxides used in them.

Problem 33.4. It is not uncommon for a glass object to crack suddenly and spontaneously. How do you account for this fact?

Problem 33.5. The setting of cement is exothermic. Elaborate precautions are taken to keep cement cool during the setting process, yet freezing must usually also be carefully avoided. How do you account for these facts?

Problem 33.6. Mica may be split much more readily, and into thinner sheets, under water than in air. Account for this fact.

Problem 33.7. What would you expect naturally occurring asbestos to look like?

Problem 33.8. Which would you expect to be the continuous phase in granite: quartz, feldspar, or mica? Why so?

Problem 33.9. Interpret the fact that granite is a much more lasting building stone than sandstone. Why, then, is the latter more commonly used?

Problem 33.10. Petrified wood is the replica of a tree which became impregnated with siliceous materials. What conditions have to be satisfied if petrified wood is to form?

Problem 33.11. Give the relative merits and demerits of steel and concrete as structural materials and interpret them in terms of the atomic structures and solid structures of the two substances.

Problem 33.12. Molded hulls made from fiber glass and plastic have been made for small boats. What may be their defects?

Problem 33.13. Calculate the radius ratio relative to oxygen for the ions listed in Table 33.2. Compare them and the corresponding coordination numbers with the data in Table 24.3.

Problem 33.14. Calcium sulfate is often scattered on fields which have been flooded with ocean water. This treatment markedly lowers the time during which plants will not flourish in the soil. Suggest a chemical interpretation.

34 COLLOIDS

SO FAR we have discussed materials and their behavior as though their properties were uniform throughout. Every atom in crystalline nickel had the same properties as every other atom, and every silver ion in crystalline silver chloride the same properties as every other ion. Very brief consideration will show that this cannot be so. Some of the atoms and ions are deep within the bulk of the crystals, and some are on the surfaces, edges, and corners. Those deep within the bulk crystal are more or less uniformly surrounded by their neighbors, those in a surface are less surrounded, and those atoms and ions in the edge and corner positions are still less surrounded. Clearly the geometrical position of certain atoms will endow them with different bonds than other atoms have and hence will give them different properties. The surface atoms will, in general, have "free bonds" with which they can form bonds to a neighboring phase.

DIMENSIONS OF COLLOIDS

Division of a substance into smaller and smaller particles increases the fraction of atoms lying in the exposed surfaces, and hence the influence of surface atoms on the over-all properties of the substance. When their contribution to the over-all behavior of the substance is appreciable the substance is said to exhibit colloidal properties and the substance, for convenience, is called a *colloid*. Colloid chemistry may, then, be described as the chemistry of surfaces, or interfaces, between two phases.

Systems with large surfaces concentrated in relatively small volumes may be of different types. They may consist of particles small in three dimensions. Examples are bubbles, fogs, and smokes, in which the particles are gas, liquid, and solid phases, respectively. They may consist of particles small in two dimensions. Examples are fibers and filaments. Particles with such shapes are usually solids, for liquids and gases, being fluid, tend to assume other shapes. Films of liquids or solids, small in only one dimension, represent the third type. Films may range in thickness from monomolecular layers to layers many molecular diameters in depth. Of these types we shall discuss chiefly the particles small in three dimensions, but the principles will also apply to the other types.

There is no sharp separation between particles of colloidal size and particles of molecular size, nor is there a sharp change in properties. Atoms, ions, and most molecules are tiny but some single molecules have sizes within the colloidal range. Viruses, with molecular weights from about one million to one billion, and the proteins, with molecular weights from a few hundred thousand to one million, have properties typical of colloids. The lower limit for the appearance of colloidal properties is at diameters of about 50 Å. The upper

Table 34.1

Types of Colloids

DISCONTINUOUS PHASE	CONTINUOUS PHASE	CLASSIFICATION	EXAMPLES
Gas	Gas	No known examples	
Liquid	Gas	Mists	fog, cloud
Solid	Gas	Smokes	dusty air
Gas	Liquid	Foams	suds
Liquid	Liquid	Emulsions	creams, mayonnaise
Solid	Liquid	Suspensions	muddy water
Gas	Solid	Solid foams	pumice
Liquid	Solid	Gels	jellies, cheese
Solid	Solid	Solid suspensions	many minerals & alloys, pearls, opals

limit is at about 10^{-5} cm., or 1000 Å. At the upper limit about 1 per cent of the atoms are on the surface of the particle.

Colloidal systems are often classified according to the phase of the colloidal particle and the phase of the medium. The colloidal particle may be gaseous, liquid, or solid in a gas, liquid, or solid medium. The colloidal particles, being suspended in the medium, are called the *discontinuous phase*, and the medium is called the *continuous phase*. Table 34.1 lists some typical examples of colloidal systems. The interactions at the surfaces between the two phases (interfaces) lead to many of the characteristic properties of the colloidal systems.

Problem 34.1. A cube one centimeter long on each edge is subdivided into cubes one-millionth centimeter long on each edge. (a) How many smaller cubes are produced? (b) What is the increase in surface area? (c) How many Ångstrom units long is each small cube? (d) If the average diameter of each atom is 3 Ångstrom units, approximately how many atoms could lie in a face of a small cube? Within each small cube?

Problem 34.2. What will be the freezing point of a water solution containing 0.01 mole of a monomer in 100 g. of water? If the monomer is now polymerized into macromolecules each containing 1000 monomeric units what will be the freezing point of the solution? Comment on the freezing point lowerings to be expected in colloidal systems.

FORMATION OF COLLOIDS

Since colloidal particles have sizes intermediate between those of bulk substances and those of individual atoms and ions, they may be prepared in one of two ways. They may be made by the disintegration of bulk materials or by the aggregation of smaller molecules. Disintegration may be accomplished by grinding (making of cement powder), by beating (mayonnaise), by impact of the bulk substance on a stationary plate (homogenized milk), by shaking (oil in soapy water), by the action of an electric arc (sparking of gold electrodes under water), or in numerous other ways of applying energy to divide bulk substances. Aggregation is brought about through formation of bubbles (gas), droplets (liquid), or crystals (solid) as molecules cluster together within a formerly homogeneous phase, but growth of the particles must stop before they exceed colloidal size. Ammonium chloride smoke from gaseous ammonia and gaseous hydrogen chloride, small crystals of silver chloride from a mixture of silver nitrate and potassium chloride solutions, or small graphite and iron grains obtained on heat treatment of white cast iron are typical of solid colloidal particles formed in gaseous, liquid, and solid media, respectively. Similar examples may be cited for the formation of the other types of colloids listed in Table 34.1.

STABILIZATION OF COLLOIDS

One of the outstanding properties of colloids is their stability. Metallic gold is highly insoluble in water, yet colloidal gold (tiny particles of gold suspended in water) prepared by Faraday in 1857 remains unprecipitated after about one hundred years of standing on a shelf and apparently will remain suspended indefinitely. Gold is much more dense than water (see Table 30.1). Why do the particles of solid gold not settle out?

There are four general reasons for the stabilities of colloidal suspensions: (1) Brownian motion, (2) similar electrical charges on the colloidal particles, (3) electrically neutral layers of adsorbed materials surrounding the particles, (4) viscosity effects.

BROWNIAN MOTION AND SETTLING OF PARTICLES

One of the very earliest observations made on small particles suspended in a continuous medium was that the particles appeared to be in rapid, more or less random, motion. The motion of these tiny particles may be observed even though the particles themselves are invisible in ordinary light. The particles are invisible since their dimensions are often less than the wave length of visible light, but they can still serve as diffraction centers for the light as long as their dimensions are not much smaller than the wave length of the light. The diffraction produces the bright scintillations observed, for instance, when a beam of light shines through a dusty atmosphere, or, for that matter, when light shines through any translucent colloidal suspension. This effect is known as the Tyndall effect. It is most readily noted at right angles to the beam of light and against a dark background.

Even before the Tyndall effect was understood, a botanist, Robert Brown, in 1827 correctly interpreted the random motion of particles suspended in a medium less dense than themselves in terms of differential molecular bombardment from various directions. For large particles this bombardment is insufficient to prevent eventual settling in a gravitational field, though it will slow the settling and cause the particles to follow tortuous paths as they settle. As the mass of the particle approaches the mass of smaller molecules, the effect of the Brownian motion increases and the particles settle out less and less completely. Instead of settling, the particles distribute themselves unequally through the column of supporting medium, a higher concentration of the particles being found in the lower portions of the medium, and a lower concentration of suspended particles being present in the upper portions of the suspending medium. A typical suspension of gum gamboge studied by Perrin gave the data in Table 34.2.

Table 34.2

Concentration of Particles in a Suspension as a Function of Height
(Gamboge: particles 2.12×10^{-5} cm in radius, $\rho = 1.206$, in water at 15°C.)

HEIGHT IN CELL (CM.)	5×10^{-4}	35×10^{-4}	65×10^{-4}	95×10^{-4}
RELATIVE CONCENTRATION	100	47	23	12

Actually, all particles whose densities differ from that of the supporting medium tend to settle. This settling effect has even been noted in a solution of lithium iodide, for instance, whirled at high speeds in a centrifuge to increase the tendency to settle. One end of the tube becomes positively charged, the other negatively charged since the denser ions are forced toward the outer end of the centrifuge tube to a greater extent than the less dense ions.

Problem 34.3. Which end of the centrifuge tube will be positive and which negative when a dilute aqueous solution of lithium iodide is centrifuged?

Problem 34.4. How do you account for the fact that the atmosphere has not separated into concentric layers of oxygen and nitrogen during the course of geologic history?

ELECTRICAL CHARGES ON COLLOID PARTICLES

Brownian motion accounts very satisfactorily for the absence of settling of small particles but it does not give any interpretation of the stability of the particles. Why do they not collide, adhere to form larger particles, and then settle out at a measurable rate? The principal reason, for most colloids, is that all their particles bear similar electrical charges, repel one another on close approach, and thus do not adhere since they do not undergo direct collisions.

The charge on a colloid may be demonstrated by electrolyzing the colloidal suspension. Positively charged colloidal particles will migrate toward the cathode; negatively charged colloids will migrate toward the anode. Some substances almost always form negative colloids (most detergents, most metals suspended in water), some substances almost always form positive colloids (ferric hydroxide), while some form either positive or negative colloids, often with equal ease (proteins, silver halides).

With the exception of the metal suspensions in which the charges may be due to extra free electrons, the electrical charges on colloidal particles usually are due to "extra" ions adsorbed on the surface of the particles. The ions are extra in the sense that they give a net charge to the particle, but they are often of the same type as ions already present in the bulk materials. Thus, silver chloride forms as a positive colloid when a dilute solution of chloride ions is mixed with an excess of a dilute solution of silver ions, whereas it forms as a negative colloid when an excess of chloride ions are present in the final solution. In each case the crystals continue to grow beyond the point where they contain equal numbers of positive

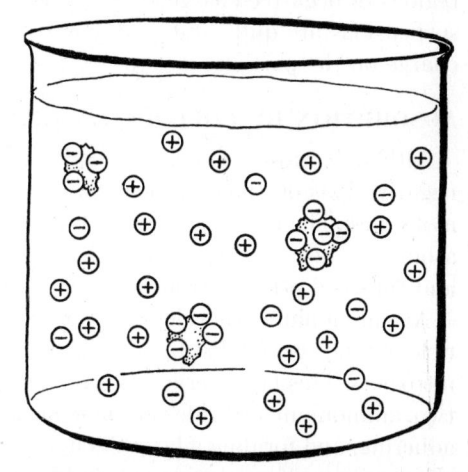

Figure 34.1.
Structure of a charged colloid. In this case negative ims are preferentially adsorbed on the colloid particles giving each particle a net negative charge of considerable magnitude. This minimizes the chance of collision between the colloid particles.

and negative ions. Some of the ions present in excess strike and adhere to the particle surface on the sites which would normally be occupied by ions of that type. The resulting charged crystals are then prevented from collision and continued growth by the similar charges. Note that if the colloidal particles are charged, the continuous phase must have the opposite charge; the system as a whole is neutral (see Figure 34.1). Many colloids will adsorb hydrogen or hydroxide ions from neutral water and so become charged even though there were few ions in the water originally. (What happens to the other ions formed?)

Most proteins will adsorb both hydrogen ions and hydroxide ions at different sites, the relative amounts depending on the ion concentrations in the solution. The resulting protein will have either positive or negative charge depending on which ion was adsorbed most. As the acidity of a solution containing a positively charged protein is slowly neutralized with base, more and more hydroxide ions are adsorbed and more and more hydrogen ions are removed by the added base. Eventually the protein becomes negatively charged, but at some particular hydrogen ion concentration the protein as a whole is neutral. It will then not migrate on electrolysis and is said to be at its *isoelectric point*. Proteins are most apt to precipitate at their isoelectric point since the particles have a net charge of zero. We shall find later, however, that the protein molecule will still have regions of positive charge and other regions of negative charge even at the isoelectric point, so that many protein suspensions are quite stable at the isoelectric point even though the over-all charge on the particles is zero.

ADSORPTION BY COLLOIDAL PARTICLES

Although most colloids are stabilized through adsorption of positive or negative ions on their surfaces, many are stabilized by adsorption of neutral molecules. The adsorption in each case results from the fact that the surface atoms are not exerting their full bonding potential within the particle itself and thus can attract strongly other atoms in the vicinity.

An ammonium chloride smoke may be electrically neutral, but each particle will be surrounded by a layer of very strongly adsorbed air (oxygen and nitrogen). This layer serves as a buffer or bumper to minimize the chances of two ammonium chloride surfaces on separate particles coming in contact, adhering, and forming a large enough particle to settle. We observed the same effect when sulfur trioxide was bubbled through water (see page 302). There the droplets of sulfuric acid formed by reaction between water vapor and gaseous sulfur trioxide became coated with a layer of adsorbed air and were then very slow to grow into larger droplets. The droplets are too heavy to move rapidly and to meet the surface of the bubble while the bubble is passing through the liquid and they are too light to settle out of the gas phase.

The bonds formed on adsorption are often as strong as any intramolecular bonds, but a given surface will form stronger bonds to some substances than to others. In general the strongest bonds will be formed with the least volatile substances and the weakest bonds with the most volatile substances. If a mixture of the inert gases were passed over a highly adsorbent substance, the gases would be adsorbed in order of decreasing boiling point, the helium being the last to be adsorbed. The commercial method of purifying helium from the other gases with which it is found is to adsorb the other gases on cold adsorbents such as charcoal. The helium being least readily adsorbed of any known substance, can then be collected as a pure substance.

Gas masks contain very finely divided charcoal, silica gel, and other adsorbents which can remove substances of low volatility from gas passing over them. For particular applications special adsorbents are used which may combine simple adsorption with chemical reaction. Thus masks for removal of ammonia vapor would contain a solid acid as adsorbent, whereas a solid base would be used as the adsorbent for hydrogen chloride. In each case adsorption and chemical reaction combine to increase the efficiency and length of service of the mask.

Adsorbents find wide use in industrial applications as means of separating substances of similar chemical nature. The higher molecular weight substances in natural gas may be removed by passing the gas over adsorbents. The substances adsorbed are then reclaimed by warming the adsorbent. This warming increases the escaping tendency of the adsorbed materials, leads to desorption, and gives a product free from the lower molecular weight substances found in the natural gas. The adsorbent is used over and over again.

Adsorption on charcoal is also used to remove the colored substances present in the juice from crushed sugar cane and beets. The sugar solution enters the adsorption bed brown, but leaves water white.

VISCOSITY EFFECTS

Brownian motion, electrical charges, and adsorbed layers are the principal stabilizing influences in gaseous and liquid colloidal suspensions, but high viscosity is most important in solid suspensions. The resistance to mass motion is so great in the solid phase that the suspended particles diffuse only very slowly and have little chance of aggregating. Solid colloidal systems are more stable on the average than any other type.

COAGULATION OF COLLOIDS

The circumstances under which colloids can be coagulated may be deduced from the factors which lead to their stability. If the stabilizing factors are minimized, the stability of the colloid will decrease. Solid colloids are stabilized primarily by their high viscosity. Therefore heating or mechanical working tends to destroy such colloidal systems, heating by increasing the thermal motion of the molecules and thus lowering the viscosity, and mechanical working by supplying higher forces which overcome the high viscosity or resistance to flow.

Heating also tends to destroy fluid colloids, primarily by increasing the kinetic energy of the particles until they can collide in spite of the repulsion of their similar charges or the buffer effect of their adsorbed layers. Cooling, on the other hand, also tends to precipitate some colloids by decreasing the Brownian motion and encouraging gravitational settling.

Colloids which owe their stability to an electrically neutral adsorbed layer become unstable with respect to coagulation when this layer is removed, and electrically stabilized colloids coagulate when their charge is neutralized. Neutralization of the charge on a colloid may be accomplished in many ways. The suspension may be electrolyzed, in which case the particles will be discharged and precipitated at the cathode if they are positively charged and at the anode if they are negatively charged. Addition of a positively charged suspension to a negatively charged suspension (say ferric hydroxide to arsenic sulfide) leads to mutual precipitation as each colloid neutralizes the other. Addition of ions of charge opposite to that of the colloid also tends to give coagulation. Highly charged ions are particularly effective, a doubly charged ion being about fifty times as effective as a singly charged ion, and a triply charged ion about one thousand times as effective as a singly charged ion. Thus a negative colloid which required $1\,f$ sodium chloride for coagulation would require about $\frac{1}{50}\,f$ calcium chloride, and $\frac{1}{1000}\,f$ aluminum chloride for the same effect. Note that the effectiveness increases much more rapidly than the charge on the ion.

Ions having an especially strong attraction for the adsorbed ions are also highly effective at coagulating suspensions. Colloidal arsenic sulfide usually owes its negative charge to excess sulfide ions so that hydrogen ions are very effective in coagulating the colloid. (You will remember that hydrogen sulfide is a weak electrolyte, hence attractions between hydrogen ions and sulfide ions are strong.) Similarly, negatively charged silver chloride is precipitated by addition of silver ions since the negative charge on the colloid results from the adsorption of excess chloride ions.

Table 34.3
Structural Formulas of Some Typical Detergents

SODIUM OLEATE: structure shown, or $C_{17}H_{33}COONa$

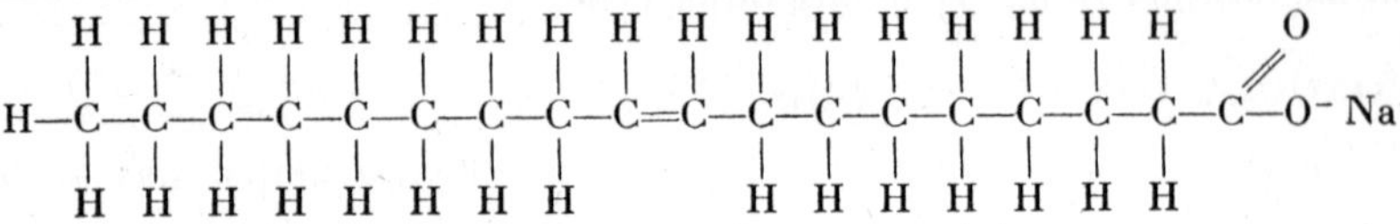

SODIUM LAURYL SULFATE: structure shown, or $C_{12}H_{25}OSO_3Na$

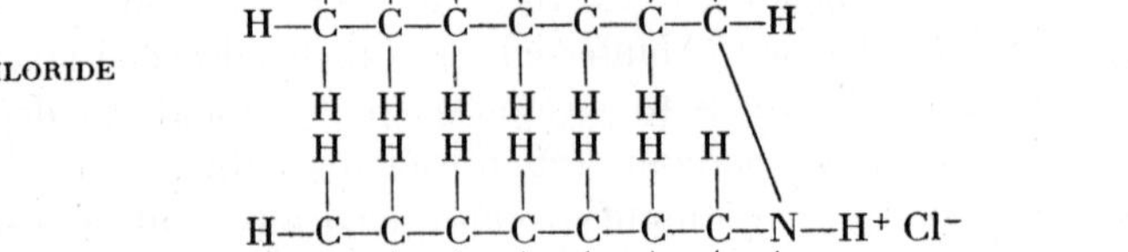

TRIHEPTYL AMMONIUM CHLORIDE: structure shown, or $(C_7H_{15})_3NHCl$

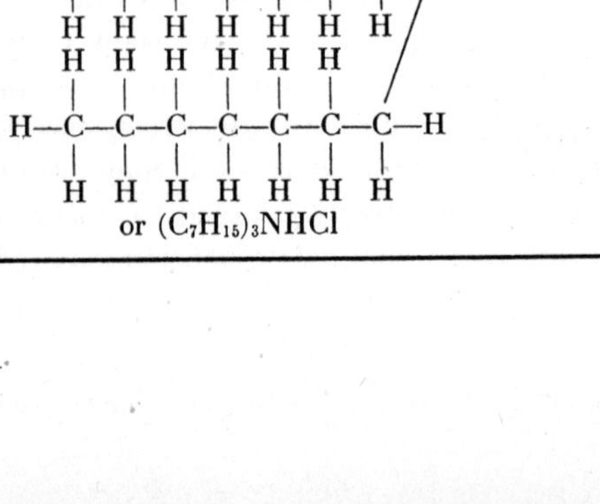

DETERGENTS

The use of detergents, including the soaps, to clean greasy surfaces with water is an excellent application of colloid principles. Grease and water do not wet one another, are insoluble in one another, and do not form a stable suspension when shaken together. When a detergent is added to the water (or to the grease), however, the two phases do wet one another, and do form a stable suspension. The detergent serves as the link between the two phases and bridges the surface between them. Some typical examples are listed in Table 34.3.

(Note that each of the detergents listed contains a long hydrocarbon portion (that is, one made up of carbon and hydrogen atoms), and an ionic portion (that is, one bearing an electric charge). The hydrocarbon portion is soluble in oils and grease but insoluble in water. The ionic portion is soluble in water but insoluble in oils and greases. Adding a detergent to pure water gives a colloidal suspension of the detergent in which the hydrocarbon ends cluster together and the ionic ends point outwards into the surface of the surrounding bulk water. Much of the detergent also concentrates at the outer surfaces of the water, the ionic end remaining in the water and the hydrocarbon end extending beyond the surface of the water. Thus the water surface is covered by a layer which will readily wet, and dissolve in, grease or oil. When the water, with its contained detergent, is agitated in the presence of oil, the oil is dispersed into droplets within the water and the detergent concentrates at the surfaces of these droplets forming a layer which stabilizes the droplets as a colloidal suspension. Note that the stabilization here involves both electrical charges and neutral fragments of the detergent molecules.

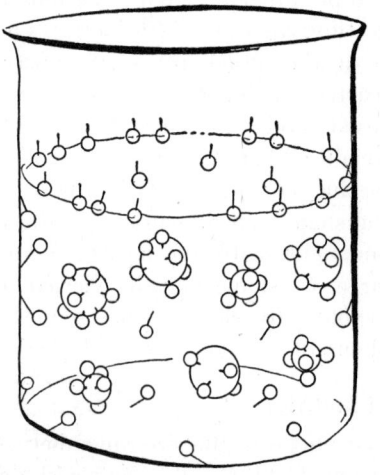

O— Molecule of Detergent (Circle represents water soluble, "tail" water insoluble portion of detergent molecule)

◯ Droplet of Dispersed Liquid (Oil)

Figure 34.2.
Structure of an emulsion stabilized by a detergent (schematic). The oil soluble portion of the detergent molecule enters the oil droplet but the water soluble part of the detergent does not. This forms a surface on the oil which water can "wet" and so keeps the oil droplet suspended in the water, and prevents the fusion of separate oil droplets when they collide due to Brownian motion.

Colloidal systems consisting of two liquid phases (for example, oil and water) are called *emulsions*. Emulsions such as mayonnaise may have relatively large amounts of oil dispersed as droplets in a water phase if the protective substance at the interface between oil and water is sufficiently stable. Figure 34.2 gives a schematic representation of an emulsion which is stabilized by a detergent.

SHAPE OF COLLOIDAL PARTICLES

Colloidal particles of all shapes are known: spheres, spheroids both oblate and prolate, cubes and other flat-sided configurations, rods, disks, and others. Settling rates and diffusion rates of substances depend on their shapes as well as on the actual sizes of the particles, as will also viscosity and the Tyndall scattering. Spheres, for instance, settle faster, diffuse faster, have lower viscosity, and show more Tyndall scattering than rods of the same molecular weight. When the shape of a colloidal particle is more or less regular and reproducible, as in many of the proteins, it is sometimes possible to determine the shape and dimensions of the particles from diffusion, settling, viscosity, and light scattering measurements. Of course, if the particle is sufficiently large, its shape may be viewed directly in the electron microscope. To be visible in the electron microscope each dimension would have to be larger than about 10^{-6} cm., or 100 Å., that is, some fifty atoms in length. See frontispiece.

SUMMARY

Particles in the size range between small single molecules of low molecular weight and bulk substances with an average radius of 10^{-4} or 10^{-5} cm. are said to be colloidal. They settle from suspensions only slowly and may be kept in suspension indefinitely by reason of Brownian motion, similar electrical charges, electrically neutral adsorbed layers, or viscosity of the suspending medium. They always contain a high proportion of surface atoms. These surface atoms adsorb substances from neighboring phases more or less tightly, this adsorption accounting for many of the typical properties of colloids. The rest of their properties may be interpreted in terms of the sizes and shapes of the colloidal particles.

Problem 34.5. Glass may be considered to be sodium silicate for the purposes of this problem. Water wets glass very well and will climb to a considerable height in a glass capillary whose lower end is submerged in water. Remember the use of the capillary pipet in qualitative analysis. How do you account for the fact that addition of a detergent to the water markedly decreases the height to which the resulting liquid will rise in the capillary when compared to pure water?

Problem 34.6. Liquid mercury is able to rise to considerable heights within a copper capillary but is depressed within a glass capillary below the level of the bulk liquid. How do you account for these facts in terms of types of bonds in the substances involved? Why are the effects greater in a capillary than in a large tube?

Problem 34.7. The freezing of mayonnaise or melting of oleomargarine usually destroys their colloidal nature with the result that layers form when the mayonnaise later thaws or the oleomargarine freezes. (Technically one says that the emulsions have been broken.) How do you account for the effect of temperature change in each instance?

Problem 34.8. Carbon black as prepared industrially (see page 92) is a poor adsorbent for the inert gases. When heated in a vacuum and then cooled in the vacuum it becomes a good adsorbent for the inert gases. The lower its temperature the better it is as an adsorbent. Yet if the black is heated very strongly in the vacuum and then cooled, it has lost most of its adsorbent powers. How do you account for these experimental facts?

Problem 34.9. Acetic acid is often used commercially to coagulate rubber latex. What is the electrical charge on the latex particles? At which electrode would rubber deposit during electrolysis of the latex suspension?

Problem 34.10. When oil is shaken with water containing a detergent, an emulsion of the oil in the water is obtained. When water is shaken with oil containing the same detergent, an emulsion of water in oil is obtained. What is the difference between an oil-in-water and a water-in-oil emulsion and why does each form under the particular conditions described?

Problem 34.11. How would you determine whether a suspension of barium sulfate in water was positively or negatively charged? Give several methods. What could cause the charge?

Problem 34.12. Calculate the surface area in 1 g. of carbon black of density 2.5 g/cm^3 if the average particle has a radius of 10^{-6} cm. and is a sphere.

Problem 34.13. Do the suds in the dishpan have any useful function? Do they, for instance, help clean the dishes?

Problem 34.14. Addition of an acid to a sudsy soap solution "kills" the suds. How do you account for this fact?

Problem 34.15. A ferric hydroxide suspension (prepared by adding a few drops of concentrated ferric chloride to hot water) is put in a cellophane bag which, in turn, is placed in a beaker of water. Chloride ions are soon detectable in the water, but none of the red colloid appears on the water side of the cellophane even on long standing. The process is known as dialysis. How do you account for the observed effects?

Problem 34.16. Name two properties which a colloidal suspension of arsenious sulfide has in common with a glue solution which justify classing these substances together as colloids. How can these properties be observed experimentally?

Problem 34.17. Discuss very briefly what is right and what is wrong in the statement: "The Brownian movement shows us the motion of molecules."

Problem 34.18. Is it possible to prepare colloidal silver iodide (a) negatively charged, (b) positively charged? If so, how? If not, why not?

Problem 34.19. What is: (a) the Tyndall effect, (b) a detergent (give an example), (c) an isoelectric point (give an example), (d) a "wetting agent" (with brief explanation of how it works), (e) a method of obtaining colloidal platinum?

35 THE HYDROCARBONS

ONE OF the earliest observed distinctions between materials from living substances and those from inanimate objects was in combustibility. The former, when heated, char to form gaseous products and carbon or in the presence of air they burn to form carbon dioxide. Noncombustible residues, the ash, were considered "inorganic" for they consist of compounds derivable from minerals. As often happens when established chemistry is applied to new fields, the eighteenth century terms "ash" and "mineral" still are used in nutrition and by the older biochemists for the elements other than carbon, hydrogen, oxygen, and nitrogen found in biological systems. Since carbon dioxide is the principal product (other than water) from the combustion of organic materials, "organic chemistry" early in chemistry (about 1750) became identified with the chemistry of carbon and its compounds. True, the carbon-containing minerals and rocks, such as the carbonates, graphite, and diamond were apparently not of organic origin, but coal, judging from its fossil leaf imprints, evidently was organic. Thus, with the exception of the carbonates and such substances as carbon monoxide and carbon dioxide, all carbon compounds became included in organic chemistry; all other compounds are included in inorganic chemistry.

In the early days of the science when chemists were intent on analyzing and classifying and on building a logical framework for chemistry, only the simpler inorganic compounds were synthesized from the elements. Living organisms were recognized as the supreme synthesizers; they took simple inorganic substances and made complicated organic material from them. The organic chemist could degrade and fragment organic material into simpler substances and could determine its ultimate composition but he could not make it. Thus, up through the first half of the nineteenth century the philosophical position was that organic substances could be made only through the operation of vital forces present in living substances, a doctrine known as vitalism. Chemistry and "chemical affinities" applied only to dead materials. In the words of Gebhardt in 1842, "La force vitale seule opère par synthèse." ("The vital force alone acts in synthesis.")

However, as has been and is still true in science, the men working in the laboratories are not permanently deterred by the dicta of philosophers. In 1828 Friedrick Wöhler (discoverer of aluminum, beryllium, and yttrium, and then only 28 years old) on heating ammonium cyanate, formula NH_4CNO, to purify it found that it was converted to urea, the principal end-product of protein metabolism in animals. The result of the experiment was unexpected. Cyanic acid and ammonia, and therefore ammonium cyanate which could be prepared from them, were regarded as inorganic although they were then prepared from organic (proteinaceous) material. Yet ammonium cyanate, an "inorganic compound," and urea, an animal substance, had the same composition and simple heating converted the former to the latter. However, because of the sources of his starting materials, Wöhler realized that he had not made an organic substance from inorganic sources and he and his contemporaries remained vitalists. The first laboratory synthesis of an unquestionably organic substance from the elements was made by Kolbe, a pupil of Wöhler, in 1845. By heating carbon and sulfur Kolbe prepared carbon disulfide. From this and chlorine he made carbon tetrachloride and then tetrachloroethylene and from this, water, and chlorine he made trichloroacetic acid which could be reduced to acetic acid, a well-known organic substance. Within the next decades many organic substances were synthesized in the laboratory and the idea of vitalism vanished from organic chemistry. Whatever of vitalism remains is in biochemistry which we shall consider in some detail in Chapter 39.

Today many more organic syntheses are carried out and many more organic compounds are made in laboratories and in industry than inorganic. Some of the newer therapeutic substances, first extracted from animal or vegetable sources, have become abundant enough and cheap enough for widespread use only after a laboratory (and then a larger scale) synthesis was developed. There are several million known carbon-containing compounds compared to some 100,000 without carbon and the difference in number grows greater daily. The majority of the synthesized carbon compounds are not found in living organisms, yet the term organic compounds still is applied to them.

SOURCES OF ORGANIC COMPOUNDS

For commercial production of many-ton lots of carbon-containing compounds large scale sources of raw materials must be available. Raising animals is, in general, a complicated and costly process and most animal products are worth more as leather, steak, chops, fur, etc., than as sources for pure compounds. Plants, on the other hand, are relatively cheap to raise on a large scale and can be used as raw materials for the synthesis of many organic compounds as well as in the fabrication of more complicated materials such as lumber, foods, etc. The cheapest substances containing carbon are limestone and coal and these are becoming increasingly important as starting materials for the synthesis of organic materials. Unfortunately, the carbon in both limestone and coal is already rather tightly bonded. High temperatures must be used to bring about initial reactions to produce materials more amenable to further synthetic steps.

The only other large scale source of carbon lies in the natural gas and petroleum fields. No one is yet sure just what the origin of these carbon compounds might have been, but they may, like coal, have been formed over the course of millions of years from ancient forests long buried under layers of rock and minerals.

The compounds in petroleum and natural gas are, in the main, composed only of carbon and hydrogen, and hence are known as hydrocarbons. Because of their importance as a source of compounds for further synthesis and because of their fundamental structure we shall begin our study of the chemistry of carbon compounds, organic chemistry, with the hydrocarbons.

THE TETRAHEDRAL CARBON ATOM

To a unique degree carbon atoms have the ability to combine with other carbon atoms, seemingly without limit. This property, together with the ability of carbon atoms to form bonds with four other atoms, results in a rich variety of compounds.

We have seen that carbon lies in the middle of Period II in the periodic table. The carbon atom with its four valence electrons is able to share these electrons with those of other atoms to form four electron-pair bonds per atom. These bonding electron-pairs are distributed as far apart as possible about the carbon atom. Hence their positions may be represented at the apexes of a regular tetrahedron having a carbon nucleus at the center.

METHANE AND SOME SIMPLE DERIVATIVES

Methane, the main constituent of natural gas, has the formula CH_4. It has the tetrahedral structure because of the directions assumed by the four bonds

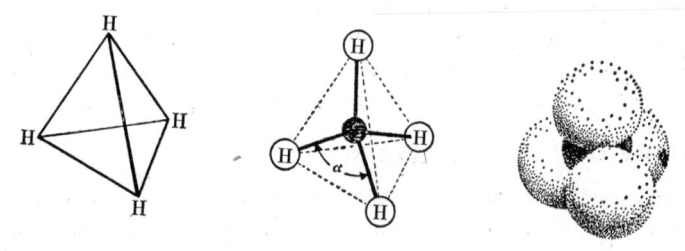

Figure 35.1.
Some different ways of representing the tetrahedral bonding by carbon in methane.

formed by carbon. Each of the hydrogen atoms lies at an apex of the tetrahedron. The hydrogen atoms are equidistant from one another and the distances between them conform to those derived from the regular tetrahedral angle, $\alpha = 109°28'$. See Figure 35.1. The equilibrium distance between carbon nucleus and hydrogen nucleus is 0.97 Å.

Problem 35.1. Given the tetrahedral angle and the measured C—H distance, calculate the distance between the hydrogen atoms (distance between nuclei) in methane.

The regular tetrahedron, a geometric figure with four sides all equal and four apexes equidistant from one another, is three-dimensional and cannot be shown on a plane in two dimensions. In consequence the formula for methane, represented in the plane of the paper as

$$\begin{matrix} & H & & & H \\ & \cdot\cdot & & & | \\ H & : C : & H & \text{or} & H—C—H \\ & \cdot\cdot & & & | \\ & H & & & H \end{matrix}$$

does not show the true spatial relations between the hydrogen atoms and the carbon atom. This fact will become evident when we consider examples of other compounds. In organic chemistry the dash, —, is used predominantly to represent an electron-pair bond.

We have seen that the halogens are able to form covalent bonds with one another and with other elements. Each halogen atom, with its seven valence

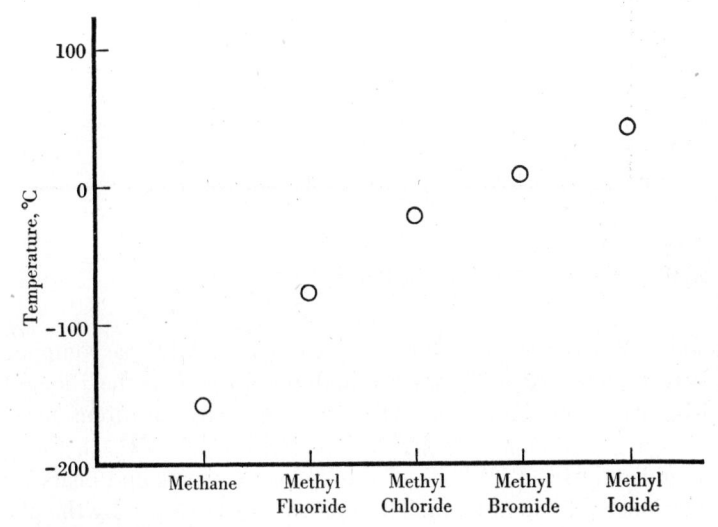

Figure 35.2.
Boiling points of the methyl halides.

electrons, can share the unpaired electron with another element. Thus each fluorine atom can form an electron-pair bond with a carbon atom, and four fluorine atoms can form four electron-pair bonds with a single carbon atom as in the molecule, CF_4. Similarly, compounds with the formulas CCl_4, CBr_4, and CI_4 can be formed. These compounds have the same tetrahedral arrangement as methane, but have different interatomic distances because of differences in

570   GENERAL CHEMISTRY

atomic size. The internuclear distances are: C—H, 0.97 Å.; C—F, 1.41 Å.; C—Cl, 1.76 Å.; C—Br, 1.91 Å.; C—I, 2.10 Å.

For compounds with similar structure, the freezing and boiling points increase with molecular volume. The increase of boiling points for the series with the formulas CH_4, CH_3F, CH_3Cl, CH_3Br, and CH_3I is shown in Figure 35.2. Consider also the series of compounds represented by the formulas CH_4, CH_3Cl, CH_2Cl_2, $CHCl_3$, and CCl_4 with the names: methane, chloromethane (methyl chloride), dichloromethane (methylene chloride), trichloromethane (chloroform), and tetrachloromethane (carbon tetrachloride), respectively. The

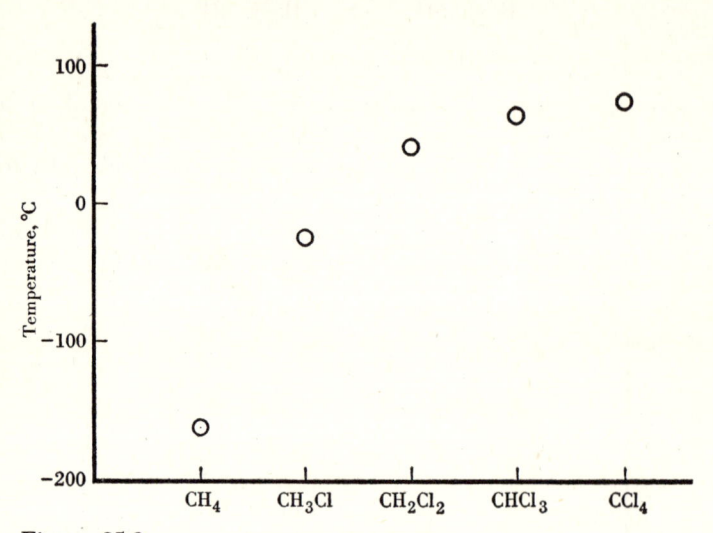

Figure 35.3.
Boiling points of the chloromethanes.

boiling points of this series are shown in Figure 35.3. All these compounds adhere closely to tetrahedral symmetry and the series may be thought of as representing the replacement, one at a time, of hydrogen atoms by chlorine atoms. This means that in a molecule with the formula CH_3Cl, the chlorine atom is equidistant from all three of the hydrogen atoms and bears the same spatial relationship to all of them. This fact cannot be shown by the plane diagram

$$H-\underset{\underset{H}{|}}{\overset{\overset{H}{|}}{C}}-Cl$$

for on such a diagram the chlorine atom appears to be adjacent to two of the hydrogen atoms but on the opposite side of the carbon atom from the third hydrogen atom. There is no experimental evidence for such difference. In mixed compounds the angles are not quite those of the regular tetrahedron but the deviations are not great.

ETHANE

The ability of a carbon atom to form an electron-pair bond with another carbon atom is illustrated by the compound, ethane, with the formula C_2H_6. In the molecule of ethane one of the four bonds of each carbon atom holds the other carbon atom and the remaining three bonds hold hydrogen atoms. In terms of a two-dimensional structure this compound can be represented as

$$\begin{array}{cc} H\ H \\ H:C:C:H \\ H\ H \end{array} \quad \text{or} \quad \begin{array}{c} H\ H \\ | \ \ | \\ H-C-C-H \\ | \ \ | \\ H\ H \end{array}$$

This compound may be thought of as one in which a CH_3— group, called a *methyl group* or *methyl radical*, is bonded to another methyl group, or as a methyl group attached in place of one of the hydrogen atoms of methane. Another possible name of ethane is methylmethane. See Figure 8.2, page 86.

The hydrogen atoms of ethane, like those of methane, may be replaced by atoms of halogens or of other elements. Consider the compound with the formula C_2H_5Cl in which a chlorine atom is substituted for a hydrogen atom. This compound may be called chloroethane or ethyl chloride. The ethyl radical C_2H_5—, like the methyl radical, has a free valence electron and is able to form a bond at that point. As a planar model chloroethane may be represented by

$$\begin{array}{c} H\ H \\ | \ \ | \\ H-C-C-Cl \\ | \ \ | \\ H\ H \end{array} \quad \text{or} \quad \begin{array}{c} H\ H \\ | \ \ | \\ H-C-C-H \\ | \ \ | \\ H\ Cl \end{array}$$

Note, however, that since the three atoms attached to each carbon atom occupy symmetrical positions, the two diagrams represent the same molecule, being merely different views of it.

If we now substitute a second chlorine atom for hydrogen in ethane two possibilities arise. If the second chlorine atom replaces one of the hydrogen atoms on the carbon atom already holding a chlorine atom the compound obtained will be

$$\begin{array}{c} H\ H \\ | \ \ | \\ H-C-C-Cl \\ | \ \ | \\ H\ Cl \end{array}$$

If the second chlorine atom replaces a hydrogen on the other carbon atom the compound will have the formula

$$\begin{array}{c} H\ H \\ | \ \ | \\ H-C-C-H \\ | \ \ | \\ Cl\ Cl \end{array}$$

572 GENERAL CHEMISTRY

The two dichloroethanes have exactly the same analysis and molar weight. Molecules of the two contain the same number of atoms of each element. They differ only in the arrangement of these atoms in the molecules. Their properties which depend on molecular structure also differ. The two dichloroethanes, since they contain the same number and same kind of atoms, are called *isomers*. Isomers which differ in the groups which are bonded to each atom are called *structural isomers*. Ammonium cyanate and urea, like the dichloroethanes, are structural isomers.

We may use the name of a compound to indicate its structure and to distinguish between isomers if the name is part of a system of nomenclature. If one of the carbon atoms is numbered 1 and the other 2, the carbon atoms to which the chlorine atoms are attached in the two dichloroethane isomers are shown by the names, 1,1-dichloroethane and 1,2-dichloroethane. This nomenclature is part of an international system adopted by the International Union of Chemistry, and is called the IUC system.

Problem 35.2. How many isomeric trichloroethanes are possible? How many tetrachloroethanes are possible? How many pentachloroethanes? How many hexachloroethanes? Name them.

PROPANE

If another carbon atom is attached to one of the carbon atoms in ethane, thus replacing a hydrogen atom, a chain of three carbon atoms is produced. If the remaining bonds of carbon are attached to hydrogen atoms the compound, propane, with the formula C_3H_8 results. When the three-dimensional structure is compressed into the plane of the paper it becomes

$$\begin{array}{ccc} & H\ \ H & \\ H & \diagdown\diagup & H \\ \diagdown & C & \diagup \\ & C\ \ \ C & \\ \diagup & | \ \ \ | & \diagdown \\ H\ H & & H\ H \end{array}$$

A number of names may be applied to propane to indicate its structure. It may be called methylethane or ethylmethane or dimethylmethane.

Hydrogen atoms in propane may be replaced by halogens to form "substituted" hydrocarbons. Compounds such as chloroethane and chloropropane are called *derivatives* of the corresponding hydrocarbons.

Observe that a question of structural isomers arises when a single chlorine atom is substituted into a propane molecule, for, obviously, there will be different structures depending on whether the chlorine atom is attached to an end carbon or to the central carbon. In the systematic nomenclature the compound having the molecular structure

THE HYDROCARBONS 573

$$\begin{array}{c} H \quad H \\ \diagdown \diagup \\ H \quad C \quad H \\ \diagdown \diagup \diagdown \diagup \\ C \quad C \\ \diagup | \quad | \diagdown \\ H \; H \quad H \; Cl \end{array}$$

is called 1-chloropropane and the compound with the structure

$$\begin{array}{c} H \quad Cl \\ \diagdown \diagup \\ H \quad C \quad H \\ \diagdown \diagup \diagdown \diagup \\ C \quad C \\ \diagup | \quad | \diagdown \\ H \; H \quad H \; H \end{array}$$

is called 2-chloropropane.

Problem 35.3. How many dichloropropanes are possible? Designate each by a systematic name.

THE METHANE SERIES

Inspection of the formulas for methane, ethane, and propane will show that the effect of replacement of a hydrogen atom by a methyl group is the addition of CH_2 to the molecule. A carbon atom that is attached to two other carbon atoms has two remaining bonds available for hydrogen atoms. The result is a *methylene group*, —CH_2—. Each of the terminal carbons in the chain can hold a third hydrogen atom. Consequently there is a family of hydrocarbons with the generalized formula C_nH_{2n+2}. The members of the family are called *paraffins* or *alkanes*. When no carbon atom is attached to more than two other carbon atoms in the chain the resulting compounds are called the *normal* paraffin hydrocarbons or *normal* alkanes. Some of the members of this series are shown in Table 35.1, together with their freezing and boiling temperatures (at atmospheric pressure). Observe that the first four members of the series are gases at room temperature and atmospheric pressure. Methane is the principal constituent of natural gases. Ethane and higher members of the series are present in natural gas in smaller and decreasing amounts. Propane and butane are also gases but they may be liquefied under pressures greater than one atmosphere at room temperature or by chilling at atmospheric pressure. Cylinders containing liquid propane or butane or mixtures of the two obtained from natural gas and petroleum are sold as "bottled gases" for domestic use in areas not supplied with gas mains. When the valve to the tank is opened the liquid fuel evaporates and passes as a gas through the valve to the burner.

The hydrocarbons containing between five and fifteen carbon atoms per molecule are liquid at room temperature and atmospheric pressure. Those having five to nine carbon atoms per molecule boil between 40 and 150°C. and are present in commercial gasoline. The kerosenes and fuel oils contain the

Table 35.1
Normal Paraffin Hydrocarbon Series
(Normal alkanes)

FORMULA	NAME	MELTING POINT IN °C.	BOILING POINT IN °C.
CH_4	Methane	−182.5	−161.5
C_2H_6	Ethane	−183.3	−88.6
C_3H_8	Propane	−187.7	−42.1
C_4H_{10}	n-Butane	−138.4	−0.5
C_5H_{12}	n-Pentane	−129.7	+36.1
C_6H_{14}	n-Hexane	−95.3	68.7
C_7H_{16}	n-Heptane	−90.6	98.4
C_8H_{18}	n-Octane	−56.8	125.7
C_9H_{20}	n-Nonane	−53.5	150.8
$C_{10}H_{22}$	n-Decane	−30	174
$C_{11}H_{24}$	n-Undecane	−26	196
$C_{12}H_{26}$	n-Dodecane	−10	216
$C_{15}H_{32}$	n-Pentadecane	+10	270
$C_{20}H_{42}$	n-Eicosane	36	345
$C_{30}H_{62}$	n-Triacontane	66	distilled at reduced pressure to avoid decomposition
$C_{40}H_{82}$	n-Tetracontane	81	
$C_{50}H_{102}$	n-Pentacontane	92	
$C_{60}H_{122}$	n-Hexacontane	99	
$C_{70}H_{142}$	n-Heptacontane	105	

members boiling between 175 and 325°C. The highest members of the paraffin series are solid at room temperature. They and their isomers form paraffin waxes. Natural petroleums also contain hydrocarbons and their derivatives from series other than the paraffin series.

THE BUTANES

We have already considered examples of structural isomers, compounds which differ in the groups attached to some atom. If we build the next higher member of the series from propane by addition of a CH_2 group we see that two different arrangements are possible. If one of the six terminal hydrogen atoms in propane is substituted by a methyl group we obtain a "straight chain" molecule with the structure

This compound is called normal butane or n-butane. Because of possible rotation of groups about a bond the molecule may have the shapes indicated, and others as well. On the other hand, if the methyl group is substituted for one of the two hydrogen atoms attached to the middle carbon in the propane, there results a compound with the structure

THE HYDROCARBONS 575

```
            H
            |
        H—C—H  H
       H     \ /   H
        \    C    /
         \  / \  /
          C    C
         / \  / \
        H   H H  H
```

This compound is called iso-butane or, in the systematic nomenclature, 2-methylpropane.

Both normal butane and iso-butane have the same formula, C_4H_{10}, but the atoms are attached in different ways to yield structural isomers with different properties. With increasing number of carbon atoms in a hydrocarbon the possible number of structural isomers of the paraffin series increases rapidly. Thus, there are three different pentanes, all with the formula C_5H_{12}. There are thirty-five different nonanes with the formula C_9H_{20}, all of which have been prepared and identified as to properties. It can be shown that over 100,000 eicosanes with the formula $C_{20}H_{42}$ are theoretically possible and over 100 million isomers of triacontane with the formula $C_{30}H_{62}$ are possible. Obviously all of these have not yet been identified. The number of possible isomers are given to indicate how, even with a relatively small number of carbon and hydrogen atoms and with fixed numbers of bonds and of angles between bonds, an enormous number of different structures and consequently of different compounds are possible. In organic chemistry even more than in inorganic chemistry one needs to be concerned with structure in order to understand how substances behave.

Problem 35.4. How many isomeric hexanes are possible? Diagram them.

NOMENCLATURE FOR THE PARAFFIN HYDROCARBONS

Organic chemists have had to use systematic names for compounds to indicate their structures, and thus to relieve the strain on their memory. All members of the paraffin series are given names which end in the suffix -ane. As a group they are called the *alkanes*. Except for the first members of the series, which bear historical names, Greek numerical prefixes indicate the number of carbon atoms per molecule. Thus, the octanes are the members of the paraffin series having eight carbon atoms per molecule. However, normal octane is the only octane to bear this name under the IUC nomenclature. Under this system the isomer of octane with the structure

```
              H
              |
      H  H—C—H  H  H  H  H  H
      |   |     |  |  |  |  |
  H—C———C————C—C—C—C—C—H
      |   |     |  |  |  |  |
      H   H     H  H  H  H  H
```

576   GENERAL CHEMISTRY

is called 2-methylheptane. It takes its name from the *longest carbon chain*. The isomer with the structure

```
                    H
                    |
                  H—C—H
                    |
        H  H  H—C—H  H  H  H
        |  |    |    |  |  |
      H—C—C————C————C—C—C—H
        |  |    |    |  |  |
        H  H    H    H  H  H
```

is called 3-ethylhexane, the longest chain having six carbon atoms. The number 3 in the name indicates the carbon atom in the longest chain (hexane) to which the ethyl radical is attached. The chains actually have the zigzag structure illustrated for *n*-butane but they are usually printed in the straight form for convenience. The monovalent radicals obtained from the normal paraffin series are designated by substituting the suffix -yl for -ane. Thus, the radical, C_2H_5— is called the ethyl radical and C_6H_{13}— the hexyl radical.

THE UNSATURATED HYDROCARBONS

In the saturated hydrocarbon series all the atoms are joined by single electron-pair bonds. Every carbon atom has four such bonds and every hydrogen atom one bond, that is, carbon is tetravalent and hydrogen is monovalent. New atoms can be substituted in such compounds only if they replace one of the atoms already present. However, there is a series of hydrocarbons having two fewer hydrogen atoms per molecule than the corresponding saturated series. The general formula of this series is C_nH_{2n}. These hydrocarbons are able to add two atoms of hydrogen or chlorine or other monovalent atoms without the displacement of any of the hydrogen atoms already present. They are therefore called *unsaturated* hydrocarbons. The first member of the series is ethylene (systematic name ethene) with the formula C_2H_4. Its electronic structure may be designated (this molecule is actually planar) as

```
        H         H
         ..     ..
          C : : C
         ..     ..
        H         H
```

If we represent electron pairs by dashes in the usual fashion it becomes

```
        H         H
         \       /
          C = C
         /       \
        H         H
```

All "-ene" compounds contain at least one *double bond*. The formula of propene (propylene), the second member of the series, is C_3H_6 and the structure is

$$\text{H—C}\begin{smallmatrix}H\\|\\H\end{smallmatrix}\text{—C}\begin{smallmatrix}H\\\\\\H\end{smallmatrix}\text{=C}\begin{smallmatrix}H\\\\\\H\end{smallmatrix}$$

Note that the names of members of this series bear the suffix -ene.

The four-carbon unsaturated hydrocarbons, the butenes, have even more isomers than butane has because different positions are possible for the double bonds as well as for the carbon atoms. If the double bond is between the first and second carbon atoms in the straight-chain compound, as in the formula

$$\text{H—C—C—C=C—H}$$

the compound is called 1-butene and if the double bond is between the two middle carbon atoms as in the formula

$$\text{H—C—C=C—C—H}$$

it is called 2-butene. Because of the symmetry of iso-butane the formation of a double bond between any pair of carbon atoms will result in the same compound

In the systematic nomenclature it is called 2-methylpropene. The members of the series are called *alkenes*, or *olefins* (oil-forming) in the older nomenclature. Ethylene itself was discovered in 1795. Table 35.2 lists some of the alkenes together with their melting and boiling points. The members of this series have *not* been found in natural petroleums. Can you postulate a reason for this?

GEOMETRIC ISOMERS

Alkenes are most reactive at the position of the double bond. The carbon atoms held together by the two electron pairs have a shorter internuclear dis-

Table 35.2
1-Alkene Series
(Normal monoolefins)

FORMULA	NAME	MELTING POINT IN °C.	BOILING POINT IN °C.
$CH_2=CH_2$	Ethene (Ethylene)	−169	−103.7
CH_3—$CH=CH_2$	Propene (Propylene)	−185	−47.7
C_2H_5—$CH=CH_2$	1-Butene	−185	−6.3
C_3H_7—$CH=CH_2$	1-Pentene	−165	+30.0
C_4H_9—$CH=CH_2$	1-Hexene	−140	64.6
C_5H_{11}—$CH=CH_2$	1-Heptene	−119	93.6
C_6H_{13}—$CH=CH_2$	1-Octene	−102	121.3
C_7H_{15}—$CH=CH_2$	1-Nonene	−81	146.9
$C_{10}H_{20}$	1-Decene	−66	170.5
$C_{15}H_{30}$	1-Pentadecene	−3.3	268.6
$C_{20}H_{40}$	1-Eicosene	+30.1	344

tance (1.34 Å.) than those held together by a single electron pair (1.54 Å.) and the electron density is high. Also, radicals joined by a single electron pair are free to rotate as though they were spinning on the axis of the bond but radicals held together by a double bond are not free to rotate. This fact has important consequences. The structure diagrammed earlier for 2-butene is not the only possible structure. Another structure is

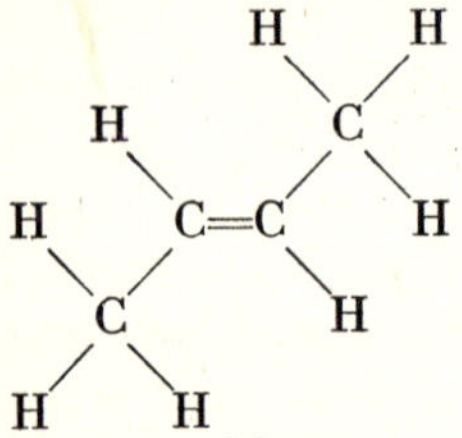

trans-2-butene   as compared with   *cis*-2-butene

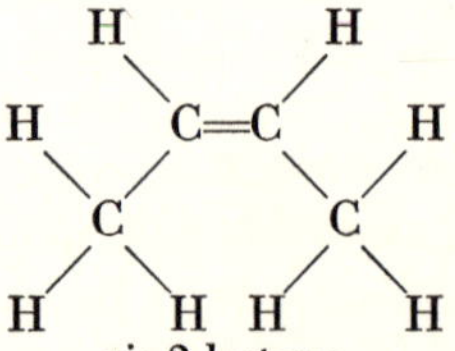

There is a compound corresponding to each of the above structures, and the two have different properties. The one with both methyl groups on the same side of the chain of doubly bonded carbon atoms is called *cis*-2-butene and the one with the methyl groups on opposite sides of the chain of doubly bonded carbon atoms is called *trans*-2-butene. The different *cis*, *trans* isomers are types of *geometric isomers*. Geometric isomers differ in spatial position within the molecules but the same atoms are bonded together. Structural isomers differ in the atoms which are bonded together (see page 572).

ACETYLENE

The alkane and alkene series of hydrocarbons are examples of *homologous series*. A third series of hydrocarbons has the general formula C_nH_{2n-2}. The members of this series have four fewer hydrogen atoms per molecule than the saturated hydrocarbons. An example is actylene with the formula C_2H_2. Here two carbon atoms are joined by three electron pairs. The result is a linear molecule with the electron structure H : C : : : C : H which may be written as H—C≡C—H. The members of the acetylene series bear the suffix -yne. Thus, the systematic name of acetylene becomes ethyne and the series name, alkynes. As in the alkene series, different isomers of the alkynes are possible depending on the position of the triple bond. Table 35.3 shows some of the members of

Table 35.3
1-Alkyne Series
(Normal acetylenes)

FORMULA	NAME	MELTING POINT IN °C.	BOILING POINT IN °C.
CH≡CH	Ethyne (Acetylene)	−81 *	−84 †
CH_3—C≡CH	Propyne (Methylacetylene)	−102.7	−23.2
C_2H_5—C≡CH	1-Butyne	−125.7	+8.1
C_3H_7—C≡CH	1-Pentyne	−106	40.2
C_4H_9—C≡CH	1-Hexyne	−132	71.4
C_5H_{11}—C≡CH	1-Heptyne	−81	99.7
C_6H_{13}—C≡CH	1-Octyne	−79.4	126.2
C_7H_{15}—C≡CH	1-Nonyne	−58	151.0
$C_{10}H_{18}$	1-Decyne	−40	174.2
$C_{15}H_{28}$	1-Pentadecyne	+9	270.7
$C_{20}H_{38}$	1-Eicosyne	39	345

* Pressure, 891 mm. rather than one standard atmosphere.
† Sublimation temperature, one atmosphere pressure.

this series. The alkynes are somewhat more reactive than the alkenes and acetylene when compressed may decompose with explosive violence. Nevertheless, acetylene and its homologues are becoming increasingly important as starting materials for the making of compounds. Acetylene can be prepared by treating calcium carbide, formula CaC_2, with water. Since calcium carbide can be prepared by heating calcium carbonate with coke in an electric furnace it follows that, through acetylene, organic compounds can be prepared from limestone, coal, and water. Thus, these very cheap sources of carbon and hydrogen become available for organic syntheses.

DIENES

Another series of hydrocarbons with the general formula C_nH_{2n-2} but related to the olefins rather than acetylenes is known. Instead of having triple bonds each molecule contains two double bonds. The first member of the diolefins is propadiene, with the formula

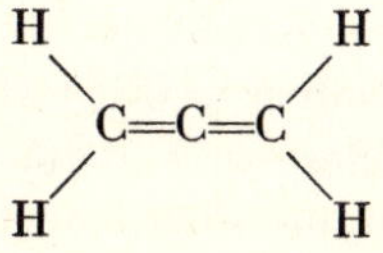

1,3-Butadiene with the formula

$$\begin{array}{c}H\\ \diagdown\\ C=\end{array}\!\!\!\!\begin{array}{c}H\\ |\\ C\end{array}\!\!-\!\!\begin{array}{c}H\\ |\\ C\end{array}\!\!=\!\!\begin{array}{c}H\\ \diagup\\ C\\ \diagdown\\ H\end{array}$$

is produced on a large scale for use in the preparation of synthetic rubbers.

HYDROCARBONS AS FUELS

Hydrocarbons today are chiefly used as fuels although to an increasing degree they are used as starting materials for preparing other organic compounds. With excess air they burn completely to carbon dioxide and water. The reaction usually takes place in the gas phase—the liquids evaporate before they burn and the solids melt and evaporate before they burn. Hence, flames (gas phase combustions) are formed. At the temperature of the flame the compounds often decompose (crack) into smaller fragments. With a deficiency of oxygen the hydrogen from the cracked hydrocarbons combines with the oxygen to form water and the carbon collects as a soot, which, even though finely divided, has the crystal structure of graphite.

The more volatile hydrocarbons pass from the gas fields through pipes directly to the consumer as natural gas. The intermediate compounds are sold as gasolines. They are evaporated and mixed with air in the carburetor of internal combustion engines to burn when ignited by a spark in the engine. The higher molar weight compounds with relatively low vapor pressures may be injected as fuels directly into hot engines of the Diesel type.

INCREASING THE AMOUNT OF GASOLINE FROM PETROLEUM

The demand for gasoline far exceeds the supply obtainable from simple distillation of crude petroleum, whereas much more kerosene and lubricating oil than can be used result from the simple distillation. Therefore, much of the higher molar weight material is decomposed at elevated temperatures and pressures (cracked) into substances of lower molar weight and higher vapor pressure for use in gasolines. When a decane, formula $C_{10}H_{22}$, is split into two fragments both cannot be saturated hydrocarbons. Thus, if one of the fragments is hexane, C_6H_{14}, the other must be butene, C_4H_8. The cracking unit also produces considerable quantities of carbon (petroleum coke) and hydrogen, indicating that some of the hydrocarbons are completely stripped of their hydrogen. This hydrogen then adds to many of the unsaturated molecules, such as butene, which had been formed and converts some of them to saturated hydrocarbons with the same chain length. The low molar weight (gaseous) materials from the cracking tower are often converted into (liquid) gasoline materials by passage through a "reforming" chamber in which they combine, in the presence of suitable catalysts, into molecules lying in the gasoline range. Thus, butane plus butene would yield an octane. Figure 35.4 shows the materials obtained from petroleum by simple distillation and by distillation with cracking.

GASOLINE AS A FUEL

The bond energies in hydrocarbons of different types are remarkably constant. Per gallon of different liquid hydrocarbons, the numbers of carbon-to-carbon bonds and carbon-to-hydrogen bonds are approximately the same. Consequently, the energy released per gallon when the fuels are burned to carbon dioxide and water remains fairly constant. However, the different types of compounds vary greatly in their burning rates and hence in their performance in a particular engine. The efficiency of engines in using the fuels also

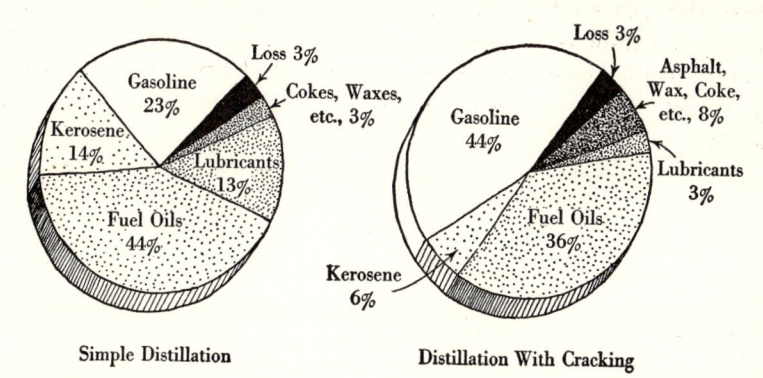

Figure 35.4.
Products from petroleum.

varies. As our petroleum sources dwindle and as fuels become more expensive, more attention is being paid to the proper relationship between the combustion process in the engine and the fuel used in it. Some substances, such as normal heptane, produce "knocking" when they burn in an automobile engine. One of the substances with excellent anti-knock qualities is an octane, 2,2,4-trimethyl pentane, also called iso-octane. An anti-knock scale has been built up in which normal heptane is given zero rating and iso-octane is given a 100 rating. If a particular gasoline performs like a mixture of 80 per cent *iso*-octane and 20 per cent *n*-heptane it is said to have an octane rating of 80. This rating scale has certain limitations because substances are now known with better anti-knock qualities than iso-octane. Lead tetraethyl, formula $Pb(C_2H_5)_4$, improves the anti-knock qualities of gasoline but it leaves a deposit of lead oxide in the engine cylinders. Large quantities of 1,2-dibromoethane are now produced for addition to the leaded gasolines. When this substance is present with the lead tetraethyl, volatile lead bromide is formed and escapes through the exhaust.

It has been shown conclusively that the anti-knock rating depends on the molecular architecture of a hydrocarbon. Extended structures such as *n*-heptane, *n*-octane, etc., knock since they burn too rapidly and tend to explode within the cylinder. More compact structures present in the branched chain molecules such as 2,2,4-trimethyl pentane or 2,2,3-trimethyl butane (which has the highest octane rating known), burn more slowly in the cylinder and give much less tendency to knock. Manufacturers of gasoline make a definite effort to produce as much as possible of the isomers which have a high anti-knock rating. The material to be made into a gasoline with high octane rating is passed through an isomerization chamber in which catalysts are present. These catalysts greatly enhance the rate of formation of the branched chain molecules at the expense of the more extended ones.

BENZENE

Benzene, first found by Faraday in 1825, gave great trouble to the early chemists who tried to explain its structure. Its molecular formula is C_6H_6 and yet it does not show the unsaturation which might be expected from a compound with so low a ratio of hydrogen to carbon. Kekule in 1865 suggested that the six carbon and six hydrogen atoms are arranged in the form of a regular hexagon as

Seven years later he suggested that the double bonds oscillate rapidly between the positions

and

Otherwise there should be two compounds of the type

and only one is known to exist.

The model for benzene proposed by Kekule is not entirely satisfactory because benzene does not have the reactivity associated with double bonds in organic compounds. Various theories and structures have been proposed to solve this problem. The experimental evidence is that benzene is a planar ring with all six hydrogen atoms in equivalent positions and all six carbon atoms in equivalent positions. The current theory is that the extra electrons, represented by the double bonds in the Kekule model are somehow shared by the ring as a whole. Note that the benzene molecule exhibits resonance (see page 299). Benzene and its radicals appear in many important organic substances. For brevity organic chemists find it very convenient to designate it by the simple hexagon

in which the individual carbon and hydrogen atoms are not shown.

The hydrogen atoms in benzene like those in the chain compounds may be replaced by other atoms or groups though under different experimental conditions. These substituted atoms and groups are shown on the hexagon. For example the compound, chlorobenzene, with the formula C_6H_5Cl, is represented in diagrammatic form as

When more than one substituent is present several isomers are possible. There are three dichlorobenzenes with the formula $C_6H_4Cl_2$. The positions of the substituents may be shown by numbering the carbon atom in the ring to which the substituent is attached, or by a verbal term. Thus, for the three dichlorobenzenes we have

1,2-dichlorobenzene, or
ortho-dichlorobenzene

1,3-dichlorobenzene, or
meta-dichlorobenzene

1,4-dichlorobenzene, or
para-dichlorobenzene

When the chlorine atoms are attached to adjacent carbon atoms the compound is called 1,2-dichlorobenzene, or alternatively, *ortho*-dichlorobenzene. Because of symmetry the compound will be the same if the substituents are in any adjacent positions, for example, in 1,6 or the 2,3 positions. When the chlorine atoms are attached to carbon atoms separated by a single carbon atom the compound is called 1,3-dichlorobenzene or *meta*-dichlorobenzene. Again, the same compound exists if the substituents are on the carbon atoms labelled 2 and 4. A new compound does not result merely because one chooses to use different numbers. When the chlorine atoms are attached to carbon atoms on opposite ends of the ring the compound is 1,4-dichlorobenzene, or *para*-dichlorobenzene; it is commonly used in "moth crystals."

DETERMINATION OF STRUCTURE

One may well ask on what experimental evidence our idea of the structure of benzene and its derivatives is based. When benzene is chlorinated to produce a substance with a formula C_6H_5Cl only one compound with this molecular formula is found. (The molecular formulas are determined from experimental molecular weight and analytical data.) Since the chlorine atom could have replaced any of the hydrogen atoms of the benzene molecules it appears that the six hydrogen atoms occupy equivalent positions in the molecule. When chlorobenzene is chlorinated further to produce dichlorobenzene a mixture of three compounds with the formula $C_6H_4Cl_2$ is produced. These compounds can be separated from one another, and each shows all the evidence of being a single pure substance. Since the compounds have different properties, including the melting and boiling temperatures shown in Table 35.4, it appears that there are

Table 35.4

Proof of Structure of the Chlorobenzenes
(According to Körner)

Dichlorobenzenes, formula $C_6H_4Cl_2$	A	B	C
Melting points, °C.	52.9	−14	−24.8
Boiling points, °C.	173	179	173
Trichlorobenzenes, formula $C_6H_3Cl_3$	D	E	F
Melting points, °C.	17	51	63
Boiling points, °C.	213	219	208

three distinct dichlorobenzenes with the chlorine atoms occupying different positions in the molecule. How could the early chemists determine which structure represents the compound with the indicated physical properties?

Let the different dichlorobenzenes be designated by the letters A, B, and C as in Table 35.4. Compound A, which is a solid at room temperature, when chlorinated further produces a single trichlorobenzene melting at 17°C. and boiling at 213°C. This trichlorobenzene with the formula $C_6H_3Cl_3$ is a pure substance. Let it be called D. Compound B, which melts at $-14°C$., when chlorinated further produces a mixture of two trichlorobenzenes. When this mixture is separated one of the pure substances obtained is compound D previously made from A. The other trichlorobenzene melts at $51°C$. and boils at $219°C$. Let this compound be called E. Compound C, which freezes at $-24.8°C$., when chlorinated further forms a mixture of three trichlorobenzenes, two of which are the compounds D and E previously found. The third is a new compound which melts at $63°C$. and boils at $208°C$. Let this compound be called F.

Now consider the proposed formulas for the dichlorobenzenes previously derived from structural considerations. Compound A must be the *para* compound, for it is symmetrical and will produce only one product when chlorine is substituted for any of the remaining hydrogen atoms. Therefore, the compound melting at $52.9°C$. must be the *para* compound. Compound B must be the *ortho* compound for the symmetry of the *ortho* compound indicates that two of the hydrogen atoms occupy equivalent positions and the other two occupy different equivalent positions. Compound C must be the *meta* compound for the symmetry of this molecule is such that there are three different hydrogen positions relative to the two chlorine atoms already present.

It follows also that compound D, which may be prepared on chlorination of any of the three dichlorobenzenes, must be 1,2,4-trichlorobenzene. Compound E, which is prepared only from the *ortho* or *meta*-dichlorobenzene must be 1,2,3-dichlorobenzene. Compound F, which is prepared only from meta-dichlorobenzene, must be 1,3,5-dichlorobenzene. These relations are shown in Table 35.5. By this logic the structure of the different chlorobenzenes was derived.

Table 35.5
Structures Derived from Table 35.4

Dichlorobenzenes	A (para-)	B (ortho-)	C (meta-)
Trichlorobenzenes	D 1,2,4-	E 1,2,3-	F 1,3,5-

The method may be applied to other benzene derivatives. Always in determining the structure of organic molecules one must apply reasoning to the results of experiments. Experiments show that there are only three different tetrachlorobenzenes, all of which may be obtained from compound D. Two of them may be obtained from E and only one from F. These facts allow us to assign structures to the different tetrachlorobenzenes prepared in the laboratory. Only one pentachlorobenzene, formula C_6HCl_5, and only one hexachlorobenzene, formula C_6Cl_6, have been prepared. Theory based on our assumed structure of benzene is in agreement.

Problem 35.5. Diagram the structure of the different tetrachlorobenzenes and decide which may be derived on chlorination of compound D, which on chlorination of compound E, and which on chlorination of compound F.

HYDROCARBON DERIVATIVES OF BENZENE

The reactions of benzene and its derivatives (aromatic hydrocarbons) differ so widely from those of the chain hydrocarbons (aliphatic hydrocarbons) that they are often treated separately in organic textbooks. When the aliphatic radicals are attached to the benzene ring the hydrogen atoms attached to the carbon atoms of the ring have the general reactivity of hydrogen on benzene and hydrogen atoms attached to the carbon atoms in the chains have the reactivities associated with hydrogen in the aliphatic series. Under proper conditions the radicals of the paraffin series may be attached to the benzene ring to form the series, methylbenzene (common name, toluene), ethylbenzene, propylbenzene, etc.

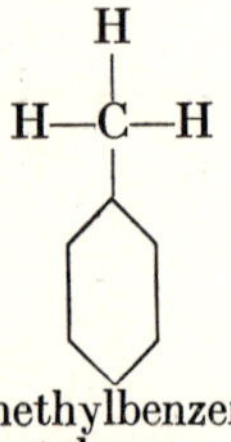

methylbenzene
toluene,
formula $CH_3 \cdot C_6H_5$

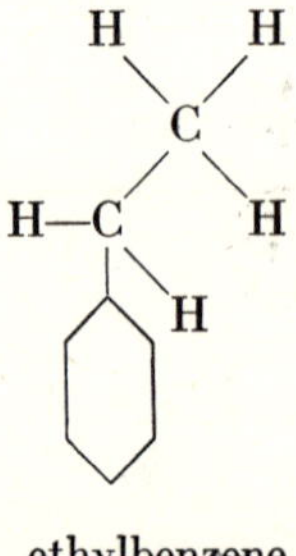

ethylbenzene,
formula $C_2H_5 \cdot C_6H_5$

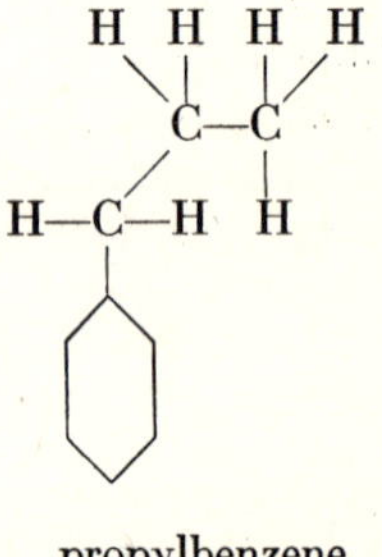

propylbenzene,
formula $C_3H_7 \cdot C_6H_5$

On the other hand, two or more radicals may be attached to benzene. There are three dimethylbenzenes with the methyl groups in the *ortho*, *meta*, and *para* positions respectively. The dimethylbenzenes are called xylenes.

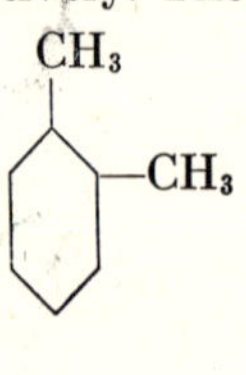

ortho-xylene

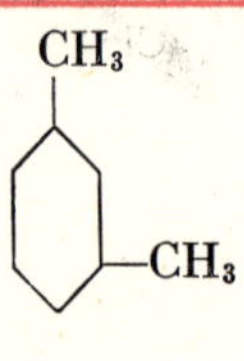

meta-xylene

para-xylene

Xylenes are structural isomers of ethylbenzene, having the same molecular formula, C_8H_{10}. The systematic name, showing structure, is always used to indicate the specific compound referred to.

For historical reasons the radical C_6H_5— is called the phenyl radical. Chlorobenzene is sometimes called phenyl chloride. When the phenyl radical is substituted for one of the hydrogen atoms in ethylene the compound phenylethylene, commonly called styrene, with the structure

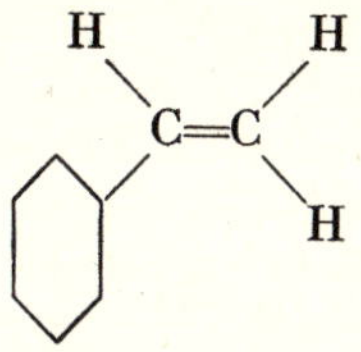

is produced. This compound is used with butadiene to make one of the common synthetic rubbers.

MULTIPLE-RING HYDROCARBONS

Ring compounds with an even lower ratio of hydrogen to carbon than in benzene are also found. One of these is naphthalene with the formula $C_{10}H_8$. It appears there are not enough hydrogen atoms to supply one for each carbon atom. The structure of this compound is represented by a double ring as

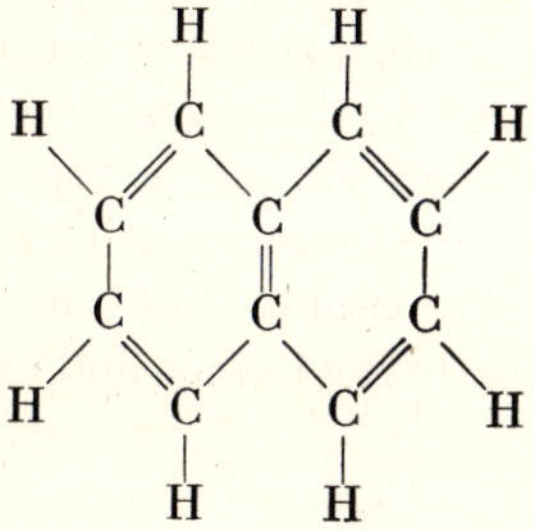

or

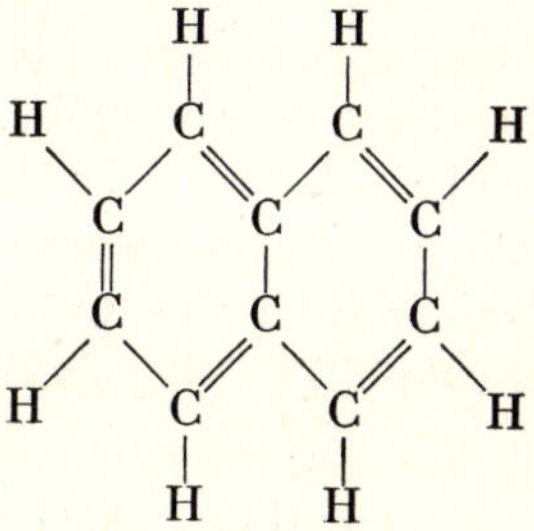

or as

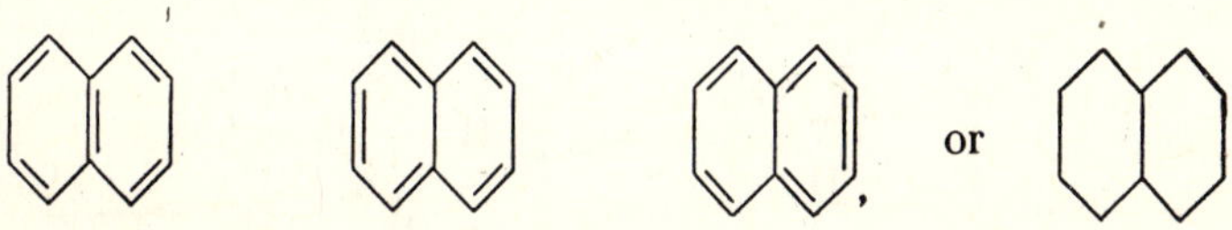

, or

There are other compounds with a still lower ratio of hydrogen to carbon. Two of them have the molecular formula $C_{14}H_{10}$. Each of these consists of three rings joined together

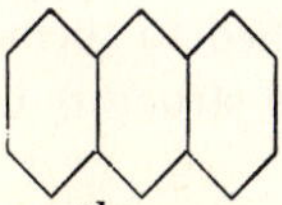

anthracene 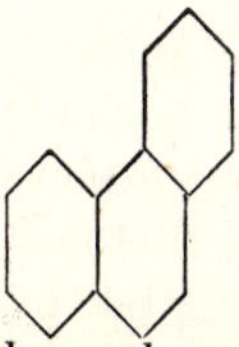   phenanthrene

588 GENERAL CHEMISTRY

The extra electrons represented by double bonds in the preceding rings are, of course, present. The phenanthrene ring structure is present in a number of compounds of great biological interest: the bile acids, sex hormones, and cancer-producing compounds.

CYCLOPARAFFINS

When benzene is reduced by hydrogen according to the reaction

benzene + 3H$_2$ = cyclohexane

it forms cyclohexane, formula C_6H_{12}. This compound in its various reactions behaves more like a saturated hydrocarbon of the paraffin series than it does like one of the benzene series. The ring of six carbon atoms no longer lies in a plane, as does benzene, but is puckered according to the zigzag structure of the paraffin carbons. Because the ends of the chain are joined, the type formula is C_nH_{2n}, like that of the monoolefins, but it is not an unsaturated hydrocarbon. The members of the series are named like the paraffins but with the prefix cyclo-. The simplest members of the series are cyclopropane and cyclobutane

cyclopropane   cyclobutane

Cyclopentane, cyclohexane, cycloheptane, and cyclooctane are fairly common, being found in petroleum and other natural materials. The syllables, pent-, hex-, etc., indicate the number of carbon atoms in the ring. Cycloparaffins with rings of five or six carbons are most common and most easily prepared. The rings may have hydrocarbon radicals attached to them. Certain cyclo compounds with large rings of particular size and structure have a musk-like odor and are synthesized for use by perfumers.

THE HYDROCARBONS 589

TRIVIAL AND PROPRIETARY NAMES

The nomenclature problem in organic chemistry is particularly vexing since a few million compounds are known and an almost infinite variety are possible. Many systems have been proposed, such as the IUC system used in the preceding material, but systematic names often become very long and complicated. They then defeat the chief purpose of a name which is to provide a reasonably simple means of recalling the substance being mentioned. Names, in other words, are nothing more than mnemonic devices for the use of man and should be as simple as possible. Trivial names have no necessarily generic relation to the structure of the compound being identified. They often arise historically because the structure was unknown when the compound was first discovered. Many of these historical names are so firmly established in the literature of chemistry that little gain would result from changing them. Thus, toluene is seldom known as methylbenzene, and acetylene is almost never called ethyne. Trivial names, because of their simplicity, may also be used for newly discovered compounds, even when the structure is well established. The compound 2,2,3-trimethyl butane is almost always called triptane, for example. It often takes less time to find in the chemical literature, which is now well indexed, the structural formula associated with a trivial name than it would to work out the structure from the systematic name. Unfortunately, also, various systems are suggested from time to time. Some names, which appear trivial now, are actually remnants of former systematic nomenclatures. Chloroform, bromoform, and iodoform might be cited as examples. Names of a third type are common in chemistry. These are the proprietary names; names originally copyrighted by a manufacturer to protect his rights in the sale of the material. Many drugs lie in this category. An outstanding example in inorganic chemistry is "pyrex." Originally this name referred to one type of glass produced by a particular manufacturer. It should, therefore, be capitalized whenever used. Actually there are many types of such glass now available and the word has become so much a part of the language that capitalization is seldom used.

Examples of all these ways of naming substances will appear in the following chapters. Current practice is to use trivial names when these are firmly established in the literature, to use systematic names for others until they become unwieldy and then to use trivial or proprietary names for substances with more complicated structures.

Problem 35.6. How does the composition of a "summer" gasoline differ from that of a "winter" gasoline? How about summer versus winter lubricating oils? Be specific in terms of actual compounds present.

Problem 35.7. Estimate the boiling point of carbon tetrabromide from Figures 35.2 and 35.3. Compare your value with the literature value.

Problem 35.8. The boiling point of carbon tetrafluoride is −128°C. In light of Figures 35.2 and 35.3 can you interpret this value in terms of the nature of the C—F bond?

Problem 35.9. Plot the melting points and boiling points in Table 35.1 as a function of the number of carbon atoms per molecule. Interpret the general shape of the curves in terms of intermolecular forces. Interpret the deviations from smooth curves in terms of intermolecular forces.

Problem 35.10. Write the equations for the formation of calcium carbide from carbon and lime and for the preparation of acetylene from calcium carbide.

36 ORGANIC COMPOUNDS CONTAINING OXYGEN

WHEN HYDROCARBONS are burned with a limited amount of oxygen, only small amounts of compounds containing carbon, hydrogen, and oxygen are produced. For instance, methane yields some methyl alcohol, formula CH_3OH, but carbon monoxide, carbon dioxide, and water are the principal products. Apparently a methane molecule, when oxidized tends to burn completely. The alcohol is more easily oxidized within the flame than is methane. These statements also apply to the higher hydrocarbons. These oxygen compounds must be made in other ways than by direct oxidation of hydrocarbons in a flame.

METHANOL

Methyl chloride when treated with potassium hydroxide yields some methyl alcohol according to the reaction

$$H-\underset{H}{\overset{H}{C}}-Cl + K^+OH^- = H-\underset{H}{\overset{H}{C}}-O-H + K^+Cl^- \qquad (36.1)$$

This method of preparation, although not commercially feasible for methyl alcohol, shows the structure of it. Methyl alcohol was formerly called wood alcohol because it was obtained in the destructive distillation of wood. Its systematic name is methanol. It is synthesized today in large quantities from carbon monoxide and hydrogen, in the presence of a zinc chromite catalyst at high temperature and pressure, as a practically pure compound.

$$CO_{(g)} + 2H_{2(g)} = CH_3OH_{(g)} \qquad (36.2)$$

Methanol in many properties reminds us of water. It is a liquid at room temperature. Its boiling point is relatively high (66°C.) for so simple a compound because it, like water, is associated (contains hydrogen bonds) in the

591

liquid phase. It is the first in a family of organic compounds called *alcohols*, which have a hydrocarbon radical attached to a hydroxyl group. They may be regarded as a derivative of water with a hydrocarbon radical substituted for a hydrogen atom. Sodium and potassium metals displace hydrogen from the alcohol though more slowly than they do from water.

$$\begin{array}{cc} \text{H} & \text{H} \\ | & | \\ \text{H—C—O—H} + \text{K} = \text{H—C—O—K} + \tfrac{1}{2}\text{H}_{2(g)} \\ | & | \\ \text{H} & \text{H} \\ \text{methyl alcohol} & \text{potassium} \\ \text{or methanol} & \text{methoxide} \end{array} \qquad (36.3)$$

Only one hydrogen atom per molecule is displaced by the metal, showing that the one hydrogen, the hydroxyl hydrogen, is attached differently than the other three. Hydrogen atoms attached directly to carbon are not replaced directly by sodium or potassium metals. The alcohols ionize only slightly. They are even less ionized than water; the ionization constants of methyl and ethyl alcohol are about 10^{-16} and 10^{-18}, respectively.

HIGHER ALCOHOLS

Since alcohols are hydroxy derivatives of the hydrocarbons they are named from them. In the systematic nomenclature the hydrocarbon suffix, -ane, is replaced by the alcohol suffix, -ol. Ethanol, the alcohol derived from ethane, has the formula C_2H_5OH and the structure

$$\begin{array}{cc} \text{H} & \text{H} \\ | & | \\ \text{H—C—C—O—H} \\ | & | \\ \text{H} & \text{H} \end{array}$$

Because of the possibilities of isomers resulting from different positions of the hydroxyl group there are two propyl alcohols with the formula C_3H_7OH. They are

$$\begin{array}{ccc} \text{H H H} & & \text{H H H} \\ | \; | \; | & & | \; | \; | \\ \text{H—C—C—C—O—H} & \text{and} & \text{H—C—C—C—H} \\ | \; | \; | & & | \; | \; | \\ \text{H H H} & & \text{H O H} \\ & & | \\ & & \text{H} \\ \text{normal propyl alcohol} & & \text{isopropyl alcohol} \\ \text{or propanol-1} & & \text{or propanol-2 (a} \\ \text{(a primary alcohol)} & & \text{secondary alcohol)} \end{array}$$

An alcohol in which the hydroxyl group is attached to an end carbon atom is called a *primary alcohol* and one in which the hydroxyl group is attached to a carbon atom between two other carbon atoms in the chain is called a *secondary alcohol*. In general there are as many isomers among the alcohols as there are possible different positions for the hydroxyl group.

In the previous chapter we found that there are two butanes. Normal butane can form the alcohols

```
      H  H  H  H                          H  H  H  H
      |  |  |  |                          |  |  |  |
   H—C—C—C—C—O—H                       H—C—C—C—C—H
      |  |  |  |                          |  |  |  |
      H  H  H  H                          H  H  O  H
                                                |
                                                H
      butanol-1                            butanol-2
```

the first being a primary alcohol and the second a secondary alcohol. Isobutane (2-methylpropane) also can form two different alcohols

```
            H                                       H
            |                                       |
      H  H—C—H  H                            H  H—C—H  H
      |     |    |                           |     |    |
   H—C     C     C—O—H       and          H—C     C     C—H
      |     |    |                           |     |    |
      H     H    H                           H     O    H
                                                   |
                                                   H
      2-methylpropanol-1                     2-methylpropanol-2
```

The first of these is a primary alcohol and the second a *tertiary* alcohol. In a *tertiary* alcohol the hydroxyl group is attached to a carbon which in turn is attached to three other carbon atoms. Thus, there are four butanols. The position of the OH group may be determined from the different reactions of the alcohols. Table 36.1 illustrates the type formulas for primary, secondary, and tertiary alcohols in which R, R', and R'' represent hydrocarbon radicals.

Table 36.1
Type Formulas for Alcohols

```
         H   H              R'  H              R'  H
         |  /               |  /               |  /
      R—C—O             R—C—O              R—C—O
         |                  |                  |
         H                  H                  R''
    primary alcohol    secondary alcohol    tertiary alcohol
```

ETHANOL

Ethanol is the most common of the alcohols. Indeed, the term alcohol when applied to a single substance means ethanol just as salt under similar usage means, specifically, sodium chloride. An ancient method of preparing ethanol is by fermentation of sugars. This method is still the most important commercially. Some of the common names of ethanol—grain alcohol and spirits of wine—reflect the source of the sugars used for the fermentation. Large quantities of ethanol are used industrially. To meet the demands, ethanol is also produced by the hydration of ethylene obtained from the cracked gases of petroleum refineries. The reactions are as follows:

$$\underset{\substack{\text{ethylene} \\ \text{gas}}}{\overset{H}{\underset{H}{>}}C=C\overset{H}{\underset{H}{<}}} + \underset{\substack{\text{concentrated} \\ \text{acid}}}{H_2SO_4} = \underset{\text{ethyl hydrogen sulfate}}{H-\overset{H}{\underset{H}{C}}-\overset{H}{\underset{H}{C}}-O-\overset{:\ddot{O}:}{\underset{:\ddot{O}:}{S}}-O-H} \quad (36.4)$$

$$H-\overset{H}{\underset{H}{C}}-\overset{H}{\underset{H}{C}}-O-\overset{:\ddot{O}:}{\underset{:\ddot{O}:}{S}}-O-H + HOH = \underset{\text{ethanol}}{H-\overset{H}{\underset{H}{C}}-\overset{H}{\underset{H}{C}}-O-H} + \underset{\substack{\text{dilute} \\ \text{acid}}}{H_2SO_4} \quad (36.5)$$

The reaction itself is an old one (1826), but it could not be used on a large scale until ethylene became available in quantity.

Ethanol, like methanol, is soluble in water without limit. Ethanol and methanol form alcoholates, corresponding to the salt hydrates, with many salts. Pharmaceutical preparations in which ethanol is used as the solvent are called *tinctures*. The smarting effect of tincture of iodine is caused by the alcohol as well as by the iodine.

POLYHYDROXYALCOHOLS

An organic molecule may have more than one alcohol group. Ethane with two carbon atoms may be made to undergo reactions so that a hydroxyl group is placed on each carbon. The result is a glycol, ethandiol-1,2, or ethylene glycol

$$H-\overset{\overset{\displaystyle H}{|}}{\underset{\underset{\displaystyle H}{|}}{C}}-\overset{\overset{\displaystyle H}{|}}{\underset{\underset{\displaystyle H}{|}}{C}}-H$$

Ethylene glycol is a liquid completely soluble in water. It has a higher boiling point than the alcohols and a correspondingly lower vapor pressure. These result from its greater degree of hydrogen bonding in the liquid phase.

Methanol, ethanol, and ethylene glycol are used in automobile radiators to lower the freezing temperature of the water. Their molar weights are low enough so that not too large amounts are necessary. However, methanol vapors are somewhat poisonous and both methanol and ethanol have fairly high vapor pressures and tend to evaporate from the radiators. The glycol has so low a vapor pressure, its boiling point being 197°C., that it is commonly used in the "permanent" antifreezes. Propylene glycol,

$$\begin{array}{c} \text{H} \quad \text{H} \quad \text{H} \\ | \quad | \quad | \\ \text{H}-\text{C}-\text{C}-\text{C}-\text{H} \\ | \quad | \quad | \\ \text{H} \quad \text{O} \quad \text{O} \\ \quad \quad | \quad | \\ \quad \quad \text{H} \quad \text{H} \end{array}$$

unlike other glycols, is used as a solvent, preservative, or softening agent in foods, pharmaceuticals, and cosmetics. Ethylene glycol is oxidized in the body to oxalate ion $C_2O_4^=$, a powerful poison.

Problem 36.1. How many dihydroxypropanes may be prepared? Diagram them. How many dihydroxybutanes are possible? Diagram them. (Compounds with two OH groups on the same carbon atom are unstable and cannot be isolated.)

The simplest trihydroxy alcohol is glycerol, commonly called glycerine. Its systematic name is propantriol-1,2,3, indicating the structure

$$\begin{array}{c} \text{H} \quad \text{H} \quad \text{H} \\ | \quad | \quad | \\ \text{H}-\text{C}-\text{C}-\text{C}-\text{H} \\ | \quad | \quad | \\ \text{O} \quad \text{O} \quad \text{O} \\ | \quad | \quad | \\ \text{H} \quad \text{H} \quad \text{H} \end{array}$$

Glycerol is completely soluble in water and has a very low vapor pressure but the water solutions are somewhat viscous so that it is not completely satisfactory as an antifreeze agent for automobile radiators. It, like propylene glycol, is nontoxic, and is used in food, medicinal, and cosmetic preparations. It is obtained from natural fats as a by-product in soap making.

ETHERS

When alcohols are treated with a dehydrating agent, such as concentrated sulfuric acid under conditions different from those used for making ethylene, the elements of water may be removed between two molecules to form a compound called an ether.

$$\begin{array}{ccccc} 2CH_3OH & = & CH_3OCH_3 & + & H_2O \\ \text{(in concentrated} & & \text{dimethyl} & & \text{(in sulfuric} \\ \text{sulfuric acid)} & & \text{ether} & & \text{acid solution)} \end{array} \quad (36.6)$$

Ethers are isomeric with alcohols, (compare the formulas CH_3OCH_3 and C_2H_5OH) but have very different properties. An ether may be considered an oxide derived from water in which both hydrogen atoms are replaced by organic radicals. The type formula is

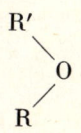

$$\begin{array}{c} R' \\ \diagdown \\ O \\ \diagup \\ R \end{array}$$

596   GENERAL CHEMISTRY

where R and R' may or may not be the same group. Diethylether, $(C_2H_5)_2O$, is the common ether used as an anaesthetic. Ethers are highly volatile, having lower boiling points than the alcohols from which they are made. The pure compounds cannot form hydrogen bonds.

The structure of ethers may be proved from reactions such as that between ethyl iodide and potassium ethoxide (obtained by reaction of potassium with ethanol).

$$\mathrm{H-\underset{\underset{H}{|}}{\overset{\overset{H}{|}}{C}}-\underset{\underset{H}{|}}{\overset{\overset{H}{|}}{C}}-I + K-O-\underset{\underset{H}{|}}{\overset{\overset{H}{|}}{C}}-\underset{\underset{H}{|}}{\overset{\overset{H}{|}}{C}}-H = H-\underset{\underset{H}{|}}{\overset{\overset{H}{|}}{C}}-\underset{\underset{H}{|}}{\overset{\overset{H}{|}}{C}}-O-\underset{\underset{H}{|}}{\overset{\overset{H}{|}}{C}}-\underset{\underset{H}{|}}{\overset{\overset{H}{|}}{C}}-H + KI} \quad (36.7)$$

This reaction may also be used to form mixed ethers, that is, ethers with different radicals. Thus, if methyl iodide is substituted for ethyl iodide in the above reaction, methyl ethyl ether, formula $CH_3OC_2H_5$, is obtained.

Problem 36.2. Interpret the differences in volatility of alcohols and ethers in terms of their structures and resulting intermolecular forces.

ALDEHYDES

When methanol is oxidized by the addition of one oxygen atom per molecule the result is not a dihydroxyalcohol as might be expected. Only under unusual conditions will there be two hydroxy groups attached to a single carbon atom. Instead, water splits out and a new type of compound called an aldehyde is formed. The reactions are

$$\mathrm{H-\underset{\underset{H}{|}}{\overset{\overset{H}{|}}{C}}-O-H + (O)} = \left[\mathrm{H-\underset{\underset{O-H}{|}}{\overset{\overset{H}{|}}{C}}-O-H} \right] = \mathrm{H-\overset{\overset{H}{|}}{C}=O + H-O-H} \quad (36.8)$$

methanol   (unstable)   methanal, or formaldehyde

The systematic name for this aldehyde is methanal, the suffix -al designating aldehydes. For historical reasons the common names for the simpler aldehydes are derived from the acids which result when the aldehydes are oxidized, the common name for methanal being formaldehyde (from formic acid).

Ethanal, with the common name acetaldehyde (from acetic acid), has the formula CH_3CHO. It may be obtained by oxidation of ethanol or by the catalytic hydration of acetylene. The general structural formula for an aldehyde may be represented by the formula

$$\mathrm{R-C\overset{\nearrow H}{\underset{\searrow O}{}}}$$

where R is an organic radical (or hydrogen for the simplest aldehyde).

KETONES

When a secondary alcohol is oxidized, the hydrogen atom bonded to the carbon atom holding the hydroxyl group is attacked and the result is

$$\underset{\text{a secondary alcohol}}{R-\underset{\underset{H}{|}}{\overset{\overset{H}{|}}{C}}-R'} + (O) = \left[\underset{\text{(unstable)}}{R-\underset{\underset{H}{\diagdown}\;\underset{H}{\diagup}}{\overset{\diagup\;\diagdown}{C}}-R'}\right] = \underset{\text{a ketone}}{R-\underset{\overset{\|}{O}}{C}-R'} + H_2O \qquad (36.9)$$

The simplest ketone, in which R and R' are methyl radicals, is called acetone. It is an important commercial solvent, as in modern lacquers. If R represents the methyl radical and R' the ethyl radical the compound is called methyl ethyl ketone.

ACIDS

When an aldehyde is oxidized, the result is an acid of the type

$$R-C\underset{\diagdown O}{\overset{\diagup O-H}{}}$$

Thus

$$\underset{\text{aldehyde}}{R-C\underset{\diagdown O}{\overset{\diagup H}{}}} + (O) = \underset{\text{acid}}{R-C\underset{\diagdown O}{\overset{\diagup O-H}{}}} \qquad (36.10)$$

The $-C\underset{\diagdown O}{\overset{\diagup O-H}{}}$ group is called the *carboxyl* group. The systematic names for acids are derived from the hydrocarbon names by use of the suffix -oic. Thus, methanoic acid, commonly called formic acid, has the formula

$$H-C\underset{\diagdown O}{\overset{\diagup O-H}{}}$$

and ethanoic acid, commonly called acetic acid, has the formula

598 GENERAL CHEMISTRY

$$\text{H-}\underset{\underset{H}{|}}{\overset{\overset{H}{|}}{C}}\text{-}C\overset{\nearrow O-H}{\searrow_O}$$

Because the acids were known long before the systematic nomenclature was established they tend to be called by their common names. Thus, the 18-carbon acid is called stearic acid rather than octadecanoic acid. The first three acids of the series are completely soluble in water. The higher members of the normal series are called fatty acids because they may be obtained from natural fats. These organic acids are relatively weak and their degree of ionization decreases only slightly for higher members of the series. The lower members of the series have a sharp odor. Those beginning with butyric (butanoic) acid have a goat-like odor, and the higher members are practically odorless. Acetic acid is the common acid in vinegar, obtained from alcoholic solutions such as cider by bacterial action. Pure acetic acid is called glacial acetic acid because it crystallizes to an ice-like solid at 17°C. Organic acids are highly associated both in the liquid and vapor phases.

The carboxyl group can be prepared by oxidation of an aldehyde group, which, in turn can be prepared by oxidation of a primary alcohol. A ketone group, obtained on oxidation of a secondary alcohol, cannot be oxidized further without disruption of the carbon chain. A tertiary alcohol cannot be oxidized without disruption.

It may be interesting to see what products are obtained if a carbon atom is oxidized to a fourth stage. With formic acid we see that the result is complete oxidation.

$$\underset{\text{formic acid}}{H-C\overset{\nearrow O-H}{\searrow_O}} + (O) = \underset{\text{carbonic acid}}{H-O-C\overset{\nearrow O-H}{\searrow_O}} = H-O-H + O=C=O \qquad (36.11)$$

$$\text{water} \qquad \text{carbon dioxide}$$

FUNCTIONAL GROUPS

One important reason for writing structural formulas is to show the presence of the parts of molecules having known kinds of reactions. In alcohols, the hydroxyl group, —OH, is characteristic, giving the alcohols certain common properties. Such a group is called a *functional group*. In aldehydes, ketones, and carboxylic acids the functional groups are

$$-C\overset{\nearrow H}{\searrow_O}, \quad \underset{}{\overset{}{\diagdown}}C=O, \quad \text{and} \quad -C\overset{\nearrow OH}{\searrow_O},$$

respectively. If one is interested only in the reactions of a substance at its functional group one usually writes semistructural formulas such as C_2H_5OH for ethyl alcohol and

$$C_2H_5C\begin{matrix} O-H \\ \\ O \end{matrix}$$

for propionic acid. Hydrocarbon radicals may also be considered functional groups.

Organic chemists subject functional groups to characteristic qualitative and quantitative tests for their presence. A methyl group may be identified by its oxidation products, alcohol, aldehyde, or acid. By a suitable variety of tests on the functional groups of a substance it is possible to derive the molecular structure of the substance. The process is logically analogous to the testing for ions in inorganic chemistry.

ESTERS

Acids and alcohols interact to produce a new type of compound called an ester. In the reaction the elements of water are removed as shown by the equation

$$R-C{\begin{matrix}O-H\\\\O\end{matrix}} + H-O-R' \underset{\text{(hydrolysis)}}{\overset{\text{(esterification)}}{\rightleftarrows}} R-C{\begin{matrix}O-R'\\\\O\end{matrix}} + HOH \quad (36.12)$$

acid   alcohol   ester   water

Esterification reactions are equilibrium reactions, and the extent of the reaction in either direction depends on the concentrations of the reacting substances. If the water concentration is kept low, the esterification reaction may be almost complete. Esters may be regarded as derivatives of organic acids in which the acidic hydrogen is replaced by an organic radical. Unlike acids and alcohols, which are associated liquids, esters are volatile, nonionized liquids, generally with lower boiling points than the acids from which they were made. When hydrolyzed they yield the original acid and alcohol.

The names of esters are derived from the interacting acids and alcohols. Thus, the ester formed from formic acid and methyl alcohol is called methyl formate. Formic acid can form esters with the other alcohols such as ethyl, propyl, and butyl alcohols. Acetic acid forms a corresponding series of esters, the simplest being methyl acetate. Cellulose, a complex alcohol, and acetic acid form the multiple ester, cellulose acetate, an important material used for making nonexplosive photographic films and certain types of rayon.

POLYACIDS

We have seen that ethylene glycol is the simplest dihydroxy alcohol. One or both of the alcohol groups may be oxidized to form the corresponding alde-

600 GENERAL CHEMISTRY

hydes and still further oxidized to form the acids. The diacid is called oxalic acid.

$$
\underset{\text{dialcohol}}{\begin{array}{c} H \\ | \\ H-C-O-H \\ | \\ H-C-O-H \\ | \\ H \end{array}} \quad \underset{-H_2O}{(+2O)} \quad \underset{\text{dialdehyde}}{\begin{array}{c} H \diagdown \diagup O \\ C \\ | \\ C \\ \diagup \diagdown \\ H \quad O \end{array}} \quad (+2O) \quad \underset{\substack{\text{diacid} \\ \text{oxalic acid}}}{\begin{array}{c} H-O \diagdown \diagup O \\ C \\ | \\ C \\ \diagup \diagdown \\ H-O \quad O \end{array}} \qquad (36.13)
$$

It is the simplest organic diacid. Its structure is that of two carboxyl groups attached to one another. Many of the acids derived from organic materials are polyacids. Thus, citric acid contains three carboxyl groups and one hydroxyl group per molecule.

A pair of isomeric diacids, maleic acid and fumaric acid, are a classical example of *cis, trans* isomerism. They have the same molecular formula, $C_4H_4O_4$. Both are diacids having two equivalents of acid per mole. Both contain a double bond as shown by their reactions with typical reagents. The structures that explain their properties are as follows:

maleic acid, *cis*-butenedioic acid
m.p. 130°C.
soluble in water

fumaric acid, *trans*-butenedioic acid
m.p. 290°C.
almost insoluble in water

Maleic acid is the *cis* diacid from butene. The two carboxyl groups lie on the same side of the double bond so that they can approach each other and can form an acid anhydride by elimination of water between them. In fumaric acid the carboxyl groups are on opposite sides of the double bond and cannot react in this way.

ACID ANHYDRIDES

We have seen that ethers result when water is split out from the hydroxyl groups of two alcohol molecules and that esters result from the splitting of water from the hydroxyl groups of an alcohol and an acid. In the presence of a dehydrating agent, water can be split out from the hydroxyl groups of two carboxylic acids to form an acid anhydride. Thus, for maleic acid

$$\text{maleic acid} = \text{HOH} + \text{maleic anhydride} \qquad (36.14)$$

Maleic anhydride, and other internal anhydrides, have a ring, one of the atoms of which is oxygen. We noted that fumaric acid because of its geometry cannot form an internal acid anhydride. Such acid anhydrides as acetic anhydride cannot be made by dehydrating the acids and must be made in other ways.

OPTICAL ISOMERISM

Tartaric acid, with the formula HOOC—CH(OH)—CH(OH)—COOH, was observed by Louis Pasteur (1860) to exist in crystals that were mirror images of each other. When the crystals were sorted by hand and dissolved in water the solutions had opposite effects on plane-polarized light. Apparently the structures of the crystals reflect differences in the structures of the molecules forming the crystals. As a result of this work LeBel and van't Hoff (1874) independently postulated that, to provide this kind of isomerism, the bonds of a carbon atom must be directed at the tetrahedral angles to form three-dimensional molecules. (Note that the fundamental structural ideas in organic chemistry predated by many years their interpretation in terms of electronic theory.)

Consider a simpler example, lactic acid, which has four different groups,

H, CH_3, OH, and COOH, attached to the central carbon atom. If they are arranged as in (a), the molecule, if held before a mirror, would appear in the mirror as (b), just as a left hand, when held before a mirror, appears in the mirror as a right hand. The hand also has four "groups" around its center, groups that may be represented by the thumb, the little finger, the front side, and the back side of the hand. By no orientation in space can a left hand be made to coincide with a right. If the thumbs, little fingers, and the front sides of the hands are brought into contact the back sides project in opposite directions. The models (a) and (b) of lactic acid behave in a similar way. Propionic acid,

```
        CH₃                    CH₃
         |                      |
    H—C—H                  H—C—H
         |                      |
         C                      C
        ╱ ╲                    ╱ ╲
       O   OH                HO   O
         (a)                    (b)
```

in which two of the groups (represented by H) are the same, does not have two isomeric forms. To be sure, models (a) and (b) are mirror images of each other, but they are also identical. By rotation in space all the groups may be made to coincide.

When light, considered as a wave motion, passes through asymmetric crystals it appears as plane-polarized light, the wave motion appearing to be in a set of parallel planes. When this polarized light is passed through a solution containing asymmetric molecules the plane of polarization is rotated to the right or to the left depending on which of the mirror-image molecules are present. The amount of rotation depends on the number and kind of molecules through which the light passes. It is, therefore, directly proportional to the concentration of these molecules and to the length of path through the solution. Mirror-image isomers are called *optical isomers*.

Optical isomers are especially important in biological reactions. When two optical isomers are possible, living organisms usually produce only one of the possible isomers. On the other hand in the usual laboratory synthesis both isomers are made in equal quantities. When the isomer which rotates plane-polarized light to the right, often called the *dextro* or *d* form, is mixed in equal amounts with the isomer which rotates the light to the left, often called the *levo*, or *l* form, the effect of each isomer is to compensate that of the other. Such a mixture, called a *racemic mixture*, is inactive toward polarized light. Thus, the compounds produced in the laboratory are racemic mixtures of the isomers.

Tartaric acid has two asymmetric carbon atoms per molecule, both alike in the groups to which they are attached. The two asymmetric groups within a molecule may reinforce each other in their effect on plane-polarized light or they may cancel each other. The isomer with the structure in which the effects cancel within the molecule is called the *meso* isomer. It, like a racemic mixture of the two active isomers, is inactive to polarized light.

Problem 36.3. Draw models of the tartaric acid molecule for each of the optically active isomers and for the *meso* isomer.

PHENOL

We have seen that a hydroxyl radical attached to an aliphatic radical forms the typical alcohol. Because of the special properties of the benzene ring, a hydroxyl radical attached to benzene is not classed as an alcohol. It is called a phenol. Its structure is

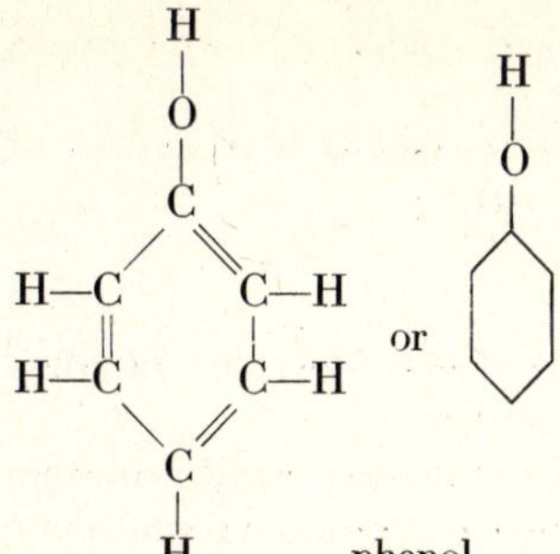

ORGANIC COMPOUNDS CONTAINING OXYGEN   603

phenol

Phenols are acidic in reaction, forming salts with strong bases. Phenol itself is a very weak acid, but the ionization of the phenol hydrogen becomes greater when the benzene ring is nitrated, as in HO—⟨ ⟩—NO₂, called nitrophenol. A phenol having a methyl group substituted for a hydrogen atom on benzene is called cresol. There are three cresols, the ortho, meta, and para compounds. Mixtures of cresols are used as disinfectants. They have a stronger bactericidal action than phenol itself. Di- and trihydroxyphenols also exist. Some of these have important commercial uses. One of them

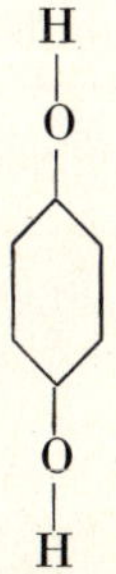

p-dihydroxybenzene (hydroquinone)

is used widely as a photographic developer because of its strong reducing action on silver halide which has been exposed to light. See page 529.

Problem 36.4. How would you prepare: (a) methyl propyl ether, (b) propyl acetate, (c) methyl propionate, (d) propanol, (e) methyl ethyl ketone, (f) ethanol?

Problem 36.5. Give examples of: (a) structural isomers, (b) geometric isomers, (c) cis-trans isomers, (d) optical isomers. List the conditions necessary for the formation of each type.

Problem 36.6. Name the compounds with the following formulas: (a) C_4H_9OH,
(b) $CH_3CH_2OC_2H_5$, (c) $CH_3-\underset{\underset{OH}{|}}{\overset{\overset{CH_3}{|}}{C}}-CH_3$, (d) $C_2H_5OC_4H_9$, (e) $CH_3\overset{\overset{O}{\|}}{C}-O-CH_3$,

(f) $C_2H_5-O-\overset{\overset{O}{\|}}{C}-C_2H_5$, (g) HO⟨ ⟩CH₃, (h) HO⟨ ⟩Cl, (i) HO⟨ ⟩.

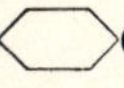

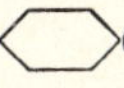

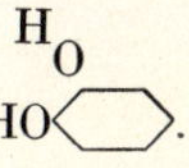

Problem 36.7. What inorganic compounds are formally analogous to (a) alcohols, (b) ethers, (c) esters?

Problem 36.8. What substances could be made to react to give the compound with the formula CH$_3$—CH$_2$—C—O—CH$_3$?
$$\underset{\text{O}}{\|}$$

Problem 36.9. How many pentanols (only one -ol group on each molecule) are possible? Outline the structure of each.

Problem 36.10. How would you prepare acetic acid from ethane?

Problem 36.11. Give the complete structural formula of each of the following: (a) butane, (b) diethyl ether, (c) formic acid, (d) methyl acetate, (e) an isomer of diethyl ketone, (f) *p*-nitrotoluene, (g) glycerine, (h) tertiary butyl alcohol, (i) naphthalene.

Problem 36.12. Outline the structure for all compounds with the formula C$_2$H$_6$O; the formula C$_3$H$_4$Cl$_2$. (There are eleven for C$_3$H$_4$Cl$_2$.) Give a systematic name to each of the compounds.

Problem 36.13. How can one determine experimentally whether a given cresol is ortho, meta or para?

Problem 36.14. Account for the marked difference in melting points of maleic acid and fumaric acid.

Problem 36.15. Diethylether boils at 35°C. The butanals, with the same empirical formula as ether, boil around 100°C. Both the ether and the butanals have about the same solubility in water. Account for these differences and similarities in terms of intermolecular forces.

37 OTHER HYDROCARBON DERIVATIVES

WE HAVE already considered some of the organic compounds containing oxygen and the halogens. Since oxygen is usually divalent, the oxygen atom in a compound may be doubly or singly bonded to a carbon atom. An oxygen atom may be bonded to a carbon atom by one bond and to a hydrogen atom by another bond to form a —C—O—H group as in alcohols or acids. On the other hand, in ethers an oxygen atom is bound to two different carbon atoms.

SULFUR

Because sulfur is a member of the oxygen family and has six valence electrons, two of them unpaired, it may be present in organic compounds in place of oxygen. Compounds, inorganic as well as organic, in which a sulfur atom replaces an oxygen atom are called *thio*compounds. Thus, there are thioalcohols, thioethers, and thioacids. Thioorganic compounds often have vile odors. Compare water and hydrogen sulfide. Primarily for this reason chemists have not worked with them as much as they have with other compounds. The characteristic odor of the skunk is a thioalcohol odor. As little as 2×10^{-12} g. per l. of thioethanol, called ethyl mercaptan, can be detected by smell.

Mustard gas, used as a war gas, is a thioether prepared from ethylene and sulfur monochloride, formula S_2Cl_2. Its formula is

$$\text{Cl}-\underset{\underset{\text{H}}{|}}{\overset{\overset{\text{H}}{|}}{\text{C}}}-\underset{\underset{\text{H}}{|}}{\overset{\overset{\text{H}}{|}}{\text{C}}}-\text{S}-\underset{\underset{\text{H}}{|}}{\overset{\overset{\text{H}}{|}}{\text{C}}}-\underset{\underset{\text{H}}{|}}{\overset{\overset{\text{H}}{|}}{\text{C}}}-\text{Cl}$$

Thioglycerol with the formula

$$\text{H}-\underset{\underset{\text{H}}{|}}{\overset{\overset{\text{H}}{|}}{\text{C}}}-\underset{\underset{\text{H}}{|}}{\overset{\overset{\text{H}}{|}}{\text{C}}}-\underset{\underset{\text{H}}{|}}{\overset{\overset{\text{H}}{|}}{\text{C}}}-\text{H}$$

was developed to counteract war gases and has other medicinal uses.

AMINES

Amines may be thought of as ammonia with organic hydrocarbon radicals substituted for hydrogen. One method of preparing amines is by treating alkyl halides with ammonia. Thus, the reaction between ethyl chloride and ammonia yields ethylamines. A compound in which only one of the hydrogen atoms of the ammonia molecule is replaced by a radical is called a *primary* amine. An amine in which two hydrogen atoms of the ammonia molecule are substituted by radicals is called a *secondary* amine, and one in which all three hydrogen atoms are substituted by radicals is called a *tertiary* amine.

$$R-N\begin{smallmatrix}H\\ \\H\end{smallmatrix} \qquad R-N\begin{smallmatrix}R'\\ \\H\end{smallmatrix} \qquad R-N\begin{smallmatrix}R'\\ \\R''\end{smallmatrix}$$

    primary amine   secondary amine   tertiary amine

The nitrogen atom in an amine retains the baselike properties it has in ammonia. Indeed, the tertiary amines are relatively strong bases. Amines will neutralize acids such as hydrochloric acid to produce salts analogous to ammonium chloride. Thus

$$C_2H_5NH_2 \ + \ HCl \ = \ C_2H_5NH_3^+Cl^- \qquad (37.1)$$
  ethyl amine, or   ethyl ammonium
   aminoethane   chloride

Benzene, like the aliphatic hydrocarbons, forms amines. Aminobenzene, commonly called aniline, has the formula

$$C_6H_5-N\begin{smallmatrix}H\\ \\H\end{smallmatrix}$$

Aniline and its derivatives, found in coal tars, for instance, are starting materials for making the aniline type of dyes.

AMINO ACIDS

Among the very important organic compounds are the amino acids. They are compounds containing at least one amino group and one carboxyl group. Some of them, the alpha amino acids, may be obtained from proteins by hydrolysis. They are the building blocks of proteins. The simplest amino acid, glycine, has the formula

$$\begin{array}{c}H\\|\\H-C-C\\|\diagdown\\N\;O\\/\;\backslash\\H\;H\end{array}\!\!\!\!\!\!=\!O$$

It may also be called aminoacetic acid. There are two different aminopropionic acids

α-aminopropionic acid, or alanine

β-aminopropionic acid

The position of the amino group in the chain attached to the carboxyl group is designated by the Greek prefix α, β, etc., the α carbon being first after the carboxyl group, the β carbon the second, etc. The naturally occurring amino acids are alpha amino acids.

Amino acids as such have interesting chemical properties. Their molecules have an acid group (COOH) as one part and a basic group (NH$_2$) as another part. The acid strength varies with the length of chain but all the amino acids are relatively weak. In a solution of a strong acid, the acid group will be practically unionized and the amino group will attract protons to form the cation

In a solution of strong base, protons are removed from the ammonium group and from the acid group to yield the anion

It follows that in electrolysis the cation will migrate toward the cathode and the anion toward the anode. There must, for a solution of each amino acid, be a concentration of hydrogen ions at which the number of anions is equal to the number of cations or at which the ions carry a positive charge at one end and a negative charge at the other and, hence, are neutral as a whole. These "neutral ions" are called *zwitter ions*.

608 GENERAL CHEMISTRY

$$R-\underset{\underset{\underset{H}{\overset{|}{N}}}{\overset{|}{C}}}{\overset{H}{|}}-\underset{O}{\overset{O-}{C}}$$

$$+$$
zwitter ion

At this concentration of hydrogen ion the amino acid ions will show no net migration toward either electrode and the amino acid is said to be at its isoelectric point. (See page 560.) This point, with its characteristic hydrogen ion concentration, will vary from amino acid to amino acid according to the ionization constant of the acid. Proteins, which are polymers built up from amino acids, have some free amino and acid groups. They show the same effects, although in more complicated form.

NITROCOMPOUNDS

An important series of compounds called nitrocompounds may be prepared from organic compounds and nitric acid. They may be illustrated by compounds from the aromatic series. Water is split out between nitric acid and benzene, especially when concentrated sulfuric acid is present to remove the water.

benzene + H—O—N(=O)(O) = nitrobenzene + H_2O (37.2)

With more drastic treatment dinitrobenzene and trinitrobenzene can be prepared. The nitrocompounds, with the large amount of oxygen available within the molecule, can burn with explosive violence, even in the absence of atmospheric oxygen. Explosives are also formed when toluene and phenol are treated with nitric acid. The products are

toluene + $3HNO_3$ = 2,4,6-trinitrotoluene, or TNT $- 3H_2O$ (37.3)

$$\text{phenol} + 3HNO_3 \xrightarrow{-3H_2O} \text{2,4,6-trinitrophenol, or picric acid} \qquad (37.4)$$

Trinitrophenol is a much stronger acid than is phenol. It has a yellow color and may be used as a dye, but it or its salts may also be used as explosives.

ORGANIC NITRATES

Nitric acid, since it is a hydroxy acid, forms ester-like substances with alcohols. Thus, with ethyl alcohol it forms ethyl nitrate.

$$\underset{\text{ethyl nitrate}}{H_3C-CH_2-O-NO_2}$$

When glycerine, a polyhydroxy compound, is treated with nitric acid it forms glyceryltrinitrate with the structure

$$\underset{\text{glyceryl trinitrate, or ''nitroglycerine''}}{\begin{array}{c} H_2C-O-NO_2 \\ HC-O-NO_2 \\ H_2C-O-NO_2 \end{array}}$$

The common name for this substance, nitroglycerine, is a misnomer, for the nitrate group, —O—NO$_2$, rather than the nitro group, —NO$_2$, is attached to the hydrocarbon radical. Starch and cellulose have many hydroxyl groups. When treated with nitric acid they form nitrates. Cellulose nitrate having a high proportion of nitrate groups is an explosive (gun cotton). If less highly nitrated, cellulose nitrate burns rapidly but not explosively. Cellulose nitrate, dissolved in suitable solvents, may be made into films, such as the older photographic films. The film remains after the solvent has been evaporated.

FATS

The principal ingredients of natural fats are esters of glycerine and normal long-chain acids. When hydrolyzed, fats yield glycerine and these acids, called fatty acids, as the principal products. Among the more common fatty acids are the 18-carbon acid, stearic acid, the 16-carbon acid, palmitic acid, and the unsaturated 18-carbon acid, oleic acid. The saturated acids are solids, but the unsaturated acids, such as oleic acid, are oily liquids. Smaller amounts of other

$$CH_3(CH_2)_{16}C\diagup^{OH}_{\diagdown O} \qquad CH_3(CH_2)_{14}C\diagup^{OH}_{\diagdown O} \qquad CH_3(CH_2)_7CH\!=\!CH(CH_2)_7C\diagup^{OH}_{\diagdown O}$$

   stearic acid   palmitic acid   oleic acid (*cis*-isomer)

unsaturated acids and of shorter-chain saturated acids are also obtained from fats. The acids containing long carbon chains are relatively odorless, but the acids of around seven carbons in length have vile, goat-like odors. The odor of rancid butter is caused by such acids, produced by hydrolysis of butter fat.

On hydrogenation, the unsaturated oleic acid is converted to stearic acid, a saturated acid, and is changed in the reaction from a liquid to a solid substance.

Since each natural fat yields more than one fatty acid the possibilities of isomers are very great. Note that optical isomers are also possible. Each fat has typical properties depending on its own mixture of isomers. Beef fat, lard, butter, and cotton seed oil have different properties because of differences in

$$\begin{array}{c} H \\ | \\ H\!-\!C\!-\!O\!-\!C\!-\!R \\ | \quad\;\;\diagup\!\diagup \\ \;\;\; O \\ H\!-\!C\!-\!O\!-\!C\!-\!R' \\ | \quad\;\;\diagup\!\diagup \\ \;\;\; O \\ H\!-\!C\!-\!O\!-\!C\!-\!R'' \\ | \quad\;\;\diagup\!\diagup \\ \;\;\; O \\ H \end{array} \qquad\qquad \begin{array}{c} H \\ | \\ H\!-\!C\!-\!O\!-\!C\!-\!C_{17}H_{35} \\ | \quad\;\;\diagup\!\diagup \\ \;\;\; O \\ H\!-\!C\!-\!O\!-\!C\!-\!C_{17}H_{35} \\ | \quad\;\;\diagup\!\diagup \\ \;\;\; O \\ H\!-\!C\!-\!O\!-\!C\!-\!C_{17}H_{35} \\ | \quad\;\;\diagup\!\diagup \\ \;\;\; O \\ H \end{array}$$

     a typical fat   glyceryl tristearate
               a fat

the kinds and proportions of the various fats. In general, liquid fats have a higher proportion of unsaturated fatty acids as constituents. When cotton seed oil and corn oil are hydrogenated somewhat, they, like their constituent fatty acids, are changed to semi-solids, or solids, depending on the amount of hydrogenation. Commercial cooking fats with the consistency of lard are produced in large quantity in this way.

Natural fats contain significant amounts of other constituents such as higher alcohols. Vitamins are also present in such fats as liver oils and butter. The fraction of fat not converted to glycerine and the salts of the fatty acids, when the fat is boiled in alkali as in soap-making, is called the nonsaponifiable fraction.

SOAPS

When fats are boiled with an alkali such as sodium hydroxide, the ester is hydrolyzed to glycerine and fatty acid. The alkali reacts with the acids produced to form the sodium salts, called soaps.

$$\begin{array}{c}\text{H}\\|\\\text{H}-\text{C}-\text{O}-\text{C}-\text{C}_{17}\text{H}_{33}\\|\quad\quad\|\\\quad\quad\text{O}\\|\\\text{H}-\text{C}-\text{O}-\text{C}-\text{C}_{17}\text{H}_{33}\\|\quad\quad\|\\\quad\quad\text{O}\\|\\\text{H}-\text{C}-\text{O}-\text{C}-\text{C}_{17}\text{H}_{33}\\|\quad\quad\|\\\quad\quad\text{O}\\|\\\text{H}\\\text{glyceryl trioleate}\\\text{a fat}\end{array} + 3\text{Na}^+\text{OH}^- = \begin{array}{c}\text{H}\\|\\\text{H}-\text{C}-\text{O}-\text{H}\\|\\\text{H}-\text{C}-\text{O}-\text{H}\\|\\\text{H}-\text{C}-\text{O}-\text{H}\\|\\\text{H}\\\text{glycerol}\end{array} + 3\text{Na}^+\text{O}^--\text{C}-\text{C}_{17}\text{H}_{33}\quad\text{(37.5)}$$
$$\text{sodium oleate}\\\text{a soap}$$

The process is called *saponification*. The term saponification is also used for the hydrolysis of any ester in the presence of a base to form an alcohol and the salt of the acid.

The sodium, potassium, and ammonium salts of the lighter fatty acids are soluble or somewhat soluble in water. Potassium soaps are softer and more likely to be liquid than the corresponding sodium soaps. The salts of the higher fatty acids are relatively insoluble in water, but often form colloidal systems. See page 563. Soaps, especially those containing cations of the heavier metals, are excellent lubricants. They are often added to lubricating oils to make better films between moving metallic parts.

Since ordinary soaps are prepared from the naturally occurring fats, they are not pure substances. Their constitution varies with the salts and the fats used in making them. For this reason fats are chosen to give the desired mixture of soaps. Coconut oil is often used because it is a source of the 12-carbon acid, lauric acid, formula $CH_3(CH_2)_{10}COOH$. The sodium salt of this acid has better lathering qualities, though not necessarily better detergent qualities, than soaps of greater molecular length.

Soaps have several limitations as detergents. We have discussed the fact that in hard water the cations of the alkaline earth group combine with the anions from the soap to form insoluble alkaline earth soaps which precipitate as curds. The fatty acids are also insoluble and precipitate when ordinary soaps are added to slightly acid solutions. Salt water tends to precipitate ordinary soaps. Synthetic detergents, having structures analogous to those of ordinary soaps, are now used in large quantities because they lack these defects.

When lauryl alcohol, formula $CH_3(CH_2)_{10}CH_2OH$, or alcohols with longer chains, are treated with sulfuric acid they form esters of the type

$$CH_3(CH_2)_{10}\overset{\overset{\text{H}}{|}}{\underset{\underset{\text{H}}{|}}{\text{C}}}-\text{O}-\overset{\overset{\text{O}}{\|}}{\underset{\underset{\text{O}}{\|}}{\text{S}}}-\text{O}-\text{H}$$

The remaining acidic hydrogen may be neutralized with sodium hydroxide to form a corresponding salt. Note that the difference between soaps and the alkyl sulfates lie in the substitution of the group

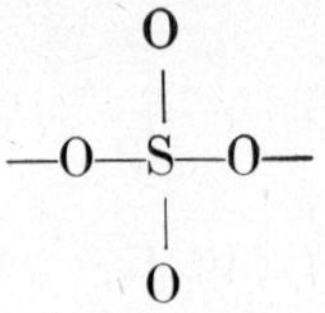

$$-O-\underset{\underset{O}{|}}{\overset{\overset{O}{\|}}{S}}-O-$$

for the

$$-\underset{\underset{O}{\|}}{C}\overset{O-}{\diagup}$$

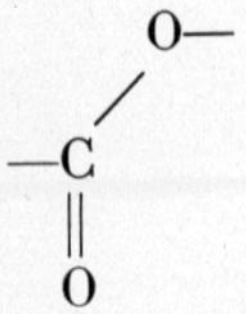

group. The higher alcohols used in such synthetic detergents may be prepared from the fats themselves or from petroleum. The synthetic detergents do not form insoluble calcium salts and hence are more useful in hard waters than the soaps. A cationic type of detergent was illustrated in Table 34.3 on page 562.

SUGARS

The sugars are members of a class of substances called carbohydrates. Common sugars may be represented by the general formula $C_n(H_2O)_m$ in which n is 6 or 5 for the simple sugars. Compounds in which n is less than 5 or more than 6 may have sugar-like properties. However, formaldehyde, CH_2O, is not a sugar. The common simple sugar, glucose, may be represented by the structure

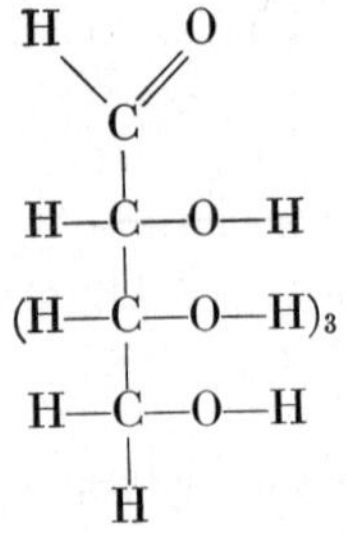

$$\begin{array}{c} H \diagdown \diagup O \\ C \\ | \\ H-C-O-H \\ | \\ (H-C-O-H)_3 \\ | \\ H-C-O-H \\ | \\ H \end{array}$$

Observe that this structure shows an oxygen atom attached to each carbon atom and the presence of one aldehyde group. This sugar is called an aldose, the prefix al- indicating the aldehyde group, the suffix -ose representing sugar. Another common simple sugar is fructose. It is a ketone sugar and is called a ketose.

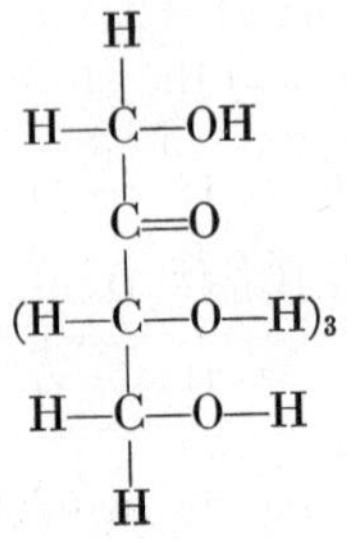

$$\begin{array}{c} H \\ | \\ H-C-OH \\ | \\ C=O \\ | \\ (H-C-O-H)_3 \\ | \\ H-C-O-H \\ | \\ H \end{array}$$

OTHER HYDROCARBON DERIVATIVES 613

Sugars containing six carbon atoms per molecule are called hexoses. The structure of the hexoses is complicated by the fact that they contain asymmetric carbon atoms with the result that numerous optical isomers are possible. The naturally occurring aldehyde hexoses are represented by the structures

```
       O                        O                        O
       ‖                        ‖                        ‖
   H—C                      H—C                      H—C
       |                        |                        |
   H—C*—O—H                 H—O—C—H                  H—C—O—H
       |                        |                        |
  H—O—C*—H                  H—O—C—H                  H—O—C—H
       |                        |                        |
   H—C*—O—H                 H—C—O—H                  H—O—C—H
       |                        |                        |
   H—C*—O—H                 H—C—O—H                  H—C—O—H
       |                        |                        |
   H—C—O—H                  H—C—O—H                  H—C—O—H
       |                        |                        |
       H                        H                        H
    glucose                  mannose                  galactose
```

All of the four starred carbons in glucose are asymmetric. For each asymmetric carbon there are two possible isomeric arrangements so that in all there are 2^4 or 16 different optical isomers. Mannose is one of these isomers and galactose is another. Both are naturally occurring hexoses. All the possible 6-carbon aldoses have been isolated or synthesized. The ketone sugar, fructose, is the only other naturally occurring hexose.

The structure of glucose is complicated by another possible arrangement. It may be crystallized in two ring arrangements called α-glucose and β-glucose. In solution these ring structures come into equilibrium with the aldehyde chain form previously shown. The rings are formed as follows: The aldehyde oxygen may receive a hydrogen atom from one of the alcohol groups. The oxygen bond thus freed joins the aldehyde carbon to form a ring as shown by the structure

```
   1.        H      O—H
              \    /
               C*
               |
   2.       H—C—O—H
               |
   3.     H—O—C—H
               |
   4.       H—C—O—H
               |
   5.       H—C—O
               |
   6.       H—C—OH
               |
               H
```

The starred carbon now has become asymmetric so that two isomers are possible. They are best shown by drawing the rings in the hexagonal forms

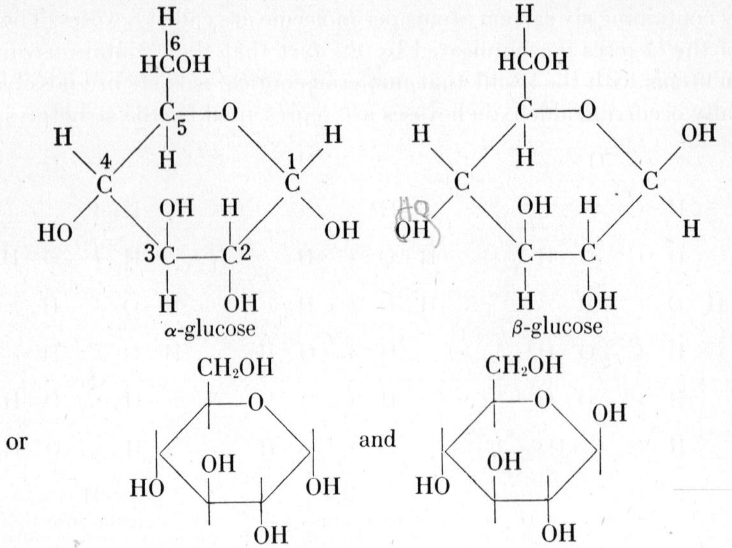

614   GENERAL CHEMISTRY

[Structures of α-glucose and β-glucose shown in open-chain and ring (Haworth) forms]

Observe that α- and β-glucose are identical except for the orientation of the H and OH groups around the first carbon.

Pentoses are not found free in nature but exist in certain polysaccharides.

DISACCHARIDES

Common table sugar, sucrose, has the formula $C_{12}H_{22}O_{11}$. Its structure and properties are the same whether it is isolated from sugar cane, sugar beets, or maple syrup. Sucrose, in the presence of a catalyst such as a dilute acid or base, reacts with water to form the two simple sugars, glucose and fructose, in equal amounts.

$$C_{12}H_{22}O_{11} + HOH = C_6H_{12}O_6 + C_6H_{12}O_6 \qquad (37.6)$$
$$\text{sucrose} \qquad\qquad \text{glucose} \quad \text{fructose}$$

One may expect to form sucrose, therefore, by removing water between glucose and fructose. This reaction is not easy to carry out in the laboratory, however, for the water must be split out in definite positions to form sucrose. The structure of sucrose appears to be

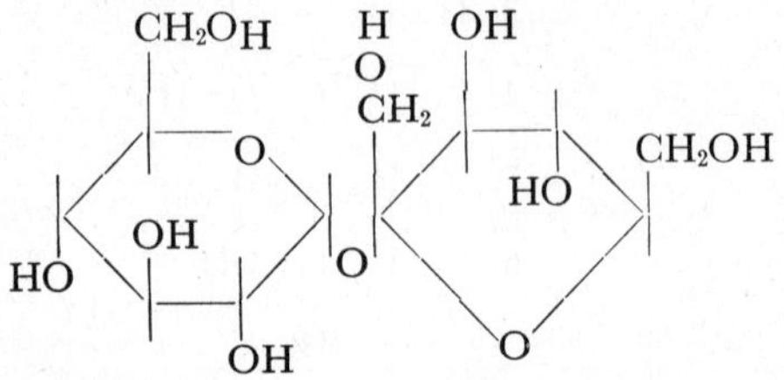

[Structure of sucrose]

Other naturally occurring disaccharides are lactose (milk sugar) and maltose. Both have the formula $C_{12}H_{22}O_{11}$. Lactose, when hydrolysed, yields galactose and glucose, while maltose yields only glucose. Another disaccharide, cellobiose, obtained in the laboratory on degradation of cellulose, also yields glucose on hydrolysis. Since maltose and cellulose yield the same products on hydrolysis their difference must be attributed to differences in structure.

We call attention again to the fact that, when optical isomers are possible, naturally occurring substances represent single specific isomers from among the great number that are possible. Table 37.1 shows some of the relations between the simple sugars and the polymers.

Table 37.1
Naturally Occurring Carbohydrates of the Hexose Series

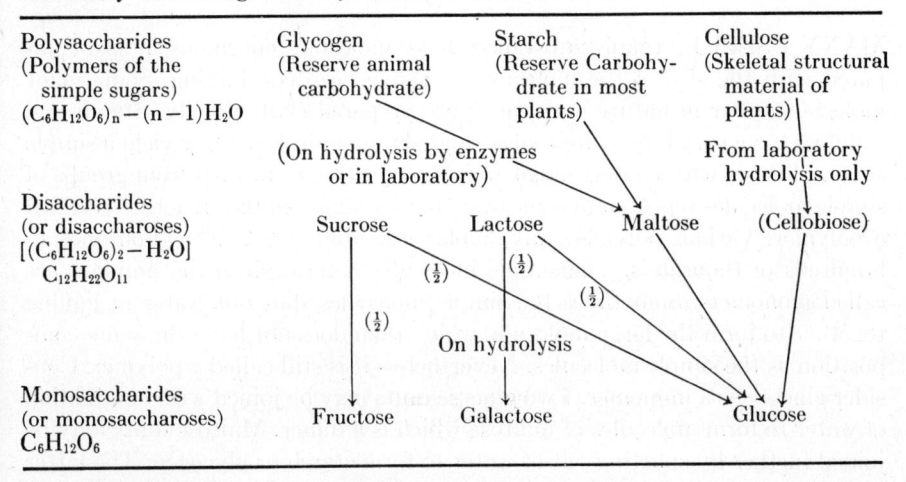

Polysaccharides (Polymers of the simple sugars) $(C_6H_{12}O_6)_n - (n-1)H_2O$	Glycogen (Reserve animal carbohydrate)	Starch (Reserve Carbohydrate in most plants)	Cellulose (Skeletal structural material of plants)
	(On hydrolysis by enzymes or in laboratory)		From laboratory hydrolysis only
Disaccharides (or disaccharoses) $[(C_6H_{12}O_6)_2 - H_2O]$ $C_{12}H_{22}O_{11}$	Sucrose	Lactose Maltose	(Cellobiose)
	($\frac{1}{2}$)	($\frac{1}{2}$) ($\frac{1}{2}$)	
	($\frac{1}{2}$)	On hydrolysis	
Monosaccharides (or monosaccharoses) $C_6H_{12}O_6$	Fructose	Galactose	Glucose

Problem 37.1. A sample of fat is analyzed and found to contain the palmitate and stearate radicals. (a) How many different kinds of fat molecules could be present? (b) If the fat also contained the oleate radical how many different kinds of fat molecules could be present?

Problem 37.2. Indicate the characteristic group in each of the following types of organic compounds: (a) alcohol, (b) fat, (c) ether, (d) soap, (e) ketone, (f) acid, (g) aldehyde, (h) ester, (i) olefin, (j) amine.

Problem 37.3. Dextrose, another name for d-glucose, is commonly said to give "quick energy" to the body. Athletes, for instance, may eat it before a contest. Why should it be more effective than common sugar, sucrose?

Problem 37.4. Why is glucose solution used in intravenous feeding of invalids rather than sucrose?

Problem 37.5. Suggest a method for making triheptyl ammonium chloride (see Table 34.3) from common starting materials.

38 POLYMERS

MANY USEFUL organic substances have molecules enormous in size compared with the size of the molecules we have been considering. Some giant molecules occur in nature and others are prepared synthetically. Starch and cellulose have very large "molecules" and yet on hydrolysis they yield a simple sugar, glucose, with modest molar weight. A substance formed from groups of simple molecules repeated in some systematic manner in the structure is called a polymer. Various polymers have molar weights ranging from thousands to hundreds of thousands. The simple molecules entering into the polymer are called monomers. Sometimes the simple molecules split out water in joining together to form the large molecule, which then does not have the same composition as the simple molecules. Nevertheless it is still called a polymer. Consider glucose as a monomer. Two glucose units may be joined with elimination of water to form molecules of maltose which is a dimer. Maltose units may be joined further by splitting out of water to form starch or glycogen. The latter are polymers.

Not all polymers are formed from monomers through elimination of water. Unsaturated molecules, having electrons available in the double bonds, can form bonds between two or more different molecules. Most synthetic rubbers are examples of polymers built up in this way. Or, polymers may be formed through the splitting out of other small molecules than water.

RUBBER

In the nineteenth century rubber subjected to destructive distillation was found to produce a liquid named isoprene. Isoprene has the empirical formula, C_5H_8. It is a diene hydrocarbon with the structural formula

$$\begin{array}{c} \text{H} \\ | \\ \text{H}-\text{C}-\text{H} \quad\quad \text{H} \quad \text{H} \\ | \quad\quad\quad | \quad\quad | \\ \text{H}-\text{C}=\text{C}-\text{C}=\text{C} \\ | \quad\quad\quad\quad\quad\quad | \\ \text{H} \quad\quad\quad\quad\quad \text{H} \end{array}$$

Liquid isoprene has a low boiling point (34°C.) but in the presence of concentrated hydrochloric acid it polymerizes to form an elastic solid with properties similar to those of natural rubber and with a very high molar weight. The combination of isoprene molecules to form the polymer appears to proceed in the following manner. The extra electrons in the double bond may separate and combine in different pairs, as shown in the following diagram, the monomers joining end to end.

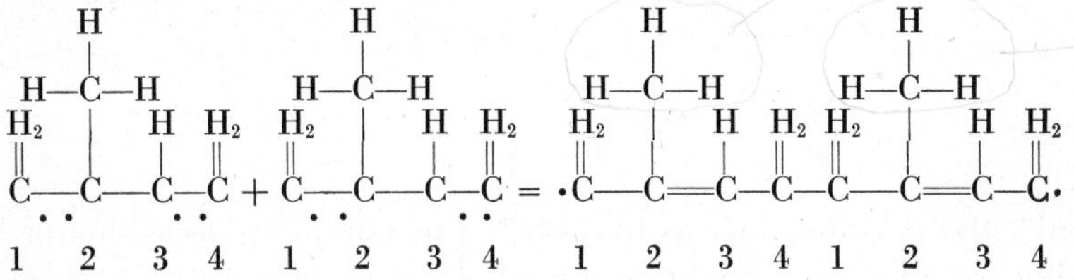

$$
\begin{array}{c}
\\
\text{H} \quad\quad\quad \text{H} \quad\quad\quad \text{H} \quad\quad\quad \text{H}\\
\text{H-C-H} \quad \text{H-C-H} \quad \text{H-C-H} \quad \text{H-C-H}\\
\text{H}_2 \;\; \text{H} \;\; \text{H}_2 \;\; \text{H}_2 \;\; \text{H} \;\; \text{H}_2 \;\; \text{H}_2 \;\; \text{H} \;\; \text{H}_2 \;\; \text{H}_2 \;\; \text{H} \;\; \text{H}_2\\
\text{C-C-C-C} + \text{C-C-C-C} = \cdot\text{C-C=C-C-C-C=C-C}\cdot \quad (38.1)\\
1 \;\; 2 \;\; 3 \;\; 4 \quad 1 \;\; 2 \;\; 3 \;\; 4 \quad 1 \;\; 2 \;\; 3 \;\; 4 \;\; 1 \;\; 2 \;\; 3 \;\; 4
\end{array}
$$

Of the four available electrons, two join to form the new double bond in the 2—3 position and two are available for forming a bond between the 4-carbon of one monomer molecule and the 1-carbon of the second. It is apparent that this process need not stop, but can proceed indefinitely, for the dimer has one unpaired electron at each end still available for bonding. Osmotic pressure, ultracentrifuge, and other methods for determining molar weights show that the molar weight of the rubber is of the order of 130,000 to 400,000. Since the molar weight of isoprene itself is only 68 this means that the average molecule of rubber consists of from 2000 to 6000 isoprene units. The formula for this polymer may therefore be written $(C_5H_8)_n$ where n has the indicated order of magnitude.

The elastic properties of rubber are explained in terms of a somewhat coiled position of the long-chain rubber molecules in the relaxed state. When rubber is stretched the coiled chains straighten out, but the molecules are long enough and intertangled enough so that they do not move past each other as a whole. When the tension is released the rubber molecules return to their original configurations. The methyl group of the chain plays an important role, for it separates the chains enough to prevent them from forming a hard solid. The double bond per monomeric unit remaining in the polymer is a position for chemical attack and it also increases pliability. Rubber when exposed to air, particularly in sunlight, becomes oxidized at the unsaturated positions. Such oxidation splits the molecule at the double bond positions. Hence, the long chains are destroyed, and the rubber properties, associated with the long chains, also disappear.

When sulfur is added to rubber the sulfur atoms may form bonds, two for each sulfur atom, with separate chains, thus linking two chains together. Through crosslinking of chains and reduction in number of double bonds remaining, the "vulcanized" rubber acquires greater mechanical strength and becomes less reactive.

$$\begin{array}{c}
\text{H} \\
| \\
\text{H}-\text{C}-\text{H} \\
\end{array}$$

[structure diagram of vulcanized rubber showing sulfur crosslinks between two polyisoprene chains]

The usual sulfur crosslink appears to consist of two sulfur atoms as shown. As more sulfur is added, more and more crosslinking occurs until *hard rubber* is formed. This vulcanized material has lost practically all of its extensibility because it is so thoroughly crosslinked. Lightly vulcanized rubber may be stretched to nine times its original length without losing its ability to return to its relaxed shape. Its cross section decreases during stretching but its density remains substantially the same, showing that the molecules of rubber have not been brought closer together but have only changed their shape. For most purposes rubber is compounded with other substances called *fillers*. Fillers such as carbon black improve the mechanical properties of rubber, undoubtedly because they form bonds between the various rubber molecules, thereby increasing hardness, strength, and resistance to chemical attack.

SYNTHETIC RUBBERS

The polymer of 2,3-dimethylbutadiene was among the first synthetic rubbers made. this compound has one more methyl group than has isoprene but could be made commercially whereas isoprene could not. The compound was called methyl rubber. The first American synthetic rubber was prepared from chloroprene, which is like isoprene except that the methyl group is replaced by chlorine. Chloroprene rubber with the structure

[structure: —C(H)(H)—C(Cl)=C(H)—C(H)(H)—C(H)(H)—C(Cl)=C(H)—C(H)(H)—]

chloroprene units

is superior to natural rubber in certain properties. It is much more resistant to oxidation and to attack by petroleum hydrocarbons, but natural rubber is still preferable for most applications. None of the synthetic rubbers is superior to natural rubber in all properties.

Butadiene was first polymerized with sodium (*natrium*) by the Germans to form a synthetic rubber named *Buna* rubber. When butadiene polymerizes, some of the monomer molecules are attached at the 1,2 positions rather than at the 1,4 positions to form less regular chains. Buna rubber was followed by a new type called Buna S because *styrene* was used with the butadiene. Because it is made of two distinct monomers, butadiene and styrene, it is called a *copolymer*. Styrene itself

forms a polymer, polystyrene, through the opening of the double bond and formation of new bonds with adjacent monomers as shown by

$$2n \begin{pmatrix} H & H_2 \\ | & \| \\ C=C \\ | \\ \bigcirc \\ \text{styrene} \end{pmatrix} = \begin{pmatrix} H & H_2 & H & H_2 \\ | & \| & | & \| \\ --C-C-C-C-- \\ | & & | \\ \bigcirc & & \bigcirc \\ \text{polystyrene} \end{pmatrix}_n \qquad (38.2)$$

The copolymer Buna S contains about 25 per cent of styrene and 75 per cent of butadiene. It may be represented as a chain of the type

Some of the chains may be crosslinked, for the double bonds remaining in the chains, like the free electrons at the end carbon atoms, are positions for chain growth. Another type of rubber, butyl rubber, is a copolymer of isobutene and small amounts of butadiene. The butadiene unit in the polymer still retains one double bond which is available for forming the necessary crosslinks in vulcanization but the isobutene, when joined in the chain of the polymer has no unsaturation left. The result is a rubber with a minimum amount of unsaturation. It is particularly useful for the inner tubes of tires, since it has a very low permeability for gases.

We have already seen (Chapter 19) that pure sulfur by forming long chains when heated to a proper temperature becomes an elastic polymer. Unfortunately these chains are not stable at room temperature; the sulfur rearranges to form crystalline sulfur having the molecular units S_8. However, polymers containing chains of hydrocarbons and S_4 units are stable. The resulting polysulfide rubbers are called *thiokols*.

620 GENERAL CHEMISTRY

THERMOPLASTIC RESINS

Rubber, unlike many polymers, retains some freedom of movement even at room temperature. A number of polymers now made are rigid at room temperature but soften and become pliable at higher temperatures. They are called *thermoplastic resins*, or often, simply *plastics*. The thermoplastic resins have polymeric molecules large in one or two dimensions. Some typical ones are, like rubbers, made from unsaturated derivatives of the hydrocarbons. The vinyl resins are examples. They are made from derivatives of the hypothetical vinyl alcohol,

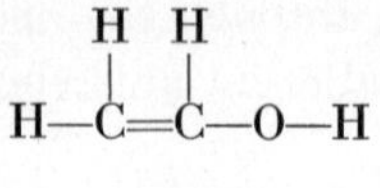

$$H-\underset{\underset{H}{|}}{C}=\underset{\underset{H}{|}}{C}-O-H$$

an unstable isomer of acetaldehyde. It cannot be isolated but its derivatives can be. Thus, vinyl acetate can be prepared. Table 38.1 shows some of the vinyl derivatives. Because of the double bond the vinyl compounds may polymerize as shown below to form a one-dimensional polymer.

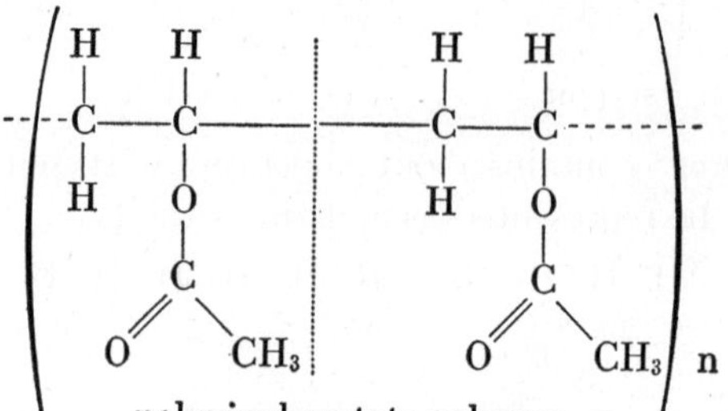

$$\left(---C-C-------C-C-----\right)_n$$
polyvinyl acetate polymer

Table 38.1
Monomers for Resins

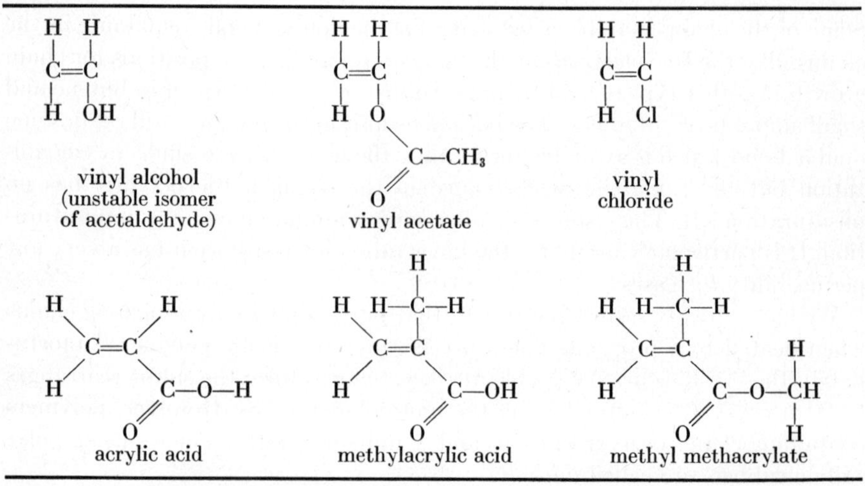

vinyl alcohol (unstable isomer of acetaldehyde)	vinyl acetate	vinyl chloride
acrylic acid	methylacrylic acid	methyl methacrylate

Another class of thermoplastic polymers is prepared from acrylic acid or its derivatives. (See Table 38.1.) The methyl ester of methylacrylic acid forms polymers sold under the trade names of Plexiglas or Lucite. These are comparatively expensive materials yet their great transparency and brilliance guarantees them a sale. Its possible ways of polymerization are:

$$\left(\begin{array}{cc} \text{CH}_3 & \text{CH}_3 \\ \text{H} \quad | \quad \text{H} \quad | \\ \text{—C—C———C—C———} \\ | \quad | \quad | \quad | \\ \text{H} \quad \text{C—O—CH}_3 \quad \text{H} \quad \text{C—O—CH}_3 \\ \quad \parallel \quad\quad\quad\quad \parallel \\ \quad \text{O} \quad\quad\quad\quad \text{O} \end{array}\right)_n \left(\begin{array}{cc} \text{CH}_3 & \text{CH}_3 \\ | \quad \text{H} \quad | \quad \text{H} \\ \text{—C—C———C—C———} \\ | \quad | \quad | \quad | \\ \text{H} \quad \text{H} \quad \text{H} \\ \text{H}_3\text{C—O—C} \quad\quad \text{C—O—CH}_3 \\ \quad\quad \parallel \quad \parallel \\ \quad\quad \text{O} \quad \text{O} \end{array}\right)_n$$

head-to-tail polymer   head-to-head polymer

These polymers are prepared by heating the monomers of the partly polymerized material in molds at suitable temperature. When cooled they become rigid. When these resins are reheated they become pliable and can be pressed into desired shapes which they retain when cooled. However, some of these resins have the interesting property of returning to their original molded shapes when warmed. Apparently the polymers are so entangled, as is rubber, so that they can change their shape under tension, but return to their original relaxed positions when the tension is removed and the temperatures are high enough to permit movement. This leads to the phenomenon of "plastic memory," and makes it desirable to cast strain-free objects which do not change shape when warmed.

The vinyl and the acrylic polymers are, in general, rather rigid at room temperatures, softening at higher temperatures. One reason for this rigidity at lower temperatures is to be found in the polar groups within the monomeric segments of the molecules. These form dipoles within each chain and lead to fairly strong dipole attractions between neighboring chains. At higher temperatures the kinetic energy becomes sufficient to overbalance the dipolar forces and the substances become more pliable.

The normal pliability of rubbery molecules, on the other hand, is partially interpreted in terms of the nonpolar nature of the bonds in these substances. Only at temperatures below usual room conditions can the weak van der Waals forces between adjacent chains give rigidity and hardness to the rubber.

The polyethylenes are another example of substances pliable at room temperature. They may be considered as made up from ethylene molecules which have condensed to form an endless chain of CH_2 units, like a long hydrocarbon molecule. The molecules are essentially nonpolar and hence have very weak intermolecular forces. Polyethylene is used in pliable bottles, pipes for plumbing, thin sheets for wrapping and covering materials, etc. It is inert, like paraffin, and is one of the cheaper plastics.

THERMOSETTING RESINS

Some polymers are formed by heating the monomers together until aggregation occurs in three dimensions. Such polymers are hard and remain hard even at higher temperatures. At high temperatures they decompose rather than become pliable as the thermoplastic resins do.

The first thermosetting resin to be produced commercially was Bakelite (1909). It is a phenol-formaldehyde resin and is still one of the cheapest resins. When phenol and formaldehyde are condensed the first result is the ortho or para product.

$$C_6H_5OH + HCHO = \text{ortho-isomer or para-isomer} \quad (38.3)$$

phenol   formaldehyde   ortho-isomer   para-isomer

These isomers can react further with phenol and formaldehyde as shown in the following scheme:

$$(38.4)$$

Thus the polymer grows in three dimensions. The smaller polymeric units are liquid but on continued heating they join together to form a fusible solid. When this is subjected to heat and pressure it will flow in a mold to form a final three-dimensional polymer that is insoluble and infusible, hence the term "thermosetting."

Another group of thermosetting resins is prepared from urea and formaldehyde.

$$\text{urea} + \text{formaldehyde} = \quad (38.5)$$

The reaction with formaldehyde continues on the second amine group and this product reacts with urea to form a three-dimensional polymer that is infusible.

RUBBERS AND RESINS

Two points of possible attachment within a monomer lead to a linear polymer; three or more possible points of attachment result in three-dimensional polymers. The former are generally rubbers or thermoplastics, the latter thermosetting resins.

The main practical distinction between "rubbers" and "resins" is the degree of extensibility of the material at room temperature. "Rubber" infers pliability and extensibility; "resin" infers hardness or horniness. Yet thermoplastics become rubbery when heated, and rubbers harden and become rigid and brittle when cooled. Structural distinctions between the rubbers and the thermoplastics are almost as arbitrary. Both are composed of long-chain, linear polymers highly intertangled. Both generally have side groups on the long chains, though some plastics do not.

Rubbers almost always have residual double bonds in the carbon chain of the polymer, permitting vulcanization. Thermoplastics almost never have residual double bonds in the carbon chain. This distinction in number of double bonds remaining is about as close as one can come to a structural differentiation; it is often stated that much of the pliability of a rubber is due to the remaining double bonds. It certainly is true that vulcanization may be carried on so far that it destroys the double bonds and extensively crosslinks the linear polymers. Such complete vulcanization completely removes the extensibility, producing a material (hard rubber) very similar to the three-dimensional thermosetting resins. Butyl rubber, polyisobutene, comes as close to being an exception to this last distinction as any for it retains some extensibility even though containing almost no double bonds.

As with most classifications, so here, continued progress introduces borderline cases and previously separate classes begin to overlap and merge. Yet the classifications still retain some usefulness as a quick way of roughly describing large groups of substances.

DRYING OILS

We have already noted that liquid fats are glyceryl esters of fatty acids, some of which are unsaturated. Some of these unsaturated acids have two or three double bonds. Drying oils, such as tung and linseed oils, have more than 75 per cent of their constituent acids with such unsaturation. They form durable dry films when exposed to air, undoubtedly through their ability to form polymers. Drying oils are used in paints and varnishes and in making products such as linoleum and oilcloth. Catalysts (dryers) are often added to increase the rate of drying. High temperatures and ultraviolet light are also favorable.

CELLULOSE

Among the most important and extensive natural polymers is cellulose, a polymer of glucose. Cotton is almost pure cellulose, and wood cellulose and lignin form most of wood. The fact that cellulose, when hydrolyzed, forms the disaccharide, cellobiose, indicates the structure. It appears that cellulose is a polymer of the type shown in Figure 38.1. Some of the polysaccharides associated with cellulose in wood are polymers of xylose, a five-carbon sugar, $C_5H_{10}O_5$.

Observe that when sucrose is formed from glucose and fructose a molecule of water is split out (see page 614). When a molecule of cellobiose is formed from two molecules of glucose, water is split out in a definite way. If an additional glucose unit is to be attached to cellobiose to form cellotriose an additional molecule of water must be split out. Thus, as the chain grows, one less molecule of water must be removed than there are glucose units in the chain. The formula for cellulose may therefore be derived as

$$\text{n } C_6H_{12}O_6 = \{\text{n } C_6H_{12}O_6 - (n-1)H_2O\} + (n-1)HOH \qquad (38.6)$$
$$\text{glucose} \qquad \text{cellulose}$$

Since there were originally five hydroxyl groups per glucose unit and since two of the five participated in the reaction to form the chain there are only three free hydroxyl groups remaining per glucose unit. That this analysis is correct is shown by the fact that when cellulose is nitrated (nitric acid reacting with the free alcohol groups to form the nitrate ester) the maximum amount of nitric acid that reacts is three moles per glucose unit. In the same way cellulose acetate has at most three acetate groups per glucose unit. The alcohol groups are also available for making ethers. In the methyl ether of cellulose, at most three methyl groups per glucose unit may be present.

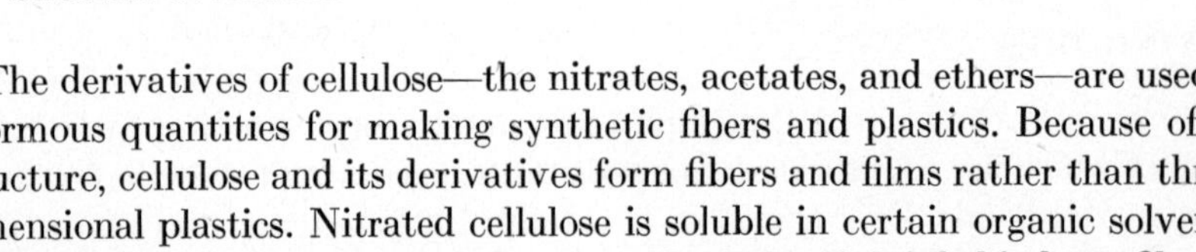

Figure 38.1.
Structure of cellulose.

The derivatives of cellulose—the nitrates, acetates, and ethers—are used in enormous quantities for making synthetic fibers and plastics. Because of its structure, cellulose and its derivatives form fibers and films rather than three-dimensional plastics. Nitrated cellulose is soluble in certain organic solvents. When the solvent is evaporated the nitrated cellulose is left behind as a film for photographic use or for lacquers. The trinitrate (three nitrate groups per monomer unit) is used as an explosive. Gun cotton is such a material. It may be dissolved and formed into desired sizes as "grains." The less highly nitrated material in solution can be extruded through tiny holes to form thin fibers.

When the solvent is removed the fibers harden and the nitrate groups may then be removed. In this way the first "artificial silk" was prepared. The fibers have a silky appearance rather than the dull appearance of cotton fibers. Because of their combustibility fabrics retaining nitrate groups are dangerous.

RAYON

The term rayon is now used instead of "artificial silk" to designate the synthetic fibers produced from cellulose. Three processes produce most of the rayon. About 75 per cent of the rayon is made by the viscose process in which cellulose is dissolved in sodium hydroxide and carbon disulfide. After standing, the colloid may be extruded as filaments into a solution of diluted acid which precipitates the cellulose. If the viscose solution is extruded through narrow slits, the regenerated cellulose will be in the form of film (cellophane).

Cellulose may be converted to the acetate ester by treating it with acetic anhydride and acetic acid. It is then partly hydrolyzed with the result that some of the acetate is removed and at the same time the cellulose molecule is partly hydrolyzed to form products containing only 200 to 300 glucose units. This material is dissolved in acetone for extrusion into filaments. The extruded filaments are then air-dryed to remove the solvent. Acetate rayon is more expensive than other types but has desirable properties that make it profitable for many uses. Unlike the other rayons, acetate rayon is not regenerated cellulose, but, rather a cellulose ester of acetic acid.

A relatively small amount of rayon is also produced by the cuprammonium process in which cellulose is dissolved in an ammoniacal solution of copper hydroxide. The filaments are again treated with dilute acid to precipitate the regenerated cellulose.

PROTEINS

Proteins are polymers of amino acids. Their molar weights are of the order of 100,000. Unlike cellulose, which is always a polymer of glucose, proteins differ according to their source. Many different proteins are known, each of which has its own special composition, structure, and properties. When a protein such as egg albumin is hydrolyzed, the product has a characteristic distribution of alpha-amino acids. In any particular protein the number of different amino acids present in the polymer is rather large but each protein lacks certain significant amino acid units. There are apparently about twenty different alpha amino acids which combine in various ways to produce the many proteins found. This fact is very important in nutrition for no diet is adequate unless it contains proteins furnishing a number of amino acids, called *essential*. About half the naturally occurring amino acids have been shown to be essential in the diet of white rats. That is, to remain healthy the rat must eat these. Many of the same amino acids have been shown to be essential to other mammals. Evidently the body is capable of synthesizing the others, but not these "essential" ones.

626 GENERAL CHEMISTRY

We have seen that amino acids contain both a carboxyl group and an amino group. In solution they may exist, depending on the hydrogen ion concentration, as cations, as anions, as neutral molecules, or as ions with no net charge. The latter ions carry a negative charge on the carboxyl group because of the acidic ionization and a positive charge on the amino group which has coordinated a proton to form an ammonium group (see page 608).

Proteins form polymers through reaction between the acid group of one molecule and the basic group of another molecule with the splitting out of water. Thus,

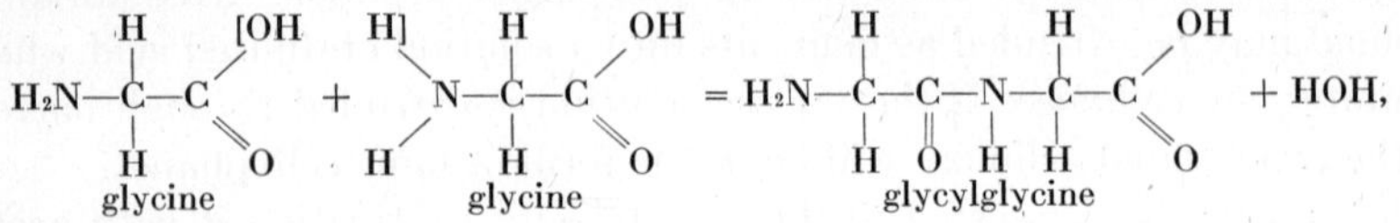

$$H_2N-\underset{\underset{H}{|}}{\overset{\overset{H}{|}}{C}}-C\overset{[OH}{\underset{O}{\diagdown}} + \overset{H]}{\underset{H}{\diagdown}}N-\underset{\underset{H}{|}}{\overset{\overset{H}{|}}{C}}-C\overset{OH}{\underset{O}{\diagdown}} = H_2N-\underset{\underset{H}{|}}{\overset{\overset{H}{|}}{C}}-\underset{\underset{O}{||}}{C}-N-\underset{\underset{H}{|}}{\overset{\overset{H}{|}}{C}}-C\overset{OH}{\underset{O}{\diagdown}} + HOH, \quad (38.7)$$

glycine glycine glycylglycine

or

$$H_2N-\underset{\underset{H}{|}}{\overset{\overset{H}{|}}{C}}-C\overset{[OH}{\underset{O}{\diagdown}} + \overset{H]}{\underset{H}{\diagdown}}N-\underset{\underset{H}{|}}{\overset{\overset{CH_3}{|}}{C}}-C\overset{OH}{\underset{O}{\diagdown}} = H_2N-\underset{\underset{H}{|}}{\overset{\overset{H}{|}}{C}}-\underset{\underset{O}{||}}{C}-N-\underset{\underset{H}{|}}{\overset{\overset{CH_3}{|}}{C}}-C\overset{OH}{\underset{O}{\diagdown}} + HOH \quad (38.8)$$

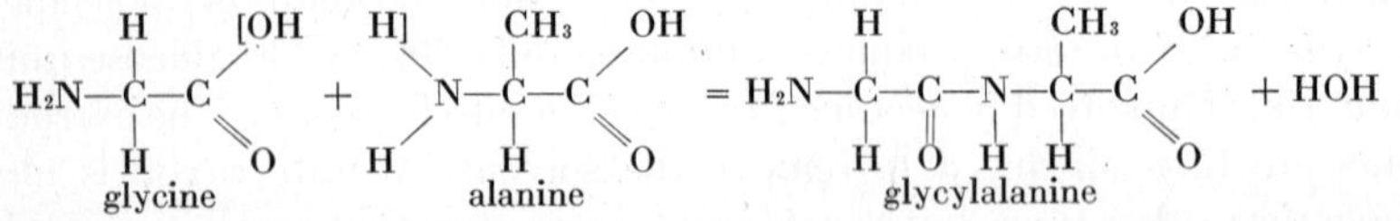

glycine alanine glycylalanine

When two different amino acids are joined in this way there are two possibilities. One is illustrated above in glycylalanine, the other will result when the acid group of alanine combines with the amino group of glycine to form alanylglycine. Since a protein molecule is a polymer containing several hundred amino acid units it is evident that many isomers are possible even with as few as two constituent amino acids. With more than twenty naturally occurring amino acids it is not surprising that there should be many different proteins. Some amino acids contain more than one amino group and some contain more than one carboxyl group. There are, therefore, possibilities for crosslinking to make three-dimensional polymers. Certain proteins, the viruses, have enormous molar weight. Tobacco mosaic virus has been shown to have a molar weight of 15,000,000 to 20,000,000.

HIGH TEMPERATURE POLYMERS

Several polymers are of unusual interest because they are stable at high temperatures, temperatures at which most organic compounds of high molar weight tend to disintegrate. One of these is prepared from tetrafluoroethylene

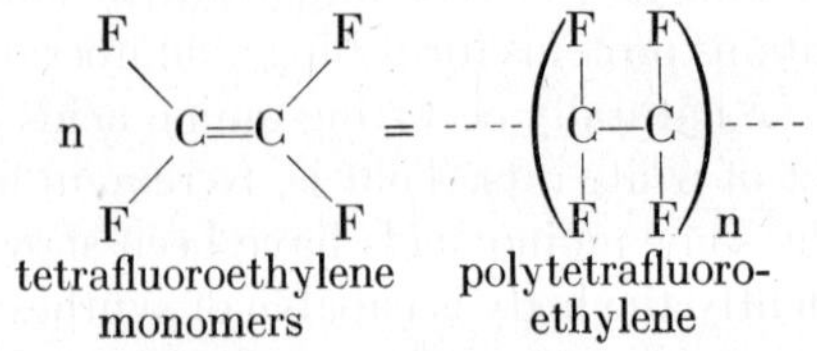

$$n \quad \underset{F}{\overset{F}{\diagdown}}C=C\underset{F}{\overset{F}{\diagdown}} = ----\left(\underset{F}{\overset{F}{\underset{|}{\overset{|}{C}}}}-\underset{F}{\overset{F}{\underset{|}{\overset{|}{C}}}}\right)_n---- \quad (38.9)$$

tetrafluoroethylene monomers   polytetrafluoroethylene

in which n is of the order of 1000. Observe that this polymer contains no hydrogen; all the bonds are carbon-carbon or carbon-fluorine bonds. This polymer is unusually resistant to solvents and even to boiling acids. It is stable at temperatures up to 325°C. Because of its inertness the polymer must be cut into desired forms after it is made. Its trade name is Teflon. It is one of the costliest of all polymers.

Another group of polymers has a silicon-oxygen chain. The silicon compound with the formula

$$\text{H--O--}\underset{\underset{CH_3}{|}}{\overset{\overset{CH_3}{|}}{Si}}\text{--O--H}$$

may be prepared from silicon tetrachloride and methyl bromide. It polymerizes with the splitting out of water to form a polymer of the type

$$2n\ \text{H--O--}\underset{\underset{CH_3}{|}}{\overset{\overset{CH_3}{|}}{Si}}\text{--OH} = \text{H--}\left(\text{--O--}\underset{\underset{CH_3}{|}}{\overset{\overset{CH_3}{|}}{Si}}\text{--O--}\underset{\underset{CH_3}{|}}{\overset{\overset{CH_3}{|}}{Si}}\text{--}\right)_n\text{--O--H} + (2n-1)\ H_2O \quad (38.10)$$

The polymer may also be formed from the monomer with the formula

$$\text{Cl--}\underset{\underset{CH_3}{|}}{\overset{\overset{CH_3}{|}}{Si}}\text{--Cl}$$

which is prepared from silicon and methyl chloride. The reaction has a number of variations; ethyl or other radicals may be substituted for the methyl radical. Also, if the number of hydrocarbon radicals and hydroxyl or chloride groups about the silicon in the monomer are varied, straight chain or branched chain polymers may be produced. The resulting polymers may be liquids, thick oils, or solids. The polymers, called silicones, are unusually stable when exposed to high temperatures and are used when temperature-resistant lubricants or other substances are required. They are currently very expensive but are used where other types of substances fail.

SYNTHETIC FIBERS

Although rayon is classed as a synthetic fiber it is prepared from a natural polymer, cellulose. New synthetic fibers are now produced from simple monomers. Among these is nylon, first produced commercially in 1940. It is a polymer with protein-like bonding and has a structure similar to that of silk. The monomers are 1,6-diaminohexane and adipic acid, a 6-carbon acid with a carboxyl group at each end. Consequently, long chains are produced by splitting out of water as in the reaction

628 GENERAL CHEMISTRY

$$HO-\underset{\underset{O}{\|}}{C}-(CH_2)_4-\underset{\underset{O}{\|}}{C}-[-OH + H-]-\underset{\underset{H}{|}}{N}-(CH_2)_6-\underset{\underset{H}{|}}{N}-H$$

adipic acid   1,6-diamino hexane

$$= HOH + HO-\underset{\underset{O}{\|}}{C}-(CH_2)_4-\underset{\underset{O}{\|}}{C}-\underset{\underset{H}{|}}{N}-(CH_2)_6-\underset{\underset{H}{|}}{N}-H \qquad (38.11)$$

water   polymer unit

The reaction can obviously continue with additional monomeric units. The monomer carbon-hydrogen chains can be derived from benzene (from coal) and hydrogen (from water or natural gas), the amino group from ammonia

Table 38.2
Synthetic Polymers for Fibers

vinyl chloride + vinyl acetate	=	Vinyon unit
vinyl chloride + vinylidene chloride	=	Saran unit
2n vinyl cyanide (acrylonitrile)	=	Orlon unit (polyacrylonitrile)
terephthalic acid + ethylene glycol	=	Dacron monomer + HOH

(air and water) and the oxygen from air. Hence the claim that nylon is made from coal, air and water.

Other new synthetic fibers are produced by the polymerization of derivatives of ethane. Examples are Vinyon (1940), Saran (1942), Orlon (1950), and Dacron (1952). Their structures are indicated in Table 38.2.

SYNTHETIC VERSUS NATURAL PRODUCTS

Chemists search for synthetics for three reasons: (1) naturally occurring materials may be unable to satisfy the market demand due to scarcity, (2) naturally occurring materials may be deficient in some desirable attribute, or (3) naturally occurring materials may be more expensive than synthetics which will do the same jobs.

Rubber, for instance, can only be raised in certain climates not generally found within the large industrial nations. If these nations wish to be self-sufficient or if they are cut off from the natural supply they must seek a synthetic source. National policy may dictate that cost is of minor importance.

Naturally occurring textiles are susceptible to wear, wrinkling, mildew, etc. Synthetics may be superior in these respects. Their desirable properties then guarantee them a market even though they cost more than the natural products.

Natural silk shows a very desirable luster yet is expensive to manufacture. Synthetics, with similar properties, yet cheaper to produce, have taken over most of the demand.

Yet many synthetics do not have as satisfactory properties as the natural materials. The question then arises, "Why not synthesize materials identical with the natural products?" For many years the problem has been known to be that of producing a single isomer. Natural polymers, in general, are formed so that each unit of the chain is identical in both formula and geometry with the other units. Plants and animals accomplish these highly specific syntheses through the use of specialized catalysts, called enzymes. The enzyme catalysts force the molecules to react in the exact position which permits the formation of one and only one of the possible isomers. One of the great unsolved problems of synthetic chemistry has been to reproduce this type of synthesis in the laboratory.

Consider the problem of synthesizing natural rubber. Many synthetics are now known, but natural rubber still has certain properties, due largely to the regular pattern in the chain, which make it superior for some uses to any known synthetic. Natural rubber is known to consist of long chains of polymerized isoprene. All the units are joined in the fashion shown in the first example in Table 38.3, known as tail-to-head, completely *cis*, 1,4 addition.

Prior to 1954 all synthetic isoprene polymers differed from the naturally occurring rubber. The disparity was known to lie in the number and kind of isomers produced, some typical dimer units being shown in Table 38.3. Thus the methyl side group and adjacent hydrogen of the polymer might be either

Table 38.3
Some Possible Combinations of Two Isoprene Monomers

$$2 \quad \underset{H}{\overset{H}{>}}C=C\underset{H}{\overset{CH_3}{-}}-C=C\underset{H}{\overset{H}{<}} \quad \text{combine:}$$

```
    H  CH₃ H  H  H  CH₃ H  H
    |  |   |  |  |  |   |  |
----C--C===C--C--C--C===C--C----   tail-to-head
    |      |  |  |      |  |
    H      H  H  H      H  H
          cis          cis
```

```
    H  CH₃       H  H  CH₃      H
    |  |        |  |  |        |
----C--C===C----C--C--C===C----C----   tail-to-head
    |       |  |  |       |   |
    H       H  H  H       H   H
           trans          trans
```

```
    H  CH₃                CH₃ H  H
    |  |                  |   |  |
----C--C===C----C--C--C===C---C----   tail-to-head
    |       |  |  |          |
    H       H  H  H          H
           trans         cis
```

```
    H  CH₃ H         H
    |  |   |        /
----C--C---C===C
    |              \
    H              H                 1,2 addition
           CH₃ H  H
           |   |  |
       H--C---C===C--C----            1,4 addition
           |         |
           H         H
              cis
```

```
    H  CH₃ H  H  H  H  CH₃ H
    |  |   |  |  |  |  |   |
----C--C===C--C--C--C===C--C----   tail-to-tail
    |      |  |  |     |   |
    H      H  H  H     H   H
          cis          cis
```

```
    H  H  CH₃ H  H  CH₃ H  H
    |  |  |   |  |  |   |  |
----C--C===C--C--C--C===C--C----   head-to-head
    |         |  |         |
    H         H  H         H
       cis          cis
```

cis or *trans* with respect to the residual double bond. Addition might occur only across one of the double bonds (called 1,2 addition), or might involve both double bonds at the end carbon atoms (called 1,4 addition). The monomers might join so that the side methyl groups were five carbon atoms apart along the carbon chain (tail-to-head addition), so that they were only four carbon atoms apart (head-to-head addition), or so that they were six carbon atoms apart (tail-to-tail addition). Many other combinations of these possibilities might also occur. Since two isoprene units can combine in so many ways, it is easy to see that there is an almost infinite variety of arrangements in any long-chain isoprene polymer.

In December of 1954 the B. F. Goodrich Co. announced that its chemists had synthesized natural rubber. The nature of the catalyst was not revealed. They may, for instance, have isolated the enzyme used by the rubber plant, or synthesized a new catalyst which would give a single isomer. Even if there were no practical advantage to such a synthesis (and actually it does appear to put a ceiling on the price of natural rubber) this synthesis would constitute one of the great feats of chemistry. If the catalyst itself is synthetic the accomplishment would rank with the greatest in the field for it is at this point that one of the great differences has existed between biological systems and laboratory reactions. Biological systems almost invariably produce and utilize only a single one of several possible isomers. Laboratory syntheses have produced mixtures of isomers.

Problem 38.1. How many isomeric "proteins" can be made from 3 molecules of alanine plus 3 molecules of glycine?

Problem 38.2. Why do you suppose natural rubber is superior to synthetic polyisoprene? That is, how do the differences in structure account for the resistance of natural rubber to wear and chemical action, and its enhanced extensibility?

Problem 38.3. Gutta-percha is a naturally occurring polyisoprene. How do you suppose it differs from rubber?

Problem 38.4. Predict two or three possible synthetic polymers and indicate how you would attempt to prepare them.

Problem 38.5. Of what importance is the fact that many biologically important substances are polymers, that is, in what respects are they superior to monomers?

Problem 38.6. Write structural formulas for the polymers and predict whether the polymers produced from the following would, at room temperature, be rubbery, be soft but not rubbery, or be hard and horny: (a) ethylene; (b) glycerol and phthalic acid, formula [benzene ring with —C(=O)—O—H and —C(=O)—O—H substituents] ; (c) the substituted butadiene with the formula

H₂C=C(C≡N)—C(H)=CH₂ ; (d) chlorotrifluoro ethylene, formula ClFC=CF₂ ; (e) 1,3,5 trihydroxybenzene and ethylene glycol.

Problem 38.7. Indicate an important industrial, medicinal, or military use for each of the following:
- a. methane
- b. benzene
- c. sodium stearate
- d. octane
- e. cellulose acetate
- f. ether
- g. glyceryl trinitrate
- h. phenol
- i. ethanol
- j. cellulose nitrate

39 BIOCHEMISTRY

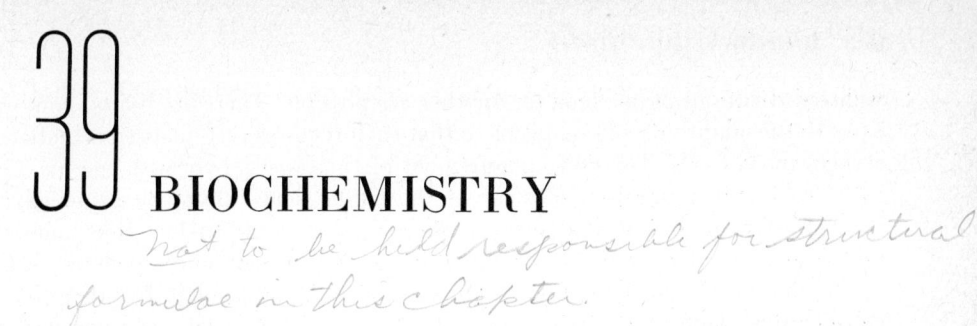

not to be held responsible for structural formulae in this chapter.

YOU WERE warned in Chapter 1 that the chemistry of the human body was much too complicated to serve as the sole material for an introductory study of chemistry. The knowledge of chemistry you have gained since then does not vitiate the statement, but it now allows you to take an informed look into some of the simpler aspects of biochemistry—the chemistry of living organisms.

The boundaries between living and nonliving matter have become increasingly ill-defined in the last twenty years, as have most of the previously established "boundaries" in science. However, living systems have the ability to assimilate relatively simple molecules, and then to synthesize more highly organized ones from them. The claim that a growing crystal of sodium chloride has the same property need not concern us here, though there are certainly analogies between such growth and that which occurs in living things.

The synthesis of the complicated molecules found in living things requires energy. Energy is also required for the movement found in animals. This energy can be provided through light absorption, as in most plants, or by the degradation of energy-rich molecules as in most animals. Many plants, for instance, can survive in light on an intake of a few simple cations and anions—sodium, potassium, chloride, phosphate, nitrate, etc.—and water and air.

From these the plants synthesize all the molecules necessary for their existence and reproduction. Some of the higher plants require rather more complicated starting materials, and all animals need to ingest fairly complicated and, often, very specific molecules in order to live. These facts might seem to indicate that the metabolisms of plants and animals are grossly different. Actually there are many similarities and even identities, but we shall concern ourselves primarily with the metabolisms in humans.

FOODS

The materials which any organism must receive from outside itself in order to maintain life are its *foods*, though air and water, both essential, are not usually called foods. Foods may vary widely in source and chemical composition and yet supply the organism's needs. So great is the synthetic and degradative skill of most organisms and so great is the complexity of most foods that wide substitutions of one food for another are possible. There are limits, however, to the adaptivity of organisms so that each requires certain *essential* substances in its foods. The daily requirement of the essential constituents may vary from gram quantities of some of the amino acids (found in proteins) through certain unsaturated fatty acids (found in fats) to less than one-millionth gram of some of the vitamins (found as traces in many foods).

The number of substances now known to be essential is small but there is considerable evidence that the small number is a reflection of our ignorance rather than a proof of almost unlimited synthetic capabilities in organisms. The fact that certain essential materials are required only in minute traces raises some of the most interesting problems to be found in biochemistry. How do these tiny amounts of less than one part per billion cause such marked effects on the whole organism?

Within an organism foods are either degraded to supply the energy for life processes, are stored for future use, or are synthesized into specific molecules required to maintain the organism. Most of the energy-producing reactions within the body are oxidations, with carbon dioxide and water as two of the most common end products. Thus, foods rich in compounds of carbon and hydrogen will be the best energy sources per gram as shown in Table 39.1. Most of the carbon dioxide is exhaled but the water may be retained to satisfy the body requirements. Some 15 per cent of the water requirements of humans comes from this metabolic water, and it is through the oxidation of the fat in their humps that camels are able to survive for such long periods without drinking. The yield of water per gram of typical foods is shown in Table 39.1.

Table 39.1

Energy and Water per Gram of Some Classes of Foods

FOOD	CALORIES * PER GRAM	GRAMS OF WATER PRODUCED PER GRAM OF FOOD
Fat	9300	1.07
Carbohydrate	4200	0.56
Protein	5600	0.41

* The "calorie" of the dietician is a different unit, being equal to the kilocalorie, or 1000 calories.

Note that fats are not only the best energy source but also the best source of water per gram.

Carbohydrates, however, are the most abundant foods in usual diets and are the primary energy source for man in spite of the fact that they are the poorest source of energy per gram as shown in Table 39.1. Proteins are less used as energy sources; their largest use is as structural substances such as muscle or hair. Fats are the most concentrated form of energy and much of the reserve food supply of the body is stored in this form though it may have been ingested as protein or as carbohydrate. Fat is the most expendable of the body constituents as an energy source. During starvation, for instance, the fat reserves in the body are used first, then the carbohydrates. Only when death is very near are the protein structures degraded rapidly in order to produce energy.

Problem 39.1. What is the amount of oxygen consumed and water produced when one mole of the fat, glyceryl trioleate, burns? What are the amounts per gram of fat?

Problem 39.2. What chemical reasons are there for the fact that fats when burned release much more energy per gram than sugars do?

Instead of being degraded for energy production, foods may be stored. Fats, as is well known, are stored as such in various parts of the body. Carbohydrates are stored mainly as the glucose polymer, glycogen, in the liver and in muscle cells, for instance. Proteins are not stored in the usual sense but are incorporated into active body structures. Hence, a protein-deficient diet leads to emaciation, for the body draws on the structural protein in order to maintain a subsistence level of other materials requiring proteins for their synthesis. Examples are the enzymes and hormones; their disappearance would lead to a more rapid death than would the loss of muscle fiber.

The storing and release of food substances is a dynamic and continuing one. Immediately after a meal the food fragments from the digestive processes enter the blood stream where their concentrations become higher than normal. As the blood flows through the cells the higher concentrations lead to increased storing rates until a balance has been reached. Thereafter until the next meal, fragments are released from storage to maintain proper concentrations in the blood. Increased activity requires use of energy-producing substances in the muscles, decreases their concentration in the blood and results in further release of fragments from storage. Thus the particular food fragments oxidized during a day's activities are probably not the same ones eaten during that day.

The third function of foods is to furnish materials for the synthesis of specific molecules. The essential foods do this by providing fragments of necessary molecules, fragments which the body is not able to synthesize from other substances. Examples are the essential amino acids (see page 625). Or the essential food may supply the whole molecule. The vitamins are outstanding examples of molecules which are incorporated into other substances almost unchanged. The proteins with the essential amino acids, on the other hand, are degraded in the intestine into the simple amino acids which are then used to build up new protein molecules or more complicated polymers needed by the organism.

Millions and millions of protein isomers are possible from the available amino acids, yet each organism confines itself to synthesizing only a small fraction of the total. And it synthesizes its own isomers with great reproducibility. As a result each protein is highly specific. Plants synthesize the amino acids needed for proteins, including the ten essential amino acids required for the nutrition of the higher animals. However, no single protein contains all of them. Zein (from wheat), for example, lacks many needed by man. Herbivorous animals, of course, must obtain all their essential amino acids from plant sources but man's vegetable foods are usually too restricted to be adequate. It is possible for a strict vegetarian to find foods of plant origin which will contribute adequate amounts of the essential amino acids but practically all "vegetarians" supplement their diet with milk, cheese, and eggs. The animal proteins in these complement the vegetable proteins in the amino acids required by man.

Fats and carbohydrates also exist in various isomeric forms but their number is much more limited and their specificity is not as great as that of proteins. Thus most of the highly specific reactions in living matter may be traced to proteinaceous material. Proteins have another valuable property in the fiberlike nature of the polymer. Muscle tissue is apparently largely constituted of these fibers, which are tough and can change length without breaking. Carbohydrate fibers carry most of the structural burden in plants but most carbohydrate polymers are too rigid to be adaptable to the movements required of animals.

ENZYMES AND ENZYME SYSTEMS

Conversion of foods into energy and body-building materials involves thousands of different chemical reactions. Most of these reactions are slow when the pure ingredients are mixed. But all organisms require rather rapid reactions if they are to survive and thus all use catalysts to increase the reaction rates. These catalysts are called *enzymes*. Hundreds of enzymes have been identified as to function, and many more certainly exist.

Though many enzymes have been identified as to function and have even been isolated and crystallized, none has had its chemical structure completely determined. All known enzymes are large proteinaceous molecules. Their names usually suggest their function and end in -ase. Thus maltase is the enzyme which catalyzes the hydrolysis of maltose, but the fact that it has a name doesn't mean that we know the composition of maltase or its detailed function.

Very often a purified enzyme is unable to catalyze reactions but becomes active when some simpler substance is added. These simpler substances may be catalysts or they may be used up in the reaction. They are called *co-enzymes*. Co-enzymes are smaller molecules than the enzymes and the two may be separated by dialysis. (See Problem 34.14.) The constitutions of many co-enzymes are known. Potassium, magnesium, calcium, and chloride ions often act as co-enzymes. An even more common one, about which we shall say more, is adenosine triphosphate, called ATP. It may be thought of as containing a nitrogenous part, a carbohydrate part, and a phosphate part.

adenosine triphosphate, "ATP"

A very similar co-enzyme—adenosine diphosphate, called ADP—is identical except that it contains only two phosphate groups, not three. These two co-enzymes, ATP and ADP, are found in all living matter and are essential to many biochemical processes.

Enzymes are highly specific in their action. Phosphorylase can convert α-D-glucose-1-phosphate (see Figure 39.1) to glycogen, but has no action on the β isomer, or on the 1-phosphates of mannose, galactose, glucose, or maltose. (See pages 612–614 for formulas of these sugars.) On the other hand, different phosphorylases—such as those of potato, jack-bean, muscle, or adipose tissue—are known, and each can accomplish the same glycogen synthesis in its own optimum environment.

The catalytic effect of enzymes is very great indeed. Cori, Cori, and Green estimate, for instance, that each molecule of phosphorylase can transform 40,000 molecules of α-D-glucose-1-phosphate into glycogen per minute on the average. As must be true of catalytic reactions in general, so with enzymes, the reactions are reversible on the enzyme and many examples are known in which the enzyme is equally important in both "forward" and "reverse" reactions. See the reactions involved in the storage of glucose as glycogen and its subsequent reconversion to glucose in Figure 39.1. (The "irreversible reactions" of biochemistry are those in which the energy evolution is so great that it is difficult to supply the energy for the reverse reaction.)

Enzymes are stored biologically in a deactivated, or masked, condition when not required. Various activating agents are known, depending on the enzymes, but metal ions, sulfides, and ascorbic acid (vitamin C) are examples. There is good reason to believe that much of the regulation of the rate of metabolism is accomplished by regulating the enzyme concentrations through greater or lesser secretion of *hormones*. Thus small changes in hormonal concentration could give a much larger change in concentration of the enzyme which would lead to a corresponding change in the rate of metabolism and energy production. But the relationships and interactions are not known, only surmised. Each molecule of the hormone insulin leads to the metabolism of glucose increasing by a rate of 3×10^6 molecules of glucose per minute, but the mechanism of the interaction is not known.

DIGESTION

Most foods are polymeric. Both carbohydrates and proteins consist of long chain and branched molecules with molecular weights in the thousands and millions. These molecules are too big to diffuse from the intestinal tract into the body fluids for transport throughout the organism. They must first be digested, that is, decomposed into smaller, preferably water-soluble, molecules. Some of the fragments diffuse directly through the aqueous fluids of the body but others are subjected to active and selective transport through cell walls—a process known as *absorption*. The mechanism of absorption is not completely understood but it appears to involve processes akin to the forming of complexes in inorganic chemistry. As a result of the process (which is limited to cells in which active metabolic reactions are occurring) cells will be richer in some substances (potassium ion, for example) than the fluid in which they are bathed. Whatever the process, the food fragments enter and leave many cells, until each enters some cell in which it reacts. It may be further degraded to give energy or be synthesized into water-insoluble, or nondiffusable polymers, which will be retained in the cell.

The conversion of carbohydrates and proteins into their respective monomers requires breaking of ether (carbohydrate) or peptide (protein) bonds in the presence of water as indicated in equations 39.1 and 39.2.

For carbohydrates: R—O—R' + H—O—H = R—O—H + R'—O—H   (39.1)
                ether   alcohol   alcohol
                group

$$\text{For proteins: } R''{-}\underset{\underset{\text{peptide group}}{}}{\overset{\overset{H}{|}}{N}}{-}\overset{\overset{O}{\|}}{C}{-}R''' + H{-}O{-}H = R''{-}\overset{\overset{H}{|}}{N}{-}H + R'''{-}\overset{\overset{O}{\|}}{C}{-}O{-}H \quad (39.2)$$
                                                                         amine   acid

These reactions when uncatalyzed are very slow but they can be catalyzed by acids, bases, and/or enzymes. The acidity and enzyme content of the mouth, stomach, and intestine vary so that each enzyme operates under favorable conditions.

All the digestible carbohydrates are decomposed in the stomach and intestine into their monosaccharides, for example, mannose, fructose, galactose, and glucose. These diffuse into the blood stream and thence to cells such as those in the muscles and liver where they are all converted into α-D-glucose-1-phosphate (see Figure 39.1) by appropriate enzyme systems. This material is then degraded to release energy or converted to stored glycogen. Note that since all digestible carbohydrates are converted into this one substance only one set of enzymes is required in further metabolism, an obvious advantage. Other carbohydrates, such as cellulose, are eliminated unchanged by humans.

Certain microorganisms do have enzyme systems which can hydrolyze cellulose to glucose. (See page 615.) Such microbes inhabit the stomachs of many ruminants (for example, cows, goats) and these animals can thus utilize glucose from cellulose.

The stomach enzymes digest proteins into smaller molecules known as peptides. The peptides are then completely decomposed into their individual amino acids in the intestine. The amino acids spread through the body by diffusion and absorption and are either incorporated into structural material such as muscle, or into specific functional molecules such as enzymes, or they are stripped of their amino groups and used as energy sources or synthesized into glucose.

Fats are not polymers in the usual sense, and their molecular weights are much lower than those of most carbohydrates and proteins. They are, however, insoluble in water. They are softened, or even liquefied, in the stomach. The mechanism of transfer from the intestines to the blood stream is not established but they are transported through the blood stream as fine droplets (emulsions) either to fat storage depots, to the liver for metabolism, or to be incorporated as structural units in tissues.

Salts, water, air, and vitamins do not need to be digested. All are somewhat soluble in blood and enter it unchanged.

CARBOHYDRATE METABOLISM

The chemistry of organic metabolism—the conversion of foods into energy and structural molecules—is only beginning to be understood. Only the simplest enzyme systems have been linked together to give a coherent picture of the fate of certain molecules. We shall treat a part of one such system, the metabolism of carbohydrates, in some detail to give an idea of the complex relations found.

The conversion of starch, a typical carbohydrate, to glucose involves only small energy changes. The subsequent complete degradation of glucose to carbon dioxide and water in the body tissues, however, releases about 686,000 calories per mole. A living system, to survive, must store part of this energy in "readily available form," but may use the rest for heat. If all the energy appeared as heat, none would be available for movement, for nerve impulses, for muscle action, or, in the electric eel, for shocking its enemies. It is rather generally accepted now that a great deal, if not all, of this energy is stored in, or by means of, ATP and that energy is converted from chemical bond energy to mechanical and other types when ATP decomposes into ADP and phosphoric acid under appropriate conditions. The mechanism of conversion is quite unknown.

Figure 39.1 illustrates the metabolism of starch to lactic acid, a process now widely accepted as occurring in humans. (Note that all the digestible carbohydrates will follow the latter part of this scheme since it includes α-D-glucose-1-phosphate which all form, as stated earlier.) Steps 3, 4, and 5 are readily reversible so that glucose can be stored (as glycogen), or transported (as

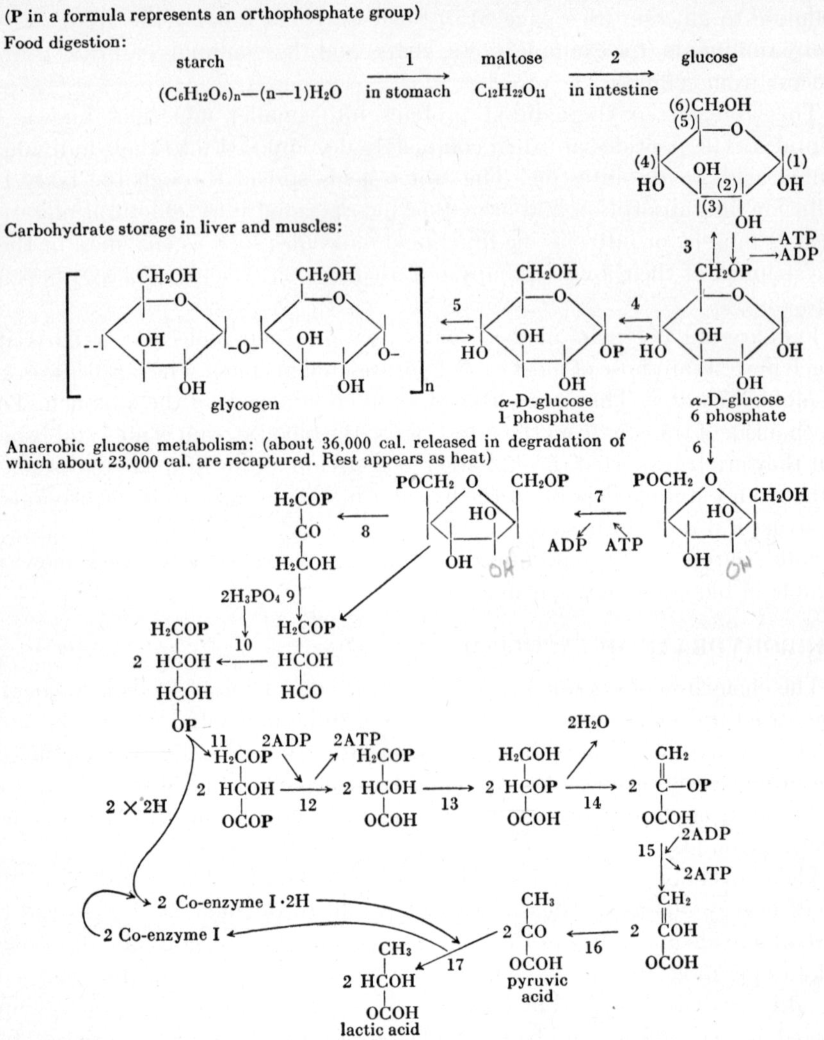

640   GENERAL CHEMISTRY

(P in a formula represents an orthophosphate group)

Food digestion:

$$(C_6H_{12}O_6)_n - (n-1)H_2O \xrightarrow[\text{in stomach}]{1} \text{maltose } C_{12}H_{22}O_{11} \xrightarrow[\text{in intestine}]{2} \text{glucose}$$

Carbohydrate storage in liver and muscles:

[glycogen structure] →5← α-D-glucose 1 phosphate →4← α-D-glucose 6 phosphate (with ATP→ADP, step 3)

Anaerobic glucose metabolism: (about 36,000 cal. released in degradation of which about 23,000 cal. are recaptured. Rest appears as heat)

[diagram of glycolysis steps 6–17, proceeding through fructose phosphates, 2H$_3$PO$_4$ (step 9), triose phosphates, through ADP/ATP exchanges (steps 11–15), yielding pyruvic acid and lactic acid with co-enzyme I · 2H / co-enzyme I cycling at step 17]

2 HCOH
OCOH
lactic acid

Figure 39.1.
Metabolism (partial) of carbohydrates.

glucose), or degraded (from α-D-glucose-6-phosphate) as the body demands. All these forms will be available at equilibrium in healthy tissues. The two hydrogen atoms removed in step 11 are reintroduced in step 17 through the action of co-enzyme I. The enzyme systems which accomplish each step of the metabolism are named in Table 39.2.

It will be noted that this complicated process merely takes glucose as far as lactic acid, that no carbon dioxide or water are produced, and that no oxygen is required. These steps constitute the anaerobic (without oxygen)

Table 39.2
Enzyme Systems for the Metabolism of Starch

REACTION (SEE FIGURE 39.1)	ENZYME	CO-ENZYME
Digestion:		
1.	at least four needed	
2.	maltases	
3.	hexokinase	ATP
Storage:		
4.	phosphoglucomutase	
5.	phosphorylase, and branching factor	phosphoric acid
Anaerobic metabolism:		
6.	oxoisomerase	
7.	phosphohexokinase	ATP
8.	aldolase	water
9.	phosphotriose isomerase	
10.	none required?	phosphoric acid
11.	triosephosphate dehydrogenase	co-enzyme I
12.	phosphoglyceric phosphokinase	ADP
13.	phosphoglyceromutase	2,3-diphosphoglyceric acid
14.	enolase	Mg^{++}
15.	pyruvic phosphokinase	ADP
16.	none required?	
17.	lactic dehydrogenase	co-enzyme I·2H

degradation of glucose. The scheme in the presence of oxygen is identical through step 16, but in aerobic metabolism the pyruvic acid, formula $CH_3COCOOH$, formed is next oxidized, with the loss of carbon dioxide, to give "active acetate." This acetate then enters a much more complicated enzyme system and is eventually completely oxidized to carbon dioxide and water.

The simple conversion of glucose to lactic acid would release about 36,000

$$\underset{\text{glucose}}{C_6H_{12}O_6} = 2\underset{\text{lactic acid}}{CH_3\text{—CHOH—COOH}} + 36{,}000 \text{ cal.} \tag{39.3}$$

calories per mole. Many steps are involved in the over-all system of Figure 39.1, but examination will show that while 2 moles of ATP (see steps 3 and 7) are used up, 4 moles of ATP (see steps 12 and 15) are generated, a net gain of 2 ATP's. The other chemicals used up are 2 moles of phosphoric acid (step 10). Thus the equation for the actual net reaction is:

$$\underset{\text{glucose}}{C_6H_{12}O_6} + 2H_3PO_4 + 2ADP = 2ATP + 2H_2O + 2\underset{\text{lactic acid}}{CH_3\text{—CHOH—COOH}} + 13{,}000 \text{ cal.} \tag{39.4}$$

The energy release here is only 13,000 calories compared to the 36,000 calories in reaction 39.3. Thus the ATP has "stored" 23,000 calories. Over 60 per cent of the available energy has been retained by the system for future use.

In the subsequent aerobic metabolism to give carbon dioxide and water some 60 per cent of the energy is again retained in ATP formed during the degradation of the glucose fragments. Thus we see in some detail how the energy of the glucose molecule is efficiently transferred to a molecule, ATP, which can deliver it quickly in a form directly useful to the body.

The degradation of carbohydrate need not proceed completely to carbon dioxide and water merely because the anaerobic degradation once starts. As a matter of fact, extra carbohydrate, beyond the immediate requirements and storage facilities of the body, is degraded to "active acetate" and the carbon then used in the synthesis of fats for which the body's storage capacity is almost unlimited. Note that this process retains most of the energy of the carbohydrate.

CONVERSION OF ENERGY IN THE BODY

The mechanisms of energy conversion in the body are not known despite intense research. Some of the chemical changes accompanying the conversions have, however, been established. In muscle cells, for instance, the following change occurs:

$$\text{ATP} + \text{extended muscle} = \text{ADP} + H_3PO_4 + \text{contracted muscle.} \quad (39.5)$$

But there is far too little ATP available to provide energy over any extended period. The ATP is, rather, regenerated at once by the reaction

$$\underset{\text{creatine phosphate}}{\text{HOOC}-CH_2-\underset{|}{N}-\underset{\|}{\overset{CH_3}{C}}-\underset{|}{\overset{NH}{N}}-\overset{H}{P}} + \text{ADP} = \text{ATP} + \underset{\text{creatine}}{\text{HOOC}-CH_2-\underset{|}{N}-\underset{\|}{\overset{CH_3}{C}}-NH_2} \quad (39.6)$$

Equation 39.6 represents a rapid, reversible equilibrium and indicates that most of the "phosphate energy" is stored in creatine phosphate but is readily available to the muscle through ATP. Extensive use of a muscle will exhaust both the ATP and creatine phosphate and the muscle will refuse to contract until more glycogen is metabolised, regenerating the ATP and the creatine phosphate. (Actually ADP can probably also donate energy by breaking a second P—O—P bond, but this need not concern us here.) It should be clear that the complicated metabolism of glycogen (Figure 39.1) will be a very slow process compared to the ATP—ADP change (equations 39.5 and 39.6) as a means of delivering energy. On the other hand during moderate work the ATP concentration will be maintained at a steady value by the continuous glucose metabolism.

FAT AND PROTEIN METABOLISM

Much less is known about the metabolism of fats than about that of the carbohydrates. Apparently, however, the liver is the principal organ for the initial metabolism; perhaps it hydrolyzes the fats to glycerol and free fatty acids. The glycerol, if not immediately degraded through aerobic processes similar to those of the carbohydrates, is almost quantitatively converted to glucose and glycogen by a reversal of much of the anaerobic glucose metabolism shown in Figure 39.1.

We have already said that carbohydrates may be converted to fats in the body, but there is little evidence that fatty acids are, in a reverse way, converted to carbohydrates. They appear, rather, to be broken down stepwise a two-carbon-atom fragment being split off at each step as "active acetate." This "active acetate" then undergoes the same aerobic degradation to carbon dioxide and water that is found for the "active acetate" from carbohydrates. Thus most of the energy of fats is also transferred to the ATP systems.

Proteins of many varieties and many compounds consisting of proteins combined with other substances are synthesized in the body from the free amino acids formed in digestion, but almost nothing is known about the mechanisms of these syntheses. A most important observation is, however, that the syntheses are very accurately reproducible, and that the end products have high specific powers as enzymes, hormones, genes, and structural tissues. Many other types of proteinaceous materials are known but their compositions, structures, and mechanism of preparation are almost a complete enigma. It is well established that the amino acids are joined in a set order into long chains by
$$R-\underset{\underset{H}{|}}{N}-\underset{\underset{}{\overset{\overset{O}{\|}}{C}}}{}-R'$$
bonds, and that these chains are held together by hydrogen bonds of the type

$$\begin{array}{c} R-\underset{\underset{H}{|}}{N}-\underset{\overset{O}{\|}}{C}-R' \\ \underset{O}{|} \quad \underset{H}{|} \quad \leftarrow \text{hydrogen bonds} \\ R-\underset{\overset{O}{\|}}{C}-\underset{\underset{}{|}}{N}-R''' \end{array}$$

Little is known of the order of the amino acids within the chains (but see insulin below), or of the orientation of the chains with respect to one another, or of the over-all shapes of the molecules. Research on protein structures is now one of the most active fields in chemistry and some of the current results give promise of much more information on the molecular architecture of proteins in the near future.

Amino acids which do not become incorporated into active structures are quickly stripped of their amino groups, probably degraded to "active acetate," with the "active acetate" then being further degraded, or else stored as glucose or glycogen.

"ACTIVE ACETATE"

You will have noted from the above that carbohydrates, fats, and proteins are all degraded to a common product, "active acetate." Up to this point each food requires its own separate enzyme sequence, but subsequently all use the

644 GENERAL CHEMISTRY

same one in transferring the energy from "active acetate" to ATP. This results in a marvelous economy in chemical reactions. Considerable effort has been expended in identifying "active acetate." It is now widely believed that this intermediate is a compound of a well-characterized substance known as co-enzyme A with a CH₃CO- (acetyl) group attached. The formula is

$$\underbrace{\text{co-enzyme A group}}_{} \qquad \underbrace{\text{acetyl group}}_{}$$

```
                          H H    CH₃ H O            O         O
       NH₂            H O O  H    |   |  ||   H H H ||  H H H  ||
        |           COPOPO—C—C—   C—C—N—C—C—C—N—C—C—S—C—CH₃
     C    N          H O O  H    |   |       H H        H H
   N    C                        CH₃ O
   ||   ||    O—C                    H
   C    C  CH /  \
  / \  /    C  H  C  H
 H   N  N   H  C   OH
            |
            OH
   ADP (or ATP)               pantothenate      β-mercapto-    acetyl
                              (vitamin B₃)      ethylamine     group
                                 group            group       "active
                                                              acetate"
```

The co-enzyme A may be considered as made up of three parts: our old friend ADP (or ATP), pantothenate (which we shall soon see is vitamin B₃), and a small fragment from β-mercapto-ethylamine which serves as a link to the CH₃CO-(acetyl) group that may have formed from the degradation of either carbohydrates, fats, or proteins.

It is this molecule which serves as the common collecting point for all further aerobic degradation of the foods, just as α-D-glucose-1-phosphate was the common collecting point before the degradation of all carbohydrates by anaerobic processes. Biochemists may well expect to find more such "collecting points" as they investigate metabolic systems, for the chemical advantages to the organism of such interchangeability are very great. Note too that these collecting points serve also as "directing stations" from which the fragments may either be sent on to further degradation and energy production, or, depending on the current requirements of the body, to synthesis for storage purposes.

These collecting points are not entirely assets to a system. They also constitute weaknesses in the sense that any attack on them by poisons or infections incapacitates practically the whole enzyme system with which they are associated. This is one reason the body is so very sensitive to certain drugs, poisons, and infections.

INORGANIC CONSTITUENTS

Calcium, magnesium, sodium, potassium, phosphate, sulfate, and chloride ions make up the principal inorganic requirements of humans. (Carbonate ions are formed within the organism. How?) Trace amounts of ferric, cupric, manganous, zinc, cobaltous, fluoride, and iodide ions are also needed. Most of these ions have several uses, but some typical examples are: calcium—bones; potassium—selectively accumulated by almost all living cells; sodium and

BIOCHEMISTRY 645

Table 39.3
Some Vitamins Essential to Man

NAMES	FORMULA	APPEARS IN	DEFICIENCY SYMPTOM	RECOMMENDED DAILY AMOUNT
A_1, β carotene (A_2 also known)	(structure of β-carotene with cyclohexene ring and polyene chain terminating in CH_2OH)		Sight impaired	2 mg.
B_1, thiamine hydrochloride	(thiamine structure with Cl^-, NH_3^+, pyrimidine and thiazolium rings, CH_2CH_2OH side chain)	Co-enzyme of oxidative decarboxylation	Beri-beri	2 mg.
B_2, riboflavin	(riboflavin structure with ribitol side chain –CH$_2$OH and isoalloxazine ring system)	All flavoproteins	Skin lesions	2 mg.
B_3, pantothenic acid	HO—C—C—C—C—N—C—C—COOH (with OH, CH$_3$, OH, O, H, H, H substituents; CH$_3$ branch)	Co-enzyme A	?	?
B_5, niacin	(pyridine ring with –COOH)	Co-enzymes I and II	Pellagra	15 mg.
B_6, pyridoxine	(pyridine ring with CH$_2$OH, HO–, CH$_2$OH, H$_3$C–, –H substituents)	Transaminase and certain decarboxylases	?	?
B_{12}, cobaltamine	(complex structure) $C_{(53-54)}H_{(77-83)}N_{12}O_{13}PCo$	?	Pernicious anaemia	0.001 mg.

646 GENERAL CHEMISTRY

Table 39.3—*Continued*

NAMES	FORMULA	APPEARS IN	DEFICIENCY SYMPTOM	RECOMMENDED DAILY AMOUNT
C, ascorbic acid	(structure of ascorbic acid)		Scurvy	75 mg.
D, (At least 10 known)	see page 648 for structure of D_3		Rickets	0.01 mg.
K, (2 known)	(structure of vitamin K)		Blood doesn't clot	?

chloride—present in large amounts in body fluids and largely responsible for osmotic balance; phosphate—ATP, bones; magnesium—co-enzyme; iron—hemoglobin and iron-containing enzymes (for example, cytochrome oxidase, peroxidase, and catalase) fluoride—teeth; iodide—thyroxine (see page 647); cobalt—vitamin B_{12} (see page 645). Iodide is probably the most commonly deficient ion but it can be supplied in iodized salt. Little is known in detail of the compounds formed by the inorganic substances.

VITAMINS

The vitamins consist of molecules which are required by the body in small amounts for the synthesis of vital substances, but which cannot themselves be synthesized by the body. Some of the essential amino acids and unsaturated fatty acids also fit this definition but are not classed as vitamins.

It is now thought that the vitamins are used in the synthesis of co-enzymes and hormones and some of these relationships have been traced. For example, pantothenic acid, vitamin B_3, (see Table 39.3) appears in co-enzyme A, as shown on page 644.

Vitamins were discovered during searches for the causes of deficiency diseases. Scurvy, pellagra, and beri-beri were known to be cured, or prevented, by eating certain foods. The term "limey" applied to Englishmen dates, for instance, from the introduction by the British Navy in 1795 of limes as standard diet to prevent scurvy among the sailors. Some 130 years later the active principle was named vitamin C, and later identified as ascorbic acid.

All the presently known vitamins, only some of which have been proved essential to humans, have been identified as to chemical structure and many are now synthesized commercially for medical use. There is general agreement in the medical world, however, that the chance of vitamin deficiency occurring in any diet based on enough, and varied, food of good quality is almost nil. In fact, certain vitamins are so widespread in occurrence and so limited in bodily demand that it has been impossible to determine the required daily dose for humans—everyone gets much more than he needs even on a very limited diet. There is a growing feeling that the use of vitamin pills should be restricted primarily to those for which clinical evidence shows a need. On the other hand, there is little evidence that anything except doses hundreds of times those feasible with pills are harmful to the individual.

Table 39.3 lists some vitamins known to be essential to man together with some of their properties. Many more vitamins essential to other organisms are known and others essential to man will almost certainly be found.

HORMONES

The hormones consist of molecules synthesized in small amounts in various glands such as the adrenals, pituitary, thyroid, ovary, testes, and pancreas. They are similar in function to the vitamins in that small amounts have very large effects on bodily functions and health, apparently largely through their influence on enzyme systems.

The chemical constitution of many hormones has been determined. Some, such as adrenaline and thyroxine, as shown in Table 39.4, are rather simple molecules. It is interesting to note the similarity between each of these two molecules and the essential amino acid, tyrosine. Similarities are also apparent between the D vitamins (10 are known) and the steroid hormones of the adrenal cortex, ovaries, and testes, many of which have the carbon skeleton shown in Table 39.5. Many other hormones are proteins or peptides.

Table 39.4

| adrenalin | thyroxine | tyrosine |

648 GENERAL CHEMISTRY

The hormone, insulin, is proteinaceous, yet much is known about its structure. It contains 16 different amino acids, has a molecular weight of about 12,000, and is composed of 4 peptide chains in two identical sets. These chains are joined by 6 S—S bonds, but are separable into A and B fractions. The B fraction is notable as being the first protein residue to have its amino acid sequence proved. The precise order in which the 30 amino acid groups composing it are arranged is known. And yet little is known of the way in which insulin operates as a control in the metabolism of carbohydrates. This situation is true throughout biochemistry. A fair amount of chemical knowledge has been attained but little is yet known about the relations between chemical

Table 39.5

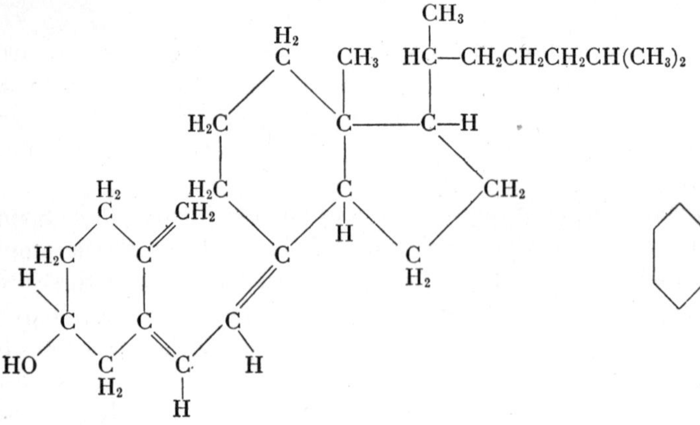

Vitamin D_3

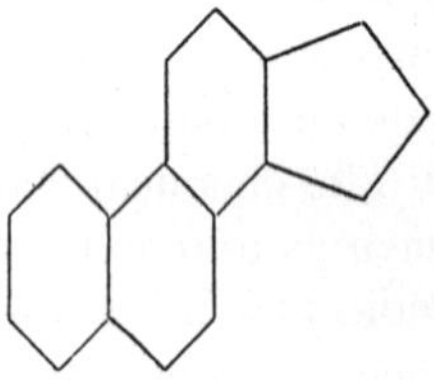

Carbon skeleton of many steroid hormones

structures and their mode of interaction. For this and other reasons biochemistry is one of the most challenging fields open to chemists.

CHEMICAL STRUCTURE AND BIOCHEMICAL ACTIVITY

While it is true that little is known as to why certain chemical structures act as they do biochemically, much knowledge has followed from the idea that similar chemical structures will have similar activity. This method of approaching biochemical systems attained fresh impetus after the discovery of the strong bactericidal action of sulfanilamide. This action was interpreted as inducing a vitamin deficiency in the bacteria by blocking their access to para-aminobenzoic acid, vitamin B_x (PAB). Thus it was suggested that the bacteria were fooled into synthesizing a co-enzyme using the sulfa drug rather than PAB, but that the resulting co-enzyme was not able to activate the enzyme system due to the very high specificity of the enzyme.

para-amino-benzoic acid (PAB) — NH₂–C₆H₄–COOH

sulfanilamide — NH₂–C₆H₄–SO₂NH₂

Thus the bacteria weaken, cease to reproduce, and are destroyed by the host organism.

Many such vitamin antagonists have since been discovered, but the field has not been very rewarding clinically since the anti-vitamins, as these ineffective vitamin substitutes are called, are generally toxic to man as well as to bacteria. In other words bacterial metabolism is similar to human metabolism in some respects. This, of course, poses one of the great problems of bacterial medicine. One must find a drug which is much more toxic to the bacteria than to the human host. Historically cut-and-try methods have always been used but the new knowledge of structures should greatly accelerate the discovery of suitable drugs for various diseases. Today it is still true, however, that the first sample of each type of drug is discovered, if not by accident, then by lengthy trial and error with many chemicals. Other chemicals with structures similar to that of the known drug are then synthesized and tested clinically in an attempt to find more potent and less toxic drugs.

Table 39.6

(dihydroxyphenyl-ethanolamine)	more powerful than	adrenalin
oxybiotin	just as effective as, and interchangeable with	biotin (vitamin B₇)

650 GENERAL CHEMISTRY

Many examples have been discovered in which a newly synthesized product is as active as or even more active than the natural or original one. See Table 39.6 for two examples. Similarly, a chloro derivative of the hormone cortisone has been synthesized which is four times as potent as cortisone itself. New penicillins have been prepared which have properties more desirable than the original.

In the same way the discovery that barbital was an anaesthetic led to the synthesis of other like molecules many of which, such as amytal and pentothal, had somewhat different properties, thus increasing the variety of available anaesthetics.

Table 39.7

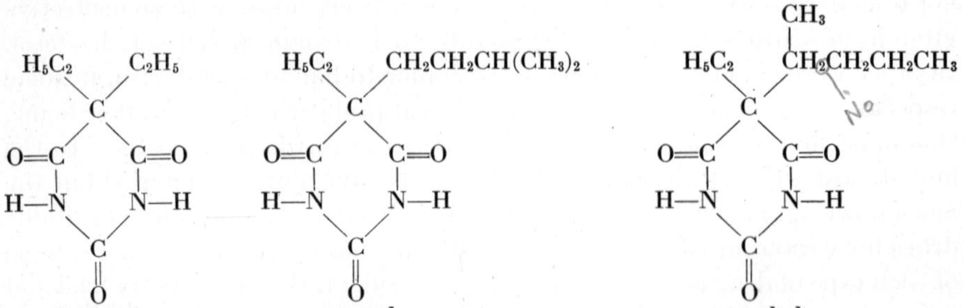

barbital (long action)

amytal (short action)

pentothal (very short action)

Note that amytal and pentothal are structural isomers

ABSORPTION BY LIVING CELLS

Except for a brief comment on absorption of food fragments by cells we have not discussed one important attribute of living organisms, namely their maintenance within their boundaries of a chemical composition different from that of their environment. Diffusion from regions of higher concentration to regions of lower concentration occurs continually for substances which can pass through cell walls but to this action is added a selective action. The cells in the kidney, for example, can remove metabolic wastes at low concentrations from the blood and concentrate them in the urine, in opposition to the diffusion effect. Living cells bathed in fluid containing sodium and potassium ions build up a higher concentration of potassium ions in the cell fluid and partially exclude sodium ion. Yet, tracer studies show that sodium and potassium ions in the cell are continually exchanging with those in the environment. Apparently the energy necessary to transport these ions against their natural diffusion processes comes from the metabolic processes for when metabolism stops the ion concentrations inside and outside the cell tend to equalize.

The transport of sodium and potassium ions is particularly interesting because these ions are so nonreactive chemically. Neither ordinarily is considered a significant complex former. Yet enzymes or other substances participating in the metabolic processes must be able to distinguish between them and to produce a net transport in opposite directions. The polymers pose no transport problem for they are too large to pass through the cell walls. In consequence, the cell concentrations of these will differ from those in the surrounding fluid. Water, of course, being free to move through cell walls will tend to flow in the direction which will equalize the concentration of the water itself.

SUMMARY

We thus see how some of the simpler parts of human physiology can be interpreted in terms of catalytic enzyme systems which regulate the rate of synthesis, degradation, and energy release from foods. The enzyme activity itself may be controlled by hormones synthesized in certain glands. Diseases may arise when materials essential for the synthesis or activation of the enzymes or hormones are withheld, or when the body is invaded by substances which block the enzyme or hormone actions. Many other types of biochemical processes and diseases occur but the great sensitivity of organisms to minute amounts of certain specific substances is at least partially interpretable by the above picture.

Furthermore, the great adaptability of the body to wide variations in food can be understood in terms of the enzyme systems linked through such common substances as α-D-glucose-1-phosphate and "active acetate."

Already the application of chemistry to biological systems has led to great results in the control of diseases and to an elementary understanding of physiology in terms of particular molecules and their behavior. Molecules with similar structures often have similar biochemical activity. On the other hand organisms often show a very high degree of selectivity and discrimination between structures which differ only slightly chemically.

A man is more than a chemical plant, but the biochemist can at least help to keep in reasonable running order that part of man which is chemical.

Problem 39.3. Plant carbohydrates are the usual precursors of animal fats, and animal fats contain an even number of carbon atoms. Postulate a general mechanism for this conversion in the animal. The fat of each animal tends to be characteristic of that species and to differ from that of other species. Is this result consistent with your general mechanism?

Problem 39.4. Discuss two possible routes by which plant cellulose could be incorporated into human glycogen.

Problem 39.5. Suggest a reason for the high rigidity of carbohydrate polymers as compared with the general flexibility of proteins. Correlate this with the still lower rigidity of fats.

Problem 39.6. Vitamins are often classified as fat or water soluble. Classify the vitamins in Table 39.3 according to this solubility grouping by examining their molecular formulas.

Problem 39.7. It has been stated that the production of radioactive isotopes of all the elements is the greatest contribution made to biochemistry since the microscope. Justify or attack the importance of the contribution even if you can't compare it with other contributions.

APPENDIX A:
REVIEW PROBLEMS

1. Compare hydrogen sulfide and hydrogen chloride with respect to the following: (a) Degree of ionization of the acid in water solution. (b) Amount of base required to "neutralize" one mole of the acid. (c) Ease of oxidation of the acid. (d) Solubility of the acid in water.
2. The following values of ionic radii represent the relative sizes of the ions: F^-, 1.36 Å.; Na^+, 0.95 Å.; Cl^-, 1.81 Å.; K^+, 1.33 Å. Why do the sizes of the ions vary in this way?
3. State the conditions of temperature, pressure, and concentration which are advisable for the synthesis of ammonia by the following reaction:

$$N_{2(g)} + 3H_{2(g)} = 2NH_{3(g)} + 21,000 \text{ cal.}$$

   Give reasons for your choice of conditions.
4. You are given a 1000 ml. flask containing an unknown gas and told to determine the molecular weight of the gas. Outline exactly what you would do and what data you would determine. Now choose some values for these data (any values you wish to use) and calculate the molecular weight of the gas.
5. Interpret the statement in a recently published chemistry book that "Less heat is necessary to heat a given weight of iron than the same weight of lead for the same change in temperature."
6. An element is isolated from a sulfide ore. The element is shiny, malleable, and conducts electricity rather well. 40.6 g. of the element combine with 8.0 g. of oxygen to give an oxide soluble in either acid or base. A volatile compound containing the element and hydrogen is found to have a molar weight of 125 g. Write the formula of the oxide and hydride and identify the element.
7. In a titration in which both an acid and a base of known formality were used it was found that 50.00 ml. of 0.500 f hydrogen ion solution were required to neutralize 2.45 g. of an unknown base to which 1.00 ml. of 0.500 f hydroxide ion solution had also been added. What is the equivalent weight of the unknown base? How many equivalents are there in 500 ml. of a 0.1 f $Ca(OH)_2$ solution?
8. The elements R, T, X, and Z have outer electron shells respectively of 8,1; 18,2; 8,7; and 18,8. Their atomic numbers increase in the order X, Z, T, R. Which elements are metallic and which nonmetallic? Which has atoms with the largest radius? Which is the bext oxidizing agent? Which element is most apt to be

naturally radioactive? Give the formulas of any combinations of atoms they form among themselves, tell whether the combinations are ionically or covalently bonded, and estimate whether the substances would melt below 0°C., above 100°C. but below 1000°C., or above 1000°C.

9. A flood in your basement leaves you confronted with four identical labelless bottles. The four contents are known to be sodium cyanide, a detergent, powdered sugar, and barium sulfate. How would you determine which was which using only the facilities of an ordinary kitchen?

10. Why is it that very pure mercury, and fairly pure copper, but no metallic sodium at all can be obtained by heating the appropriate sulfides in air, yet in every case, the sulfur in the sulfide is burned completely to sulfur dioxide? Write equations for all reactions involved.

11. Where does the heat come from that melts the ice when salt is spread on an icy sidewalk?

12. A well-known chemistry text states: "Ammonia can be cracked into its elements by heating in contact with the very catalysts used in its synthesis, proving that both reactions are in equilibrium: $2NH_{3(g)} = N_{2(g)} + 3H_{2(g)}$. The cracking is 99.8% complete at equilibrium." How is this behavior consistent with the fact that ammonia is prepared in 15% yield by passing nitrogen and hydrogen over this same catalyst until equilibrium is attained? The temperature is 500°C. in both instances.

13. Account for the following in terms of atomic structure:
    a. Variation in size in the periodic table row from Na to Cl.
    b. Variation in size in the Group 1 ions Li^+ to Cs^+.
    c. Variation in chemical inertness in the Cu, Ag, Au group.
    d. Variation in acid strength between HNO_3 and HNO_2.

14. Outline two experimental proofs that elements adjacent to one another in the periodic table differ by a unit positive charge in the nucleus.

15. Experimentation shows that a sodium thiosulfate solution will dissolve silver bromide but not silver iodide. Silver bromide does not dissolve in a $3f$ ammonia solution which does dissolve silver chloride. Will silver chloride dissolve in the thiosulfate solution? Give the reasons for your conclusion and write equations for the solution processes.

16. If you were asked to pick a location for each of the following types of industrial plants, what criteria would you use and what general locale would you recommend? Answer for any *two* plants.
    a. Manufacture of metallic magnesium.
    b. Manufacture of ammonia.
    c. Manufacture of chlorine.

17. Which of the following would polymerize to give rubbery materials? Give the structural formulas of all polymers.

    a. $CH_2=CH-CH=CH_2$
    b. $CH_2=CCl-CH=CH_2$
    c. $CH_2=CCl-CH_2-CH_3$
    d. $CH_2=CHCl$

18. Only those indium compounds containing indium (In, atomic number 49) of 3+ oxidation number are stable whereas thallium (Tl, atomic number 81) exists in both 1+ and 3+ stable oxidation states in compounds. How do you interpret this

difference? Which would be more soluble in 6 f NaOH, thallous or thallic hydroxide? Give equations for the two possible reactions.

19. You are assigned to produce a low melting alloy, melting point below 100°C., and containing no mercury. No reference books are available, but chemicals and equipment are unlimited. Outline the steps you would follow, giving reasons for each.

20. Give a practical, commercial use of any four of the following. Write the equation for each use chosen.
    a. Formation of a complex ion.
    b. Oxidation and reduction in an electric cell.
    c. Hydrolysis.
    d. Extraction of a chemical substance from sea water.
    e. Extraction of a chemical substance from the air.

21. In what respect is the bonding in boron hydride with the formula B_2H_6 greatly different from that of most other chemical compounds?

22. When borax is dissolved in water the resulting solution is alkaline but when solid borax is melted on a piece of metal copper it "dissolves" the basic metallic oxide and leaves a bright metal surface. Explain each type of reaction and write the equations.

23. Indicate whether the reaction represented by each of the following equations tend to proceed in the forward or the reverse direction:
    a. $2Cu^+ = Cu_{(s)} + Cu^{++}$
                  red   blue
    b. $2Cu^{++} + 5I^- = 2CuI_{(s)} + I_3^-$
          blue   brown   brown
    c. $Cu_{(s)} + 2Ag^+ = Cu^{++} + 2Ag_{(s)}$
         red   blue
    d. $CuS_{(s)} + 4NH_3 + H_2O = Cu(NH_3)_4^{++} + HS^- + OH^-$
        black   deep blue

24. Write equations for the net reaction that takes place, if any does, in each of the following. If there is no reaction, so state: (a) 1 f hydrochloric acid solution is added to solid calcium carbonate, (b) Ammonia water is added to solid silver chloride, (c) 1 f sodium bicarbonate and 1 f calcium chloride solutions are mixed, (d) Dilute hydrochloric acid solution is added to a solution containing the $Ag(S_2O_3)_2^{---}$ ion, (e) 1 f sulfuric acid solution is added to solid calcium chloride and the mixture evaporated to dryness, (f) 1 f sodium hydroxide solution is added to solid ammonium chloride.

25. What substances are present in solution in moderate or large amounts after the following are mixed:
    a. 0.1 mole of stannic sulfide and 1 mole of fresh ammonium sulfide in 1 l. of water
    b. 0.1 mole of mercuric chloride and 0.1 mole of stannous chloride in 1 l. of water
    c. 0.1 mole of ferric chloride and 1 mole of hydrogen sulfide in 1 l. of water
    d. 0.1 mole of calcium and 0.4 mole of hydrogen chloride in 1 l. of water
    e. 0.01 mole of calcium chloride and 0.02 mole of carbonic acid in 1 l. of water

26. What new species if any, are likely to form when solutions of the following are mixed: (a) IO_3^-, SO_3^{--}, and H^+ ions, (b) Fe^{++} ions and chlorine, (c) I^- ions and hydrogen sulfide, (d) hydrogen sulfide and sulfur dioxide, (e) Fe^{+++} ions and sulfur dioxide, (f) chlorine and OH^- ions?

656 GENERAL CHEMISTRY

27. An equivalent of an oxidizing or reducing agent is that amount of it which reacts with or yields one mole of electrons. A normal solution contains one equivalent per liter. If 0.3 g. of iron are dissolved in dilute hydrochloric acid solution in the absence of air, what volume of 0.2 normal potassium permanganate solution is needed to oxidize the ferrous chloride solution thus obtained?

28. Which of the following chemicals should be chosen for each of the listed purposes? Name only one for each purpose. Calcium sulfide, calcium carbonate, calcium sulfate hemihydrate, sodium hydroxide, magnesium, sodium chloride, sodium, aluminum, sodium tetraborate, phenolphthalein, ammonia water, calcium chloride, ammonium chloride, anhydrous calcium sulfate, magnesium oxide, sodium sulfate decahydrate, sodium hexametaphosphate.

   a. As electrical conductor
   b. For welding
   c. For plaster cast
   d. As building material
   e. To dissolve silver chloride
   f. To titrate potassium hydroxide
   g. As incendiaries
   h. As raw material in preparation of washing soda
   i. As water softener
   j. To dissolve aluminum hydroxide

29. Complete the equation for a reaction in acid solution involving the following species:

$$AgCNS_{(s)} + BiO_3^- = Ag^+ + CO_{2(g)} + NO_3^- + SO_4^{--} + Bi^{+++}$$

30. What approximate volume of oxygen, measured at standard conditions, is required to burn the acetylene given off by the action of water on 1.28 g. of calcium carbide?

31. Gaseous hydrogen sulfide measuring 1.12 l. at 0°C. and 1 atmosphere pressure is passed into 100 ml. of a solution containing .025 moles of ferric chloride and .025 moles of hydrogen chloride. Supply the numerical values in the following table:

SPECIES	BEFORE THE HYDROGEN SULFIDE IS ADDED		AFTER HYDROGEN SULFIDE IS ADDED	
	Number of moles	Concentration	Number of moles	Concentration
Fe^{++}	___	___	___	___
Fe^{+++}	___	___	___	___
Cl^-	___	___	___	___
H_2S	___	—(in gas)—	___	___
H^+	___	___	___	___
Any other products (identify them)	___	___	___	___

32. State the main chemical substances present in each of the following: (a) solder, (b) water glass, (c) clay, (d) soda glass, (e) automobile battery, (f) red lead, (g) baking powder.

33. How many electrons are there in the $3d$ shell of: (a) arsenic atoms, (b) calcium atoms, (c) scandium atoms?

34. In each of the following groups, underline the formula of each substance or species having the characteristic asked for:

a. Dissolves in ammonium sulfide solution: As_2S_3, Fe_2S_3, ZnS, CuS, SnS_2.
b. Strongest oxidizing agent: Cu^{++}, I_2, Cl_2, SnO_2, PbO_2.
c. Largest radius: Na^+, K^+, Mg^{++}, Al^{+++}, Li^+.
d. Forms most soluble sulfate: Fe^{++}, Pb^{++}, Ca^{++}, Ba^{++}, Ra^{++}.
e. Is most strongly hydrolyzed: Na^+, NH_4^+, Sn^{++}, Sn^{++++}, Ca^{++}.

35. Give the chemical names of the substances having the following formulas:
(a) $C_{10}H_{22}$, (b) H_2CO, (c) $HCCl_3$, (d) CH_3OH, (e) $(CH_3)_2CO$, (f) C_2H_2, (g) HCOOH, (h) $C_6H_5NH_2$ (aromatic), (i) C_6H_6 (aromatic), (j) C_2H_5—O—C_3H_7, (k) limestone, (l) slaked lime, (m) ruby, (n) alum, (o) ClO^-, (p) $KClO_4$, (q) Rn, (r) washing soda, (s) muriatic acid, (t) caustic soda.

36. How could you prepare (a) solid sodium hydrogen sulfite, (b) sulfur dioxide from sulfuric acid, (c) $S_2O_3^{--}$ ion from SO_3^{--} ion, (d) sulfur from hydrogen sulfide, (e) sulfuric acid from sulfur (f) sulfur dioxide from hydrogen sulfide?

37. How could you test for small amounts of the first named species in the presence of large amounts of the second in each of the following: (a) Fe^{+++} ions with Fe^{++} ions, (b) Hg_2^{++} ions with Hg^{++} ions, (c) Ag^+ ions with Cu^{++} ions, (d) copper sulfide with copper oxide, (e) copper with silver, (f) mercuric chloride with mercurous chloride (g) ferrous sulfide with zinc sulfide?

38. How could you test for traces of the first named substances in the presence of much of the second in each of the following?
    a. Calcium sulfate in barium sulfate.
    b. Ferrous hydroxide in ferric hydroxide.
    c. Zinc sulfide in ferrous sulfide.
    d. Ferrous sulfide in zinc sulfide.
    e. Cupric sulfide in silver sulfide.
    f. Mercuric chloride in mercurous chloride.
    g. Mercuric sulfide in mercuric oxide.
    h. Mercury in silver.
    i. Cupric sulfide in cupric oxide.
    j. Ferrous chloride in ferric chloride.

39. Steam is heated with carbon monoxide until equilibrium is established according to the reaction: $CO_{(g)} + H_2O_{(g)} = CO_{2(g)} + H_{2(g)}$. At 959°K. and 2 atm. the partial pressures at equilibrium were:
P_{CO} = 0.57 atm.; P_{H_2O}= 0.57 atm.; P_{CO_2} = 0.43 atm.; P_{H_2} = 0.43 atm.
At 1500°K. and 2 atm. the partial pressures were:
P_{CO} = 0.36 atm.; P_{H_2O} = 0.36 atm.; P_{CO_2} = 0.64 atm.; P_{H_2} = 0.64 atm.
Is the reaction exothermic or endothermic? Explain briefly.

40. Problems 40a through 40h deal with unknowns. On the basis of the information given in each case select the substances that must be present, those that must be absent, and those that might be either present or absent among those listed in each part.

40a. An unknown solution has been made by dissolving one or more of the following solids: mercurous nitrate, silver nitrate, zinc chloride, ammonium nitrate, potassium hydroxide. The solution is alkaline and on addition of dilute nitric acid gives a white precipitate insoluble in excess acid.

40b. An unknown mixture may contain one or more of the following: calcium sulfate, mercuric sulfate, ferric hydroxide, zinc oxide, cupric sulfate. The mixture dissolves readily in dilute hydrochloric acid solution (1 f) and the solution gives a whitish precipitate with hydrogen sulfide. The filtrate from this gives no precipitate when made slightly alkaline with sodium hydroxide.

40c. An unknown solid mixture is made from one or more of the following: calcium oxide, silver nitrate, ferric oxide, zinc sulfide, cupric oxide. Treatment with water gives a dark precipitate and a colorless solution. Treatment with dilute hydrochloric acid gives a white precipitate and a colorless solution.

40d. A clear solution is made by dissolving one or more of the following solids in water: ammonium nitrate, potassium hydroxide, calcium nitrate, ferric nitrate, mercurous nitrate, zinc nitrate, silver nitrate. Sample of the solution gave a yellow color with indigo carmine. The solution when treated with 6 f hydrochloric acid gave a white precipitate, insoluble in excess of acid.

40e. An unknown mixture may contain one or more of the following solids: calcium carbonate, zinc sulfide, mercuric sulfide, ferric chloride. The mixture leaves a residue when treated with water, but dissolves without residue in dilute hydrochloric acid. A precipitate forms when this solution is made alkaline with ammonia water.

40f. An unknown white solid is soluble in water, in hydrochloric acid, and in sulfuric acid. The water solution is acidic and colorless and gives no precipitate when treated with silver nitrate. What single compound of the ions H^+, Na^+, K^+, Ag^+, Cu^{++}, Ca^{++}, Zn^{++}, NH_4^+, OH^-, Cl^-, NO_3^-, CO_3^{--}, SO_4^{--}, S^{--}, could be the white solid?

40g. An unknown solid is made up of one or more of the following: calcium carbonate, barium chloride, sodium sulfate, silver nitrate, zinc sulfate, sodium hydroxide, ammonium chloride. The solid is completely soluble in water; the solution is odorless, and gives a red color with phenolphthalein. When 1 f hydrochloric acid solution is added, a precipitate is produced which dissolves in excess of the acid.

40h. An unknown solution may contain two or more of the following species: Al^{+++}, Cr^{+++}, Fe^{+++}, NH_4^+, Ag^+, Hg^{++}, H^+, OH^-, SO_4^{--}, Cl^-, NO_3^-, CO_3^{--}. When 2 f sodium hydroxide was slowly added in excess a green precipitate was seen to appear and then to dissolve completely. When 0.1 f hydrochloric acid was added to a fresh portion of the original unknown solution a white precipitate was formed. After filtration this precipitate proved to be soluble in ammonia water.

APPENDIX B:
SOME CONVERSION FACTORS

1 inch equals 2.5400 centimeters
1 quart (U. S. liquid) equals 946.36 cubic centimeters
1 pound (avoirdupois) equals 453.59 grams

Use of the above three conversion factors in addition to the usual relations among the units within the English and within the metric system permits one to convert any of the usual English units of length, volume, or weight into the corresponding metric unit. However a few more conversion factors, derivable from the above ones, are listed here:
1 yard equals 0.91440 meters
1 cubic foot equals 28.316 liters
1 fluid ounce (U.S.) equals 29.573 milliliters
1 mile equals 1.6093 kilometers

The following prefixes have the meanings indicated when used in connection with metric units:
micro- means millionths of. (1 microliter is one millionth of a liter.)
milli- means thousandths of. (1 milligram means one thousandth of a gram.)
centi- means hundredths of. (1 centimeter means one hundredth of a meter.)
deci- means tenths of. (1 decimeter means one tenth of a meter.)
kilo- means thousands of. (1 kilogram means one thousand grams.)

The following conversions within the metric system are often useful:
1 liter equals 1000 milliliters equals 1000.028 cubic centimeters.
1 Ångstrom unit equals 10^{-10} meters equals 10^{-8} centimeters.

SUBJECT INDEX

Page entries in *italics* refer to data in tables or to figures. **Bold-face** entries refer to the most important of several entries. Most references to the elements or their compounds are entered under the Group numbers of the elements. For example, there are some entries under Sodium but sodium and its compounds are also discussed, and indexed, under Group 1a.

"a" and "b" Groups in periodic table
  differentiation between, 496
  origin of, 155–158
  resemblances between, 505
Absolute zero, 105
Absorption by living cells, 650
Abundance
  of elements, *77, 543*
    in air, *65*
    in ocean water, *453*
  of isotopes, *172, 488*
  of rare earths, *488*
Acceptor atom, 203, 501
Acetic acid, 282, 597–598
Acid, definition of, 241, 243
  hydroxy, 411
  organic, 597–599
  oxides and, 421
  strength of, 297, 326, 410–415
  strong, 283
  weak, 283
Acid anhydride, 411, 425–426
  organic, 600–601
Acid-base, indicators, 283, *285*
  strength, 326, 410–415, 512
  theory, 241, 243, 409, 489
Acidic oxides, 239
Actinium, *see* Group 3b, actinide subgroup
Activated complex, 88
Activation energy, 87, *88*, 232–233
Active acetate, 643–644
Adrenalin, 647
Adsorption, 560
Air, composition of dry, *65*
  liquid, 64
  oxygen in, *66*

Alcohol, 591–595
Aldehydes, 596–597
Allotropes, 81–82
Alloys, 528, 534–542
  properties of, 35, 538–539
  types of, 536–537
Alpha rays, 20, **22,** 25, 334–337
  bombardment with, 342–344
  emission of, 170, 339
  size of, 165
Alum, 484
Aluminum, *see also* Group 3a
  as a reducing agent, 462
  halides of, 484
  hydroxide of, 483–484
  metal, 483–484
  metallurgy, 454–455, 463, *464*
  oxygen and, 38
  welding, 70
Amalgam mining, 456
Americium, *see* Group 3b, actinide subgroup
Amines, 606
Amino acid, 606
  essential, 625–626
Ammonia, 356
  analysis for, 376, 386
  coordination of, 359
  from coal, 94
Ammonia water, 357
Ammonium, 360
  ion, 354
  salts, 359
Ammonium hydroxide, *see* Ammonia water
Amorphous substances, 79, 81
Ampere, 212
Amphoterism, 388, 423–425

661

SUBJECT INDEX

Analysis, for alkali elements, 478
  for alkaline earth elements, 482
  for halides, 329
  for solids, 389
  qualitative, 374–390
Aniline, 606
Anions, 210
  from oxides, 422
Anode, 210, 436
Antimony, metallurgy, 458, *see also* Group 5a
Aqua regia, 527
Argon, *see* Group 0
Arsenic, metallurgy, 458, *see also* Group 5a
Astatine, *see* Group 7a
Atmosphere, 64–75
  composition, 65, *66*
Atmospheric pressure, standard, 104
Atom, definition of, 32, 42, 49
Atomic bomb, 436
Atomic energy, 345
Atomic energy levels, 191
Atomic kernel, 195
Atomic mass, standard, 164
Atomic pile, 342, 348
Atomic radii, *178*, *180–181*, 504
Atomic size, 157
Atomic structure, 166, 175
Atomic theory, 37, 41
Atomic volume, 174, 544
Atomic weights, 114, 124–125, 143–144
  average, 160
  individual, 162–165
Atoms, 32–48
ATP (ADP), adenosine triphosphate, 636–637
  in carbohydrate metabolism, 639–642
Avogadro's number, 45, 249
Avogram, 45

Bakelite, 622
Baking powders, 476
Barium, *see* Group 2a
Barometer, 98
  gravity effect on, 105
  temperature effect on, 99
Barriers, selective, 265
  semipermeable, 266
Base, *see also* Acid, *and* Acid-base
  definition of, 241, 243
  strong, 420
Basic anhydrides, *419*
Basic oxides, 239, 418–420, 425
Basic strength, 420
Benzene, 582–584
  derivatives, 586–587
  structure, 584–586
Berkelium, *see* Group 3b, actinide subgroup

Beryllium, electronic structure, 185, *see also* Group 2a
Beta rays, 20, **22**, *25*, 334
  bombardment with, 342–345
  emission, 171, 338–340
  positive, 338–339
  source, 341
Biochemistry, 633–652
Bismuth, metallurgy, 456, *see also* Group 5a
Black, carbon, 618
  gas, 91
  lamp, 91
Blast furnace, 459, *461*
Boiling point, 103, 104
  of 1-alkenes, *578*
  of 1-alkynes, *579*
  of elements, *156*, *497*
  of normal hydrocarbons, *574*
  of solutions, 262, 264
Bombardment, nuclear, 338
  machines for, 341
  reactions, 342
Bond, coordinate, 203, 305
  covalent, 201
  dipole, 219, 621
  directions of, 204, *206*
  distance, 199
  double, 203, 576, 579
  electrovalent, 214
  energy, 199
  hydrogen, 222, 643
  ionic, 214, 218
  metallic, 216
  nonpolar, 202, 218
  polar, 218
  resonance, 203–204
  triple, 203, 579
  types, *222*
  van der Waals, 56, 206
Bonding, chemical, 197, 224
Bordeaux mixture, 528
Boron, *see also* Group 3a
  compounds of, 417
  electronic structure, 186
  flame color, *177*
  properties of element, 468, *469*
Boyle, data of, *101*
Brittleness, 215
Bromine, *see* Group 7a
Brownian motion, 250, 557
Butadiene, 580
Butane, 85, 574

Cadmium, metallurgy, 458, *see also* Group 2b
Calcium, *see also* Group 2a
  carbide of, 96
  electronic structure, 186

Californium, see Group 3b, actinide subgroup
Calomel, 530
Calorie, 212
　definition, 59, 634
Carbides, 96, 517, 579
Carbohydrates, *615*, 634–636
　digestion of, 638
　metabolism of, 639–642
Carbon, 76, 84
　binary compounds of, 95
　combustion, 87–90
　　of compounds, 90
　compounds of, 85–97
　　organic, 566–652
　electronic structure, 186
　forms of, 76
　tetrahedral atom, 568, 601
Carbon dioxide, crystal, *221*
　cycle, *72*
　formation, 87
　in air, *65*, 71
　poisoning, 71
　structure, *57*
Carbon disulfide, 96
Carbon monoxide, formation, 89
　structure, *57*
Carbon tetrachloride, 96
　structure, 221
Carbonates, fusion, 480
　insoluble, 388
　natural, 97
Carbonyls, 501, 524
Cast iron, 539
Catalysis, 233, 286, 513
Cathode, 209, 436
Cations, 209
Caves, 480
Cell (electric), concentration, 440–442
　diagrams, 432–438
　voltages, 438–446
　work by, 436
Cellophane, 625
Cellulose, 624
Cement, 553
Centigrade, 103, *107*
Ceramics, 553
Cerium, see Group 3b, rare earth subgroup
Cesium, chloride crystal structure, 215, see also Group 1a
Chain reaction, 89, 342
Charcoals, 89, 93, 94, 560
Charge density, acid strength and, 326–328
　crystal stability and, 401
Chemical bonding, 197–224
Chemical equilibrium, 271–289
Chemical reactions, 225–249

Chlorine, see also Group 7a
　insoluble chlorides, 381
　isotopes, 163
Chromium, 518, see also Group 6b
　compounds of, 518–522
　metallurgy, 452, 458, 462
　trioxide of, 241
Clathrate compounds, 225
Clouds, 72
Coal, 92, *93*
　gas from, 94
　tar from, 94
Cobalt, 523–524, see also Group 10b
　as a radioactive source, 341
　metallurgy, 458
Co-enzyme, 636, 639–642
Coke, 89, 93
　in metallurgy, 457, 458, 459–462
Colloids, 250, 555–565
　Brownian motion and, 557
　coagulation of, 561–562
　dimensions, 555
　electrical charge and, 558
　formation, 557
　shape of, 564
　stabilization, 557
Color, analysis and, 375
　causes, 491, 506, *508*
　flame, *177*
Columbium, see Group 5b *and* Niobium
Combining volumes of gases, **37,** 50
Combining weights, 38
Combustion, heats of, *62*
　phlogiston theory of, 69
　spontaneous, 91
Common ion effect, 281
Complex ion, equilibrium and, 284
　formation, 508–512
　stabilization, 502, 522, 524
Composition, definite, laws of, 33, 35
　of atmosphere, *65*
　of earth's crust, *71*
　of sun's atmosphere, *77*
　per cent and, 66
Compounds, 49–63
　binary, 95
　definition of, 13, 33
　metallic, 537
Concentration, electric cells and, 440–446
　pressure effect on, 257
　temperature effect on, 256
　units, 252
Condensation, 127
Conductivity, electrical, 465, 535, 538
Contact process, 300
Coordination number, 412
Copolymer, 619

664 SUBJECT INDEX

Copper, *see also* Group 1b
  flame color, *177*
  isotopes, 163, *169*
  metallurgy, 454, 457, 465
Corrosion, alloys and, 539
  electrolytic, 526
    protective coatings, and, 316, 472, 502, 526–527, 530
  rusting, and, 525–527
Corrosive sublimate, 530
Coulomb, 212
Counter-current flow, 460
Covalent bond, 201, 232
Covalent radii, *178*, *180–181*, 311–312
Critical state, 128, 135, 140–141
Crookes tube, 30, 160
Cryolite, 464
Crystal structures, 393–402
Crystals, 78, 81
  charge density and, 401
  coordination number in, 396–398
  formation of, 128
  free rotation in, 221
  ionic, 215
  ionic shape in, 402
  macromolecular, *78*, *79*, 81, 208, 394
  metallic, *217*
  molecular, 74, 81, *221*
  radius ratio and, 396, *399*
  relative ionic size in, 398
  relative numbers of ions in, 401
  solubility of, 391–406
  structure of salt, 393, *395*
Curium, 350, *see also* Group 3b, actinide subgroup
Cycloparaffins, 588

Deacon process, 317
Density, 8
  of elements, 472, *497*
Detergents, 135, 563, 610–612
Deuteron, 27, 342–343
Diagonal relationships in periodic table, 407
Diamond, density of, 82
  natural, 77
  stability of, 82
  structure of, *78*
  synthetic, 82
Dienes, 579–580
Diffusion, in gases, 121, 133
  in liquids, 133
  in solids, 133
Digestion, 638–639
Dipole bonds, 219
Dipole moment, 218, *219*
Disaccharides, 614–615
Disproportionation, 502, 524
Dissociation constant, 380
Distillation, 11–13, 456
Distribution equilibrium, 259
Dolomite, 97
Donor atom, 203, 501, *510–511*
Downs cell, *319*
Dry cell, 447
Drying oils, 623
Dulong and Petit law, 143
Dysprosium, *see* Group 3b, rare earth subgroup

Ease of oxidation, 502
Electric cells, 432
Electricity, conduction of, 209, *211*
  nature of, 22, 23
Electrochemistry, 429–449
Electrode, 209
  anode, 210
  cathode, 209
  potentials at, 442, 472, *497*, 504
  reactions at, 209, *431*
Electrolysis, 209
  colloids and, 558–560
  corrosion and, 526
  Faraday's laws of, 211
  halide solutions and, 317, 319
  metallurgy and, 457, 463
  of fused salts, 210, 463
  of magnesium chloride, 210
  of sodium chloride, 318–319
  oxidation-reduction and, 238
  refining by, 465–466
Electrolyte, non-, 281
  strong, 281
  weak, 281
Electromotive force, sources of, 439
  standard, *431*
Electronegativity, relative, 218, *220*
Electron structure, 175, *189–190*, *191*, *192–193*, 504
Electron volt, definition, 30
Electronic structure of atoms, 174–196
Electrons, charge, 23, *24*
  Crookes tube and, 30
  inert pair, 498, 499
  mass, *169*
  pairs, 187, 201, 244
  transfer, 227
  unpaired, 187
  valence, 197
Electropositive element, 468–486
Electrostatic separation, 454
Elements, and atoms, 32–48
  boiling points, *156*
  definition, 13, 15, *195*
  discovery, 149, *150*
  ease of oxidation, 503, *504*

Elements—*Continued*
heat capacity, of gaseous, 123, *124*
of solid, 143–144
in central region of periodic table, part I, 496–515
part II, 516–533
sources, *451*
EMF, *see* Electromotive force
Emulsions, 563
Endothermic reactions, 60
Energy, activation, 87
bond, 199
chemical reaction and, 59
internal, 59
kinetic, 120
mass and, 29
potential, 136, 199
Energy levels, electron, 176–194
molecular, 245
nuclear, 171
Enzymes, 629, 636–638
carbohydrate metabolism and, 639–642
digestive, 638–639
Equations, chemical, 58
net reaction, 280
oxidation-reduction, 306, 429
partial, 228, 429, *431*
thermochemical, 60
Equilibrium, complex ion, 284, 321
distribution between phases and, 269
dynamic, 271
in bromine water, 321
liquid-gas, 138
of hydrogen iodide, 273
oxidation-reduction, 286, 501
phase, 135
quantitative treatment of, 273
shift of, 272
solubility, 254, 379
vapor, 72, 138
weak electrolyte, 281–285
Equilibrium constant, **274–279**, 379, 444–446
Equivalent weights, 38
Erbium, *see* Group 3b, rare earth subgroup
Error, 34, 47
Escaping tendency, **255**, 257, 262, 264, 391
Esters, 599
Ethane, 85, 571
structure, *86*
Ethanol, 593–594
Ethers, 595–596
Ethylene glycol, 594
Europium, *see* Group 3b, rare earth subgroup
Eutectic, 537
Exothermic reactions, 60
Explosions, 328, 367

Fahrenheit, 103, *107*
Faraday unit, 212
Fats, 608, 634–636
digestion, 639
metabolism, 642–643
Fertilizer, 371
Fibers, synthetic, 627–629
Fission, nuclear, 342, 344, 347
Flame colors, *177*
Flotation, 454
Fluorine, *see also* Group 7a
discovery of, 150
electronic structure, 186
Flux, 529
Food, 633–636
inorganic, 644
Fool's gold, 295
Formality, 252
Formulas, 49–63
empirical, 54, 217
of compounds, 54
of elements, 53, 74
of molecules, 51, 74
phase, 61
Francium, *see* Group 1a, alkali elements
Freezing point, of solutions, 263, 264, *see also* Melting point
Frequency (light), 177
Fuels, 92, 94–95, 580–582
Fulminate, 530
Functional group, 598–599
Fundamental particles, 18–31, *28*, 165

Gadolinium, *see* Group 3b, rare earth subgroup
Gallium, *see* Group 3a
Gamma rays, 20, **21**, 22, 25
emission of, 171
Gas, carbon black from, 92
coal, 94
fuel, *95*
natural, 85, 561
producer, 95
water, 94
Gas behavior, 98–119
kinetic theory of, 120–130
Gases, amount of, 108
atomic weights in, 114
definition, 131
diffusion in, 121
heat capacity of, 123, *124*
ideal, 110
laws of, 118
molar volume in, 110, *111*
molar weights of, 112
real, 110
solutions of, 115
Gasoline, 91, 580–582

Geologic clocks, 337
Germanium, properties, *152, see also* Group 4a
Geysers, 146
Glass, 146, 551–553
Glucose, 612–614
Glycerine, 595
Gold, metallurgy, 455–456, 466, 467, *see also* Group 1b
Goldschmidt reaction, 462
Granite, 9
Graphite, 76
  density, 82
  stability of, 82
  structure, *79*
Ground state, 176
Group 0, inert gases, 192–193
  boiling points of, *65*
  crystals, *81*
  discovery, 69
  electron structure, 200, *201, 229*
  in air, *65*
  periodic table and, 155
  reactions of, 225
  uses, 70, 71
Group 1a, alkali elements, 192–193
  analysis for, 226, 228, 468
  covalent radii, *471*
  crystal forms, 470
  densities, 472
  electrode potentials, 472
  flame colors, *177*
  halide crystals, 399
  hydrides of, 473–474
  hydroxides of, 419
  ionic radii, *471*
  ionization potentials, 472
  metallurgy, 463
  oxides of, *418*
  salts of, 474–478
Group 1b, 192–193, 527–529
  properties of elements, *497*
Group 2a, alkaline earth elements, 192–193, 228, 468
  analysis for, 482
  covalent radii, *471*
  crystal forms, 470
  densities, *472*
  electrode potentials, 472
  flame colors, *177*
  hard water and, 481
  hydroxides of, *419*
  ionic radii, *471*
  ionization potentials, 172
  metallurgy, 463, 479
  occurrence, 479

Group 2a—*Continued*
  oxides of, *418*
  properties of elements, *469*
  salts of, 480
Group 2b, 192–193, 529–531
  properties of elements, *497*
Group 3a, 192–193, 531
  covalent radii, *471*
  crystal forms, 470
  densities, 472
  electrode potentials, 472
  ionic radii, *471*
  ionization potentials, 472
  properties of elements, *469, 483, 497*
Group 3b, 192–193
  actinide subgroup, 192–193, 494
  covalent radii, *471*
  crystal forms, 470
  densities, 472
  electrode potentials, *469*
  ionic radii, *471*
  ionization potentials, 472
  properties of elements, *469,* 483
  rare earth subgroup, 192–193, 468, 487–495
    acidity, 489, *490*
    analysis for, 492
    color, 491
    magnetism, 490
    metallurgy, 494
    occurrence, 488
    oxidation states, *488*
Group 4a, 192–193, 531–532
  properties of elements, *497*
Group 4b, 192–193, 516–517
  properties of elements, *497*
Group 4b through 4a, 192–193
  acid-base relationships, 512
  atomic radii, 504
  catalysis and, 513
  color, 506
  complexes, 501, 508–512
  ease of oxidation, 503
  metallic nature, 514
  oxidation states, 499, 501
  properties of elements, *497*
  zero oxidation number and, 501
Group 5a, nitrogen family, 192–193, 351–373
  acids of, 366, 369, 410–413, *415,* 416
  elements, 352, 371
  halogen compounds of, 361
  hydrogen compounds of, 354
  occurrence, 351, 371
  oxides of, 362–366, 368
Group 5b, 192–193, 517
  properties of elements, *497*

SUBJECT INDEX 667

Group 6a, chalcogen family, 192–193, 290–309
  hydrogen compounds of, 296
  ion formation, 230
  oxidation states, 294
  oxides of, 298
  oxygen acids of, 300–305
  properties of elements, 290–294
Group 6b, 192–193, 518
  properties of elements, *497*
Group 7a, halogen family, 192–193, 226, 230, 310–333
  analysis for, 329
  bonding, 311–314
  hydrogen compounds of, 323–328
  nonaqueous solutions of, 322
  occurrence, 314
  oxidation states, 310, 328
  oxygen compounds of, 323, 328
  preparation, 315–320
  properties of elements, 310–312
  reaction with water, 320
  salt crystals of, 393, *399*, 400
Group 7b, 192–193, 522–523
  properties of elements, *497*
Group 8b, 192–193, 522–527
  properties of elements, *497*
Group 9b, 192–193, 522–527
  properties of elements, *497*
Group 10b, 192–193, 522–527
  properties of elements, *497*
Gunpowder, 367

Hafnium, 516–517, *see also* Group 4b
Half life, 171, *172*
Half reaction, 306, 429
Hardness, 216, 535, 539
Heat, content, 60
  of combustion, 56, *62*
  of condensation, 137
  of evaporation, 73, 137
  of freezing (melting), 142
  of reaction, 60
Heat capacity, 59
  of elements, 143–144
  of gases, 123, *124*
  of liquids, 142
  of solids, 142–144
Helium, *see also* Group 0
  alpha particles and, 26
  electronic structure, 184
  ions, *25*
  isotopic masses, *169*
  liquid, 71
  occurrence, 85
  volume change of, 175
Heterogeneous substance, 8
Homogeneous substance, 8

Hooker Type S cell, 318
Hormones, 637–638, 647–648
Humidity, 73
Hydration, 403
  and electrode potentials, 473
Hydride, 231, 473
Hydrocarbons, 566–590
  derivatives of, 591–615
  fuels and, 580–582
  gaseous, 85
  liquid, 87
  nomenclature of, 575–576
  normal, 573–574
  oxygenated derivatives of, 591–604
  unsaturated, 576–577
Hydrocyanic acid, 282
Hydrogen, as a reducing agent, 462
  boiling point, 65
  bomb, 345, 347
  bonds, 221, 596
  combination with oxygen, 35
  electronic structure, 183
  formula, 51
  from methane, 92
  halides, polarities of, *219*
  in air, *65*
  isotopic masses, *169*
  molecular structure, *88*
Hydrogen iodide, equilibrium and, 273
  formation of, *88*
Hydrolysis, 283, 382, 422, **425,** 476
Hydrosphere, 64
Hydroxides, amphoteric, 388
  insoluble, 386
  of alkali elements, 477
Hypo, 529

Ideal gas, 110
Ideal solution, 253
Indicators, acid-base, 241–242, 283, *285*
Indium, 531, *see also* Group 3a
  radioactivity, 337
Insulin, 648
Interhalogen compounds, 320
Interstitial solid solutions, 537
Iodine, structure of, *88, see also* Group 7a
Ion exchange resins, 481–482, 492, 549
Ionic bonds, 214
Ionization constants, 282
Ionization of water, 282
Ionization potentials, 178, *179, 180–181, 182,* 472, *497*
Ions, 209
  determination of charge on, 212–214
  electron structure in, 229
  formation of, 228
  gaseous, 161
  hydrogen, 230

668   SUBJECT INDEX

Ions—*Continued*
 in salts, 213
 shape of, 402
 sizes of, *157*
 stable, 229
Iridium, 527, *see also* Group 9b
Iron, 523–527, *see also* Group 8b
 alloys, 540–541
 carbide of, 96
 cast, 462, 539
 heat treatment, 540–541
 metallurgy, 454, 458, *459*
 pig, 462
 rusting, 525–526
 wrought, 540
Isoelectric point, 560, 608
Isomers, cis-trans, 578, 630
 geometric, 577–578
 head-tail, 621, 630–631
 o, m, p, 584–586
 optical, 601–602
 production of single, 629–631
 structural, 572, 575, 578, 584–586
Isomorphism, 154, 291, 545
Isotopes, 42, *162*
 abundance, 172, 488
 exact masses of, 168–170
 nomenclature, 168
 radio-, 349
 radioactive series of, 335
 separation, 347

K-capture, 339
Kelvin temperature, 106, *107*
Kernel, 197
Ketones, 597
Kindling temperature, 89
Kinetic theory, 120
 escaping tendency and, 255
 of gases, 120–130
 pressure and, 125–126
 vapor pressure and, 261
Kinetics, 286
"Knock," 581
Krypton, *see* Group 0

Lanthanide contraction, 504
Lanthanides, *see* Group 3b, rare earth subgroup
Lanthanum, *see* Group 3b, rare earth subgroup
Law, Avogadro's, 51
 Boyle's, 100
 Charles', 105
 combining volumes of gases, 50
 combining weights, 40
 conservation of mass, 13
 conservation of mass-energy, 29
 Dalton's, 115

Law—*Continued*
 definite composition, 33
 Dulong and Petit, 143
 Faraday's, 211
 gas, 118
 Gay-Lussac's, 105
 Graham's, 121
 Henry's, 258
 Le Chatelier's, 140, **272**
 mass action, 274
 multiple proportions, 40
Lead, *see also* Group 4a
 metallurgy, 456, 457
 storage battery, 446
Lead chamber process, 303
Lead tetraethyl, 581
Le Chatelier's principle, 140, 257, **272**
Lifting power, 70
Light, 176–177
Lime, 97, 239
 -soda water softening, 481
Liquids, 131–148
 definition of, 131
 formation of, 128
 heat capacities of, 142
Lithium, electron structure, 185, *see also* Group 1a
Lithopone, 530
Lithosphere, 64

Macromolecular crystals, *78, 79*, 81, 208
Magnesium, *see also* Group 2a
 as a reducing agent, 463
 heat capacity, *144*
 metallurgy, 210, 455, 463
Magnetic separation, 454
Magnetism, 245, 490
Manganese, *see also* Group 7b
 analysis for, 376
 metallurgy, 458, 462
Mass, definition of, 14
 energy and, 29
 isotopic, 168–170
 of fundamental particles, *27, 169*
 units of, 28
 velocity and, 29
Mass action, 274
Mass number, 163
Mass spectrograph, 44, 161, *162*
Matches, 371
Matter, particle nature of, 21, 26, 31, 32, 37–51
Mean free path, 125
Mechanism of reaction, 233, 371, 458, 459–460, 525
Melting points, 103
 of 1-alkenes, *578*
 of 1-alkynes, *579*

Melting points—*Continued*
of elements, *497*
of normal hydrocarbons, *574*
of solutions, 263
Mercurous ion, 501
Mercury, *see also* Group 2b
barometer, 98
density, 104
metallurgy, 457
Meson, 27
Metallurgy, 450–467
Metals, alloys and, 534–542
bonds in, 216
compounds of, 217, 537
crystals of, *217*
elements and, 514
properties, 534–535
pure, 535
Methane, 85, *568*
combustion of, 90
derivatives of, 568
structure of, *86*, *568*
Methanol, 591
Methyl group, 571
Mica, 549
Minerals, 450
Molality, 252
Molar volume, 55, 110, *111*
Molar weights, 55, **112**, 124, **264**, 268
Molarity, 252
Mole, definition of, 55, 110
Mole fraction, 116, 252
Molecular crystals, 74, 81, *221*
Molecular energy levels, 245
Molecular shape, 205, *206*
Molecular velocities, 121, 126–127
Molecular weights, 51, 55, 110, 124
Molecule, definition of, 49
Molybdenum, 518, *see also* Group 6b
metallurgy, 458
Mond process, 524
Monel, 524
Mustard gas, 605

Naphthalene, 587
Neodymium, *see* Group 3b, rare earth subgroup
Neon, isotopes of, 163, *see also* Group 0
Neptunium, in a radioactive series, 335, *see also* Group 3b, actinide subgroup
Net reaction, 280
Neutralization, 242
Neutrino, *27*
Neutron, *27*
mass of, *169*
secondary, 342, 348
Neutron-proton structure of the nucleus, 167–171, 338–339

Nickel, 523–524, *see also* Group 10b
metallurgy, 458, 466
Niobium, 517, *see also* Group 5b
Nitrates, organic, 609
Nitric acid, 366–368
Nitrocompounds, 608
Nitrogen, *see also* Group 5a
acids of, 366–368
boiling point, 65
electron structure, 186
formula, 51, 200
in air, *66*, 67
Nitroglycerine, 608
Nomenclature, of binary compounds, 96, 97
of energy levels, 191–195
of halogen compounds, *313*
of IUC, 572
of -ol ions, 512
of oxidation states, *313*
of ternary compounds, 97
of -yl ions, 512
proprietary, 589
trivial, 589
Nuclear chemistry, 334–350
Nuclear structure, 160–173
Nucleus, 166
bombardments of, 339–344
energy of, 345
fission of, 342, 344, 347
fusion of, 344
spallation of, 344
structure of, 166–171, 338
Nylon, 627–628

Ocean water, composition of, *453*
Octane rating, 581
-ol ions, 512
Olefins, 577
Optical isomerism, 601–602
Orbital, 191
Ores, 450–455
Osmium, 527, *see also* Group 8b
Osmosis, 265–268
Oxidation number, *192–193*, 194, 198, 236, 306
acid strength and, *415*
group, 499
maximum, 320
trends of in periodic table, *500*
Oxidation-reduction, 237, 286
reactions involving, **306**, **429**, *430*
Oxides, 239, 407–428
and their reactions with water, 407–428
coatings of, 472, 503, 525
ionic, 417–421
macromolecular, 421–425
molecular, 408–416
per-, 417, *418*

SUBJECT INDEX

Oxides—*Continued*
  super-, 417, *418*
  water-insoluble, 421
Oxygen, *see also* Group 6a
  allotropes, 81, 82
  atomic weight standard, 45, 164
  boiling point, *65*, *291*
  combination, with aluminum, 38
    with hydrogen, 35
  combining weight standard, 39, 57
  coordination number, 412
  electron structure of, 186, 198
  heats of combustion with, *62*
  in air, *66*, 67
  molecular structure, 57, 244, 290
  organic compounds containing, 591–604
Ozone, 82, 290
Ozonides, 418

Paired electrons, 187, 201, 244
Palladium, 527, *see also* Group 10b
Paraffins, 572
Paris green, 528
Parkes process, 456
Partial pressure, 115, 277
Particles, fundamental, 18–31
Periodic classification of elements, 149–159
Periodic table, *153*, *158*
  atomic and ionic size and, *157*
  diagonal relationships in, 407
  families in, 159
  groups in, 159
  periods in, 159
Peroxides, 417, *418*
  analysis for, 521
Persulfates, 304
Phase diagram of water, 145
Phases, definition of, 8, 10
  separation of, 9
Phenol, 602
Phlogiston, 69
Phosgene, 96
Phosphorus, molecular structure, *205*, *see also* Group 5a
Photographic process, 528–529, 603
Photons, 25, 26
Physical scale of atomic weights, 164
Plastics, 620–621
Platinum, 527, *see also* Group 10b
  metallurgy of, 453, 466
Plutonium, 346–348, *see also* Group 3b, actinide subgroup
Poisoning, carbon dioxide, 71
  carbon monoxide, 89
  corrosive sublimate, 531
  heavy metal, 530
  lead, 532
  mercury, 530–531

Polonium, 336, *see also* Group 6a
Polyacids, 599–600
Polyethylene, 621
Polyions, 550–551
Polymer, 616–632
Positron, 27, 339
Potash, 476
Potassium, *see also* Group 1a
  heat capacity, *144*
  metallurgy, 454
Potential, concentration, 440
  contact, 439
  solution, 439
Potential energy, 136
Praseodymium, *see* Group 3b rare earth subgroup
Pressure, absolute, 102
  concentration and, 257
  gage, 102
  kinetic theory of, 125
  measurement of, 98
  partial, 115, 277
  standard, 104
Prometheum, *see* Group 3b, rare earth subgroup
Propane, 85, 572
Properties, extensive, 7
  intensive, 8
Proprietary names, 589
Protactinium, 336, *see also* Group 3b, actinide subgroup
Proteins, 606, 625, 634–636
  digestion of, 639
  metabolism of, 642, 643
Proton, 27
  acceptor-donor, 243
  bombardments, 342–343, 345
  -neutron nucleus, 167, 338
  size, 165
Pure substances, 10, 250
Pyrites, 295

Qualitative analysis, 374–390
Quanta, 25, 26
Quantum number, 194
Quartz, 58

Radiation, counters of, 21
  genetic effects of, 340
  mass and charge of, 25
  particle nature of, 20
  types, 20
Radicals, 284
Radii, atomic, 470
  covalent, *178*, *180–181*, 311, 470
  ionic, *180–181*, 311, 470
  van der Waals, 312, 470

SUBJECT INDEX 671

Radioactivity, disintegration series and, *336*
  geologic time and, 337
  half life and, 171, *172*, 337
  induced, 27
  isotopes and, 349
  natural, 19, 170–171, 334
  processes in, 338
Radium, 336, *see also* Group 2a
  as source of alpha particles, 341
  with beryllium as neutron source, 341
Radius ratio, 396
Radon, 70, 336, *see also* Group 0
Rare earth elements, 487–495
Rate of reaction, 227
  between solids, 458
  catalysts and, 286
  concentration and, 273
  corrosion and, 526
  rusting and, 525–527
  structure and, 410
Rayon, 625
Reactions, analytical, 378
  competitive, 234, 271
  half-, 306, 429, *431*
  mechanism of, 233, 371, 459–460, 525
  net, 280
  oxidation-reduction, 237, **306**
  rate of, 227, 273, 286, 410, 458
  solid-gas, 226
Real gases, 110
Real solutions, 253
Resins, 620–623
Resonance, 299, 583
Rhenium, 522, *see also* Group 7b
Rhodium, 527, *see also* Group 9b
Roasting minerals, 457
Rubber, Buna (-S), 618–619
  hard, 618
  natural, 616–618, 629–631
  properties of, 617, 621, 623
  synthetic, 618–619, 629–631
  thiokol, 619
  vulcanized, 617
Rubidium, metallurgy of, 450, *see also* Group 1a
Rusting, 525–527
Ruthenium, 527, *see also* Group 8b

Salts, 209
  brittleness in, 215
  formation of, 225
  ions in, 213
  solubility of, in water, 391–406
  structure of, 393
  water and, 392
Samarium, *see* Group 3b, rare earth subgroup
Saturation, 254

Scandium, *see* Group 3b
Selective distillation, precipitation, and solution, 455
Selenium, *see* Group 6a
Senses, five, 6
Significant figures, 47
Silicates, 543–554
  types of, 546–550
Silicon, *see* Group 4a *and* Silicates
Silver, metallurgy, 455–456, 457, 466, *see also* Group 1b
Slag, 459
Smog, 65
Soap, 595, 610
Soda, 475, 476
Sodium, *see also* Group 1a
  as a reducing agent, 462, 464
  bicarbonate of, 475, 476
  carbonate of, 474
  chloride crystal structure, *215*
  electron structure, 186
  hydroxide of, 476
  metallurgy, *319*, 463
Sodium sulfide reagent, 384
Solar energy, 345
Solids, 131–148
  heat capacities of, 142–144
Solubility, equilibrium and, 254, 279
  nonelectrolytes and, 391
  of salts, 391–406
  rules of, 391
  tables of, *381*, *383*, *387*, *392*, *419*
Solubility product constant, 276, 279–281, *379*, *381*, *382*, *383*, *387*, *490*
Solute, 251
Solutions, 250–270
  boiling of, 11
  constant boiling and freezing, 12
  definition of, 11
  freezing of, 11
  gaseous, 115
  solid, 537
  types of, *251*
Solvent, 251
  nonaqueous, 405
  vapor pressure of, 258
Specific heat capacity, 123
Spinel, 520
Spontaneous combustion, 91
Stable chemical systems, 279
Steel, 540–541
Strontium, *see* Group 2a
Structural materials, 472, 543
Structure, *see also* Bond
  atomic, 166, 175
  benzene derivatives and, 584–586
  biochemical activity and, 648–650
  crystal, 393–402

672 SUBJECT INDEX

Structure—*Continued*
  electronic, 175, 192–193, 504
  molecular, 56, *57*
  nuclear, 167–171, 338, 339
Sublimation, 315
Substances, kinds of, 5–17
  pure, 10
Substitution, in alloys, 537
  in ores, 450
  in silicates, 545
Substitutional solid solutions, 537
Sucrose, 614
Sugar of lead, 531
Sugars, 612–615
Sulfides, insoluble, 382, 388
  metallic, 295
  poly-, 298
Sulfur, *see also* Group 6a
  dioxide, 239, 299
  mining, 293
  molecular structure, *203, 205,* 291
  oxidation states of, 294
  trioxide of, 240, 299
Sulfuric acid, 240, 300, *301–304,* 413–414
Sulfurous acid (sulfites), 240, 300, 410
Superheating, 146, 256
Superoxides, 417, *418*
Supersaturation, 254, 256
Surface tension, 134
Suspensions, 250
Symbols, alchemical, *43*
  chemical, 42
  phase, 61
  weight, 44
Synthetics vs natural products, 629
System, definition of, 8

Tantalum, 517, *see also* Group 5b
  metallurgy, 462–463
Technetium, 522, *see also* Group 7b
Tellurium, *see* Group 6a
Temperature, absolute, 105
  concentration and, 256
  equilibrium and, 278
  Kelvin, 106, *107*
  measurement of, 102
  scales of, 103, 106, *107*
  standards of, *107*
Terbium, see Group 3b, rare earth subgroup
Tetrahedral angle, 205
Thallium, 531, *see also* Group 3a
Thermal expansion, 132
Thermite reaction, 462
Thermoplastic resins, 620–621
Thermosetting resins, 622
Thio-anions, 306, 384
Thio-compounds, 305, 605
Thiosulfates, 304

Thorium, **453,** *see also* Group 3b, actinide subgroup
  in natural radioactivity, 335, 336
  source of nuclear energy, 347–348
Thulium, *see* Group 3b, rare earth subgroup
Tin, *see also* Group 4a
  gray-white, 497
  metallurgy, 454
Tincture, 594
Titanium, 516–517, *see also* Group 4b
  metallurgy, 462–463
Transistors, 531
Transmutations, natural, 18, 170–171, 334–337
Transparency, 216
Triton, *27*
Trivial names, 589
Tungsten, 518, *see also* Group 6b
  metallurgy, 458, 459, 463

Undercooling, 73, 146, 256
Unit cell, 80, *81,* 84
Units, concentration, 252
Unsaturated hydrocarbons, 576
Unsaturation in solutions, 254
Uranium, *see also* Group 3b, actinide subgroup
  and age of earth, 337–338
  in natural radioactivity, 335, *336*
  in nuclear fission, 342, 344–348
  ions of, 512
Urea, 567

Valence electron, 197
Vanadium, 517, *see also* Group 5b
  metallurgy, 462
Van der Waals forces, 86, **206,** 312, 470
Vapor equilibrium, 72
Vapor pressure, 116, 138, 258, 264
  of water, *140*
Velocities, molecular, 121, 126–127
Vinegar, 598
Viscosity, 134, 561
Vitalism, 567
Vitamins, *645–646,* 646–647
  antagonists of, 648–649
Volt, 212, 429
Volumes, atomic, 174, 544
  combining, in gases, 37, **50**
  gram-atomic, 144, *156*
  molar, 55, 110, *111*
Vulcanization, 617

Water, acidic oxides and, 239, 409
  ammonia and, 357
  antifreezes for, 594
  basic oxides and, 239
  complexes of, 360, 509, 527

Water—*Continued*
  food and, 634
  formula of, 52
  hard, 481
  in air, 72
  ionization of, 282, 297
  oxides and, 409–428
  phase diagram for, 145
  softening of, 481
  solubilities in, 404
  structure of, *57*, 393, 403
  vapor pressure of, *140*, *141*
Watt, 212
Weak electrolyte equilibrium, 281
Weather, 73, 74
Weight, atomic, 45, *46*, **112**, 124–125, 143–144
  combining, 38, 57
  equivalent, 38, 57
  formula, 52
  gram-atomic, 45

Weight—*Continued*
  molar, 55, 112, 124, 264, 268
  molecular, 51
  symbol, 44
White lead, 532
Wilson cloud chamber, 22

Xenon, *see* Group 0
X-rays, 30
  crystal study with, 80, 213

-yl ions, 512
Ytterbium, *see* Group 3b, rare earth subgroup
Yttrium, *see* Group 3b, rare earth subgroup

Zeolites, 481, 549
Zinc, metallurgy, 458, *see also* Group 2b
Zirconium, 516–517, *see also* Group 4b
  metallurgy, 462–463
Zwitter ions, 607

NAME INDEX

Amontons, 103
Arrhenius, 243
Avogadro, 49, 110
Balmer, 183
Becquerel, 19
Berthollet, 33
Berzelius, 42, 44, 51
Bohr, 176
Boyle, 13, 100
Bragg, 80
Brønsted, 243
Brouncker, 100
Brown, 132
Cannizzaro, 114
Castner, 463, 477
Cavendish, 69
Celsius, 103
Charles, 105
Cori, 637
Dalton, 37, 40, 41, 52, 115
Della Porta, 102
Desch, 83
Döbereiner, 151
Einstein, 29
Faraday, 211, 436, 557, 582
Galileo, 99, 102
Galvani, 463
Gay-Lussac, 50, 105
Gebhardt, 566
Graham, 121
Hall, 464
Hannay, 83
Henry, 258
Heroult, 464
Hesiod, 98
Hooke, 100
Jewett, 464
Joule, 212
Kekule, 582

Kolbe, 567
Körner, 584
Laue, 80
Lavoisier, 13, 33, 69
Le Chatelier, 140
Leonardo da Vinci, 64
Lewis, 243
Lockyer, 70
Lyman, 183
Mao-Khoa, 64
Marignac, 33
Maxwell, 126
Mendeleeff, 152, 488
Meyer, 152
Millikan, 23, 24, 249
Moissan, 82, 83, 150
Morley, 35
Moseley, 195
Newlands, 151
Pasteur, 601
Pauling, 471
Priestley, 69
Proust, 33
Ramsay, 70
Rankine, 106, 107
Rayleigh, 70
Reaumur, 103
Rey, 102
Rutherford, 166
Scheele, 69
Stas, 33
Stoney, 23
Thomson, 161
Torricelli, 98
Townley, 100
Tyndall, 558
Van't Hoff, 601
Von Guericke, 100
Wöhler, 567